Marihuana:
An Annotated Bibliography, Volume II

Coy W. Waller, Ph.D., University of Minnesota, is former Director of the Research Institute of Pharmaceutical Sciences at The University of Mississippi where he is presently Professor of Pharmaceutics. He has served on the FDA/NIDA Drug Abuse Research Advisory Committee, FDA-NIMH Psychotomimetic Agents Advisory Committee and as a Special Consultant to the National Institute of Mental Health on marihuana. Dr. Waller continues his research in the exploitation of cannabis and its constituents for medicinal usefulness and is presently a special consultant to the FDA.

Rashmi S. Nair, Ph.D., University of Mississippi, is Senior Toxicologist for Monsanto Company in St. Louis, Missouri.

Ann F. McAllister, M.L.S., University of Mississippi, is now a Technical Information Specialist at the National Library of Medicine in Bethesda, Maryland.

Beverly S. Urbanek, M.L.S., University of Mississippi, is a Research Associate for the Research Institute of Pharmaceutical Sciences at The University of Mississippi.

Carlton E. Turner, Ph.D., University of Southern Mississippi, is Director (on leave) of the Research Institute of Pharmaceutical Sciences at The University of Mississippi. He is currently Senior Policy Advisor for Drug Policy in the Office of Policy Development at The White House. Dr. Turner was Project Director for NIDA's Cannabis-coca Project at The University of Mississippi from 1971-1981 during which time his group developed an internationally recognized analytical methodology for the analysis of cannabis and the cannabinoids.

Marihuana:
An Annotated Bibliography, Volume II

Coy W. Waller
Rashmi S. Nair
Ann F. McAllister
Beverly S. Urbanek
Carlton E. Turner
Research Institute of Pharmaceutical Sciences
University of Mississippi

MACMILLAN PUBLISHING CO., INC.
NEW YORK

Collier Macmillan Publishers
LONDON

Professional Books Division
Macmillan Publishing Co., Inc.
866 Third Avenue, New York, N.Y. 10022

Collier Macmillan Canada, Inc.

Library of Congress Catalog Card Number: 76-20635

Printed in the United States of America

printing number

1   2   3   4   5   6   7   8   9   10

Library of Congress Cataloging in Publication Data (Revised)

Main entry under title:

Marihuana, an annotated bibliography.

  Includes indexes.
   1. Marihuana—Bibliography—Collected works.
2. Cannabis--Bibliography--Collected works.
I. Waller, Coy Webster
Z7164.N17M32   [HV5822.M3]   016.615′7827   76-20635
ISBN 0-02-699820-3 (v. 2)   AACR2

TABLE OF CONTENTS

	Page
Preface	vii
Foreword	viii
Abbreviations	ix
Numbering of the Cannabinoids	x
Tables 1-11 Structures of the Cannabinoid Compounds, 1-61	xi
Table 12 Nitrogenous Compounds, 62-81	xix
Table 13 Amino Acids, 82-99	xxi
Table 14 Proteinatious Compounds, 100-108	xxi
Table 15 Sugars and Related Compounds, 109-142	xxii
Table 16 Hydrocarbons, 143-199	xxiii
Table 17 Simple Alcohols, 193-199	xxv
Table 18 Simple Aldehydes, 200-211	xxv
Table 19 Simple Ketones, 212-224	xxvi
Table 20 Simple Acids, 225-244	xxvi
Table 21 Fatty Acids, 245-256	xxvii
Table 22 Esters and Lactones, 257-269	xxviii

CONTENTS (continued)

Page

Table 23
Steroids, 270-280.. xxviii

Table 24
Terpenes, 281-383... xxix

Table 25
Non Cannabinoid Phenols, 384-399.. xxxiii

Table 26
Flavonoid Glycosides, 400-418... xxxiv

Table 27
Vitamins, 419... xxxv

Table 28
Pigments, 420-421.. xxxv

Addendum.. 1

References and Annotations... 23

Addendum II... 371

1979 Supplement.. 375

U.S. Patents... 431

Author Index... 439

Subject Index.. 475

PREFACE

The Research Institute of Pharmaceutical Sciences at the University of Mississippi is conducting an intensive research program involving all of the published research that has been done on marihuana world-wide. This project was begun in 1968 and includes works published from 1964-1980. We are now credited with housing the most extensive collection of marihuana research papers in the world. We believe that this project is necessary to acquaint scientists, educators and students with the vast amount of information that is available. It is to this end that we now offer *Marihuana, An Annotated Bibliography, Vol. II.*

Every effort has been made to make this bibliography as comprehensive as possible. The previous volume covers all facets of cannabis research from 1964-1974. Vol. II contains 2,669 entries covering international scientific publications from 1975-1979. The literature references prior to 1964 can be found in *The Question of Cannabis, Cannabis Bibliography* (United Nations Commission on Narcotic Drugs, E/CN7/479, 1965) edited by the late Dr. Nathan B. Eddy.

Marihuana, An Annotated Bibliography, Vol. II offers a broader format than Vol. I. The introductory section on structures of naturally occurring compounds has been expanded (Turner, et al.)* to include the structures of all different types of cannabinoids as well as other different classes of compounds. Cannabinoids are usually identified as the group of C_{21} compounds typical of and present in *Cannabis sativa*, their carboxylic acids, analogs and transformation products.

The Addendum includes citations prior to 1975 which were omitted from Vol. I. Entries are arranged alphabetically by senior author and are numbered consecutively with Vol. I. Unsigned articles are listed under anonymous. In order to make the bibliography as complete as possible, Addendum II was inserted to include the material received after typing of the book was underway. The 1979 citations are followed by a list of United States Patents. The patents are also listed alphabetically by author. However, they are indexed numerically according to patent number and referenced by annotation number. We are delighted to offer a greatly expanded subject index. Though it was designed particularly with the researcher in mind, it includes enough diversity to meet the needs of anyone with an interest in marihuana. It is our belief that this feature will be well received and hopefully well used by everyone.

We would like to express our appreciation to the staff members of the Research Institute of Pharmaceutical Sciences for their valuable assistance. We especially appreciate the untiring efforts of Mr. James Coffey and the technical staff of the data center. We would also like to thank Dr. Lumir Hanus, Dr. Lucio Merlini, Dr. Hala Elsohly and Ms. Kathleen Baran for their assistance in translations. A special thank you is in order to Mrs. Jackie Johnson for much of the groundwork in the early days of the bibliography. Finally, we wish to thank Mrs. Jean Brannan and Mrs. Barbara Lago for months of dedicated typing.

----

*Turner, C. E.; Elsohly, M. A.; and Boeren, E. G.; J. Nat. Prod., 43(2), 169-234(1980).

FOREWORD

The broad acceptance of *Marihuana, An Annotated Bibliography* by the scientific and lay community validates the usefulness of our approach to making scientific information, previously hidden in deep corners of libraries, readily available and useful.

Volume I, published in 1976, has proven a valuable classroom tool in various professional and non-professional educational programs. The format for Vol. I was developed for fellow scientists. Shortly after publication, it became apparent that the lay public found the book a valuable reference source because of the author and subject index. In an attempt to further increase its usefulness, the format of Vol. II has been expanded. Scientists and lay people will find the extensive subject and key word index of Vol. II much more complete and useful. Also, to help those interested in understanding the complex, crude drug known as marihuana, we have listed all chemicals (421) known to occur in the cannabis plant.

Keeping abreast of all scientific literature even in a chosen field such as cannabis, marihuana, etc. is next to impossible. However, with Vol. I and Vol. II one has 5,715 literature citations at their fingertips.

The desire of the Research Institute of Pharmaceutical Sciences (RIPS) and those involved with our bibliographic services is to provide an abstract of all cannabis literature citations. We think our annotated bibliography on marihuana and future volumes on coca and cocaine will be extremely beneficial to those individuals interested in the rapidly changing medical and social conditions caused by these drugs. Computer printouts of literature citations, since Vol. II was published, can be obtained from RIPS for a nominal fee. Special literature searches can also be done by RIPS personnel.

Your comments on the format and how it can be improved in future bibliographies would be appreciated.

Carlton E. Turner, Ph. D., Director
Research Institute of Pharmaceutical Sciences
School of Pharmacy
University of Mississippi
June 1, 1981

ABBREVIATIONS

ACTH - adrenocorticotropic hormone

β-HHC - (±)-9-*nor*-9-beta-OH-hexahydrocannabinol

BP - blood pressure

cAMP - cyclic AMP (adenosine monophosphate)

CBC or CBCH - cannabichromene

CBD - cannabidiol

CBE - cannabielsoin

CBG - cannabigerol

CBN - cannabinol

CBV - cannabivarin

CNS - central nervous system

DA - dopamine

DMHP - dimethylheptylpyran

EEG - electroencephalogram

EPI - epinephrine

GABA - gamma-amino-butyric acid

GAD - glutamic acid decarboxylase

GC/MS - gas chromatography-mass spectrometry

GLC - gas liquid chromatography

HPLC - high-pressure liquid chromatography

5-HIAA - 5-hydroxyindolacetic acid

5-HT - serotonin (5hydroxytryptamine)

IR - infrared

MS - mass spectrometry

NE - norepinephrine, noradrenaline

NMR - nuclear magnetic resonance

REM - rapid eye movement

RIA - radioimmunoassay

SAR - structure-activity relationship

THC - tetrahydrocannabinol

THCV - tetrahydrocannabivarol

TLC - thin layer chromatography

UV - ultra violet

mg - milligrams

kg - kilograms

μg - micrograms

ml - milliliters

ng - nanograms

wt - weight

hr - hour

wk - week

da - day

i.p. - intraperitoneal

i.m. - intramuscular

p.o. - orally

i.v. - intravenous

s.c. - subcutaneous

NUMBERING OF THE CANNABINOIDS

Dibenzopyran Numbering

Numbering used by TODD

Diphenyl Numbering

Monoterpene Numbering (Based on p-cymene)

Monoterpene Numbering

TABLE 1

	Cannabigerol-type	R_1	R_2	R_3
1.	Cannabigerolic acid	COOH	C_5H_{11}	H
2.	Cannabigerolic acid monomethylether	COOH	C_5H_{11}	CH_3
3.	Cannabigerol	H	C_5H_{11}	H
4.	Cannabigerol monomethylether	H	C_5H_{11}	CH_3
5.	Cannabigerovarinic acid	COOH	C_3H_7	H
6.	Cannabigerovarin	H	C_3H_7	H

TABLE 2

	Cannabichromene-type	R_1	R_2
7.	Cannabichromenic acid	COOH	C_5H_{11}
8.	Cannabichromene	H	C_5H_{11}
9.	Cannabichromevarinic acid	COOH	C_3H_7
10.	Cannabichromevarin	H	C_3H_7

TABLE 3

	Cannabidiol-type	R_1	R_2	R_3
11.	Cannabidiolic acid	COOH	C_5H_{11}	H
12.	Cannabidiol	H	C_5H_{11}	H
13.	Cannabidiol monomethylether	H	C_5H_{11}	CH_3
14.	Cannabidiol-C_4	H	C_4H_9	H
15.	Cannabidivarinic acid	COOH	C_3H_7	H
16.	Cannabidivarin	H	C_3H_7	H
17.	Cannabidiorcol	H	CH_3	H

TABLE 4

	Δ^9-(*trans*)-Tetrahydrocannabinol-type	R_1	R_2	R_3	R_4
18.	Δ^9-(*trans*)-Tetrahydrocannabinolic acid A	H	COOH	C_5H_{11}	H
19.	Δ^9-(*trans*)-Tetrahydrocannabinolic acid B	H	H	C_5H_{11}	COOH
20.	Δ^9-(*trans*)-Tetrahydrocannabinol	H	H	C_5H_{11}	H
21.	Δ^9-(*trans*)-Tetrahydrocannabinolic acid - C_4	H	COOH or H	C_4H_9	H or COOH
22.	Δ^9-(*trans*)-Tetrahydrocannabinol - C_4	H	H	C_4H_9	H
23.	Δ^9-(*trans*)-Tetrahydrocannabivarinic acid	H	COOH	C_3H_7	H
24.	Δ^9-(*trans*)-Tetrahydrocannabivarin	H	H	C_3H_7	H
25.	Δ^9-(*trans*)-Tetrahydrocannabiorcolic acid	H	COOH or H	CH_3	H or COOH
26.	Δ^9-(*trans*)-Tetrahydrocannabiorcol	H	H	CH_3	H

TABLE 5

	$\triangle^8$-(*trans*)-Tetrahydrocannabinol-type	R
27.	$\triangle^8$-(*trans*)-Tetrahydrocannabinolic acid	COOH
28.	$\triangle^8$-(*trans*)-Tetrahydrocannabinol	H

TABLE 6

	Cannabicyclol-type	R_1	R_2
29.	Cannabicyclolic acid	COOH	C_5H_{11}
30.	Cannabicyclol	H	C_5H_{11}
31.	Cannabicyclovarin	H	C_3H_7

TABLE 7

	Cannabielsoin-type	R_1	R_2
32.	Cannabielsoic acid **A**	COOH	H
33.	Cannabielsoic acid **B**	H	COOH
34.	Cannabielsoin	H	H

TABLE 8

	Cannabinol-type	R_1	R_2	R_3
35.	Cannabinolic acid	H	COOH	C_5H_{11}
36.	Cannabinol	H	H	C_5H_{11}
37.	Cannabinol methylether	CH_3	H	C_5H_{11}
38.	Cannabinol-C_4	H	H	C_4H_9
39.	Cannabivarin	H	H	C_3H_7
40.	Cannabiorcol	H	H	CH_3

TABLE 9

	Cannabinodiol-type	R
41.	Cannabinodiol	C_5H_{11}
42.	Cannabinodivarin	C_3H_7

TABLE 10

	Cannabitriol-type	R_1	R_2
43.	(-)-Cannabitriol	H	OH
44.	(+)-Cannabitriol	H	OH
45.	(±)-9,10-dihydroxy-$\Delta^{6a(10a)}$-tetrahydrocannabinol	H	OH
46.	(-)-10-ethoxy-9-hydroxy-$\Delta^{6a(10a)}$-tetrahydrocannabinol	H	OEt
47.	(±)-8,9-dihydroxy-$\Delta^{6a(10a)}$-tetrahydrocannabinol	OH	H
48.	Cannabidiolic acid tetrahydrocannabitriol ester (CBD-THO) (CBDA ester at 9-OH group)	H	H

TABLE 11

49.

50.

51.

52.

Miscellaneous

---

49. Dehydrocannabifuran

50. Cannabifuran

51. Cannabichromanon

52. Cannabicitran

53.

54.

xvii

TABLE II (continued)

55.

56.

---

53. 10-Oxo-Δ6a(10a)-Tetrahydrocannabinol

54. Δ9-(6a,10a,*cis*)-Tetrahydrocannabinol

55. 3,4,5,6-Tetrahydro-7-hydroxy-α,α-2-trimethyl-9-*n*-propyl-2,6-methano-2H-1-benzoxocin-5-methanol

56. (-)-(6aR,9S,10S,10aR)-9,10-Dihydroxyhexahydrocannabinol (Cannabiripsol)

57

61

---

57. 6a,7,10a-Trihydroxy-Δ9-Tetrahydrocannabinol

---

58. Cannabichromanone-C_3

59. Cannabielsoin-C_3

60. Cannabielsoin acid B-C_3

61. Cannabicoumaronone

TABLE 12

NITROGENOUS COMPOUNDS

QUATERNARY BASES

62.　　Choline

63.　　Trigonelline

64.　　Muscarine

65.　　L-(+)-isoleucine betaine

66.　　Neurine

AMIDES

67.　　N-(p-hydroxy-β-phenylethyl)-p-hydroxy-(*trans*)-cinnamide

----

SIMPLE AMINES

68.　　Piperidine

69.　　Hordenine

70.　　Ammonia

71.　　Methylamine

72.　　Ethylamine

73.　　*n*-propylamine

74.　　*n*-Butylamine

75.　　Iso-butylamine

76.　　Sec-butylamine

77.　　Dimethylamine

78.　　Diethylamine

79.　　Pyrrolidine

Tentatively Identified

iso-Amylamine

β-Phenethylamine

n-Pentylamine

Cadaverine

Ethanolamine or histamine

Benzylamine or tyramine

SPERMIDINE ALKALOIDS

80.

81.

80.   Cannabisativine

81.   Anhydrocannabisativine

TABLE 13

AMINO ACIDS

82. Alanine

83. Aspartic acid

84. Cystine

85. Glutamic acid

86. Glycine

87. Serine

88. Arginine

89. Histidine

90. Isoleucine

91. Leucine

92. Lysine

93. Methionine

94. Phenylalanine

95. Proline

96. Threonine

97. Tryptophane

98. Tyrosine

99. Valine

TABLE 14

PROTEINS, GLYCOPROTEINS, AND ENZYMES

100. Edestin

101. Zeatin

102. Zeatin nucleoside

103. Edestinase

104. Glucosidase (emulsin)

105. Polyphenol oxidase

106. Peptidase (ereptase)

107. Peroxidase

108. Adenosine-5-phosphatase

TABLE 15

SUGARS AND RELATED COMPOUNDS

Monosaccharides

109. Arabinose

110. Fructose

111. Galactose

112. Galacturonic acid

113. α-D-glucose

114. β-D-glucose

115. *altro*-Heptulose (*sedo*-heptulose)

116. D-*manno*-heptulose

117. Mannose

118. D-*glycerol*-D-*manno*-Octulose

119. Rhamnose

120. Ribose

121. Xylose

Disaccharides

122. Sucrose (saccharose)

123. Maltose

Polysaccharides

124. Raffinose (oligosaccharide)

125. Cellulose

126. Hemicellulose

127. Pectin

128. Xylan

Sugar alcohols and cyclitols

129. Arabitol (arabinitol)

130. Erythritol

131. Galactitol

132. Glycerol

133. Mannitol

TABLE 15 (Continued)

134.	Ribitol
135.	Sorbitol
136.	Xylitol
137.	D(-)-Bornesitol
138.	(+)-Inositol
139.	*myo*-Inositol
140.	(+)-Quebrachitol (1 L-2-O-methyl-*chiro*-inositol)

Amino sugars

141.	Galactosamine
142.	Glucosamine

TABLE 16

HYDROCARBONS

143.	C_9H_{20}	*n*-Nonane
144.	$C_{10}H_{22}$	*n*-Decane
145.	$C_{11}H_{24}$	*n*-Undecane
146.	$C_{12}H_{26}$	*n*-Dodecane
147.	$C_{13}H_{28}$	*n*-Tridecane
148.	$C_{14}H_{30}$	*n*-Tetradecane
149.	$C_{15}H_{32}$	3,6-Dimethyl-tridecane
150.	$C_{15}H_{32}$	*n*-Pentadecane
151.	$C_{16}H_{34}$	2,6-Dimethyl-tetradecane
152.	$C_{16}H_{34}$	*n*-Hexadecane
153.	$C_{17}H_{36}$	*n*-Heptadecane
154.	$C_{18}H_{38}$	2,6-Dimethyl-hexadecane
155.	$C_{18}H_{38}$	*n*-Octadecane
156.	$C_{19}H_{40}$	3,6-Dimethyl-heptadecane
157.	$C_{19}H_{40}$	3,7-Dimethyl-heptadecane
158.	$C_{19}H_{40}$	*n*-Nonadecane
159.	$C_{20}H_{42}$	3,6-Dimethyl-octadecane
160.	$C_{20}H_{42}$	3,7-Dimethyl-octadecane

TABLE 16 (Continued)

161. $C_{20}H_{42}$ *n*-Eicosane

162. $C_{21}H_{44}$ *n*-Heneicosane

163. $C_{22}H_{46}$ 3-Methyl-heneicosane

164. $C_{22}H_{46}$ *n*-Docosane

165. $C_{23}H_{48}$ *n*-Tricosane

166. $C_{24}H_{50}$ 3-Methyl-tricosane

167. $C_{24}H_{50}$ *n*-Tetracosane

168. $C_{25}H_{52}$ 2-Methyl-tetracosane

169. $C_{25}H_{52}$ *n*-Pentacosane

170. $C_{26}H_{54}$ *n*-Hexacosane

171. $C_{26}H_{54}$ 3-Methyl-pentacosane

172. $C_{27}H_{56}$ 2-Methyl-hexacosane

173. $C_{27}H_{56}$ *n*-Heptacosane

174. $C_{28}H_{58}$ 3-Methyl-heptacosane

175. $C_{28}H_{58}$ *n*-Octacosane

176. $C_{29}H_{60}$ 2-Methyl-octacosane

177. $C_{29}H_{60}$ 9-Methyl-octacosane

178. $C_{29}H_{60}$ *n*-Nonacosane

179. $C_{31}H_{64}$ 3-Methyl-triacontane

180. $C_{30}H_{62}$ *n*-Triacotane

181. $C_{32}H_{66}$ 2-Methyl-hentriacontane

182. $C_{31}H_{64}$ *n*-Hentriacontane

183. $C_{32}H_{66}$ 3-Methyl-hentriacontane

184. $C_{32}H_{66}$ *n*-Dotriacontane

185. $C_{33}H_{68}$ 2-Methyl-dotriacontane

186. $C_{33}H_{68}$ *n*-Tritriacontane

187. $C_{34}H_{70}$ Tetra-triacontane

188. $C_{35}H_{72}$ Pentatriacontane

189. $C_{36}H_{74}$ Hexatriacontane

190. $C_{37}H_{76}$ Heptatriacontane

191. $C_{38}H_{78}$ Octatriacontane

192. $C_{39}H_{80}$ Nonatriacontane

TABLE 17

SIMPLE ALCOHOLS

193. Methanol

194. Ethanol

195. 1-Octene-3-01

196. Octanol-1

197. Octanol-3

198. Nonanol-1

199. Hexadecanol-1

TABLE 18

SIMPLE ALDEHYDES

200. Acetaldehyde

201. Isobutyraldehyde

202. Pentanal

203. Hexanal

204. Heptanal

205. Octanal

206. Nonanal

207. Decanal

208. Undecanal

209. Dodecanal

210. Tridecanal

211. *p*-Ethylbenzaldehyde

TABLE 19

SIMPLE KETONES

---

212. Acetone

213. Heptanone-2

214. 2-Methyl-2-heptene-6-one

215. Decanone-2

216. Undecanone-2

217. Dodecanone-2

218. Pentadecanone-2

219. Octanone-3

220. 2,2,6-Trimethyl cyclohexanone

221. 2,2,6-Trimethyl-5-cyclohexenone

222. 3-Decene-5-one

223. 6,10-Dimethyl undecanone-2

224. 6,10,14-Trimethyl pentadecanone-2

TABLE 20

SIMPLE ACIDS

---

225. Arabinic

226. Azelaic

227. *trans*-Cinnamic

228. Citric

229. Glucaric

230. Gluconic

231. Glyceric

232. *p*-Hydroxybenzoic

233. *p*-Hydroxycinnamic (*p*-Coumarie)

234. Isocitric

235. Malic

236. Malonic

237. 2-C-Methylaldotetronic

238. 3-Methoxy-4-hydroxycinnamic (Ferulic)

TABLE 20 (Continued)

239. Phosphoric

240. Pyroglutamic

241. Quinic

242. Succinic

243. Threonic

244. Vanillic

TABLE 21

FATTY ACIDS

245. Arachidic

246. Behenic

247. Eicosadienic

248. Eicosemic

249. Linoleic

250. Linolenic

251. Myristic

252. Oleic

253. Palmitic

254. Palmitoleic

255. Sativic

256. Stearic

TABLE 22

SIMPLE ESTERS AND LACTONES

257. Benzyl acetate

258. *p*-Ethyl benzyl acetate

259. *cis*-3-Hexenyl caproate

260. Hexyl acetate

261. Hexyl butyrate

262. Hexyl caproate

263. Hexyl isobutyrate

264. Methyl acetate

265. 2-C-Methyl-aldotetronolactone

266. Methyl linoleate

267. Methyl palmitate

268. Methyl salicylate

269. Octyl caproate

TABLE 23

STEROIDS

270. Campesterol

271. Campest-5-en-3β-ol-7-one

272. Campest-4-en-3-one

273. Ergosterol

274. β-Sitosterol

275. 5α-Stigmasta-7,24(28)-dien-3β-ol

276. Stigmasta-5,22-dien-3β-ol-7-one

277. Stigmasta-4,22-dien-3-one

278. Stigmast-5-en-3β-ol-7-one (7-Keto-β-sitosterol)

279. Stigmast-4-en-3-one

280. Stigmasterol

TABLE 24

TERPENES

Monoterpenes

281. Borneol

282. Bornyl acetate

283. Camphene

284. Camphenehydrate

285. Camphor

286. Δ^3-Carene

287. Δ^4-Carene

288. Carvacrol

289. Carvone

290. β-Cyclocitral

291. 1,4-Cineol

292. 1,8-Cineol

293. Citral B

294. Citronellol

295. *p*-Cymene

296. *p*-Cymene-8-ol

297. Dihydrocarveyl acetate

298. Dihydrocarvone

299. Fenchyl alcohol

300. Fenchone

301. Geraniol

302. Geranyl acetone

303. Limonene

304. Linalool

305. *cis*-Linalool oxide

306. *trans*-Linalool oxide

307. *m*-Mentha-1,8(9)-dien-5-ol

308. 1-Methyl-4-*iso*-propenylbenzene

309. Myrcene

TABLE 24 (Continued)

310. Nerol

311. Nerolidol

312. *cis*-β-Ocimene

313. *trans*-β-Ocimene

314. Perillene

315. α-Phellandrene

316. β-Phellandrene

317. 3-Phenyl-2-methyl-prop-1-ene

318. α-Pinene

319. β-Pinene

320. α-Pinene oxide

321. Pinocarveol

322. Pinocarvone

323. Piperitenone

324. Piperitone oxide

325. Piperitenone oxide

326. Pulegone

327. Sabinene

328. *trans*-Sabinene hydrate

329. Sabinol

330. Safranal

331. α-Thujene

332. α-Terpinene

333. γ-Terpinene

334. α-Terpinene-4-ol

335. α-Terpinolene

336. α-Terpineol

337. β-Terpineol

338. Thujyl alcohol

TABLE 24 (Continued)

Sesquiterpenes

339. Allo-aromadendrene

340. α-*trans*-Bergamotene

341. β-Bisabolene

342. α-Bisabolol

343. Calamenene

344. Caryophyllene

345. α-Caryophyllene (Humulene)

346. β-Caryophyllene

347. α-Caryophyllene alcohol (Caryophyllenol)

348. *iso*-Caryophyllene

349. Caryophyllene oxide (Caryophyllene epoxide)

350. α-Cedrene

351. γ-Cadinene

352. δ-Cadinene

353. α-Copaene

354. α-Cubebene

355. α-Curcumene

356. β-Curcumene

357. γ-Elemene

358. γ-Eudesmol

359. β-Farnesene

360. (Z)-β-Farnesene

361. *trans-trans*-α-Farnesene

362. Farnesol

363. Farnesyl acetone

364. α-Gurjunene

365. Guaiol

366. β-Humulene

367. Humulene epoxide I

368. Humulene epoxide II

TABLE 24 (Continued)

369   Ledol

370.   Longifolene

371.   Nerolidol

372.   epi-β-Santalene

373.   α-Selinene

374.   β-Selinene

375.   Selina-3,7(11)-diene

376.   Selina-4(14),7(11)-diene

Diterpenes

377.   Phytol

Triterpenes

378.   Friedelin (Friedelan-3-one)

379.   Epifriedelanol

Miscellaneous compounds of terpenoid origin

380.   Vomifoliol (blumenol A)

381.   Dihydrovomifolio (blumenol B)

382.   β-Ionone

383.   Dihydroactinidiolide

TABLE 25

NON CANNABINOID PHENOLS

Spiro-Indan-type	R_1	R_2	R_3	R_4
384. Acetylcannabispirol	H	CH_3	OAc	H
385. Cannabispiradienone	H	CH_3	$\overset{O}{\underset{}{C}}$	diene α,β and α,β to carbonyl
386. β-Cannabispiranol (cannabispirol)	H	CH_3	OH	H
387. Cannabispirenone (dehydrocannabispiran)	H	CH_3	$\overset{O}{\underset{}{C}}$	$\Delta\alpha,\beta$ to carbonyl
388. Cannabispirenone isomer	CH_3	H	$\overset{O}{\underset{}{C}}$	$\Delta\alpha,\beta$ to carbonyl
389. Cannabispirone (cannabispiran)	H	CH_3	$\overset{O}{\underset{}{C}}$	

TABLE 25 (Continued)

Dihydrostilbene-type

-----

390. 3-{ 2-(4-hydroxyphenyl) ethyl }-5-methoxyphenol

391. 3-{ 2-(3-hydroxy-4-methoxyphenyl) ethyl }-5-methoxyphenol

392. 3-{ 2-(3-isoprenyl-4-hydroxy-5-methoxyphenyl) ethyl }-5-methoxyphenol

393. 3-{ 2-(2-isoprenyl-3-hydroxy-4-methoxyphenyl)-ethyl }-5-methoxyphenol (canniprene)

-----

394. Cannabidihydrophenanthrene

395. Eugenol

396. iso-Eugenol

397. *cis*-Anethol

398. *trans*-Anethol

399. Methyleugenol

TABLE 26

FLAVONOID GLYCOSIDES

-----

400. Apigenine-7-O-*p*-coumarylglucoside

401. Apigenin-7-O-glucoside (Cosmosioside)

402. Apigenin-O-glycoside

403. Isovitexin-7-O-glucoarabinoside

404. Isovitexin-O-glucoside

405. Isovitexin-7-O-rhamnoglucoside

406. Kaempferol-O-glycoside(s)

407. Luteolin-O-glycoside

TABLE 26 (Continued)

408.   Orientin

409.   Orientin-7-O-glucoside

410.   Orientin-O-glucoside (in sugar moiety)

411.   Orientin-O-glucoside

412.   Orientin-7-O-rhamnoglucoside

413.   Quercetin-O-glucoside(s)

414.   Vitexin-7-O-(6"-glucoside)

415.   Vitexin-O-glucoside

416.   Vitexin-O-rhamnoglucoside

417.   2"-O-glucopyranosylorientin

418.   2"-O-glucopyranosylvitexin

TABLE 27

VITAMINS

419.   Vitamin K

TABLE 28

PIGMENTS

420.   Carotene

421.   Xanthophylls

ADDENDUM

A

3046   Adams, P. M.; Barratt, E. S., Fed. Proc. *33*(3), 540 (1974).

Effects of Chronic Marijuana Administration on Stages of Primate Sleep-Wakefulness (abstract).

The 24 hr. sleep-wakefulness activity after the administration of 1.2 mg/kg Δ^9-THC (by intubation) was studied in squirrel monkeys.

3047   Albrecht, S. L., Sociol. Soc. Res., *57*(2), 196-207 (1973).

Verbal Attitudes and Significant Other's Expectations as Predictors of Marijuana Use.

Perceived norms and personal attitude toward marihuana greatly predicted marihuana use behavior. Prediction was most powerful when both these factors were in concordance.

3048   Annis, H. M.; and Smart, R. G., in *Committee on Problem of Drug Dependence, 1974.* Division of Medical Sciences, National Research Council, National Academy of Sciences, Washington, D.C., 1974, pp. 764-69.

Adverse Reactions and Recurrences from Marihuana Use.

An epidemiological study among high school students in Ontario revealed that adverse effects after marihuana use were observed. A study of the questionnaires answered by the students showed that recurrence of marihuana effects in a drug-free state were also seen in this population.

3049   Anonymous, J. La. St. Med. Soc., *126*(12), 445-47 (1974).

The Marijuana Myth.

This editorial summarizes the testimony of scientists appearing before the Senate Subcommittee on Internal Security during May, 1974, and the conclusions of the committee that marihuana is not an innocuous drug. It also calls on physicians to assume leadership in a program of drug abuse education aimed at eradicating the marihuana epidemic.

3050   Askew, W. E., Diss. Abstr. Int. B. *34*(11), 5397 (1974).

Neurochemical Role of Adenosine 3´,5´-Cyclic Monophosphate and Guanosine 3´,5´-Cyclic Monophosphate and their Relation to Neurotransmitters; Effect of Tetrahydrocannabinols.

Δ^8-THC and Δ^9-THC and not Δ^8-OH-THC depleted whole rat brain actylcholine. Δ^8-THC increased cyclic AMP in the rat midbrain and decreased it in the cerebellum. The effect of adenosine 3´,5´-monophosphate and guanosine 3´,5´-monosphosphate on various brain neurotransmitters in cannulated rats was also described.

B

3051   Beaconsfield, P.; Oakley, C.; Carpi, A.; Rainsbury, R.; and Del Basso, P., Eur. J. Cardiol.; *2*(2), 167-73 (1974).

Cardiac Effect of Δ^9-Tetrahydrocannabinol on a Heart-Lung Preparation and on the Intact Animal.

The cardiac effect of cannabis is secondary to circulatory effects elsewhere when smoking a marihuana cigarette containing about 10 mg of Δ^9-THC. This effect in humans is confirmed in animals when the heart-lung preparation of the guinea pig is used. Excessive amount, however, will have direct toxic effect on the specialized conductive tissue of the heart.

3052 Beahrs, J. O.; Carlin, A. S.; and Shehorn, J., Amer. J. Clin. Hypn., 16(4), 267-69 (1974).

Impact on Psychoactive Drugs on Hypnotizability.

Smoking marihuana or treatment with haloperidol did not significantly influence the hypnotic susceptibility of marihuana users.

3053 Bercht, C. A. L.; and Paris, M. R., Bull. Tech. Gattefosse SFPA, pp. 87-90 (1974).

Contribution a l'Etude de l'Essence de *Cannabis sativa L.* [Oil of *Cannabis sativa L.*]

The essential oil of *Cannabis sativa L.* was separated in a hydrocarbon fraction and a fraction containing the oxygenated compounds. Analysis by gas chromatography-mass spectrometry revealed the presence of nine new terpenes.

3054 Bercht, C. A. L.; and Salemink, C. A., United Nations Document, ST/SOA/SER. S/21,22 August, 1969.

On the Basic Principles of *Cannabis*.

A schematic presentation of a qualitative method for identification of the quaternary nitrogen bases found in cannabis seeds was furnished. The isolation and physical characteristics of a new substance were also reported.

3055 Biggs, D. A.; Orcutt, J. B.; and Bakkenist, N., J. Coll. Student Personnel, 15(1), 22-30 (1974).

Correlates of Marijuana and Alcohol Use Among College Students.

The study was conducted on college students to compare the correlates of marihuana and alcohol use in order to ascertain distinctive variables which would help explain the differences in the use of these two drugs.

3056 Bloom, R.; Hays, J. R.; and Winburn, G. M., Int. J. Addict., 9(2), 329-35 (1974).

Marijuana Use in Urban Secondary Schools: A Three-Year Comparison.

The purpose of the present study is to compare reported marihuana use among Houston high school students in order to determine whether a shift in pattern of use among the socioeconomic classes has occurred and whether there has been a growth in reported use over the three years of study (1970 to 1972). Results of the comparison are discussed.

3057 Bloomquist, E. R., pp. 178-86 in *Drugs and Youth* (Proc. Rutgers Symp. Drug Abuse), edited by J. R. Wittenborn, H. Brill, J. P. Smith, and S. A. Wittenborn. Springfield, Illinois, Charles C. Thomas, 1969.

Some Observations on the Contemporary Use of Cannabis.

Marihuana users are classified as either

ntisocial, psychedelics, or otherwise normal subjects. The latter group's decision to use pot is influenced by a variety of societal stimuli, which are discussed in the paper.

3058 Burstein, S.; and Raz, A., Prostaglandins, 2(5), 369-74 (1972).

Inhibition of Prostaglandin E_2 Biosynthesis by $\triangle^1$-Tetrahydrocannabinol.

Indomethacin and $\triangle^9$-THC inhibited the synthesis of prostaglandin E_2 from arachidonic acid in sheep seminal vesicle preparation. The former agent was more potent.

C

3059 Campo, R. A., J. Pharmacol. Exp. Ther., 184(3), 521-27 (1973).

Development of Tolerance in Pigeons to Behavioral Effects of a New Benzoypran Derivative.

SP-1, a synthetic nitrogen-containing cannabinoid, disrupted the behavior of pigeons trained under a multiple fixed ratio, fixed interval schedule of food presentation. Repeated administration of the agent resulted in a marked and long lasting tolerance to its behavioral effects.

3060 Carlini, A. S.; and Post, R. D., Int. J. Addict., 9(3), 401-10 (1974).

Drug Use and Achievement.

Use of marihuana or psychedelic drugs was inversely related to the level of individual achievement.

3061 Carlini, E. A., Arch. Invest. Med., 5(1), 161-72 (1974).

Cannabis sativa and Aggressive Behavior in Laboratory Animals.

In several animal species, cannabis blocks aggression in nonstressed subjects. Under chronic conditions or in stressed animals, however, cannabis induces aggression. The involvement of brain amines is suggested.

3062 Carlini, E. A., pp. 31-43 in *Pharmacology and the Future of Man, Vol. 1, Drug Abuse and Contraception* (Proc. Fifth Int. Cong. Pharmacol., San Francisco, Calif., July 23-28, 1972), edited by J. Cochin. New York, Karger, 1973.

Acute and Chronic Behavioral Effects of *Cannabis sativa*.

Under acute conditions cannabis acts either as a depressant, stimulant or hallucinogen. Tolerance and reverse tolerance to its effects develop after chronic use. The effect of cannabis on aggression is influenced by stress.

3063 Carlini, E. A.; and Lindsey, C. J., Aggress. Behav., 1, 81-99 (1974).

Pharmacological Manipulations of Brain Catecholamines and the Aggressive Behavior Induced by Marihuana in REM-Sleep-Deprived Rats.

Marihuana, amphetamine or apomorphine induced aggression in REM-sleep deprived rats. Evidence presented suggests that DA facilitates, whereas NE inhibits, this marihuana-induced effect.

3064 Chan, M. L.; Whetsell, C.; and McChesney, J. D., J. Chromatogr. Sci., 12(9), 512-16 (1974).

Use of High Pressure Liquid Chromatography for the Separation of Drugs of Abuse.

4

Separation techniques are described which are useful in the identification of 16 common street drugs. The use of HPLC is shown to provide the rapid preliminary purification necessary to process a large number of samples.

3065   Cohn, R. A., Diss. Abstr. Int. B, *35*(5), 2342 (1974).

Sex Differences in Responses of Rats to Marijuana Extract.

The effects of marihuana extract distillate (MED) administered orally or intravenously to male and female rats was studied using a behavioral rating scale. The results indicated that female rats responded differently to the drug compared to the males. The effects of alteration of hormonal balance on response of rats to MED were also studied. Finally the distribution of marihuana rats was carried out using a new technique.

3066   Cole, J. O., pp. 212-16 in *Drugs and Youth* (Proc. Rutgers Symp. Drug Abuse), Edited by J. R. Wittenborn, H. Brill, J. P. Smith, and S. A. Wittenborn, Springfield, Illinois, Charles C. Thomas, 1969.

LSD and Marijuana: Research Needs.

Hurdles to LSD and marihuana research are abundant. Clinical research with the latter should be pursued.

3067   Coper, H.; and Fernandes, M.; pp. 135-41 in *Psychic Dependence: Definition, Assessment in Animals and Man, Theoretical and Clinical Implications*, edited by L. Goldberg and F. Hoffmeister. New York, Springer-Verlag, 1973.

Interaction between Cannabis and Other Drugs.

Cannabis extract increased the toxicity of morphine and pentobarbitone in a dose-dependent manner. It also markedly decreased amphetamine toxicity and prolonged hexobarbitone sleeping time but did not considerably change ethanol LD50 in rats. Hepatic metabolism of type I compounds was inhibited by the cannabinoids, with CBD being a stronger inhibitor than either Δ^9-THC or CBN.

3068   Cormier, D.; Bourassa, M.; and Landreville, I., Toxicomanies, *6*(4), 371-83 (1973).

La Tolerance a la Frustration et le Recours a la Marijuana [Tolerance to Frustration and the Use of Marihuana].

Marihuana users responded to frustration in the same manner as did nonusers, but were more non-conformist than nonusers.

3069   Cormier, D.; Bourassa, M.; and Panquin, D., Toxicomanies, *6*(3), 267-85 (1973).

Characteristiques de la Personnalite de l' Usager de Drogues Benignes: Comparaison Interculterelle [Personal Characteristics of Soft Drug Users: A Cross-Cultural Comparison].

American marihuana users, unlike their Canadian counterparts, were better satisfied with their inner selves and reluctant to depend on others. These and other relevant cultural factors were discussed.

3070   Crawford, H. J. W., Diss. Abstr. Int. B, *35*(6), (1974).

The Effects of Marijuana on Primary Suggestibility.

Marihuana enhanced behavioral and experiential primary suggestibility under double-blind drug administration.

3071   Cross, H. J.; and Davis, G. L., J. Counsel. Psychol., *19*(1), 65-67 (1972).

College Students' Adjustment and Frequency of Marijuana Use.

Students' use of marihuana and their personal adjustment were not related. However, when compared to total sample, the heaviest users admitted to more maladjustment.

D

3072   de Faubert Maunder, M. J., J. Ass. Pub. Anal., *7*, 24-30 (1969).

A Simple and Specific Test for Cannabis.

A field test for cannabis was described which included extraction of a very small amount of material with petroleum ether on a filter paper followed by testing with Fast Blue B salt. Red to violet color was taken as a possible positive. Caution in interpretation of the test was given. Several other plant samples were tested with negative results except for mace and nutmeg.

3073   de Faubert Maunder, M. J., J. Ass. Pub. Anal., *8*, 42-47 (1970).

A Comparative Evaluation of the Δ^9-Tetrahydrocannabinol Content of Cannabis Plants.

A rapid TLC method was described for identifying various components of *Cannabis sativa* from one flower, seed, or small piece of leaf. The two dimensional procedure described allowed identification of the geographical origin of the plant material. CBD was absent from many samples, but was the major component in plants from the Middle East. CBN was a major component of most samples, but a minor one in Middle Eastern plants and most English-grown plants. Δ^9-THC, CBD, CBN, and two unknowns were monitored in the TLC systems in order to classify plant origin.

3074   Deliyannakis, E.; Panagopoulos, C.; and Huott, A. D., Clin. Electroencephalogr., *1*(4), 128-40 (1970).

The Influence of Hashish on Human EEG.

The effect of chronic hashish use on human EEG varied greatly. EEG disturbances were, however, evident in most subjects experiencing hallucination.

3075   Dittrich, A. and Woggon, B., Int. Pharmacopsychiat., *9*(3), 138-51 (1974).

Subjektive Veranderungen unter (-)-Δ^9-*trans*-Tetrahydrocannabinol bei Cannabisnaiven Probanden [Subjective Changes under the Effect of (-)-Δ^9-*trans*-Tetrahydrocannabinol in Cannabis-Naive Subjects].

Δ^9-THC caused profound depersonalization and derealization syndromes in human subjects when it was given in a dose of 350 mg/kg orally.

3076   Du Toit, B. M., S. Aft. J. Sci., *70*, 266-70 (1974).

Cannabis sativa in Sub-Saharan Africa.

A brief review attempting to reconstruct the origin and spread of cannabis in sub-Saharan Africa is provided.

3077 Dykstra, L. and McMillan, D. E., Fed. Proc., *33*(3), 516 (1974).

Shock-intensity Adjustment by Squirrel Monkeys under a Titration Procedure Following Administration of Morphine, Nalorphine, Pentazocine Propoxyphene, Δ^8-Tetrahydrocannabinol (Δ^8-THC) or Chlorpromazine (abstract).

30 min. after the injections of Δ^8-THC (15 mg/kg) or after one of several different analgesics, monkeys adjusted the shock intensity of the electric current applied to their tails to higher levels as compared to normal values.

E

3078 Edwards, G., Acta Psychiat. Scand., Suppl. *251*, 1-62 (1974).

Cannabis and the Criteria for Legalization of a Currently Prohibited Recreational Drug: Groundwork for a Debate.

Paper sets forth an experimental design for the study of "recreational" drugs, and as such serves as a protocol which might be included in any pharmacology or toxicology text. The paper addresses itself to such classic areas as: animal and human pharmacology, psychopharmacology, extrapolation of animal data to man, epidemiological testing, teratogenicity, carcinogenicity, mutagenicity, cannabis and crime, cannabis and escalation to other drug use, and cannabis and other health problems. Appendix lists some research needs and serves as an overview of the paper, and as such

could serve as the basis of a protocol.

3079 Emboden, W., Econ. Bot., *28*(3), 304-10 (1974).

Cannabis - a Polytypic Genus.

A literature review of cannabis. Emphasis is placed on proving cannabis polytypic. Three "species" are listed: *C. sativa, C. indica,* and *C. ruderalis.* Five additional "species" are mentioned as being valid with a total of twelve different "species" having been referred to in the literature.

3080 Emboden, W. A., pp. 214-36 in *Flesh of the Gods: the Ritual Use of Hallucinogens,* edited by P. T. Furst. New York, Praeger Publishers, 1972.

Ritual Use of *Cannabis sativa L.*: a Historical-Ethnographic Survey.

A complete description of *Cannabis sativa L.* as a plant is provided. In addition, its historical and cultural uses in China, the ancient Mediterranean area, Arabia, Asia Minor, Africa, India, Europe, Mexico and the United States are reviewed.

F

3081 Farnsworth, D. L.; Brill, H.; and Robitscher, J. Transact. Studies Coll. Physicians, Philadelphia, *36*(2), 63-95 (1968).

Drug Abuse: Legal and Ethnical Implications of the Non-Medicinal Use of Hallucinogenic and Narcotic Drugs (Mary Scott Newbold Symposium).

Medical, legal and social problems stemming from the abuse of drugs including marihuana, LSD and amphetamine cannot be neglected. Participation of all segments of population, including the younger generation, is required in order to decide on appropriate courses of action.

3082 Farnsworth, D. L.; and Weiss, S. T., pp. 168-77 in *Drugs and Youth* (Proc. Rutgers Symp. Drug Abuse), edited by J. R. Wittenborn, H. Brill, J. P. Smith, and S. A. Wittenborn. Springfield, Illinois, Charles C. Thomas, 1969.

Marijuana: the Conditions and Consequence of Use and the Treatment of Users.

Marihuana, the most often used drug by youth, is not devoid of harmful effects. Treatment of users should deal with predisposing factors to its use.

3083 Farnsworth, N. R., J. Psychedelic Drugs, *5*(1), 67-84 (1972).

Psychotomimetic and Related Higher Plants.

Plants possessing psychotomimetic activity were listed by plant family. *Cannabis indica* and *Cannabis sativa* were listed under the Moraceae family.

3084 Ferraro, D. P.; and Billings, D. K., Int. J. Addict., *9*(2), 321-327 (1974).

Marihuana Use by College Students: Three-Year Trends, 1970-1972.

The use of marihuana by college students (in the 3 years of the present study) has been increasing and most likely will continue to do so. It is suggested that the rate of increase in marihuana use may be diminishing. Precollege first exposure to marihuana has increased from 55.3% in 1970 to 70.7% in 1972.

3085 Ford, R. D., Diss. Abstr. Int. B, *35*(6), 2925 (1974).

Some Effects of Chronic Δ^9-Tetrahydrocannabinol Administration on the Behavior of Pigeons, Monkeys, Rats, and Spiders.

Tolerance and cross-tolerance between Δ^8- and Δ^9-THC were demonstrated in pigeons, rats, squirrel monkeys and orb-web building spiders. Cumulative effects were only detected in spiders.

G

3086 Gergen, M. K.; and Gergen, K. J., J. Appl. Soc. Psychol., *2*(1), 1-16 (1972).

Correlates of Marijuana Use among College Students.

Religious affiliation, sex and region of the country were the major demographic characteristics separating marihuana users from nonusers. A variety of factors including anti-war activities, gradepoint average and the student's academic aspiration also proved to be important.

3087 Gibbs, F. A., Clin. Electroencephalogr., *1*(4), 127 (1970).

Editorial.

Cannabis does not appreciably alter the electroencephalogram.

3088 Goode, E., Amer. J. Psychiat., *128*(10), 1272-76 (1972).

Drug Use and Sexual Activity on a College Campus.

Positive correlation between the extent of marihuana use and increased sexual activity was found for this sample of college students.

3089 Graham, J. D. P.; Lewis, M. J.; and Williams, J., Brit. J. Pharmacol., *52*, 446 (1974).

The effect of Δ^1-Tetrahydrocannabinol on the Noradrenaline and Dopamine Content of the Brain and Heart of the Rat.

Δ^9-THC (10 mg/kg, p.o.) decreased the levels of nonepinephrine in rat brain but not in the heart. It also reduced dopamine levels in both of the above organs. Tween 80, which was used as a vehicle, also produced the same effects.

3090 Grisham, M. G.; and Ferraro, D. P., Psychopharmacologia, *27*, 163-69 (1972).

Biphasic Effects of Δ^9-Tetrahydrocannabinol on Variable Interval Schedule Performance in Rats.

Although doses of 0.25 to 2 mg/kg of Δ^9-THC increased rate of responding of rats trained under variable interval schedule of water presentation, higher doses (12 and 16 mg/kg) decreased responding.

3091 Grupp, S. E., *The Marihuana Muddle*. Lexington, Massachusetts, Lexington Books, 1973. 181 pp.

Thirteen sociologically oriented research papers (both new and revised) grouped around the main themes of initiation of marihuana use, patterns of use of marihuana and other drugs, the interrelationship between marihuana and heroin, and control of marihuana.

3092 Gupta, L.; Tayal, G.; Agarwal, S. S.; and Bhardwaj, S. L., J. Res. Indian Med., *9*(1), 102-04 (1974).

Toxicity Studies on *Cannabis indica.*

Chronic oral administration of alcoholic extracts of *Cannabis indica* (100, 200, and 300 mg/kg) for 3 weeks to rats of either sex caused cessation of body weight gain. Change to the next higher dose was made when tolerance was determined to have developed as evidenced by resumption of normal food intake and of normal behavioral pattern. A 6 weeks regimen of alcoholic extracts of 50 and 100 mg/kg, p.o. caused no prominent histopathological alteration in the liver, heart, kidney, spleen or brain.

H

3093 Halki, J. J., Diss. Abstr. Int. B., *34*(12), 6137-38 (1974).

The Effects of Dextroamphetamine, Dimethyltryptamine, Lysergic Acid Diethylamide and Tetrahydrocannabinol upon Pregnancy and the Offspring.

The effects of d-amphetamine, dimethyltryptamine, LSD and THC upon the gestation or gestational productivity in rats were described. Learning capacity of the first generation offspring of treated animals was also investigated.

3094 Harmon, J. W.; and Aliapoulios, M. A., Surg. Forum, *25*, 423-25 (1974).

Marijuana-Induced Gynecomastia: Clinical and Laboratory Experience.

Diethylstilbesterol antagonized the THC (1 mg/kg, s.c. -induced) stimulation of rat breast tissue development.

3095   Hauck, V. G.; and Mo, H. R., Beitr. Gerichtl. Med., 32, 221-26 (1974).

Tests for the Determination of the Cannabis Contents of Exhaled Air.

TLC and GC methods for the detection of the major cannabinoids in exhaled air are described.

3096   Hirschhorn, I. D.; and Rosecrans, J. A., Fed. Proc., 33(3), 549 (1974).

Tolerance to the Stimulus Effects of Morphine and Δ^9-Tetrahydrocannabinol (abstract).

A high degree of discriminated responding occurred with Δ^9-THC (4 mg/kg) or morphine (10 mg/kg) in a lever-operant test chamber. After supplemental injections of morphine and Δ^9-THC animals continued to discriminate but to a lesser extent between the vehicle and Δ^9-THC or morphine. Naloxone precipated withdrawal symptoms in both groups of rats.

3097   Hollister, L. E., pp. 177-85 in *Psychic Dependence: Definition, Assessment in Animals and Man, Theoretical and Clinical Implications*, edited by L. Goldberg and F. Hoffmeister. New York, Springer-Verlag, 1973.

Clinical Pharmacology of Cannabis in Relation to its Social Use.

A brief review of the clinical pharmacology, including physiological, neurophysiological, biochemical and psychological effects, of cannabis is provided. Natural cannabis, cannabis extracts and synthetic Δ^9-THC or its isomers and homologs have been used (by different routes of administration) in studying these effects. Study techniques, along with difficulties encountered, are also discussed.

3098   Hollister, L. E.; and Gillespie, H. K., pp. 208-11 in *Drugs and Youth* (Proc. Rutgers Symp. Drug Abuse), edited by J. R. Wittenborn, H. Brill, J. P. Smith, and S. A. Wittenborn. Springfield, Illinois, Charles C. Thomas, 1969.

Comments: Similarities and Differences between the Effects of Lysergic Acid Diethylamide and Tetrahydrocannabinol in Man.

THC (30-70 mg) caused similar effects to those induced by LSD in humans. THC, however, was a better euphoriant and lacked any sympathomimetic effects.

3099   Hoton-Dorge, M., J. Pharm. Belg., 29(5), 415-22 (1974).

Isolement des Principaux Constituants Phenoliques du *Chanvre indien*, pas Chromatographie sur Colonne et Chromatographie Preparative [Isolation of the Principal Phenolic Constituents of *Cannabis sativa* by Column Chromatography and Preparative Chromatography].

Phenol derivatives from Indian hemp were partially separated on TLC plates. Complete separation was achieved on silicagel columns.

The isolated products were studied by ultra violet spectroscopy and a fluroescence reaction according to De Clercq, Massart, and Vercruysse.

I

3100   Izquierdo, I., Psychopharmacologia, *38* (3), 259-66 (1974).

Effect on Pseudoconditioning of Drugs with Known Central Nervous Activity.

Female rats of 60-80 days age were pseudoconditioned to cross a midline barrier in a conventional shuttle-box by the random interspersion of buzzers and shock without a temporal association. Having previously tested several of the drugs used in this experiment on a shuttle-box avoidance procedure, the author feels that a differentiation of pseudoconditioned and conditioned responses and comparison can be made. Whereas CBD has been observed to depress shuttle avoidance conditioning it has no effect on pseudomg/kg, i.p., immediately before placing rats in shuttle boxes for a test session.

J

3101   Johnson, B. D., *Marihuana Users and Drug Subcultures*. New York, John Wiley & Sons, Inc., 1973. 290 pp.

The author urges the liberalization of drug laws on the grounds that marihuana users have no legal way to obtain supplies and therefore marihuana selling (and involvement in drug subcultures) emerges from marihuana use.

3102   Jones, R. T., pp. 71-86 in *Psychopathology and Psychopharmacology*, edited

by J. O. Cole, A. M. Freedman, and A. J. Friedhoff. Baltimore, Johns Hopkins University Press, 1973.

Drug Models of Schizophrenia - - Cannabis.

Cannabis is capable of producing a schizophrenic-like state in users. This depends, however, on the interaction of many complex variables such as setting, expectations and personality.

K

3103   Kaplan, J., pp. 461-73 in *Pharmacology, Toxicology and Abuse of Psychotomimetics (Hallucinogens)*, edited by S. Radouco-Thomas, A. Villeneuve, and C. Radouco-Thomas. Quebec, Les Presses do l'Universite Laval, 1974.

The Cost of Marijuana Laws.

Marihuana laws in California turn first-time offenders into felons and contribute to the generation gap and misinformation about drugs. They also are costly; whether social benefits outweigh costs remains an unresolved issue.

3104   Karler, R.; and Cely, W., Fed. Proc., *33*, 540 (1974).

Fate of 3H-Δ^9-Tetrahydrocannabinol in Rat and Mouse Brain (abstract).

The anticonvulsant effect of Δ^9-THC in rats and mice did not temporally correlate with brain levels of Δ^9-THC or metabolites.

3105   Kaymakcalan, S., Ankara Univ. Tip Fak. Mecm., *27*(1-2), 482-99 (1974).

Esrarin Muhtemel Zarar ve Tehlikeleri

[Possible Harm and Dangers Due to cannabis].

A review (with 46 references) of the adverse effects of cannabis.

3106 Keeler, M. H., pp. 186-90 in *Drugs and Youth* (Proc. Rutgers Symp. Drug Abuse), edited by J. R. Wittenborn, H. Brill, J. P. Smith, and S. A. Wittenborn. Springfield, Illinois, Charles C. Thomas, 1969.

Comments: What Are the Questions Concerning Marijuana?

Marihuana is either used or abused as a relaxant, intoxicant or psychotomimetic. It may precipitate psychotic reactions and its legalization would result in greater use.

3107 Khare, B. P., Gupta, S. B. and Chandra, S., Indian J. Agr. Res., *8*(4), 243-248 (1974).

Biological Efficacy of Some Plant Materials against *Sitophilus oryzae Linneaeous.*

A powdered cannabis preparation (bhang) was tested as an insect repellant and insecticide against sitophilus oryzae. There is potential as a repellant only.

3108 Kirchegessner, W. G.; DiPasqua, A. C.; Anderson, W. A.; and Delaney, G. V. J. Forensic Sci., *19*(2), 313-16 (1974).

Drug Identification by the Application of Gas Chromatography/Time-of-Flight Mass Spectrometer Technique.

The authors list mass spectral data for 36 common street drugs including cannabinoids extracted from marihuana, derivatized heroin, cocaine, d-amphetamine, etc. The value of the GC-MS system in forensic science is discussed.

3109 Knight, R. C.; Sheposh, J. P.; and Bryson, J. B., J. Health Soc. Behav., *15*(1), 28-35 (1974).

College Student Marijuana Use and Societal Alienation.

The relationship between four levels of marijuana use (non-users, experimenters, recreational users and heads) and two forms of alienation (personal and societal) were studied. The degree of marijuana use was related to societal alienation but not to personal alienation. Heavy users felt themselves to be targets of legal and social harassment.

3110 Kokka, N.; and Garcia, J. F., Life Sci., *15*(2), 330-38 (1974).

Effect of Δ^9-THC on Growth Hormones and ACTH Secretion in Rats.

Acute and chronic intraperitoneal administration of Δ^9-THC to adult male rats were utilized to demonstrate Δ^9-THC effects on the interactions of the pituitary, hypothalamus, and adrenals. Adult doses of THC (5-20 mg/kg, i.p.) resulted in increased ACTH secretion and a concomitant inhibition of GH secretion. Their former effect was blocked by pretreatment with dexamethasone as doses of 0.2 and 0.4 mg and was blocked partially by pentobarbital at doses of 50 mg/kg, i.p.; the latter effect was not modified by either compound. Tolerance to the neuroendocrine effects of THC was not observed after 20 days at 20 mg/kg. Blood sugar chemistry was not affected by the doses of Δ^9-THC employed.

L

3111 Leuchtenberger, C.; Leuchtenberger, R.; and Schneider, A., Nature, *241*, 137-39 (1973).

12

Effects of Marijuana and Tobacco Smoke on Human Lung Physiology.

Explants of normal human lungs exposed to marihuana or tobacco smoke developed cytotoxic effects including pycnosis, necrosis, and cell death, along with a significant reduction of mitosis and DNA synthesis. These effects were less severe in marihuana than in tobacco-exposed explants.

3112   Li, H.-L., Econ. Bot., *28*, 437-48 (1974).

An Archaeological and Historical Account of Cannabis in China.

Cannabis is indigenous in China. In ancient times, it was used for its analgesic effects and as a hallucinogen, and in Neolithic culture for painted pottery, shoes and fabric. From the Middle Ages to the present time, cannabis has been an important fiber plant in northern China.

3113   Li, H.-L., Econ. Both., *28*(3), 293-301 (1974).

The Origin and Use of Cannabis in Eastern Asia: Linguistic-Cultural Implications.

A continuous record of cannabis from Neolithic to present time is found in northern China. It was cultivated as a fiber plant (hemp); for food, one of the major grains of the ancients; and an important medicinal plant. Cannabis was used widely and its use in everyday life and language is given.

3114   Louria, D. B., pp. 753-61 in *Controversy in Internal Medicine 2*, edited by F. J. Ingelfinger, R. V. Ebert, M. Finland, and A. S. Relman. Philadelphia, W. B. Saunders Company, 1974.

The Marihuana Debate: Doubts about Legalization.

The author discusses the dangers of single or repetitive use of marihuana, the problem of escalation to other drugs and the issue of how many intoxicants our society wishes to legitimatize. He also stresses that decision on the matter of legalization should be made after a dispassionate assessment of the potential public health risks of marihuana.

M

3115   Maitre, L.; Waldmeier, P. C.; and Baumann, P. A., pp. 1015-20 in *Frontiers in Catecholamine Research* (Proc. 3rd Int. Catecholamine Symp.), edited by E. Usdin and S. H. Snyder. Oxford, Pergamon Press, 1973.

Effects of some Tetrahydrocannabinols on the Biosynthesis and Utilisation of Catecholamines in the Rat Brain.

Following tyrosine, Δ^9-THC, Δ^8-THC and DMHP increased the accumulation of rat brain NE and, to a lesser extent, brain DA. All three cannabinoids also accelerated the disappearance of NE, but only DMHP accelerated that of DA. Striatal HVA content remained constant, whereas that of dihydroxyphenylacetic acid increased.

3116   Maker, H. S.; Khan, M. A.; and Lehrer, G. M., Fed. Proc., *33*, 540 (1974).

The Effect of Self Regulated Δ^9-Tetrahydrocannabinol Consumption on Pregnant Mice and Offspring (abstract).

Mice allowed access to Δ^9-THC in their diet were reluctant to consume it. Exposure to THC during gestation and lactation did not, however, result in noticeable adverse effects.

3117 Manning, F. J., Fed. Proc., *33*(3), 481 (1974).

Tolerance to Effects of Δ^9-Tetrahydrocannabinol (THC) on Free-Operant Shock Avoidance (abstract).

Subacute Δ^9-THC administration (30 mg/kg, i.g.) significantly altered both response and shock rates of rats trained in a freely operant shock-avoidance test. Tolerance to the inhibitory, but not the excitatory, effects of THC developed following its repeated administration.

3118 Manno, J.; Manno, B.; Walsworth, D.; and Herd, R., J. Forensic. Sci., *19*, 884-90 (1974).

Analysis and Interpretation of the Cannabinolic Content of Confiscated Marihuana Samples.

Report on the variability of cannabidiol, tetrahydrocannabinol and cannabinol concentrations from marihuana samples confiscated in 1971, 1972 and 1973. There is some increase in THC concentration in the more recent samples. Low concentration of CBN is interpreted to indicate a short delay between harvesting and confiscation prior to analysis.

3119 Mantilla-Plata, B.; Clewe, G. L.; and Harbison, R. D., Fed. Proc., *32*, 736 (1973).

Teratogenic and Mutagenic Studies of Δ^9-Tetrahydrocannabinol in Mice (abstract).

Pregnant mice treated with Δ^9-THC developed more in utero death, had more resorptions and their offspring had higher incidence of cleft palate and lower weight. Lethal mutations in-creased after subacute treatment of pregnant mice with THC, and fecundity and total implants per pregnancy decreased after chronic treatment.

3120 Manys, S.; and Kasprzak, A., Prace Inst. Przemyslu Wlokien Lykowych, *16*, 97-122 (1969).

Badanie Zawartosci Karotenoidow i Substancji Mineralnych w Lisciach Konopi i w Maczce z Lisci Konopi [Carotenoids and Mineral Substances in Hemp Leaves].

Mineral contents and the presence of carotenoids in four varieties of cannabis grown in eastern Europe were discussed. Hemp meal was also investigated. Caroten content in leaves was 330-438.5 mg/kg and xantophylls content was 468-628 mg/kg. Carotenoids content in tested meal was 190-310 mg/kg.

3121 Martin, B. R.; Harris, L. S.; and Dewey, W. L., Fed. Proc., *33*, 540 (1974).

Behavioral and Pharmacological Properties of 11-methyl- and 9-*nor*-Δ^8-Tetrahydrocannabinol (abstract).

11-methyl- and 9-*nor*-Δ^8-THC exhibited behavioral and cardiovascular effects in dogs similar to those seen after administration of Δ^8-THC.

3122 Marx, M. R., Diss. Abstr. Int. B., *34*(7), 3468-69 (1974).

Residual Effects of Recurrent Use of Marihuana on Immediate and Short Term Memory Processes (with special reference to LSD).

Short term and immediate memory functioning were examined in users and non-users of drugs. No significant differences were observed between users and non-users of drugs. Time lapse of brief structured mental activity appeared more sensitive to group differences.

3123   Matsuyama, S.; Yen, F. S.; Jarvik, L. F.; and Fu, T. K., Genetics, *74*, s175 (1973).

Marijuana and Human Chromosomes.

Marihuana caused no significant chromosomal damage in leukocyte cultures of human users.

3124   Maugh, T. H., Science, *185*(4152), 683-85 (1974).

Marihuana: The Grass May No Longer Be Greener.

Contrary to the assumptions of the advocates of marihuana legalization, ample evidence indicates its potential health hazards.

3125   McClean, D. K., Diss. Abstr. Int. B., *34*(9), 4258-59 (1974).

Cell Division and Macromolecular Synthesis in *Tetrahymena pyriformis*: The Action of Tetrahydrocannabinol, Morphine, Levorphanol and Levallorphan.

Δ^9-THC, morphine, levorphanol and levallorphan markedly affect macromolecular synthesis and associated cell division in *Tetrahymena pyriformis*. The study indicated that tetrahymena is a sensitive organism for the evaluation of drug action.

3126   McKillip, J.; Johnson, J. E.; and Petzel, T. P., J. Drug Educ., *3*(1), 1-12 (1973).

Patterns and Correlates of Drug Use Among Urban High School Students.

A high proportion of high school students surveyed admitted to drug use. Drug users were then divided according to their use of hard or social drugs. The latter group included marihuana and alcohol. An individual's drug use habits correlated best with those of close friends and least with those of parents.

3127   McMillan, D. E.; Harris, L. S.; Frankenheim, J. M.; and Kennedy, J. S., Science, *169*, 501-03 (1970).

1-Δ^9-*trans*-Tetrahydrocannabinol in Pigeons: Tolerance to the Behavioral Effects.

Δ^9-THC disrupted responding in pigeons trained under multiple fixed interval, fixed ratio schedule of food presentation. Tolerance to this initial disrupting effect developed after repeated drug administration.

3128   Medek, A., Navratil, J., Hrbek, J., Komenda, S., Krejci, Z.; and Rozhold, O., Acta Univ. Palacki. Olomuc. Fac. Med., *68*, 135-43 (1974).

The Effect of Drugs on the Recall of the Fixed Conditioned Alimentary Motor Reflexes in Cats. Tetrahydrocannabinol and Nicotine, Part I.

Nicotine alone (0.3 mg/kg, s.c.) and in combination with THC (0.6 mg/kg, p.o.) were evaluated in cats of either sex for their effects on performance of a lever-press response for food reinforcement in the presence of auditory discriminative stimulus. Nicotine caused a decrease in the number of correct responses at 0, 15, 30, and 60 min. post injection. Combination treatment (THC-nicotine) resulted in a greater percentage of correct responses at 15 and 60 min. post injection when compared with nicotine alone.

3129   Miras, C. J., pp. 191-98 in *Drugs and Youth* (Proc. Rutgers Symp. Drug Abuse), edited by J. R. Wittenborn, H. Brill, J. P. Smith, and S. A. Wittenborn. Springfield, Illinois, Charles C. Thomas, 1969.

Experience with Chronic Hashish Smokers.

Cannabis users may progress from beginner to regular and then to chronic. Characteristics of chronic users include undernourished appearance, accidental confusional syndrome and EEG changes.

3130   Mohan Ram, H. Y.; and Jaiswal, V. S., pp. 987-96 in *Plant Growth Substances, Proc. Int. Conf. on Plant Growth Substances, 8th, 1973.* Tokyo, Japan, Hirokawa Publishing Co., Inc., 1974.

The Possible Role of Ethylene and Gibberellins in Flower Sex Differentation in *Cannabis sativa*.

Male cannabis plants treated with ethephon formed female flowers while female plants treated with gibberellins formed male flowers. Although ethephon and gibberellins antagonized the action of each other, their effects were dose-dependent. Implications of the findings were discussed.

N

3131   Naditch, M. P., J. Abnorm. Psychol., *83*(4), 394-403 (1974).

Acute Adverse Reactions to Psychoactive Drugs, Drug Usage, and Psychopathology.

Acute adverse reactions to marihuana, used by 92% of this sample, were less severe than those experienced after LSD/mescaline, despite the similarities in patterns. Adjustment, regression and schizophrenia correlated with drug use.

3132   Nahas, G. G.; Suciu-Foca, N.; Desoize, B.; Armand, J. P.; and Morishima, A., Science, *185*(4150), 544 (1974).

Possible Noninhibition of Cellular-Mediated Immunity in Marihuana Smoker. Reply to Comments.

Nahas *et al* defended their work on cell immunity as criticized by Segelman and Segelman in this same issue.

3133   Navratil, J.; Medek, A.; Hrbek, J.; Komenda, S.; Krejci, Z.; and Dvorak, M., Acta Univ. Palacki. Olomuc. Fac. Med., *68*, 145-54 (1974).

The Effects of Drugs on the Recall of the Fixed Conditioned Alimentary Motor Reflexes in Cats. Tetrahydrocannabinol and Nicotine. Part II.

Interaction of THC (0.6 mg/kg, p.o.) and nicotine was studied in cats trained to lever press for food reinforcement. Behavioral disruption resulted when nicotine was injected s.c. 15 or 60 min. following THC administration.

3134   Noyes, R.; and Baram, D.A., Comor. Psychiat., *15*(6), 531-35 (1974).

Cannabis Analgesia.

A brief history of use of marihuana as an analgesic is presented, followed by five case histories in which marihuana was successfully used to reduce pain of the post-surgical type as well as migraine headaches. It is pointed out that this effect is patient-dependent and that concentration on pain may heighten its effects.

O

3135 Orcutt, J. D., Sociol. Soc. Res., *56*(2), 242-53 (1972).

Toward a Sociological Theory of Drug Effects: A Comparison of Marijuana and Alcohol.

Alcohol use is clearly defined by normative expectations, whereas intimate interaction is associated with marihuana use. Alcohol, but not marihuana, is indigenous to middle class American culture.

P

3136 Paton, W. D., Intra-Sci. Chem. Rep., *8*(13), 225-31 (1974).

Pharmacological Factors in the Establishment of Drug Dependence.

Although the issue of cannabis dependence is vague, it is still possible to recognize the drug-seeking habits and the pursuit of its mind-altering properties by users. Cannabis also possesses several properties that make it liable to induce dependence.

3137 Pickens, R.; Thompson, T.; and Muchow, D. C., pp. 78-86 in *Psychic Dependence: Definition, Assessment in Animals and Man. Theoretical and Clinical Implications*, edited by L. Goldberg and F. Hoffmeister. New York, Springer-Verlag, 1973.

Cannabis and Phencyclidine Self-Administration by Animals.

Rhesus monkeys self-administered both Δ^9-THC and phencyclidine i.v. and cannabis by smoking. Responding was initially increased following substitution of phencyclidine for cocaine and Δ^9-THC for phencyclidine, a condition perhaps reflecting in part extinction responding, with a low response rate then being obtained. Other aspects of this self-administration behavior were also discussed.

3138 Pillard, R. C., pp. 762-68 in *Controversy in Internal Medicine 2*, edited by F. J. Ingelfinger, R. V. Ebert, M. Finland, and A. S. Relman. Philadelphia, W. B. Saunders Company, 1974.

Marihuana Is Not a Public Health Menace: It Is Time to Relax Our Social Policy.

The author actively supports the recommendations of the National Commission on Marihuana and Drug Abuse and briefly reviews the various forms of marihuana use and its adverse reactions and effects in heavy users. "Curiosity" and "peer social pressure" were the commonest reasons for casual marihuana use.

3139 Pohl, K. D., Arch. Kriminol., *150*, 93-101 (1972).

Methodische Beitrage zum Nachweis des Synthetischen (-)-Δ^9-Tetrahydrocannabinols [Methodological Contribution to the Detection of (-)-Δ^9-Tetrahydrocannabinol].

Analysis of synthetic Δ^9-THC, synthesized under improved conditions, was conducted by TLC and GC methods. All methods confirmed its presence.

3140 Pradhan, S. N.; Bailey, P. T.; and Ghosh, P., Psychon. Sci., *27*(3), 179-81 (1972).

Effects of $\triangle^9$-Tetrahydrocannabinol on a Timing Behavior in Rats.

$\triangle^9$-THC exerted a biphasic dose-related effect on the response rate in rats trained under DRL-schedule of food reinforcement. Most responses occurred within the first 10 second time category.

3141 Prendergast, T. J., Int. J. Addict., *9*(6), 827-39 (1974).

Family Characteristics Associated with Marijuana Use Among Adolescents.

Less conservative attitude of parents toward marihuana, lax control by mothers and a habit of prescribed drug use by fathers positively predict the possibility of marihuana use by adolescents.

R

3142 Reid, L. D.; Ibrahim, M. K. F.; Miller, R. D.; and Hansteen, R. W., Society of Automotive Engineers Congress, Technical Paper No. 730092, Detroit, Michigan, January, 1973.

The Influence of Alcohol and Marijuana on a Manual Tracking Task.

A useful technique to study the effects of drugs on human performance (i.e., car driving) using linear mathematical models was assessed. Both alcohol and marihuana caused significant alterations in this manual tracking task.

S

3143 Sabelli, H. C.; Vazque, A. J.; Mosnaim, A. D.; and Madrid-Pedemonte, L., Nature, 248(5444), 144-45 (1974).

2-Phenylethylamine as a Possible Mediator for $\triangle^9$-Tetrahydrocannabinol-Induced Stimulation.

The effect of an acute i.v. administration of $\triangle^9$-THC (3 mg/kg) and a chronic one (0.3 mg/kg for 8 days) on the level of 2-phenylethylamine of the rabbit brain was studied. Behavioral effects were also noted in mice before and after treatment with monoamine oxidase inhibitors.

3144 Santavy, F., Acta Univ. Palacki. Olomuc. Fac. Med., *35*, 5-9 (1964).

Notes on the Structure in Cannabidiol Compounds.

The position of the double bond in CBD is discussed. Optical rotation values of several derivatives of CBD are presented, but the author stated that definite assignment can only be obtained from the NMR.

3145 Scherer, S. E., Int. J. Addict., *8*(5), 755-66 (1973).

Hard and Soft Hallucinogenic Drug Users: Their Drug Taking Patterns and Objectives.

College students using LSD, amphetamine and other hard drugs reported higher frequencies of cannabis use than did soft drug users (cannabis only). Greater similarities were found among heavy cannabis users and hard drug users. Findings also indicated that most drug users started their habits before entering college and that parents of users tended to use more drugs than parents of non-users.

3146 Schultes, R. E., Bull. Narcotics, *21*(4), 15-271 (1969).

The Plant Kingdom and Hallucinogens (Part II).

An ethnobotanical review of hallucinogenic plants was presented. Cannabis is a widely spread and used, but poorly understood, hallucinogen.

3147   Sigg, E. B.; Keim, K. L.; Kovacs, J. L.; and Sigg, T. D., Fed. Proc., *32*(3), 221 (1973).

Selective Effect of Psychotropic Agents on Preganglionic Sympathetic Outflow in Cat (abstract).

Δ^9-THC, diphenylhydantoin or chloropromazine diminished the evoked potential in the stimulated splanchnic nerve of anesthetized cats. That of the cervical sympathetic nerve was not influenced.

3148   Simpson, D. D.; and Sells, S. B., Int. J. Addict., *9*(2), 301-14 (1974).

Patterns of Multiple Drug Abuse: 1969-1971.

Marihuana was reported to be used on a weekly basis by 16.6% of this sample of patients entering drug-abuse treatment programs. Heroin was the most abused drug.

3149   Sinnett, E. R.; Wampler, K. S.; and Harvey, W. M., Psychol. Rep., *34*, 47-53 (1974).

Marihuana - A Psychedelic Drug?

When marihuana was compared to several different psychedelics, the judgement of users of marihuana indicated its misclassification as a psychedelic agent.

3150   Small, E., Greenhouse-Garden-Grass, *11*, 46-52 (1972).

The Hemp Problem in Canada.

A description of cannabis cultivation in Canada is presented. Marihuana and hashish are discussed briefly and a detailed description of the cannabis genus is given. For the control of cannabis 2,4-d (1 lb./25 gal. water/acre) is recognized as effective, as are granular herbicides applied prior to germination in early spring.

3151   Small, E., Microgram, *7*(2), 131-32 (1974).

American Law and the Species Problem in Cannabis.

A discussion on the legal definition of cannabis is presented. Only one species, *Cannabis sativa L.* is considered.

3152   Smart, R. G., J. Safety Res., *6*(4), 155-58 (1974).

Marihuana and Driving Risk Among College Students.

A survey of college students indicated that alcohol caused three times as many accidents and driving charges as marihuana. Implications of findings and of differences in driving frequencies under the influence of marihuana and alcohol were discussed.

3153   Smart, R. G.; and Krakowski, M., J. Drug Educ., *2*(3), 279-88 (1972).

Selective Exposure to Information about the Harmful Effects of Marijuana and Tranquilizers.

Selective exposure to marihuana-related information was not related to whether subjects used it or not.

3154   Stanton, M. D., Arch. Gen. Psychiat., *26*, 279-86 (1972).

Drug Use in Vietnam: A Survey Among Army Personnel in the Two Northern Corps.

During the Vietnam tour, an increased incidence of marihuana use along with heavier consumption was reported by a surveyed sample of enlisted men. Correlation between drug use, rank and marihuana use was also estimated.

3155   Stringaris, M. G., *Die Haschischsucht: Pharmakologie, Geschicte, Psychopathologie, Klinik, Soziologie [Hashish Addiction: Pharmacology, History, Psychopathology, Clinical, Sociology]*. Berlin, Springer-Verlag, 1972. 150 pp.

An update of a 1939 publication. Contains 11 pages of references, many of which are more recent than the original publication date.

3156   Szara, S., pp. 707-09 in *Psychopharmacology, Sexual Disorders and Drug Abuse*, edited by Ban, T. A., Boissier, J. R., Gessa, G. J., Heimann, H., Hossister, L., Lehmann, H. E., Munkvad, I., Steinberg, H., Sulser, F., Sundwall, A., and Vinar, O. Amsterdam-London, North Holland Publishing Company, 1973.

Δ^9-Tetrahydrocannabinol-Potential Precursor of "False Hormones"?

Due to the unknown long-term effects of cannabinoids but observed short-term effects in animals, metabolites of Δ^9-THC are proposed as "false hormones". Probable mechanism of false hormones is by selective binding to specific receptors in the hypothalamus and hippocampus.

T

3157   Tec, N., J. Marriage Fam., *32*(4), 656-64 (1970).

Family and Differential Involvement with Marihuana: A Study of Suburban Teenagers.

A survey of 1700 youths, aged 15 to 18, revealed that those who come from broken homes and/or do not live with both parents are more likely to use marihuana than are youths who come from intact families. Other family roles and characteristics, such as warmth and reliability, also proved to be important determinants of marihuana use.

3158   Tec, N., Int. J. Soc. Psychiat., *20*(3-4), 173-79 (1974).

Marihuana and Other Illegal Drugs.

The assumption that marihuana use in itself leads to more potent drug use (the stepping stone theory) is analyzed. Pharmacologically the properties of marihuana do not create a need for other more potent drugs. Psychologically it is assumed that some individuals are prone to drug involvement no matter what the consequences. These people would start out with any drug but because of marihuana's relatively low price and availability it is the drug of choice. The only area where the stepping stone theory can find support is with a sociocultural interpretation. Marihuana is accepted in all socioeconomic levels of the young. Such favorable attitudes reduce the resistance to the use of more potent drugs.

3159   Thoden, J. S.; Mosher, R.; MacConaill, M.; and Ling, G., Med. Sci. Sports, *6*(1), 81 (1974).

Effects of Marihuana on Treadmill Performance (abstract).

Marihuana smoking (6-7 mg Δ^1-THC by groups of volunteers produced significant increases in heart rate and ventilation at rest and while inspiring 7% CO_2. No significant group changes, however, were observed in exercise function.

3160 Tinklenberg, J. R.; and Murphy, P., J. Psychedelic Drugs, *5*(2), 183-91 (1972).

Marihuana and Crime: A Survey Report.

Reviewed pertinent research revealed that marihuana, in and by itself, does not lead to criminal behavior. Rather, it tends to suppress aggression.

3161 Tinklenberg, J. R.; Murphy, P. L.; Murphy, P.; Darley, C. F.; Roth, W. T.; and Kopell, B. S., Arch. Gen. Psychiat., *30*(5), 685-89 (1974).

Drug Involvement in Criminal Assaults by Adolescents.

Being under the influence of drugs constituted a major contributing factor in adolescents engaging in criminal assaults. Marihuana was implicated in 6 out of 56 analyzed cases.

3162 Tinklenberg, J. R.; and Woodrow, K. M., Aggression, *52*, 209-24 (1974).

Drug Use Among Youthful Assaultive and Sexual Offenders.

In adolescents who were serious offenders, alcohol and secorbarbital were most closely associated with assaultive behavior. Marihuana was associated with decreased aggressiveness.

3163 Triesman, D., Int. J. Addict., *8*(4), 667-82 (1973).

Logical Problems in Contemporary Cannabis Research.

Cannabis use is a socially unacceptable phenomenon in the western world. Researchers are therefore predetermined to show cannabis use as detrimental to society and health. This bias and the inherent problems in the research methodologies followed distort the picture completely.

3164 Turkanis, S. A., Fed. Proc., *33*, 540 (1974).

Anticonvulsant Activity and Motor Toxicity of Five Cannabinoids (abstract).

1-*trans*-Δ^9-THC, 11-OH-Δ^9-THC, 1-*trans*-Δ^8-THC, CBD and dimethylheptylpyran were all effective anticonvulsants at much lower than toxic doses.

3165 Tylden, E., Aust. Fam. Physician, *1*, (Feb. 1972).

Cannabis and LSD.

A brief review of cannabis and LSD with discussion of use, effects, problems and treatment.

3166 Tylden, E., Newcastle Med. J., *30*(6), (Dec. 1968).

Cannabis Taking in England.

A discussion of cannabis as a popular drug among young people in England. The source of the drug, its pharmacology and types of users are described.

Chronic use causes a characteristic chronic psychosis. Ninety-five percent of heroin addicts started their use of drugs with cannabis.

U

3167 Uyeno, E. T., Fed. Proc., *33*(3), 540 (1974).

Δ^9-Tetrahydrocannabinol and the Competitive Behavior of the Rat (abstract).

Δ^9-THC inhibited the dominant behavior of male Wister rats in competition for a female in estrus. The ED50 is 1.76 μm/kg.

V

3168 Vachon, L.; Sulkowski, A.; and Rich, E., Psychopharmacologia, *39*, 1-11 (1974).

Marihuana Effects on Learning, Attention and Time Estimation.

Ten male subjects smoked 1 gm cigarettes with 2.5% Δ^9-THC. SS were to rate the quality of the cigarettes and the "high" experienced. Marihuana-induced tachycardia was observed; blood pressure showed systolic elevation; and conjunctival reddening was more apparent after marihuana than placebo. SS rated more intense "high" after marihuana while "pleasantness" of trip varied. One subject had a "bad trip" with anxiety, restlessness and transient paranoid ideation. Memory acquisition process was disrupted on tasks performed along with impaired time perception.

W

3169 Wagner, H., pp. 67-76 in *Rauschgift-Drogen [Intoxicating Drugs]*. Berlin, Springer-Verlag, 1969.

Indischer Hanf (Haschisch, Marihuana) [Indian Hemp (Hashish, Marihuana)].

A technical and historical discussion of hashish in the old world.

3170 Wardell, D. and Mehra, N., J. Coll. Student Personnel, *15*(1), 31-33 (1974).

Prediction of Marihuana Usage Among Students in a University Residence.

The results of the study conducted on university resident students indicated that drug users were less moralistic, more alienated in their view of God, more likely to endorse the "have a good time and get by" attitude toward college and less likely to come from a family in which the father is semi-skilled and the mother is employed.

3171 Warner, E. G., pp. 161-67 in *Drugs and Youth* (Proc. Rutgers Symp. Drug Abuse), edited by J. R. Wittenborn, H. Brill, J. P. Smith, and S. A. Wittenborn. Springfield, Illinois, Charles C. Thomas, 1969.

Sources of Hallucinogenic Drugs, Including Marijuana: The Nature and Economic Significance of the Trade.

Clandestine laboratories easily manufacture drugs such as LSD. Marihuana and hashish are mainly smuggled from Mexico and the Middle East, respectively. Dealing of the Bureau of Narcotics and Dangerous Drugs with these sources was discussed.

3172 Weil, A., pp. 14-23 in *Management of Adolescent Drug Misuse: Clinical, Psychological and Legal Perspectives* (Proc. Second Annual Symp. of the Student Association for the Study of Hallucinogens), edited by J. R. Gamage, Beloit, Wisconsin, Stash Press, 1973.

Toxic Reactions to Marihuana.

The majority of psychotic reactions to marihuana are panic reactions caused by drug-induced anxiety. True psychotic reactions, which are rare, seem to occur in persons with a history of psychosis or hallucinogenic-drug experimentation.

3173 Werner, G.; and Erdmann, G., Naunyn Schmeidebergs Arch. Pharmacol., *282* (Suppl. R105), 22 (1974).

Autoradiographic Investigation of 14c-Tetrahydrocannabinol Distribution in the Monkey (abstract).

A contact procedure was used to prepare autoradiograms of cryostat sections from monkey injected i.v. with labelled Δ^8- and Δ^9-THC and sacrificed 30 min. later. Localization of radioactive Δ^8- and Δ^9-THC was then studied in various organs.

3174 Wilson, C. W. M., editor, *The Pharmacological and Epidemiological Aspects of Adolescent Drug Dependence* (Proc. Society for the Study of Addiction to Alcohol and Other Drugs, London, Sept. 1 and 2, 1966). New York, Pergamon Press, 1968.

This book reports the proceedings of a symposium and contains sections entitled: The Use of Cannabis in Relation to the Adolescent, Drug Dependence of the Cannabis Type, and Marijuana-Heroin Interdependence.

3175 Winek, C. L., pp. 109-27 in *Everything You Wanted to Know About Drug Abuse...but Were Afraid to Ask*. New York, Marcel Dekker, Inc., 1974.

Marihuana and Hashish.

Questions regarding marihuana and its use were asked and answers were provided. Among the questions were the general dose used, potency, identification, physiological and psychological effects and differences between marihuana and other abused drugs.

3176 Woggon, B., *Haschisch: Konsum and Wirkung [Hashish: Consumption and Effects]*. Berlin, Springer-Verlag, 1974. 152 pp.

Information on the historic and actual distribution of hashish consumption, effects of hashish on man and animals, and the possible consequences of long term consumption. 749 references are included.

Z

3177 Zimmerman, A. M.; and McClean, D. K., pp. 67-94 in *Drugs and the Cell Cycle*, edited by A. M. Zimmerman, G. M. Padilla, and L. L. Cameron. New York, Academic Press, 1973.

Action of Narcotic and Hallucinogenic Agents on the Cell Cycle.

Δ^9-THC, morphine, levorphanol and levallorphan reduced RNA, DNA and protein synthesis and increased lipid synthesis of *Tetrahymena*. Δ^9-THC was an effective inhibitor of microsomal drug metabolism and, along with Δ^8-THC, decreased the mitotic index in HeLa cells. Additional research on the action of narcotics and hallucinogens in single cellular system is needed.

A

3178   Abbott, B. J.; Fukuda, D. S.; and Archer, R. A., Experientia, *33*(6), 718-20 (1977).

Microbiological Transformation of Cannabinoids.

By using microorganisms the authors produced several cannabinoid derivatives through biotransformation of $\Delta^{6a, 10a}$-THC and nabilone. The microorganisms used were randomly selected soil isolates, some of which were identified. The several derivatives were given as well as some of the separation procedures. Details of the structural assignments will be published elsewhere.

3179   Abbott, S. R.; Aou-Shumays, A.; Loeffler, K. O.; and Forrest, I. S., Res. Commun. Chem. Pathol. Pharmacol., *10*(1), 9-19 (1975).

High Pressure Liquid Chromatography of Cannabinoids as Their Fluorescent Dansyl Derivatives.

Four synthetic cannabinoids were derivatized with 1-dimethylaminonaphthalene-5-sulfonate (dansyl) and separated using HPLC. Separation by HPLC required 20 min. Maximum sensitivity for fluorescence detection was 5 picograms as compared to 3 nanograms for absorbance detection. Specifics on HPLC system are given.

3180   Abboud, R. T.; and Sanders, H. D., Chest, *70*(4), 480-85 (1976).

Effect of Oral Administration of Delta-9-Tetrahydrocannabinol on Airway Mechanics in Normal and Asthmatic Subjects.

This study revealed that although 10 mg of Δ^9-THC p.o. may produce a slight but significant increase in pulmonary function in normal patients, its effectiveness in asthmatic patients is questionable. In fact one of the asthmatic patients developed severe bronchoconstriction in this study. Thus the therapeutic usefulness of Δ^9-THC for treatment of asthma is doubtful.

3181   Abel, E. L., Behav. Biol., *15*(3), 255-81 (1975).

Cannabis: Effects on Hunger and Thirst.

Cannabis use stimulated hunger in humans, while it inhibited consummatory behavior in animals. The possible causes for this difference were dosage, route of administration, inhibition of alimentary tract activity, differences in fluid intake, changes in blood glucose, neurochemical changes, development of tolerance, and the suggestibility of humans.

3182   Abel, E. L., Behav. Biol., *14*, 1-20 (1975).

Cannabis and Aggression in Animals.

This article cites literature dealing with the effects of cannabis on aggressive animals. The author concludes from his study that a distinction must be made between the acute and chronic effects of the drug and the condition of the subject at the time of drug treatment.

3183   Abel, E. L., ed., The Scientific Study of Marihuana. Chicago, Nelson-Hall, 1976. 299 pp.

This book consists of 31 papers on cannabis, all of which had been previously published and most of which were annotated in our 1976 bibliography. The papers deal with the effects of cannabis on humans.

3184   Abel, E. L., Fed. Proc., *34*(3), 743 (1975).

Suppression of Maternal Behavior in the Mouse by Δ^9-Tetrahydrocannabinol (Δ^9-THC).

Maternal behavior of mice was evaluated following acute (0.2-20 mg/kg, i.p.) and chronic (5 mg/kg/day for 5 days) Δ^9-THC administration. Acute doses decreased maternal activities, especially nursing. Tolerance developed to all.

3185   Abel, E. L., Int. Rev. Neurobiol., *18*, 329-56 (1975).

Marihuana, Learning, and Memory.

A review of the methods for memory and learning research in animals and man with respect to marihuana and its various modes of administration was presented. Marihuana has been shown both to affect and not affect learning and memory in animals. No conclusions were stated on the effects of marihuana on the cognitive process in animals. However, in humans it was generally accepted that marihuana impairs acquisition but not retrieval of information. Ninety references were given.

3186   Abel, E. L., Psychol. Bull., *84*(2), 193-211 (1977).

The Relationship Between Cannabis and Violence: A Review.

After reviewing pertinent literature, it was concluded that casual cannabis use is not a major cause for aggression or violence, but may still precipitate them in certain predisposed individuals. Relevant factors to be considered were also outlined.

3187   Abel, E. L.; and Siemens, A. J., Fed. Proc., *35*(3), 506 (1976).

Response to Δ^9-Tetrahydrocannabinol, Barbiturates and Ethanol in Lactating, Virgin Female and Male Mice.

The responsiveness of lactating, virgin female and male mice to depressant drugs with different mechanisms was reported. Δ^9-THC (0.1 mg/kg) produced significant elevation of body temperature in males. Ten mg/kg of Δ^9-THC decreased body temperature of lactating mice.

3188   Abruzzi, W., Int. J. Addict., *12*(1), 183-93 (1977).

Drug-Induced Psychosis.

Drug-induced psychosis is common among users. Marihuana is no exception. Flashbacks are also precipitated by marihuana use.

3189   Ackerman, N. R., Toxicol. Appl. Pharmacol., *41*(2), 321-28 (1977).

The Lack of an Effect of Δ^9-THC on Pulmonary Smooth Muscle Function in the Guinea Pig.

THC was found to be devoid of any direct bronchodilating, antihistaminic and anticholinergic activities in guinea pigs.

3190   Acosta-Urquidi, J.; and Chase, R., Can. J. Physiol. Pharmacol., *53*(5), 793-98 (1975).

The Effects of Δ^9-Tetrahydrocannabinol on Action Potentials in the Mollusc *Aplysia.*

The effect of Δ^9-THC (10^{-4} - 10^{-5} M) and its water soluble derivative SP-111A on the neuronal membranes of a parieto-visceral ganglia and paired buccal ganglia of the mollusc *Aplysia californica* was examined. THC depressed neuronal excitability; however, the soma was affected more than the axon.

3191   Adamec, C.; Pihl, R. O.; and Leiter, L., Int. J. Addict., *11*(2), 295-307 (1976).

An Analysis of the Subjective Marijuana Experience.

Marihuana users in this Canadian sample were mostly single, 18-31 years old, highly educated and creative. Subcultural differences with a comparable California sample were pointed out. Included were frequency of drug use and minimal levels of intoxication.

3192   Adamec, C. S.; and Pihl, R. O., Psychol. Women Quart., *2*(4), 334-53 (1978).

Sex Differences in Response to Marijuana in a Social Setting.

Female subjects experienced more positive attitude, mood, interaction and pleasure under marihuana influence than did male counterparts under controlled experimental setting.

3193   Adams, A. J., pp. 93-105 in *Frontiers in Visual Science*, Vol. 8 (Proc. Univ. Houston Coll. Optom. Ded. Symp., Houston, Texas, March 1977), edited by S. J. Cool and E. L. Smith. New York, Springer-Verlag, 1977.

Acute Effects of Alcohol and Marijuana on Vision.

Human subjects exhibited visual deficits after administration of alcohol or mari-huana under double-blind clinical conditions. The effects were more profound in the former case. These deficits involved more oculomotor than visuo-sensory changes.

3194   Adams, A. J.; Brown, B.; Flom, M. C.; Haegerstrom-Portnoy, G.; and Jones, R. T., Psychopharmacology, *56*(1), 81-86 (1978).

Marijuana, Alcohol, and Combined Drug Effects on the Time Course of Glare Recovery.

Studies on light adaptation after intense light exposure were found to be significantly delayed by alcohol, marihuana and a combined dose of alcohol and marihuana. These effects were found in a double blind experiment using 10 subjects. The experimental treatments were placebo, 0.75 mg/kg of 95% ethanol, 8 and 15 mg of THC and 0.75 mg/kg of 95% ethanol together with 15 mg of THC.

3195   Adams, A. J.; Brown, B.; Flom, M. C.; Jones, R. T.; and Jampolsky, A., Amer. J. Optom. Physiol. Optics, *52*(11), 729-35 (1975).

Alcohol and Marijuana Effects on Static Visual Acuity.

Dosages of 95% ethanol (1.0 and 0.5 mg/kg) or marihuana (8 and 15 mg Δ^9-THC) were administered to volunteers, and static high-low contrast visual acuity was evaluated. No change was detected up to 6 hrs. post-injection.

3196   Adams, A. J.; Brown, B.; Haegerstrom-Portnoy, G.; Flom, M. C.; and Jones, R. T., Percept. Psychophys., *20*(2), 119-24 (1976).

Evidence for Acute Effects of Alcohol and Marihuana on Color Discrimination.

Post-drug changes in color perception were measured after doses of alcohol or marihuana. A deficiency in hue discrimination in the blue region was observed for both drugs. Alcohol also created a deficiency in the yellow-green region which lasted for at least 90 minutes post-consumption. Marihuana caused a deficiency in the red region which returned to control levels within 90 minutes.

3197   Adams, M. D.; Chait, L. D.; and Earnhardt, J. T., Brit. J. Pharmacol., *56*, 43-48 (1976).

Tolerance to the Cardiovascular Effects of Δ^9-Tetrahydrocannabinol in the Rat.

Rats were administered daily i.p. injections of Δ^9-THC, 10 mg/kg, for 28 days. Treated rats did not gain weight for 5 days after first treatment. Then tolerance developed and weight increased at the same rate as controls. Tolerance also developed to the hypothermic and BP responses, but not to the depressant effects of THC on spontaneous motor activity.

3198   Adams, M. D.; Earnhardt, J. T.; Dewey, W. L.; and Harris, L. S., J. Pharmacol. Exp. Ther., *196*(3), 649-56 (1976).

Vasoconstrictor Actions of Δ^8- and Δ^9-Tetrahydrocannabinol in the Rat.

Δ^8- and Δ^9-THC (0.1-3 mg/kg, i.v.) increased BP in rats in a dose-related manner. This initial BP increase was followed by hypotension and bradycardia. Intra-arterial infusion of either cannabinoid resulted in vasoconstriction which was effectively blocked by phentolamine and reserpine. Other data presented suggested that the THC-induced increase of BP is the result of tyramine-like action.

3199   Adams, M. D.; Earnhardt, J. T.; Martin, B. R.; Harris, L. S.; Dewey, W. L.; and Razdan, R. K., Experientia, *33*(9), 1204-05 (1977).

A Cannabinoid with Cardiovascular Activity, but No Overt Behavioral Effects.

Synthetic congeners of Δ^8-THC and CBD, each with transposed phenoxyl and pentyl side chain groups, failed to elicit behavioral effects in the dog. The CBD congener did produce hypotension and bradycardia in anesthetized dogs, but without observable CNS effects at doses used.

3200   Adams, P. M.; and Barratt, E. S., Biol. Psychiat., *10*(3), 315-22 (1975).

Effect of Chronic Marijuana Administration on Stages of Primate Sleep-Wakefulness.

Chronic Δ^9-THC (1.2 mg/kg, p.o., for 60 days) altered all 5 stages of the sleep-wakefulness cycle in chronically implanted monkeys. Disturbances in neurotransmitter balance caused by THC may have been responsible for the above mentioned changes.

3201   Adams, P. M.; and Barratt, E. S., Electroencephalogr. Clin. Neurophysiol., *39*(6), 621-25 (1975).

Role of Biogenic Amines in the Effects of Marijuana on EEG Patterns in Cats.

Agents altering brain biogenic amines modified the behavioral and EEG effects manifested in cats treated with Δ^9-THC

(2.7 mg/kg, p.o.). A specific serotonergic involvement was indicated for Δ^9-THC.

3202 Adams, P. M.; and Barratt, E. S., Physiol. Psychol., 4(2), 155-58 (1976).

The Effects of a Marijuana Extract on Two-Choice Discrimination Learning in the Squirrel Monkey.

Δ^9-THC (0.68 mg/kg, p.o.) significantly impaired form- and color-cued learning in trained monkeys. Therefore it was suggested that marihuana induces motor and learning deficiencies.

3203 Adams, T. C., Jr.; and Jones, L. A., Agric. Food Chem., 23(2), 352-53 (1975).

Phytosterols of Cannabis Smoke.

The β-hydroxysterols: campesterol, stigmasterol, and β-sitosterol were identified and quantitated in marihuana smoke. The levels of the individual sterols are essentially in the same ratio as that found in the plant material smoked in the study.

3204 Agnew, W. F.; Rumbaugh, C. L.; and Cheng, J. T., Brain Res., 109(2), 355-66 (1976).

The Uptake of Δ^9-Tetrahydrocannabinol in Choroid Plexus and Brain Cortex In Vitro and In Vivo.

Studies of the CNS uptake and distribution of labelled THC in rabbits indicated that it is actively transported by the choroidal epithelium and cerebral cortical slices. Various characteristics of this active transport process were reported.

3205 Agrell, J., Lakartidningen, 73(45), 3876-78 (1976).

Cannabis- -Range of Misuse and Future Trends.

Certain aspects of cannabis misuse were examined. It was found to be fairly popular among the national servicemen in Sweden. Although the authors could not statistically prove that cannabis use led to use of other hard drugs, they did find that many of the addicts initially abused marijuana. Cannabis use was also more popular in large cities than in rural areas.

3206 Agurell, S., Lakartidningen, 73(45) 3860-63 (1976).

Detecting Cannabis Use and Relation of Pharmacokinetics to Effects in Man.

Since the concentration of THC in blood is very low after smoking cannabis, the use of advanced analytical techniques such as mass fragmentography and radio-immunological methods are necessary. The application of these techniques is discussed.

3207 Agurell, S.; Binder, M.; Fonseka, K.; Lindgren, J.-E.; Leander, K.; Martin, B.; Nilsson, I. M.; Nordquivst, M.; Ohlsson, A.; and Widman, M., pp. 141-55 in Marihuana: Chemistry, Biochemistry, and Cellular Effects, edited by G. G. Nahas. New York, Springer-Verlag, 1976.

Cannabinoids: Metabolites Hydroxylated in the Pentyl Side Chain.

Side chain hydroxylated cannabinoids are discussed. The ultimate goal is to establish to what extent, if any, side chain

28

hydroxylated Δ^9-THC metabolites contribute to the effects of Δ^9-THC and marihuana in man. Over a dozen previously unknown side chain hydroxylated metabolites are also discussed.

3208   Agurell, S.; Levander, S.; Binder, M.; Bader-Bartfai, A; Gustafsson, B.; Leander, K.; Lindgren, J-E.; Ohlsson, A.; and Tobisson, B., pp. 49-61 in *The Pharmacology of Marihuana, Vol. 1*, edited by M. C. Braude and S. Szara. New York, Raven Press, 1976.

Pharmacokinetics of Δ^8-Tetrahydrocannabinol in Man After Smoking: Relations to Physiological and Psychological Effects.

A new method for the detection of Δ^8-THC by MS is described. Plasma levels of human volunteers smoking 8.3 or 21 mg of Δ^8-THC were determined by this method on a LKB Model 9000 GC/MS. This new method can detect 0.3 ng Δ^8-THC/ml of plasma. The pattern of plasma concentration and heart rate are similar to that seen with Δ^9-THC.

3209   Agurell, S.; Lindgren, J.-E.; Edery, H.; Leander, K.; Martin, B.; Nordqvist, M.; Widman, M.; Yisak, W.; Mechoulam, R.; and Rosell, S., Acta Pharm. Suecica, *14*(suppl.), 28 (1977).

Cannabinoids- -Metabolic Patterns Versus Biological Activity.

A discussion of the complicated patterns of cannabinoid metabolism in man and animals and the assignment of biological activity to certain metabolites. The authors considered both *in vivo* and *in vitro* studies, clinical studies, and species differences.

3210   Aldrich, M. R., J. Psychedelic Drugs., *9*(3), 227-33 (1977).

Tantric Cannabis Use In India.

Rituals of Tantric practice are described. Cannabis is used to intensify actions and to allow worshipers to sense the divinity inside and outside themselves.

3211   Aldridge, J. W.; and Pomeranz, B., Comp. Biochem. Physiol. [c], *57*C(1), 75-77 (1977).

Δ^1-Tetrahydrocannabinol Derivative Enhances Excitatory Synaptic Potentials Through a Presynaptic Mechanism in Crayfish Neuromuscular Junction.

Δ^1-THC was tested on a crayfish neuromuscular junction which is a glutamate synapse. PH changes were noted to affect drug potency at the synapse. Δ^1-THC was shown not to interfere with post-synaptic binding or action of glutamate, but to enhance junction potential. The enhancement is suggested to be presynaptic and four possible mechanisms are discussed.

3212   Alessandro, A.; Mari, F.; and Mazzi, G., Boll. Chim. Farm., *114*, 21-25 (1975).

Metodo Rapido Per L'identificazione Dei Principi Attivi Della "Cannabis" Mediante Cromatografia Su Strato Sottile Circolare [Rapid Method for the Identification of the Active Principles of Cannabis by Means of Circular Thin-Layer Chromatography].

Chromatographic methods to separate the major components of cannabis are described. Two solvent systems are used which allow for excellent separation of CBD, THC and CBN. Problems with minor components or other interfering compounds are not described.

3213   Alexander, P. C.; Crawford, W. J.; Merritt, J. C.; Curry, C. L.; and Barnes, B. O., Clin. Res., *26*(3), 286a (1978).

Cardiovascular Responses in Glaucoma Patients after Inhalation of Tetrahydrocannabinol.

THC increased heart rate and decreased BP in hypertensive- and normotensive-glaucoma patients.

3214   Alikaridis, P.; Michael, C. M.; Papadakis, D. P.; Kephalas, T. A.; and Kiburis, J., United Nations, ST/SOA/SER.S/55, June 17, 1977. GE. 77-7339.

Chemical Aspects of Cannabis Smoke Produced Through Water Pipes.

Cannabis was smoked by a machine and the particulate matter and effluent gases were analyzed. The cannabis was mixed with a tobacco commonly used by water pipe smokers and smoked through a water pipe. Approximately 10% of the originally smoked cannabis got through to the machine with a calculated 25% of the initial amount of CBD, CBN, and THC.

3215   Allen, L. V., U. S. Pharmacist, $3(4)$, 65-75 (1978).

History and Effects of Marijuana.

Available data point to the hazards associated with marihuana intoxication and also to its possible therapeutic benefits. More objective studies are needed.

3216   Allen, T., New Eng. J. Med., $294(3)$, 168 (1976).

Tetrahydrocannabinol and Chemotherapy.

Letter to the editor calls attention to the antiemetic properties of Δ^9-THC and cannabis by quoting from "How Could I Not Be Among You?" by poet Ted Rosenthal, who succumbed to leukemia in 1972.

3217   Alli, B. A., J. Natl. Med. Ass., $70(9)$, 677-80 (1978).

Marijuana and the Adolescent.

Physicians, the public and authorities should assume more rational and responsible positions in dealing with marihuana use by adolescents, which seems to be increasing.

3218   Altman, J. L.; Albert, J.-M.; Milstein, S. L.; and Greenberg, I., Psychopharmacol. Commun., $2(4)$, 327-30 (1976).

Drugs as Discriminative Events in Humans.

A list of drugs is presented along with literature citations for tasks tested for dissociated learning in humans. Three references are listed for the various parameters tested in humans using marihuana.

3219   Alvares, A. P., Clin. Pharmacokinetics, 3, 462-77 (1978).

Interactions Between Environmental Chemicals and Drug Biotransformation in Man.

A brief review of the literature on Δ^9-THC in regard to metabolism is presented. Speculations on the effects of marijuana smoke are briefly mentioned.

3220   Amit, Z.; Levitan, D. E.; Brown, Z. W.; and Rogan, F., Neuropharmacology, $16(2)$, 121-24 (1977).

Possible Involvement of Central Factors in the Mediation of Conditioned Taste Aversion.

30 ug of THC injected in the dorsal hippocampus (DH) produced a conditioned taste aversion (CTA) to saccharin in male wistar rats. Ip injection of 5 mg/kg THC produced CTA also.

When THC was injected i.p. and into the DH simultaneously the effects on CTA were additive. Although both morphine and ethanol produced CTA when given i.p., no CTA was observed when these drugs were given in the DH. Thus, THC produces CTA by both peripheral and central components and the latter is located in the dorsal hippocampus.

3221 Anderson, E., Int. Rev. Mod. Sociol., 7(2), 212-23 (1977).

A Comparison of Male and Female Adolescents' Attachment to Parents and Differential Involvement With Marijuana.

Questioning a sample of high school students revealed that value congruence and affectional identification with parents were inversely related to youth involvement with marihuana. Importance of differential socialization patterns of young males and females for involvement with drug use was also emphasized.

3222 Anderson, P. F.; Jackson, D. M.; Chesher, G. B.; and Malor, R., Psychopharmacologia, 43(1), 31-36 (1975).

Tolerance to the Effects of Δ^9-Tetrahydrocannabinol in Mice on Intestinal Motility, Temperature and Locomotor Activity.

Female mice were administered 1 ml/100 g body weight Δ^9-THC by gavage. Tolerance developed to the hypothermic effect and to the depressant effect of THC on locomotor activity and on intestinal motility.

3223 Andre, C.; and Vercruysse, A., Planta Med., 29(4), 361-66 (1976).

Histochemical Study of the Stalked Glandular Hairs of the Female Cannabis Plants, Using Fast Blue Salt.

Use of fast blue B in detecting cannabinoids is discussed. Histochemical observations on stalked and sessile glandular hairs of cannabis plants showed concentration of cannabinoids inside, but not outside cuticles of intact hairs.

3224 Andrews, J.; and Conley, J., Amer. Ann. Deaf, 122(6), 557-67 (1977).

Beer, Pot, and Shoplifting: Teenage Abuses.

Marihuana smoking, shoplifting and accidents are prevalent social teenage problems. By relying on the mass media to obtain information, deaf youths often have misconceptions of the nature and consequences of such crimes. To help the deaf obtain accurate and appropriate information, reading and writing skills should be improved. Ways to do so are proposed.

3225 Anokhina, I. P.; Bondarenko, T. T.; Zabrodin, G. D.; and Khristolyubova, N. A., Zh. Nevropatol. Psikhiatr. Im. S. S. Korsakova, 75(2), 264-74 (1975). (Russ.)

General Principles of the Mechanism of the Central Action of Psychotomimetics.

LSD (20-60 ug/kg/day), hashish extracts or phenamine (10-20 mg/kg/day) were injected i.v. into rabbits or into several brain areas. EEG showed increased activity; especially sensitive were the mid brain and limbic system. The adrenergic substrate and serotoninergic structures of brain stem and limbic system were also affected.

3226 Anonymous, Brit. J. Addict., *73*(4), 337-38 (1978).

Cannabis: Memories of the Future (editorial).

Satirical comment on British policy in regard to cannabis.

3227 Anonymous, Brit. Med. J., *1*(6111), 460-61 (1978).

Cannabis and the Cardiovascular System.

The effects of cannabis smoking on the heart of normal individuals and/or those with heart diseases is discussed. The interaction of THC with other drugs and the action of cannabis and THC on BP were also discussed.

3228 Anonymous, Brit. Med. J., *2*(6044), 1092-93 (1976).

Cannabis Psychosis (editorial).

This paper points out that there is little agreement about the clinical basis of differentiation of cannabis psychosis from functional disorders, including pre-existing neuroses.

3229 Anonymous, *Cannabis: A Discussion Paper.* Royal Commission into the Non-Medical Use of Drugs, South Australia, 1978. 132 pp.

The purpose of this publication is to discuss the possible alternatives for the regulation of marihuana (cannabis) use in Australia, with reference to evidence on the effects of use, the extent of use at present, current regulation, and the history of regulation elsewhere. It does not present recommendations, but does ask for comments from readers.

3230 Anonymous, Chem. Eng. News, *53*(49), 27-28 (1975).

Cancer Risk Higher for Pot Smokers.

More than 150 potentially carcinogenic polynuclear aromatic hydrocarbons have been isolated from the smoke condensate of Mexican marihuana. Pyrolysis of cannabinoids yields polynuclear aromatic hydrocarbons. Increased carcinogens may derive from the combustion of high potency marihuana.

3231 Anonymous, Conn. Med., *42*(6), 337-80 (1978).

Health Aspects of Marihuana Use.

After reviewing the convincing evidence pointing to the hazardous consequences of marihuana use to individuals and society, the AMA Council on Scientific Affairs recommended the discouragement of marihuana use in a report delivered in 1977.

3232 Anonymous, Consumer Rep., *40*, 256-66 (1975).

Marijuana: The Legal Question.

A paper in favor of decriminalizing marihuana.

3233 Anonymous, Drugs Drug Abuse Educ., *6*(10), 1-3 (1975).

Marijuana Use Increasing.

Results of four studies indicate that marihuana use is increasing to the point of joining alcohol and tobacco as a widely used recreational drug. Long-term effects are still unknown; yet moderate use does not seem to be a health hazard. Studies indicating brain and chromosome damage are still challenged by other researchers. Studies concentrating on the cumulative effects of marihuana are needed.

3234   Anonymous, J. Amer. Med. Ass., *233*(12), 1251, 1255 (1975).

Test Monkeys Display 'Marihuana Syndrome'.

2.4 mg/kg/day of THC was administered orally to rhesus monkeys. Hormonal levels were checked and no physiological changes were observed. However, there were behavioral and social changes. After 3 or 4 months tolerance developed. The drugged females rose through the ranks and were more aggressive. Lower ranking males had to be removed from the cages after 7 months.

3235   Anonymous, J. Amer. Med. Ass., *235*(12), 1199, 1201 (1976).

Marihuana Ingredient Has Various Medical Uses.

Potential therapeutic applications of marihuana as far as patients with glaucoma, asthma and terminal cancer are discussed. Results in these areas are only preliminary and patient improvement may be due to drug-induced psychological effects.

3236   Anonymous, J. Sch. Health, *45*(9), 544-46 (1975).

National Survey of Marijuana Use and Attitudes.

A national survey revealed that 49% of American adults between the ages of 18 and 25 have tried marihuana; adults 50 and older have hardly used

it, while teenagers hold an intermediate position. The sample was evenly divided on the issue of decriminalization with the greatest difference seen between users and never users.

3237   Anonymous, Lancet, *1*(7908), 667-69 (1975).

Therapeutic Possibilities in Cannabinoids.

Possible therapeutic applications of cannabinoids are discussed with emphasis on their relatively prolonged bronchodilation. Other effects discussed include: tranquillization, analgesia, anticonvulsion, hypothermia, hypotension, appetite stimulation, lowering of intraocular tension, and immunosuppression.

3238   Anonymous, Lancet, *2*(8027), 49 (1977).

The Law on Possession of Cannabis.

The legal changes concerning cannabis use in Britain were discussed.

3239   Anonymous, *Marihuana and Health*. Fifth Annual Report to the U.S. Congress from the Secretary of Health, Education, and Welfare, Superintendent of Documents, U. S. Government Printing Office, Washington, D. C., 1975. 145 pp.

Progress in the field of marihuana research was reviewed. Cannabis use in the U.S. is on the rise. Chemical, pharmacological and behavioral characteristics of marihuana in both humans and animals were among the topics discussed.

3240   Anonymous, *Marihuana and Health*. Sixth Annual Report to the U. S. Congress from the Secretary of Health, Education, and Welfare, Superintendent of Documents, U. S. Government Printing Office, Washington, D. C., 1976. GPO Stock No. 017-024-00570-3. 44 pp.

The 6th annual report on the progress of marihuana research during 1976 is compiled by the Department of Health, Education, and Welfare for Congress in compliance with Title V of PL 91-296. This review is non-technical and deals only with current knowledge. Six general areas of marihuana research are outlined and include marihuana use patterns and use trends in the USA with emphasis on at-risk populations; chemistry and metabolism of cannabis; animal research; human research and areas of public health concern; therapeutic applications for cannabinoid products; and future research directions.

3241 Anonymous, *Marihuana and Health*. Seventh Annual Report to the U. S. Congress from the Secretary of Health, Education, and Welfare, Superintendent of Documents, U. S. Government Printing Office, Washington, D. C., 1977. 52 pp.

Annual progress report on marihuana research. Trends in marihuana use, pharmacological advances, both in man and animals and possible therapeutic applications were among the issues discussed.

3242 Anonymous, *Marihuana-Hashish Epidemic and its Impact on United States Security. The Continuing Escalation.* Hearings before the Subcommittee to Investigate the Administration of the Internal Security Act and Other Internal Security Laws of the Committee on the Judiciary, United States Senate, Ninety-Fourth Congress, First Session, Part 2, May 8, 1975. U. S. Government Printing Office, Washington, D. C., 1975.

Continued upward escalation in cannabis use and in potency of cannabis preparations points to a more careful scrutiny of the drug prior to any major revisions in U. S. policy towards marihuana. Testimony of: Jerry N. Jensen, Deputy Administrator, Department of Justice; Carlton E. Turner, Director of Marihuana Project, University of Mississippi; Coy W. Waller, Director, Research Institute, University of Mississippi; Robert L. Dupont, Director, National Institute on Drug Abuse.

3243 Anonymous, Mass. Phys., *36*, 18-19 (1977).

Ethanol and Cannabis.

A comparison was carried out between the effects and the legality or illegality of cannabis and alcohol.

3244 Anonymous, Med. J. Aust., *1*(7), 201-02 (1977).

Chronic Cannabis Use and Psychomotor Function (editorial).

A brief synopsis of the findings of several studies concerned with chronic marihuana use is presented. The studies include those conducted by the U. S. Government on users in Jamaica, Greece, and Costa Rica, as well as those conducted by Sharma in Nepal and by Soueif in Egypt. The findings reached in the latter two studies, concerning the presence of an amotivational syndrome, contradict the findings reached in the studies conducted by the U. S. Government.

3245 Anonymous, Med. J. Aust., *1*(21), 771 (1976).

Cannabis and Road Accidents (editorial).

An editorial advocating the use of the newly derived means of detection of cannabinoids in blood or urine by means of a simple radioimmunoassay to monitor levels in unsafe automobile drivers.

3246 Anonymous, Med. J. Aust., *1*(25), 767-68 (1975).

Marihuana - Evidence for the Prosecution.

A comment on the effects of marihuana. There are enough proven adverse effects of marihuana (toxic psychosis, panic reactions, DNA inhibition and chromosomal breakage) that possible therapeutic applications and personal use carry definite dangers.

3247 Anonymous, Med. Lett. Drugs Ther., *18*(17), 69-70 (1976).

Marihuana.

Conclusions based upon current literature about marihuana include the observations that: no physical dependence has been shown, driving under the influence of marijuana can be dangerous, and the drug should not be used by pregnant women.

3248 Anonymous, N. Y. State J. Med., *75*(5), 774-76 (1975).

Questions and Answers.

Chronic use of marihuana produced gynecomastia in some males and alterations in reproductive physiology were noted. The effects may be the result of direct action of THC on the breast or a direct CNS effect on the pituitary in the release of prolactin and testicular output of androgen.

3249 Anonymous, Pa. Med., *79*(1), 14 (1976).

Decriminalize, Don't Legalize. The Society's Marihuana Position - - Modify Law.

The official position of the Pennsylvania Medical Society with respect to marihuana is presented as supportive of decriminalization with continued close scrutiny on future developments in the areas of toxicity, benefits, and abuse of the drug.

3250 Anonymous, Pediatrics, *56*(1), 134-43 (1975).

Effects of Marihuana on Man.

The Committee on Drugs reports that only 4% of the adults and youths who use marihuana are heavy smokers. The adverse effects (physiological, psychological, mutagenic, and teratogenic) are discussed. The committee recommends that one should not drive while intoxicated with marihuana and that no criminal penalties should be imposed for possession or use.

3251 Anonymous, Prof. Pharmacy, *5*(1), 4 (1978).

Investigator 'High' on New Glaucoma Treatment.

The recent data collected on marihuana as an anti-glaucoma agent were summarized. Δ^9-THC was effective in reducing IOP in man and animals.

3252 Anonymous, Science, *192*(4238), 450 (1976).

House Chops Sex-Pot Probe.

Funds for the Southern Illinois University (rubin) project to investigate marihuana effects on human sexual behavior (arousal) have been cancelled in a highly unorthodox manner by the House of Representatives. Opposition was on financial and moral grounds.

3253 Anonymous, Science, *201*(4357), 694 (1978).

Medical Marijuana Substitute Under Development.

The new synthetic cannabinoid, Nabilone, of Eli Lilly and Co. is being investigated as a potential antiemetic agent in cancer patients undergoing chemotherapy. The agent is at phase III of its clinical trial and the company hopes to file for a new drug application next year.

3254 Anonymous, Sci. News, *109*(8), 119 (1976).

Marijuana Report: Another Approach.

Summary of the report prepared by the Department of HEW. Marihuana's therapeutic uses are enumerated: 1) for glaucoma and asthma; 2) as an anticonvulsant agent; 3) as a sedative hypnotic; 4) as an antinauseant and antiemetic in cancer patients undergoing chemotherapy; and 5) as an analgesic, preanesthetic and antidepressant in treating alcoholics and relieving heroin withdrawal symptoms.

3255 Anonymous, United Nations, Division of Narcotic Drugs, MNAR/15/1976 GE. 77-1387.

The Botany and Chemotaxonomy of Cannabis.

This is a report of a working group sponsored by the United Nations to study the botany and chemotaxonomy of cannabis and to define specific areas where further research is still needed. A list of known chemicals in cannabis is given. It was agreed that it was impossible to subdivide the species with current scientific knowledge.

3256 Anonymous, United Nations Document, MNAR/6/1975 GE. 75-5104, Athens, 21-25 April 1975.

The Chemistry of Cannabis Smoke.

A summary of the patterns of cannabis use and a review of experimental procedures, apparatus, the "standard" of marihuana, and pyrolytic aspects of cannabis are given.

3257 Anonymous, United Nations Information Letter, Division of Narcotic Drugs, NAR/Inf. Lett./1976-5, May 1976.

Pakistan. Workshop on Drug Abuse Prevention. Cannabis.

In spite of the restrictive action taken by the Pakistani Government, illicit traffic of charas (resin from the cannabis plant) continues.

3258 Anonymous, United Nations Information Letter, Division of Narcotic Drugs, NAR/Inf. Lett./1975-6, June 1975.

Cannabis Effects in Animal Brain.

Rats given 20 mg THC/kg body weight performed differently on tests than drug-free rats. The natural attrition of brain cells was accellerated, and with a long exposure to cannabis the deterioration of learning and motor skills would become permanent.

3259   Archer, R. A.; Blanchard, W. B.; Day, W. A.; Johnson, D. W.; Lavagnino, E.; Ryan, C. W.; and Baldwin, J. E., J. Org. Chem., 42(13), 2277-84 (1977).

Cannabinoids. 3. Synthetic Approaches to 9-Ketocannabinoids. Total Synthesis of Nabilone.

Five methods for the synthesis of 9-keto-cannabinoids were outlined, two of which had been reported before. The new methods are based on coupling olivetol (or an olivetol derivative) with a suitable monoterpene.

3260   Archer, R. A.; Johnson, D. W.; Hagaman, E. W.; Moreno, L. N.; and Wenkert, E., J. Org. Chem., 42(3), 490-95 (1977).

Carbon-13 Nuclear Magnetic Resonance Spectroscopy of Naturally Occurring Substances. 47. Cannabinoid Compounds.

Structural analyses of 4 THCs and 4 related ketones are described using ^{13}C-NMR spectroscopy. Differentiation is possible between natural THC products and their positional and stereochemical isomers. The synthesis, purification, and physical properties of each ketone are detailed. A procedure to locate phenolic groups at specific aromatic carbons by pyridine-induced shifts in ^{13}C-NMR spectra is given.

3261   Arnone, A.; Bernardi, R.; Merlini, L.; and Servi, S., Gazz. Chim. Ital., 105, 9-10 (1975).

XXVI. Spectroscopic Methods for Distinguishing Tricyclic Cannabinoids from "Abnormal" Synthetic Isomers.

One step in the synthesis of many cannabinoids involves the alkylation of olivetol or of another 5-alkylresorcinol with a monoterpene. This condensation may lead to two isomeric products. A distinct difference in the position of the aromatic protons is observed for these isomers when the NMR spectra run in benzene and CCL_4 are compared.

3262   Arnone, A.; Merlini, L.; and Servi, S., Tetrahedron, 31(24), 3903-96 (1975).

Hashish. Synthesis of (+)-Δ^4-Tetrahydrocannabinol.

The synthesis of (+)-Δ^4-THC and its abnormal isomer was effected by alkylating olivetol with p-menth-4-en-3,8-diol which also resulted in the formation of other side products.

3263   Aronow, W. S.; and Cassidy, J., Clin. Pharmacol. Ther., 17(5), 549-54 (1975).

Effect of Smoking Marihuana and of a High-Nicotine Cigarette on Angina Pectoris.

In 10 anginal pectoris patients, smoking marihuana (1 cigarette) or 1 high-nicotine cigarette decreased exercise performance until the onset of angina pectoris. This decrease was greater after marihuana smoking than after high-nicotine cigarette.

3264   Arrigo Reina, R.; Scoto, G. M.; Spadero, C.; and Mazzone, G., Boll. Soc. Ital. Biol. Sper., 54(23), 2348-54 (1978).

Effetti Comportamentali Nel Ratto Di Un Estratto Di Cannabis: Ruolo Delle Catecolamine [Behavioral Effects of a Cannabis Extract in Rats: Role of Catecholamines].

Rats treated with cannabis extract exhibited signs of abnormal behavior. These behavioral changes were mediated by catecholamines and acetylcholine.

3265 Asch, R. H.; Fernandez, E. O.; Smith, C. G.; and Pauerstein, C. J., Fertil. Steril., *29*(2), 250 (1978).

Δ^9-Tetrahydrocannabinol Inhibits the Ovulatory Reflex in Rabbits.

No ovulation occurred in naturally mated rabbits treated with Δ^9-THC (5 mg/kg/day for 4 days). Ovulation did occur, however, in rabbits (control and Δ^9-THC-treated) receiving human chorionic gonadotropin and in naturally mated controls.

3266 Auld, J., pp. 261-78 in *Drugs and Politics*, edited by P. E. Rock. New Brunswick, Transactions, Inc., 1977.

Cannabis, Alcohol, and the Management of Intoxication.

The use of alcohol, which is socially acceptable and accessible in western societies, is compared to the use of the not so acceptable and accessible marihuana. While the outcome of alcohol intoxication is well-defined and predictable, that of marihuana is much less so. The author proposes that in order to understand the problem, more attention should be focused on why and how the marihuana users stop or alter their pattern of drug-taking.

3267 Austin, G. A., pp. 178-83 in *Perspectives on the History of Psychoactive Substance Use*, NIDA Research Issues 24, 1978.

Cannabis (Ganja): Jamaica, 1845-1974.

A brief chronological description of cannabis history (introduction, spread, public concern, regulation and legislation) in Jamaica is given.

3268 Austin, G. A., pp. 236-45 in *Perspectives on the History of Psychoactive Substance Use*, NIDA Research Issues 24, 1978.

Cannabis (Marihuana): United States, 1900-1944.

A brief chronological description of marihuana use and regulation in the United States is given.

3269 Ayalon, D.; NIR, I.; Cordova, T.; Bauminger, S.; Puder, M.; Naor, Z.; Kashi, R.; Zor, U.; Harell, A.; and Lindner, H. R., Neuroendocrinology, *23*(1), 31-42 (1977).

Acute Effect of Δ^1-Tetrahydrocannabinol on the Hypothalamo-Pituitary-Ovarian Axis in the Rat.

The THC-induced blockade of ovulation in rats is thought to be due to both a direct effect on the ovary and a suppression of proestrous gonadotropin secretion at the hypothalamic level.

3270 Aye, U. T., Forensic Sci. Int., *12*(2), 145-49 (1978).

Indian Hemp Eradication Campaign in Burma and the Characterization of Burmese Hemp Type of Thin-Layer Chromatography. A Case Report.

A report on cannabis eradication in Burma and TLC analysis of CBD, Δ^9-THC, and CBN. Range for Δ^9-THC is 2.00 to 6.60, CBD nil to 0.05, and CBN from 0 to 0.81. Burmese cannabis has high Δ^9-THC and low CBD content.

B

3271 Babor, T. F., pp. 149-79 in *Self-Administration of Abused Substances: Methods for Study*, NIDA Research Monograph 20, 1978.

Studying Social Reactions to Drug Self-Administration.

Single and repeated doses of marihuana and heroin result in a general suppression of social interaction. Unlike marihuana, however, chronic heroin intoxication is associated with almost total withdrawal from the social environment.

3272 Babor, T. F.; Mendelson, J. H.; Gallant, D.; and Kuehnle, J. C., Int. J. Addict., *13*(1), 89-102 (1978).

Interpersonal Behavior in Group Discussion During Marijuana Intoxication.

Linear and quadratic trend analyses revealed that moderate marihuana users were less task-oriented and participated less than heavy or no-drug users during a four-person group interaction setting. Ratings of "high" and marihuana consumption were, however, higher for heavy than for moderate users.

3273 Babor, T. F.; Mendelson, J. H.; Greenberg, I.; and Kuehle, J. C., Arch. Gen. Psychiat., *32*(12), 1548-52 (1975).

Marijuana Consumption and Tolerance to Physiological and Subjective Effects.

Moderate and heavy (daily) marihuana smokers were studied for the effect on pulse rate, subjective responses, and tolerance development. Heavy smokers developed tolerance and consumed almost twice as much marihuana as moderate users. However, development of tolerance and increased consumption are not always linked in humans.

3274 Babor, T. F.; Mendelson, J. H.; and Kuehnle, J., in *Committee on Problems of Drug Dependence, 1976*. Division of Medical Sciences, National Research Council, National Academy of Sciences, Washington, D. C., 1976, pp. 485-503.

Marihuana and Human Physical Activity.

Marihuana caused an immediate reduction in the physical activity of both moderate and heavy users and altered the waking activity of only the latter. Other aspects of marihuana use were also discussed.

3275 Babor, T. F.; Mendelson, J. H.; and Kuehnle, J., in *Committee on Problems of Drug Dependence, 1978*. Division of Medical Sciences, National Research Council, National Academy of Sciences, Washington, D. C., 1977, pp. 667-77.

Experimental Analysis of Marihuana Self-Administration.

Monetary cost was found to have a powerful effect, both directly and indirectly, on the frequency and patterning of marihuana consumption. Other findings, including tolerance development to the physiological and psychological effects of marihuana and an almost total lack of mood change following acute doses of marihuana, were also discussed.

3276 Babor, T. F.; Mendelson, J. H.; and Kuehnle, J., Psychopharmacology, *50*(1), 11-19 (1976).

Marihuana and Human Physical Activity.

Marihuana caused an immediate reduction in the physical activity of both moderate and heavy users but altered the waking activity of only the latter. Other aspects of marihuana use were also discussed.

3277 Babor, T. F.; Mendelson, J. H.; Uhly, B.; and Kuehnle, J. E., Int. J. Addict., *13*(6), 947-59 (1978)

Social Effects of Marihuana Use in a Recreational Setting.

Given free access to marihuana, moderate, but not heavy, users exhibited less interaction during intoxication.

3278 Babst, D. V., J. Drug Educ., *6*(1), 23-41 (1976).

The Relationship Between Friends' Marihuana Use, Family Cohesion, School Interest and Drug Abuse Prevention.

This study points out the need for awareness of the possible differences in the target audience during the planning of drug abuse prevention programs. Those students most involved with drugs are least receptive to traditional education programs. The reasons for drug use, knowledge about drugs, attitudes toward education and use of other drugs, alcohol, and tobacco are discussed.

3279 Babu, R.; Roy, A. N.; Gupta, Y. K.; and Gupta, M. N., Curr. Sci. India, *46*(20), 719-20 (1977).

Fungi Associated with Deteriorating Seeds of *Cannabis sativa L*.

Seeds of *Cannabis sativa L*. were surface washed with 0.1% mercurous chloride. Sixteen fungal species were cultured from the washings and ten from the seeds. Five species such as *Aspergillus niger*, and *Penicillium chrysogenum* were isolated from external and internal surfaces of the seed. Of the ten internally-born fungi, only *Penicillium* was found to be pathogenic to the seeds and to leaves of the adult plant.

3280 Bach, D.; Bursuker, I.; and Goldman, R., Biochim. Biophys. Acta, *469*(2), 171-79 (1977).

Differential Scanning Calorimetry and Enzymic Activity of Rat Liver Microsomes in the Presence and Absence of Δ^1-Tetrahydrocannabinol.

THC altered the thermotrophic behavior of microsomal lipids and liver microsomes and also abolished the break seen in the Arrhenius plot of nitroanisol dealkylation by microsomal enzymes.

3281 Bach, D.; Raz, A.; and Goldman, R., Biochem. Pharmacol., *25*, 1241-44 (1976).

The Interaction of Hashish Compounds with Planar Lipid Bilayer Membranes (BLM).

A transient decrease in the electrical resistance of lecithin membranes was noted due to the asymmetric distribution of CBD across these membranes. A membrane potential was also generated under the same conditions. No similar events, however, were detected during symmetric distribution of CBD or THC'

3282 Bach, D.; Raz, A.; and Goldman, R., Biochim. Biophys. Acta, *436*(4), 889-94 (1976).

The Effect of Hashish Compounds on Phospholipid Phase Transition.

The influence of Δ^9-THC and CBD on the electrical resistance of planar bilayer membranes was studied. It was concluded that both Δ^9-THC and CBD can affect the transition of phospholipids from gel to liquid crystalline state. Cannabinoids might trigger a localized phase transition of phospholipids at a constant temperature. Differential scanning calorimetry thermograms are presented for dipalmitoyl phosphatidyl choline and for dipalmitoyl phosphatidyl choline/cannabinoid mixtures.

3283 Backhouse, C. I., Brit. Med. J., *1*, 360-62 (1975).

Peak Expiratory Flow in Youths with Varying Cigarette Smoking Habits.

Initial peak of expiratory flow for marihuana smokers, unlike that of cigarette smokers, did not show any impairment.

3284 Bahr, R., New Physician, *25*, 34-37 (1976).

Dealing in Bethesda Gold

Two legal sources of marihuana and its purified active ingredients are described. The first source mentioned is the National Institute of Mental Health at Bethesda, Md., which contracts for its marihuana supply from the University of Mississippi which maintains several strains of Cannabis. The second source is Polysciences of Warrington, Pa. The procedure involved in obtaining a license to research a controlled substance such as marihuana is briefly outlined as are some possible medical applications for marihuana or its purified derivatives.

3285 Bailey, K., J. Chromatogr., *160*(1), 288-90 (1978).

Formation of Olivetol During Gas Chromatography of Cannabinoids.

Olivetol (I) was detected and proved to be present in the GC of cannabis extracts. The study indicated that (I) was formed as a product of decomposition of CBD or CBG at high inlet temperatures (above 150° C.)

3286 Bailey, K.; and Gagne, D., J. Pharm. Sci., *64*(10), 1719-20 (1975).

Distinction of Synthetic Cannabidiol, Cannabichromene, and Cannabivarin by GLC Using On-Column Methylation.

Methyl ethers of CBD, CBC and CBV were produced by an on-column methylation procedure using synthetic cannabinoids and trimethylanilinium hydroxide. Separation parameters for GLC systems are reported.

3287 Baker, B.; and Rogers, S., Res. Commun. Chem. Pathol. Pharmacol., *21*(3), 569-72 (1978).

Trans-Delta-9-Tetrahydrocannabinol: Effects on Macromolecular Content of Mouse Liver Tissue.

Δ^9-THC treatment increased liver RNA and decreased protein levels in previously starved mice. However, DNA and glycogen levels remained unaltered.

3288 Baker, P. B.; and Fowler, R., Proc. Anal. Div. Chem. Soc., *15*(12), 347-49 (1978).

Analytical Aspects of the Chemistry of Cannabis.

Samples of confiscated cannabis were analyzed for their cannabinoid content and the data compared with those samples of known origin. Two dimensional TLC and HPLC methods were used.

3289 Balster, R. L.; and Ford, R. D., pp. 131-47 in *Drug Discrimination and State Dependent Learning*, edited by B. T. Ho, D. W. Richards, and D. L. Chute. New York, Academic Press, 1978.

The Discriminative Stimulus Properties of Cannabinoids: A Review.

Literature reviewed pointed to the possible establishment of discriminative stimulus properties of cannabinoids in several animal species under a variety of performance conditions. Tolerance to these effects develops slowly. 11-OH-Δ^9-THC and 11-OH-Δ^8-THC substituted for Δ^9-THC while several psychoactive agents did not.

3290   Banerjee, A.; Poddar, M. K.; Saha, S.; and Ghosh, J. J., Biochem. Pharmacol., 24, 1435-36 (1975).

Effect of Δ^9-Tetrahydrocannabinol on Monoamine Oxidase Activity of Rat Tissues *in vivo*.

Δ^9-THC was injected i.p. (10 mg/kg or 50 mg/kg) in rats which were then sacrificed and the mitochondrial fraction from the brain, hypothalamus, liver, kidney and heart was isolated. An increase in MOA was observed in the whole brain, hypothalamus and heart with little or no effect in the liver and kidney mitochondria. This study suggests that an important site of action of Δ^9-THC is the central monoamine neurons.

3291   Banerjee, B. N.; Galbreath, C.; and Sofia, R. D., Teratology, 11(1), 99-101 (1975).

Teratologic Evaluation of Synthetic Delta-9-Tetrahydrocannabinol in Rats.

The s.c. administration of Δ^9-THC (up to 100 mg/kg) to pregnant rats did not produce fetal mortality.

3292   Banerjee, B. N.; Sofia, R. D.; Erikson, D.; and Ivins, N. J., J. Toxicol. Environ. Health, 1(5), 769-76 (1976).

Toxicity of Δ^9-Tetrahydrocannabinol (THC) Administered Subcutaneously for 13 Days to Female Rabbits.

Δ^9-THC (3-100 mg/kg/day/13 days, s.c.) resulted in anorexia, local dermal irritation and significant alteration in several blood chemistry parameters of treated rabbits.

3293   Banerjee, S. P.; Snyder, S. H.; and Mechoulam, R., J. Pharmacol. Exp. Ther., 194(1), 74-81 (1975).

Cannabinoids: Influence on Neurotransmitter Uptake in Rat Brain Synaptosomes.

Studies of uptake inhibition by cannabinoids in which the drugs were dissolved in DMSO and then added to Krebs-Henseleit incubation media revealed that THC and its analogs exhibit comparable potency in inhibiting 5-HT and NE uptake into synaptosomes in homogenates of rat brain, while they tend to be less potent in altering GABA accumulation.

3294   Banerji, A.; Poddar, M. K.; and Ghosh, J. J., Toxicol. Appl. Pharmacol., 40(2), 347-54 (1977).

Action of Δ^9-Tetrahydrocannabinol on Membrane-Bound Monoamine Oxidase Activity.

Tissue mitochondrial fractions and blood platelets of rats were used to study changes in the kinetic parameters of MAO activity following acute (10 and 50 mg/kg., i.p.) and subacute (10 mg/kg/day, i.p. for 15 days) THC administration. A wide range of effects was obtained and their implications discussed.

3295   Barry, H.; and Krimmer, E. C., Fed. Proc., 34(3), 743 (1975).

Discriminative Δ^9-Tetrahydrocannabinol Stimulus Tested with Several Doses, Routes, Intervals and Related Compounds.

In rats trained to discriminate the stimulus properties of Δ^9-THC (2 mg/kg, i.p.), the ED_{50} values were 0.87, 0.27 and 2.9 mg/kg for the i.p., i.v. and p.o. routes, respectively. Δ^8-THC, 11-OH-Δ^8-THC or marihuana extract elicited the Δ^9-THC-response, whereas chlordiazepoxide, alcohol or pentobarbital did not.

3296   Barry, H.; and Krimmer, E. C., pp. 535-38 in the *Pharmacology of Marihuana, Vol. 2*, edited by M. C. Braude and S. Szara. NY, Raven Press, 1976.

Discriminative Δ^9-Tetrahydrocannabinol Stimulus Tested with Several Doses, Routes, Intervals, and a Marihuana Extract.

Testing the effects of various routes of administration and time intervals in male rats trained to discriminate the stimulus properties of THC (2 mg/kg, i.p.) on food reinforced operant behavior resulted in ED_{50} values of THC in the following order: 0.27, 0.82, and 2.92 mg/kg by i.v., i.p., and p.o., respectively. Time of peak effect was 30 min post-drug administration and marihuana extract was more potent than pure THC.

3297   Barry, H., and Krimmer, E. C., Psychopharmacology, *58*(2), 3 (1978).

Similarities and Differences in Discriminative Stimulus Effects of Chlordiazepoxide, Pentobarbital, Ethanol and Other Sedatives (abstract).

The discriminative stimulus effects of pentobarbital and chlordiazepoxide do not generalize to Δ^9-THC, chlorpromazine or morphine at behaviorally depressant doses. Pentobarbital stimulus generalizes to ethanol only under negative stimulus conditions.

3298   Bartl, K.; Kraatz, U.; and Korte, F., Justus Liebigs Ann. Chem., *3*, 407-11 (1976).

Synthese von Δ^8-Tetrahydrodibenzol (b, d)pyran-6-onen und ihre Aminolyse zu Δ^8-Tetrahydrophenanthridin-6-onen [Synthesis of Δ^8-Tetrahydrodibenzo (b,d) pyran-6-ones and their Aminolysis to Δ^8-Tetrahydrophenathridin-6-ones.]

Δ^8-Tetrahydrodibenzo (b,d)pyran-6-ones and Δ^8-Tetrahydrophenanthridin-6-ones (cannabinoid analogs) were synthesized. The synthesis of compounds having the C_0 and C_1 side chain instead of the C_5 side chain were also reported. The structures of the synthesized compounds were confirmed by spectrometrical data: NMR, IR, and MS.

3299   Bartle, K. D.; Lee, M. L.; and Novotny, M., Analyst, *102*(1219), 731-38 (1977).

Identification of Environmental Polynuclear Aromatic Hydrocarbons by Pulse Fourier-transform ^{1}H Nuclear Magnetic Resonance Spectroscopy.

Methyl derivatives of polynuclear aromatic hydrocarbons in marihuana smoke condensates were identified by NMR and GC-MS spectra.

3300   Bartova, A.; and Birmingham, M. K., J. Biol. Chem., *251*(16), 5002-06 (1976).

Effect of Δ^9-Tetrahydrocannabinol on Mitochondrial NADH-Oxidase Activity. Δ^9-THC inhibited mitochondrial NADH-oxidase activity by 70% in the heart and, to a varying degree, in various regions of rat brain. THC was a more effective inhibitor than deoxycorticosterone.

3301 Batra, S. W. T., Kans. Entomol. Soc. J., *49*(3), 385-88 (1976).

Some Insects Associated With Hemp or Marijuana (*Cannabis sativa L.*) in Northern India.

Insects were collected from mature cannabis growing in three locations in India. Among others, 35 plant-eating species were identified, including an aphid common to the United States.

3302 Battistich, V. A.; and Huffman, S., Int. J. Addict., *13*(6), 975-80 (1978).

Psychoactive Drug Use in a Midwestern High School: Extent of Current Use and Future Trends.

Alcohol, tobacco and marihuana were the drugs more frequently used by high school students. Although drug use is declining, users of the former agents indicated their intention of continued use.

3303 Baytop, T.; and Savic, Y., Istanbul Univ. Eczacilik Fak. Mecm., *11*(2), 129-37 (1975).

Quantitative Determination of THC in the Cultivated Species of *Cannabis sativa* in Turkey.

A densitometric method was adopted for the quantitative estimation of THC content in the flowering tops of both the male and female plants of *Cannabis sativa*, collected in Turkey from different regions and under different climatic conditions.

3304 Bazzaz, F. A.; Dusek, D.; Seigler, D.S.; and Haney, A. W., Biochem. Syst. Ecol., *3*, 15-18 (1975).

Photosynthesis and Cannabinoid Content of Temperate and Tropical Populations of *Cannabis sativa*.

Photosynthesis rates were compared for plants produced by seeds from Illinois, Nepal, Jamaica, and Panama. Rates were similar for Illinois and Nepal (temperate). Jamaica and Panama (tropical) were similar. Rates were evaluated at various temperatures.

3305 Bearden, W. O.; and Woodside, A. G., J. Health Soc. Behav., *19*(2), 199-204 (1978).

Normative and Attitudinal Control as Moderating Influences on Marijuana Use.

Attitudinally influenced marihuana users were heavier consumers and less fearful of the legal and physical consequences of use than were normative users. The study utilized Fishbein's extended model of behavioral intention. Other differences were also found.

3306 Bearden, W. O.; and Woodside, A. G., J. Soc. Psychol., *106*, 57-67 (1978).

Situational and Extended Attitude Models as Predictors of Marijuana Intentions and Reported Behavior.

Both Fishbein's extended model and Rokeach framework were better predictors of behavioral intentions than reported marihuana use in this sample of college students. The former model also indicated the continuing influence of social environment.

3307 Beautrais, A. L.; and Marks, D. F., Psychopharmacologia, *46*(1), 37-40 (1976).

A Test of State Dependency Effects in Marihuana Intoxication for the Learning of Psychomotor Tasks.

Marihuana impaired human psychomotor performance regardless of prior training conditions. Performance of subjects did not differ whether training occurred under marihuana influence or not.

3308 Becker, B. M.; and Reid, L. D., Bull. Psychon. Soc., *10*(4), 325-27 (1977).

Daily 1-Δ^9-Tetrahydrocannabinol and Pressing for Hypothalamic Stimulation.

THC-induced initial depression of rat intracranial stimulation behavior subsided following its repeated administration. Sites of hypothalamic electrodes are thought to be important factors in similar studies.

3309 Bellville, J. W.; Gasser, J. C.; Miyake, T.; and Aqleh, K., J. Pharmacol. Exp. Ther., *197*(2), 326-31 (1976).

Tolerance to the Respiratory Effects of Marihuana In Man.

Respiratory depression following marihuana smoking was monitored in 8 male adults by responses to CO_2 inhalation. Changes in time-effect and peak-effect curves were significant over a 90-day period and indicated a development of tolerance. Changes in marihuana-induced pulse rate increase over the 90-day period were shown not to be significant.

3310 Bellville, J. W.; Gasser, J. C.; Miyake, T.; and Aqleh, K., Pharmacologist, *17*(2), 180 (1975).

Tolerance to the Respiratory Depression of Marihuana.

Tolerance to marihuana depression of respiration developed in subjects smoking marihuana, (900 mg cigarettes with 2.2% Δ^9-THC), *ad libitum* for 90 days.

3311 Bellville, J. W.; Swanson, G. D.; and Aqleh, K. A., Clin. Pharmacol. Ther., *17*(5), 541-48 (1975).

Respiratory Effects of Delta-9-Tetrahydrocannabinol.

Smoking marihuana cigarettes containing 7.5 or 22.5 mg THC caused a slight respiratory depression in human subjects, as did pentobarbital in high dose. Ethanol gave a mixed response.

3312 Ben-Zvi, Z.; Bergen, J. R.; Burstein, S.; Sehgal, P. K.; and Varanelli, C., pp. 63-75 in the *Pharmacology of Marihuana, Vol. 1*, edited by M. C. Braude and S. Szara. NY, Raven Press, 1976.

The Metabolism of Δ^1-Tetrahydrocannabinol in the Rhesus Monkey.

Data presented show that Δ^1-THC is metabolized to CBN-7-oic-acid after i.v. administration of 14-C-Δ^1-THC (30 mg) in the rhesus monkey. Separation of this and other metabolites from urine is done by TLC. Metabolites were eluted and further purified on LH-Sephaden column. Their structure is confirmed by GLC-MS. The brain is also shown to be capable of metabolizing Δ^1-THC to CBN-7-oic-acid. Only Δ^1-THC was present in the feces.

3313   Ben-Zvi, Z.; and Burstein, S., Biochem. Pharmacol., *24*, 1130-31 (1975).

Transformation of Δ^1-Tetrahydrocannabinol (THC) by Rabbit Liver Microsomes.

Liver homogenates of female albino rabbits were incubated with ^{14}C-Δ^1-THC. Products were isolated and identified with GLC/MS.

3314   Benowitz, N. L.; and Jones, R. T., Clin. Pharmacol. Ther., *18*(3), 287-97 (1975).

Cardiovascular Effects of Prolonged Delta-9-Tetrahydrocannabinol Ingestion.

Twelve male users were treated orally with Δ^9-THC (210 mg) and evaluated on six consecutive phases. Blood samples were collected daily and a complete cardiovascular examination was performed. Development of tolerance was noted with a lowering of BP and slowing of heart rate.

3315   Benowitz, N. L.; and Jones, R. T., Clin. Pharmacol. Ther., *21*(3), 336-42 (1977).

Prolonged Delta-9-Tetrahydrocannabinol Ingestion: Effects of Sympathomimetic Amines and Autonomic Blockades.

Heart rate and BP were monitored in hospitalized subjects treated with agents altering sympathetic and parasympathetic activities prior to and after two weeks of daily THC (2.57 ± 0.78 mg/kg, p.o.) administration. Findings and implications were discussed.

3316   Benowitz, N. L.; and Jones, R. T., Clin. Pharmacol. Ther., *22*(3), 259-68 (1977).

Effects of Delta-9-Tetrahydrocannabinol on Drug Distribution and Metabolism.

THC (60-180 mg/day) was found to depress the disappearance rate of pentobarbital, antipyrine and ethanol from blood of human volunteers. A weak metabolic inhibitory effect was also detected. The possible mechanisms of action were discussed.

3317   Benowitz, N. L.; and Jones, R. T., Fed. Proc., *36*(3), 1027 (1977).

Tolerance to Cardiovascular Effects of Chronic Δ^9-Tetrahydrocannabinol (THC) in Man.

Atropine and propranolol antagonized Δ^9-THC-induced cardiovascular effects in human subjects. Tolerance to THC-induced cardiovascular and psychological effects developed after repeated dosing.

3318   Benowitz, N. L.; Jones, R. T.; and Lerner, C. B., J. Clin. Endocrinol. Metab., *42*(5), 938-41 (1976).

Depression of Growth Hormone and Cortisol Response to Insulin-Induced Hypoglycemia After Prolonged Oral Δ^9-Tetrahydrocannabinol Administration in Man.

After 15 days of treatment with THC (210 mg/day, p.o.) six adult, male volunteers exhibited depressed growth hormone and cortisol responses to insulin-induced hypoglycemia, although baseline levels of these hormones were not changed. A discussion of possible mechanisms and correlation with other data published in this area is presented.

3319   Benowitz, N. L.; Rosenberg, J.; Rogers, W.; and Jones, R. T., Fed. Proc., *37*(3), 737 (1978).

Autonomic Nervous Mechanisms of the Cardiovascular (COV) effects of Delta-9-

Tetrahydrocannabinol (THC) in Man (abstract).

Atropine and propranolol attenuated the changes in vascular resistance and fore-arm blood flow and the increase in heart rate induced by Δ^9-THC (35 ug/kg, i.v.) in four human volunteers. An additional subject developed hyperten-sion associated with increased vascular resistance following marihuana smoking (10 mg Δ^9-THC).

3320 Bensemana, D.; and Gascon, A. L., Can. J. Physiol. Pharmacol., 56(5), 721-30 (1978).

Relationship Between Analgesia and Turnover of Brain Biogenic Amines.

Morphine and sodium salicylate induced analgesia correlated with elevated turn-over rate of DA, 5-HT and NE. That of Δ^9-THC involved DA and 5-HT only.

3321 Bercht, C. A. L.; Samrah, H. M.; Lous-berg, R. J. J.; Theuns, H.; and Salemink, C. A., Phytochemistry, 15(5), 830-31 (1976).

Isolation of Vomifoliol and Dihydro-vomifoliol from *Cannabis*.

Two compounds of the isophorone structure, vomifoliol and dihydrovomi-foliol, were isolated from the leaves and stems of Dutch grown hemp. The com-pounds are characterized by comparison of MS optical rotation, NMR and IR with reference data from reference standards. The yield of compound per kg of plant material was 25 mg for dihydrovomifoliol and 65 mg for vomi-foliol.

3322 Bercht, C. A. L.; Van Dongen, J. P. C. M.; Heerma, W.; Lousberg, R. J. J. Ch.; and Kuppers, F. J. E. M., Tetrahedron, 32(33), 2939-43 (1976).

Cannabispirone and Cannabispirenone, Two Naturally Occurring Spiro-Com-pounds.

Phytochemical investigation of the polar constituents obtained from South African Cannabis cultivated in France resulted in the isolation of two new spiro-com-pounds, cannabispirone and cannabi-spirenone. The structures of these two compounds were determined by spectral means. Special attention was given to the ^{13}C-NMR of these compounds which were chemically interrelated.

3323 Bernstein, J. G.; Kuehnle, J. C.; and Mendelson, J. H., Amer. J. Drug Alco-hol Abuse, 3(2), 347-61 (1976).

Medical Implications of Marihuana Use.

Marihuana users experienced tachycardia and minimal changes in temperature when smoking it under inpatient condi-tions. Except for some changes in pulmonary function, various initial clini-cal examinations did not reveal any abnormalities associated with marihuana.

3324 Bertulli, G.; Mosca, L.; and Pedroni, G., Boll. Chim. Farm., 115(10), 714-19 (1976).

Rapid Method for the Detection and Identification of Cannabinols in Canna-bis.

A simple, accurate and economical TLC method for detecting and identifying cannabinols was described.

3325 Besch, N. F.; Besch, P. K.; Moore, S. C.; Smith, M. T.; and Smith, C. G., Clin. Chem., *22*(7), 1184 (1976).

The Effect of Marihuana (Delta-9-Tetrahydrocannabinol) on the Secretion of Lutenizing Hormone in the Mature Female Rhesus Monkey.

The authors studied the effect of acute dosing of THC (2.5 or 5.0 mg/kg, i.m.) in four mature overiectomized monkeys. The results for the lower dose were not consistent, but the higher dose resulted in at least a 50% decrease in LH levels in all animals. The effect lasted for 12-24 hours and returned to control levels within 18-48 hours.

3326 Besch, N. F.; Smith, C. G.; Besch, P. K.; and Kaufman, R. H., Amer. J. Obstet. Gynecol., *128*(6), 635-42 (1977).

The Effect of Marihuana (Delta-9-Tetrahydrocannabinol) on the Secretion of Luteinizing Hormone in the Ovariectomized Rhesus Monkey.

Short-term i.m. administration of THC (2.5 and 5.0 mg/kg) depressed the level of LH in ovariectomized monkeys.

3327 Besch, N. F.; and Smith, R. G., Pharmacologist, *20*(3), 165 (1978).

The Effect of Cannabidiol on the Secretion of Gonadotrophins in the Ovariectomized Rhesus Monkey (abstract)

CBD, unlike Δ^9-THC, did not inhibit the secretion of LH and FSH in ovariectomized monkeys.

3328 Beuthin, F., J. Amer. Med. Ass., *233*(13), 1357 (1975).

Marihuana: Can It Hurt You?

Adverse reaction to a biased presentation of marihuana research is given. The author feels that Kolansky and Moore performed a disservice to the scientific community by selective reporting of data.

3329 Bhakuni, D. S., J. Sci. Ind. Res., *36*(10), 490-509 (1977).

Biosynthesis of Biologically Active Mevalonate Derived Natural Products: Part II. Non-steroids.

This article reviews the tracer experiments conducted during the last 10 years to verify the biosynthetic speculations on the formation of the biologically active non-steroidal, mevalonate-derived natural products. These included the ergot, vinca, ipecac, cinchona and rauwolfia alkaloids, cannabinoids, santonin and rotenoids.

3330 Bhargava, H. N., Eur. J. Pharmacol., *36*(1), 259-62 (1976).

Inhibition of Naloxone-Induced Withdrawal in Morphine Dependent Mice by 1-*trans*-Δ^9-Tetrahydrocannabinol.

Morphine dependent mice were injected with Δ^9-THC (2.5, 5.0, and 10.0 mg/kg, i.p.) and 30 minutes later were challenged with naloxone (s.c.). Δ^9-THC blocked naloxone-induced withdrawal syndrome. The mechanism of Δ^9-THC inhibitions of morphine abstinence is unknown although the syndrome is associated with increased brain DA and cyclic AMP and decreased acetylcholine.

3331 Bhargava, H. N., Gen. Pharmacol., *9*(4), 195-213 (1978).

Potential Therapeutic Applications of Naturally Occurring and Synthetic Cannabinoids.

Due to the unique pharmacological profile of Cannabis, many possible therapeutic applications were found when Cannabis literature was reviewed. Among the major promising areas are the appetite stimulant effects in cancer patients following chemotherapy and the treatment of glaucoma. Limitations include the psychotomimetic effects and the insolubility of the naturally occurring cannabinoids.

3332 Bhargava, H. N., Pharmacol. Biochem. Behav., *8*(1), 7-11 (1978).

Time Course of the Effects of Naturally Occurring Cannabinoids on Morphine Abstinence Syndrome.

Mice rendered morphine dependent by pellet implantation were used to study the effects of a single i.p. injection (10 mg/kg) of the cannabinoids Δ^9-THC, Δ^8-THC and 11-OH-Δ^8-THC on the abstinence syndrome. Δ^9-THC was found to have a longer duration of action than other cannabinoids in inhibiting the naloxone-precipitated jumping response.

3333 Bhargava, H. N., Psychopharmacology, *49*(3), 267-70 (1976).

Effect of Some Cannabinoids on Naloxone-Precipitated Abstinence in Morphine-Dependent Mice.

Antagonism of naloxone-induced withdrawal jumping by several cannabinoids (2.5-20 mg/kg, i.p.) is demonstrated in male mice dependent on morphine. All cannabinoids increased the ED_{50} of naloxone but suppressed defecation and rearing behavior. Order of decreasing potency for withdrawal prevention is: Δ^9-THC > Δ^8-THC > 11-OH-Δ^8-THC > CBD > CBN. Non-psychotomimetic cannabinoids may facilitate narcotic detoxification.

3334 Bhargava, H. N., *Seventh International Congress of Pharmacology: Abstracts*, Paris, France, July 16-21, 1978, p. 357.

Studies with Naturally Occurring Cannabinoids and Metabolites on Morphine Dependence.

Δ^9-THC, Δ^8-THC, 11-OH-Δ^8-THC, CBD and CBN in this order inhibited the stereotyped jumping response, withdrawal defecation and rearing, when administered 30 min. before naloxone to mice dependent on morphine. These and other findings indicated the possible usefulness of cannabinoids in controlling morphine abstinence syndrome and thus in narcotic detoxification.

3335 Bieniek, D.; and Korte, F., Deut. Apth.-Ztg., *118*(51-52), 1933-35 (1978).

Neuere Ergebnisse zur Chemie und Pharmakologie des Haschisch [Recent Results on the Chemistry and Pharmacology of Hashish].

A short review of the constituents of cannabis with a brief description of the stereospecific synthesis of Δ^8- and Δ^9-THC is given.

3336 Bier, M. M.; and Steahly, L. P., pp. 163-67 in *Acute Drug Abuse Emergencies: A Treatment Manual*, edited by P. G. Bourne. NY, Academic Press, 1976.

Emergency Treatment of Marihuana Complicating Diabetes.

Since the possibility of marihuana use leading to Ketoacidosis in latent and overt diabetics is not far-fetched, detection of marihuana ingestion is advised. A treatment regimen for diagnosed Ketoacidosis is described.

3337 Billets, S.; El-Feraly, F.; Fetterman, P. S.; and Turner, C. E., Org. Mass Spectom., *11*, 741-51 (1976).

Constituents of *Cannabis Sativa L*. XII - Mass Spectral Fragmentation Patterns for Some Cannabinoid Acids as Their TMS Derivatives.

The fragmentation patterns of a number of cannabinoid acid derivatives are described and compared to the corresponding neutral compounds. The compounds are analyzed as TMS derivatives and deuterium labeling is used to describe the fragmentation. High resolution analysis is used in the description of the fragmentation mechanisms.

3338   Binder, M., Helv. Chim. Acta, *59*(8), 1674-84 (1976).

Microbial Transformation of (-)-Δ^1-3,4-*trans*-Tetrahydrocannabinol by *Cunninghamella blakesleeana* LENDER.

Three new hydroxylated metabolites of Δ^9-THC were identified after conversion by a microorganism. Sufficient quantities of these compounds were isolated to allow NMR analysis although emphasis is put on mass spectral analysis. A metabolic conversion rate of less than 3% is observed for the major product.

3339   Binder, M., pp. 159-67 in *Marihuana: Chemistry, Biochemistry, and Cellular Effects*, edited by G. G. Nahas. NY, Springer-Verlag, 1976.

Identification of Hydroxylated Cannabinoids by PMR and Mass Spectroscopy.

A general method for identifying side chain hydroxylated cannabinoids, regardless of the basic type of cannabinoid, is presented using PMR and MS studies. PMR and MS spectra of a number of synthetic side chain hydroxylated cannabinoids were investigated.

3340   Binder, M.; and Meisenberg, G., Eur. J. Appl. Microbiol. Biotechnol., *5*(1), 37-50 (1978).

Microbial Transformation of Cannabinoids. Part 2. A Screening of Different Microorganisms.

A two-dimensional TLC technique was employed to characterize various microbial and fungal metabolites of Δ^9-THC. Of the 163 strains of microorganisms tested, 51 transformed Δ^9-THC to Fast Blue B Salt positive metabolites on TLC. Two major patterns of metabolism, "Fusarium type" and "Botrytis type", were found to be common to large groups of microorganisms: their characteristics were discussed.

3341   Binitie, A., Psychopharmacologia, *44*(3), 301-02 (1975).

Psychosis Following Ingestion of Hemp in Children.

Two case reports of a 3 year old and an 11 year old puffing hemp and the toxic psychosis that followed.

3342   Birmingham, M. K.; and Bartova, A., pp. 425-38 in *Marihuana: Chemistry, Biochemistry, and Cellular Effects*, edited by G. G. Nahas. NY, Springer-Verlag, 1976.

Effects of Cannabinol Derivatives on Blood Pressure, Body Weight, Pituitary-Adrenal Function and Mitochondrial Respiration in the Rat.

Sites of action of cannabinoids that could be pertinent to their antihypertensive potency were investigated. The authors assessed the effects of Δ^9-THC administered both *in vitro* and *in vivo* on adrenal function and on mitochondrial metabolism of various tissues. The *in vivo* studies also included a comparison of the effects of Δ^8-THC with those of Δ^9-THC on BP, body weight, and adrenal functions in rats with adrenal regeneration hypertension.

3343 Biswas, B.; Deb, G.; Ghosh, J. J., Acta Endocrinol., *80*, 329-38 (1975).

Changes in Rat Adrenal Medulla Following Δ^9-Tetrahydrocannabinol Treatment: A Histochemical Study.

Acute Δ^9-THC (10 mg/kg) decreased adrenal catecholamine level and increased activities of ATPase, butyryl- and acetyl-cholinesterases. After 30 days of this treatment, THC preferentially increased the release of Epi.

3344 Biswas, B.; Dey, S. K.; and Ghosh, J. J., Endocrinol. Exp. (Bratisl.), *10*(2), 139-48 (1976).

Adrenocortical Changes in Rats During Acute and Chronic Administration of Delta-9-Tetrahydrocannabinol.

Acute Δ^9-THC depleted cholesterol containing neutral lipids and ascorbic acid of rat adrenocortical tissues. After 15 days of THC administration, the former lipids accumulated and the latter acid slightly increased. The increased activity of Δ^5-3β -hydroxysteroid and G-6-P-dehydrogenase, encountered after acute THC administration was attenuated and hypertrophy of adrenal glands was evident.

3345 Blackly, P. H., pp. 405-15 in *Chronic Cannabis Use*, edited by R. L. Dornbush, A. M. Freedman, and M. Fink. NY, Annals of the New York Academy of Sciences, V. 282, 1976.

Effects of Decriminalization of Marihuana in Oregon.

A survey of attitudes toward decriminalization of marihuana in Oregon (1973) was conducted by means of questionnaries distributed to members of that state's police-judicial-parole system and to state educators at the high school and collegiate levels. Divergent opinions were expressed about the impact of marihuana decriminalization on drug use patterns and on society in general.

3346 Blaine, J. D.; Meacham, M. P.; Janowsky, D. S.; Schoor, M.; and Bozzette, L. P., pp. 445-47 in the *Pharmacology of Marihuana, Vol. 1*, edited by M. C. Braude and S. Szara. NY, Raven Press, 1976.

Marihuana Smoking and Simulated Flying Performance.

Testing of flying performance of human marihuana smokers (0.09 mg Δ^9-THC/kg) by simulated flight instruments revealed significant increase in the number of major and minor errors. The effects were seen 30 mins. post smoking and lasted several hours.

3347 Blakey, D., J. Miss. State Med. Ass., *16*(5), 153-54 (1975).

Is the Grass Greener?

The author tells of marihuana's six cumulative health hazards: (1) chromosome damage; (2) cellular metabolism and immune system effects; (3) hormone effects; (4) damage to respiratory tract; (5) personality changes; and (6) brain damage.

3348 Blevins, R. D.; and Regan, J. D., Fed. Proc., *35*(2), 127-35 (1976).

Δ^9-Tetrahydrocannabinol: Effect on Macromolecular Synthesis in Human and Other Mammalian Cells.

Inhibition of uptake of ^{14}C-thymidine, ^{14}C-uridine and ^{14}C-leucine into DNA, RNA and protein was observed in human fibroblasts, neuroblastoma cells and mouse neuroblastoma cells. At 3.2 x 10^{-7} M concentration of THC only 11-17% inhibition of incorporated radioactive precursors was seen in all cell types. No effect was noted on protein synthesis. THC (10^{-5} M) inhibited nucleic acid synthesis 40-50% and protein synthesis 30-40%. The intracellular pool size of precursors was decreased by 50% with administration of THC.

3349   Blevins, R. D.; and Regan, J. D., pp. 213-21 in *Marihuana: Chemistry, Biochemistry, and Cellular Effects*, edited by G. G. Nahas. NY, Springer-Verlag, 1976.

Δ^9-Tetrahydrocannabinol: Effect on Macromolecular Synthesis in Human and Other Mammalian Cells.

Studies on the effect of Δ^9-THC on the macromolecular synthesis show that Δ^9-THC inhibits the incorporation of ^{3}-H-thymidine, ^{3}-H-uridine, and ^{14}C-leucine into DNA, RNA and protein, respectively, in normal human fibroblasts, human neuroblastoma cells and mouse neuroblastoma cells.

3350   Blizard, J., Med. J. Aust., *2*(7), 228-(1977).

Marihuana, Cigarettes and Alcohol (letter).

Seventeen percent of 157 marihuana users questioned believed that long term marihuana use is bad for health. The majority of respondents thought the use of cigarettes or alcohol would be detrimental to health.

3351   Bloch, E.; Thysen, B.; Morrill, G. A.; Gardner, E.; and Fujimoto, G., pp. 203-58 in *Vitamins and Hormones, 36*, edited by P. L. Munson, J. Glover, E. Diczfalusy, and R. E. Olson. NY, Academic Press, 1978.

Effects of Cannabinoids on Reproduction and Development.

Literature reviewed indicated that cannabinoids inhibited testicular and reproductive function and reduced LH concentration in studied species. Cannabinoids also inhibited the weight gain in pregnant rats, reduced lactation and inhibited prostaglandin synthesis. They stimulated sexual behavior after acute, and inhibited it after chronic, administration. Cannabinoids also exerted teratogenic effects.

3352   Bloom, A. S.; and Dewey, W. L., Psychopharmacology, *57*(3), 243-48 (1978).

A comparison of Some Pharmacological Actions of Morphine and Δ^9-Tetrahydrocannabinol in the Mouse.

Morphine was a more potent antinociceptive than THC, whereas the latter was a more potent hypothermic agent in mice. A greater increase of NE synthesis resulted after THC than after morphine, while the reverse was true for DA. Naloxone partially antagonized some THC effects and an asymmetrical cross-tolerance between THC and morphine was demonstrated.

3353   Bloom, A. S.; Dewey, W. L.; Harris, L. S.; and Brosius, K., Neurosci. Abstr., *5*, 242 (1975).

Brain Catecholamines and the Antinociceptive Action of (±)-9-nor-9β -OH-Hexahydrocannabinol.

Unlike Δ^9-THC, β-HHC was similar to

52

morphine and other narcotic analgesics in producing analgesia and increasing brain catecholamine synthesis. Naloxone antagonized both effects.

3354   Bloom, A. S.; Dewey, W. L.; Harris, L. S.; and Brosius, K. , J. Pharmacol. Exp. Ther., *200*(2), 263-70 (1977).

9-*nor*-9-β-Hydroxyhexahydrocannabinol, A Cannabinoid with Potent Antinociceptive Activity: Comparisons with Morphine.

Antinociceptive activity of β-HHC was examined in male ICR mice and compared to that of morphine. Changes in brain catecholamines were also examined. β-HHC was found to be equipotent to morphine; however, no cross tolerance was observed between the two.

3355   Bloom, A. S.; Haavik, C. O.; and Hardman, H. F., Fed. Proc., *36*(3), 1027 (1977).

Effect of Δ^9-Tetrahydrocannabinol (THC) *in vitro* on ATPases in Mouse Brain Subcellular Fractions.

Δ^9-THC inhibited NA-K- and Mg-Ca ATPase activity in subcellular fractions of the mouse brain. Effects were dose-related.

3356   Bloom, A. S.; Haavik, C. O.; and Strehlow, D., Life Sci., *23*(13), 1399-1404 (1978).

Effects of Δ^9-Tetrahydrocannabinol on ATPases in Mouse Brain Subcellular Fractions.

Δ^9-THC elevated Mg^{2+}-ATPase activity in mitochondrial and inhibited it in microsomal fractions of the mouse brain. THC, however, inhibited NA^+-K^+-and mg^{2+}-Ca^{2+}-ATPases in all tested fractions.

3357   Bloom, A. S.; Johnson, K. M.; Bowman, F. J.; and Dewey, W. L., Fed. Proc., *35*(3), 506 (1976).

Correlation Between the Effects of Several Cannabinoids on Catecholamine Synthesis, Body Temperature, and Behavior.

The effects of five cannabinoids, Δ^9-THC, β-HHC, α-HHC, CBN and CBD on body temperature, catecholamine synthesis and behavior were examined in mice. Compounds which produced behavioral changes also produced hypothermia, along with an accumulation of newly synthesized catecholamine.

3358   Bloom, A. S.; Johnson, K. M.; and Dewey, W. L., Res. Commun. Chem. Pathol. Pharmacol., *20*(1), 51-57 (1978).

The Effects of Cannabinoids on Body Temperature and Brain Catecholamine Synthesis.

Δ^9-THC, 11-OH-Δ^9-THC and β-HHC were found to decrease body temperature and to increase the accumulation of newly synthesized brain catecholamines in mice. The effects were dose related. CBN and CBD were without significant effect on those measures.

3359   Bloom, A. S.; Kiernan, C. J.; and Haavik, C. O., Fed. Proc., *37*(3), 737 (1978).

Δ^9-Tetrahydrocannabinol (THC) Induced Increase in Brain Catecholamine Synthesis and Plasma Corticosterone (CS) Levels in the Absence of Hypothermia.

Δ^9-THC (2 to 16 mg/kg, i.v.) produced a dose-related increase in brain NE and DA synthesis but did not alter body temperature at 31°. Plasma corticosterone levels were also increased at both 20° and 31°.

3360 Bloom, A. S.; Kiernan, C. J.; and Halloin, T. J., *Seventh International Congress of Pharmacology: Abstracts*, Paris, France, July 16-21, 1978, p. 607.

Effect of Δ^9-Tetrahydrocannabinol (THC) on the Synthesis of Catecholamines in Brain Synaptosomes.

Δ^9-THC (3-100 μm) significantly increased the conversion of ^{3}H tyrosine to DA and NE. The high concentrations, 30 and 100 μm, were less effective than the lower ones and also significantly inhibited the active uptake of tyrosine into mouse brain synaptosomes.

3361 Blum, K.; Briggs, A. H.; Feinglass, S. J.; Domey, R.; and Wallace, J. E., Curr. Ther. Res., *21*(2), 241-44 (1977).

Effects of Δ^9-Tetrahydrocannabinol (Δ^9-THC) on Amphetamine-Aggregate Toxicity in Mice.

Low doses of THC (0.75 mg/kg) decreased while higher doses (3.0 mg/kg) increased the amphetamine-induced toxicity in aggregated mice. Implications and possible mechanisms of action were discussed.

3362 Boeren, E. G.; Elsohly, M. A.; Turner, C. E.; and Salemink, C. A., Experientia, *33*(7), 848 (1977).

β-Cannabispiranol: A New Non-Cannabinoid Phenol From *Cannabis sativa L.*

The structure of β-cannabispiranol was determined by means of spectrochemical analysis (NMR, IR, UV, MS) and by correlation with cannabispiran.

3363 Boeren, E. G.; Heerma, W.; Terlouw, J. K., Org. Mass Spectrom., *11*, 659-63 (1976).

The Use of Labelled Analogues for the Determination of Mass Spectrometric Fragmentation Mechanisms of Cannabinoids.

The formation of the most abundant fragment ion $C_{15} H_{19} O_2$ (M/e 231) in the mass spectrum of Δ^8-THC was proven to occur through a one-step mechanism and through a retrodiels-alder reaction followed by a methyl elimination. The mechanism of the one-step process is discussed in detail.

3364 Bogg, R. A., Can. J. Pub. Health, *66*, 369-73 (1975).

Stress-Seeking and Hallucinogenic Drug Usage.

The author shows a correlation between drug abuse and tendencies to hitchhike, attend rock festivals, ride motorcycles and join protest groups. Inferences are presented that drug usage is actually a means of seeking stress rather than of escaping it. Hashish and marihuana are considered separately as their use is correlated to the above mentioned activities.

3365 Bogg, R. A., Drug Forum, *5*(1), 55-67 (1975-1976).

Drinking as a Precursor to Hallucinogenic Drug Usage.

Among surveyed high school seniors, marihuana users were found to have consumed alcohol before marihuana. The attitude of marihuana-naive alcohol drinkers was much more relaxed toward the future use of marihuana than that of non-drinkers. Other differences were also indicated and findings discussed.

3366 Boisio, M. L.; Med. Leg. Assicur., *24*(1-4), 45-60 (1976).

Separazione Su Strato Sottile Di Cannabinoidi Da Fitosteroli E Da Componenti Del Tabacco [Thin-Layer Separation of Cannabinoids From Phytosterols and Tobacco Components.]

Successful separation of THC, CBN, CBD and beta-sitosterol from each other and from tobacco components was accomplished by TLC. GC was used for the quantitative analysis of the above cannabinoids.

3367   Borg, J.; Gershon, S.; and Alpert, M., Psychopharmacologia, *42*(3), 211-18 (1975).

Dose Effects of Smoked Marihuana on Human Cognitive and Motor Function

Marihuana cigarettes containing 70 to 250 μg/Kg of Δ^9-THC decreased the speed of human performance in a dose-related fashion. This decrease was more impressive in simple automatic and motor functions than in functions of greater cognitive involvement.

3368   Borison, H. L.; McCarthy, L. E.; and London, S. W., New Eng. J. Med., *298*(26), 1480-81 (1978).

Cannabinoids and Emesis (letter).

Nabilone, a synthetic cannabinoid, protected cats from emesis induced by treatment with antineoplastic or emetic agents. Implications of findings were discussed.

3369   Boucher, F.; Paris, M.; and Cosson, L., Phytochemistry, *16*(9), 1445-48 (1977).

Mise En Evidence De Deux Types Chimiques Chez Le *Cannabis sativa* Originaire D' Afrique Du Sud [Demonstration of Two Chemotypes in *Cannabis sativa* from South Africa.]

A study carried out on the flowering tops of *Cannabis sativa*, obtained from South African seeds and grown in a phytotron, shows the presence of two chemotypes varying in concentration of tetrahydrocannabinolic and tetrahydrocannabivarolic acids. These results are attributable to genetic heterogeneity.

3370   Bouhuys, A.; and Zuskin, E., Ann. Intern. Med., *84*(4), 398-405 (1976).

Chronic Respiratory Disease in Hemp Workers.

Questionnaires were given to soft-hemp workers in Spain first in 1967 and then in 1974 for a followup study. Older hemp workers showed more chronic lung disease and lower forced expiratory volume (FEV) than did controls of the same age. Even after exposure to dust ceased, chronic respiratory symptoms developed. FEV was a good index for the progression of disease. A decline in FEV was more prevalent among hemp workers than controls.

3371   Boulougouris, J. C.; Liakos, A.; and Stefanis, C., pp. 17-23 in *Chronic Cannabis Use*, edited by R. L. Dornbush, A. M. Freedman, and M. Fink. NY, Annals of the New York Academy of Sciences, V. 282, 1976.

Social Traits of Heavy Hashish Users and matched Controls.

Sociological characteristics of chronic hashish users in Greece were examined. The test population had little education and consumed about 3.0 g of hashish per day. Initiation of cannabis use was not related either to environmental factors or family histories. Hashish users generally held less skilled jobs when compared to non-users and also had a greater frequency of imprisonments.

The authors, however, failed to find a significant correlation between cannabis use and antisocial behavior.

3372 Boulougouris, J. C.; Panayiotopoulos, C. P.; Antypos, E.; Liakos, A.; and Stefanis, C., pp. 168-72 in *Chronic Cannabis Use*, edited by R. L. Dornbush, A. M. Freedman, and M. Fink. NY, Annals of the New York Academy of Sciences, V. 282, 1976.

Effects of Chronic Hashish Use on Medical Status in 44 Users Compared with 38 Controls.

Chronic cannabis users ($\bar{x}$=23 yrs) and matched controls are contrasted with respect to drug effects on physical and mental status. Methods of evaluation included medical histories, thorough clinical examinations of the respiratory, cardiovascular, and alimentary systems, and neurologic examinations. Users were physically and neurologically healthy.

3373 Bourdon, R., Eur. J. Toxicol. Environ. Hyg., *9*(1), 11-21 (1976).

Dosage Fluorimetrique Du Delta-9-Tetrahydrocannabinol Et De Ses Metabolites Dans L'urine [Fluorometric Determination of Delta-9-Tetrahydrocannabinol and its Metabolites in Urine.]

A new highly specific fluorometric method to characterize and determine the amount of THC and its metabolites in the urine is described. Metabolic and structural considerations were taken into account.

3374 Bourdon, R., pp. 111-21 in *Marihuana: Chemistry, Biochemistry, and Cellular Effects*, edited by G. G. Nahas. NY, Springer-Verlag, 1976.

Identification and Quantification of Cannabinoids in Urine by Gallium Chelate Formation.

The author presents an identification and quantification of cannabinoids in urine through their transformation into o-o´-dihydroxy azo compounds able to give highly fluorescent gallium chelates. All cannabinoids having a nonsubstituted carbon atom between the phenol group and the side chain are able to give gallium chelates.

3375 Boutet, M.; Roy, P. E.; and Huy, N. D., Clin. Res., *23*(5), 608a (1975).

Chronic Inhalation of Marijuana in Dogs: A Light and Electronmicroscopic Study of the Heart.

Cardiac tissues of Beagles which voluntarily inhaled 4 marihuana cigarettes per day for 30 mos. did not differ histologically from control's as determined by light and electron microscopes.

3376 Bowd, A.; Swann, D. A.; Towell, B.; and Turnbull, J. H., pp. 128-34 in *Excited States of Biological Molecules*, Proc. Intl. Conf., April 18-24, 1974, Lisbon, edited by John B. Birks. Chichester, Eng., Wiley, 1976.

Cannabinols: Photochemistry and Determination in Biological Fluids.

CBD, CBN, Δ^8-THC and Δ^9-THC irradiated at 285 nm produce a flourescent product which was found to be substituted 4-hydroxy phenanthrene. This reaction can be applied to quantitate cannabinoids in biological fluids.

3377 Bowd, A.; Swann, D. A.; and Turnbull, J. H.; J. Chem. Soc. Chem. Commun., No. *19*, 797-98 (1975).

Photochemical Transformations of Cannabinol.

CBN, when subjected to photochemical (UV-irradiation) conditions, produced an isomeric diol which formed the highly fluorescent hydroxyphenanthrene. The solvent was ethanol.

3378   Bowker, L. H., Drug Forum, 7(1), 69-80 (1978-79).

The Relationship Between Sex, Drugs, and Sexual Behavior on a College Campus.

Analysis of a questionnaire indicated that males dominate the college drug distribution system and that they generally introduce and supply females with drugs (including marihuana) on a continuing basis. Drug seductions are also performed by males to make females more sexually willing and responsive.

3379   Boyd, E. H.; Boyd, E. S.; and Brown, L. E., Neuropharmacology, 14, 533-36 (1975).

Differential Effects of a Tetrahydrocannabinol and Pentobarbital on Cerebral Cortical Neurons.

Unlike pentobarbital, Δ^9-THC (1.5 mg/kg, i.v.) enhanced several parameters related to the late and later phases of the response evoked by electrical stimulation of somatosensory cortex of monkeys.

3380   Boyd, E. S.; Boyd, E. H.; and Brown, L. E., Psychopharmacology, 47(1), 119-22 (1976).

Effects of Δ^9-Tetrahydrocannabinol and Pentobarbital on a Cortical Response Evoked During Conditioning.

Δ^9-THC and pentobarbital depressed evoked cortical activity in trained monkeys.

3381   Boyd, E. S.; Boyd, E. H.; and Brown, L. E., J. Pharmacol. Exp. Ther., 207(2), 521-31 (1978).

Effects of Some Psychotropic Drugs on M-Wave and Operant Behavior in the Squirrel Monkey.

Nabilone (0.125-1.0 mg/kg, p.o.) and chlorpromazine tended to decrease the amplitude of the evoked M-wave and to depress conditioned behavior in squirrel monkeys. Effects of other psychotropic drugs on the above mentioned parameters were also investigated.

3382   Bracs, P.; Jackson, D. M.; and Chesher, G. B., J. Pharm. Pharmacol., 27(9), 713-15 (1975).

The Effects of Δ^9-Tetrahydrocannabinol on Brain Amine Concentration and Turnover in Whole Rat Brain and in Various Regions of the Brain.

Male rats were administered THC, p.o. (20 mg/kg) or vehicle 1 hr. before decapitation. No significant difference was noted in whole brain concentrations of DA, 5-HT, or NE.

3383   Bradley, S. G.; Munson, A. E.; Dewey, W. L.; and Harris, L. S., Infect. Immun., 17(2), 325-29 (1977).

Enhanced Susceptibility of Mice to Combinations of Δ^9-Tetrahydrocannabinol and Live or Killed Gram-Negative Bacteria.

A hyperadditive mortality was observed in mice when THC was combined with various bacterial endotoxins. The possible mechanisms involved were discussed.

3384   Brady, K. T.; Balster, R. L.; and Harris, L. S., Fed. Proc., 37(3), 737 (1978).

Antagonism by Cannabidiol of Δ^9-Tetrahydrocannabinol Induced Suppression of

Operant Behavior in Rhesus Monkeys.

Δ^9-THC (0.3 and 1.0 mg/kg, i.m.) suppressed operant behavior in monkeys. CBD (30 mg/kg) pretreatment completely reversed the suppression induced by the lower dose of Δ^9-THC, but failed to antagonize the effects exerted by the higher dose.

3385   Bram, S.; and Brachet, P., pp. 207-11 in *Marihuana: Chemistry, Biochemistry, and Cellular Effects*, edited by G. G. Nahas. NY, Springer-Verlag, 1976.

Inhibition of Proliferation and Differentiation of *Dictyostelium discoideum* Amoebae by Tetrahydrocannabinol and Cannabinol.

Marihuana cytotoxicity was studied using the slime mold *Dictyostelium discoideum.* Results showed that above a critical concentration, Δ^9-THC and CBN were found to affect both growth and differentiation of the mold.

3386   Branda, L. A.; Ackerman, M. J.; Daley, J. D.; and Rosenfeld, J. M., IRCS Med. Sci., Libr. Compend., *6*(1), 44 (1978).

Perfusion of Human Placenta with Δ^9-Tetrahydrocannabinol.

THC perfused through the maternal side of human placenta was not significantly detected on the fetal side. Implications of the findings were discussed.

3387   Brannan, M. D., Diss. Abstr. Int. B, *37*(4), 1637-38 (1976).

A Study of the Mechanisms of the Cardiovascular Effects of Delta-8-Tetrahydrocannabinol in the Anesthetized Dog.

Cardiovascular effects of Δ^8-THC (0.5 mg/kg, i.v.) are described in the anesthesized dog.

Hypotension induced with THC correlates with neurally mediated vasodilation of hindlimbs and not with bradycardia. No direct inotropic effect is detected and metabolic conversion of THC is not essential for cardiovascular activity.

3388   Brannan, M. D.; Proctor, J. D.; and Wasserman, A. J., Fed. Proc., *34*(3), 744 (1975).

Cardiovascular Effects of 9-NOR-Δ^8-Tetrahydrocannabinol (9-NOR) and Δ^8-Tetrahydrocannabinol (Δ^8) in Anesthetized Dogs.

Δ^8-THC and its 9-Nor derivative at a dose of 0.5 mg/kg, i.v. produced a decrease in mean arterial BP, contractility, and heart rate in the pentobarbital anesthetized, mechanically ventilated, open-chested dog. Peak responses were seen within 15 min. and responses persisted for 1 hr. Cardiac output was unaffected.

3389   Braude, M. C., pp. 693-97 in *Pharmacology of Marihuana, Vol. 2*, edited by M. C. Braude and S. Szara. NY, Raven Press, 1976.

Genetics: An Introduction.

A summary of results concerning studies conducted in the last 10 years on the effects of marihuana on reproduction and genetics is tabulated. The conflicting reports may be due to varying the route of administration, species and type of marihuana used. THC was also found to produce agalactia.

3390   Braude, M. C., pp. 21-26 in *Pharmacology of Marihuana, Vol. 1*, edited by M. C. Braude and S. Szara. NY, Raven Press, 1976.

Five Years of Preclinical Marihuana Research.

Brief chemophysiological and pharmacological profiles of marihuana data compiled over 5 yrs. of preclinical research are presented. Large numbers of diverse compounds have been isolated from marihuana plant materials. Techniques of identification and quantitation include GC, GC-MS, mass fragmentography, electron capture detection, and RIA. Pharmacological aspects of marihuana research encompass the biphasic activity of cannabinoids, tolerance development and reversal, dosing technique evolution, and the hazards of animal data extrapolation to the human situation.

3391   Braude, M. C.; Szara, S., eds., *Pharmacology of Marihuana, Vol. 1 and Vol. 2*, New York, Raven Press, 1976. 865 pp.

These two volumes are a compilation of papers presented at a meeting in Savannah, Georgia in 1974, by experts in the field at that time. Abstracts of each chapter can be found under individual senior author.

3392   Brecher, E. M.; and Editors, Consumer Reports, Contemp. Drug Probl., 4(2), 115-40 (1975).

Marijuana: The Health Questions/The Legal Question.

A review of scientific evidence concerning the harmful effects of marihuana in humans including irreversible brain damage, lowering of body resistance, increases in the likelihood of birth defects, induction of precancerous lung changes and possible sterility and/or impotence among men. Conflicts with regard to the above mentioned evidence were analyzed along with some findings of the Jamaica study. Also implications of the Oregon experience with marihuana decriminalization were discussed.

3393   Bright, T. P.; Farber, M. O.; Brown, D. J.; and Forney, R. B., Toxicol. Appl. Pharmacol., 31(3), 100-106 (1975).

Cardiopulmonary Toxicity of Δ^9-Tetrahydrocannabinol in the Anesthetized Dog.

In the anesthetized, ventilated dog, 0.5 mg/kg THC i.v. produced changes in pulmonary resistance as mediated through a vagal mechanism with no change in pulmonary compliance or arterial blood gases. In some animals a decrease in cardiac output and blood pH was associated with the THC induced increase in pulmonary resistance, and generally was associated with an increased scatter of R_L measurements.

3394   Bright, T. P.; Farber, M. O.; Brown, D. J.; Lewis, S. C.; and Forney, R. B., Toxicol. Appl. Pharmacol., 31, 520-26 (1975).

Cardiopulmonary Effects of Cannabidiol in Anesthetized Mongrel Dogs.

Female dogs were administered CBD (0.5 mg/kg or 1.0 mg/kg) via the femoral vein to the right ventricle to examine cardiopulmonary effects.   CBD had little effect on arterial blood but a decrease in lung clearance was noted, with no metabolic acidosis. CBD effects are compared to THC's.

3395   Bro, P.; and Schou, J., New Eng. J. Med., 293(20), 1049-50 (1975).

Cannabis Poisoning with Analytical Verification.

The case of a four year old girl accidentally ingesting 1.5 g cannabis resin was presented with physiological and behavioral observations.

3396   Bromley, B.; Gordon, J.; and Zimmermann, E., Fed. Proc., 36(3), 1026 (1977).

Δ^9-Tetrahydrocannabinol Inhibition of Ether and Perphenazine-Induced Release of Prolactin in Male Rats.

Δ^9-THC suppressed stress- and perphenazine-induced prolactin release in rats.

3397   Bromley, B. L.; Rabii, J.; Gordon, J. H.; and Zimmermann, E., Endocrine Res. Commun., 5(4), 271-78 (1978).

Delta-9-Tetrahydrocannabinol Inhibition of Suckling-Induced Prolactin Release in the Lactating Rat.

Δ^9-THC (1.25 or 4.0 mg/kg, i.v.) antagonized suckling-induced increase in plasma prolactin level in lactating rats. Δ^9-THC also inhibited maternal behavior toward pups.

3398   Bron, B., Prax. Kinderpsychol. Kinderpsychiat., 25(4), 128-39 (1976).

Motivation Und Effekt Des Phantastica-Konsums [Motivation and Effect of Consumption of Hallucinogens].

Marihuana and LSD users expect to alleviate interpsychic conflicts and tensions by drug consumption. Psychodynamic and social factor analysis indicated, however, that drug consumption aggravated, rather than alleviated, these symptoms.

3399   Bron, B.; Froscher, W.; and Gehlen, W., Fortschr. Neurol. Psychiatr., 44(12), 673-82 (1976).

Differential Diagnostische Und Syndromgenetische Probleme Und Aspekte Drogeninduzierter Psychosen Bei Jugendlichen [Differential Diagnosis and Syndrome-Genetic Problems and Aspects of Drug-Induced Psychoses in Juveniles].

Hashish-, LSD- or amphetamine-induced psychosis complicates the psychosis differential diagnostic process in adolescents.   Factors to consider before diagnosis were discussed.

3400   Brook, J. S.; Lukoff, I. F.; and Whiteman, M., J. Genetic Psychol., 133(2), 261-71 (1978).

Family Socialization and Adolescent Personality and Their Association with Adolescent Use of Marijuana.

Among interviewed adolescents, those conforming to parental rules were less likely to use marihuana. Parent socialization and personality/attitudinal factors bear direct but independent reltionship to adolescent use of marihuana.

3401   Brook, J. S.; Lukoff, I. F.; and Whiteman, M., Yale J. Biol. Med., 50(4), 383-90 (1977).

Correlates of Adolescent Marijuana Use as Related to Age, Sex, and Ethnicity.

Regardless of age, sex or ethnicity factors, the modeling of familial or peer drug use and nonconformity to conventional values contributed most to the marihuana use prevalent in 19% of 403 interviewed adolescents.

3402   Brown, A.; and Stickgold, A., J. Psychedelic Drugs, 8(4), 275-83 (1976).

Marijuana Flashback Phenomena.

Analysis and a discussion of the clinical implications of 13 cases of self-diagnosed marihuana flashbacks were presented.

3403   Brown, B.; Adams, A. J.; Haegerstrom-Portnoy, G.; Jones, R. T.; and Flom, M. C., Amer. J. Ophthalmol., 83(3), 350-54 (1977).

Pupil Size After Use of Marihuana and Alcohol.

Pupil size of human volunteers after ingestion of THC and/or alcohol was examined. THC (8-15 mg) produced a dose related pupillary constriction, whereas alcohol (0.75 mg/kg) produced no significant change in pupil size. Persons consuming both alcohol and THC also showed no change in pupil size.

3404 Brown, B.; Adams, A. J.; Haegerstrom-Portnoy, G.; Jones, R. T.; and Flom, M. C., Percept. Psychophys., *18*(6), 441-46 (1975).

Effects of Alcohol and Marijuana on Dynamic Visual Acuity: I. Threshold Measurements.

Ten subjects participated in a double-blind study of the alcohol and marihuana (8 and 15 mg of Δ^9-THC) effects on dynamic visual activity (DVA). Both agents produced significant dose-related reductions in DVA but those produced by alcohol were greater than for "equivalent" doses of marihuana. Implications of the findings on alcohol-related traffic accidents were discussed.

3405 Brown, J. E., Diss. Abstr. Int. B., *37*(6), 2774-75 (1976).

Effects of Δ^9-Tetrahydrocannabinol on Food Intake, Taste Preferences and Hypothalamic Concentrations of Norepinephrine and Serotonin in the Rat.

Δ^9-THC (0.25 and 0.40 mg/kg, p.o.) treated rats initially consumed more food than controls, but the difference was negligible within 24 hrs. Initial differences in caloric intake were attributed to the preference of THC-treated rats for highly concentrated sucrose solutions. These effects are associated with changes in hypothalamic NE and 5-HT within 1 or 2 hrs. after THC ingestion.

3406 Brown, J. E.; Kassouny, M.; and Cross, J. K., Behav. Biol., *20*(1), 104-10 (1977).

Kinetic Studies of Food Intake and Sucrose Solution Preference by Rats Treated with Low Doses of Δ^9-Tetrahydrocannabinol.

Rats treated with Δ^9-THC (0.25 and 0.4 mg/kg, p.o.) exhibited time and dose-dependent temporal increase in the consumption of strong sucrose solution (0.8m) and dry chow. Total 24 hr.-kilocaloric consumption was, however, similar in both treated and control groups.

3407 Brown, J. E.; and Kassouny, M. E., Fed. Proc., *35*(3), 341 (1976).

Marihuana Induced Alterations in Feeding Behavior and Hypothalamic Concentrations of Norepinephrine and Serotonin in the Rat.

Oral Δ^9-THC (0.25 and 0.4 mg/kg) initially increased the feeding behavior of rats and altered hypothalamic NE and 5-HT concentrations.

3408 Brown, J. K.; and Malone, M. H., Clin. Toxicol., *9*(2), 145-68 (1976).

Status of Drug Quality in the Street-Drug Market - - An Update.

Some 3700 street-drug samples were analyzed for content. Approximately 90% of samples collected were *Cannabis sativa* or preparations thereof. No street samples were pure THC, but supposedly pure THC samples usually contained phencyclidine. Some supposed opium samples were found to be hashish.

3409 Brunk, S. F.; Noyes, R.; Avery, D. H.; and Canter, A., J. Clin. Pharmacol., *15*(7), 554 (1975).

The Analgesic Effect of Delta-9-Tetrahydrocannabinol.

Thirty-four cancer patients received placebo, 10 and 20 mg THC, and 60 and 120 mg codeine in a double-blind study. Low doses of THC and codeine produced similar analgesic effects. The effects of 20 mg THC make it not therapeutically useful.

3410 Brunnemann, K. D.; and Hoffmann, D., J. Chromatogr. Sci., *13*(4), 159-63 (1975).

Chemical Studies on Tobacco Smoke XXXIV. Gas Chromatographic Determination of Ammonia in Cigarette and Cigar Smoke.

Presence and inhalation of ammonia in cigarette smoke is thought to cause acceleration of breathing rate due to lung irritation. Quantitation was by GC using methylamine-^{14}C as internal standard. A marihuana cigarette was found to contain 188 micrograms per gram ammonia. This was higher than a standard cigarette but lower than any cigars tested.

3411 Brunnemann, K. D.; Yu, L.; and Hoffmann, D., J. Anal. Toxicol., *1*(1), 38-42 (1977).

Chemical Studies on Tobacco Smoke. XLIX. Gas Chromatographic Determination of Hydrogen Cyanide and Cyanogen in Tobacco Smoke.

This paper is chiefly concerned with analytical determinations of HCN in smoke and particulate matter from cigarettes and cigars. Total HCN in mainstream smoke of non-filtered marihuana cigarettes was comparable to that in a standard non-filtered tobacco cigarette. The non-inhaled sidestream smoke of the marihuana cigarette contained more HCN than its tobacco counterpart.

3412 Brunner, T. F., J. Psychedelic Drugs, *9*(3), 221-25 (1977).

Marijuana in Ancient Greece and Rome? The Literary Evidence.

In reviewing pertinent Greek and Roman literature, the author presented evidence to prove that marihuana was then employed in medicine and that its alleged use for hallucinogenic purposes was not substantiated.

3413 Buckingham, G. A.; and Dahl, C. J., *Rep. Invest.: Aust. Gov. Anal. Lab.*, *56* (1977). 31 pp.

The Preparation and Identification of Cannabinoid Acids and Derivatives.

This is a report on preparation, separation, and spectra data of cannabinoid acids. Spectra data are given for the methyl esters. Decarboxylation procedures are also provided. Analysis was by GLC, TLC, UV, NMR, IR, and MS.

3414 Bueno, O. F. A.; Carlini, E. A.; Finkelfarb, E.; and Suzuki, J. S., Psychopharmacologia, *46*, 235-43 (1976).

Δ^9-Tetrahydrocannabinol, Ethanol, and Amphetamine as Discriminative Stimuli-Generalization Tests with Other Drugs.

In rats trained to discriminate Δ^9-THC, only Δ^8-THC and CBN elicited like responses. Pentobarbital induced ethanol-like responses, whereas only Δ^9-THC and apomorphine induced amphetamine-like responses in ethanol- and amphetamine-trained rats, respectively.

3415 Burdsal, C.; Greenberg, G.; Bell, M.; and Reynolds, S., J. Clin. Psychol., *31*(3), 568-72 (1975).

A Factor-Analytic Examination of Sexual Behaviors and Attitudes and Marihuana Usage.

A sample drawn from undergraduates at Wichita State University was questioned about marihuana and sex. Specific conclusions included: (1) Persons with liberal sexual views are likely to use marihuana and to favor its liberalization; (2) Marihuana users feel that marihuana has beneficial effects on sexual intercourse and favor marihuana liberalization; (3) Persons with avant-garde sexual attitudes favor liberalization of marihuana laws; and (4) Females use marihuana less frequently than men.

3416　Burgers, P. C.; Dijkstra, G.; Heerma, W.; Terlouw, J. K.; Boon, A.; Kramer, H. F.; Kuppers, F. J. E. M.; Lousberg, R. J. J. C.; and Salemink, C. A., Adv. Mass Spectrom. Biochem Med., *1*, 391-400 (1976).

The Utility of Metastable Ion Characteristics in the Determination of Ion Structures of Cannabinoids.

Metastable measurements and isotopic labelling were used in the mass spectral study of cannabinoids. Six cannabinoids with M. W. 314 were used. The major fragmentation of these compounds to give the ion at m/e 231 was studied and a new mechanism for the formation of such ion was given.

3417　Burkett, S. R., J. Drug Issues, 7(3), 263-73 (1977).

Religion, Parental Influence, and Adolescent Alcohol and Marijuana Use.

An inverse relationship between religious involvement and alcohol or marihuana use was found to exist among high school seniors. Parents influenced the religious beliefs, but not the morality of personal asceticism, of their children. Other findings were also discussed.

3418　Burkett, S. R., Pac. Sociol. Rev., *20*(2), 181-201 (1977).

School Ties, Peer Influence, and Adolescent Marijuana Use.

A questionnaire on marihuana use was administered to high school students. When responses were analyzed, it was concluded that marihuana use was more common among the less successful students and that, due to the illegality involved, such a practice was a peer-supported activity.

3419　Burns, M.; and Sharma, S., Psychol. Rep., *38*(2), 543-46 (1976).

Marihuana "High" - A First-Time Effect?

Marihuana users begin their usage by 18 yrs of age, use marihuana 1-7 times per week, rarely initiate usage when alone, are highly influenced toward marihuana consumption by curiosity coupled to peer pressure, and rarely achieve an enjoyable subjective "high" on the first try. These conclusions were drawn from a survey of college students.

3420　Burrell, C. D., J. Sch. Health. *46*(3), 148-57 (1976).

The Future of Mind-Altering Substances.

A vice-president of a pharmaceutical company gives his views on the positive and negative aspects of the utilization of mind-altering substances. Some moral, legal, and social implications of drug abuse, therapeutic drug use, and the search for more drugs were discussed. Included was a discussion of past, present, and future uses of marijuana.

3421   Burstein, S., pp. 19-33 in *The Therapeutic Potential of Marihuana*, edited by S. Cohen and R. Stillman. NY, Plenum Medical Book Company, 1976.

Prostaglandins and Cannabis - - IV: A Biochemical Basis for Therapeutic Applications.

Literature evidence implicating cannabis actions in prostaglandin (PG) synthesis inhibition was provided. The importance of cellular cultures in studying cannabis action on PG was suggested as a step in providing a biochemical basis for therapeutic applications of cannabis.

3422   Burstein, S.; and Hunter, S. A., Biochem. Pharmacol., *27*(8), 1275-80 (1978).

Prostaglandins and Cannabis VI. Release of Arachidonic Acid from HeLa Cells by $\triangle^1$-Tetrahydrocannabinol and Other Cannabinoids.

THC, CBN and CBC released, in a dose-related manner, the previously bound arachidonic acid from HeLa cells culture. Other cannabinoids and non-cannabinoids were also tested and relationship of the data to prostaglandin synthesis was discussed.

3423   Burstein, S.; and Hunter, S. A., Prostaglandins, *15*(4), 702 (1978).

Release of Arachidonic Acid From HeLa Cells by $\triangle^1$-Tetrahydrocannabinol and Other Cannabinoids.

THC, CBN and CBC released, in a dose-related manner, the previously bound arachidonic acid from HeLa cells culture. Other cannabinoids and non-cannabinoids were also tested and relationship of the data to prostaglandin synthesis was discussed.

3424   Burstein, S.; Hunter, S. A.; and Shoupe, T. S., Life Sci., *23*(9), 979-81 (1978).

Inhibition of Cholesterol Esterases by $\triangle^1$-Tetrahydrocannabinol.

$\triangle^1$-THC inhibited cholesterol esterase of the rat adrenal and luteinized ovary in a dose-related manner.

3425   Burstein, S.; Hunter, S. A.; Shoupe, T. S.; and Taylor, P., Res. Commun. Chem. Pathol. Pharmacol., *19*(3), 557-60 (1978).

Cannabinoid Inhibition of Testosterone Synthesis by Mouse Leydig Cells.

Both THC and CBN inhibited testosterone production by Leydig cells of the mouse testes, with THC being more potent than CBN.

3426   Burstein, S.; Taylor, P.; El-Feraly, F. S.; and Turner, C., Biochem. Pharmacol., *25*(17), 2003-04 (1976).

Prostaglandins and Cannabis. V. Identification of *p*-Vinylphenol as a Potent

Inhibitor of Prostaglandin Synthesis.

p-Vinylphenol, a substance present in cannabis smoke and steam distillate, is a strong inhibitor of PG synthesis. p-Vinylphenol can be obtained from p-hydroxycinnamic acid, a natural constituent of cannabis; however, p-hydroxycinnamic acid is found to be a moderate stimulator of PG synthesis. Thus, caution must be observed in ascribing the biological activity of cannabis to any single compound.

3427   Burstein, S.; and Varanelli, C., Res. Commun. Chem. Pathol. Pharmacol., *11*(3), 343-54 (1975).

Transformations of Cannabinol in the Mouse.

A possible role for CBN formed *in vivo* in the pharmacological profile of Δ^9-THC is suggested after studying the metabolic pathways of CBN in mice.

3428   Burstein, S.; Varanelli, C.; and Slade, L. T., Biochem. Pharmacol., *24*, 1053-54 (1975).

Prostaglandins and Cannabis III. Inhibition of Biosynthesis by Essential Oil Compounds of Marihuana.

The inhibiting effect of the volatile fraction of cannabis on the conversion of ^{14}C-8,11,14-eicosatrienoic acid to PGE by bovine seminal vesicle microsomes was studied.

3429   Butler, J. L.; Gaines, L. S.; and Lenox, J. R., Percept. Motor Skills, *42*(3, pt. 2), 1059-65 (1976).

Effects of Marijuana, Expectation and "Suggestibility" on Cognitive Functioning.

Volunteers were first categorized as to their suggestibility and then tested under the influence of marihuana to see if pre-dosing suggestions as to dosage strength would influence ability to perform in cognitive tasks and subjective evaluations. Results showed that many performance deficits during marihuana "highs" were not sensitive to prior opinions or perceptions.

3430   Butler, J. R.; Peek, L.; Regelson, W.; Moore, M.; and Lubin, L., pp. 313-28 in *The Therapeutic Potential of Marihuana*, edited by S. Cohen and R. Stillman. NY, Plenum Medical Book Company, 1976.

Treatment Effects of Δ^9-THC in an Advanced Cancer Population.

THC (0.1 mg/kg, t.i.d.) given to terminal cancer patients acted as an euphoriant and mild tranquilizer. Pain, nausea and vomiting were suppressed and a tendency to maintain weight was evident in these patients.

3431   Butler, R. C.; Sorber, W. A.; and Harclerode, J. E., IRCS Med. Sci., Libr. Compend., *4*(7), 311 (1976).

Delta-9-Tetrahydrocannabinol Suppresses Humoral Immunity.

High doses of THC reduced the number of plaque-forming cells, an immune response to antigens in sensitized mice.

C

3432 Cais, M.; Dani, S.; Joseph, Y.; Modiano, A.; Gershon, H.; and Mechoulam, R., FEBS Lett., 55(1), 257-60 (1975).

Studies of Cannabinoid Metabolites - A Free Radical Immunoassay.

Protein conjugates of Δ^6-THC derivatives were synthesized with bovine serum albumin and ovalbumin. Spin-labelled haptens of some Δ^6-THC derivatives were also prepared. The use of these materials for the detection of cannabinoid metabolites in the urine of hashish smokers by a free radical immunoassay was studied.

3433 Calil, H. M., Psychopharmacology, 56(1), 87-92 (1978).

Screening Hallucinogenic Drugs. II. Systematic Study of Two Behavioral Tests.

In rats trained to discriminate Δ^9-THC, no generalization to other drugs could be made. Implications of the findings were discussed.

3434 Campbell, I., pp. 33-36 in Chronic Cannabis Use, edited by R. L. Dornbush, A. M. Freedman, and M. Fink. N.Y., Annals of the New York Academy of Sciences, V. 282, 1976.

The Amotivational Syndrome and Cannabis Use with Emphasis on the Canadian Scene.

Under controlled clinical setting, large mandatory doses of marihuana led to decreased productivity and motivation but consumption of desirable amount of the agent did not. It was suggested that academic performance deterioration and possible amotivational syndrome may result only after high marihuana intake.

3435 Campos Rodriguez, R., Univ. Cent. Venez., Fac. Farm. Rev., 38, 64-116 (1977).

Modificaciones De Comportamiento Por Efectos De La Marihuana, Del THC Y Similares, En Palomas [Behavior Modifications by the Effects of Marijuana, THC and Similar Derivatives in Doves].

Δ^9-THC, SP-1 and marihuana extract affected behavior of pigeons under reinforcement schedule and concurrent punishment. Tolerance and cross-tolerance to the behavioral effects of these cannabinoids developed after repeated administration.

3436 Canale, M., Zacchia, 12(1), 32-43 (1976).

Recenti Acquisizioni Farmacologiche Sulla Canapa Indiana E Problemi Medico-Legali [Recent Pharmacological Acquisitions on Indian Hemp and Medicolegal Problems.]

The pharmacology of Indian hemp was reviewed along with methods for its identification and quantitation.

3437 Capek, R.; and Esplin, B., pp. 383-95 in Marihuana: Chemistry, Biochemistry, and Cellular Effects, edited by G. G. Nahas. N.Y., Springer-Verlag, 1976.

Effects of Δ^9-Tetrahydrocannabinol on the Homosynaptic Depression in the Spinal Monosynaptic Pathway: Implications for Transmitter Dynamics in the Primary Afferents.

Administration of Δ^9-THC (5 mg/kg, i.v.) to anesthetized cats deepened the usual decline in the evoked responses of spinal monosynaptic pathways. Relationship of the above response to transmitter dynamics was studied.

3438 Capelle, N.; Atrault-Jarrier, M.; Hoellinger, H.; and Scherrmann, J. M., Eur. J. Toxicol., 9(1), 5-9 (1976).

Liaison du Δ^8-THC aux Proteines Seriques Humaines: Etude de sa Fixation en Fonction de la Composition Lipoproteinique [Binding of Δ^8-THC to Human Serum Proteins: Study of Binding as a Function of Lipoprotein Composition.]

The ability of Δ^8-THC to bind serum proteins was studied. The outcome of the experiment indicated that phospholipids are the only lipoprotein constituents involved in Δ^8-THC binding mechanisms. The procedure followed is described in detail.

3439 Carasso, R. L.; Yehuda, S.; and Frommer, R., Int. J. Neurosci., 8(2), 65-69 (1978).

The Anticonvulsant and Thermal Effects of Various Cannabinoids in Rats.

Δ^6-THC and Δ^6-THC-DMH did not protect rats against pentylenetetrazol (PTZ) or PTZ-d-amphetamine induced seizures, whereas SP-175 did. Δ^6-THC was the only cannabinoid to induce hypothermia and to enhance the hypothermic effect of d-amphetamine in rats kept at 4° C.

3440 Carchman, R. A.; Harris, L. S.; and Munson, A. E., Cancer Res., 36, 95-100 (1976).

The Inhibition of DNA Synthesis by Cannabinoids.

Δ^9-THC, CBN, Δ^8-THC and 2 metabolites inhibited DNA synthesis as measured by in vitro thymidine uptake by isolated Lewis lung cells, L 1210 leukemia cells and bone marrow cells. CBD and its 1-OH-3-n-pentyl metabolite were less active. Except for the latter two compounds which were either inactive or stimulated tumor growth in vivo, a good correlation existed between the in vivo and in vitro findings.

3441 Carchman, R. A.; Martin, B. R.; Ambrose, A. M.; and Friedman, M. A., Fed. Proc., 36(3), 1027 (1977).

The Demonstration of Cannabinoid Binding Site(s) in HTC Cells in Tissue Culture.

Evidence presented suggested the crude nuclear fraction of HTC cells to be the binding site for Δ^8-THC.

3442 Carchman, R. A.; Warner, W.; White, A. C.; and Harris, L. S., pp. 329-45 in Marihuana: Chemistry, Biochemistry, and Cellular Effects, edited by G. G. Nahas. NY, Springer-Verlag, 1976.

Cannabinoids and Neoplastic Growth.

The authors evaluated the action of cannabinoids at different cellular levels. In addition, the effects of Δ^9-THC on Lewis lung cells in vitro and in culture, on steroid-secreting cells in vitro, and on normal and malignant cells, were evaluated.

3443 Carder, B., pp. 90-102 in Behavioral Tolerance: Research and Treatment Implications, NIDA Research Monograph 18, 1978.

Environmental Influences on Marihuana Tolerance.

Arguments against the notion that behavioral tolerance always involves a learned adjustment are presented. The author suggests that there is no essential difference between pharmacologic and environmental events in their effects on the CNS and that CNS function can be altered by both. Environmental influences on the development of tolerance to drugs is fundamental to understanding the etiology of drug addiction.

3444 Carder, B., Science, *190*(4214), 590 (1975).

Blockade of Morphine Abstinence by Δ^9-Tetrahydrocannabinol.

A possible therapeutic role for Δ^9-THC as a suppressant of narcotic abstinence syndrome is criticized based on laboratory results obtained with rats. Although THC did protect against wet shakes and defecation, the general sedative effect could not account for suppression of some behavioral abstinence symptoms.

3445 Carlin, A. S.; and Trupin, E. W., Int. J. Addict., *12*(5), 617-24 (1977).

The Effect of Long-Term Chronic Marijuana Use on Neuropsychological Functioning.

When the Halstead neuropsychological test battery was applied to chronic marihuana users and matched control nonusers, no significant differences were observed between the two groups. Implications of findings were discussed.

3446 Carlini, E. A., pp. 82-102 in *Psychopharmacology of Aggression, Modern Problems of Pharmacopsychiatry, 13*. Basel, Karger, 1978. 180 pp.

Effects of Cannabinoid Compounds on Aggressive Behavior.

A review of the literature indicated that acute cannabis administration to nonstressed rats suppressed, whereas chronic

treatment induced or increased, aggressive behavior. Aggression in stressed animals, however, was apparent under both acute and chronic cannabis administration.

3447 Carlini, E. A., Psychopharmacology, *53*(2), 135-45 (1977).

Further Studies of the Aggressive Behavior Induced by Δ^9-Tetrahydrocannabinol in REM Sleep-Deprived Rats.

THC induced aggressive behavior in REM sleep-deprived rats and also affected the topography of such a behavior.

3448 Carlini, E. A.; Lindsey, C. J.; and Tufik, S., pp. 229-42 in *Interactions of Drug Abuse*, edited by E. S. Vesell and M. C. Braude. NY, Annals of the New York Academy of Sciences, V. 281, 1976.

Environmental and Drug Interference with Effects of Marihuana.

Stressful situations such as starvation and deprivation of REM-sleep altered the behavioral effects observed in THC treated rats. The use of several agents influencing brain NE and DA indicated that the cannabis-induced bahavioral excitation in stressed animals is dopaminergically mediated.

3449 Carlini, E. A.; Lindsey, C. J.; Musty, R. E.; and Monti, J. M., pp. 515-34 in *Pharmacology of Marihuana, Vol. 2*, edited by M. C. Braude and S. Szara. NY, Raven Press, 1976.

Marihuana-Aggressiveness in REM Sleep-Deprived Rats: Neurochemical and Neurophysiological Correlates.

To help understand the mechanism by which marihuana (10 mg/kg) induces aggressive behavior in REM-sleep deprived rats, several different experiments were performed to manipulate central dopaminergic and noradrenergic systems. Results indicated that marihuana possibly induces such a behavioral effect either by blocking the central NE inhibitory system or by directly stimulating the excitatory DA system.

3450 Carlini, E. A.; Lindsey, C. J.; and Tufik, S., Brit. J. Pharmacol., *61*(3), 371-79 (1977).

Cannabis, Catecholamines, Rapid Eye Movement Sleep and Aggressive Behaviour.

In REM sleep-deprived rats, cannabis administration resulted in an aggressive behavior irritation, enhanced THC-induced hypothermia and decreased brain DA turnover. The relationship among REM sleep-deprivation, THC effects and catecholamines was further explored.

3451 Carlini, E. A.; Mechoulam, R.; and Lander, N., Res. Commun. Chem. Pathol. Pharmacol., *12*(1), 1-15 (1975).

Anticonvulsant Activity of Four Oxygenated Cannabidiol Derivatives.

Pentobarbital sleeping time increased with CBD and all four derivatives, CBD aldehyde-diacetate, 6-oxo-CBD-diacetate, 6-OH-CBD-triacetate, and 9-OH-CBD-triacetate. All but CBD aldehyde-diacetate, which was very toxic, were found to protect mice from convulsions.

3452 Carney, J. M.; Uwaydah, E. M.; and Balster, R. L., Pharmacol., Biochem. Behav., *7*(4), 357-64 (1977).

Evaluation of a Suspension System for Intravenous Self-Administration Studies of Water-Insoluble Compounds in the Rhesus Monkey.

A lipoid suspension of Emulphor, ethanol and saline was found suitable for i.v. delivery of insoluble compounds. Among these, β-HHC, a cannabinoid, disrupted food-reinforced behavior in monkeys.

3453 Carr, R. R., Intellect, *104*(12), 235-36 (1975).

Oregon's Marijuana Decriminalization: One Year Later.

A survey of marihuana usage patterns in Oregon one year after its decriminalization is presented. Results indicate that 20% of the adult population have tried marihuana and 9% are current users. Of the current users, most are between 18-29 yrs. of age, are males by 4 to 1, and are college graduates. No increase in use was detected.

3454 Carranza, J., *Eleventh Collegium Internationale Neuro-Psychopharmacologicum: Abstracts*, Vienna, Austria, July 9-14, 1978, p. 146.

Long Term Effects of Cannabis in Man.

Fifty chronic marihuana users participated in a study aimed at evaluating the long-term effects of cannabis in humans. Family integrations, problems related to interaction with parents, depression, psychotic thinking and hallucinations were among the parameters studied.

3455 Carter, W. E.; and Doughty, P. L., pp. 2-16 in *Chronic Cannabis Use*, edited by R. L. Dornbush, A. M. Freedman, and M. Fink. NY, Annals of the New York Academy of Sciences, V. 282, 1976.

Social and Cultural Aspects of Cannabis Use in Costa Rica.

Costa Rican cannabis users showed socio-cultural characteristics similar to those seen in American users. Delinquent students were more likely to become cannabis users. Parents of users, especially the mothers, usually did not abuse marihuana, and most users seldom used other drugs like cocaine and heroin.

3456   Casswell, S., Percept. Mot. Skills, *41*(2), 423-34 (1975).

Cannabis Intoxication: Effects of Monetary Incentive on Performance, a Controlled Investigation of Behavioural Tolerance in Moderate Users of Cannabis.

Cannabis (2-4 mg Δ^9-THC) and placebo treatment were investigated in money motivated/non-motivated naive and experienced cannabis users with respect to disruptive influences on performance. Dose-related decrements in performance were observed in four of the five tasks. No differences were detected in the performances of experienced marihuana users relative to naive subjects.

3457   Cates, W.; and Pope, J. N., Amer. J. Surg., *134*(5), 613-15 (1977).

Gynecomastia and Cannabis Smoking. A Nonassociation Among U.S. Army Soldiers.

In a case-control study involving U.S. soldiers, no correlation was found to exist between idiopathic gynecomastia and chronic cannabis use.

3458   Cates, W., Jr.; and Warren, J. W., J. Amer. Med. Ass., *234*(9), 930-34 (1975).

Hepatitis B in Nuremberg, Germany; Epidemiology of a Drug-Associated Epidemic Among U.S. Army Soldiers.

An epidemilogical study of hepatitis B prevalence in American military personnel in the Nuremberg, Germany area is outlined. Epidemic viral hepatitis most readily developed in illicit drug users sharing parenteral equipment with infected individuals. Cannabis smoking may serve to transmit the virus nonparenterally.

3459   Cely, W.; Karler, R.; and Turkanis, S., Clin. Res., *23*(2), 88a (1975).

Anticonvulsant Activity of Marihuana.

In mice, rats or frogs, the amounts of Δ^9-THC and metabolites were found to reach a maximum level considerably later than anticonvulsant activity. Chronic administration of Δ^9-THC to mice resulted in rapid development of tolerance to its anticonvulsant activity.

3460   Chakravarty, I.; and Ghosh, J. J., Biochem. Pharmacol., *26*(9), 859-62 (1977).

Effect of Cannabis Extract on Uterine Glycogen Metabolism in Prepubertal Rats under Normal and Estradiol-Treated Conditions.

Daily injections of cannabis extract for 11 days in young female rats affected uterine glycogen metabolism which was also varied by estradiol treatment. In both normal and estradiol-treated animals, glycogen synthetase activity was inhibited. In normal animals, THC treatment also increased the synthesis of phosphorylase and its conversion to phosphorylase a, whereas estradiol treatment prevented an increase in the level of phosphorylase a.

3461   Chakravarty, I.; and Ghosh, J. J., Quart. J. Surg. Sci., *14*(1-2), 89-92 (1978).

Effect of Cannabis on Female Reproduction.

Δ^9-THC (10 mg/kg) antagonized estradiol action on rat uterus.

3462 Chakravarty, I.; Sengupta, D.; Bhattacharyya, P.; and Ghosh, J. J., Toxicol. Appl. Pharmacol., *34*(3), 513-16 (1975).

Effect of Treatment with Cannabis Extract on the Water and Glycogen Contents of the Uterus in Normal and Estradiol-Treated Prepubertal Rats.

Cannabis extract administration caused a significant dehydrating effect in normal prepubertal rat uterus and inhibited the water uptake and glycogen accumulation induced by estradiol.

3463 Chakravarty, I.; Sengupta, D.; Bhattacharya, P.; and Ghosh, J. J., Biochem. Pharmacol., *25*(4), 377-78 (1976).

Effect of Cannabis Extract on the Uterine Monoamine Oxidase Activity of Normal and Estradiol Treated Rats.

MAO activity was evaluated in the nonprimed and primed (estradiol benzoate) uterine tissue of prepubertal female rats following 11 days of exposure to 10 mg Δ^9-THC/kg, s.c. Although estradiol benzoate decreased MAO activity by itself, THC partially reversed the suppression and increased MAO activity of control rats.

3464 Chakravarty, I., Sheth, A. R.; and Ghosh, J. J., Fertil. Steril., *26*(9), 947-48 (1975).

Effect of Acute Δ^9-Tetrahydrocannabinol treatment on Serum Luteinizing Hormone and Prolactin Levels in Adult Female Rats.

Δ^9-THC (50 mg/kg, i.p.) administered acutely to adult female rats on day of estrus significantly reduced serum LH and prolactin levels. Reduction was probably caused by inhibition of hormone release.

3465 Chan, M. Y.; and Tse, A., Biochem. Pharmacol., *27*(13), 1725-28 (1978).

The Effect of Cannabinoids (Δ^9-THC and Δ^8-THC) on Hepatic Microsomal Metabolism of Testosterone *In Vitro*.

Δ^8-THC was more potent than Δ^9-THC in inhibiting testosterone hydroxylation by hepatic microsomes. Only Δ^9-THC, however, inhibited its 5α-reduction.

3466 Chan, W. R.; Magnus, K. E.; and Watson, H. A., Experientia, *32*(3), 283-84 (1976).

The Structure of Cannabitriol.

A novel cannabinoid, cannabitriol, was isolated and its structure determined by spectrochemical means and by chemical reactions.

3467 Chao, F.-C.; Green, D. E.; Forrest, I. S.; Kaplan, J. N.; Winship-Ball, A.; and Braude, M., Res. Commun. Chem. Pathol. Pharmacol., *15*(2), 303-17 (1976).

The Passage of ^{14}C-Δ^9-Tetrahydrocannabinol into the Milk of Lactating Squirrel Monkeys.

Prior to tracer amounts of ^{14}C-THC, nursing monkeys were maintained on oral THC (2 mg/kg) for 8 or 20 wks. Percentage of total dosage appearing in their milk, feces, and urine were 0.2%, 42%, and 1% respectively. Excretion into milk was maximal within 2 hrs. Suckling infants eliminated radioactivity primarily via the feces. THC dosing did not suppress milk formation or infant growth rate.

3468   Chari-Bitron, A., pp. 272-81 in *Marihuana: Chemistry, Biochemistry, and Cellular Effects*, edited by G. G. Nahas. NY, Springer-Verlag, 1976.

Effect of $\triangle^1$-Tetrahydrocannabinol on Red Blood Cell Membranes and on Alveolar Macrophages.

This report contains two parts: a discussion of the dose-dependent action of THC on membranes, based on biochemical and morphological findings and a review of recent studies involving THC and alveolar macrophages.

3469   Chase, A. R.; Kelley, P. R.; Taunton-Rigby, A., pp. 1-9 in *Cannabinoid Assays in Humans*, NIDA Research Monograph, No. 7, 1976.

Quantitation of Cannabinoids in Biological Fluids by Radioimmunoassay.

Synthesis of two conjugates of $\triangle^9$-THC is presented and a RIA based on tritium is described. Cross reactivity studies between $\triangle^9$-THC, other cannabinoids, and other compounds are provided. RIA has cross reactivity with metabolites. Data from the urine of two patients are presented.

3470   Cheema, A. M.; and Inayat, Y., Pak. J. Zool., *9*(2), 137-44 (1977).

Effects of Chloroform Extracted Cannabinoids on Insulin Release and its Role in Cellular Uptake of Blood Sugar.

Cannabis extract (50 mg/kg) impaired glucose tolerance, inhibited the action of exogenous insulin and antagonized the stimulated release of endogenous insulin in treated rabbits.

3471   Chesher, G. B.; Franks, H. M.; Hensley, V. R.; Hensley, W. J.; Jackson, D. M.; Starmer, G. A.; and Teo, R. K. C., Med. J. Aust., *2*(5), 159-63 (1976).

The Interactions of Ethanol and $\triangle^9$-Tetrahydrocannabinol in Man. Effects on Perceptual, Cognitive, and Motor Functions.

THC (10 mg/70kg, p.o.) and ethanol interactions are assessed in experienced university students. A battery of tests designed to discriminate ethanol-induced changes in perceptual, cognitive, and motor skills was used. Although solitary drug treatments caused minimal performance decrement, combinations of THC-ETOH caused pronounced disruption. THC prolonged blood alcohol levels and introduced anxiety/tension into an otherwise relaxed alcohol situation.

3472   Chesher, G. B.; Franks, H. M.; Jackson, D. M.; Starmer, G. A.; and Teo, R. K. C., Med. J. Aust., *1*(14), 478-81 (1977).

Ethanol and $\triangle^9$-Tetrahydrocannabinol: Interactive Effects on Human Perceptual, Cognitive and Motor Functions. II.

The results reported in this paper confirm earlier findings of an additive effect of THC and alcohol in man, as measured by performance in perceptual, cognitive and motor function tests. However, the complexity of this interaction is evidenced by the results which show an additive effect in the first hour after dosing but an apparent antagonistic effect in the next hour.

3473   Chesher, G. B.; Jackson, D. M.; and Malor, R. M., J. Pharm. Pharmacol., *27*(8), 608-09 (1975).

Interactions of $\triangle^9$-Tetrahydrocannabinol and Cannabidiol with Phenobarbitone in Protecting Mice from Electrically Induced Convulsions.

72

THC and CBD at 50 mg/kg dose were administered to mice by gavage 1 hr. before phenobarbitone (i.p.) and 2 hr. before maximum electroshock seizures. CBD was less active than THC in potentiation of the activity of phenobarbitone.

3474 Chiarotti, M.; Guiusti, G. V.; Passatore, M.; Carnevale, A.; and Fiori, A., Acta Med. Rom., *13*(6), 423-26 (1975).

Muscular Dystrophy in Adult Mice Chronically Treated with Cannabinoids at Behavioral Doses. II-Biochemical Findings.

Treatment of mice with cannabinoids produced symptoms similar to those of muscular dystrophy, with chronic Δ^9-THC causing the most marked changes. The hydroxyproline content rose and protein levels decreased in gastrocnemius muscle of mice pretreated with either THC, CBD, or CBN. Histopathological findings supported the biochemical data.

3475 Chiu, P., Diss. Abstr. Int. B, *39*(6), 2762 (1978).

The Influence of Cannabidiol and Delta-9-Tetrahydrocannabinol on Cobalt Epilepsy in Rats.

Unlike Δ^9-THC and its 11-OH metabolite, CBD protected rats against focal epilepsy without exerting overt CNS excitation.

3476 Chiu, P.; Karler, R.; Craven, C.; Olsen, D. M.; and Turkanis, S. A., Res. Commun. Chem. Pathol. Pharmacol., *12*(2), 267-86 (1975).

The Influence of Δ^9-Tetrahydrocannabinol, Cannabinol and Cannabidiol on Tissue Oxygen Consumption.

THC, CBD and CBN were administered in various vehicles in order to investigate the mechanism of hypothermia. The vehicles were evaluated for their effects on *in vitro* tissue oxygen consumption. Homogenates of brain, heart, skeletal muscle and liver were examined.

3477 Chopa, G. S.; and Jandu, B. S., pp. 95-108 in *Chronic Cannabis Use*, edited by R. L. Dornbush, A. M. Freeman, and M. Fink. New York, Annals of the New York Academy of Science, V. 282, 1976.

Psychoclinical Effects of Long-Term Marijuana Use in 275 Indian Chronic Users. A Comparative Assessment of Effects in Indian and USA Users.

The pattern of marihuana use in the Indian drug culture was assessed. Chronic high doses of marihuana produced: psychopathology, poor physical health, decreased fertility and sexuality, neurologic deterioration, an amotivational syndrome, and increased antisocial behavior. The pattern of use in India differed markedly from that in the USA.

3478 Choulis, N. H., pp. 288-303 in *Identification Procedures of Drugs of Abuse*, Ghent, Belgium, European Press, 1977.

Hallucinogens. II. Marihuana.

A short review of the current procedures used in the identification of cannabis preparations. In particular, TLC and GLC procedures are described for *in vitro* and *in vivo* testing.

3479 Christensen, S. B., Arch. Pharm. Chemi., *82*(23), 1237-47 (1975).

De Euforiserende Forbindelser I *Cannabis sativa L*. Syntese Samt Struktur I Relation Til Biologisk Aktivitet [The Euphoric Compounds in *Cannabis sativa L*. Synthesis and Structure in Relation to Biological Activity].

A review of the relation between cannabinoid structure and pharmacological activity is presented. Synthesis of active (naturally occurring) cannabinoids is included. The SAR of the synthetic cannabinoid derivatives is also discussed. Forty-six references are given.

3480 Christie, R. M.; Rickards, R. W.; and Watson, W. P., Aust. J. Chem. *31*(8), 1799-807 (1978).

Microbial Transformation of Cannabinoids. I. Metabolism of (-)-Δ^9-6a, 10a-*trans*-Tetrahydrocannabinol by *Chaetomium globosum*.

Chaetomium globosum was found as a contaminate along with other fungi on the flowering tops of Cannabis plant. The organism was grown on standard Czapek-Dox agar in the presence of 0.01% cannabis resin. Incubation of Δ^9-THC with liquid cultures of the organism resulted in the identification of the three metabolites (3´-OH-Δ^9-THC, 11-OH-Δ^9-THC and 3´, 11-dihydroxy-Δ^9-THC). Identification was by synthesis and MS comparisons.

3481 Chrusciel, T. L., Int. J. Clin. Pharmacol., 12(1/2), 57-62 (1975).

Recent Progress in the Long-Term Pharmacological Research on Cannabis.

Since the long-term study of marihuana is so complex, a joint effort of pharmacologists, behavioral scientists, psychiatrists and various other health professionals is required. Variables increase in long-term studies and controls are difficult but necessary for good experimental design. A study in Jamaica is cited and the problem of classifying cannabis psychosis is discussed.

3482 Chusid, M. J.; Gelfand, J. A.; Nutter, C.; and Fauci, A. S., Ann. Intern. Med., *82*(5), 682-83 (1975).

Pulmonary Aspergillosis, Inhalation of Contaminated Marijuana Smoke, Chronic Granulomatous Disease.

A case history of a 17-yr. old male debilitated by an *Aspergillus fumigatus* infection is described. Marihuana contaminated by aging in the soil is the most likely source of the aspergillosis.

3483 Clark, S. C., Pharmacol. Biochem. Behav., *3*, 299-306 (1975).

Marihuana and the Cardiovascular System.

A review of the use of marihuana with a pharmacological emphasis on the cardiovascular system. Sixty-seven references are given.

3484 Clark, S. C.; Rootman, I.; and Maclean, B., Bull. Narcotics, *29*(1), 1-11 (1977).

Contacts with a Canadian Drug Information and Crisis Centre, 1971-74.

The number of crisis contacts associated with cannabis dropped 73% over the 3 year period covered in this study.

3485 Clarke, D. E.: and Jandhyala, B., Res. Commun. Chem. Pathol. Pharmacol. *17*(3), 471-80 (1977).

Acute and Chronic Effects of Tetrahydrocannabinols on Monoamine Oxidase Activity: Possible Vehicle/Tetrahydrocannabinol Interactions.

The acute administration of Δ^8-THC, Δ^9-THC, ethanol or Tween 80 did not influence MAO activity in rat organs. However, subacute (14 days) Δ^8-THC or Δ^9-THC treatment reversed the Tween 80-induced decrease of MAO activity in rat brain and lungs.

3486   Clarke, R. C., *The Botany and Ecology of Cannabis*. Ben Lomond, California, Pods Press, 1977. 57 pp.

A botanical account of cannabis. Characteristics of plant organs, determinants of sex and phases of flowering were discussed. Suitable ecological conditions for the vigorous growth of the plant were also described.

3487   Co, B. T.; Goodwin, D. W.; Gado, M.; Mikhael, M.; and Hill, S. Y., J. Amer. Med. Ass., *237*(12), 1229-30 (1977).

Absence of Cerebral Atrophy in Chronic Cannabis Users - - Evaluation by Computerized Transaxial Tomography.

Chronic cannabis users did not show any evidence of cerebral atrophy. Computerized transaxial tomography was employed in arriving at this conclusion.

3488   Cockerham, W., Int. J. Addict., *11*(2), 209-20 (1976).

Drug Use Among White and American Indian High School Youth.

Data from a population of 511 high school students of both sexes (391 white, 120 American Indian) suggests that Indians are more likely to try marijuana and at a younger age than whites, but are no more likely to continue use of the drug than are whites.

3489   Cockerham, W. C., Int. J. Addict., *12*(2-3), 271-85 (1977).

Patterns of Alcohol and Multiple Drug Use Among Rural White and American Indian Adolescents.

The results of this study support the hypothesis that users of any one drug, including alcohol and marihuana, will show an increased probability to use another drug. Indian adolescents were more likely to be involved with alcohol, marihuana and hard drugs than were white adolescents.

3490   Coffman, C. B.; and Gentner, W. A., Agron. J., *69*(5), 832-36 (1977).

Responses of Greenhouse-grown *Cannabis sativa L*. to Nitrogen, Phosporus, and Potassium.

THC and CBD concentration along with tissue yield and plant growth in greenhouse-grown cannabis plants were positively correlated with soil phosphorus level. N and K levels did not exhibit a similar correlation. It is indicated that this analysis may be helpful in determining the origin of cannabis plants.

3491   Coffman, C. B.; and Gentner, W. A., Agron. J., *67*(4), 491-97 (1975).

Cannabinoid Profile and Elemental Uptake of *Cannabis sativa L*. as Influenced by Soil Characteristics.

As reported, soil types alter morphological characteristics of cannabis plants. No significant differences were observed between soils for CBD and CBC but differences were observed for Δ^9-THC and CBN. Ratios of Ca/Mg from leaf tissue was positively correlated with Δ^9-THC leaf concentrations. Other correlations are also reported. Also included is a discussion on geographical origin.

3492   Coffman, C. B.; and Gentner, W. A., Proc. Northeast Weed Sci. Soc., *32*, 9 (1978).

Cannabis sativa L. Response to Paraquat.

Data are given on the effectiveness of paraquat in controlling cannabis. Cannabinoid content (CBD, Δ^9-THC) is reported. Plants were from a Jamaican variant and were grown in a greenhouse.

3493 Coggins, W. J., pp. 667-72 in *Pharmacology of Marihuana, Vol. 2*, edited by M. C. Braude and S. Szara. NY, Raven Press, 1976.

The Costa Rica Cannabis Project: An Interim Report on the Medical Aspects.

Medical screening of 74 marihuana smokers and 149 control male subjects showed significant differences between these groups. Smokers had differences for syphilis, abnormal chest x-ray, conjunctival infection and unilateral testicular atrophy. Six clinical test batteries are now being investigated. Analysis of street marihuana samples in Costa Rica is presented.

3494 Coggins, W. J.; Swensen, E. W.; Dawson, W. W.; Fernandez-Salas, A.; Hernandez-Bolanos, J.; Jiminez-Antillon, R. F.; Solano, J. R.; Vinocour, R.; and Faerron-Valdez, F., pp. 148-61 in *Chronic Cannabis Use*, edited by R. L. Dornbush, A. M. Freedman, and M. Fink. NY, Annals of the New York Academy of Sciences, V. 282, 1976.

Health Status of Chronic Heavy Cannabis Users.

A two-part survey of marihuana use in Costa Rica was presented. As compared to control, chronic marihuana use did not alter sexual functioning or plasma testosterone levels. GI tract disturbances and lower body weight were, however, evident. Thus chronic marihuana use did not impair normal functioning.

3495 Cohen, D. R., Psychol. Today, *12*(6), 36, 39 (1978).

Pot for Patient Patients.

Marihuana is moving from being regarded as a drug of high abuse potential and little medical value to the position of a drug with potential therapeutic effects.

3496 Cohen, M. J.; Rickles, W. H.; and Naliboff, B. D., Pharmacol. Biochem. Behav., *3*(2), 195-200 (1975).

Marijuana Influenced Changes in GSR Activation Peaking During Paired-Associate Learning.

Experienced users, after acute exposure to marihuana under double-blind conditions, were challenged to learn a 9-word paired-associated list. Δ^9-THC (14.0 mg) impaired the learning process. Inhibition may be linked to the anticholinergic effects of Δ^9-THC in the CNS.

3497 Cohen, S., J. Amer. Med. Ass., *240*(16), 1761-63 (1978).

Marijuana: Does it Have a Possible Therapeutic Use?

In some cases cannabis was an effective remedial agent in ancient times. At present, the new water soluble cannabinoids may prove to be very beneficial therapeutic agents lacking psychoactive properties.

3498 Cohen, S., pp. 194-225 in *Marihuana Research Findings: 1976*, NIDA Research Monograph, No. 14, 1977.

Therapeutic Aspects.

Research dealing with the potential therapeutic effects of cannabinoids was reviewed. Among the more promising areas discussed are the reduction of IOP, the alleviation of cancer chemotherapy side effects and bronchodilation.

3499 Cohen, S., pp. 211-20 in *Chronic Cannabis Use*, edited by R. L. Dornbush, A. M. Freedman, and M. Fink. NY, Annals of the New York Academy of Sciences, V. 282, 1976.

The 94-Day Cannabis Study.

Subchronic marihuana administration under controlled clinical setting to moderate and heavy users resulted in maintenance of learning and task performance, bronchodilation along with a decrease in airway resistance and a fall in IOP. Other reported findings include: depression in plasma testosterone and LH, tachycardia to which tolerance developed, altered hemispheric dominance and EEG changes.

3500 Cohen, S., Drug Abuse Alcohol. Newsl., *4*(1), 1975.

Marihuana Today.

Some of the effects of marihuana are summarized. THC reduces and delays cell division in tetrahymena. Marihuana users show a decrease in testosterone levels and are more likely to develop sinusitis, pharyngitis, emphysema and other respiratory difficulties in one year, as opposed to 10 to 20 years in cigarette smokers. Amotivational syndrome and deterioration of mental performance are observed in chronic marihuana users.

3501 Cohen, S., pp. 357-69 in *Principles of Psychopharmacology*, 2nd. ed., edited by W. G. Clark and J. del Giudice. New York, Academic Press, 1978.

Psychotomimetics (Hallucinogens) and Cannabis.

Δ^9-THC has been extensively studied in man and animal. Its possible therapeutic potentials include reduction of IOP, bronchodilation and daytime sedation.

3502 Cohen, S., Psychol. Today, *11*, 60, 62, 64, 73 (1978).

Marijuana as Medicine.

The therapeutic potentials of marihuana in glaucoma and cancer are promising. Clinical research is, however, complicated by its chemical properties and bureaucratic red tape.

3503 Cohen, S.; Lessin, P. J.; Hahn, P. M.; and Tyrrell, E. D., pp. 621-26 in *Pharmacology of Marihuana, Vol. 2*, edited by M. C. Braude and S. Szara. NY, Raven Press, 1976.

A 94-Day Cannabis Study.

A large battery of pharmacological and psychological tests were conducted on 28 paid volunteer male subjects. Tests were over a 94-day hospital stay involving periods of intoxication (daily average of 100 mg THC) and non-intoxication with marihuana. Protocol used is described.

3504 Cohen, S.; and Stillman, R., eds., *The Therapeutic Potential of Marihuana*. NY, Plenum Medical Book Company, 1976.

This book has 28 chapters. Eight chapters deal with marihuana and the remaining twenty with the therapeutic potential of pure cannabinoids.

3505 Coleman, J. H.; Tacker, H. L.; Evans, W. E.; Lemmi, H.; and Britton, E. L., Dis. Nerv. Syst., *37*(1), 29 (1976).

Neurological Manifestations of Chronic

Marihuana Intoxication. Part I: Paresis of the Fourth Cranial Nerve.

Frontal and temporal headaches of ocular etiology are the most commonly observed complaints in young users of marihuana. Of the patients seen, 82.6% manifest a hyperphoria which probably is related to paresis of the ipsilateral superior oblique muscle caused by damage to the fourth cranial nerve. Although paresis is permanent, headaches are attenuated by the use of corrective prism lenses.

3506 Collins, F. G.; and Haavik, C. O., Fed. Proc., *34*(3), 744 (1975).

Inhibition of Mouse Cardiac Sarcoplasmic Reticulum C^{++} Stimulated Mg^{++} Dependent-ATPase (Ca^{++}-ATPase) by Δ^9-Tetrahydrocannabinol (Δ^9-THC).

Δ^9-THC inhibits the activation of a microsomal membrane bound C^{++}-ATPase isolated from pooled samples of mouse cardiac tissue. It is suggested that Δ^9-THC interacts with membrane bound Ca^{++}-ATPase to produce its various *in-vivo* actions.

3507 Collu, R., Life Sci., *18*(2), 223-30 (1976).

Endocrine Effects of Chronic Intraventricular Administration of Δ^9-Tetrahydrocannabinol to Prepuberal and Adult Male Rats.

Δ^9-THC administered i.v.t. to prepuberal and adult rats for a week did not induce behavioral changes. Compared to controls, prepuberal rats had smaller prostate and brain, while adult rats had lower body weight and larger brain and adrenal weight. Prolactin levels increased in both groups, while growth hormone levels increased in prepuberal rats only.

3508 Collu, R.; Letarte, J.; Leboeuf, G.; and Ducharme, J. R., Life Sci., *16*(4), 533-42 (1975).

Endocrine Effects of Chronic Administration of Psychoactive Drugs to Prepuberal Male Rats. I: Δ^9-Tetrahydrocannabinol.

Male rats were administered 1 mg/kg or 10 mg/kg THC 3 times a week. They were decapitated, organs weighed and radioimmunoassays performed on blood. Growth Hormone (GH), FSH levels, brain levels of 5-HT, NE, DA and 5-HIAA were examined. Levels of GH and LH were decreased and prostate growth was inhibited. Other endocrine levels were comparable to controls.

3509 Comitas, L., pp. 24-32 in *Chronic Cannabis Use*, edited by R. L. Dornbush, A. M. Freedman, and M. Fink. NY, Annals of the New York Academy of Sciences, V. 282, 1976.

Cannabis and Work in Jamaica: A Refutation of the Amotivational Syndrome.

A study of Jamaican farm workers showed that those workers who used cannabis (ganja) did just as much work as those who did not. The results also showed that workers who used cannabis felt that they worked better under the influence of cannabis. The workers were also more cohesive socially.

3510 Connell, P. H.; and Dorn, N., eds., *Cannabis and Man: Psychological and Clinical Aspects and Patterns of Use.* New York, Churchill Livingstone, 1975. 236 pp.

This book is composed of 14 papers delivered and summarized discussion held at the Third International Cannabis Conference, organized by the Institute for the

Study of Drug Dependence.

3511   Consroe, P.; Jones, B.; and Laird, H.,
        pp. 198-211 in *Interactions of Drug
        Abuse*, edited by E. S. Vesell and M. C.
        Braude. NY, Annals of the New York
        Academy of Sciences, V. 281, 1976.

Interactions of Δ^9-Tetrahydrocannabinol
with Other Pharmacological Agents.

The effect of i.v. administration of THC
on the EEG and behavior of rabbits
differed in adapted and non-adapted
situations. Recent and previously reported findings by the authors on the
antagonistic effect of different classes
of CNS stimulants, in addition to the
convulsive activity of cannabinoids in
susceptible rabbits, were discussed.

3512   Consroe, P.; Jones, B.; Laird, H.; and
        Reinking, J., pp. 363-82 in *The Thera-
        peutic Potential of Marihuana*, edited
        by S. Cohen and R. Stillman. NY,
        Plenum Medical Book Company, 1976.

Anticonvulsant-Convulsant Effects of Δ^9-
Tetrahydrocannabinol.

THC protected rabbits against the maximal seizures induced by either electroshock or PTZ but not strychnine. THC
was ineffective in protecting animals
against minimal seizures or lethality due
to convulsants and induced seizure activity in prone subjects.

3513   Consroe, P.; Martin, P.; and Eisenstein,
        D., Res. Commun. Chem. Pathol. Phar-
        macol., *16*(1), 1-13 (1977).

Anticonvulsant Drug Antagonism of Δ^9-
Tetrahydrocannabinol-Induced Seizures
in Rabbits.

Δ^9-THC and CBN produced convulsions in susceptible rabbits. CBD was
ineffective alone and protected animals

when given concomitantly with Δ^9-
THC. Several anticonvulsants used to
control grand mal epilepsy were effective in blocking THC-induced convulsions.

3514   Consroe, P.; and Wolkin, A., J. Pharmacol.
        Exp. Ther., *201*(1), 26-32 (1977).

Cannabidiol - Antiepileptic Drug Comparisons and Interactions in Experimentally Induced Seizures in Rats.

The relative anticonvulsant activity and
motor toxicity of CBD, CBN and THC
were studied and compared with a
number of clinically employed antiepileptic drugs. CBD proved to be
effective against the maximal electroshock and audiogenic seizure tests.
CBD also enhanced the anticonvulsant
properties of phenytoin while decreasing
the effectiveness of a few of the other
antiepileptic drugs studied. Implications of the results were discussed.

3515   Consroe, P. F.; Jones, B. C.; and Akins,
        F., Neuropharmacology, *14*(5/6), 377-
        83 (1975).

Δ^9-Tetrahydrocannabinol-Methamphe-
tamine Interaction in the Rabbit.

An increase in mean cortical electrogenesis induced in rabbits by Δ^9-THC
(0.5 mg/kg, i.v.) was reversed by methamphetamine. Likewise, postural and
behavioral effects induced by Δ^9-THC
were antagonized by methamphetamine.
Bizarre behavior was evoked by the
Δ^9-THC-methamphetamine combination.

3516   Consroe, P. F.; Jones, B. C.; and Chin,
        L., Pharmacol. Biochem. Behav., *3*(2),
        173-77 (1975).

Δ^9-Tetrahydrocannabinol, EEG and Behavior: The Importance of Adaption
to the Testing Milieu.

Δ^9-THC was administered i.v. (0.01, 0.05, 0.1, 0.5 and 1.0 mg/kg) to rabbits adapted to the testing chamber. Non-adapted rabbits were given the highest dose only. Cortical and hippocampal EEG's, along with postural and activity behaviors, were recorded. The results suggest that the behavioral actions are largely dependent upon the animal's existing state of arousal.

3517 Consroe, P.; Jones, B.; and Laird, H., Psychopharmacology, 50(1), 47-52 (1976).

EEG and Behavioral Effects of Δ^9-Tetrahydrocannabinol in Combination with Stimulant Drugs in Rabbits.

Cocaine, methamphetamine and caffeine, but not apomorphine, antagonized Δ^9-THC-induced increases in cortical electrogenesis in rabbits. Methamphetamine and caffeine antagonized most of the behavioral effects of THC. The latter was less toxic.

3518 Consroe, P. F.; and Wolkin, A. L., J. Pharm. Pharmacol., 29(8), 500-01 (1977).

Anticonvulsant Interaction of Cannabidiol and Ethosuximide in Rats.

CBD was found to increase and SKF 525-A decreased the ED_{50} of the anticonvulsant ethosuximide when given concurrently. These results suggest that the interaction between CBD and ethosuximide is not dependent on the hepatic actions of CBD.

3519 Consroe, P. F.; Wood, G. C.; and Buchsbaum, H., J. Amer. Med. Ass., 234(3), 306-07 (1975).

Anticonvulsant Nature of Marihuana Smoking.

A case report of a 24-year old male with grand mal epilepsy. Marihuana smoke along with his prescribed regimen of phenobarbital and diphenylhydantoin controlled his seizures. Approximately 6.15 μ g/kg of Δ^9-THC was used per joint.

3520 Cook, C. E.; Hawes, M. L.; Amerson, E. W.; Pitt, C. G.; and Williams, D., pp. 15-27 in Cannabinoid Assays in Humans, NIDA Research Monograph Series, No. 7, 1976.

Radioimmunoassay of Δ^9-Tetrahydrocannabinol.

Paper contains a discussion of problems involved in using a RIA method to quantitate cannabinoids in body fluids. The synthesis of a Δ^8-THC antigen and data on cross reactivity of Δ^9- and Δ^8-THC antigen are presented. Data are given for four human plasma samples spiked with Δ^9-THC. Structure-binding relationship for various antisera for cannabinoids are given.

3521 Cooler, P.; and Gregg, J., pp. 77-87 in The Therapeutic Potential of Marihuana, edited by S. Cohen and R. Stillman. NY, Plenum Medical Book Company, 1976.

The Effect of Δ^9-Tetrahydrocannabinol on Intraocular Pressure in Humans.

I.V. administered THC in 1.5 and 3.0 mg doses lowered the IOP and increased the heart rate of normal subjects but had no effect on respiration or BP. THC also caused an increase in anxiety as compared to diazepam or placebo. Dysphoria and unpleasant sensations were also observed.

3522 Cooler, P.; and Gregg, J. M., South. Med. J., 70(8), 951-54 (1977).

Effect of Delta-9-Tetrahydrocannabinol on Intraocular Pressure in Humans.

Δ^9-THC lowered IOP while valium was less effective. The peak activity was between 30 and 60 min. Three of ten subjects had marked hypotension. Other general pharmacological findings are discussed.

3523 Cooper, H., S. Afr. Med. J., *50*(24), 913 (1976).

Cannabis Not Guilty.

The author points out several weaknesses in a clinical case presented in the South African Medical Journal, *50*: 639 (1976) by G. Schweitzer and A. Levin. A withdrawal episode was attributed to cannabis abstinence, but could more rationally have been attributed to alcohol abstinence. The precipitating cause of the abstinence syndrome was orthopedic surgery.

3524 Cooper, J. T.; and Goldstein, S., Can. J. Physiol. Pharmacol., *54*(4), 541-45 (1976).

Toxicity Testing *In Vitro*. I. The Effects of Δ^9-Tetrahydrocannabinol and Aflatoxin B_1 on the Growth of Cultured Human Fibroblasts.

Δ^9-THC produced no inhibitory effects at less than 1 μgm/ml, but did depress cell plating efficiency at higher concentrations. Since *in vitro* cultures of normal diploid human cells closely resemble the *in vivo* situation, considerable merit may exist in this model as a toxicological screen on a chronic and acute basis.

3525 Corcoran, M. E.; McCaughran, J. A.; and Wada, J. A.;, Epilepsia, *19*(1), 47-55 (1978).

Antiepileptic and Prophylactic Effects of Tetrahydrocannabinols in Amygdaloid Kindled Rats.

High toxic doses of Δ^9-THC or Δ^8-THC were required to reliably protect rats from seizures induced by electrical stimulation of the amygdala. Tolerance to such a protective effect developed rapidly after repeated cannabinoid administration. A prolonged duration of seizure was also noted on the nondrug days in rats receiving high doses of THC. The possible mechanisms involved were discussed.

3526 Corrigan, D.; and Lynch, J. J., Planta Med., *33*(3), 269-70 (1978).

A Histochemical Test for *Cannabis sativa L*.

A new selective method employing a reagent composed of vanillin in ethanolic sulphuric acid was successfully used to detect illicit cannabis preparations. This vanillin reagent stains the gland in both cannabis bracts and resin with a deep reddish purple color.

3527 Costa, G.; De Pasquale, R. C.; and Scarpignato, C., Farm. Ed. Prat., *32*(4), 180-85 (1977).

Behavior of Cerebral Serotonin in the Rat Subjected to Audiogenic Stress. Effect of Cannabis Resin.

THC (14 mg/kg) increased brain 5-HT levels and antagonized the audiogenic stress-induced decrease in brain 5-HT concentration.

3528 Costa, G.; and Scarpignato, C., Farm. Ed. Prat., *32*(3), 152-56 (1977).

Cerebral Homovanillic Acid and Audiogenic Stress in Rats: Effect of Cannabis Resins.

The audiogenic stress-induced fall in cerebral HVA was antagonized in rats by pretreatment with cannabis extract.

3529   Cottereau, M.-J.; and Loo, H., Ann. Med. Psychol., *136*(2) 255-85 (1978).

Le Cannabis [Cannabis].

A review on cannabis and its resin which deals mainly with the psychotropic effects of the drug. 103 references.

3530   Cox, B.; ten Ham, M.; Loskota, W. J.; and Lomax, P., Proc. West. Pharmacol. Soc., *18*, 154-57 (1975).

The Anticonvulsant Activity of Cannabinoids in Seizure Sensitive Gerbils.

THC, in doses high enough to produce marked toxic effect, protected seizure susceptible gerbils from exhibiting spontaneous seizure activity. Tolerance to the protective effect developed after six days of daily administration of THC (50 mg/kg, i.p.) while toxicity persisted and became more severe.

3531   Coyle, I.; Wayner, M. J.; and Singer, G., Pharmacol. Biochem. Behav., *4*(2), 191-200 (1976).

Behavioral Teratogenesis: A Critical Evaluation.

A comprehensive review of the literature pertaining to behavioral teratogenesis is presented with emphasis on significance and relevance. A reference is given for a study showing transient delay in behavioral maturation of offspring from maternal organisms given toxic doses of Δ^9-THC.

3532   Craven, C.; and Karler, R., Clin. Res., *23*(2), 88a (1975).

Relationship Between the Hypothermic Activity of Marihuana and its Effect on Tissue Respiration.

In vitro Δ^9-THC depresses the respiratory rate of mouse brain, liver, heart, and skeletal muscle regardless of the vehicle (Tween 80, pluronic, ethanol, bovine albumin). Brain tissue was most sensitive to Δ^9-THC (10^{-6}M), and skeletal muscle was the least sensitive (10^{-4}M).

3533   Crawford, W. J.; Alexander, P. C.; Gelbart, S. S.; and Andouze, A. L., Clin. Res., *26*(5), 657a (1978).

Effect of Marihuana on Intraocular and Blood Pressure in Glaucoma.

Marihuana treatment lowered IOP and BP and increased heart rate in glaucoma patients.

3534   Crawford, W. J.; Alexander, P.C.; Merritt, J. C.; Thombs, M. J.; and Curry, C. L., Prev. Med., *7*(1), 54 (1978).

Tetrahydrocannabinol Effects on Elevated Blood Pressure in Humans.

THC increased heart rate and decreased BP in both hypertensive- and normotensive-glaucoma patients. The effects on BP were more pronounced in the former group.

3535   Crockett, D.; Klonoff, H.; and Clark, C., J. Pers. Assess., *40*(6), 582-87 (1976).

The Effects of Marijuana on Verbalization and Thought Processes.

Variables of the Thematic Apperception Test (namely abstraction, multiple meaning, anxiety, organization quality and negative emotions) discriminated between marihuana-treated and control subjects and also between low and high marihuana doses.

3536   Crombie, L.; and Crombie, W. M. L., pp. 43-76 in *Cannabis and Health*, edited by J. D. P. Graham. London, Academic Press, 1976.

Chemistry of the Cannabinoids.

A discussion of the chemistry of the major cannabinoids was given. The occurrence of methyl ethers and cannabinoid acids and other constituents was discussed. A biosynthetic proposal for the cannabinoids was presented. Also included is the synthesis of cannabinoids.

3537   Crombie, L.; and Crombie, W. M. L., Phytochemistry, *14*, 213-20 (1975).

Cannabinoid Bis-Homologues: Miniaturised Synthesis and GLC Study.

Synthetic procedures were reported for C_1, C_3, C_5, and C_7 homologues of cannabinoids. TLC and GLC data were given. In all, 32 cannabinoids were reported.

3538   Crombie, L.; and Crombie, W. M. L., Phytochemistry, *14*(2), 409-12 (1975).

Cannabinoid Formation in *Cannabis sativa* Grafted Interracially, and With Two Humulus Species.

Grafting experiments between *Cannabis sativa* and two humulus species were successful and consistent with their close botanical relationship. However, grafting did not cause any significant alteration in the composition of the mixture of cannabinoids.

3539   Crombie, L.; and Crombie, W. M. L., Phytochemistry, *16*(9), 1413-20 (1977).

Cannabinoid Acids and Esters: Miniaturized Synthesis and Chromatographic Study.

A brief review of the biosynthesis, storage, isolation, stability, and derivitization of many of the cannabinoids is presented. A small-scale synthetic procedure for most of these is outlined along with TLC and GLC data.

3540   Crombie, L.; and Crombie, W. M. L., Tetrahedron Lett., *47*, 4711-14 (1978).

Dihydrostilbenes of Thailand Cannabis.

Three dihydrostilbenes were isolated from Thailand cannabis. Structures and spectral data are provided. In addition cannabispiran, dehydrocannabispiran and cannabispiranol were isolated.

3541   Crombie, L.; Crombie, W. M. L.; Forbes, Roger; and Whitaker, Alison, J. of Chem. Res. (*S*) 114-15 (1977).

Synthesis of Cannabinoid Methyl Esters and Acids.

A procedure for the synthesis of methylesters of the cannabinoids using methylolivetolate is reported. Decarboxylation yielded the carboxylic acids. Techniques used and physical data are listed.

3542   Crombie, W. M. L., pp. 21-41 in *Cannabis and Health*, edited by J. D. P. Graham. London, Academic Press, 1976.

The Analysis of Cannabis.

Early identification and analytical tests for cannabis and some test limitations were discussed. The use of TLC, GC, and GC-MS for detection of cannabinoids was presented. Extraction, chromatographic separation, and the use of IR, UV, NMR, MS, and VIV graphs for their identification were also given. RIA for Δ^9-THC and other metabolites was included.

3543   Crombie, W. M. L., in Phytochemistry, *16*(9), 1369-71 (1977).

The Influence of Photosynthesis and SKF Inhibitors on Cannabinoid Production in *Cannabis sativa*.

This study examines the relationship between cannabinoid formation and the presence of chlorophyll using various techniques. Also the effects of some terpenoid/steroid-biosynthesis inhibitors such as SKF 7732-A_3, SKF 7997-A_3, SKF 525-A and SKF 3301-A are reported.

3544   Cross, C. E.; and Last, J. A., Chest, *74*(4), 358-59 (1978).

Paraquat Goes to Pot.

The adverse pulmonary effects resulting from inhalation of marihuana contaminated with paraquat are not as yet well established. More studies are needed.

3545   Cruickshank, E. K., pp. 162-67 in *Chronic Cannabis Use*, edited by R. L. Dornbush, A. M. Freedman, and M. Fink. NY, Annals of the New York Academy of Sciences, V. 282, 1976.

Physical Assessment of 30 Chronic Cannabis Users and 30 Matched Controls.

Chronic marihuana smokers did not differ significantly from carefully matched controls with respect to liver and lung function, cardiovascular status, hematology, peripheral thyroxine levels, steroid excretion, or chromasomal integrity.

3546   Cuendet, J. F.; Shapiro, D.; Calanca, A.; Faggioni, R.; and Ducrey, N., Ophthalmologica, *172*, (2-3), 122-27 (1976).

Action Du Delta-9-Tetrahydrocannabinol Sur L'ophtalmotonus. [Action of Delta-9-Tetrahydrocannabinol on the Eye.]

Low doses of THC decreased occular pressure. The authors propose the use of THC as an adjunctive therapy in the treatment of glaucoma.

3547   Currie, R. F.; Perlman, D.; and Walker, L., Brit. J. Addict., *72*(2), 159-65 (1977).

Marijuana Use Among Calgary Youths as a Function of Sampling and Locus of Control.

In a Canadian survey, 26% of the youth respondents admitted recent use of marihuana. This use was similar in both in and out of school students and higher among individuals of high socio-economic level, broken homes or families with drug taking habits. Also, externally oriented respondents were more likely to use marihuana than were internally oriented ones.

3548   Curtis, B.; and Simpson, D. D., Int. J. Addict., *11*(1), 161-73 (1976).

Demographic Characteristics of Groups Classified by Patterns of Multiple Drug Abuse: A 1969-1971 Sample.

Reports on 11,380 drug abuse patients admitted to the NIDA-TCU Drug Abuse Reporting Program during 1969-1971 were analyzed. Drug use patterns were classified according to the combinations of drugs used prior to admission. Marihuana was included in 7 of 9 categories. Comparisons were made within the 9 categories according to age, sex, and race/ethnic criteria.

3549   Cushman, Jr., P., Amer. J. Drug. Alcohol Abuse, *2*(2), 269-75 (1975).

Plasma Testosterone Levels in Healthy Male Marijuana Smokers.

Liver function and plasma testosterone, FSH, and LH did not differ between marihuana users and non-users although broad fluctuations in normal values did occur. Heavy marihuana consumption is probably associated with lower, normal-range, testosterone levels.

3550   Cushman, P., Life Sci., *19*(6), 875-86 (1976).

Cannabinols and the Rosette Forming Properties of Lymphocytes *In Vitro*.

In vitro, thymus-derived lymphocytes exposed to cannabinoids such as THC, CBD, CBN, and olivetol show a dose-related decrease in early rosette formation that attains a maximal suppression of 50%. Suppression is greater in T-cells from marihuana-naive individuals than in those from experienced users. THC-induced alteration of T-cell and sheep red blood cell plasma membranes is discussed as the cause of early rosette suppression.

3551 Cushman, P.; Grieco, M.; and Gupta, S., Int. J. Clin. Pharmacol. Biopharm., *12*(1/2), 217-20 (1975).

Reduction in T-Lymphocytes Forming Active Rosettes in Chronic Marihuana Smokers.

Venous blood was drawn from 23 marihuana smokers and 23 non-smokers and separated for lymphocytes. The authors observed an impairment in T-cell rosette formation in some chronic smokers.

3552 Cushman, P.; and Khurana, R., Clin. Pharmacol. Ther., *19*(3), 310-17 (1976).

Marijuana and T-Lymphocyte Rosettes.

Marihuana use significantly decreased rosette formation by early T-lymphocytes, but the effect was short lived and recovered to control levels within 96 hours. No change in later or total peripheral T-lymphocyte rosette formation was detected.

3553 Cushman, P.; and Khurana, R., Clin. Res., *24*(3), 326a (1976).

Controlled Marijuana Smoking: T- and B-Cell Rosettes.

In experienced users, marihuana use resulted in decreased early T-cell rosette formation but no change in early or late B-cell rosette formation, white blood cells, lymphocytes, or late T-cell rosette formation. It is assumed that depressed early T-cell rosette formation relates to the impaired cell-mediated immunity often seen with Δ^9-THC.

3554 Cushman, P.; and Khurana, R., Fed. Proc., *34*(3), 783 (1975).

Effects of Marihuana Smoking and Tetrahydrocannabinol on T-Cell Rosettes.

Marihuana smoking reduces rosette formation when human T-lymphocytes are brought into contact with sheep cells. *In vitro* THC at 9.0×10^{-7} M reduced rosette formation as did CBN and CBD. T-lymphocyte function is impaired by marihuana ingestion, probably via a cell membrane effect.

3555 Cushman, P.; and Khurana, R., Life Sci., *20*(6), 971-80 (1977).

Controlled Cycle of Tetrahydrocannabinol Smoking: T and B Cell Rosette Formation.

Human volunteers smoking THC cigarettes (20 mg THC) showed decreased early T-cell rosette formation with sheep red blood cells. There was no change in total white blood cell count, percent lymphocytes, B-cell and late T-cell rosette formation, but there appeared to be a functional change in lymphocytes.

3556 Cushman, P.; Khurana, R.; and Hashim, G., pp. 207-09 in *Pharmacology of Marihuana, Vol. 1*, edited by M. C. Braude and S. Szara. NY, Raven Press, 1976.

Tetrahydrocannabinol: Evidence for Reduced Rosette Formation by Normal T Lymphocytes.

Treatment with Δ^9-THC (9×10^{-9} to 3×10^{-3} M) *in vitro* resulted in decreased rosette formation in normal human T lymphocytes. The number of sheep cells/rosetting cells and multirosetted cells were also decreased at the high dose level. Probably, Δ^9-THC reacts with the cell-wall resulting in decreased adherence of sheep cells with lymphocytes.

3557 Cuskey, W. R.; Berger, L. H.; and Richardson, A. H., Contemp. Drug Probl., 7(4), 491-532 (1978).

The Effects of Marijuana Decriminalization on Drug Use Patterns: A Literature Review and Research Critique.

Marihuana decriminalization laws, enacted by many states, will have impact on all levels of society. Therefore, an in-depth comprehensive analysis should be undertaken to determine the consequences of such a significant social policy.

3558 Cutler, M. G.; and Mackintosh, J. H., Psychopharmacologia, 44, 287-89 (1975).

Effects of Delta-9-Tetrahydrocannabinol on Social Behaviour in the Laboratory Mouse and Rat.

Rats and mice received 5 mg/kg THC i.p. and were paired with animals that received the same volume of 4% Tween 80 in saline. No species difference in behavior was found. Dosed animals showed increased immobility and flight elements with a decrease in non-social activity and in social and sexual investigation. Aggression was not significantly altered.

3559 Cutler, M. G.; Mackintosh, J. H.; and Chance, M. R. A., Psychopharmacologia, 41, 271-76 (1975).

Effects of Cannabis Resin on Social Behaviour in the Laboratory Mouse.

The effects of several doses of cannabis (4 to 100 mg/kg, i.p.) were studied by an ethological analysis of encounters between male mice injected with drug and partners injected with Tween-saline. Duration of immobility was directly related to logarithm of the dose given. A straight line relationship existed between the logarithm of flight/aggression and the logarithm of cannabis administered. An ataxic gait and Straub tails were observed in some mice receiving 25 to 100 mg cannabis/kg.

3560 Cutler, M. G.; Mackintosh, J. H.; and Chance, M. R. A., Psychopharmacologia, 44(2), 173-77 (1975).

Behavioural Changes in Laboratory Mice During Cannabis Feeding and Withdrawal.

When mice from different pairs were put together, the dominant mouse became more so while the behavior of the subordinate mouse remained unchanged. After daily ingestion of 23 mg cannabis the cannabis group also preferred the untreated- over cannabis-treated chow. After cannabis withdrawal, aggression levels rose and then tapered off.

3561 Cutler, M. G.; Mackintosh, J. H.; and Chance, M. R. A., Psychopharmacologia, 45(1), 129-31 (1975).

Cannabis Resin and Sexual Behavior in the Laboratory Mouse.

Cannabis administered i.p. (12.5 or 25 mg/kg) to male mice inhibited mounting behavior and caused periods of immobility and frequent non-social behavior. The effects increased with dose.

D

3562 Dahiya, M. S., Indian Drugs, *14*(3), 66-79 (1976).

Chemistry and Pharmacology of Cannabis.

In reviewing the up-to-date knowledge concerning the chemistry and pharmacology of marihuana, the author stresses the fact that marihuana is not an innocuous, low toxicity drug.

3563 Dahiya, M. S.; and Jain, G. C., Indian Drugs, *14*(4), 76-79 (1977).

Inhibitory Effects of Cannabidiol and Tetrahydrocannabinol Against Some Soil Inhabiting Fungi.

THC and CBD inhibited the activity of several fungi, but were ineffective against *Penicillium chrysogenum* and *Aspergillus niger*.

3564 Dahiya, M.S.; and Jain, G. C., Indian Drugs Pharm. Ind., *12*(4), 31-34 (1977).

Antibacterial Activity of Cannabidiol and Tetrahydrocannabinol.

Both THC and CBD exhibited antibacterial activity. Degrees of inhibition varied among the two cannabinoids and depended on the organism tested.

3565 Dahiya, M. S.; and Jain, G. C., Indian J. Criminol., *5*(2), 96-104 (1977).

Analysis and Identification of *Cannabis sativa L.* Constituents from Smoke by Thin Layer Chromatography.

A TLC procedure was developed for detection of cannabinoids in the smoke obtained from Indian marihuana and hashish. The drugs were burned in a smoking pipe and sucked into a chamber where the smoke bubbled into a series of solvents including urine, saliva, water, petroleum ether, kerosine oil, benzene, toluene, chloroform, methanol and ethanol. TLC of these solvents using neutral plates or alkaline plates showed the presence of different cannabinoids: Δ^9-THC, CBD and CBN in all solvents, as well as on the walls of the smoking chamber.

3566 Dahiya, M. S.; and Jain, G. C., Indian J. Pharm., *40*(1), 1-4 (1978).

Enhancement of Depressant Properties of Datura in Combination with Δ^9-Tetrahydrocannabinol.

THC in combination with Datura induced sleeping in rats. This was not seen when either agent was administered alone. THC also potentiated the paralysis caused by high doses of Datura.

3567 Dahiya, M. S.; and Shrivastava, R. K., IRCS Med. Sci., Libr. Compend., *6*(3), 108 (1978).

Δ^9-THC and Metabolism of Neutral 17-Ketosteroids in Rats.

THC (40 mg/kg/day for 7 days) increased the levels of 17-ketosteroids in rat testes and spleen, while it decreased urinary, hepatic, and adrenal levels.

3568 Dalterio, S.; Bartke, A.; and Burstein, S., Science, *196*(4297), 1472-73 (1977).

Cannabinoids Inhibit Testosterone Secretion by Mouse Testes *In Vitro*.

In the incubation medium of decapsulated mouse testes, 25 mg/ml of THC resulted in 86% inhibition of testosterone accumulation. CBN at 25 and 250 mg/ml resulted in 73 and 95% testosterone inhibition respectively. Implications of findings were discussed.

3569 Dalterio, S.; Bartke, A.; Roberson, C.; Watson, D.; and Burstein, S., Pharmacol. Biochem. Behav., *8*(6), 673-78 (1978).

Direct and Pituitary-Mediated Effects of Δ^9-THC and Cannabinol on the Testis.

Only in the presence of human chorionic gonadotropin (HCG) did THC inhibit *in-vitro* progesterone and testosterone production by mouse testes and have no effect on their precursors. However, *in-vivo* and in the absence of HCG, CBN inhibited testosterone production while THC decreased plasma testosterone, LH and FSH levels and inhibited copulatory behavior.

3570   Dalterio, S. L. S., Diss. Abstr. Int. B, *39*(3), 1534-35 (1978).

Effects of Cannabinoids on Male Reproductive Function in Mice.

Acute Δ^9-THC (50 mg/kg, p.o.) reduced plasma testosterone, LH and FSH levels and decreased copulatory behavior of male mice, while CBN did not induce similar effects. Under chronic conditions, both agents impaired sexual behavior. Other related experiments were also carried out.

3571   Dalton, W. S., Diss. Abstr. Int. B, *37*(8), 3898 (1977).

The Influence of Cannabidiol on the Effects of Δ^9-Tetrahydrocannabinol.

CBD, ineffective by itself, attenuated the THC-induced euphoria and, to a lesser extent, its psychomotor impairment when administered simultaneously, but not before THC, to human subjects. Further investigation suggests that such an interaction is competitive in nature.

3572   Dalton, W. S.; Martz, R.; Lemberger, L.; Rodda, B. E.; and Forney, R. B., Clin. Pharmacol. Ther., *18*(3), 298-304 (1975).

Effects of Marihuana Combined with Secobarbital.

Fifty min. before smoking a marihuana cigarette (0 to 25 μg/kg THC), either secobarbital (150 mg/70kg) or placebo was administered to 12 subjects. Their psychological response and psychomotor performance were studied. A table is given of the various results. There was no interaction of effects between THC and secobarbital. The effects were additive.

3573   Dalton, W. S.; Martz, R.; Lemberger, L.; Rodda, B. E.; and Forney, R. B., Clin. Pharmacol. Ther., *19*(3), 300-09 (1976).

Influence of Cannabidiol on Delta-9-Tetrahydrocannabinol Effects.

Male subjects smoked 500 mg cigarettes which delivered THC (0 or 25 μg/kg) and CBD (0 or 150 μg/kg) simultaneously. Mental and motor performances were observed. No significant interaction was observed between THC and CBD in these parameters. CBD alone did not produce euphoria and in combination with THC the psychologic "high" was significantly reduced. CBD administered 30 min. before THC had no effect on THC euphoria.

3574   Dalton, W. S.; Martz, R.; Rodda, B. E.; Lemberger, L.; and Forney, R., Toxicol. Appl. Pharmacol., *37*(1), 135 (1976).

Clinical Effects of Cannabidiol and Secobarbital in Man.

As CBD has been reported to be a potent inhibitor of drug metabolism in animals, the effects of CBD (0, 150, 500 μg/kg) on secobarbital metabolism were examined in humans. No changes in plasma half-life, peak plasma levels of secobarbital and time to peak levels were observed with CBD.

3575   Dalton, W. S.; Martz, R.; Rodda, B. E.; Lemberger, L.; and Forney, R. B., Clin. Pharmacol. Ther., *20*(6), 695-700 (1976).

Influence of Cannabidiol on Secobarbital Effects and Plasma Kinetics.

In six male adults receiving 150 mg/kg sodium secobarbital orally and up to 500 mg/kg CBD via inhalation, no evidence was shown of changes in baseline liver enzyme kinetics or metabolism of secobarbital.

3576   Dalton, W. S.; Martz, R.; Rodda, B. E.; Lemberger, L.; and Forney, R. B., Forensic Sci., 5(2), 118 (1975).

Combined Effects of Δ^9-THC and CBD in Man.

Male volunteers smoked 0 to 25 µg/kg THC combined with 0 or 150 µg/kg CBD. It was shown that CBD attenuated the THC euphoria. In a second test THC was smoked 20 min. prior to CBD. In this case CBD had no effect on THC responses.

3577   Darley, C. F.; Tinklenberg, J. R.; Roth, W. T.; Vemon, S.; and Kopell, B. S., Psychopharmacology, 52(3), 239-41 (1977).

Marijuana Effects on Long-Term Memory Assessment and Retrieval.

THC (0.3 mg/kg, p.o.) did not alter retreival of non-experimentally presented information from long-term memory nor did it change the subjects' recognition performance.

3578   Daskalopoulos, N.; Schmitt, H.; and Laubie, M., Encephale, 1(2), 121-32 (1975).

Action du Delta 9-Tetrahydrocannabinol sur la Regulation Cardiovasculaire Centrale: Mechanisme et Localisation. [Effect of Delta-9-Tetrahydrocannabinol on Central Cardiovascular Control: Mechanism and Site of Action).

The medulla oblongata appeared to be the main site of action of Δ^9-THC (30-300 µg/kg, i.v.) in cats and dogs.

3579   Daul, C. D.; and Heath, R. G., Life Sci., 17(6), 875-82 (1975).

The Effect of Chronic Marihuana Usage on the Immunological Status of Rhesus Monkeys.

Monkeys were chronically exposed to marihuana smoke containing three different levels of Δ^9-THC. In vitro lymphocytes and immunoglobulin levels were then determined. Changes in cellular reactivity were observed.

3580   Davalos, S. G.; Boucher, F.; Fournier, G.; and Paris, M., Experientia, 33(12), 1562-63 (1977).

Analysis of a Population of Cannabis sativa L.Originating from Mexico and Cultivated in France.

Qualitative and quantitative studies were done on male and female plants of Cannabis sativa L., originating from Mexico and cultivated in France, to evaluate their cannabinoid content. Statistical analysis indicated variability which was correlated with genetic heterogeneity of the seeds.

3581   Davalos, S. G.; Fournier, G.; and Boucher, F., J. Pharm. Belg., 32(1), 89-99 (1977).

Contribution A L'etude De La Marihuana Mexicaine. Estudes Preliminaires: Cannabinoides Et Huile Essentielle [Contribution to the Study of Mexican Marihuana. Preliminary Studies: Cannabinoids and Essential Oil.]

Three Mexican samples of cannabis did not contain any CBD, while their THC content, differed according to their geographic origins. The Oaxaca sample had the highest THC content, followed by the Michoacan and Durango samples.

3582 Davies, B. H.; Radcliffe, S.; Seaton, A.; and Graham, J. D. P., Thorax, *30*(1), 80-85 (1975).

A Trial of Oral $\triangle^1$-(*Trans*)-Tetrahydrocannabinol in Reversible Airways Obstruction.

Sixteen human subjects were given $\triangle^1$-THC in a dose of 10 mg. The results indicated that the agent is not an effective oral bronchodilator in patients with reversible airways obstruction.

3583 Davis, C. S., Drug Forum, *6*(4), 315-26 (1977-78).

Marijuana and Psychedelic Use: Are They Deviant Responses?

Psychological health of young marihuana users did not appreciably differ from that of non-users or psychedelic users.

3584 Davis, E. M., Police Chief, *42*(1), 34-35 (1975).

Position Paper on Marihuana.

A report from the Los Angeles chief of police opposing the legalization of marihuana.

3585 Davis, G. S.; and Brody, A. R., Amer. Rev. Resp. Dis., *117*(4 pt. 2), 229 (1978).

Changes in Surface Morphology of Human Alveolar Macrophages Induced by Tobacco and Marijuana Smoking (abstract).

Chronic marihuana and tobacco smoking induced significant changes in the morphology, number and heterogeneity of human alveolar macrophages.

3586 Davis, R. E.; Midalia, N. D.; and Curnow, D. H., Med. J. Aust., *1*(11), 617-20 (1978).

Illegal Drugs and Nutrition in Undergraduate Students.

The nutritional status of marihuana users did not differ from that of non-users in this sample of Australian undergraduates. A high incidence of multiple drug use was indicated.

3587 Davis, W. M.; and Borgen, L. A., Arch. Int. Pharmacodyn. Ther., *213*(1), 97-112 (1975).

Tolerance Development to the Effect of $\triangle^9$-Tetrahydrocannabinol on Contioned Behavior: Role of Treatment Interval and Influence of Microsomal Metabolism.

Naive rats received $\triangle^9$-THC (10 mg/kg or less, i.p.) while being tested in a food-reinforcement operant procedure. Tolerance to THC-induced behavioral depression was most evident in animals with the highest frequency of exposure to drug. Pretreatment with SKF-525A enhanced, whereas that of phenobarbital blocked, the behavioral effects of THC.

3588 Dawson, W. W., Invest. Ophthalmol., *15*(4), 243-54 (1976).

Cannabis and Eye Function.

Marihuana's effects on eye function and vision are reviewed briefly. Consistent ocular ramifications attendant to acute marihuana use include: (1) decreased lacrimation and intraocular pressure; (2) photophobia and blepharospasm; (3) conjunctival injection and pupillary constriction; (4) increased exposure of corneal nerves; and (5) accommodative or refractive changes. The data on ocular function in chronic use situations are sparse, but available clinical observations indicate no gross pathology relative to cigarette (tobacco) smoking.

3589 Dawson, W. W.; Jimenez-Antillon, C. F.; Perez, J. M.; and Zeskind, J. A., Invest. Ophthalmol., *16*(8), 689-99 (1977).

Marijuana and Vision - After Ten Years' Use in Costa Rica.

Pupil, intraocular pressure, dark-adaptation, decimal activity, color matching, lacrimal secretion and fundus evaluations were made on marihuana users and socioanthropological non-users. Results are reported for each area investigated and compared to known data obtained from diseased eyes. Chronic users had an increase in IOP. An apparent optically uncorrectable acuity deficit was found in chronic users.

3590   Dayanandan, P.; and Kaufman, P. B., Amer. J. Bot., *63*(5), 578-91 (1976).

Trichomes of *Cannabis sativa L.* (Cannabaceae).

A comparison between silicification, calcification and nonglandular hairs of *Cannabis sativa, Humulus lupulus,* and *Lantana camera* is presented. Pistillate and staminate were investigated and found to contain same types of glandular and non-glandular hairs.

3591   De Faubert Maunder, M. J., Med. Sci. Law, *16*(2), 78-89 (1976).

The Forensic Significance of the Age and Origin of Cannabis.

Samples of confiscated cannabis preparations are classified as to color, shape, weight, packaging, odor, etc. Using TLC analysis and physical characteristics it is possible to generally determine geographical origin and age of sample. Photographs of seized samples of various resins and herbs are presented along with a written description of the various types. Absence of CBD noted for some variants.

3592   De Pasquale, A.; Costa, G.; and Scarpignato, C., Riv. Farmacol. Ter., *8*(1), 71-78 (1977).

Noradrenalina E Serotonina Cerebrali Dopo Stress Audiogeno Nel Ratto: Influenza Della Resina Di "Cannabis" [Cerebral Noradrenaline and Serotonin in Rats after Audiogenic Stress: Effect of Cannabis Resin].

Cannabis resin antagonized the audiogenic stress-induced decrease in rat brain NE, 5-HT, and 5-HIAA levels.

3593   De Pasquale, A.; Costa, G.; and Trovato, A., Bull. Narcotics, *30*(2), 55-61 (1978).

Effects of Cannabis Resin on Learning by Repetition in the Rat.

Cannabis resin improved learning in the water-filled maze technique and the conditioned avoidance reflex when administered to rats at a dose corresponding to 0.5 mg/kg of Δ^9-THC. Opposite effects were observed with the higher dose (5.0 mg/kg of Δ^9-THC).

3594   De Pasquale, A.; Costa, G.; and Trovato, A., Bull. Narcotics, *30*(3), 33-41 (1978).

The Influence of Cannabis on Glucoregulation.

Δ^9-THC increased plasma levels of glucose and amonia and decreased immunoreactive insulin levels in treated dogs. Tolerance to glucose was also suppressed.

3595   De Souza, H.; and Palermo Neto, J., J. Pharm. Pharmacol., *30*(9), 591-92 (1978).

Effects of Anti-Acetylcholine Drugs on Aggressive Behavior Induced by *Cannabis sativa* in REM Sleep-Deprived Rats.

Atropine sulphate or scopolamine decreased cannabis extract-induced aggression in REM sleep-deprived rats.

3596   De Souza, H.; Trajano, E.; De Carvalho, F. V.; and Palermo Neto, J., Jap. J. Pharmacol., *28*(3), 507-10 (1978).

Effects of Acute and Long-Term Cannabis Treatment on Restraint-Induced Gastric Ulceration in Rats.

Cannabis extract protected rats against restraint-induced ulceration under acute, but not long term, conditions.

3597 Deikel, S. M.; and Carder, B., Psychopharmacol. Commun., 2(1), 61-65 (1976).

Attentuation of Precipitated Abstinence in Methadone-Dependent Rats by Δ^9-THC.

A critique and rebuttal on the question of whether or not Δ^9-THC can antagonize specifically (separate from its non-specific sedative effects) naloxone-precipitated methadone abstinence.

3598 Del Castillo, J.; Anderson, M.; and Rubottom, G. M., Nature, 253(5490), 365-66 (1975).

Marihuana, Absinthe and the Central Nervous System.

The essential oils of absinthol and cannabis were investigated. Thujone and THC have similar geometric structure and functional groups available for metabolism. The similarity in psychological actions of these two drugs was explained as a common receptor site in the CNS.

3599 Dell, D. D.; and Snyder, J. A., Amer. J. Nurs., 77(4), 630-35 (1977).

Marijuana: Pro and Con.

In reviewing available literature concerning the benefits and hazards of marihuana use, the authors concluded that when consumed in small amounts marihuana does not cause an irreversible damage. However, it is reasonable to expect both harmful and unpleasant side effects if excessive quantities are used.

3600 Dembo, R.; and Miran, M., Int. J. Addict.. 11(5), 881-903 (1976).

Evaluation of Drug Prevention Programs by Youths in a Middle-Class Community.

Drug prevention program formats and their effectiveness at the junior and senior high school levels were evaluated. Utilization of a questionnaire and statistical analysis of the results were also discussed.

3601 Dembo, R.; Schmeidler, J.; and Koval, M., J. Health Soc. Behav., 17, 177-87 (1976).

Demographic, Value, and Behavior Correlates of Marijuana Use Among Middle-Class Youths.

Youths from a suburban school, grades 7 through 12, were surveyed to ascertain their reasons for using marihuana. Socioeconomic status was found to be independent of marihuana use and both sexes had similar rates of use. Marihuana use was an affirmation of a set of peer-supported values and activities and a quest for new sensations. A high correlation was found between drug use and risk orientation and attendance at parties.

3602 Desoize, B.; Hsu, J.; Nahas, G. G.; and Morishima, A., Fed. Proc., 34(3), 783 (1975).

Inhibition of Human Lymphocyte Transformation In Vitro by Natural Cannabinoids and Olivetol.

Lymphocytic responsiveness to phytohemagglutinin or allogenic cells was inhibited 50% by Δ^9-THC and 11-OH-Δ^9-THC at 2.0×10^{-4} M and 100% at 5.0×10^{-4} M. Additional cannabinoids including olivetol possessed comparable antimitotic activity.

3603   Desoize, B.; Jardillier, J. C.; Leger, C.;
        and Nahas, G. G., Brit. J. Pharmacol.,
        58(3), 419P (1976).

        Delta-9-Tetrahydrocannabinol (THC) and
        Macromoleculary Synthesis: Mechanisms
        of Action.

        The inhibitory effect of Δ^9-THC on the
        incorporation of leucine, uridine and
        thymidine in the biosynthesis of protein,
        RNA and DNA was studied. Interference
        with transport enzymes of the plasma
        membrane was suggested as a mechanism
        of action.

3604   Desoize, B.; Leger, C.; and Nahas, G.,
        Ann. Med. Nancy, 17, 413-14, 416
        (1978).

        Effects Cellulaires du Cannabis [Cellular
        Effects of Cannabis].

        The effects of Δ^9-THC, CBD, CBN,
        CBG, CBC and CBL on cell life and cell
        division were reviewed. Toxic effects
        were observed. ^{3}H-Thymidine uptake
        was recorded for these cannabinoids
        and dose concentration relationship curves
        were given.

3605   Desoize, B.; Leger, C.; and Nahas, G.,
        C. R. Acad. Sci. Ser. D., 287(16), 1441-
        44 (1978).

        Inhibition par le Delta-9-Tetrahydrocan-
        nabinol (THC) du Systeme de Transport
        Membranaire de la Thymidine [Inhibition
        of the Membrane Transport System of
        Thymidine by Delta-9-Tetrahydrocannabi-
        nol (THC).

        The effects of Δ^9-THC on the membrane
        systems responsible for the transport of
        thymidine are studied using culture of
        L1210 murine lymphoma cells and
        huma lymphocytes at 37° and 0°. At
        37° Δ^9-THC decreased the uptake of
        ^{3}H-Thymidine within 15 sec., while at
        0° the drug did not have any effect.

        These results indicate that the action
        of Δ^9-THC on the membrane is non-
        specific. Δ^9-THC inhibits DNA synthe-
        sis through change in the membrane
        configuration.

3606   Desoize, B.; and Nahas, G., C. R. Acad.
        Sci. Ser. D., 281, 474-78 (1975).

        Effet Inhibiteur du Delta 9-Tetrahydro-
        cannabinol sur la Synthese des Proteines
        et des Acides Nucleiques [Inhibitory
        Effect of Delta-9-Tetrahydrocannabinol
        ·on Protein and Nucleic Acid Synthesis].

        Δ^9-THC inhibits the incorporation of
        intracellular and intramolecular tritiated
        thymidine, leucine and uridine in cul-
        tures of lymphocytes. This occurs
        within the first hours after addition of
        Δ^9-THC to lymphocyte cultures.

3607   Desoize, B.; and Nahas, G. G., J. Pharma-
        col. (Paris), 7(4), 421-32 (1976).

        Delta-9-Tetrahydrocannabinol and Nu-
        cleic and Protein Synthesis in Cultured
        Lymphocytes.

        Addition of THC to cultured lympho-
        cytes stimulated by phytohemagglutinin
        quickly inhibited incorporation of thy-
        midine, uridine, and leucine. This inhibi-
        tion was reversible by washing the cells
        and was lessened by diluting the culture
        medium with serum. Kinetic evaluation
        suggested a very similar non-competi-
        tive inhibition for all three precursors.

3608   Detrick, R.; and Foltz, R. L., pp. 88-95 in
        Cannabinoid Assays in Humans, NIDA
        Research Monograph Series, No. 7,
        1976.

        Quantitation of Δ^9-Tetrahydrocannabinol
        in Body Fluids by Gas Chromatography/
        Chemical Ionization-Mass Spectrometry.

        A procedure for the quantitation of
        Δ^9-THC in plasma samples was developed.

Cleanup of the samples was done by a modification of the solvent extraction procedure developed at the Research Triangle Institute. Silylation of the samples was followed by GC-MS analysis and selective ion monitoring. This method also made use of the collision-induced mass spectra to improve the sensitivity.

3609 Dewey, W. L.; Johnson, K. M.; and Bloom, A. S., pp. 190-97 in *Interactions of Drug Abuse*, edited by E. S. Vesell and M. C. Braude. NY, Annals of the New York Academy of Sciences, V. 281, 1976.

Interaction of Active Constituents of Marihuana with Other Drugs in the Neuron.

Forty-five percent of radiolabeled THC and metabolites were found in the brain crude mitochondrial fraction of mice, rats, and dogs treated with THC. Reserpine does not influence THC-binding, whereas THC and other cannabinoids influence the binding of reserpine. Naloxone antagonized the antinociception and elevation of catecholamine synthesis resulting from treatment with β-HHC and also blocked the hypothermia and the increased catecholamine synthesis produced by THC.

3610 Dewey, W. L.; Martin, B. R.; Beckner, J. S.; and Harris, L. S., pp. 349-65 in *Marihuana: Chemistry, Biochemistry, and Cellular Effects*, edited by G. G. Hahas. NY, Springer-Verlag, 1976.

A Comparison of the Subcellular Distribution of Cannabinoids in the Brains of Tolerant and Nontolerant Dogs, Rats, and Mice after Injecting Radiolabeled Δ^9-Tetrahydrocannabinol.

A comparison of the subcellular distribution of Δ^9-THC in the brains of tolerant and nontolerant rats and mice

was carried out. The study was designed to investigate the significant decrease in radioactivity in the synaptic vesicle fraction of tolerant as compared to nontolerant dogs. The study also investigated the subcellular distribution of Δ^9-THC in the brains of rodents.

3611 Dewey, W. L.; Martin, B. R.; and Harris, L. S., pp. 585-94 in *Pharmacology of Marihuana, Vol. 2*, edited by M. C. Braude and S. Szara. NY, Raven Press, 1976.

Chronic Effects of Δ^9-THC in Animals: Tolerance and Biochemical Changes.

Rate of absorption, tissue distribution and plasma concentration of THC were the same in tolerant and nontolerant pigeons. In dogs, tolerance to marihuana-induced static ataxia was not due to changes in plasma concentration or distribution in peripheral organs. The significant decrease in the amount of THC found in synaptic vesicles of tolerant dogs may be the cause of such a behavioral tolerance.

3612 Di Ciommo, M.; and Merlini, L., Gazz. Chim. Ital., *106*(9-10), 967-69 (2976).

XXVII. Cannabinoid-Like Benzoxocinols from *p*-Menthadienes and Olivetol.

Benzoxocinols with a cannabinoid-like structure were synthesized by coupling of *p*-menthadiens with olivetol. The structures of the compounds were determined by MS and NMR and by comparison with compound with similar structures.

3613 Dibenedetto, M., Arch. Phys. Med. Rehabil., *57*(2), 62-66 (1976).

Electrodiagnostic Evidence of Subclinical Disease States in Drug Abusers.

Peripheral nerve stimulation in 100 healthy drug abusers was used to detect possible nerve damage. Changes in nerve conduction were noted in persons using heroin, methadone, LSD, or barbiturates, but no abnormalities were shown in marijuana smokers.

3614   Dibenedetto, M.; McNamee, H. B.; Kuehnle, J. C.; and Mendelson, J. H., Brit. J. Psychiat., *131*, 361-65 (1977).

Cannabis and the Peripheral Nervous System.

Tests were run on 27 chronic medium and heavy male users of marihuana to see if alterations in the anatomy of nervous structures could be detected after 21 days exposure to marihuana cigarettes. The study showed no deterioration of peripheral nerve function.

3615   Dike, S. Y.; Kamath, M.; and Merchant, J. R., Experientia, *33*(8), 985 (1977).

A New One-Step Synthesis of Hexahydrocannabinoid Analogs.

The synthesis of two analogs of hexahydrocannabinol is reported. Citronellal was reacted with one aromatic ketone and one aromatic aldehyde pyridine as the solvent. Yields were approximately 7%.

3616   Dike, S. Y.; and Merchant, J. R., Bull. Chem. Soc. Japan, *51*(7), 2145-47 (1978).

Studies on the Cannabinoid Field: Synthesis of New Cannabinoids from 4-Hydroxycoumarin and 4-Hydroxythiocoumarin by Pyridine-catalyzed Condensation of Citral and Citronellal.

Analogs of THC and HHC were prepared by pyridine catalyzed condensation of 4-hydroxycoumarin with citral and citronellal respectively. The corresponding thioderivatives were prepared starting from 4-hydroxythiocoumarin. In the latter case the thiocoumarin structure was not retained. Instead, the alternate thiochromene structure was obtained. Spectral data are given.

3617   Dionyssiou-Asteriou, A.; and Miras, C. J., J. Pharm. Pharmacol., *27*(2), 135-36 (1975).

Fluorescence of Cannabinoids.

Induction of cannabinoid fluorescence by thermal treatment allows for fluorometric analysis. Some decomposition of THC occurred during the sample preparation. Induced fluorescence was also observed for CBD and CBN. The thermally treated product, from THC, yielded seven spots on TLC indicating considerable decomposition or rearrangement of the starting material. This technique was used to identify cannabinoids in the urine of marihuana smokers.

3618   Dittrich, A.; Bickel, P.; Schopf, J.; and Zimmer, D., Arch. Psychiat. Nervenkr., *223*(1), 77-87 (1976).

Vergleich veranderter BewuBtseinszustande unter den Halluzinogenen (-)-Δ^9-*trans*-Tetrahydrocannabinol (Δ^9-THC) und N,N-Dimethyltryptamin (DMT). [Comparison of Altered States of Consciousness Induced by Hallucinoens (-)-Δ^9-*Trans*-Tetrahydrocannabinol and N,N-Dimethyltryptamine.]

The effects of Δ^9-THC (250 μ m/kg, p.o.) and N,N-Dimethyltryptamine (DMT; 250 μm/kg, i.m.), with respect to altered states of consciousness were assessed via questionnaires directed at eight criteria of mental testing. Both hallucinogens altered consciousness although no significant differences between the two were reached.

3619 Dittrich, A.; Bickel, P.; and Zimmer, D., Psychopharmacologia, *40*, 351-58 (1975).

Effekte von (-)-Δ^9-*trans*-Tetrahydrocannabinol auf Psychotizismus-Tests [Effects of (-)-Δ^9-*trans*-Tetrahydrocannabinol on Tests of Psychosis].

The effects of Δ^9-THC (250 μ/g/kg, p.o.) on objective and performance tests measuring psychosis were assessed in human volunteers.

3620 Dixit, V. P.; Arya, M.; and Lohiya, N. K., Endokrinologie, 66(3), 365-68 (1975).

The Effect of Chronically Administered Cannabis Extract on the Female Genital Tract of Mice and Rats.

Chronic marihuana extract drastically reduced ovarian weights and interrupted estrous cycle in 'treated rats and mice. Treatment also induced significant histological and biochemical alterations.

3621 Dixit, V. P.; Arya, M.; and Lohiya, N. K., Indian J. Physiol. Pharmacol. 20(1), 38-41 (1976).

Mechanism of Action of Chronically Administered Cannabis Extract on the Female Genital Tract of Gerbils.

Toxic effects of chronic i.p. cannabis (2.5 mg/day for 60 days) in gerbils include (1) degenerative changes in the ovaries with atresia of the ovarian follicles and suppression of luteinization; (2) decrease in RNA, protein, sialic acid and glycogen content of the uterus; and (3) failure to show a regular estrous cycle. These results suggest that cannabis has anti-estrogenic effects.

3622 Dixit, V. P.; Gupta, C. L.; and Agrawal, M., Endokrinologie, 69(3), 299-305 (1977).

Testicular Degeneration and Necrosis Induced by Chronic Administration of Cannabis Extract in Dogs.

Subacute administration of cannabis extract (12.5 mg/kg/day for 30 days) inhibited spermatogenesis in dogs and resulted in exfoliation and fibrosis of the seminiferous elements. Other pathologic and biochemical testicular alterations were also detected.

3623 Dixit, V. P.; Jain, H. E.; Verma, O. P.; and Sharma, A. N., Indian J. Exp. Biol., 15(7), 555-57 (1977).

Effects of Cannabis Extract on the Testicular Function of the Toad *Bufo andersonii* Boulenger.

Toads treated with cannabis extract (10 mg/day, i.p. for 14 days) showed marked inhibition of spermatogenesis but no hepatic pathology. Implications of the findings were discussed.

3624 Dixit, V. P.; and Lohiya, N. K., Indian J. Physiol. Pharmacol., 19(2), 98-100 (1975).

Effects of Cannabis Extract on the Response of Accessory Sex Organs of Adult Male Mice To testosterone.

Castrated male mice were sacrificed 24 hr. after final dose of cannabis extract i.p. (10 mg/ml) and testosterone s.c. (6 mg), alone or in combination. Cannabis extract caused a marked reduction in body weight, seminal vesicles, ventral prostate, epididymus, preputial glands and perineal complex. The adrenals increased in weight significantly. Testosterone's stimulatory effects on accessory sex organs were inhibited by cannabis extract: an anti-adrogenic effect.

3625 Dodge, D. L., Int. J. Addict., 12(7), 971-81 (1977).

Dimensions of Marijuana Use in a Midwest Catholic University: Subcultural Considerations.

A sample of male Catholic college students was questioned on several aspects of marihuana use. Findings indicated that in contrast to nonusers, users were uncertain regarding the harmful or beneficial effects of marihuana use, yet they believed marihuana should be legalized. Users also believed that friends' attitudes were more in line with theirs than did nonusers. Prominent differences between systematic and heavy users in this subculture were not reflected.

3626   Dodge, D. L., J. Amer. Coll. Health Ass., 25(2), 102-08 (1976).

Survey of Students and Drugs at the University of Notre Dame: An Overview.

On the basis of a questionnaire given to 134 students of the University of Notre Dame in 1972, it was concluded that for the population studied, essentially all drug users smoked marijuana while some of them also used other drugs. The bulk of the paper deals with the differing beliefs between users and nonusers of drugs about legal and social aspects of drug use.

3627   Dolby, T. W., Diss. Abst. Int. B., 35(7), 3203 (1975).

Marihuana Components and Cyclic Nucleotide Alterations in the Central Nervous System.

Low doses of Δ^9-THC, i.p., elevated cyclic AMP levels in mouse brains and specific regions by 50-160% over controls. High doses of THC decreased whole brain cyclic AMP by 30-60%. THC, 11-OH-THC and CBN have no effect on adrenyl cyclase activity or phosphodiesterase activity until adrenyl cyclase is stimulated by NE. Correlations are observed in the behavioral and physiological actions of cannabinoids in mammals which may be mediated by the mechanisms of cyclic AMP.

3628   Dolby, T. W.; and Kleinsmith, L. J., Can. J. Physiol. Pharmacol., 55(4), 934-42 (1977).

Cannabinoid Effects on Adenylate Cyclase and Phosphodiesterase Activities of Mouse Brain.

THC, 11-OH-THC, and CBN, at specific doses, were shown to alter adenylate cyclase activity in vivo directly and also indirectly by increasing or decreasing sensitivity to stimulation by neurotransmitters. The cannabinoids also were shown to cause changes in the properties of whole-brain phosphodiesterase after prolonged administration in mice. The overall activity of the "changed" esterase was similar to control enzyme activity except that calcium ions no longer stimulated cyclic AMP breakdown.

3629   Domino, E., pp. 407-13 in Marihuana: Chemistry, Biochemistry, and Cellular Effects, edited by G. G. Nahas. NY, Springer-Verlag, 1976.

Effects of Δ^9-Tetrahydrocannabinol and Cannabinol on Rat Brain Acetylcholine.

Effects of THC and CBN on rat brain acetylcholine were studied. Results provided additional evidence that large doses of THC elevate rat brain acetylcholine and reduce its utilization. CBN in this respect is much less effective.

3630   Domino, E. F.; Donelson, A. C.; and Tuttle, T., pp. 673-78 in Cholinergic Mechanisms and Psychopharmacology, Vol. 24 (Adv. Behav. Biol.), edited by D. J. Jenden. New York, Plenum Press, 1977.

Effects of Δ^9-Tetrahydrocannabinol on Regional Brain Acetylcholine.

Δ^9-THC (1 to 32 mg/kg, i.p.) induced behavioral changes in rats. Δ^9-THC did not affect regional rat brain ACh levels although it increased previously depleted ACh levels in the hippocampus.

3631 Domino, E. F.; Rennick, P.; and Pearl, J. H., pp. 393-417 in *Pharmacology of Marihuana, Vol. 1*, edited by M. C. Braude and S. Szara. NY, Raven Press, 1976.

Short-Term Neuropsychopharmacological Effects of Marihuana Smoking in Experienced Male Users.

A battery of tests were performed to assess the neurophysiological, pharmacological, subjective and cognitive effects of Δ^9-THC. A maximum of 4 cigarettes of 300 mg each containing 0, 0.5, and 2.9% THC were smoked. Pharmacological effects observed include tachycardia, elevated systolic and diastolic pressure, a decrease in palpebral fissure, an increase in dizziness and a decrease in clear thinking. Neurophysiological tests showed impairment of ability to name colors. Cognitive effects included a slight loss of short term memory and impaired ability to perform conceptual tests.

3632 Dornbush, R. L., pp. 103-14 in *Marijuana and Health Hazards*, edited by J. R. Tinklenberg. NY, Academic Press, 1975.

Marijuana and the Central Nervous System.

A critical evaluation of studies conducted to determine the CNS effects of marihuana is made. The author indicates the weak points in each study and appraises the work of Klonoff *et al.* (1973) as being a good model for future studies. The issue of whether or not marihuana damages the CNS requires very carefully planned, designed, executed and interpreted prospective studies.

3633 Dornbush, R. L.; and Freedman, A. M., pp. vii-viii in *Chronic Cannabis Use*, edited by R. L. Dornbush, A. M. Freedman, and M. Fink. NY, Annals of the New York Academy of Sciences, V., 282, 1976.

Introduction.

Consequences of chronic cannabis use for drug subcultures in Jamaica, Greece, Costa Rica, India and Egypt were documented. Extrapolation of these data to the possible outcome of social cannabis use was also provided. Emphasis was placed on CNS functioning and health implications.

3634 Dornbush, R. L.; Freedman, A. M.; and Fink, M., eds. Annals of the New York Academy of Sciences, Vol. 282, *Chronic Cannabis Use*. NY, New York Academy of Sciences, 1976. 430 pp.

Papers presented at a conference held Jan. 26-28, 1976, sponsored by the New York Academy of Sciences, NIDA, and New York Medical College. Book chapters have individual entries.

3635 Dornbush, R. L.; and Kokkevi, A., pp. 313-22 in *Chronic Cannabis Use*, edited by R. L. Dornbush, A. M. Freedman, and M. Fink. NY, Annals of the New York Academy of Sciences, V., 282, 1976.

Acute Effects of Cannabis on Cognitive, Perceptual, and Motor Performance in Chronic Hashish Users.

The effects of hashish, marihuana and Δ^9-THC (100 mg) on short-term memory, alertness, time sense, mental coordination and motor performance were as-

98

sessed in Greek chronic cannabis users. Comparison between American short-term users and Greek chronic users demonstrated that cannabis use impaired performance on complex tasks only.

3636 Dornbush, R. L.; and Kokkevi, A., pp. 421-27 in *Pharmacology of Marihuana, Vol. 1*, edited by M. C. Braude and S. Szara. NY, Raven Press, 1976.

The Acute Effects of Various Cannabis Substances on Cognitive, Perceptual, and Motor Performance in Very Long-Term Hashish Users.

The acute effects of very high doses of cannabis preparations (marihuana equivalent to 80 mg Δ^9-THC), hashish (equivalent to 180 and 190 mg Δ^9-THC) and pure Δ^9-THC (100 mg) on psychomotor behavior of chronic hashish users were described. Although no disruption of behavior was observed in simple tasks, ability to perform complex tasks was impaired. It was also noted that the effects produced by pure Δ^9-THC were different than those produced by smoking hashish or marihuana. An interaction due to the presence of CBN and CBD in the latter two preparations was suggested.

3637 Dorr, M.; and Steinberg, H., Psychopharmacolocy, *47*, 87-91 (1976).

Effects of Δ^9-Tetrahydrocannabinol on Social Behaviour in Mice. Comparison Between Two Vehicles.

Decreased social behavior was achieved by lower doses of Δ^9-THC when the vehicle was propylene glycol than when Tween-80 was used. The latter stimulated behavior when used alone.

3638 Drachler, D. H., New Eng. J. Med., *293*(13), 667 (1975).

Hashish and the Transmission of Hepatitis.

Soldiers with no history of blood transfusions had sporadic Type B hepatitis. Most of them smoked hashish and shared the same pipe. Saliva is a vehicle for transmitting the hepatitis virus.

3639 Dren, A. T., pp. 439-55 in *The Therapeutic Potential of Marihuana*, edited by S. Cohen and R. Stillman. NY, Plenum Medical Book Company, 1976.

Preclinical Neuropharmacology of Three Nitrogen-Containing Heterocyclic Benzopyrans Derived from the Cannabinoid Nucleus.

Compared to reference agents, the synthetic nitrogen-benzopyran cannabinoid-like compounds SP-1, SP-106 and SPA-80 were found to possess tranquilizing, analgesic and sedative-hypnotic effects in laboratory animals in addition to lowering the IOP. A water-soluble derivative, SP-106, failed to maintain the self-administration behavior in dependent monkeys.

3640 Dren, A. T.; Bopp, B. A.; and Ebert, D. M., Pharmacologist, *17*, 257 (1975).

Nitrogen-Containing Benzopyran Analogs: Reduction of Intraocular Pressure in Rabbits.

Administration of ABBOTT-40656 and ABBOTT-40174, two nitrogen containing benzopyran (cannabinoid-like) analogs, reduced IOP in rabbits. The former agent was also effective systemically and antagonized arachidonic acid increase of IOP.

3641 Drewnowski, A.; and Gray, J. A., Psychopharmacologia, *43*(3), 233-37 (1975).

Influence of $\triangle^9$-Tetrahydrocannabinol on Partial Reinforcement Effects.

Rats were trained in a food reinforcement study that compared THC (5 mg/kg, i.p.) to placebo under the contingencies of partial and continuous reinforcement. THC, during acquisition or extinction, disrupted partial reinforcement extinction effect. In this respect, $\triangle^9$-THC resembled alcohol and amylobarbitone.

3642   Drewnowski, A.; and Grinker, J. A., Pharmacol. Biochem. Behav., 9(5), 619-30 (1978).

Food and Water Intake, Meal Patterns and Activity of Obese and Lean Zucker Rats Following Chronic and Acute Treatment with $\triangle^9$-Tetrahydrocannabinol.

Fifteen-day treatment with $\triangle^9$-THC decreased food and water intakes of obese and lean rats. Further investigations revealed that THC reduced meal size and initially increased, then decreased, meal frequency.

3643   Drewnowski, A.; and Grinker, J. A., Behav. Biol., 23(1), 112-17 (1978).

Temporal Effects of $\triangle^9$-Tetrahydrocannabinol on Feeding Patterns and Activity of Obese and Lean Zucker Rats.

THC did not alter food intake, although it changed the feeding pattern of lean and obese rats. A later phase of THC-induced anorexia paralleled a reduction in animals' activity. Implications of the findings relative to potential anorectic drugs were discussed.

3644   Du Toit, B. M., Afr. Econ. Hist., 1, 17-35 (1976).

Man and Cannabis in Africa: A Study of Diffusion.

The author discusses the introduction of cannabis to Africa and offers an elaborate analysis of evidence at the historical, linguistic and social levels.

3645   Du Toit, B. M., pp. 75-99 in Drugs, Rituals, and Altered States of Consciousness, edited by B. M. Du Toit. Rotterdam, Balkema, 1977.

Ethnicity and Patterning in South African Drug Use.

The patterns of drug use in South Africa were analyzed within and against the historical traditions and values of that area. A sample of cannabis users including Coloured, White, Indian, and African participants were screened. Results indicated that the wide traditional use of cannabis did not lead to hard drug use. The social significance of the ritual of first use was also discussed.

3646   Du Toit, B. M., J. Asian Afr. Stud., 11(3-4), 203-08 (1976).

Continuity and Change in Cannabis Use by Africans in South Africa.

The author compares the old and new ways of using cannabis in South Africa. He blames the government for ignoring cultural heterogeneity, available evidence on cannabis use and existing research avenues when formulating legislation concerning cannabis abuse.

3647   Du Toit, B. M., J. Psychedelic Drugs, 9(3), 235-46 (1977).

Historical and Cultural Factors Influencing Cannabis Use Among Indians in South Africa.

South Africans of Indian origin preserve and continue to exercise a lot of traditional behavioral and belief patterns pertaining to India. Their pattern of cannabis use has similarities to both African and Indian styles.

3648 Dube, K. C.; Kumar, A.; Kumar, N.; and Gupta, S. P., Bull. Narcotics, *29*(1), 47-61 (1977).

Drug Use Among College Students - An Interim Report.

Upon questioning a sample of Indian post-graduate and senior medical students, more males than females and more medical than non-medical students had experienced some sort of drug use. Cannabis was among the drugs used and its habitual use was regarded as leading to involvement with more potent drugs.

3649 Dube, K. C.; Kumar, A.; Kumar, N.; and Gupta, S. P., Acta Psychiat. Scand., *57*(4), 336-56 (1978).

Prevalence and Pattern of Drug Use Amongst College Students.

A survey of 1192 college students revealed that 50.8% used dependence-producing drugs, including marihuana. The highest rate was among male medical students. Alcohol and marihuana were preferred by males, whereas females had a preference for meprobamate followed by alcohol. The influence of several factors, such as peer pressure and family attitude, on drug use were also discussed.

3650 Duggan, J. F.; and Aust, M., Acta Psiquiat. Psicol. Amer. Lat., *22*(1), 63-70 (1976).

Pscosis Por Marihuana [Marihuana Psychosis].

Chronic marihuana use resulted in toxic psychosis resembling schizophrenia in 4 out of 5 subjects studied.

3651 Dukes, M. N. G., pp. 17-20 in *Side Effects of Drugs Annual 1*, edited by M. N. G. Dukes. Amsterdam, Excerpta Medica, 1977. 420 pp.

Social Drugs: Cannabis '77.

Evidence supporting the concept of marihuanas harmful effects on humans can easily be obtained by reviewing pertinent marihuana literature. A review of some recent research (23 references).

3652 Duncan, D. F., Brit. J. Addict., *70*(2), 192-97 (1975).

Marijuana and Heroin: A Study of Initiation of Drug Use by Heroin Addicts.

In two samples of heroin addicts, prison inmates and methadone patients, marihuana was not the main first drug. For the inmates 61.6% started with speed and for the methadone patients 73.6% started with alcohol. The crucial factor in heroin use lies within the person and the environment and not in the pharmacology of the drug.

3653 Duncan, G. E.; and Dagirmanjian, R., Fed. Proc., *37*(3), 275 (1978).

Δ^9-Tetrahydrocannabinol Sensitization of the Rat Brain to Direct Cholinergic Stimulation.

Δ^9-THC (3 and 6 mg/kg, i.p.) potentiated the drinking and the abnormal motor responses induced in rats by carbachol injection into the lateral septal nucleus. Atropine completely blocked the drinking response elicited by carbachol alone and partially antagonized the response to the combination.

3654 Dupont, R. L., pp. 311-20 in *Interactions of Drug Abuse*, edited by E. S. Vesell and M. C. Braude. NY, Annals of the New York Academy of Sciences, V. 281, 1976.

Polydrug Abuse and the Maturing National Drug Abuse Data Base.

This report is an edited speech on drug-abuse research given by the director of NIDA. The main theme is concerned with new and more useful sources of data for this area of research. From one source it can be seen that people who do not use marihuana rarely abuse drugs, and the same can be said about alcohol. Another concept derived from the same data is that heroin users also use marihuana and most other drugs.

3655   Dupont, R. L., in *Committee on Problem of Drug Dependence*, 1977. Division of Medical Sciences, National Research Council, National Academy of Sciences, Washington, D.C., 1977, pp. 41-48.

Science, Values, and the Marihuana Issue.

Research improvement so as to resolve some of the present uncertainty regarding risks involved in marihuana use is recommended by NIDA.

3656   Dupont, R. L., Drug Alcohol Depend., *1*(3), 233-40 (1976).

The Future of Federal Drug Abuse Research: How Can We Best Maximize Scarce Resources?

The author discusses the trend of increasing federal funding for drug abuse investigation as well as the relative percentages of this funding that are allotted to different agencies. Budgeting and goals of NIDA and other similar agencies are touched upon. There is some mention of general attitudes in marijuana and opiate research.

3657   Dupont, R. L., Med. Times, *104*(1), 120-33 (1976).

Just What Can You Tell Your Patients About Marihuana?

A non-hysterical approach to the issue of recreational drug abuse is urged for physicians. Statistics are presented that delineate the population that uses marihuana and the expected effects for which it is consumed. Some known and potential health hazards associated with chronic marihuana use are enumerated and discussed briefly. Without condemning marihuana use, decriminalization of use is suggested as a more rational approach to dealing with drug abuse. The physician has a critical role in dealing with recreational drug abuse and a unique opportunity to bridge the generation gap that exists with regards to marihuana experimentation.

3658   Dupont, R. L., pp. 3-8 in *Pharmacology of Marihuana, Vol. 1*, edited by M. C. Braude and S. Szara. NY, Raven Press, 1976.

Marihuana: An Issue Comes of Age.

A synopsis of the scientific, societal and legalistic evolution of interest in marihuana is given with primary attention focused on the American drug scene. Marihuana use and experimentation is traced from the 1937 marihuana tax act through the 1970 federal controlled substance act to the recent congressional committees. Recent surveys have established the magnitude of marihuana abuse. Interest in programs to discourage marihuana use is mounting because of possible health hazards attributable to more frequent use of higher potency products in ever younger populations. The need for restraint in marihuana use and for additional information on its effects is emphasized.

3659   Dupont, R. L., Science, *192*(4240), 647-49 (1976).

Marihuana: A Conversation with NIDA's Robert L. Dupont.

The patterns of marihuana use are changing and are more like cigarette smoking than drinking alcohol. Street marihuana is rising in potency. The level of exposure to marihuana is increasing. In the 18 to 25 year age group, 53% have used marihuana and 6.2% of high school seniors use it every day. Health consequences of marihuana use are of greatest importance.

3660   Dwivedi, C.; and Harbison, R. D., Toxicol. Appl. Pharmacol., *31*(3), 452-58 (1975).

Anticonvulsant Activities of Δ^8- and Δ^9-Tetrahydrocannabinol and Uridine.

The protective effect of Δ^8- and Δ^9-THC against experimentally induced seizures in male mice is described here along with a comparison of these agents to other known anticonvulsants.

3661   Dykstra, L. A.; McMillan, D. E.; and Harris, L. S., Pharmacol. Biochem. Behav., *3*(1), 29-32 (1975).

Effects of Δ^9-THC and a Water Soluble Ester of Δ^9-THC on Schedule-Controlled Behavior.

Both Δ^9-THC and SP-111, a THC water soluble ester, reduced the rate of pigeons responding under a variable interval schedule or a multiple fixed ratio-fixed interval schedule of food presentation. The former was more potent and had a faster onset of action.

E

3662   Earnhardt, J. T., Diss. Abstr. Int. B., *38*(4), 1671 (1977).

Characterization of the Pressor and Vasoconstrictor Actions of Δ^9-Tetrahydrocannabinol in the Rat.

Cardiovascular effects of Δ^9-THC and Δ^8-THC after i.v. or i.a. injection into perfused hindquarters of urethane-anesthetized rats, and i.v. injection into pithed rats are discussed. Animals tolerant to immediate transient bradycardia and prolonged hypotension were not tolerant to the transient hypertension obtained with Δ^9-THC. The use of phentolamine, reserpine, indomethacin, NE, and vasopressin to elucidate the mechanism of action of the cardiovascular effects observed is discussed.

3663   Earnhardt, J. T.; and Adams, M. D., Fed. Proc., *35*(3), 643 (1976).

Mechanism of Vasoconstrictor Action of Δ^9-Tetrahydrocannabinol in Pithed and Anesthetized Rats.

Administration of Δ^9-THC (i.v. 0.3, 1.0 and 3.0 mg/kg) produced dose related transient increases in BP with no increase in heart rate in urethane-anesthetized rats (AR) and pithed rats. In AR, hypotension and bradycardia followed initial increase. Other data were presented to support the hypothesis that i.v^9 Δ^9-THC produces vasoconstriction which is mediated in part through the adrenergic mechanism.

3664   Earnhardt, J. T.; Martin, B. R.; and Adams, M. D., Fed. Proc., *34*(3), 744 (1975).

Separation of Cardiovascular and Behavioral Effects of Synthetic Cannabinoids in the Dog.

Δ^9-THC, Δ^8-THC, 9-nor-9-α - and β - HHC, CBD, 1-pentyl-3-OH-CBD and 1-pentyl-3-OH-Δ^8-THC were investigated in dogs for behavioral and cardiovascular effects. Of the seven cannabinoids, separation of behavioral from cardiovascular activity was successful for 1-pentyl-3-OH-CBD at doses of 0.5 and 2 mg/kg, i.v. A procedure for an antihypertensive cannabinoid devoid of psychotometic activity was established.

3665   Ebert, D. M.; and Dren, A. T., Pharmacologist, *19*(2), 230 (1977).

Intraocular Pressure Lowering Properties of ABBOTT-43981, a Cannabinoid-Derived Heterocyclic Benzopyran with Minimal CNS Activities.

ABBOTT-43981, when administered topically (0.1% solution) or intravenously (0.05-1 mg/kg) to rabbits, was found to decrease intraocular pressure by 32% and 20-40%, respectively. However, the drug was relatively inactive when given by oral or intramuscular routes. It did not produce hyperexcitability in dogs and had no effects in neuropharmacological screening tests in rats and mice.

3666   Edery, H.; and Gottesfeld, Z., Brit. J. Pharmacol., *54*(3), 406-08 (1975).

The Gamma-Aminobutyric Acid System in Rat Cerebellum During Cannabinoid Induced Cataleptoid State.

Rats were administered 20 mg/kg $\Delta^{1,6}$-THC i.p. for two weeks. Within 30 min. of injection cataleptoid reactions appeared. Repeated doses induced an increase in GABA concentration and a decrease in glutamic acid decarboxylase in certain brain areas. The effects of $\Delta^{1,6}$-THC may be due to a change in excitability of the brain.

3667   Edwards, G., pp. 321-40 in *Cannabis and Health*, edited by J.D.P. Graham. London, Academic Press, 1976.

Cannabis and the Psychiatric Position.

In searching the available literature on cannabis, the author sorted out the main psychiatric consequences of cannabis use. These ranged from acute mental disturbances and flashbacks to chronic psychotic symptoms. Each one of these consequences was analyzed in relation to clinical and pathological findings.

3668   Egan, S. M.; Graham, J. D. P.; and Lewis, M. J., Brit. J. Pharmacol., *56*(4), 413-16 (1976).

The Uptake of Tritiated Δ^1-Tetrahydrocannabinol by the Isolated Vas Deferens of the Rat.

When added to the incubation media, desmethylimipramine inhibited the uptake of Δ^9-THC or NE by rat vas deferens. Pretreatment with 6-hydroxydopamine also reduced uptake of Δ^9-THC and abolished that of NE.

3669   Eichel, G. R.; and Troiden, R. R., J. Psychedelic Drugs, *10*(2), 133-36 (1978).

The Domestication of Drug Effects: The Case of Marijuana.

Cross-cultural comparison between Jamaican and American marihuana users revealed that what is experienced under the influence of marihuana depends greatly on cultural predispositions and expectations.

3670   Einstein, R.; Hughes, I. E.; and Hindmarch, I., Brit. J. Addict., *70*(2), 145-50 (1975).

Patterns of Use of Alcohol, Cannabis and Tobacco in a Student Population.

Positive correlations between alcohol consumption or cigarette smoking and cannabis use were found to exist in this surveyed undergraduate sample.

3671   El-Feraly, F. S.; Elsohly, M. A.; Boeren, E. G.; Turner, C. E.; Ottersen, T.; and Aasen, A., Tetrahedron, *33*(18), 2373-87 (1977).

Crystal and Molecular Structure of Cannabispiran and its Correlation to Dehydrocannabispiran. Two Novel Cannabis Constituents.

The isolation of cannabispiran and dehydrocannabispiran, two novel spiro compounds, was reported and their structures presented. The detailed crystallographic data on cannabispiran were given.

3672   El-Feraly, F. S.; Elsohly, M. A.; and Turner, C. E., Acta Pharm. Jugoslav., *27*(1), 43-46 (1977).

Anisaldehyde as a Spray Reagent for Cannabinoids and Their Methyl Ethers.

Anisaldehyde-sulfuric acid was found to be a superior spray reagent for detecting cannabinoids and their methyl ethers. Advantages of this reagent over the commonly used Fast Blue Salt B were the detection of natural and synthetic methyl ethers and the formation of different colors with different cannabinoids. The developed colors are given, as well as the synthesis of various mono- and dimethyl derivatives of cannabinoids.

3673   El-Feraly, F. S.; and Turner, C. E., Phytochemistry, *14*(10), 2304 (1975).

Alkaloids of *Cannabis sativa* Leaves.

Hordenine was isolated from cannabis plant material for the first time. Physical data and separation techniques are given.

3674 El-Feraly, F. S.; and Turner, C. E., United Nations Document, ST/SOA/SER. S/52, 28 November 1975.

The Isolation and Characterization of the Alkaloid Cannabisativine from the Leaves of a Thailand Variant of *Cannabis sativa L.*

The alkaloid cannabisativine was isolated from cannabis leaves. Cannabisativine was not found in all cannabis variants and thus may be important in the division of cannabis into drug and fiber type. Physical data for cannabisativine are given.

3675 Elliott, H. W., Int. J. Clin. Pharmacol., *12*(1/2), 134-40 (1975).

Effects of Street Drugs on Anesthesia.

A report on the difficulties of administering anesthetics to persons taking unknown drugs. THC is not a major problem in anesthetic requirements and is difficult to identify pharmacologically.

3676 Ellis, C. G., Practitioner, *216*, 93-94 (1976).

A Bizarre Cause of Rectal Trauma.

A prisoner would conceal dagga wrapped in cellophane in his rectum and then sell it to inmates. The money he made would also be concealed in the rectum, except for the coins which would be swallowed.

3677 Ellis, C. G., S. Afr. Med. J., *50*(12), 462 (1976).

Dagga Offences.

The legal status of dagga possession in the U.S.A. is traced from its legality in Alaska to its misdemeanor status in Oregon to its felony status in New York. Social use of dagga and its legislative evolution have not resulted in hard drug addiction as has been feared by the government of South Africa. The author denounces excessively punitive sentences for dagga use in South Africa.

3678 Ellner, M., pp. 147-53 in *A Multicultural View of Drug Abuse,* Proc. Natl. Drug Abuse Conf., 1977, edited by D. E. Smith, S. M. Anderson, M. Buxton, N. Gottlieb, W. Harvey, and T. Chung. Cambridge, Massachusetts, Schenkman Publishing Co., Inc., 1978.

Marijuana Use by Heroin Abusers as a Factor in Program Retention.

A study of primary heroin abusers who voluntarily remained in a drug free treatment center an average of nine months indicated that marihuana was used by these subjects as a heroin substitute. Marihuana users were also more apt to remain in the treatment program than were non-users.

3679 Ellner, M., J. Consult Clin. Psychol., *45*(4), 709-10 (1977).

Marijuana Use by Heroin Abusers as a Factor in Program Retention.

Marihuana was used by heroin abusers, who remained in a voluntary drug-free treatment program, as a heroin substitute. This use seems to have constituted an incentive for the users to remain in the program.

3680 Elsmore, T. F., Pharmacol. Biochem. Behav., *5*(2), 123-28 (1976).

The Role of Reinforcement Loss in Tolerance to Chronic Δ^9-Tetrahydrocannabinol Effects of Operant Behavior of Rhesus Monkeys.

Adult rhesus monkeys treated orally with Δ^9-THC (1 mg/kg) for 40 days were evaluated for behavioral tolerance by means of an alternating multiple F-I 120 sec., DRL 120 sec. schedule in which food reward is coupled to task performance via auditory cues. A test of the "reinforcement loss" hypothesis of behavioral tolerance was attempted. In agreement with the hypothesis, tolerance developed most readily to the DRL component of the multiple schedule where increased responding led to reductions in food reinforcement.

3681   Elsohly, M. A.; Boeren, E. G.; and Turner, C. E., Experientia, *34*(9), 1127-28 (1978).

($\pm$)9,10-Dihydroxy-$\Delta^{6a(10a)}$-Tetrahydrocannabinol and ($\pm$)8,9-Dihydroxy-$\Delta^{6a(10a)}$-Tetrahydrocannabinol: 2 New Cannabinoids from *Cannabis sativa L*.

The title compounds were isolated from a hexane extract of Indian Cannabis. The compounds were chemically correlated with CBN. The acetates, methyl and TMS ethers and other derivatives were prepared. Spectral data are given.

3682   Elsohly, M. A.; Boeren, E. G.; and Turner, C. E., J. Heterocycl. Chem., *15*(4), 699-700 (1978).

An Improved Method for the Synthesis of dl-Cannabichromene.

A new procedure for efficient synthesis of CBC was given which involved the reflux of citral and olivetol in the presence of equimolar concentration of t-butylamine. Only trace amounts of iso-CBC, CBL and cannabicitran were formed.

3683   Elsohly, M. A.; El-Feraly, F. S.; and Turner, C. E., Lloydia, *40*(3), 275-80 (1977).

Isolation and Characterization of ($\pm$)-Cannabitriol and (-)-10-ethoxy-9-hydroxy-$\Delta^{6a-[10a]}$-tetrahydrocannabinol: Two New Cannabinoids from *Cannabis sativa L*. Extract.

The title compounds were isolated from a cannabis extract and their structures determined by chemical and spectral means and by conversion to cannabinol.

3684   Elsohly, M. A.; and Turner, C. E., Pharm. Weekbl., *111*(43), 1069-75 (1976).

A Review of Nitrogen Containing Compounds from *Cannabis sativa L*.

An up-to-date review on all nitrogenous compounds isolated from cannabis is presented with structures, physical constants, references, and isolation procedures.

3685   Elsohly, M. A.; and Turner, C. E., United Nations Document, ST/SOA/SER.S/54, 1977.

Screening of Cannabis Grown from Seed of Various Geographical Origins for the Alkaloids Hordenine, Cannabisative, and Anhydrocannabisative.

Samples of cannabis grown under the same conditions from seeds obtained from 15 different geographical locations were screened for alkaloids. All samples examined showed the presence of the alkaloids hordenine, cannabisativine and anhydrocannabisativine.

3686   Elsohly, M. A.; and Turner, C. E., United Nations Document, ST/SOA/SER.S/53, 1976.

Anhydrocannabisativine: A New Alkaloid Isolated from *Cannabis sativa L*.

A new spermidine type alkaloid named anhydrocannabisativine was isolated from the leaves and small stems of *Cannabis sativa L*. The structure elucidation was based on spectrochemical data (IR, MS) and the conversion of cannabisativine to anhydrocannabisativine was followed.

3687 Elsohly, M. A.; Turner, C. E.; Phoeba, C. H.; Knapp, J. E.; Schiff, P. L.; and Slatkin, D. J., J. Pharm. Sci., *67*(1), 124 (1978).

Anhydrocannabisativine, A New Alkaloid from *Cannabis sativa L*.

The structure of a new spermidine alkaloid (anhydrocannabisativine), isolated from the roots and leaves of *Cannabis sativa L*. was determined by spectral analysis as well as correlation with cannabisativine.

3688 Ely, D. L.; Henry, J. P.; and Jarosz, C. J., Behav. Biol., *13*(3), 263-76 (1975).

Effects of Marihuana (Δ^9-THC) on Behavior Patterns and Social Roles in Colonies of CBA Mice.

The behavioral effects of Δ^9-THC in a freely interacting mixed set group of rodents living in population cages are dependent upon social position, composition of groups, and dosage of Δ^9-THC (0.5, 2, and 20 mg/kg, i.v.).

3689 Emboden, W. A., Taxon, *26*(1), 110 (1977).

A Taxonomy for Cannabis.

The author feels that taxonomy should concern itself with taxonomic rather than social judgements. The Small and Cronquist article on cannabis (Taxon *25*, 405-35, 1976) violated this philosophy.

3690 End, D. W.; Thoursen, K.; Dewey, W. L.; and Carchman, R. A., Mol. Pharmacol., *13*(5), 864-71 (1977).

Comparative Study of the Disposition of (-)-Δ^9-Tetrahydrocannabinol in Neuroblastoma and Glioma Cells in Tissue Culture: Relation to Cellular Impairment.

Mouse neuroblastoma cells (NB2A) were severely affected by concentrations of THC that had little effect on rat glioma cells (C6) in tissue cultures. Subcellular distribution of labelled THC and intracellular binding in the two cell systems did not differ markedly but the NB2A cells took up a 10-fold larger amount of the drug.

3691 Endo, M., Kagaku (Kyoto), *33*(3), 213-19 (1978).

Marihuana.

A brief general discussion about the history, botany, preparations, cannabinoids, identification, pharmacology, and laws of marihuana with no references.

3692 Erdmann, G.; Just, W. W.; Thel, S.; Werner, G.; and Wiechmann, M., Psychopharmacology, *47*(1), 53-58 (1976).

Comparative Autoradiographic and Metabolic Study of Δ^8- and Δ^9-Tetrahydrocannabinol in the Brain of the Marmoset *Callithrix jacchus*.

Monkeys treated with Δ^8- or Δ^9-THC displayed initial heavy labeling in their brain gray matter as indicated by autoradiography. Brain regions involved in processing visual and acoustic information and motor control had the most accumulation.

3693 Erickson, P. G., J. Crim. Law Criminol., *67*(2), 222-32 (1976).

Deterrence and Deviance: The Example of Cannabis Prohibition.

The complicated problem of relating frequency of marihuana use to deterrence effects of a legal sort in the United States and Canada is presented. A somewhat philosophical discussion introduces the hypothesis that the deterrent effect of the ever-lessening legal penalties can be increased by increasing the probabilities of punishment rather than severity, since even a severe penalty is not ominous when the chances of getting caught are nil. The research reported shows, however, that increased severity and certainty of punishment had no deterrent effect upon users who had already been prosecuted for marihuana use.

3694   Esber, H. J.; Kuo, E. H.; Rosenkrantz, H.; and Braude, M. C., Fed. Proc., *34*(3), 783 (1975).

Serum Hormone Levels in Non-Pregnant and Pregnant Rats After Chronic Oral Treatment with Delta-9-Tetrahydrocannabinol.

Non-pregnant and pregnant Fischer rats were treated chronically with oral THC (1-50 mg/kg). Non-pregnant rats exhibited aggressiveness within 28 days and neurotoxicity within 90 days. Serum LH, FSH, and GH were elevated 60-180% initially, but returned to normal within 28 days. Pregnant rats showed decreases in LH and FSH, but an increase in estrogens at higher doses of THC. Deliveries were uneventful and no teratogenicity was detected.

3695   Esber, H. J.; Luthra, Y. K.; and Rosenkrantz, H., Abstracts of the Annual Meeting of the American Society for Microbiology, *78*, 67 (1978).

Assessment of Tolerance to Immunosuppression Induced by Δ^9-Tetrahydrocannabinol (abstract).

Tolerance did not develop to the immunosuppressive effect of Δ^9-THC (6 or 12 mg/kg) during its subacute oral administration.

3696   Esplin, B.; and Capek, R., Res. Commun. Chem. Pathol. Pharmacol., *15*(1), 199-202 (1976).

Quantitative Characterization of THC and Ethanol Interaction.

Anticonvulsant activities of Δ^9-THC, ethanol, and combinations of the two drugs were evaluated by means of the mouse maximal electroshock test. THC and ethanol produce additive anticonvulsant effects.

3697   Evans, M. A., Diss. Abst. Int. B., *35*(7), 3488 (1975).

Clinical Studies with Marihuana and Dextroamphetamine Combination.

Secobarbital and ethanol impaired the behavioral performance of human subjects, whereas d-amphetamine caused a slight improvement and marihuana, a slight reduction, of performance. Also, the psychological and cardiovascular interactions of amphetamine and marihuana were additive in nature.

3698   Evans, M. A.; and Brown, D. J., Fed. Proc., *34*(3), 743 (1975).

Effect of Δ^9-Tetrahydrocannabinol on Methamphetamine-Induced Hyperactivity in Mice.

Administration of Δ^9-THC resulted in a dose-related biphasic effect on locomotor activity of aggregated mice but only decreased the activity of isolated ones. When combined with methamphetamine, low doses of Δ^9-THC greatly increased the locomotor activity under aggregated conditions while decreasing it under isolation.

3699   Evans, M. A.; and Harbison, R. D., pp. 195-208 in *Drug Abuse in Pregnancy and Neonatal Effects*, edited by J. L. Rementeria. St. Louis, Mo., C. V. Mosby Company, 1977.

Cocaine, Marihuana, LSD: Pharmacological Effects in the Fetus and Newborn.

This chapter is an overview of the effects of cocaine, marihuana, and LSD on fetal toxicity. The absorption and metabolite formation of Δ^9-THC were discussed. Δ^9-THC and its metabolites were shown to be present in fetal tissues and evidence of teratogenicity from cannabis administration was indicated in rats, hamsters, and rabbits. Fetal resorptions were induced in these species and in mice.

3700   Evans, M. A.; Harbison, R. D.; Brown, D. J.; and Forney, R. B., Psychopharmacol., *50*(3), 245-50 (1976).

Stimulant Actions of Δ^9-Tetrahydrocannabinol in Mice.

Δ^9-THC (15 mg/kg, i.p.) synergized with methamphetamine in aggregated conditions to increase locomotor activity and methamphetamine lethality. In isolated mice THC opposed the methamphetamine stimulation of locomotor activity without affecting its lethality. Isolated and aggregated mice eliminated methamphetamine and its metabolites from plasma, liver, and brain at the same rates. Synergism of THC with methamphetamine is related to aggregation and not to metabolic interactions of the drugs.

3701   Evans, M. A.; Martz, R.; Rodda, B. E.; Lemberger, L.; Forney, R. B., Clin. Pharmacol. Ther., *20*(3), 350-58 (1976).

Effects of Marihuana-Dextroamphetamine Combination.

Heart rate and BP increased additively in subjects receiving oral d-amphetamine and smoking marihuana (50 μ g/kg of Δ^9-THC). Impairment of psychomotor performance after 25 μ g/kg of THC was not, however, altered by the two drug-combined treatment.

3702   Evans, R. G.; Schill, T. R.; and Monroe, S., J. Clin. Psychol., *34*(4), 999-1000 (1978).

The Relationship Between Guilt and Quality of Drug Experiences.

High guilt subjects were less likely to use marihuana and other drugs than were low guilt ones. More unpleasant trips were experienced by high guilt users.

F

3703 Fabre, L. F.; Mclendon, D. M.; and Stark, P., Curr. Ther. Res., *24*(2), 161-69 (1978).

Nabilone, A Cannabinoid, in the Treatment of Anxiety: An Open-Label and Double-Blind Study.

Nabilone, a synthetic cannabinoid, was found to be quite effective in relieving anxiety symptoms. Its side effects are thought to be dose related.

3704 Fairbairn, J. W., pp. 3-19 in *Cannabis and Health*, edited by J. D. P. Graham. London, Academic Press, 1976.

The Pharmacognosy of Cannabis.

The history and uses of cannabis as a source of hemp fibers, for its seeds and as a narcotic drug were discussed. The identification of cannabis plant using both morphological and chemical means was mentioned. The active constituents of cannabis, and the use of the CBD Δ^9-THC ratio in the classification of cannabis into 2 or 3 races were discussed.

3705 Fairbairn, J. W.; Liebmann, J. A.; and Rowan, M. G., J. Pharm. Pharmacol., *28*, 1-7 (1976).

The Stability of Cannabis and its Preparations on Storage.

Cannabis resin, synthetic cannabinoids and herbal preparations were stored for 2 yrs under various conditions. Data are given on stability observed in different solvents, etc. Data from other storage studies are also discussed.

3706 Fairbairn, J. W.; and Rowan, M. G., J. Pharm. Pharmacol., *27*(suppl.), 90P (1975).

Cannabinoid Pattern in *Cannabis sativa L.* Seedlings as an Indication of Chemical Race (abstract).

CBD and THC ratio in a Mexican and a Turkish variant is given.

3707 Fairlie, K.; and Fox, B. L., J. Chromatogr. Sci., *14*(7), 334-35 (1976).

Rapid, Quantitative Determination of Tetrahydrocannabinol in Marihuana by Gas Chromatography.

A simple device is described for solid-sample injections of marihuana. Some experimental details are provided.

3708 Fairshter, R. D.; and Wildson, A. F., Chest. *74*(4), 357-58 (1978).

Paraquat and Marihuana: Assessing the Hazard.

Available evidence does not indicate any possible adverse effects to marihuana users as a result of paraquat contamination.

3709 Falek, A., pp. 1-16 in *Marijuana and Health Hazards*, edited by J. R. Tinklenberg. NY, Academic Press, 1975.

Genetic Studies of Marijuana: Current Findings and New Directions.

Methods used to detect genetic alterations are limited and studies done on this subject proved contradictory. Future genetic experimentations, including those of marihuana, should follow standardized protocols and should be run in several laboratories. Newer and more sensitive chromosome banding techniques should be employed and evaluation at the level of DNA-base-pair substitution should be included.

3710 Farber, S. J.; and Huertas, V. E., Arch. Intern. Med., *136*(3), 337-39 (1976).

Intravenously Injected Marihuana Syndrome.

The clinical courses of two male patients who injected crude marihuana intravenously is given. Abuse of marihuana by the intravenous route is characterized by severe hypotension, renal insufficiency, thrombocytopenia, and rhabdomyolysis. All symptoms of intoxication appear to be reversible without permanent dysfunction.

3711   Farkas, J.; and Andrassy, E., Acta Aliment., 5(1), 57-67 (1976).

The Sporostatic Effect of Cannabidiolic Acid.

The inhibitory effect of CBD-acid on the spores of bacillus cereus was found to be equivalent with the antibiotics nisin and tylosin. It was shown that CBD-acid was heat stable in neutral solutions and had a high radiation resistance. However, there was a loss of activity in media which contained proteins. This fact limits the use of CBD-acid in the canning industry.

3712   Farnsworth, D. L., pp. 1 in Chronic Cannabis Use, edited by R. L. Dornbush, A. M. Freedman, and M. Fink. NY, Annals of the New York Academy of Sciences, V., 282, 1976.

Introduction: What is the Evidence for an Amotivational Syndrome in Cannabis Users?

Emotionality pervades the debate of the influence of cannabis on amotivational syndrome. Evidence indicates that excessive drug use for pleasure can decrease motivation, but a specific capacity for inhibition of motivation by cannabis has not yet been demonstrated.

3713   Farnsworth, N. R.; and Cordell, G. A., J. Psychedelic Drugs, 8(2), 151-55 (1976).

New Potential Hazard Regarding Use of Marijuana - - Treatment of Plants with Liquid Fertilizers.

Since catechols and amines are present in the cannabis plant, application of a liquid fertilizer containing nitrates may enhance formation of carcinogens in the plant.

3714   Fatray, Z.; Simon, L. M.; and Matkovics, B., Biochem. Physiol. Pflanz., 167(4), 367-70 (1975).

In vitro Hydroxylation and Transformation, 26. Pyridine Hydroxylation Experiments with Plant Tissue.

Of the plants and plant tissues examined, Cannabis sativa was the only one capable of transforming pyridine to 3-hydroxypyridine.

3715   Fauman, B.; Aldinger, G.; Fauman, M.; and Rosen, P., Clin. Toxicol., 9(4), 529-38 (1976).

Psychiatric Sequelae of Phencyclidine Abuse.

Phencyclidine-induced psychosis was compared to that of cannabis, LSD and amphetamine. Differences and similarities were pointed out.

3716   Feeney, D. M., Behav. Biol., 18(4), 455-71 (1976).

The Marijuana Window: A Theory of Cannabis Use.

From available neurophysiological, behavioral and subjective data, it was postulated that marihuana increases the variability of information processing by limbic and cortical brain structures. This effect increases experiential and behavioral variability, retards drug habituation and produces dishabituation.

3717   Feeney, D. M., J. Amer. Med. Ass., 235(11), 1105 (1976).

Marihuana Use Among Epileptics (letter).

Of convulsive disorder patients under 30 yrs. of age, 29% reported use of marihuana, 10% amphetamines, 4% LSD,

2% barbiturates, 2% cocaine and none use of heroin. This illegal drug use was rarely (4%) discussed with physicians even though these drugs may interact with prescribed medication. Older patients did not abuse drugs.

3718   Feeney, D. M., Science, *197*(4310), 1301-1302 (1977).

Marihuana and Epilepsy. Comments.

The author suggests that the seizures observed by Martin and Consroe are perhaps an idiosyncratic strain-specific response of their rabbits and the relevance to human epilepsy is unclear. Species differences with respect to seizure activity induced by marihuana are conceded. The mechanism of action of cannabinoid-induced epileptic activity is related to their anticholinergic actions.

3719   Feeney, D. M.; Spiker, M.; and Weiss, G., pp. 343-62 in *The Therapeutic Potential of Marihuana*, edited by S. Cohen and R. Stillman. NY, Plenum Medical Book Company, 1976.

Marihuana and Epilepsy: Activation of Symptoms by Delta-9-THC.

THC (5 mg/kg) was found to exacerbate seizure activity in epileptic dogs and also in cats implanted with electrodes in the motor cortex.

3720   Fehr, K. A.; Kalant, H.; and Leblanc, A. E., Science, *192*, 1249-51 (1976).

Residual Learning Deficit After Heavy Exposure to Cannabis or Alcohol in Rats.

THC was administered 10 mg/kg by intubation 1 hr. before testing rats trained in a closed-field maze. No learning impairments were observed until after 6 mos of THC and deficits were still apparent after 2 mos of free drug state. Ethanol (2 g/kg - 6 g/kg over 2 wks) showed impairment of cognitive and motor tasks comparable to THC.

3721   Fehr, K. A.; Kalant, H.; Leblanc, A. E.; and Knox, G. V., pp. 495-505 in *Marihuana: Chemistry, Biochemistry, and Cellular Effects*, edited by G. G. Nahas. NY, Springer-Verlag, 1976.

Permanent Learning Impairment After Chronic Heavy Exposure to Cannabis or Ethanol in the Rat.

The authors examined the effects of cannabis and alcohol in the rat on the learning and performance of a food-motivated maze test chronic intoxication. The results suggest strongly that permanent impairment can be produced by prolonged heavy dosage with either drug.

3722   Feinberg, I.; Jones, R.; Walker, J.; Cavness, C.; and Floyd, T., Clin. Pharmacol. Ther., *19*(6), 782-94 (1976).

Effects of Marijuana Tetrahydrocannabinol on Electroencephalographic Sleep Patterns.

Sleep cycle effects of oral marihuana extract (70-120 mg Δ^9-THC/24 hrs for 21-32 days) are compared to the same effects of oral Δ^9-THC at identical doses. Both treatments elicited similar sleep cycle changes with decreased REM sleep and eye movement density to which tolerance developed and which showed rebounds upon drug withdrawal. Similarities exist between THC- and lithium-induced sleep cycle changes.

3723   Feinberg, I.; Jones, R.; Walker, J. M.; Cavness, C.; and March, J., Clin. Pharmacol. Ther., *17*(4), 458-66 (1975).

Effects of High Dosage Delta-9-Tetrahydrocannabinol on Sleep Patterns in Man.

Administration and withdrawal of high dosages of THC induced striking changes in EEG sleep patterns in human marihuana users. The relationship between the behavioral effects of psychotic agents and their effects on sleep has not yet been defined.

3724 Fenimore, D. C.; Davis, C. M.; and Horn, A. H., pp. 42-47 in *Cannabinoid Assays in Humans*, NIDA Research Monograph Series, No. 7, 1976.

Determination of Δ^9-Tetrahydrocannabinol in Human Blood Serum by Electron Capture Gas Chromatography.

A dual column-dual oven GLC instrument is described. Sample clean up is on a packed column. Effluent is trapped from the packed column by a microvalve system, which allows the described amount of effluent to be processed through the capillary column. Detection is by a ECD of a fluoro-derivative. Human blood serum levels of Δ^9-THC are reported.

3725 Fennessy, M. R.; and Taylor, D. A., Brit. J. Pharmacol., *60*(1), 65-71 (1977).

The Effect of Δ^9-Tetrahydrocannabinol on Body Temperature and Brain Amine Concentrations in the Rat at Different Ambient Temperatures.

While THC (2 mg/kg, i.v.) induced behavioral excitation followed by depression in rats tested at 4 different ambient temperatures, its hypothermic effect was only evident at 4° and 21°. Alteration of brain 5-HT metabolism may be responsible for the THC-induced hypothermia.

3726 Fennessy, M. R.; and Taylor, D. A., Brit. J. Pharmacol., *63*(2), 267-73 (1978).

Antagonism of the Effects on Thermoregulation of Δ^9-Tetrahydrocannabinol by Clomipramine in the Rat.

Clomipramine, a tricyclic antidepressant, modified the biphasic dose-dependent effects of THC on body temperature and brain concentration of 5-HIAA acid in rats. The possible mechanism of action of clomipramine was discussed.

3727 Fenselau, S.; Kelly, S.; Salmon, M.; and Billets, S., Food Cosmet. Toxicol., *14*(1), 35-39 (1976).

The Absence of Tetrahydrocannabinol from Hops.

Past work with *Humulus lupulus* utilizing color reactions of questionnaire sensitivity have failed to show THC in the hops plant. The authors describe the use of GC-MS in the selected-ion monitoring mode to detect THC if present in amounts equal to or greater than one nanogram. Of 17 different samples analyzed, none showed detectable amounts of THC.

3728 Fenz, W. D.; and Young, M. J., Psychosom. Med., *37*(1), 88-89 (1975).

Psychophysiological Reactions to *Cannabis sativa* in Chronic Users.

Individual response hierarchies of 15 chronic male users of marihuana were established under various conditions of physical and mental stress before and after smoking. Findings indicate dissonance between the subjective experience of marihuana intoxication and the physiological objective state of the organism.

3729 Fernandez, E. O.; Asch, R. H.; Smith, C. G.; and Pauerstein, C. J., Fertil. Steril., *29*(2), 239 (1978).

Effect of Antigonadotropins During the Luteal Phase of the Rhesus Monkey: Danazol and Δ^9-Tetrahydrocannabinol.

Monkeys treated daily with 2.5 mg/kg of Δ^9-THC from the first postovulatory day until mensus exhibited normal luteal phases during the treatment cycles. None of these animals, however, ovulated during the post-therapy cycles. Danazol effects were also investigated and discussed.

114

3730 Fernandez-Guardiola, A.; Salgado, A.; Contreras, C. M.; Condes, M.; Gonzalez-Estrada, T.; Solis, H.; Calvo, J. M.; and Ayala, F., pp. 335-43 in *Pharmacology of Marihuana, Vol. 1*, edited by M. C. Braude and S. Szara. NY, Raven Press, 1976.

Multiunit Activity and Polygraphic Recordings of the Pharmacological Effects of Δ^9-THC.

The CNS effects of Δ^9-THC (25 mg/kg orally in humans and 1 mg/kg, i.v. in cats) were monitored. Significant findings in humans include a depression of alpha-rhythm of EEG increase in galvanic skin response, increase in reaction time and contraction latency of the muscles of dominant forearm, and increase in time estimation. In cats, multiunit activity was accelerated in cerebral cortex and Purkinje cells but depressed in the red nucleus. CNS depression was also noted as decreased response to painful stimulus.

3731 Ferraro, D. P., pp. 103-17 in *Behavioral Tolerance: Research and Treatment Implications*, NIDA Research Monograph 18, 1978.

Behavioral Tolerance to Marihuana.

Distinction between empirical and theoretical behavioral tolerance, as it applies to marihuana, is made. Significance and implications of these two types of tolerance are discussed.

3732 Ferraro, D. P., pp. 86-102 in *Marihuana Research Findings: 1976*, NIDA Research Monograph, 14, 1977.

Preclinical Effects: Unlearned Behavior.

The recent renewed interest in the effects of cannabinoids on unconditioned animal behavior was indicated as a means of investigating the interaction of cannabinoids with each other and with other psychotropic agents. Relevant new studies were cited.

3733 Ferraro, D. P., pp. 103-17 in *Marihuana Research Findings: 1976*, NIDA Research Monograph, 14, 1977.

Preclinical Effects: Learned Behavior.

Literature reviewed indicated that THC and other cannabinoids are capable of influencing learned behavior in animals depending on the tasks learned and on drug parameters. The discriminative stimulus properties of some cannabinoids were also pointed out.

3734 Ferraro, D. P., pp. 118-27 in *Marihuana Research Findings: 1976*, NIDA Research Monograph, 14, 1977.

Preclinical Chronic Effects: Unlearned and Learned Behavior.

Review of available literature indicated that tolerance to the cannabinoid-induced behavioral effects develops, in several animal species and under various experimental conditions, following their chronic administration. Usefulness of the tetrahydrocannabinols in narcotic detoxification programs was also discussed.

3735 Ferraro, D. P., pp. 539-40 in *Pharmacology of Marihuana, Vol. 2*, edited by M. C. Braude and S. Szara. NY, Raven Press, 1976.

Behavioral Pharmacology: Summary.

Increased recognition of the different factors involved in determining the behavioral effects of cannabis is of great importance and research in this area is getting more sophisticated. A brief reminder of this session's papers is presented.

3736 Ferraro, D.P., pp. 475-86 in *Pharmacology of Marihuana, Vol. 2*, edited by M. C. Braude and S. Szara. NY, Raven Press, 1976.

A Behavioral Model of Marihuana Tolerance.

Changes in learned conditions in animals may be related to adverse environmental consequences; to tolerance not exerting adverse effects on behavior and environment; to whether or not response occurs under the influence of the drug and to the relative simplicity or complexity of tasks. Drug-behavior and environment interactions are important factors in understanding such a tolerance phenomenon.

3737 Ferraro, D. P.; Huthsing, K. B.; and Fetterold, D.J., Behav. Biol., *17*(4), 567-72 (1976).

Time Course of Δ^9-THC Effects on Water Consumption in Rats.

Δ^9-THC (2,4 and 8 mg/kg) produced a biphasic effect on rat water consumption which was characterized by an initial decrease of behavior followed by a compensatory increase. However, no disruption of the circadian stimulus control of drinking behavior was encountered.

3738 Fink, M., pp. 387-98 in *Chronic Cannabis Use*, edited by R. L. Dornbush, A.M. Freedman, and M. Fink. NY, Annals of the New York Academy of Sciences, V. 282, 1976.

Effects of Acute and Chronic Inhalation of Hashish, Marijuana, and Δ^9-Tetrahyrocannabinol on Brain Electrical Activity in Man: Evidence for Tissue Tolerance.

EEG effects of cannabis were qualitatively similar in U.S. users and chronic Greek users. Increased α-activity, decreased β-activity and mean EEG frequencies were evident along with experienced subjective euphoria and increased heart rate. Tissue tolerance developed after repeated cannabis inhalation and persisted for one to three weeks after cessation of drug.

3739 Fink, M., pp. 427-30 in *Chronic Cannabis Use*, edited by R. L. Dornbush, A. M. Freedman, and M. Fink. NY, Annals of the New York Academy of Sciences, V. 282, 1976.

Conference Summary.

Chronic marihuana use was not associated with brain damage, psychosis, amotivational syndrome or physical dependence. Tissue tolerance developed rapidly but abstinence syndrome was not commonly observed.

3740 Fink, M.; Volavka, J.; Panayiotopoulos, C. P.; and Stefanis, C., pp. 383-91 in *Pharmacology of Marihuana, Vol. 1*, edited by M. C. Braude and S. Szara. NY, Raven Press, 1976.

Quantitative EEG Studies of Marihuana, Δ^9-THC and Hashish in Man.

A computerized quantitative study was undertaken to compare the EEG changes caused by Δ^9-THC in occasional users with those in chronic hashish users. Although similar changes were observed in both groups, higher dosages of Δ^9-THC were required in chronic hashish users. Thus, tolerance develops to the effects of THC. EEG changes also correlated well with changes in psychological moods and tachycardia.

3741 Fisher, A., *Nature/Sci. Ann.*, Time-Life Books, 155-65 (1976).

The Real Dope on Pot: New Tests Suggest Marihuana May Have Harmful Effects.

A review of marihuana summarizing that chronic high doses of marihuana may be harmful in several areas: reduction of immunoresponse system; lung damage, maybe cancer; physical impairment; and decreased motor ability, especially in driving. The therapeutic effects are also discussed along with some botanical aspects of the marihuana plant.

3742 Fleischman, R. W.; Hayden, D. W.; Braude, M. C.; and Rosenkrantz, H., Toxicol. Appl. Pharmacol., 34(3), 467-78 (1975).

Chronic Marihuana Inhalation Toxicity in Rats.

Chronic exposure of rats to marihuana smoke led to cumulative toxic manifestations such as CNS inhibition, hypopnea, hypothermia, neurotoxic reactions and pathological changes including focal pneumonitis. Also, tolerance to these toxic symptoms developed. Males were more susceptible to marihuana toxicity than females.

3743 Fleischman, R. W.; Hayden, D. W.; Rosenkrantz, H.; and Braude, M., Teratology, 12(1), 47-50 (1975).

Teratologic Evaluation of Δ^9-Tetrahydrocannabinol in Mice, Including a Review of the Literature.

Pregnant mice received Δ^9-THC (5, 15, 50 and 150 mg/kg/day p.o.) on 6-15 days of gestation. Treatment shows Δ^9-THC is not teratogenic in mice.

3744 Fletcher, J. M.; and Satz, P., Bull. Narcotics, 29(2), 29-34 (1977).

A Methodological Commentary on the Egyptian Study of Chronic Hashish Use.

The authors criticized the Soueif study of chronic hashish use in Egypt and suggested that the study could have had more impact if further careful analyses of data were carried out.

3745 Fletcher, J. M.; Satz, A.; and Carter, W. E., Contemp. Drug Probl., 7(1), 3-34 (1978).

Chronic Cannabis Use: Recent Cross-Cultural Evidence from Costa Rica and Other Countries.

Studying the long-term consequences of marihuana use in the U.S.A. is not advisable since the level of use there is well below chronic levels. The methodological deficits for major cross-cultural studies on marihuana were many. Steps for sound and valid future research on the subject were proposed.

3746 Flom, M. C.; Adams, A. J.; and Jones, R. T., Invest. Ophthalmol., 14(1), 52-55 (1975).

Marijuana Smoking and Reduced Pressure in Human Eyes: Drug Action or Epiphenomenon?

IOP change is not related to pulse-rate increment, but is positively related to the maximum "high" rating and to the score on a scale pertaining to peaceful relaxation and tiredness. The amount of marihuana experience is inversely related to above parameters and is independent of pulse increase.

3747 Flom, M. C.; Brown, B.; Adams, A. J.; and Jones, R. T., Amer. J. Optom. Physiol. Opt., 53(12), 764-73 (1976).

Alcohol and Marijuana Effects on Ocular Tracking.

Experienced users of alcohol and marijuana were asked to track a circular light spot with their eyes. The frequencies at which alterations in smooth- and saccadic-tracking occurred were decreased by low doses of alcohol but not by marijuana or placebo.

3748 Florvaag, E., Tidsskr. Norske Laegeforen., *97*(12), 563-64 (1977).

Rhino-Konjunktival Hasjisjallergi?
[Rhino-Conjunctival Hashish Allergy?]

Hashish or marihuana seldom cause
allergic reactions, although in some
patients perforation of the nasal mucous
membrane has been reported. Certain
marihuana constituents may produce
rhino-conjunctival allergies.

3749 Florvaag, E., Tidsskr. Nor. Laegeforen,
98(3), 142-44 (1978).

Cannabis og Luftveiene [Cannabis and
the Airways].

Cannabis smoking may cause irritation of the bronchial tubes and may
also cause allergic reactions. The pharmacological action of Δ^9-THC and
CBD on the lungs is briefly discussed.

3750 Fonseka, K.; and Widman, M., J. Chromatogr., *120*(2), 343-48 (1976).

Chromatographic Separation of Cannabinoids and Their Monooxygenated Derivatives.

Monooxygenated metabolites of cannabinoids (CBD, CBN, Δ^9-THC, Δ^8-THC)
are separated on Sephadex LH-20.
Solvents were light petroleum (b.p.
40-60°-chloroform-ethanol (10:10-1).
In CBD the order of separation was
2"-, 1"-, 3"-, 4"-, and 5"-hydroxylat
compounds. Hydroxylated 3"- and
4"- in all series were poorly separated;
TLC and GC did separate: . 11-OH,
β-OH, and 8-α-OH-Δ^9-THC were best
separated by TLC and/or GC.

3751 Fonseka, K.; and Widman, M., J. Pharm.
Pharmacol., *29*(1), 12-14 (1977).

Dihydroxylated Metabolites of Cannabinol Formed by Rat Liver *in vitro*.

Metabolic studies with rat liver *in vitro*
revealed that tritium-labelled CBN had
four dihydroxylated metabolites. These
included 1",7-dihydroxy-CBN, 2",7-di-
hydroxy-CBN, 3",7-dihydroxy-CBN and
4",7-dihydroxy-CBN. These metabolites
were separated by TLC and their structures were confirmed by NMR and
GC-MS.

3752 Forbes, J. E.; Debski, B. F.; Dewey,
W. L.; and Johnson, D. N., Fed. Proc.,
36(3), 1039 (1977).

The Effect of Cannabinoids on Ganglionic Transmission in Rat Superior
Cervical Ganglia.

Δ^8-THC and 11-OH-Δ^9-THC facilitated
electrically evoked postganglionic potentials. CBN produced biphasic effects, whereas CBD inhibited them.

3753 Ford, R. D.; and Balster, R. L., Fed.
Proc., *34*(3), 743 (1975).

The Discriminative Stimulus Properties
of Δ^9-Tetrahydrocannabinol (Δ^9-THC):
Generalization to Some Metabolites and
Derivatives.

Rats trained to press selectively a particular lever when THC (3 mg/kg) was
administered also pressed the same lever
when substitution for THC was made
with 11-OH-Δ^9-THC (0.3-1.0 mg/kg),
9-*nor*-9-α-OH-hexahydrocannabinol (0.3-
1.0 mg/kg), or 9-*nor*-Δ^8-THC (60 mg/kg),
but not when substitution was with
8-α - and 8β -11-di-OH-Δ^9-THC (12
mg/kg), 8-α-OH-Δ^9-THC (15-60 mg/kg),
8-β-OH-Δ^9-THC (3-30 mg/kg), or 9-*nor*-
9-α -OH-hexahydrocannabinol (1-10
mg/kg).

3754 Ford, R. D.; Balster, R. L.; and Beckner,
J. S., Fed. Proc., *35*(3), 644 (1976).

Δ^9-Tetrahydrocannabinol (Δ^9-THC) and
11-OH-Δ^9-THC: Onset, Pattern and
Duration of Behavioral Effects and
Tolerance in Rats.

118

In trained rats behavior suppression by 11-OH-Δ^9-THC was rapid, complete, dose dependent and short-lived. Behavioral suppression after Δ^9-THC exhibited reverse characteristics. Tolerance and cross-tolerance to equipotent doses of the THC's developed at the same rate. 11-OH-Δ^9-THC is responsible for the behavioral effects of Δ^9-THC.

3755 Ford, R. D.; Balster, R. L.; and Dewey, W. L., Life Sci., *20*(12), 1993-2004 (1977).

Δ^9-THC and 11-OH-Δ^9-THC: Behavioral Effects and Relationship to Plasma and Brain Levels.

Under DRL-15 and FI-90 sec. schedule of food reinforcement, both THC and 11-OH-Δ^9-THC decreased responding when administered in high i.p. doses. The latter agent exhibited faster onset and shorter duration of action while the reverse was true for THC. The behavioral effects of these two compounds correlated well with their plasma and brain levels.

3756 Forney, R.; Martz, R.; Lemberger, L.; Rodda, B.; and Evans, M., pp. 162-170 in *Interactions of Drug Abuse*, edited by E. S. Vesell and M. C. Braude. NY, Annals of the New York Academy of Sciences, V. 281, 1976.

The Combined Effect of Marihuana and Dextroamphetamine.

THC in a dose of 15 mg/kg, i.p. was more effective in increasing locomotor activity in mice than higher doses. The same dose resulted in increased motor activity in methamphetamine-treated mice. The effects of THC (25 μg/kg) combined with amphetamine on several different subjective and objective tests were studied in 12 male students.

3757 Forrest, D. V.; Ryan, J. H.; and Zeidenberg, P., Amer. J. Psychiat., *134*(1), 92 (1977).

Elimination of the Reverse Heisenberg (Ho) Effect by Closed-Circuit Television.

Subjects receiving placebo treatment and untreated observers have passively gotten "high" from fumes of near-by marihuana smokers. The author reports elimination of this problem with the use of closed-circuit television techniques.

3758 Fort, J., Contemp. Drug Probl., *5*, 1-3 (1976).

Marihuana, Alcohol, Tobacco and the Criminal Law (Editor's page).

The author argues that social and legal emphasis should be placed on combating alcohol and tobacco use rather than on the present preoccupation with trivia such as marihuana use.

3759 Fournier, E.; Rosenberg, E.; Hardy, N.; and Nahas, G., pp. 457-68 in *Marihuana: Chemistry, Biochemistry, and Cellular Effects*, edited by G. G. Nahas. NY, Springer-Verlag, 1976.

Teratologic Effects of Cannabis Extracts in Rabbits: A Preliminary Study.

Results of the teratogenic effects of cannabis extracts in the rabbit are presented. Teratological effects observed might be attributed to the inhibitory effect of cannabinoids and their metabolites on DNA, RNA, and protein anabolism.

3760 Fournier, G.; and Paris, M., Ann. Med. Nancy, *17*, 401-04 (1978).

Progres Recents de la Pharmacognosie du Chanvre: *Cannabis sativa L*. Cannabinacees [Current Progress in Hemp Pharmacognosy: *Cannabis sativa L*.

A review in which the chemical constituents were briefly outlined, especially the types of cannabinoids, nitrogenous compounds, terpenes, etc. The complexity of the chemical composition of the cannabis plant is emphasized.

3761 Fournier, G.; Paris, M. R.; Fourniat, M. C.; and Quero, A. M., Ann. Pharm. Fr., *36*(11-12), 603-06 (1978).

Activite Bacteriostatique D'Huiles Essentielles de *Cannabis sativa L*. [Bacteriostatic Activity of *Cannabis sativa L*. Essential Oil].

The bacteriostatic effect of the volatile oil of fiber and drug types of cannabis and of hashish was determined using five strains of bacteria. The minimum inhibitory concentration of each oil was determined for each strain. The Gram + bacteria were the most sensitive to Cannabis essential oil.

3762 Frank, I. M.; Lessin, P. J.; Tyrrell, E. D.; Hahn, P. M.; and Szara, S., pp. 673-79 in *Pharmacology of Marihuana, Vol. 2*, edited by M. C. Braude and S. Szara. NY, Raven Press, 1976.

Acute and Cumulative Effects of Marihuana Smoking in Hospitalized Subjects: A 36-Day Study.

In a controlled hospital setting, the effects of smoking marihuana (7 mg/kg) for 28 days on several physiological, psychological and clinical parameters were tested in 36 carefully screened male subjects. Marihuana caused a dose-related increase in subjective "high" and heart rate and a slight but acute elevation in systolic and diastolic blood pressures. No changes in temperature, respiration or psychological tests conducted were observed. Results of the clinical lab tests were also presented.

3763 Frank, M.; and Rosenthal, E., *Marijuana Grower's Guide*. Berkeley, California, And/Or Press, 1978. 330 pp.

Detailed information on steps needed to ensure the growing of healthy cannabis plants is given.

3764 Fredericks, A. B.; and Benowitz, N. L., Fed. Proc., *36*(3), 1027 (1977).

Effects of Chronic Δ^9-Tetrahydrocannabinol (THC) on Autonomic Control of the Cardiovascular (CV) System of Conscious Rhesus Monkeys.

Repeated i.v. administration of Δ^9-THC resulted in partial tolerance to its induced bradycardia and hypotension in monkeys. Evidence also pointed to modification of autonomic control of the cardiovascular system by THC.

3765 Frederickson, R. C. A.; Hewes, C. R.; and Aiken, J. W., J. Pharmacol. Exp. Ther., *199*(2), 375-84 (1976).

Correlation Between *In Vivo* and an *In Vitro* Expression of Opiate Withdrawal Precipitated by Naloxone: Their Antagonism by l-(-)-Δ^9-Tetrahydrocannabinol.

l-(-)-Δ^9-THC (1-10 mg, p.o.) stereospecifically and in a dose-dependent manner antagonises naloxone-induced withdrawal in morphine-dependent guinea pigs and rats. THC inhibited behavioral symptoms and weight loss while sedatives predominantly blocked behavioral hyperactivity. *In vitro*, ileum from morphine-dependent guinea pigs contracted upon exposure to naloxone l-(-)-Δ^9-THC blocked the contraction without modifying ach-induced motility. THC may be adaptable to opiate detoxification.

3766 Freedman, D. X., pp. 167-71 in *Marijuana and Health Hazards*, edited by J. R. Tinklenberg. NY, Academic Press, 1975.

Passions, Pot and Science Policy.

Scientific training is needed to evaluate and appreciate the significance of data. Researchers have to answer not only to the general public but also to their colleagues. Available studies did not indicate the relative seriousness of marihuana health hazards. Continuing research is needed.

3767 Freemon, F. R.; and Al-Marashi, M. S. H., Drug Alcohol Depend., 2(1), 39-43 (1977).

Long-Term Changes in the Sleep of Normal Volunteers Administered Multiple Doses of Delta-9-Tetrahydrocannabinol.

Two subjects were given 20 mg of THC orally on nights 7 and 18 of a 30 night study monitoring their sleep patterns. Sleep polygraphic records were obtained and analyzed and the results discussed.

3768 Freemon, F. R.; Rosenblatt, J. E.; and El-Yousef, M. K., Clin. Pharmacol. Ther., 17(2), 121-26 (1975).

Interaction of Physostigmine and Delta-9-Tetrahydrocannabinol in Man.

In human subjects, physostigmine partially counteracted THC effects on heart rate and conjunctival injection while it did not affect the neurologic assessment measures nor change the peak behavioral effects of THC.

3769 Fried, P. A., Behav. Biol., 21(2), 163-96 (1977).

Behavioral and Electroencephalographic Correlates of the Chronic Use of Marijuana - A Review.

Extensive literature surveys and analyses indicated that tolerance develops to the behavioral and electrophysiological depressant effects, but not to the excitatory aspects, of marihuana following its chronic use. Learning factors influence such a tolerance and correlations between human and animal studies can be found.

3770 Fried, P. A., Pharmacol. Biochem. Behav., 4(6), 635-38 (1976).

Cross-Tolerance Between Inhaled Cannabis and Intraperitoneal Injection of Δ^9-THC.

Rats exposed to cannabis smoke (16.5 mg/kg, THC every 48 hrs.) initially showed hypoactivity, then tolerance developed after 13 successive exposures. These rats were also cross-tolerant to i.p. THC (4 mg/kg) in a sex-related manner.

3771 Fried, P. A., Psychopharmacology, 50(3), 285-91 (1976).

Short- and Long-Term Effects of Pre-Natal Cannabis Inhalation Upon Rat Offspring.

Gravid rats exposed to cannabis smoke exhibited increased resorptions while delivered progeny had lower birth weights and demonstrated delayed physiological maturation. In-utero exposure to Δ^9-THC was associated with retained sensitivity to subsequent THC exposures. EEG recordings indicated tolerance development to THC (4-8 mg/kg, i.p.) given repeatedly to rat pups.

3772 Friedman, E.; Gershon, S.; Hine, B.; Torrelio, M.; and Moss, I. R., Brit. J. Pharmacol., 59(4), 561-63 (1977).

Cardiovascular Effects of Δ^9-Tetrahydrocannabinol in Conscious and Anaesthetized Dogs.

THC (0.1-0.5 mg/kg, i.v.) produced bradycardia in both conscious and anesthetized dogs and caused a fall in BP under the latter condition only. Implications of the findings were discussed.

3773 Friedman, E.; Hanin, I.; and Gershon, S., J. Pharmacol. Exp. Ther., *196*(2), 339-45 (1976).

Effect of Tetrahydrocannabinols on 3H-Acetylcholine Biosynthesis in Various Rat Brain Slices.

Δ^8- and Δ^9-THC (5-40 mg/kg, i.p.), but not CBD (20-40 mg/kg), inhibited ACh synthesis in the cortex, hypothalamus and striatum of male rat brain slices. These treatments, however, did not impair choline acetyltransferase activity or uptake of choline in brain slices. The inhibiting effect of the two cannabinoids was antagonized by high K^+ in the incubation medium. Mechanisms involved were interpreted.

3774 Friedman, J. G., New Eng. J. Med., *292*(9), 484 (1975).

Marihuana and Testosterone Levels.

The author is critical of the study of Mendelson *et al.* (N. Eng. J. Med., *291*: 1051, 1974) who evaluated plasma testosterone levels in chronic marihuana smokers without the inclusion of adequate nonsmoker controls. The long half-life of THC precludes the establishment of a baseline response with chronic marihuana smokers.

3775 Friedman, M. A., Cancer Biochem. Biophys., *2*(2), 51-54 (1977).

In Vivo Effects of Cannabinoids on Macromolecular Biosynthesis in Lewis Lung Carcinomas.

Δ^9-THC, Δ^8-THC and CBD failed to inhibit tumor macromolecular biosynthesis in Lewis lung tumor-bearing mice. Implications of the findings were discussed.

3776 Friedman, M. A., Fed. Proc., *35*(3), 623 (1976).

Inhibition of DNA Synthesis by Δ^9-Tetrahydrocannabinol in L1210 Murine Leukemia.

Anticancer effects of Δ^9-THC (200 mg/kg, i.p.) were studied in BDF1 mice inoculated i.p. with 10^{-5} L1210 leukemic cells. The uptake of tritiated thymidine was suppressed by 66% and 23% at 1½ and 3 hrs. post Δ^9-THC. Oral Δ^9-THC also inhibited DNA synthesis. Incorporation of cytidine into RNA was enhanced although total RNA was unchanged. Refractoriness to the anti-tumor effects of Δ^9-THC developed rapidly.

3777 Friedman, M. A., Res. Commun. Chem. Pathol. Pharmacol., *15*(3), 541-52 (1976).

Inhibition of Arylhydrocarbon Hydroxylase Induction in BALB/C Mouse Liver by Δ^9-Tetrahydrocannabinol.

A single oral treatment of male BALB/C mice with THC (200 mg/kg) caused a nonsignificant increase in hepatic mixed-function oxidase activity. Simultaneous administration of THC with phenobarbital or 3-methyocholanthrene suppressed the induction of arylhydrocarbon hydroxylase and aminopyrine N-demethylose suppression correlated with impaired nuclear RNA synthesis.

3778 Friedman, M. A.; Kooshian, L. K.; and Harris, L. S., Pharmacologist, *17*(2), 181 (1975).

Suppression of Murine Mixed Function Oxidase Induction by Δ^9-THC.

Mice treated with either THC (200 mg/kg, p.o.) and/or phenobarbital (75 mg/kg, i.p.) were killed and enzyme assays were performed on the microsomes to study the effect of the drugs on arylhydrocarbon hydroxylase activity and aminopyrine demethylase activity.

3779 Friedman, M. A.; and Staub, J., Cancer Biochem. Biophys., *2*, 99-104 (1978).

122

Effects of Cannabinoids on L1210 Murine Leukemia. II. Induction by Cannabinoids of Single Strand Breaks in L1210 Tumor DNA.

Δ^9-THC, Δ^8-THC, CBD and abnormal CBD induced marked single strand breaks in the DNA of L1210 murine leukemia cells, whereas CBN did not. The characteristics of DNA breaks, as well as the time course of these cannabinoids' effects, were discussed.

3780   Friedman, M. A.; and Wrenn, J. M., Toxicol. Appl. Pharmacol., *41*(2), 345-52 (1977).

Suppression by Δ^9-Tetrahydrocannabinol of Induction of Hepatic Tyrosine Aminotransferase and Tryptophan Oxygenase.

Δ^9-THC alone did not inhibit tyrosine aminotransferase (TAT) activity, but did decrease the level of induction of TAT by hydrocortisone. Dose relationships and time sequences are given. Some small effect of THC on induction of TAT or tryptophan oxygenase by tryptophan was seen in mouse liver, but not in rat liver.

3781   Friedrich-Fiechtl, J.; and Spiteller, G., Tetrahedron, *31*(6), 479-87 (1975).

Neue Cannabinoide I. [New Cannabinoids I.].

Four new cannabinoids were isolated by micropreparative GC. Trivial names are cannabichromanon, cannabifuran, dehydrocannabifuran, and 2-Oxo-Δ^3-THC. Physical constant and data are included. All four have C_5 side chains.

3782   Frischknecht, H. R.; and Waser, P. G., Gen. Pharmacol., *9*(5), 369-73 (1978).

Actions of Hallucinogens on Ants (*Formica pratensis*). I. Brain Levels of LSD and THC Following Oral Administration.

Ants fed LSD or Δ^9-THC in their diet exhibited brain peak values at 12-24 hrs. and 24-48 hrs. respectively. THC had half-life time of 3 days, whereas LSD had that of half-a-day.

3783   Frischknecht, H. R.; and Waser, P. G., Gen. Pharmacol., *9*(5), 375-80 (1978).

Actions of Hallucinogens on Ants (*Formica pratensis*). II. Effects of Amphetamine, LSD and Delta-9-Tetrahydrocannabinol.

Δ^9-THC, in the dose administered, did not alter ants' behavior appreciably, whereas amphetamine and LSD induced significant changes.

3784   Frizza, J.; Chesher, G. B.; Jackson, D. M.; Malor, R.; and Starmer, G. A., Psychopharmacology, *55*(1), 103-07 (1977).

The Effect of Δ^9-Tetrahydrocannabinol, Cannabidiol, and Cannabinol on the Anaesthesia Induced by Various Anaesthetic Agents in Mice.

THC prolonged the action of several anesthetics in mice. CBD affected pentobarbital anesthesia only while CBN was inactive. Complex interactions were found to exist between the cannabinoids and the anesthetics tested.

3785   Fujiwara, M.; and Ueki, S., Physiol. Behav., *21*(4), 581-85 (1978).

Muricide Induced by Single Injection of Δ^9-Tetrahydrocannabinol.

Regardless of duration, isolation precipitated muricidal behavior in Δ^9-THC treated male rats.

3786   Fukuda, D.; Archer, R. A.; and Abbott, B. J., Appl. Environ. Microbiol., *33*(5), 1134-40 (1977).

Microbiological Transformations of $\Delta^{6a,10a}$-Tetrahydrocannabinol.

Modification of $\Delta^{6a,10a}$-THC by a large number of micro-organisms was undertaken and findings discussed. The possible application of this approach to generate therapeutically desirable cannabinoids was advocated.

3787   Furr, M., Diss. Abstr. Int. B., *37*(8), 3740-41 (1977).

Ontogeny, Structure, and Histochemical Analyses of Unbranched Non-Articulated Laticifers in *Cannabis sativa L.*

Unbranched non-articulated laticifers of *Cannabis sativa L.* from seedling, vegetative, and floral organs were investigated by light and electron microscopy. The latex and laticifers had positive color test for alkaloids and cannabinoids.

G

3788 Gagliardi, L.; Bonifazi, A.; and Chiavarelli, S., Farmaco Ed. Prat., *31*(1), 18-22 (1976).

Studio Su Una Reazione Colorimetrica Della *Cannabis Indica* [Studies on the Colorimetric Reaction of *Cannabis Indica*].

A sensitive and specific procedure for the detection of cannabis was described. This colorimetric reaction involves the use of hydrochloric acid in ethanol.

3789 Gagnon, M-A.; and Elie, R., Union Med. Can., *104*(6), 914-21 (1975).

Les Effets de la Marijuana et de la D-Amphetamine sur L'Appetit, la Consommation Alimentaire et Quelques Variables Cardio-Respiratories Chez L' Homme [Effects of Marihuana and of D-Amphetamine on Appetite, Food Intake and Some Cardio-Respiratory Variables in Man].

Nine equal groups of marihuana users received one of the following combinations of drug-dose: d-amphetamine orally, 0, 10 or 20 mg; and Δ^9-THC, smoked, 0, 10 or 20 mg. Food intake was measured and a questionnaire determined appetite. Marihuana produced a biphasic response at the higher doses. Appetite and intake were inhibited, then they were stimulated with a decrease in satiety.

3790 Galanter, M., Amer. J. Psychiat., *133*(6), 635-40 (1976).

The "Intoxication State of Consciousness": A Model for Alcohol and Drug Abuse.

The author discusses some psychiatric aspects of marijuana intoxication including changes in awareness and responses to stimuli. Subjective research shows that physical responses to marijuana intoxication were fairly consistent among users, while perceptual and mental responses were not. The use of social intoxicants and their attractiveness to abusers is discussed, along with substitution of drug intoxication with transcendental meditation.

3791 Galbraith, G., Bus. Soc. Rev., *27*, 58-60 (1978).

The Economic Necessity of Marijuana.

The author feels that reasons to continue regarding marihuana as illegal are feeble. Rather than importing pot, U.S. farmers should benefit from its commercial cultivation. The states should handle it and sell decent marihuana to the public.

3792 Galchus, D. S.; and Galchus, K. E., Drug Forum, *6*(1), 65-76 (1977/78).

Drug Use: Some Comparisons of Black and White College Students.

When questioned, 46% and 50.9% of white and black students, respectively, admitted either frequent or occasional use of marihuana. Patterns of alcohol and tobacco use were similar among the two groups, while blacks used more heroin and cocaine and whites used more amphetamine and barbiturates.

3793 Galliher, J. F.; and Walker, A., Soc. Probl., *24*(3), 367-76 (1977).

The Puzzle of the Social Origins of the Marihuana Tax Act of 1937.

Passage of the Marihuana Tax Act of 1937 was not mainly due to the Federal Bureau of Narcotics propaganda efforts or to a national crisis but rather to well-timed common sense.

3794   Gangadnara, M.; and Ihamdar, J. A., Plant Syst. Evol., *127*, 121-37 (1977).

Trichomes and Stomata, and Their Taxonomic Significance in the *Urticales*.

Differences and similarities between the stomata and trichomes in the *Urticales* were pointed out. *Urticales* were suggested to be a natural order of four different plant families that included the *Cannabaceae*.

3795   Ganz, V. P.; and Volkmar, F., J. Amer. Coll. Health Ass., *25*(2), 93-96 (1976).

Adverse Reactions to Marihuana Use Among College Students.

Five case reports are presented in which college students who were using marihuana to suppress anxiety or who were suffering anxiety and using marihuana, found their anxiety to increase to the extent that they sought professional help. In 4 of the 5 cases, Diazepam was prescribed along with cessation of marihuana use. Symptoms and anxiety disappeared even after Diazepam was withdrawn, but reappeared if marihuana was used again.

3796   Garber, A. S., J. Psychedelic Drugs, *10*(3), 217-26 (1978).

Potential Tax Revenues from a Regulatory Marketing Scheme for Marijuana.

The author estimated that the tax revenues that could be raised by selling marihuana to the American public through a regulatory marketing scheme would be $1.8 billion. Suggestions on how this money should be spent were included.

3797   Garrett, C. P. O.; Braithwaite, R. A.; and Teale, J. D., Brit. Med. J., *2*(6080), 166-67 (1977).

Unusual Case of Tetrahydrocannabinol Intoxication Confirmed by Radioimmunoassay.

A case of acute THC intoxication was reported. Hallucination, confusion, restlessness and excitement were among the many symptoms observed.

3798   Garrett, E. R.; Gouyette, A. J.; and Roseboom, H., J. Pharm. Sci., *67*(1), 27-31 (1978).

Stability of Tetrahydrocannabinols II.

The biphasic degradation of Δ^9-THC was studied under acidic conditions and the degradation products identified by GC and GC-MS. HPLC was used for the purification of Δ^9- and Δ^8-THC and the degradation products. Kinetic studies on the degradation of both Δ^9- and Δ^8-THC were also carried out.

3799   Garrett, E. R.; and Hunt, C. A., pp. 33-41 in *Cannabinoid Assays in Humans*, NIDA Research Monograph Series, 7, 1976.

Separation and Sensitive Analysis of Tetrahydrocannabinol in Biological Fluids by HPLC and GLC.

A HPLC procedure is described for separating Δ^9-THC from endogenous materials and metabolites in plasma and other biological fluids. Analysis of Δ^9-THC is then carried out with GLC. Lower limit is 1 ng/ml. Data were checked using labeled molecules.

3800   Garrett, E. R.; and Hunt, C. A., J. Pharm. Sci., *66*(1), 20-26 (1977).

Separation and Analysis of Δ^9-Tetrahydrocannabinol in Biological Fluids by High-Pressure Liquid Chromatography and GLC.

A HPLC system is reported for the separation of several natural and synthetic cannabinoids and metabolites. Specifics are given for extracting the cannabinoids and metabolites from biological fluids. Emphasis is placed on Δ^9-THC and 11-OH-Δ^9-THC. Two GLC methods are discussed with purification procedures and calibration curves being reported.

3801 Garrett, E. κ.; and Hunt, C. A.; J. Pharm. Sci., 66(3), 395-407 (1977).

Pharmacokinetics of Δ^9-Tetrahydrocannabinol in Dogs.

The pharmacokinetics of intravenous ^{14}C-Δ^9-THC (0.1, 0.5, and 2.0 mg/kg) were assessed in dogs. THC demonstrated a biphasic disappearance from plasma. Metabolites of THC were totally and rapidly eliminated in the bile and urine with 10-15% undergoing enterohepatic recirculation. The rate-limiting step of THC elimination was postulated.

3802 Gascon, A. L.; and Bensemana, D., Res. Commun. Chem. Pathol. Pharmacol., 12(3), 449-63 (1975).

An Attempt to Correlate Analgesia to Changes in Brain Neuromediators in Rats.

The analgesic activity of Δ^9-THC (.25 to 6 mg/kg, i.p.), morphine sulfate (1.25 to 10 mg/kg, s.c.) and sodium salicylate (75 to 600 mg/kg, i.p.) and the effects on brain amine levels were studied. The degree of analgesia with THC was correlated with an increase in brain stem levels of 5-HT and NE.

3803 Gash, A.; Karliner, J. S.; Janowsky, D.; and Lake, C. R., Ann. Intern. Med., 89(4), 448-52 (1978).

Effects of Smoking Marihuana on Left Ventricular Performance and Plasma Norepinephrine: Studies in Normal Men.

After smoking marihuana (6 mg of Δ^9-THC), subjects exhibited significant increases of heart rate and left ventricular performance. Plasma NE increased 30 minutes after the onset of tachycardia.

3804 Gaul, C. C.; and Mellors, A., Res. Commun. Chem. Pathol. Pharmacol., 10(3), 559-64 (1975).

Δ^9-Tetrahydrocannabinol and Decreased Macrophage Migration Inhibition Activity.

Δ^9-THC decreased the ability of lymphocytes, in peritoneal exudates, to inhibit the migration of macrophages induced by prior immunization of rats.

3805 Gawin, F. H., J. Psychedelic Drugs, 10(3), 227-36 (1978).

Drugs and Eros: Reflections on Aphrodisiacs.

An expanded definition of aphrodisiacs is proposed by the author and the effects of several agents, including marihuana, on sexual activity are reviewed.

3806 Geller, I.; Hartmann, R. J.; and Randle, S., Proc. West. Pharmacol. Soc., 19, 416-20 (1976).

Effects of Δ^9-THC on Operant Behavior of Laboratory Rats.

Δ^9-THC, unlike the anti-anxiety agents meprobamate and chlordiazepoxide, did not impair discrimination task performance or suppress conflict behavior at doses less than totally disruptive of operant behavior in rats.

3807 Genest, P.; Huy, N. D.; and Roy, P. E., Res. Commun. Psychol. Psychist. Behav., 1(2), 283-90 (1976).

Toxicity Study of Marihuana in Dogs: Effects on the Mitotic Index and the Chromosomes.

Lymphocyte cultures from chronic marihuana smoking dogs showed no significant adverse chromosomal effects. Implications of the findings were discussed.

3808 Ghosh, J. J.; Mitra, G.; Poddar, M. K.; and Chatterjee, D. K.; Biochem. Pharmacol., 26(19), 1797-1801 (1977).

Effect of Δ^9-Tetrahydrocannabinol Administration on Hepatic Functions.

Chronic THC administration (10 mg/kg/day, i.p. for 21 days) altered several of the hepatic functions studied, whereas acute THC (10 or 50 mg/kg, i.p.) only inhibited microsomal lipid peroxidation and enhanced Mg^{+2}-ATPase activity.

3809 Ghosh, J. J.; Poddar, M. K.; Mitra, G.; Bannerjee, A.; and Sarkar, C., *Eleventh Collegium Internationale Neuro-Psychopharmacologicum: Abstracts*, Vienna, Austria, July 9-14, 1978, p. 144.

Neurobiochemical Studies on the Mode of Action of Delta-9-Tetrahydrocannabinol.

Δ^9-THC induced changes in the lipid microenvironment of membranes in the brain and other tissues. Both synaptosomal (Na-K-ATPase, AChE) and mitochondrial (MAO) membrane-bound enzymes were affected with concomitant changes in the phospholipid and ganglioside compositions of these subcellular preparations.

3810 Ghosh, P.; and Bhattacharya, S. K., Psychopharmacology, 59(3), 293-97 (1978).

Anticonvulsant Action of Cannabis in the Rat: Role of Brain Monoamines.

P-chlorophenylalanine, methysergide and cyproheptadine antagonized the anticonvulsant action of cannabis resin in rats. After reserpine, 5-hydroxytrypto-

phan restored the action of cannabis. This and other evidence suggested the involvement of 5-HT and not catecholamines in the anticonvulsant properties of cannabis.

3811 Gianutsos, R.; and Litwack, A. R., Bull. Psychon. Soc., 7(3), 277-79 (1976).

Chronic Marijuana Smokers Show Reduced Coding into Long-Term Storage.

The disruptive effects of chronic high-frequency marihuana usage on a recall paradigm was assessed in a sample drawn from undergraduate university students. Marihuana usage depressed word recall ability and the degree of depression was proportional to the length of the reading task.

3812 Gibbins, R. J.; McDougall, J.; Miles, C. G.; and Marshman, J. A., Acta Pharmacol. Toxicol., 39(1), 65-76 (1976).

Tolerance to Marihuana-Induced Tachycardia in Man.

Tolerance to the marihuana-induced increase in human heart rate developed following daily smoking of marihuana cigarettes (totaling 16 mg of THC) for 27 days.

3813 Gibermann, E.; Gothilf, S.; Shahar, A.; and Bino, T.; J. Reprod. Fertil., 42(2), 389-90 (1975).

Effect of Δ^9-Tetrahydrocannabinol on the Membrane Permeability of Bull Spermatozoa to Potassium.

Δ^9-THC drastically changes the cation permeability of the bull sperm cells.

3814 Gilbert, J. C.; Pertwee, R. G.; and Wyllie, M. G., Brit. J. Pharmacol., 59(4), 599-601 (1977).

Effects of Δ^9-Tetrahydrocannabinol and Cannabidiol on a Mg^{+2}-ATPase of Synaptic Vesicles Prepared from Rat Cerebral Cortex.

Both THC and CBD inhibited vesicular mg^{+2}-ATPase activity of rat cerebral cortex synaptosomes at concentrations of 0.1 mM and above, while lower concentrations of THC increased such an enzymatic activity. The relationship between enzyme inhibition and anticonvulsant activity was discussed.

3815   Gildea, M. L.; and Bourn, W. M., Life Sci., 21(6), 829-32 (1977).

The Effect of Delta-9-Tetrahydrocannabinol on Barbituate Withdrawal Convulsions in the Rat.

THC protected rats, in a dose related manner, against audiogenic seizures during barbital withdrawal.

3816   Gill, E. W., pp. 151-61 in Interactions of Drug Abuse, edited by E. S. Vesell and M. C. Braude. NY, Annals of the New York Academy of Sciences, V. 281, 1976.

The Effects of Cannabinoids and Other CNS Depressants on Cell Membrane Models.

The electron spin resonance technique was used to detect perturbations of liposome bilayers by cannabinoids and some physico-chemically related steroids. Perturbation caused by low doses of THC was similar to that induced by the steroids studied indicating that the site of action of these compounds is the lipid phase of cell membranes. Whether or not THC shares the same site of action with several CNS depressants is discussed.

3817   Gill, E. W.; and Lawrence, D. K., pp. 147-55 in Pharmacology of Marihuana, Vol. 1, edited by M. C. Braude and S. Szara. NY, Raven Press, 1976.

The Physicochemical Mode of Action of Tetrahydrocannabinol on Cell Membranes.

The influence of THC on lipid soluble part of a cell membrane was studied. Pertubation of this membrane system was followed by electron spin resonance signals. With the various cannabinoids studied, the amount of fluidization produced correlated well with their pharmacological effects. Fluidization by Δ^9-THC was similar to that of steroid anesthetics.

3818   Ginsberg, I. J.; and Greenley, J. R., J. Health Soc. Behav., 19(1), 22-34 (1978).

Competing Theories of Marijuana Use: A Longitudinal Study.

When a sample of college students was surveyed, a high rate of marihuana use was found to exist among those who admired users and associated with them and also among the less committed and the psychologically distressed. A follow-up study was conducted and the importance of the above factors on influencing marihuana use was assessed.

3819   Ginsburg, H. J.; Norris, S. A.; and Hudson, G., Bull. Psychon. Soc., 10(5), 361-63 (1977).

Δ^9-Tetrahydrocannabinol Affects Consummatory but not Appetitive Sequence of Interspecific Aggression in the Mongolian Gerbil (Meriones unquiculatus).

THC (5 mg/kg, i.p.) depressed the aggressive behavior of gerbils toward mice. Such a depression was specific in nature.

3820   Giono-Barber, P.; Bertuletti, G.; and Giono-Barber, H., C. R. Soc. Biol. (Paris), 169(1), 264-70 (1975).

Action du Cannabis sur l'apprentissage chez le Singe Cynocephale (Papio papio) [The Action of Cannabis on the Learning Ability of the Monkey (Papio papio)].

The effect of chronic oral treatment with cannabis resin (1-75% Δ^9-THC) on the learning ability of monkeys was investigated. Two sets of experiments were carried out in which the resin was given either before or after acquisition of learned behavior.

3821   Girdano, D. D.; and Girdano, D. A.; J. Amer. Coll. Health Ass., 25(2), 117-19 (1976).

College Drug Use - A Five-Year Survey.

A study of drug use by undergraduates at the University of Maryland shows alcohol abuse to be the biggest problem and increasing. Marijuana and hashish were less of a problem and their use was declining. Other drugs discussed were used even less. People who drank, smoked, or both, had a higher rate of marijuana abuse.

3822   Giusti, G. V., Acta Med. Rom., 15(4-5), 339-48 (1977).

Muscular Dystrophy in Mice after Treatment with Cannabinoids.

Histological, biochemical and functional tests indicated the development of muscular dystrophy in mice treated with Δ^9-THC for one month. Pathological changes were attenuated when Δ^9-THC was given in combination with α-tocopherol.

3823   Giusti, G. V.; and Carnevale, A., Arch. Toxicol., 34, 169-72 (1975).

Myeloid Hyperplasia in Growing Rats After Chronic Treatment with Δ^9-THC at Behavioral Doses.

Rats were injected with 1 mg/kg Δ^9-THC s.c. for 30 days. Half were sacrificed immediately and the others four months later. Changes occurred in the proportion of red to white blood cells.

Δ^9-THC appears to have a toxic effect (the development of myeloid hyperplasia) on bone marrow.

3824   Giusti, G. V.; and Canevale, A., Drug Alcohol Depend., 2(1), 31-37 (1977).

Effects of Cannabinoids on Bone Marrow Activity in Adult Mice.

The effects of Δ^9-THC, CBN, CBD and crude resin extract on bone marrow activity was examined after both acute and chronic administration. Acutely, the effect of CBN was opposite to that of THC while chronically all cannabinoids initially depressed erythropoiesis and stimulated myelopoiesis followed by a tendency toward control levels.

3825   Giusti, G. V.; Chiarotti, M.; and Gentile, V., Acta Med. Rom., 16(4), 446-50 (1978).

Iperplasia Delle Cellule Tubulari Nella Capsula Di Bowman Del Topo a Seguito Di Trattaminto Con Cannabinoidi [Tubular Cells Hyperplasia in Bowman's Capsule of Mice after Treatment with Cannabinoids].

Δ^9-THC, CBN and CBD, after subchronic treatment, induced hyperplasia in tubular cells of Bowman's capsule in mice.

3826   Giusti, G. V.; Chiarotti, M.; and Passatore, M., Experientia, 33(2), 257-58 (1977).

Muscular Dystrophy in Adult Mice Chronically Treated with Δ^9-THC at Behavioural Doses.

Mice treated with Δ^9-THC (1 mg/kg, s.c.) for 30 days exhibited changes in their gastrocnemius muscle responsiveness and histology that simulated muscular dystrophy. The effect may be related to THC blocking action at the neuromuscular junction.

3827 Giusti, G. V.; Chiarotti, M.; Passatore, M.; Gentile, V.; and Fiori, A., Forensic Sci., *10*, 133-40 (1977).

Muscular Dystrophy in Mice after Chronic Subcutaneous Treatment with Cannabinoids.

Active muscle tension was lower in the stimulated gastrocnemius muscle of mice treated with THC or CBD (1 mg/kg, s.c.) for 30 days. CBN, however, caused strong enhancement of tension. Histologic lesions and biochemical changes in the muscle were highest in THC-treated and lowest in CBD-treated mice.

3828 Globus, G. G.; Cohen, H. B.; Kramer, J. C.; Elliott, H. W.; and Sharp, R., J. Psychedelic Drugs, *10*(1), 71-76 (1978).

Effect of Marijuana Induced 'Altered State of Consciousness' on Auditory Perception.

In subjects trained under drug-free state to increase the intensity of a test tone to reach a fixed loudness level, marihuana administration resulted in reproduced tones substantially louder than baseline. Subjects initially trained under marihuana influence, however, reproduced tones at baseline levels.

3829 Gobar, A. H., Bull. Narcotics, *28*(2), 1-11 (1976).

Drug Abuse in Afghanistan.

Drug abuse research is simplified in Afghanistan since all drug addicts institutionalized are processed through one central hospital. Drugs listed as abused are hashish, opium, and alcohol. Causes for abuse, availability, price, distribution, patterns of abuse, production and sale of hashish and opium are discussed. Treatment of hashish overdose is administration of phenothiazines.

3830 Goldman, H.; Dagirmanjian, R.; Drew, W. G.; and Murphy, S., Life Sci., *17*(3), 477-82 (1975).

Δ^9-Tetrahydrocannabinol Alters Flow of Blood to Subcortical Areas of the Conscious Rat Brain.

Cataleptoid postures and a "pop corn" jumping appeared in rats administered Δ^9-THC (1 mg/kg, i.v.). The flow of blood was reduced to the cerebellum, hypothalamus basal ganglia and the dorsal hippocampus. The toxic effects of THC seemed to be exerted on the hippocampal complex. Vascularity does not seem as important as specific receptor-binding or lipid solubility to the distribution and chronic effects of Δ^9-THC.

3831 Goldstein, F. J.; Vernot, E. T.; and Strahlendorf, H. K., Neuropharmacology, *16*(1), 71-72 (1977).

Potentiation of Catecholamine Inhibition of Ganglionic Transmission by Δ^9-Tetrahydrocannabinol.

In the *in situ* rabbit cervical ganglia, higher doses of THC (175-500 μg/kg, i.v.) depressed electrically initiated transmission, while lower doses (7.5-15 μg/kg) potentiated the ganglionic transmission inhibition of NE and EPI, but not those of DA.

3832 Goldstein, H.; Harclerode, J.; and Nyquist, S. E., Life Sci., *20*(6), 951-54 (1977).

Effects of Chronic Administration of Delta-9-Tetrahydrocannabinol and Cannabidiol on Rat Testicular Esterase Isozymes.

Treatment with 2 mg/kg, i.p. of THC or CBD for 10 days resulted in testicular weight reduction (77%). Examination of testicular esterase isozymes indicated a specific inhibition of the Leydig cell esterase isozyme.

3833 Goode, E., Contemp. Drug Probl., *4*(4), 397-445 (1975).

Sociological Aspects of Marijuana Use.

A thorough examination and social profile of marihuana users is given. Background (economic, parental use of drugs), situational factors, social and behavioral correlates (sexual attitudes, political ideology, religion and use of other drugs) are studied. Age is more closely related to marihuana use than any other single factor. Social pressure is next. Criminal behavior and use of marihuana is presented and legal considerations are given.

3834 Gordon, J. H.; Bromley, B. L.; Gorski, R. A.; and Zimmermann, E., Pharmacol. Biochem. Behav., *8*(5), 603-08 (1978).

Δ^9-Tetrahydrocannabinol Enhancement of Lordosis Behavior in Estrogen Treated Female Rats.

THC treatment did not induce lordosis behavior in ovariectomized rats, but enhanced this behavior in estradiol treated rats. Evidence presented indicated that adrenal steroids are not involved in THC action and suggested that alterations in biogenic amines may be the cause.

3835 Gordon, R.; Gordon, R. J.; and Sofia, R. D., Eur. J. Pharmacol., *35*(2), 309-13 (1976).

Antitussive Activity of Some Naturally Occurring Cannabinoids in Anesthetized Cats.

THC (i.v.) suppressed experimentally-induced cough in anesthetized cats. Neither CBN nor CBD was effective.

3836 Gottesfeld, Z.; and Edery, H., Isr. J. Med. Sci., *11*(8), 862 (1975).

Gamma Aminobutyric Acid System and Cannabinoid-Induced Motor Disturbances (Abstract).

Acute injection of Δ^8-THC into rats at 20 mg/kg resulted in severe ataxia with cerebella levels of GABA and glutamic acid decarboxylase unchanged during peak response. Chronic Δ^8-THC at 10 mg/kg, i.p. for 14 days suppressed glutamic acid decarboxylase and increased the influx of $[^3H]$-GABA into cerebellar synaptosomes.

3837 Gottschalk, L. A.; Aronow, W. S.; and Prakash, R., Biol. Psychiat., *12*(2), 255-266 (1977).

Effect of Marijuana and Placebo-Marijuana Smoking on Psychological State and on Psychophysiological Cardiovascular Functioning in Anginal Patients.

Various psychological and physiological tests indicated that marihuana smoking did not help anginal patients. In fact, it worsened their conditions.

3838 Gough, A. L.; and Gough, N. E., Int. J. Bio-Med. Computing, *9*(2), 81-100 (1978).

Computer Analysis of Interacting Dopaminergic and Cholinergic Control Mechanisms in the Extrapyramidal System.

Δ^9-THC and haploperidol were found to affect extrapyramidal dopaminergic and cholinergic balance when using a simulated computerized model representing their respective control systems. The former caused presynaptic, whereas the latter caused postsynaptic, disturbances.

3839 Gough, A. L.; and Olley, J. E., J. Pharm. Pharmacol., *27*(1), 62-63 (1975).

Cannabis and Amphetamine-Induced Stereotypy in Rats.

A dose-dependent alteration in amphetamine-induced stereotypy in rats was observed when cannabis extract was administered i.p. 30 min. prior to amphetamine (2.5 mg/kg).

3840 Gough, A. L.; and Olley, J. E., Neuropharmacology, *17*(2), 137-44 (1978).

Catalepsy Induced by Intrastriatal Injections of $\triangle^9$-THC and 11-OH-$\triangle^9$-THC in the Rat.

Dose-dependent catalepsy was obtained in the rat following injection of either $\triangle^9$-THC or its 11-OH derivative into the corpus striatum, but not following injection into globus pallidus. Further data suggest cholinergic involvement in catalepsy induction by these cannabinoids in the caudate-putamen. Amphetamine lessened the catalepsy in the striatum and enhanced it in the globus pallidus, suggesting DA involvement.

3841 Gough, A. L.; and Olley, J. E., Psychopharmacology, *54*(1), 87-99 (1977).

$\triangle^9$-Tetrahydrocannabinol and the Extrapyramidal System.

Evidence supporting the involvement of the extrapyramidal dopaminergic system in THC-induced catalepsy in rats was presented.

3842 Graham, J. D. P., ed., *Cannabis and Health*. London, Academic Press, 1976. 480 pp.

This book is divided into three main sections. Section I deals with the Nature of Cannabis and the Cannabinoids, Section II with the Action of Cannabis and its Effects on Health, and Section III with Cannabis and Society. The above three sections include a total of 12 chapters. Abstracts of these are found under the respective authors.

3843 Graham, J. D. P., pp. 121-42 in *Cannabis and Health*, edited by J. D. P. Graham. London, Academic Press, 1976.

The Effect of Cannabis on A: The Mind of Man, B: Animal Behavior.

Smoking cannabis results in a pleasant and harmless experience in most but not all users. Marihuana causes an initial depression followed by irritation and severe sedation in animals and humans. Cannabis also accumulates in the body and may impair motor and mental functions and disrupt well-learned behavior.

3844 Graham, J. D. P., pp. 143-269 in *Cannabis and Health*, edited by J. D. P. Graham. London, Academic Press, 1976.

The Pharmacology of Cannabis and Cannabinoids.

An excellent pharmacological review of cannabis is presented. Cannabis affects not only the brain but also various body organs and functions with little effect on the endocrine system. In animals, it impairs heat production and has analgesic and anticonvulsive properties. Effects on human muscular function is a neglected research area. Interactive studies between THC, other cannabis constituents and drugs, especially alcohol, were cited.

3845 Graham, J. D. P., pp. 271-320 in *Cannabis and Health*, edited by J. D. P. Graham. London, Academic Press, 1976.

Cannabis and Health.

The acute toxicity of cannabis in humans is due to overdose, hypersensitivity or adulterants. Death from cannabis is uncommon in humans. THC depresses the immune response, accumulates in the lung, may damage the liver, reduces the alpha waves of EEG and causes increased chromosomal aberations. Tolerance to cannabis is reported in humans and in animals.

3846   Graham, J. D. P., pp. 417-37 in *Cannabis and Health*, edited by J. D. P. Graham. London, Academic Press, 1976.

If Cannabis Were a New Drug.

Available literature on animal and clinical experimentations with cannabis was utilized to try to predict what would be the case if cannabis were tried out as a possible beneficial therapeutic agent. Steps of such a "new drug" development and marketing were analyzed.

3847   Graham, J. D. P., Brit. Med. J., *1*(6116), 857 (1978).

Cannabis and the Cardiovascular System (Letter).

The author argues that disturbance of the cardiovascular system following cannabis smoking is likely to be only transient in healthy subjects.

3848   Graham, J. D. P., *Cannabis Now*. Great Britain, HM+M Publishers, Ltd., 1977.

Marihuana is used in countries throughout the world. In moderation, marihuana smoking is not harmful and evidence to the contrary in chronic users is still not convincing. Its subjective effects are greatly influenced by setting and expectations. The present British law regards marihuana as an illegal substance. The author argued in favor of liberalization of the law.

3849   Graham, J. D. P.; Davies, B. H.; Seaton, A.; and Weatherstone, R. M., pp. 269-76 in *Pharmacology of Marihuana, Vol. 1*, edited by M. C. Braude and S. Szara. NY, Raven Press, 1976.

Bronchodilator Action of Extract of Cannabis and Δ^1-Tetrahydrocannabinol.

Oral administration of 10 mg Δ^1-THC failed to produce significant bronchodilator effects in patients suffering from reversible airway obstruction. Asthmatic patients failed to show any bronchodilator effects with 3 mg of Δ^1-THC in an aerosol preparation. However, THC was detected in the plasma of these patients.

3850   Graham, J. D. P.; Grey, A. C.; Henderson, A. H.; and Lewis, M. J., Brit. J. Pharmacol., *62*(1), 153-56 (1978).

Effects of Δ^1-*Trans*-Tetrahydrocannabinol on Mechanical Performance of Isolated Heart Muscle Preparations.

Isolated papillary muscle preparations of cat and rat hearts were used to study the effect of Δ^1-THC on peak rate of tension development and decline, time to peak force, half isometric relaxation time, total tension, and contraction velocity. When compared to controls, only those muscles treated with at least 29 μg/ml solutions of THC exhibited significant decline in any parameters and of those, only two were depressed: -8% in developed tension and -11% in contraction velocity.

3851   Grant-Whyte, H., Addict. Dis., *3*(1), 61-64 (1977).

The Present Status of Drug Dependence in South Africa.

Drug abuse is as widely spread in South Africa as it is in other countries. Cannabis (dagga) is the drug most abused although LSD, heroin, amphetamines, barbiturates, analgesics and tranquilizers are also abused. Patients under 24 years constituted the majority of drug abusers. Medical, social, psychiatric and religious approaches are employed for treatment.

3852   Green, D. E., pp. 70-87 in *Cannabinoid Assays in Humans*, NIDA Research Monograph Series, 7, 1976.

134

Quantitation of Cannabinoids in Biological Specimens using Probability Based Matching Gas Chromatography/Mass Spectrometry.

The "Olfax" method (GC screening combined with PBM mass spectrum matching) is recommended for quantitative cannabinoid (metabolite) analyses. Possibly the only advantage of this method over the GC-MS methods is its speed and convenience. Procedures (extraction, silylation) and programs which were used are given in detail. The results presented illustrate the validity of the method.

3853   Green, D. E.; Killam, E. E. K.; Loeffler, K. O.; Chao, F.; and Forrest, I., Pharmacologist, $17(1)$, 268 (1975).

Fecal Excretion of $^{14}C\text{-}\Delta^9\text{-}THC$ Derivatives in Baboon (Abstract).

After oral dosing, Δ^9-THC was mainly excreted unchanged or as its 11-OH-metabolite in the feces.

3854   Green, H. I.; and Levy, M. H., pp. 169-222 in *Drug Misuse...Human Abuse*, NY, Marcel, Inc., 1976.

Facts About Cannabis

This chapter provides non-referenced information regarding various preparations of cannabis. Some of the scientific data is easily understandable and fairly accurate. The book states that little or no tolerance develops to cannabis. This and other information is not current with research findings.

3855   Green, K., Invest. Ophthalmol., $14(4)$, 261-63 (1975).

Marihuana and the Eye.

This paper discusses recent advances on the effects of marihuana and Δ^9-THC on the eye. Discussion is centered around the reduction in IOP in man following the administration of either marihuana or Δ^9-THC.

3856   Green, K., J. Psychedelic Drugs, $10(3)$, 207-10 (1978).

Is There a Scientific Basis to the Legislation of Marijuana as a Medicant?

Research on individual cannabinoids should continue in order to establish which proves most efficacious in the treatment of specific diseases such as glaucoma and, at the same time, is possibly devoid of the psychoactive effects of marihuana. The author also cautions against the legalization of marihuana before proper and sufficient testing is performed.

3857   Green, K.; Bigger, J. F.; Kim, K.; and Bowman, K., Exp. Eye Res., $24(2)$, 189-96 (1977).

Cannabinoid Action on the Eye as Mediated Through the Central Nervous System and Local Adrenergic Activity.

THC, SP-1 and SP-106 decreased the IOP of normal and ganglionectomized rabbit eyes through local and central pathways with the local pathways being more significant in the SP-106 case. β- and, to a lesser extent, α-adrenergic blockers antagonized the THC effects.

3858   Green, K.; Bigger, J. F.; Kim, K.; and Bowman, K., Exp. Eye Res., $24(2)$, 197-205 (1977).

Cannabinoid Penetration and Chronic Effects in the Eye.

THC was most effective in reducing the IOP of rabbit eyes when topically applied in the least viscous oily vehicle. SP-1 and SP-106 were both effective in reducing the IOP with no tolerance development. Chronic administration of SP-106, a water soluble cannabinoid, caused a greater response in ganglionectomized eyes.

3859   Green, K.; and Bowman, K., pp. 803-13 in *Pharmacology of Marihuana Vol. 2*, edited by M. C. Braude and S. Szara. NY, Raven Press, 1976.

Effect of Marihuana and Derivatives on Aqueous Humor Dynamics in the Rabbit.

THC at a concentration of (5×10^{-7}) mg/ml exerted profound effects on isolated ciliary body preparation leading to increased membrane permeability. Administration of THC (i.v.) decreased IOP and increased total outflow facility in both anesthetized and unanesthetized rabbits. Among the cannabinoids tested, $11\text{-OH-}\Delta^9\text{-THC}$ was the most potent. Results of this study were calculated and analyzed.

3860   Green, K.; and Kim, K., Exp. Eye Res., *23*(4), 443-48 (1976).

Mediation of Ocular Tetrahydrocannabinol Effects by Adrenergic Nervous System.

$\Delta^9\text{-THC}$ $(5 \times 10^{-5}$ mg/mg plasma, i.v.) reduced IOP and increased total outflow facility (TOF) by 25% in the normal rabbit eye. Ganglionic blockade reduced the THC lowering of IOP without altering TOF, whereas ganglionectomy reduced both effects. THC lowers IOP by β-adrenergic and CNS interaction and increases TOF by a direct α-adrenergic effect associated with prostaglandin synthetase inhibition.

3861   Green, K.; and Kim, K., Exp. Eye Res., *24*(2), 207-12 (1977).

Papaverine and Verapamil Interaction with Prostaglandin E_2 and Δ^9-Tetrahydrocannabinol in the Eye.

Papaverine was more effective in antagonizing the THC-induced fall in IOP of rabbit eye while verapamil was more effective in antagonizing the PGE_2-induced changes. Mechanisms and sites of action of these agents were discussed.

3862   Green, K.; and Kim, K., Invest. Ophthalmol., *15*(2), 102-12 (1976).

Interaction of Adrenergic Antagonists with Prostaglandin E_2 and Tetrahydrocannabinol in the Eye.

Phentolamine, phenoxybenzamine and propranolol partially antagonized the THC-induced fall in rabbit IOP, whereas sotalol completely abolished this fall. The THC-induced increase in total outflow facility was blocked only by the α-adrenergic antagonists. Effects of the above adrenergic receptor blockers on the increases in IOP and total outflow facility elicited by PGE_2 were also investigated.

3863   Green, K.; and Kim, K., Proc. Soc. Exp. Biol. Med., *154*(2), 228-31 (1977).

Acute Dose Response of Intraocular Pressure to Topical and Oral Cannabinoids.

Nitrogen-containing analogs of cannabinoids produced a fall of IOP when administered either topically (0.001 to 1%) or orally (0.3 mg/kg) to rabbits. In rhesus monkeys, topical applications (0.5%) caused a substantial decrease of IOP. The decreases were dose-dependent.

3864   Green, K.; Kim, K.; and Bowman, K., pp. 49-62 in *The Therapeutic Potential of Marihuana*, edited by S. Cohen and R. Stillman. NY, Plenum Medical Book Company, 1976.

Ocular Effects of Δ^9-Tetrahydrocannabinol.

The possible therapeutic use of THC for glaucoma treatment was explored. In rabbits, THC decreased the IOP and increased total outflow facility by direct effects on adrenergic receptors. Ocular penetration studies also indicated a systemic absorption of THC by orbital tissues.

3865 Green, K.; Kim, K.; Wynn, H.; and Shimp, R. G., Exp. Eye Res., 25(5), 465-71 (1977).

Intraocular Pressure, Organ Weights and the Chronic Use of Cannabinoid Derivatives in Rabbits for One Year.

Chronic administration of SP-1, SP-106 and SP-204 did not result in tolerance to the decrease in rabbit IOP produced by these synthetic cannabinoids. These agents, however, caused a significant decrease in liver weights of all treated animals.

3866 Green, K.; Wynn, H.; and Bowman, K. A., Exp. Eye Res., 27(2), 239-46 (1978).

A Comparison of Topical Cannabinoids on Intraocular Pressure.

The efficacy of 11 cannabinoids was determined for reduction of IOP in ganglionectomized rabbits. Δ^8-THC > 8α-11-dihydroxy-Δ^9-THC > 8α-OH-Δ^9-THC > Δ^9-THC > 8β-11-dihydroxy-Δ^9-THC > CBD > 11-OH-Δ^8-THC > 8β-OH-Δ^9-THC. The others were inactive. Mineral oil was a better vehicle than was sesame oil. Topical application does not always follow efficacy of i.v. or other methods. Dose regimen is discussed.

3867 Green, K.; Wynn, H.; and Padgett, D., Exp. Eye Res., 26(1), 65-69 (1978).

Effects of Δ^9-Tetrahydrocannabinol on Ocular Blood Flow and Aqueous Humor Formation.

THC decreased the aqueous humor formation and increased the blood flow in rabbit ocular tissues. The possible mechanisms involved in THC-Induced reduction of IOP were discussed.

3868 Greenberg, I.; Kuehnle, J. C.; Mendelson, J. H.; and Bernstein, J. G., Psychopharmacology, 49(1), 79-84 (1976).

Effects of Marihuana Use on Body Weight and Caloric Intake in Humans.

After 21 days of inpatient marihuana smoking, both body weight gain and caloric consumption were higher in casual and heavy users than in control subjects.

3869 Greenberg, I.; Kuhn, D.; and Appel, J. B., Pharmacol. Biochem. Behav., 3(5), 931-34 (1975).

Comparison of the Discriminative Stimulus Properties of Δ^9-THC and Psilocybin in Rats.

Rats were lever trained and administered THC (1.0 mg/kg) or psilocybin (1.0 mg/kg, i.p.) to test for cross-tolerance and drug discrimination. No cross-tolerance was observed and THC and psilocybin differentially controlled the learned behavior.

3870 Greenberg, I.; Mendelson, J. H.; Kuehnle, J. C.; Mello, N.; and Babor, T. F., pp. 72-84 in Chronic Cannabis Use, edited by R. L. Dornbush, A. M. Freedman, and M. Fink. NY, Annals of the New York Academy of Sciences, V. 282, 1976.

Psychiatric and Behavioral Observations of Casual and Heavy Marihuana Users in a Controlled Research Setting.

Heavy and casual marihuana users, in a controlled clinical setting, were challenged to perform a simple operant task on a FI 1-sec schedule of money reinforcement. Long-term marihuana use resulted in behavior disturbances which were clinically minor. Heavy, sustained marihuana intake did produce a psychiatric profile indicating some psychopathology.

3871 Greenberg, J. H.; and Mellors, A., Biochem. Pharmacol., 27(3), 329-33 (1978).

Specific Inhibition of an Acyltransferase by $\triangle^9$-Tetrahydrocannabinol.

The authors present evidence that $\triangle^9$-THC in low concentrations and other cannabinoids at higher concentrations inhibit an acyltransferase located in the rat lymphocyte plasma membrane, in vitro. Since $\triangle^9$-THC also inhibits an acyltransferase located in mouse brain synaptosomes, a possible mechanism for psychoactivity is suggested. Excellent methods for ^{14}C-labeling studies, measurement of lipid membrane activity, and correlation with erythrocyte hemolysis are discussed.

3872 Greenberg, J. H.; and Mellors, A., Biochem. Soc. Trans., 5(1), 108-10 (1977).

Modification of Acyltransferase Activity in Lymphocyte Membranes by Cannabinoids and Other Lipids.

In mouse lymphocytes, small amounts of $\triangle^9$-THC decreased the activity of acyltransferase by almost 38%, while the other 5 cannabinoids tested increased activity by roughly the same amount.

3873 Greenberg, J. H.; Mellors, A.; and McGowan, J. C., J. Med. Chem., 21(12), 1208-12 (1978).

Molar Volume Relationships and the Specific Inhibition of a Synaptosomal Enzyme by Psychoactive Cannabinoids.

Only psychoactive cannabinoids inhibited mouse-brain synaptosomal lysophosphatidylcholine acyltransferase at much lower concentrations than those required to show anesthetic activity. This specific inhibition was further evaluated.

3874 Greenberg, J. H.; Saunders, M. E.; and Mellors, A., Science, 197(4302), 475-77 (1977).

Inhibition of a Lymphocyte Membrane Enzyme by $\triangle^9$-Tetrahydrocannabinol in vitro.

Lysolecithin acyltransferase, a membrane bound lymphocytic enzyme, was inhibited by low levels of THC. The level of this enzyme in T-cells was generally increased by mitogens such as concanavalin A. The response to concanavalin A was abolished by THC. It is suggested that the lipophilic THC was changing the lipid phase of the lymphocytic membrane, thereby increasing the fluidity of these structures.

3875 Greene, M. H.; Nightingale, S. L.; and Dupont, R. L., Ann. Intern. Med., 83(3), 402-11 (1975).

Evolving Patterns of Drug Abuse.

Sources of available relevant data on drug abuse were pointed out. Marihuana use is rising and is more common among privileged classes.

3876 Gregg, J. M.; Campbell, R. L.; Levin, K. J.; Ghia, J.; and Elliott, R. A., Anesth. Analg. Curr. Res., 55(2), 203-13 (1976).

Cardiovascular Effects of Cannabinol During Oral Surgery.

THC pretreatment induced a dose-related sustained tachycardia and a tendency to syncopal hypotension in patients undergoing elective oral surgery. Large doses of THC exerted antiarrhythmic activity whereas premedication with atropine synergized with THC or its metabolites to produce an abnormally sustained post-operative tachycardia. Other THC effects and interactions under similar settings were discussed.

3877 Gregg, J. M.; Small, E. W.; Moore, R.; Raft, D.; and Toomey, T. C., J. Oral Surg., *34*(4), 301-13 (1976).

Emotional Response to Intravenous Δ^9-Tetrahydrocannabinol During Oral Surgery.

Surgically stressed patients receiving Δ^9-THC (0.022 and 0.044 mg/kg, i.v.), exhibited intense autonomic responses, experienced a drastic distortion for the perception of pain and showed pronounced elevation of anxiety states. The importance of environmental conditions in determining the emotional response to THC was indicated.

3878 Griffin, B. S.; and Griffin, C. T., Drug Forum, *7*(2), 155-65 (1978-79).

Marihuana Use Among Students and Peers.

Peer action definitions were the most powerful predictors for possible marihuana use by college students. Parental and attitudinal definitions were also relevant.

3879 Grilly, D. M., J. Psychedelic Drugs, *9*(4), 311-16 (1977).

People's Views on Marihuana, Drugs, and Driving: A Changing Scene.

Marihuana was perceived by two samples of college students to be detrimental to the driving skills of both themselves and other people, but ranked second to alcohol, LSD, barbiturates and narcotics in this regard. Other aspects of the survey were discussed.

3880 Gross, S. J.; and Soares, J. R., pp. 10-14 in *Cannabinoid Assays in Humans*, NIDA Research Monograph Series, 7, 1976.

Separate Radioimmune Measurements of Body Fluid Δ^9-THC and 11-Nor-9-Carboxy-Δ^9-THC.

Data are presented on a RIA using tritium. Reactivity of RIA to Δ^9-THC and THC equivalents is given for humans before and after smoking. Urine samples were used. Plasma samples were obtained from eight patients. Δ^9-THC was almost undetectable in plasma 1-2 hours after exposure.

3881 Gross, S. J.; and Soares, J. R., J. Anal. Toxicol., *2*(3), 98-100 (1978).

Validated Direct Blood Δ^9-THC Radioimmune Quantitation.

RIA for direct determination of Δ^9-THC in plasma was developed. The Δ^9-THC antiserum was found to discriminate between closely related cannabinoids. The procedure has forensic implications since Δ^9-THC concentrations in blood might allow assessment of recent versus distant exposure to marihuana.

3882 Grote, H.; and Spiteller, G., J. Chromatogr., *154*(1), 13-23 (1978).

Neue Cannabinoide. II [New Cannabinoids. II].

The isolation of water soluble cannabinoids, especially cannabinoid acids from cannabis extracts, was carried out by adsorption on XAD resins. The new cannabinoids C_3-cannabichromanone, C_3-cannabielsoin and cannabielsoic acid B were detected by GC/MS. The major compound was an acid with the same skeleton as a previously isolated compound of mass 328. The C_3-homolog and its acid were also detected.

3883   Grote, H.; and Spiteller, G., Tetrahedron, *34*(21), 3207-13 (1978).

Neue Cannabinoide. III. Die Strucktur des Cannabicumaronons und Analoger Verbindungen [New Cannabinoids. III. The Structure of Cannabicoumaronon and Related Analogs].

A new cannabis constituent with benzofuran skeleton was isolated from hashish extract. Its structure was determined by spectral evidence and conversion to cannabichromanone. Other related compounds were also detected.

3884   Guinn, R., J. Psychedelic Drugs, *9*(4), 341-43 (1977).

The Phenomenology of Marijuana Use Among Mexican-American Youth.

No clear cut relationship was found between the socioeconomic level and marihuana use in a sample of Mexican-American students in secondary schools. Several sociological factors involved with marihuana use are discussed.

3885   Gulas, I.; and King, F. W., J. Psychol., *92*(first half), 65-69 (1976).

On the Question of Pre-Existing Personality Differences Between Users and Nonusers of Drugs.

This study examined the Gordon Personal Profiles from 90 male college seniors who used marijuana and other drugs only after entering college, or not at all, but who filled out the profiles before entering college. Relationships of drug habits, pre-existing personality traits, and results of other studies are discussed.

3886   Gupta, R. C., Clin. Toxicol., *9*(2), 281-93 (1976).

Street Drug Identification Program.

Results of the analysis of several samples of abused drugs were reported. THC was among the drugs identified.

H

3887 Haar, J., Contemp. Drug Probl., 5(2), 161-85 (1976).

In Pursuit of Happiness: An Evaluation of the Constitutional Right to Private Use of Marijuana.

The author states that decriminalization of marihuana home use should be enacted as a part of the constitutional right to privacy.

3888 Haavik, C. O., Fed. Proc., 36(12), 2595-98 (1977).

Profound Hypothermia in Mammals Treated with Tetrahydrocannabinols, Morphine, or Chlorpromazine.

The THC-induced hypothermia in mice results from reduced heat production and occupies an intermediate position between hypothermias caused by morphine and chlorpromazine. Inhibition of membrane ATPase is also thought to be responsible for the hypothermic effect of THC.

3889 Haavik, C. O.; Arora, S.; and Collins, F., pp. 255-67 in Pharmacology of Marihuana, Vol. 1, edited by M. C. Braude and S. Szara. NY, Raven Press, 1976.

Effect of Cannabis on Temperature Regulation.

Imbalance of any one neurotransmitter or inhibition of prostaglandin synthesis was not responsible for the hypothermic response of Δ^9-THC (1-16 mg/kg, i.v.) in mice. Δ^9-THC may be binding to biomembranes causing Ca^{++} imbalance which would affect the release of various neurotransmitters and thus produce a hypothermic response.

3890 Haavik, C. O.; Bloom, A. S.; and Hardman, H. F., Seventh International Congress of Pharmacology: Abstracts, Paris, France, July 16-21, 1978, p. 79.

Effect of Sodium and Calcium Ions of Delta-9-Tetrahydrocannabinol Induced Hypothermia in the Mouse.

I.v. administration of NaCl (10-400 mg/kg) and $CaCl_2$ (25-100 mg/kg) to mice caused a respective dose-related elevation and decrease in body temperature. The lowest dose of NaCl potentiated, while higher doses antagonized, the hypothermia induced by Δ^9-THC (1 mg/kg). Also, hypothermia resulting from 16 mg/kg of Δ^9-THC was not significantly altered by NaCl pretreatment.

3891 Haddad, L. M., Amer. Fam. Physician, 14(1), 82-87 (1976).

Management of Hallucinogen Abuse.

This study presents useful tips for management of a patient who may have abused hallucinogenic drugs such as LSD, phencyclidine, cannabinols, etc. Initially the patient should be pacified in a quiet room and the clinical symptoms carefully observed. Urine and blood samples can be analyzed to confirm diagnosis, but gastric lavage is not recommended for hallucinogens. No pharmacological agent should be used except for diazepam to decrease hyperactivity.

3892 Hagel, D.; Laverty, V.; Santo, J.; and Fein, A., pp. 119-40 in Trace Analysis Detection in the Environment, Sixth Annual Proceedings, 1975. Edgewood Arsenal Special Publication *(U.S. Dep. Army), 1976. EO-SP-76001.

Detection of Vapor Phase Compounds of Illicit Narcotics.

Head vapor analyses are reported for hashish and marihuana. Special vapor trace sampler is used. Chromatograms are enclosed for various cannabis samples. Indications are that terpenes and other products may be useful in field detectors.

3893 Halikas, J. A.; Shapiro, T. M.; and Weller, R. A., pp. 161-83 in *Treatment Aspects Drug Dependence*, edited by A. Schecter and S. J. Mule. West Palm Beach, Florida, CRC, 1978.

Marijuana: A Critical Review of Sociological, Medical, and Psychiatric Questions.

Although marihuana has been in existence and use since ancient times, real scientific research studying its pharmacological effects on human users has just begun. Science may help to point out the harmful or harmless effects of marihuana, but the issue of use is strictly a social one and should be treated as such.

3894 Hall, F. B.; Klein, A. L.; and Waters, J. E., J. Alter. State Conscious., 2(2), 161-70 (1975-76).

Long Term Effects of Marijuana Smoking.

College students who used marihuana did not exhibit significant adverse effects on motivation, memory, muscular coordination, or sustained attention. The choice of test group may explain this unexpected result, as may the shorter term of usage than that of previous studies.

3895 Halle, S.; Labrecque, G.; Morin, G.; Berthiaume, A.; and Morin, P. J., Clin. Res., 23(5), 608A (1975).

Penicillin Convulsions Resulting from Acute or Chronic Marijuana Smoking in Dogs.

Mongrel dogs received morphine and penicillin G i.v. following acute Δ^9-THC (6 mg by inhalation) and chronic Δ^9-THC (3 mg/day for 10 weeks by inhalation) treatment. Penicillin G caused coarse tremors and epileptiform waves in 90% of the acutely dosed dogs while precipitating frank epileptiform episodes in 50% of chronically dosed dogs. This antibiotic should be avoided by known marihuana smokers.

3896 Hamed, A.; and Jandhyala, B. S., Pharmacologist, 20(3), 164 (1978).

Systemic and Pulmonary Effects of Δ^9-Tetrahydrocannabinol (Δ^9-THC) in Conscious Dogs and in those Anesthetized with Morphine Plus Chloralose (M+C) (Abstract).

Anesthesia interfered with Δ^9-THC-induced pulmonary and systemic hemodynamic changes in dogs.

3897 Hammond, C. T.; and Mahlberg, P. G., Amer. J. Bot., 65(2), 140-51 (1978).

Ultrastructural Development of Capitate Glandular Hairs of *Cannabis sativa L.* (Cannabaceae).

Formation and secretory stages of gland development in cannabis are discussed. Highly modified plastids were observed. It is suggested that unique plastid complement may play a role in cannabinoid synthesis. The ultrastructure of cannabis glands fits pattern for terpene secreting glands. Much data (obtained with electron microscope) on cellular structures are given.

3898 Hammond, C. T.; and Mahlberg, P. G., Amer. J. Bot., 64(8), 1023-31 (1977).

Morphogenesis of Capitate Glandular Hairs of *Cannabis sativa* (Cannabaceae).

Of the glandular hairs of cannabis, both bulbous and capitate-sessile develop on young bracts, while capitate-stalked glands develop at later stages of bract growth. The secretory portion of the gland also differs with the type of gland. Further anatomical analysis of these three glands was undertaken.

3899   Handrick, G. R.; Razdan, R. K.; Uliss, D. B.; Dalzell, H. C.; and Boger, E., J. Org. Chem., *42*(15), 2563-68 (1977).

Hashish. Synthesis of [+]-Delta-1- and Delta-6-3, 4-cis-Cannabidiols and their Isomerization by Acid Catalysis.

[+]-Δ^1- and Δ^{6-3}, 4-cis-CBD were synthesized by two independent routes. Catalyzed cyclization of the cannabidiols resulted in the formation of different products which included cannabicitran and iso-THC derivatives. The amount of each product was dependent on the acid concentration. Detailed procedures are outlined.

3900   Haney, A.; and Kutscheid, B. B., Amer. Midl. Natur., *93*(1), 1-24 (1975).

An Ecological Study of Naturalized Hemp (*Cannabis sativa L.*) in East-Central Illinois.

A review of the early cultivation of hemp in the U.S. and a thorough ecological study (soil, foliage, height, sex, biomass, insects, etc.) of wild *Cannabis sativa L*.

3901   Hanley, J.; Tyrrell, E.; and Hahn, P., pp. 187-204 in *The Therapeutic Potential of Marihuana*, edited by S. Cohen and R. Stillman. NY, Plenum Medical Book Company, 1976.

Therapeutic Aspects of Marihuana: Computer Analyses of Electroencephalographic Data from Human Users of *Cannabis sativa*.

Computer analysis of EEG waves recorded for marihuana users and nonusers indicated a possible differentiation of these two states. Protocols of experiment and computer usage were described. The possible therapeutic value of marihuana as an anticonvulsant was also suggested since it decreases the energy of EEG signals.

3902   Hanna, J. M.; Hong, S. K.; Strauss, R. H.; Itagaki, B.; Bindon, J.; Stanyon, R.; and Kwon, W. J., Fed. Proc., *34*(3), 478 (1975).

Marijuana Smoking and Cold Exposure in Nude Men.

The effect of marihuana smoking on 4 physiological parameters was determined in nude men under cold exposure conditions (cold air and water). Skin temperature, metabolic rate, and heart rate were increased but rectal temperature was unchanged.

3903   Hanna, J. M.; Strauss, R. H.; Itagaki, B.; Kwon, W. J.; Stanyon, R.; Bindon, J.; and Hong, S. K., Aviat. Space Environ. Med., *47*(6), 634-39 (1976).

Marijuana Smoking and Cold Tolerance in Man.

In contrast to other animal species, human volunteers smoking marihuana (118 to 176 µg THC/kg) failed to show any rectal hypothermia when exposed to either cold air or cold water at 20°. Marihuana also increased the amount of heat produced in human volunteers exposed to cold temperatures. The mechanism of tachycardia produced with marihuana is also discussed.

3904 Hansteen, R. W.; Miller, R. D.; Lonero, L.; Reid, L. D.; and Jones, B., pp. 240-56 in *Chronic Cannabis Use*, edited by R. L. Dornbush, A. M. Freedman, and M. Fink. NY, Annals of the New York Academy of Sciences, V. 282, 1976.

Effects of Cannabis and Alcohol on Automobile Driving and Psychomotor Tracking.

High doses of Δ^9-THC produced performance decrement on automobile driving and psychomotor tracking tasks in experienced users. Also, Δ^9-THC, in low doses or in combination with alcohol, increased errors in complex tracking tasks with the combination causing additional impairment.

3905 Hanus, L., Acta Univ. Palacki. Olomuc. Fac. Med., *73*, 233-39 (1975).

The Present State of Knowledge in the Chemistry of Substances of *Cannabis sativa L*. III. Terpenoid Substances.

A review article on the terpenoid substances found in cannabis. Structures and physical data are given. This paper covers terpenoids identified prior to 1974. 15 references are given.

3906 Hanus, L., Acta Univ. Palacki. Olomuc. Fac. Med., *73*, 241-44 (1975).

The Present State of Knowledge in the Chemistry of Substances of *Cannabis sativa L*. IV. Nitrogen Containing Compounds.

A review of the nitrogen containing compounds found in cannabis. All compounds isolated prior to 1974 are included. Physical and structural data are given. 23 references are used.

3907 Hanus, L., Acta Univ. Palacki. Olomuc. Fac. Med., *76*, 153-66 (1976).

The Present State of Knowledge in the Chemistry of Substances of *Cannabis sativa L*. V. Addendum to Part I-IV.

A review of the constituents of *Cannabis sativa L*. including the hydrocarbons, cyclitols, sugars, noncannabinoid phenols, phytosterols, fatty acids, flavonoids and miscellaneous. 41 references are given.

3908 Hanus, L., Acta Univ. Palacki. Olomuc. Fac. Med., *76*, 167-73 (1976).

The Present State of Knowledge in the Chemistry of Substances of *Cannabis sativa L*. VI. The Other Contained Substances.

A review of the constituents of *Cannabis sativa L*. including the cannabinoids, cannabinoid metabolites, terpenoids, and nitrogen metabolites, terpenoids, and nitrogen containing compounds. 69 references are given.

3909 Hanus, L., Activ. Nerv. Super., *20*(4), 282-84 (1978).

A Contribution to the Content of the Psychotomimetically Active Δ^9-Tetrahydrocannabinol in Female (Marijuana) and Male Flowering Tops of *Cannabis sativa L*. Cultivated in Climatic Conditions of Czechoslovakia.

Male and female plants of a Czechoslovak variety of cannabis were examined for their cannabinoid content by TLC and capillary GC. The cannabinoid ratios were similar in both sexes. CBD and its acid prevailed over Δ^9-THC and its acid. However, the latter compounds were shown to prevail at certain stages of growth.

3910 Hanus, L.; Hruban, L.; and Krejci, Z., Acta Univ. Palacki. Olomuc. Fac. Med., *74*, 167-72 (1975).

Isolation of Cannabidiolic Acid from Turkish Variety of Cannabis Cultivated for Fiber.

Procedures used are for the isolation of cannabidiolic acid from plant material. IR, MS and NMR patterns are presented and described. The physical properties of methyl ester derivatives are also described. Other acids isolated during the extraction were not characterized.

3911   Hanus, L.; and Krejci, Z., Acta Univ. Palacki. Olomuc. Fac. Med., *74*, 161-66 (1975).

Isolation of Two New Cannabinoid Acids from *Cannabis sativa L.* of Czechoslovak Origin.

The isolation and identification of two new cannabinoid acids was reported. The acids were isolated as their methyl ethers and further purified by column chromatography. Spectroscopical data (NMR, IR, UV, MS) of the ethers indicated that one of the compounds was Δ^8-THC-acid and the structure of the other compound could not be determined but was tentatively named cannabioxoic acid.

3912   Hanus, L.; Yoshida, T.; and Krejci, Z., Acta Univ. Palacki. Olomuc. Fac. Med., *74*, 173-80 (1975).

Production of Δ^9-Tetrahydrocannabinol from Hemp Cultivated in Climatic Conditions of Czechoslovakia.

It was proven that hemp cultivated in Czechoslovakia can produce Δ^9-THC and Δ^9-THC acid in such quantities that 1 gram of hemp can produce a "high" when smoked.

3913   Harbison, R. D.; Mantilla-Plata, B.; and Lubin, D. J., J. Pharmacol. Exp. Ther., *202*(2), 455-65 (1977).

Alteration of Δ^9-Tetrahydrocannabinol-Induced Teratogenicity by Stimulation and Inhibition of its Metabolism.

Although pretreatment of pregnant mice with phenobarbital or SKF-525A enhanced the teratogenic effects of THC, the former decreased whereas the latter increased the levels of THC and metabolites in fetal and placental fluids. An intermediate THC metabolite is thought to be responsible for its induced teratogenesis.

3914   Hardman, H. F.; and Hosko, M. J., pp. 231-38 in *Pharmacology of Marihuana, Vol. 1*, edited by M. C. Braude and S. Szara. NY, Raven Press, 1976.

An Overview of the Cardiovascular-Autonomic Actions of Cannabis.

A review of the literature on the cardiovascular effects of THC. In cats and dogs, THC produces hypotension along with bradycardia. In humans tachycardis and increased BP is found. However, orthostatic hypotension is also present. Hypotension can be produced by stress and chronic THC use. There are probably two pharmacological effects of THC in the brain.

3915   Harmon, J. W.; Locke, D.; Aliapoulios, M. A.; and Macindoe, J. H., Surg. Forum, *27*(62), 350-52 (1976).

Interference with Testicular Development by Δ^9-THC.

Rats treated with Δ^9-THC (8 mg/kg, p.o.) not only had decreased testicular weight compared to controls, but also had decreased serum testosterone levels and increased serum FSH levels. Histological examination of the testis also showed that spermatogenesis was depressed.

3916 Harper, I., N. Z. Med. J., *81*, 361-62 (1975).

Cannabis Misuse.

The author opposes legalization of marihuana in New Zealand and gives three principal facts to support his position.

3917 Harper, J. W.; Heath, R. G.; and Myers, W. A., J. Neurosci. Res., *3*(2), 87-93 (1977).

Effects of *Cannabis sativa* on Ultrastructure of the Synapse in Monkey Brain.

Monkeys which had previously shown electroencephalographic changes following 3 months of marihuana dosing (equivalent to 7 joints a day in man) were shown to have been affected at the level of the synapse of a selected area of the septal brain region. Opaque granules appeared in the synaptic cleft region and there was some clumping of vesicles along with a widening of the cleft.

3918 Harris, L. S., pp. 299-312 in *The Therapeutic Potential of Marihuana*, edited by S. Cohen and R. Stillman. NY, Plenum Medical Book Company, 1976.

Analgesic and Antitumor Potential of the Cannabinoids.

Unlike THC, 9-OH-9-nor hexahydrocannabinol produced analgesia in animals. THC was the most efficacious cannabinoid tested as an antitumor agent both *in vivo* and *in vitro*, while CBD enhanced carcinogenicity.

3919 Harris, L. S., pp. 1565-74 in *Psychopharmacology: A Generation of Progress*, edited by M. A. Lipton, A. Dimascio, and K. F. Killam. New York, Raven Press, 1978.

Cannabis: A Review of Progress.

Advances in the field of marihuana research during the last decade were summarized. Some interesting highlights included the epidemiological studies conducted by NIDA and the Drug Abuse Council and the potential therapeutic effects of marihuana.

3920 Harris, L. S.; Carchman, R. A.; and Martin, B. R., Life Sci., *22*(13-15), 1131-37 (1978).

Evidence for the Existence of Specific Cannabinoid Binding Sites.

Data presented indicate that binding of Δ^9-THC to rat brain homogenate is specific and dependent on protein concentration and temperature. A high degree of binding also took place in hepatoma tissue culture cells. The possible stereospecificity of such a binding was discussed.

3921 Harris, L. S.; Carchman, R. A.; and Munson, A. E., Pharmacologist, *17*(1), 265 (1975).

Structure-Antitumor Activity of Cannabinoids.

After testing 21 cannabinoids, it was found that the location of double bond in the A ring does not influence antitumor activity, whereas the opening of the B ring enhances tumor growth. Other conclusions were also drawn.

3922 Harris, L. S.; Dewey, W. L.; and Razdan, R. K., pp. 371-429 in *Handbook of Experimental Pharmacology, Vol. 45, Drug Addiction 2: Amphetamine, Psychotogen and Marihuana Dependence*, edited by W. R. Martin. NY, Springer-Verlag, 1977.

Cannabis: Its Chemistry, Pharmacology,

and Toxicology.

A general review which includes the chemistry and isolation of cannabinoids and their absorption, distribution and fate after marihuana use. The pharmacology, toxicology, tolerance and therapeutic potential were also discussed.

3923   Harris, L. S.; Martin, B. R.; and Dewey, W. L., *Eleventh Collegium Internationale Neuro-Psychopharmacologicum: Abstracts*, Vienna, Austria, July 9-14, 1978, p. 145.

Role of Distribution and Metabolism in the Development of Tolerance to the Cannabinoids.

Tolerance development to the behavioral and other effects of cannabinoids, including Δ^9-THC, cannot be accounted for by distributional or metabolic factors.

3924   Harris, L. S.; Munson, A. E.; and Carchman, R. A., pp. 749-62 in *Pharmacology of Marihuana, Vol. 2*, edited by M. C. Braude and S. Szara. NY, Raven Press, 1976.

Antitumor Properties of Cannabinoids.

Δ^9-THC (25, 50 and 200 mg/kg, p.o.), Δ^9-THC and CBN inhibited primary Lewis lung tumor growth and increased the life expectancy of mice bearing it. *In vitro* studies indicated that a concentration of (2.5×10^{-6} M) of Δ^8-, Δ^9-THC and CBN inhibited the uptake of 3H-thymidine in these tumor cells. CBD, both *in vivo* and *in vitro*, was ineffective. The use of L1210 leukemia and normal bone marrow cells is also discussed.

3925   Harshman, R. A.; Crawford, H.; and Hecht, E., pp. 205-54 in *The Therapeutic Potential of Marihuana*, edited by S. Cohen and R. Stillman. NY, Plenum Medical Book Company, 1976.

Marihuana, Cognitive Style, and Lateralized Hemispheric Functions.

Marihuana intoxication shifts the cognition style by impairing functions closely associated with the left hemisphere and enhancing those related to the right hemisphere. Such a shift is partially accomplished by decreasing participation of the former and increasing that of the latter. Lateralized tests conducted on marihuana users supported these concepts but small sample size prevented statistical significance. Description of the protocol and samples of tests conducted were provided.

3926   Hart, R. H., J. Amer. Acad. Psychiat. Neurol., *1*(1), 25-26 (1976).

Chronic Effects of Cannabis.

The harmful physical and psychological effects of chronic cannabis use were cited in an effort to warn laymen against the dangers of cannabis use.

3927   Hart, R. H., J. Amer. Acad. Psychiat. Neurol., *1*(4), 83-97 (1976).

A Psychiatric Classification of Cannabis Intoxication.

Twelve case histories of marihuana intoxication illustrate a clinical classification of psychiatric conditions. Cannabis experiences have been erroneous compared to schizophrenic conditions, but are organic brain syndromes (psychotic or non-psychotic). Changing patterns of cannabis use are discussed from clinical experience.

3928   Hartelius, J., Lakartidningen, *73*(45), 3879-81 (1976).

Cannabis - Narkotikakonventioner, Lagstiftning och Lagstiftngdebatt [Narcotics Conventions, Legislation and Legal Debate].

Laws, treaties and legislation on cannabis use and cannabis traffic are discussed.

3929 Hartelius, J., Lakartidningen, *73*(45), 3882-85 (1976).

Cannabis - Subkulturer och Psykedelisk Filosof [Cannabis Subcultures and Psychedelic Philosophy].

This sociological review on cannabis abuse includes 9 references.

3930 Hartley, J. P. R.; Nogrady, S. G.; Seaton, A.; and Graham, J. D. P., *Seventh International Congress of Pharmacology: Abstracts*, Paris, France, July 16-21, 1978, p. 73.

Bronchodilator Effect of Δ^1-Tetrahydrocannabinol.

A dose-related bronchodilation was produced in asthmatic patients given 50, 100 and 200 µg of Δ^1-THC. A single dose of 100 µg, which is effective in 30 min. and lasts for at least 4 hrs., is suggested. Propranolol pretreatment failed to abolish this dilator effect of Δ^1-THC.

3931 Hartley, J. P. R.; Nogrady, S. G.; Seaton, A.; and Graham, J. D. P., Brit. J. Clin. Pharmacol., *5*(6), 523-25 (1978).

Bronchodilator Effect of Δ^1-Tetrahydrocannabinol.

A clinical study using 5 female patients examined the effects of Δ^9-THC on ventilatory function. Three doses of Δ^9-THC (50, 100 and 200 µg) administered by inhalation were found to increase peak expiratory flow rate and forced expiratory volume in 1 second in a dose-related manner.

3932 Harvey, D. J., Biomed. Mass Spectrom., *4*(2), 88-93 (1977).

Cyclic Alkylboronates as Derivatives for the Characterization of Cannabinolic Acids by Combined Gas Chromatography and Mass Spectrometry.

Formation of cyclic alkylboronate derivatives is proposed as superior to TMS derivatization in preparing cannabinolic acids for GC-MS analysis. The splitting patterns are more characteristic of the free (decarboxylated) cannabinoids, and increased versatility is claimed with respect to identification of isomeric cannabinolic acids.

3933 Harvey, D. J., Biomed. Mass Spectrom., *4*(4), 265-74 (1977).

Allyldimethylsilyl Ethers as Derivatives for the Characterization of Steroids and Cannabinoids by Combined Gas Chromatography and Mass Spectrometry.

MS data are presented for allyldimethylsilyl ethers of several cannabinoids. Fragmentation patterns are discussed. Fragmentation of allyl- and *t*-butyldimethylsilyl derivatives produced more abundant ions than did the regular TMS derivatives.

3934 Harvey, D. J., J. Chromatogr., *147*, 291-98 (1978).

Comparison of Fourteen Substituted Silyl Derivatives for the Characterization of Alcohols, Steroids and Cannabinoids by Combined Gas-Liquid Chromatography and Mass Spectrometry.

The GC-MS characteristics of 14 different silyl derivatives of the cannabinoids Δ^9-THC, CBD, CBN and 11-OH-Δ^9-THC and some aliphatic alcohols and steroids are studied. The methylene unit values of these derivatives are given. These derivatives include TMS, DMS, ADMS, PDMS, TBDMS, CMDMS, DCMDMC, DCMMS, PhDMS, BZDMS, TES, TPS, TBS and THC.

148

3935   Harvey, D. J., J. Pharm. Pharmacol., *28*, 280-85 (1976).

Characterization of the Butyl Homologues of Δ^1-Tetrahydrocannabinol, Cannabinol and Cannabidiol in Samples of Cannabis by Combined Gas Chromatography and Mass Spectrometry.

Identification of an even-numbered carbon side-chain homolog of Δ^9-THC using GC and GC/MS techniques is described. Samples were analyzed as TMS derivatives; the corresponding acid of the butyl homolog was also described. Extrapolation of methylene unit plot data accurately described the retention characteristics of the butyl homolog.

3936   Harvey, D. J.; Martin, B. R.; and Paton, W. D. M., pp. 403-28 in *Mass Spectrometry in Drug Metabolism, (Proc. Int. Symp.) 1976*, edited by A. Frigerio and E. L. Ghisalberti. NY, Plenum, 1977.

Characterization of *in vivo* Liver Metabolites of Delta-1-Tetrahydrocannabinol by EI and CI Mass Spectrometry.

The *in vivo* liver metabolism of Δ^9-THC was studied in the rat, mouse, and guinea-pig by electron impact and chemical ionization MS. Twenty-four metabolites were listed and the large degree of species variation was discussed. The metabolism of Δ^9-THC in the mouse and rat was similar, but fewer trisubstituted metabolites were observed in the mouse.

3937   Harvey, D. J.; Martin, B. R.; and Paton, W. D.M., Biochem. Pharmacol., *25*(19), 2217-19 (1976).

Identification of the Glucuronides of Cannabidiol and Hydroxy-Cannabidiols in Mouse Liver.

Hepatic metabolism of CBD is studied in male mice given CBD twice at 100 mg/kg, i.p. Following polar extraction of metabolites with ethyl acetate, purification of samples was conducted by means of column chromatography. Enzymatic hydrolysis with β-glucuronidase and GLC-MS were used to establish glucuronidation. Direct evidence for CBD and 47-OH CBD glucuronides is noted while the formation of 6-α-OH CBD glucuronide is suggested.

3938   Harvey, D. J.; Martin, B. R.; and Paton, W. D. M., Biomed. Mass Spectrom., *4*(6), 364-69 (1977).

In vivo Metabolism of Cannabinol by the Mouse and Rat and a Comparison with the Metabolism of Δ^1-THC and Cannabidiol.

The metabolism of CBN (100 mg/kg) following an i.p. injection was studied in the mouse and the rat. The metabolites isolated from liver were identified by GC-MS. The major metabolite identified was cannabinol glucuronide. Minor Metabolites included 7-OH-CBN, CBN-7-oic acid and two disubstituted metabolites.

3939   Harvey, D. J.; Martin, B. R.; and Paton, W. D. M., pp. 161-84 in *Recent Developments in Mass Spectrometry in Biochemistry and Medicine, (Proc. Int. Symp., 4th, 1977)*, edited by A. Frigerio. NY, Plenum, 1978.

Comparative *in vivo* Metabolism of Δ^1-Tetrahydrocannabinol (Δ^1-THC), Cannabidiol (CBD) and Cannabinol (CBN) by Several Species.

Major metabolic pathways for Δ^9-THC, CBN and CBD were investigated in mice, rats, and guinea pigs. It was found that CBN lacked allylic substitution and glucuronide formation was almost absent for Δ^9-THC biotransformation.

3940 Harvey, D. J.; Martin, B. R.; and Paton, W. D. M., J. Pharm. Pharmacol., *29*(8), 482-86 (1977).

Identification of Di- and Tri-Substituted Hydroxy and Ketone Metabolites of Δ^1-Tetrahydrocannabinol in Mouse Liver.

In vivo mouse liver metabolites of Δ^1-THC were analyzed as their TMS or methyloxime derivatives by GC-MS. Several new dihydroxylated and other oxygenated (ketones and hydroxy acids) could be detected.

3941 Harvey, D. J.; Martin, B. R.; and Paton, W. D. M., J. Pharm. Pharmacol., *29*(8), 495-97 (1977).

Identification of Metabolites of Δ^1- and $\Delta^{1\ (6)}$-Tetrahydrocannabinol Containing a Reduced Double Bond.

Metabolites of Δ^9-THC and Δ^8-THC obtained by *in vivo* metabolism in mice were examined by GC-MS analyses of their TMS-derivatives. The metabolites were found to be substituted HHC's.

3942 Harvey, D. J.; Martin, B. R.; and Paton, W. D. M., Res. Commun. Chem. Pathol. Pharmacol., *16*(2), 265-79 (1977).

Identification of Glucuronides as *in vivo* Liver Conjugates of Seven Cannabinoids and Some of their Hydroxy and Acid Metabolites.

Metabolic studies with various cannabinoids revealed that glucuronidation plays some role in the metabolism of these compounds. These metabolites were identified from liver extracts of mice treated with 100 mg/kg/dose (2 doses) of the cannabinoid by a combination of GC and GC-MS. Quantitatively CBD and CBN and their metabolites showed more extensive glucuronidation that Δ^9-THC and Δ^8-THC.

3943 Harvey, D. P.; and Paton, W. D. M., *Seventh International Congress of Pharmacology: Abstracts*, Paris, France, July 16-21, 1978, p. 455.

Effect of Deuterium Labelling on the Production of *in vivo* Metabolites of Δ^1-Tetrahydrocannabinol.

In animals treated with deuterium-labelled Δ^9-THC, displacement of deuterium or reduction of the concentration of metabolites involving attack at the labelled site can give information both on the structure of the metabolite and the mechanism for its formation. In fact, thirty metabolites have been identified using deuterium labelling.

3944 Harvey, D. J.; and Paton, W. D. M., J. Chromatogr., *109*(1), 73-80 (1975).

Use of Trimethylsilyl and Other Homologous Trialkylsilyl Derivatives for the Separation and Characterization of Mono- and Dihydroxycannabinoids by Combined Gas Chromatography and Mass Spectrometry.

A study of GC retention characteristics of various alkyl substituted silyl derivatized cannabinoids. Separation using the SE-30 column is largely mass dependent and retention times increase with the number of hydroxy groups available for derivatization. Increasing alkyl chain size from methyl through hexyl also leads to increased retention times. The large mass of the tri-*n*-hexyl group limited its utility in MS analysis.

3945 Harvey, D. J.; and Paton, W. D. M., J. Pharm. Pharmacol., *29*(8), 498-500 (1977).

In vivo Metabolites of $\Delta^{1\ (6)}$-Tetrahydrocannabinol Produced by the Mouse via the Epoxide-Diol Pathway.

Chromatography and MS analysis were used to isolate and identify four new metabolites of Δ^8-THC from mouse liver. Apparently microsomal peroxide formation occurs across the 1-6 carbons, followed by diol formation and subsequent hydroxylations of the alkyl chain.

3946   Harvey, D. J.; and Paton, W. D. M., pp. 93-109 in *Marihuana: Chemistry, Biochemistry, and Cellular Effects*, edited by G. G. Nahas. NY, Springer-Verlag, 1976.

Examination of the Metabolites of Δ^1-Tetrahydrocannabinol in Mouse Liver, Heart, and Lung by Combined Gas Chromatography and Mass Spectrometry.

This paper describes the extraction and GC/MS characterization of Δ^9-THC and several of its metabolites from mouse tissue (liver, heart and lung) after large i.p. doses were administered. Metabolites of Δ^9-THC so far identified in mouse were cited.

3947   Harvey, D. J.; and Paton, W. D. M., Res. Commun. Chem. Pathol. Pharmacol., *13*(4), 585-99 (1976).

Characterization of Three Monohydroxy-acid and Two Dihydroxyacid Metabolites of Δ^1-Tetrahydrocannabinol in Mouse Liver.

High doses of Δ^9-THC (750 mg/kg, i.p.) were given to mice on 2 successive days. Separation of the resulting metabolites from their liver extracts was carried out using Sephadex LH-20. Metabolites were then analyzed as their corresponding TMS-,d$_9$-TMS-,methylester-TMS-, and ethyl ester-TMS derivatives using combined GC-MS. Interpretation of results is discussed.

3948   Harvey, D. J.; and Paton, W. D. M., Res. Commun. Chem. Pathol. Pharmacol., *21*(3), 435-46 (1978).

Identification of Six Substituted 4"-Hydroxy-Metabolites of Δ^1-Tetrahydrocannabinol in Mouse Liver.

Mice treated with Δ^9-THC (10 to 750 mg/kg) were found to form six 4"-hydroxy-metabolites in their liver. Identification of these new metabolites involved the use of a combination of GC-MS techniques.

3949   Hasleton, S.; and Simmonds, D., Brit. J. Addict., *70*(3), 325-34 (1975).

Is Australia Going to Pot: Some Trends Relating to Marihuana.

A probability sample of the Australian population suggested that some relaxations of marihuana use may be tolerated. If these trends continue, modifications of marihuana laws might be necessary.

3950   Hattendorf, C.; Hattendorf, M.; Coper, H.; and Fernandes, M., Psychopharmacology, *54*(2), 177-82 (1977).

Interaction Between Δ^9-Tetrahydrocannabinol and *d*-Amphetamine.

THC (10 mg/kg) enhanced *d*-amphetamine-induced anorexia and prolonged its stereotypic effect in rats. The motor stimulant and hyperthermic effects of amphetamine were also antagonized by THC. No evidence of cross tolerance was found between the two agents and the effects of the combined treatment on brain catecholamine levels were reported.

3951   Hattori, T.; and McGeer, P. L., Toxicol. Appl. Pharmacol., *39*(2), 307-11 (1977).

Electron Microscopic Autoradiography on Δ^8-[^{3}H] Tetrahydrocannabinol Localization in Brain Tissue.

Labeled Δ^8-THC was found to accumulate preferentially in the terminal boutons of young and adult rat brains. The THC-induced inhibition of protein and nucleic acid synthesis is thought to affect its localization in certain brain regions.

3952 Hawks, D., pp. 379-416 in *Cannabis and Health*, edited by J. D. P. Graham. London, Academic Press, 1976.

The Law Relating to Cannabis 1964-1973: How Subtle an Ass?

There is no need to reform or revive the present British law relative to cannabis use since its benefits are much more than credited and its cost is exaggerated. The law, as implemented, is quite different than that in the U.S.A.; hence extrapolation of findings from one country to the other is hazardous.

3953 Heath, R. G., pp. 507-20 in *Marihuana: Chemistry, Biochemistry, and Cellular Effects*, edited by G. G. Nahas. NY, Springer-Verlag, 1976.

Cannabis sativa Derivatives: Effects on Brain Function of Monkeys.

Studies were undertaken on *Cannabis sativa* derivatives in rhesus monkeys under accurately controlled conditions. Experiments were designed to determine if ingredients of *C. sativa L.* administered in dosages used by some human subjects caused alterations in brain functions or irreversible brain damage, as well as altered behavior in rhesus monkeys.

3954 Heath, R. G., pp. 345-56 in *Pharmacology of Marihuana, Vol. 1*, edited by M. C. Braude and S. Szara. NY, Raven Press, 1976.

Marihuana and Δ^9-Tetrahydrocannabinol: Acute and Chronic Effects on Brain Function of Monkeys.

Acute effects of Δ^9-THC in monkeys included lack of awareness of the environment, decreased response to internal stimuli, blank staring and changes in the recordings of electrodes in the hippocampus, amygdala, and septal areas. Permanent organic brain damage was noted after chronic exposure. Two lethalities were noted at the highest dose, probably due to lung complications.

3955 Hembree, M. W.; Nahas, G. G.; and Zeidenberg, P., Bull. Acad. Natl. Med., *160*(1), 101-06 (1976).

Oligospermie des Fumeurs de Chanvre [Oligospermia in Cannabis Smokers].

In this work the authors reported the inhibitory effect of cannabis on spermatogenesis in chronic cannabis smokers.

3956 Hembree, W. C.; Nahas, G. G.; Zeidenberg, P.; and Dyrenfurth, I., Clin. Res., *24*(3), 272A (1976).

Marihuana Effects upon the Human Testis.

Marihuana (90-250 cigarettes/week, each containing 20 mg THC) produced decrease in sperm count and motility without a concomitant change in LH and FSH levels. These results suggest that THC may be affecting sperm function by a direct effect on the germinal epithelium of the testis.

3957 Hembree, W. C.; Zeidenberg, P.; and Nahas, G., pp. 521-32 in *Marihuana: Chemistry, Biochemistry, and Cellular Effects*, edited by G. G. Nahas. NY, Springer-Verlag, 1976.

Marihuana's Effects on Human Gonadal Functions.

Effects of marihuana on human gonadal function are studied. Human volunteers smoked increasing amounts of marihuana after which serum samples were taken and analyzed for testosterone, LH, and FSH by RIA. Semen samples were obtained and qualitatively and quantitatively studied using different techniques.

3958   Hemphill, J. K.; Mahlberg, P. G.; Turner, J. C.; and Hughes, W., Plant Physiol., *57*(5), 106 (1976).

Effects of Wavelengths of Light on Cannabinoid Composition in Cannabis.

A THC-strain of cannabis grown under light of different wavelenghts was analyzed for CBD/CBC, CBN and THC. The influence of the wavelength on cannabinoid composition was discussed.

3959   Hemphill, J. K.; Turner, J. C.; and Mahlberg, P. G., Lloydia, *41*(5), 453-62 (1978).

Studies on Growth and Cannabinoid Composition of Callus Derived from Different Strains of *Cannabis sativa*.

Culture media influenced the growth of cellus derived from Mexican and Turkish cannabis plant organs. The ability of these callus strains to synthesize cannabinoids was influenced by manipulating experimental conditions.

3960   Hendriks, H.; Malingre, T. M.; Batterman, S.; and Bos. R., Pharm. Weekbl., *113*(17), 413-24 (1978).

The Essential Oil of *Cannabis sativa L*.

The chemical composition of the steam distilled essential oil of cannabis was studied and compared with that of *Humulus lupulus* (hops). Fractions of the volatile oil containing alkanes, terpenes and oxygenated compounds were prepared through column chromatography. Each fraction was analyzed by GC/MS.

3961   Hendriks, H.; Malingre, T. M.; Batterman, S.; and Bos. R., Phytochemistry, *14*, 814-15 (1975).

Mono- and Sesqui-Terpene Hydrocarbons of the Essential Oil of *Cannabis sativa*.

Mono- and sesqui-terpene hydrocarbons were isolated and listed with those previously reported. Isocaryophyllene, β-seliene, selina-3,7(11) diene and selina-4(14),7(11) diene were identified in cannabis for the first time.

3962   Hendriks, H.; Malingre, T. M.; Batterman, S.; and Bos. R., Phytochemistry, *16*(6), 719-21 (1977).

Alkanes of the Essential Oil of *Cannabis sativa*.

Essential oil of *Cannabis sativa* when column chromatographed gave a waxy fraction, shown by GC-MS to consist of n-alkanes ranging from C_9 to C_{39}, 2-methyl and 3-methyl alkanes and some dimethyl alkanes (GLC on OV-1 and OV-17). The qualitative and quantitative composition of this fraction has been compared with the alkane fraction obtained by extraction of the herb.

3963   Hendriks, H.; Malingre, T. M.; Batterman, S.; and Bos. R., Planta Med., *33*(3), 280-81 (1978).

The Essential Oil of *Cannabis sativa L*.

An abstract comparing the essential oil of cannabis with that of humulus.

3964   Henke, G., J. Radioanal. Chem., *39*(1), 69-83 (1977).

Activation Analysis of Rare-Earth Elements in Opium and Cannabis Samples.

If cannabis resins and plant materials contained a low or extremely high level of rare-earth elements or ratios thereof, the detection of cannabis material would be facilitated through the technique of neutron activation analysis. This report, however, states that the relative levels of these elements in cannabis and opium samples is similar to that of the upper continental earth's crust and not unique.

3965   Henriksson, B. G.; Johansson, J. O.; and Jarbe, T. U. C., Pharmacol. Biochem. Behav., *3*, 771-74 (1975).

Δ^9-Tetrahydrocannabinol Produced Discrimination in Pigeons.

Pigeons differentially responded in drugged and nondrugged states of THC. They could also discriminate THC from CBN, CBD, pentobarbital, *d*-amphetamine and ditran but LSD-25 confused them.

3966   Hepler, R. S.; Frank, I. M.; and Petrus, R., pp. 815-28 in *Pharmacology of Marihuana, Vol. 2*, edited by M. C. Braude and S. Szara. NY, Raven Press, 1976.

Ocular Effects of Marihuana Smoking.

Acute or chronic marihuana administration, smoked or taken orally, reduced the ocular pressure in normal subjects and in 7/11 glaucoma patients. Marihuana smoke or marihuana applied topically also decreased the ocular pressure in rabbits.

3967   Hepler, R. S.; and Petrus, R., pp. 63-75 in *The Therapeutic Potential of Marihuana*, edited by S. Cohen and R. Stillman. NY, Plenum Medical Book Company, 1976.

Experiences with Administration of Marihuana to Glaucoma Patients.

Marihuana smoking reduced the IOP in a high percentage of glaucoma patients. The possible use of marihuana as an adjunct therapy to conventional medications of glaucoma was suggested.

3968   Herman, T. S.; Jones, S. E.; Dean, J.; Leigh, S.; Dorr, R.; Moon, T. E.; and Salmon, S. E., Biomedicine, *27*(9-10), 331-34 (1977).

Nabilone: A Potent Antiemetic Cannabinol with Minimal Euphoria.

In patients under cancer chemotherapy, the synthetic cannabinol nabilone exerted strong antiemetic effects while producing minimal euphoria and acceptable side effects.

3969   Hernandez-Bolanos, J.; Swenson, E. W.; and Coggins, W. J., Amer. Rev. Resp. Dis., *113*(4), 100 (1976).

Preservation of Pulmonary Function in Regular, Heavy, Long-Term Marijuana Smokers.

Chronic, heavy, adult male marihuana smokers matched for cigarette consumption and age were subjected to a battery of lung function tests. Results indicate improvement in oxygen flow in small airways in the presence of bronchodilatation.

3970   Hershkowitz, M.; Goldman, R.; and Raz, A.; Biochem. Pharmacol., *26*(14), 1327-31 (1977).

Effect of Cannabinoids on Neurotransmitter Uptake, ATPase Activity and Morphology of Mouse Brain Synaptosomes.

Uptake of NE, DA, 5-HT, and GABA by mouse brain synaptosomes was inhibited in a dose-related manner by

THC and CBD. Na^+-K^+-ATPase and Mg-ATPase were also inhibited by the two cannabinoids. The possible mechanisms involved in neurotransmitter uptake inhibition were discussed.

3971 Hildebrand, D. C.; and McCain, A. H., Phytopathology, *68*(7), 1099-1101 (1978).

The Use of Various Substrates for Large-Scale Production of *Fusarium oxysporum f. sp. Cannabis* Inoculum.

Large-scale production of *Fusarium oxysporum f. sp. cannabis* which could be an ideal fungus for biological control of *Cannabis sativa*.

3972 Hill, R. D.; and Dodder, R. A., Int. Rev. Mod. Sociol., *8*(1), 75-87 (1978).

A Reference Group Theory of Marihuana Use.

Children of parents opposed to marihuana would not use it to the extent that they are affectively satisfied with their parents and have ideological similarity to them. Otherwise, association with marihuana users will lead to its use.

3973 Hill, S. Y.; and Goodwin, D., pp. 139-52 in *The Therapeutic Potential of Marihuana*, edited by S. Cohen and R. Stillman. NY, Plenum Medical Book Company, 1976.

Stimulant Effects of Marihuana on Three Neuropsychological Systems.

Marihuana was found to produce a state dependent learning for tasks sensitive to dissociation, to enhance the critical flicker fusion threshold and to have no analgesic activity when inhaled (12 mg of THC) by experienced smokers. Protocols employed were described.

3974 Hillestad, A.; and Wold, J. K., Phytochemistry, *16*(12), 1947-51 (1977).

Water-Soluble Glycoproteins from *Cannabis sativa* (South Africa).

Chemical studies carried out on the glycoprotein fractions indicated that the carbohydrate and protein are connected via serine-*O*-galactoside linkage. Further analysis of the carbohydrate part was carried out.

3975 Hillestad, A.; Wold, J. K.; and Engen, T., Phytochemistry, *16*(12), 1953-56 (1977).

Water-Soluble Glycoproteins from *Cannabis sativa* (Thailand).

Several glycoproteins were isolated from aqueous extracts of cannabis leaves (plants of Thai origin). Separation and characterization of carbohydrate moeties are discussed. The Thailand material differed mostly from corresponding South African cannabis leaves in that the former contained no hydroxyproline.

3976 Hillestad, A.; Wold, J. K.; and Paulsen, B. S., Carbohyd. Res., *57*, 135-44 (1977).

Structural Studies of Water-Soluble Glycoproteins from *Cannabis sativa L.*

Arabinose, galactose, mannose, galacturonic acid, 2-acetamido-2-deoxyglucose and 2-acetamido-2-deoxygalactose were detected in a carbohydrate-protein fraction of *Cannabis sativa L.* Purification, characterization and some structure details of this fraction were also reported.

3977 Hindmarch, I., Brit. J. Addict., *73*(1), 75-76 (1978).

Some Aspects of Chronic Cannabis Use in the United Kingdom.

Habitual cannabis users in the U.K. seemed satisfied with cannabis samples low in THC. A freer availability of cannabis may only result in more potent substances that would be much more hazardous.

3978   Hindmarch, I.; Hughes, I.; and Einstein, R., Bull. Narcotics, *27*(1), 27-36 (1975).

Attitudes to Drug Users and to the Use of Alcohol, Tobacco and Cannabis on the Campus of a Provincial University.

Cannabis was not considered a social drug among this student sample. Unlike alcohol and tobacco, the attitude of cannabis users differed greatly from that of non-users. The degree of use also reflected attitude held by users.

3979   Hine, B.; Friedman, E.; Torrellio, M.; and Gershon, S., Neuropharmacology, *14*(8), 607-10 (1975).

Tetrahydrocannabinol-Attenuated Abstinence and Induced Rotation in Morphine-Dependent Rats: Possible Involvement of Dopamine.

The authors suggest that the synergism between haloperidol and Δ^9-THC in attenuating morphine abstinence, and the attenuation by haloperidol of THC-induced rotation could have important implications for clinical narcotic detoxification programs.

3980   Hine, B.; Friedman, E.; Torrelio, M.; and Gershon, S., Science, *187*, 443-45 (1975).

Morphine-Dependent Rats: Blockade of Precipitated Abstinence by Tetrahydrocannabinol.

Rats were implanted with s.c. morphine pellets, then injected i.p. with 4 mg/kg naloxone 72 hours later. Treatment with 1, 2, 5 or 10 mg/kg Δ^9-THC OR 10 mg/kg CBD 1 hour prior to naloxone administration was investigated. Cannabinoids did not induce abstinence, but 2, 5 and 10 mg/kg THC did significantly reduce the appearance of several symptoms associated with naloxone-induced withdrawal.

3981   Hine, B.; Friedman, E.; Torrelio, M.; and Gershon, S., Science, *190*(4214), 590-01 (1975).

Blockade of Morphine Abstinence by Delta-9-Tetrahydrocannabinol.

Δ^9-THC at doses of 2 mg/kg or higher causes a significant dose-dependent decrease in 9 components of a naloxone-precipitated abstinence syndrome. The mode of THC administration as a source of response variability is discussed.

3982   Hine, B.; Torrelio, M.; and Gershon, S., Life Sci., *17*(6), 851-58 (1975).

Interactions Between Cannabidiol and Δ^9-THC During Abstinence in Morphine-Dependent Rats.

CBD (10 mg/kg, i.p.) was administered to rats implanted with 75 mg morphine pellets. CBD did not prevent the abstinence signs of morphine dependent rats when naloxone was administered as Δ^9-THC does. CBD did potentiate the abstinence attenuating properties of Δ^9-THC and the rotational behavior.

3983   Hine, B.; Torrelio, M.; and Gershon, S., Pharmacology, *15*(1), 65-72 (1977).

Analgesic, Heart Rate, and Temperature Effects of Δ^8-THC During Acute and Chronic Administration to Conscious Rats.

Δ^8-THC induces analgesia and hypothermia and decreases the heart rate in

156

rats. Tolerance to these responses, especially the latter, develops after repeated administration.

3984　Hine, B.; Torrelio, M.; and Gershon, S., Psychopharmacol. Commun., *1*(3), 275-83 (1975).

Attenuation of Precipitated Abstinence in Methadone-Dependent Rats by Δ^9-THC.

Methadone-dependent rats given 10 mg/kg of Δ^9-THC one hour before challenge with naloxone were blocked of abstinence signs almost identically with that reported for morphine-dependent animals. Abstinence signs were not blocked by CBD in dependent animals.

3985　Hine, B.; Torrelio, M.; and Gershon, S., Res. Commun. Chem. Pathol. Pharmacol., *12*(1), 185-88 (1975).

Differential Effects of Cannabinol and Cannabidiol on THC-Induced Responses During Abstinence in Morphine-Dependent Rats.

A pellet of morphine base (75 mg) was implanted in male rats. Two i.p. injections of CBN (10 or 50 mg/kg), CBD (1 mg/kg), or Δ^9-THC (2 mg/kg) were administered. CBN increased abstinence-attenuating properties of Δ^9-THC. The amount of turning was half as great as observed with CBD on THC-induced rotation. Marihuana may ameliorate narcotic withdrawal.

3986　Ho, B. T.; and Johnson, K. M., pp. 367-82 in *Marihuana: Chemistry, Biochemistry, and Cellular Effects*, edited by G. G. Nahas. NY, Springer-Verlag, 1976.

Sites of Neurochemical Action of Δ^9-Tetrahydrocannabinol Interaction with Reserpine.

Due to a limited knowledge of the mechanism of action of Δ^9-THC on the brain, the authors studied the interactions of Δ^9-THC with reserpine to determine the site of action of some neurochemical effects of Δ^9-THC.

3987　Hochhauser, M., Amer. J. Drug Alcohol Abuse, *4*(1), 65-76 (1977).

Alcohol and Marijuana Consumption Among Undergraduate Polydrug Users.

In a sample of undergraduates, marihuana was the most preferred drug after alcohol. While the latter was the first to be used, it was later combined with marihuana. Polydrug use was also expanded in some cases to 14 combinations.

3988　Hoekman, T. B.; Dettbarn, W.-D.; and Klausner, H. A., Neuropharmacology, *15*(5), 315-19 (1976).

Actions of Δ^9-Tetrahydrocannabinol on Neuromuscular Transmission in the Rat Diaphragm.

Although no difference was detected in resting membrane potentials between control and Δ^9-THC treated rat phrenic nerve-diaphragm preparations, there was an increase in both amplitude and frequency of miniature and plate potentials (MEPP). The duration of MEPP at 50% of peak amplitude also increased without a concomitant increase in amplitude. Δ^9-THC effects on other aspects of synaptic transmission electro-dynamics and cholinesterase activity were also investigated.

3989　Hoellinger, H.; Nguyen-Hoang-Nam; Decauchereux, J.-F.; and Pichat, L., J. Label. Compd. Radiopharm., *13*(3), 401-15 (1977).

Synthese de $\triangle^8$- et $\triangle^9$-Tetrahydrocannabinol Deuteries et Trities [Synthesis of Deuterated and Tritiated $\triangle^8$- and $\triangle^9$-Tetrahydrocannabinol].

Deuterated and tritiated $\triangle^8$- and $\triangle^9$-THC were prepared by catalytic reduction of the corresponding 4',5'-dehydroderivatives with deuterium and tritium, respectively. A procedure was outlined for the synthesis of the 4',5'-dehydroderivatives.

3990   Hoellinger, H.; Scherrmann, J.; Nguyen-Hoang-Nam; and Fournier, E., Ann. Med. Nancy, *17*, 405-06, 08 (1978).

Methodes d'Identification et de Dosage du Delta-9-THC dans les Fluides Biologiques [Methods for the Identification and Determination of Delta-9-THC in Biological Fluids].

The authors compared different methods for the detection and analysis of $\triangle^9$-THC in biological fluids (plasma and urine). A table was presented with the sensitivity, specificity and reproducibility of each method with certain biological fluids. Discussion was given for toxicological and medicolegal aspects.

3991   Hoffmann, D.; Brunnemann, K. D.; Gori, G. B.; and Wynder, E. L., Rec. Adv. in Phytochem., *9*, 63-81 (1975).

On the Carcinogenicity of Marijuana Smoke.

Marihuana and tobacco smoke were analyzed for toxic and teratogenic agents. Particulate matter for organic gas phases of the smokes were qualitatively similar, with much more isoprene in tobacco smoke. Particulate matter analyses showed 50% more volatile phenois (promoters) in tobacco smoke and also a 6-fold increase in $\triangle^9$-THC content over marihuana leaves.

Marihuana smoke contained 50% more polycyclic hydrocarbons (carcinogenic) than did tobacco smoke.

3992   Holley, J. H.; Hadley, K. W.; and Turner, C. E., J. Pharm. Sci., *64*(5), 892-95 (1975).

Constituents of *Cannabis sativa L*. XI. Cannabidiol and Cannabichromene in Samples of Known Geographical Origin.

An investigation into the variation of cannabinoid contents in cannabis from known geographical origins is presented. The ratios and abundance of CBD and CBC in freshly grown cannabis material are given. CBD is absent in many variants. A separation procedure is given for CBD and CBC.

3993   Hollister, L. E., *Eleventh Collegium Internationale Neuro-psychopharmacologicum: Abstracts*, Vienna, Austria, July 9-14, 1978, p. 143.

Cannabis Constituents and Homologs: Clinical Studies.

Attempts have been made to correlate the plasma concentrations of $\triangle^9$-THC with its clinical effects. Also, investigations of the therapeutic actions of various THC homologs disclosed that nabilone was not as effective as diazepam in an experimental model of human anxiety. The question of whether cannabis will prove to be a therapeutic agent remains to be answered.

3994   Hollister, L. E., pp. 212-18 in *Interactions of Drug Abuse*, edited by E. S. Vesell and M. C. Braude. NY, Annals of the New York Academy of Sciences, V. 281, 1976.

Interactions of $\triangle^9$-Tetrahydrocannabinol with Other Drugs.

Alcohol, the most frequently used drug with marihuana, was the only drug studied and found to possess additive effects to marihuana. The use of several widely different agents, such as phenitrone, tamarind or ice cream, did not antagonize the effects of marihuana. Studies on the interaction between THC and cannabinoids or agents affecting brain amines were discussed. The rate of metabolism and the setting in which marihuana was taken did not explain the wide individual differences in response to the agents.

3995   Hollister, L. E., Life Sci., *17*(5), 661-68 (1975).

Minireview: Drugs and Sexual Behavior in Man.

The influence of drugs, cannabis included, on human sexual behavior is a complex issue. In low doses, cannabis acts as an aphrodisiac. In high doses, the reverse is true.

3996   Hollister, L. E., pp. 35-36 in *Pharmacology of Marihuana, Vol. 1*, edited by M. C. Braude and S. Szara. NY, Raven Press, 1976.

Reflections on Marihuana Research.

The proliferation of marihuana data has been stimulated primarily by NIDA through its supply program and funding allocations. The evolution of marihuana research is outlined with recent evidence suggesting some therapeutic utility. Social marihuana use must be predicted on an informed risk-benefit estimate.

3997   Hollister, L. E., Psychopharmacol. Bull., *11*(3), 44 (1975).

Drugs and Sexual Behavior in Man.

Social drugs and their effect on sexual behavior and function are discussed. Very few are actual aphrodisiacs. Hallucinogens and marihuana may enhance orgasm, but endocrine changes diminish sexual functions with prolonged use.

3998   Hollister, L. E.; and Gillespie, H., Clin. Pharmacol. Ther., *18*(1), 80-83 (1975).

Interactions in Man of Delta-9-Tetrahydrocannabinol. II. Cannabinol and Cannabidiol.

Fifteen volunteer subjects received either a combined treatment of 20 mg of THC with extracted marihuana placebo, with 40 mg of CBN or with 40 mg of CBD. Clinical evaluations indicated insignificant alteration of THC effect when combined with other cannabinoids and compared to THC alone.

3999   Hollister, L. E.; and Gillespie, H. K., Clin. Pharmacol. Ther., *18*(6), 714-19 (1975).

Action of Delta-9-Tetrahydrocannabinol.

Subjects were rated as rapid or slow hydroxylators according to the results of antipyrine and phenylbutazone plasma disappearance rates. They then received 50 μg/kg THC, i.v. No correlations were found between rate of metabolism and effects of THC.

4000   Hollister, L. E.; and Overall, J. E., Drug Alcohol Depend., *1*, 155-64 (1975/1976).

Dimensions of Marihuana Experience.

A questionnaire of 72 adjectives was completed by 182 subjects as to the amount of marihuana and effects most experienced (somatic, perceptual, social, etc.). The results showed that experiences are subjective and multidimensional.

4001   Hollister, L. E.; Overall, J. E.; and Gerber, M. L., Arch. Gen. Psychiat., 32(6), 798-80 (1975).

Marihuana and Setting.

Twelve male casual users of marihuana were given either placebo cigarettes or ones containing 19 mg THC in favorable and unfavorable environments. Results showed that effects depend more on the subject and the drug than on the setting.

4002   Holmstedt, B., Laekartidningen, 73(45), 3853-56 (1976).

Cannabis-Kulturhistorisk och Vetenskaplig Utveckling [Cannabis-Its History and Scientific Development].

This historical review on cannabis use includes 37 references.

4003   Hood, L. V. S.; and Barry, G. T., J. Chromatogr., 166(2), 499-506 (1978).

Headspace Volatiles of Marihuana and Hashish: Gas Chromatographic Analysis of Samples of Different Geographic Origin.

Headspace volatiles of different marihuana samples and hashish of different goegraphical origins were analyzed by GC method on two different columns (OV-101 and Reoplex-400). Although no correlation between the composition and geography of the volatiles was possible, the data could be useful in the forensic problem of relating samples to common source.

4004   Hornung, R., Soz. Praeventivmed., 21(5), 221-22 (1976).

Furchterregung der Botschaft, Glaubwurdigkeit des Kommunikators und die Einstellung zu Haschisch [Fear Arousal of the Message, Credibility of the Communicator, and Attitude to Hashish].

Communicator credibility influenced teenagers' attitude toward hashish.

4005   Horowitz, L. G.; and Nersasian, R. R., J. Amer. Dent. Ass., 96(6), 983-86 (1978).

A Review of Marijuana in Relation to Stress-Response Mechanisms in the Dental Patient.

A comprehensive review of a number of complicating factors which should be considered in the preoperative, operative and postoperative management of a chronic marihuana user needing dental treatment was undertaken. These factors are cardiovascular in nature and may be life threatening under stressful conditions such as oral surgery.

4006   Horowitz, M., Bull. Narcotics, 29(1), 75-84 (1977).

Herbicidal Treatments for Control of Cannabis sativa L.

A series of 49 commercially available herbicides were tested for the ability to destroy illicit stands of cannabis. Each herbicide was tested on greenhouse-grown plants and in field experiments. Agents were chosen which would be effective pre- and early post-emergents. Data on the persistence in soil and crop selectivity is included.

4007   Hosko, M. J.; and Hardman, H. F., pp. 239-53 in Pharmacology of Marihuana, Vol. 1, edited by M. C. Braude and S. Szara. NY, Raven Press, 1976.

Evidence for a Dual Mechanism of Action of Cannabis on Central Cardiovascular Control.

BP was depressed in response to Δ^9-THC (1.0 mg/kg, i.v.) in cats anesthetized by choralose-urethane (CU) or dialkylbarbiturate urethane (DU). Cervical transection of spinal cord resulted in loss of ability of Δ^9-THC to reduce BP but midbrain section did not affect this response. Pressor response produced by electrical stimulation in the medullary vasomotor center was depressed by THC in CU anesthetized cats but increased in DU treated cats. Human studies confirmed the above hypothesis.

4008 Houser, V. P., Physiol. Psychol., 3(2), 157-61 (1975).

The Effects of Δ^9-Tetrahydrocannabinol Upon Fear-Motivated Behavior in Squirrel Monkeys.

Three doses of THC (40, 80 and 120 mg/kg) were administered orally to six squirrel monkeys which were subjected to a Sidman nondiscriminated avoidance schedule that superimposed conditioned stimuli. Some behavioral measures were affected by all THC doses while the highest dose affected avoidance response and higher shock rates. Response-facilitation-ratio measures are more sensitive to the effects of THC than the simple overall response ratio.

4009 Howes, J. F.; and Osgood, P. F., pp. 415-24 in Marihuana: Chemistry, Biochemistry, and Cellular Effects, edited by G. G. Nahas. NY, Springer-Verlag, 1976.

Cannabinoids and the Inhibition of Prostaglandin Synthesis.

Direct and indirect pharmacological evidences are accumulating to show that Δ^9-THC and other cannabinoid-like agents affect prostaglandin synthesis. This is indicated by physiological changes that are attributable to inhibition of prostaglandin synthesis.

4010 Hrbek, J.; Komenda, S.; Macakova, J.; Siroka, A.; and Carbol, L., Acta Univ. Palacki. Olomuc. Fac. Med., 75, 423-33 (1975).

On the Acute Effect of Some Drugs on the Higher Nervous Activity in Man. Smoking Tetrahydrocannabinol with Tobacco. Part 33A. A Partial Analysis of the Effect of the Drugs Merely on the Couples of Involved Optic Associations.

No significant differences were caused by Δ^9-THC (8, 16 and 24 mg with tobacco) on the formation of artificial conditioned speech connections accomplished in 16 volunteers by means of two optic associations (among a total of six).

4011 Hrbek, J.; Komenda, S.; Macakova, J.; Siroka, A.; Chmelikova, M., Acta Univ. Palacki. Olomuc. Fac. Med., 75, 435-46 (1975).

On the Acute Effect of Some Drugs on the Higher Nervous Activity in Man. Smoking Tetrahydrocannabinol with Tobacco. Part 33B. A Partial Analysis of the Effect of the Drugs Merely on the Couples of Involved Complex Tactile Associations.

Effects of smoking THC (8, 16 and 24 mg) with tobacco or a placebo on the formation of artificial conditioned speech connections in 16 volunteers were investigated. A significant improvement was found in the number of necessary repetitions 15 min. after smoking a mixture of 8 mg THC + 1.0 g tobacco.

4012 Hrbek, J.; Komenda, S.; Macakova, J.; Siroka, A.; Chmelikova, M., Acta Univ. Palacki. Olomuc. Fac. Med., 75, 447-58 (1975).

On the Acute Effect of Some Drugs on the Higher Nervous Activity in Man. Smoking Tetrahydrocannabinol with Tobacco. Part 33C. A Partial Analysis of the Effect of the Drugs Merely on the Couples of Involved Acoustic Associations.

Human performance as measured by means of couples of acoustic associations improved significantly after 75 minutes of smoking THC.

4013   Hrbek, J.; Komenda, S.; Navratil, J.; and Siroka, A., Agressologie, *19D*, 197-99 (1978).

Comparative Effects of Smoking Marihuana (with Tobacco) in Men and Women.

Females were more susceptible to marihuana impairment of performance than were males.

4014   Hrbek, J.; Komenda, S.; Siroka, A.; Mackova, J.; and Vedlich, L., Acta Univ. Palacki. Olomuc. Fac. Med., *75*, 409-22 (1975).

On the Acute Effect of Some Drugs on the Higher Nervous Activity in Man. Smoking Tetrahydrocannabinol with Tobacco. Part 33.

Δ^9-THC (8 mg with tobacco) induced a certain degree of improvement in the formation of artificial conditioned speech connections 15 min. after its administration to 16 healthy volunteers. A marked improvement in the number of correct responses and the number of necessary repetitions was detected 75 min. after the administration of 8 and 16 mg of Δ^9-THC.

4015   Hrbek, J.; Komenda, S.; Siroka, A.; Navatil, J.; and Macakova, J.; Agressologie, *19D*, 201-02 (1978).

The Effect of Smoking THC on Verbal Associations.

The effects of smoking denicotinized tobacco impregnated with Δ^9-THC (4, 12 and 24 mg) on artificial conditioned speech connections were investigated in 16 university students. Although the number of correct reactions was decreased by the higher doses of THC, the number of necessary repetitions was not markedly affected.

4016   Huang, H. F. S.; Nahas, G. G.; and Hembree, W. C., Fed. Proc., *37*(3), 739 (1978).

Morphological Changes of Spermatozoa During Marihuana Induced Depression of Human Spermatogenesis.

A significant decrease in total spermatozoa count was noted in 12 of 16 male marihuana users in spite of unchanged LH, FSH and testosterone levels. Abnormal types of spermatozoa included small heads, tapered heads and amorphous forms.

4017   Huber, G.; O'Connel, D.; McCarthy, C.; Pereira, W.; Mahajan, V.; and Mullane, J., Clin. Res., *24*(3), 255A (1976).

Toxicologic Pharmacology of Tetrahydrocannabinol (THC) and Marijuana (MJ) Smoke Components (Abstract).

THC and whole marijuana smoke was found to depress immune response to *S. aureus* in rat lung. Analysis of the smoke components revealed that a water soluble component of the gas phase contained the cytotoxins. This component, however, had no psychomimetic effect.

4018   Huber, G. L.; Simmons, G. A.; McCarthy, C. R.; Cutting, M. B.; Laguarda, R.; and Pereira, W., Chest, *68*(6), 769-73 (1975).

Depressant Effect of Marihuana Smoke on Antibactericidal Activity on Pulmonary Alveolar Macrophages.

Marihuana was cytotoxic to alveolar macrophages. THC itself did not show this effect. Bacterial phagocytosis was also depressed.

4019   Hughes, R. B.; and Warner, V. J., J. Forensic Sci., *23*(2), 304-10 (1978).

A Study of False Positives in the Chemical Identification of Marihuana.

A color test (modified Duquenois-Levine) combined with TLC was carried out on various substances reported by different authors to give a positive response to color tests considered to be specific for marihuana. The authors conclude that the modified Duquenois-Levine color test, when used on sample of fresh coffee, can be mistaken for marihuana. However, this problem is resolved by TLC, as CBN, THC and CBD have different Rf values and develop different colors than coffee extracts sprayed with Fast Blue B salt.

4020 Hunt, C. A., Diss. Abstr. Int. B., *37*(7), 3356-57 (1975).

The Pharmacokinetics and Metabolism of Δ^9-Tetrahydrocannabinol.

HPLC and TLC revealed that after i.v. administration to dogs, Δ^9-THC was rapidly metabolized, had prolonged plasma half-life and was preferentially eliminated in the feces, mainly as metabolites. Biliary THC metabolites were either phenolic, weak or strong acidic, or highly polar compounds. These metabolites were highly bound to plasma proteins.

4021 Hunt, D. F.; and Crow, F. W., Anal. Chem., *50*(13), 1781-84 (1978).

Electron Capture Negative Ion Chemical Ionization Mass Spectrometry.

Positive and negative ion chemical ionization (CI) MS are reported for several derivatives of phenols and amines under GC conditions. Greater sensitivity was found by the use of electron capture-CI/MS. Detection limits for Δ^9-THC, amphetamine and dopamine were in the femtogram range using this technique. The signal to noise ratio was improved through the use of conversion dynode electron multiplier.

4022 Huot, J., pp. 313-27 in *Marihuana: Chemistry, Biochemistry, and Cellular Effects*, edited by G. G. Nahas. NY, Springer-Verlag, 1976.

Cellular and Biochemical Alterations Induced *in Vitro* by Δ^1-Tetrahydrocannabinol: Effects on Cell Proliferation, Nucleic Acids, Plasma Cell Membrane ATPase, and Adenylate Cyclase.

This work describes some cellular and biochemical alterations induced by Δ^1-THC in cells cultivated *in vitro*. The results of such *in vitro* studies should not be extrapolated hastily to interpret the action of this drug in man.

4023 Husain, S.; and Lame, M., Fed. Proc., *37*(3), 738 (1978).

Delta-9-Tetrahydrocannabinol Induced Alteration of Glucose Metabolism in Rat Testicular Tissue.

Preincubation exposure of rat testicular tissues to Δ^9-THC caused a dose-dependent inhibition of $^{14}CO_2$ production from glucose 6-C^{14}.

4024 Husain, S.; Pryor, G. T.; and Mitoma, C., Pharmacologist, *17*(2), 182 (1975).

Kinetic Interactions of Delta-9-Tetrahydrocannabinol (THC) with Phencyclidine (PC), Phenobarbital (PB), and Cocaine (COC) (Abstract).

THC (10 mg/kg, p.o.) and other drugs were studied to determine metabolic interactions. Cocaine and THC showed no interactions except the subacute level of cocaine reduced the amount of C^{14}-THC.

4025 Huszar, L. A.; Greenberg, J. H.; and Mellors, A., Mol. Pharmacol., *13*(6), 1086-91 (1977).

Effects of Δ^9-Tetrahydrocannabinol on Lymphocyte and Synaptosomal Lysophosphatidylcholine Acyltransferases *in Vivo*.

Mouse brain synaptosomal lysophospha-tidylcholine (LPC) acyltransferase was greatly inhibited by THC (15-70 mg/kg, i.v.). The decrease in lymphocyte LPC acyltransferase activity caused by THC was accompanied by blastogenesis inhibition.

4026   Huy, N. D.; Belleau, R.; and Roy, P. E., Int. J. Clin. Pharmacol. Biopharm., *12*(1/2), 267-76 (1975).

Toxicity of Marijuana and Tobacco Smoking in the Beagle.

Dogs chronically exposed to marihuana smoke exhibited varied food consumption, reduced body weight gain, increased heart rate, depressed serum triglycerides and alpha 1-globulin and some alterations of hematological values. Behavioral changes included learning deficits and auditory hypersensitivity.

4027   Huy, N. D.; Gailis, L.; Cote, G.; and Roy, P. E., Int. J. Clin. Pharmacol. Biopharm., *12*, 284-89 (1975).

Effects of Chronic Administration of Delta-9-Tetrahydrocannabinol (Δ^9-THC) in Guinea-Pigs.

The study evaluates physiological, biochemical (blood serum) and pathological (organs) changes in guinea pigs treated i.p. with Δ^9-THC (3 mg/kg) for six months. The authors suggest that the toxic effect of Δ^9-THC is caused by its accumulation in the liver, which provokes an inhibition of certain liver enzymatic systems.

4028   Huy, N. D.; Laurent, B.; Belleau, R.; Tremblay, R.; Nadeau, A.; and Roy, P. E., Clin. Res., *23*(5), 609A (1975).

The Chronic Inhalation of Marihuana and Tobacco in Dogs: Effects on Body Weight and Blood Chemistry.

In spite of an initial increase in food consumption, a slowing of weight gain was noted in dogs smoking marihuana under chronic conditions. Among other findings reported, plasma testosterone and cellular mitotic index were not altered significantly in these dogs. Effects of tobacco smoking were also investigated and compared to those of marihuana.

4029   Huy, N. D.; and Roy, P. E., Res. Commun. Chem. Pathol. Pharmacol., *13*(3), 465-72 (1976).

Inhalation of Tobacco and Marijuana in Dog over a Period of 30 Months: Effect on Body Weight, Food Intake and Organ Weight.

A 27-month inhalation study was performed in beagle dogs. No significant alterations in food intake, body weight gain or organ weights were observed at the end of the study despite an initial depression of body weight gain by both tobacco and marihuana.

4030   Hyun, B. H.; Gulliani, G. L.; Moss, S. W.; and Parekh, A. K., J. Med. Soc. N. J., *75*(12), 853-54 (1978).

Adverse Reaction to Intravenously Injected Marihuana.

Gastrointestinal, renal, hepatic and hematologic toxic disturbances were experienced in two subjects after administration of crude marihuana extract intravenously. Toxic symptoms were reversed after one week of treatment.

I

4031 Ilaria, R. L.; and Fann, W. E., Fed. Proc., *37*(3), 619 (1978).

Nabilone, a Cannabinol Derivative, in Anxiety Neurosis.

Nabilone was found to be an effective antianxiety agent in neurotic patients. Side effects were limited mainly to orthostatic hypotension.

4032 Inayama, S.; Sawa, A.; and Hosoya, E., Chem. Pharm. Bull., *24*(9), 2209-18 (1976).

Mass Spectrometry of Oxidation Products of Δ^1- and Δ^6-Tetrahydrocannabinols.

The MS of Δ^9- and Δ^8-THC, 8-α- and 8-β-OH-Δ^9-THC, 11-OH-Δ^9-THC, 11-OH- and 11-oxo THC, CBN, 11-OH, 8-OH- and 11-oxo-CBN and the acetates of these cannabinoids were given using high resolution MS and d_3-acetyl derivatives. Structure correlations and principal fragmentations were studied.

4033 Ingall, G. B., Diss. Abstr. Int. B., *39*(6), 2766 (1978).

Effects of Acute and Subacute Cannabidiol Treatment on Hepatic Drug Metabolism.

CBD prolonged hexobarbital sleeping time and decreased its rate of metabolism and cytochrome P-450 concentration. Tolerance to these CBD-induced effects developed in mice.

4034 Ingall, G. B.; Borys, H. K.; Turkanis, S. A.; and Karler, R., Fed. Proc., *37*(3), 738 (1978).

Effects of Acute and Subacute Cannabidiol Treatment on Drug Metabolism.

No detectable cytochrome P-450 inhibitory complexes were found following the acute administration of CBD (120 mg/kg, i.p.). A 30% decline in cytochrome P-450 was detected, but did not parallel the time course of the prolongation of hexobarbital sleep time. Other findings indicated hepatic microsomal induction due to subchronic CBD administration.

4035 Irvin, J. E.; and Mellors, A., Biochem. Pharmacol., *24*(2), 305-07 (1975).

Δ^9-Tetrahydrocannabinol - Uptake by Rat Liver Lysosomes.

^{14}C-Δ^9-THC injected i.v. was found to accumulate in the liver lysosomes causing toxicity. After 5 min. 8.7% of the dose was found in the liver, 15.5% at 15 min. and 7.5% at 1 hr. Five min. after injection was the maximum of relative specific activity and of percentage total protein.

4036 Issidorides, M. R., Lancet, 2(8091), 688 (1978).

Sperm Basic Proteins in Cervical Carcinogenesis (Letter).

Sperm basic protein ratio was altered in chronic cannabis users. The possibility of that happening with other drugs was raised. Implications of findings were also discussed.

4037 Itokawa, H.; Takeya, K.; and Akasu, M., Chem. Pharm. Bull., *24*(7), 1681-83 (1976).

Sterochemistry in Oxidation of Primary Allylic Alcohols by Cell-Free System of Callus Induced from *Cannabis sativa L*.

Incubation of (S)-*trans*-cinnamyl alcohol-1-D and (S)-geraniol-1-D with cell free system of callus induced from *Cannabis sativa L*. for for 4 hr at 26 degrees, resulted in the formation of the respective *cis*- and *trans*-aldehydes in which the pro-R hydrogen was abstracted.

4038 Itokawa, H.; Takeya, K.; and Mihashi, S., Chem. Pharm. Bull., *25*(8), 1941-46 (1977).

Biotransformation of Cannabinoid Precursors and Related Alcohols by Suspension Cultures of Callus Induced from *Cannabis sativa L*.

Alcohols which are thought to condense during biotransformation to form cannabinoids were suspended in culture using cannabi callus. The system did not produce cannabinoids, but conversion of 1 and 2 allylic alcohols to the aldehydes did occur. This conversion was specific for cyclic alcohols and was catalyzed by an alcohol oxidase.

J

4039 Jackson, D. M.; Malor, R.; Chesher, G. B.; Starmer, G. A.; Welburn, P. J.; and Bailey, R., Psychopharmacology, *47*(2), 187-93 (1976).

The Interaction Between Prostaglandin E_1 and Δ^9-Tetrahydrocannabinol on Intestinal Motility and on the Abdominal Constriction Response in the Mouse.

Low dose (0.25 mg/kg) of Δ^9-THC antagonized PGE_1-decrease of mouse intestinal motility and higher doses (0.75-1.0 mg/kg) potentiated it. Moreover, Δ^9-THC antagonized the increased intestinal motility induced by $PGF_{2\alpha}$.

4040 Jacobs, B. L.; Trulson, M. E.; and Stern, W. C., Brain Res., *132*(2), 301-24 (1977).

Behavioral Effects of LSD in the Cat: Proposal of an Animal Behavior Model for Studying the Actions of Hallucinogenic Drugs.

Unlike psilocybin, Δ^9-THC did not mimic LSD in inducing hallucinatory-like behavior in cats. Limb flick and abortive grooming characterized LSD-like compounds.

4041 Jaffe, J. H., pp. 153-58 in *Marijuana and Health Hazards*, edited by J. R. Tinklenberg. NY, Academic Press, 1975.

Psychiatric Consequences of Marijuana.

Concerns of adverse consequences of marihuana use should be made in comparison to those of likely alternatives such as alcohol. Available long-term studies reported negative findings of intellectual impairment by marihuana. The issue of whether marihuana is less harmful to both society and user than alcohol is raised.

4042 Jakubovic, A.; and McGeer, P. L., pp. 223-41 in *Marihuana: Chemistry, Biochemistry, and Cellular Effects*, edited by G. G. Nahas. NY, Springer-Verlag, 1976.

In Vitro Inhibition of Protein and Nucleic Acid Synthesis in Rat Testicular Tissue by Cannabinoids.

Different cannabinoids were tested for their possible effects on macromolecular synthesis in rat testis slices. The results show that all tested cannabinoids, in incubation with various labeled metabolites, significantly changed the biosynthesis of proteins, nucleic acids, and lipids.

4043 Jakubovic, A.; and McGeer, P. L., Toxicol. Appl. Pharmacol., *41*(3), 473-86 (1977).

Biochemical Changes in Rat Testicular Cells *In Vitro* Produced by Cannabinoids and Alcohol: Metabolism and Incorporation of Labeled Glucose, Amino Acids, and Nucleic Acid Precursors.

The *in vitro* effects of THC and other cannabinoids, and a water soluble derivative, SP-111A, on metabolism in the rat testis were studied. Various cannabinoids were shown to inhibit protein, nucleic acid, and lipid synthesis. Furthermore, results suggest that decreased concentrations of nucleotides might be correlated with decreased nucleic acid synthesis that might be the result of a decrease in ATP.

4044 Jakubovic, A.; McGeer, P. L.; and Fitzsimmons, R. C., J. Toxicol. Environ. Health, *1*(3), 441-47 (1976).

Effects of Δ^9-Tetrahydrocannabinol and Ethanol on Body Weight Protein and Nucleic Acid Synthesis in Chick Embryos.

Repetitive injection of the yolk sac of chick eggs with $\triangle^9$-THC retarded embryo development without any overt teratogenicity. Body and brain weights decreased, whereas liver weight increased. Lingering metabolic effects were also evident.

4045   Jandhyala, B. S., Res. Commun. Chem. Pathol. Pharmacol., *20*(3), 489-505 (1978).

Effects of Prolonged Administration of $\triangle^9$-Tetrahydrocannabinol on the Autonomic and Cardiovascular Function and Regional Hemodynamics in Mongrel Dogs.

THC (2 mg/kg/day) for 35 days) potentiated pentobarbital anesthesia in dogs, but tolerance developed to its vagolytic effects and also to its interaction with pentobarbital at the central vagal structures. Chronic THC treatment did not induce essential changes in the hemodynamic parameters measured or in myocardial function and contractility. Further investigations were also carried out.

4046   Jandhyala, B. S.; and Buckley, J. P., Eur. J. Pharmacol., *44*(1), 9-16 (1977).

Influence of Several Anesthetic Agents on the Effects of $\triangle^9$-Tetrahydrocannabinol on the Heart Rate and Blood Pressure of the Mongrel Dog.

THC-induced cardiovascular effects in dogs were found to depend on the state of consciousness and the type of anesthetic employed. The possible mechanisms involved were discussed.

4047   Jandhyala, B. S.; and Buckley, J. P., Res. Commun. Chem. Pathol. Pharmacol., *16*(4), 593-607 (1977).

Autonomic and Cardiovascular Effects of Chronic $\triangle^9$-Tetrahydrocannabinol Administration in Mongrel Dogs.

Various hemodynamic and cardiac parameters were measured after chronic administration of THC (1 mg/kg, twice a day for 7 days, s.c.) in anesthetized mongrel dogs. Except for some bradycardia, no significant change was observed in all parameters. Studies with perfused hind limb of a dog revealed no change in neurogenic tone but a decrease in intrinsic vascular tone along with increased circulating catecholamines.

4048   Jandhyala, B. S.; and Hamed, A. T., Eur. J. Pharmacol., *53*(1), 63-68 (1978).

Pulmonary and Systemic Hemodynamic Effects of $\triangle^9$-Tetrahydrocannabinol in Conscious and Morphine-Chloralose-Anesthetized Dogs: Anesthetic Influence on Drug Action.

$\triangle^9$-THC (1.0 and 2.5 mg/kg, i.v.) produced a decrease in the heart rate and cardiac output of conscious dogs along with an increase in the pulmonary arterial pressure, pulmonary vascular resistance and right ventricular stroke work. Exactly opposite results were obtained in the morphine-chloralose-anesthetized dogs.

4049   Jandhyala, B. S.; Malloy, K. P.; and Buckley, J. P., Eur. J. Pharmacol., *38*(1), 183-87 (1976).

Effects of Acute Administration of $\triangle^9$-THC on Pulmonary Hemodynamics of Anesthetized Dogs.

Dogs treated with $\triangle^9$-THC (2.5 mg/kg, i.v.) demonstrated bradycardia, decreased total peripheral resistance and plasma blood flow associated with increased pulmonary vascular resistance (PVR) and arterial pressure. Mechanical pacing attenuated the PVR-increase whereas bilateral vagotomy or hexamethonium completely antagonized it.

4050 Jandhyala, B. S.; Malloy, K. P.; and Buckley, J. P., Fed. Proc., *34*(3), 744 (1975).

Effects of Δ^9-Tetrahydrocannabinol (Δ^9-THC) on Pulmonary Circulation.

Anesthetized mongrel dogs, given THC at 2.5 mg/kg, i.v., exhibited a decreased heart rate and pulmonary blood flow associated with an increased pulmonary vascular resistance and right ventricular stroke work. Maintenance of heart rate by a pacemaker caused a reduction in right ventricula stroke volume although pulmonary blood flow was reduced and pulmonary vascular resistance was elevated.

4051 Jandhyala, B. S.; Malloy, K. P.; and Buckley, J. P., Fed. Proc., *35*(3), 643 (1976).

Chronic Cardiovascular Effects of Δ^9-Tetrahydrocannabinol (Δ^9-THC) in the Mongrel Dogs (Abstract).

Cardiovascular effects of Δ^9-THC in mongrel dogs was investigated for 7 days. Chronic Δ^9-THC antagonized the effect of pentobarbital and intrinsic tone of the vascular smooth muscles of limbs was observed. Data demonstrated that certain effects of Δ^9-THC for 7 days differ qualitatively and quantitatively from those observed for a single injection.

4052 Jandyhala, B. S.; Malloy, K. P.; and Buckley, J. P., Res. Commun. Chem. Pathol. Pharmacol., *14*(1), 201-04 (1976).

Effects of Chronic Administration of Δ^9-Tetrahydrocannabinol on the Heart Rate of Mongrel Dogs.

Mongrel dogs of either sex were administered Δ^9-THC, 1 mg/kg, s.c. twice a day for 7 days. Pulse rate was monitored at resting condition prior to and following pentobarbital anesthesia. No significant differences were noted in peripheral sympathetic transmission to the heart. THC appeared to have an inhibitory effect on central vagal neurons and potentiated the anesthetic effects of pentobarbital.

4053 Jandhyala, B. S.; Pariani, H. K.; and Lokhandwala, M. F., Fed. Proc., *36*(3), 948 (1977).

The Role of Central α-Adrenergic Receptors in the Hypotension and Bradycardia Produced by Δ^9-Tetrahydrocannabinol (Δ^9-THC) in the Anesthetized Cat.

Phentolamine antagonized Δ^9-THC and intraventricular NE-induced bradycardia and hypotension in cats.

4054 Janowsky, D. S.; Meacham, M. P.; Blaine, J. D.; Schoor, M.; and Bozzetti, L. P., Amer. J. Psychiat., *133*(4), 384-88 (1976).

Marihuana Effects on Simulated Flying Ability.

Marihuana smoking (0.09 mg/kg of THC) disrupted simulated flight performance in professional pilots, an effect mainly attributed to marihuana disruption of short term memory and time perception. Deviations from normal simulated flight patterns were significant.

4055 Janowsky, D. S.; Meacham, M. P.; Blaine, J. D.; Schoor, M.; and Bozzetti, L. P., Aviat. Space Environ. Med., *47*, 124-28 (1976).

Simulated Flying Performance After Marihuana Intoxication.

In a double blind experiment using placebo and $\triangle^9$-THC, social doses of the latter increased both major and minor errors, altitude and heading deviations, and radio navigation errors. Effects lasted for 2 hours, disappearing by 4 to 6 hours post administration.

4056 Janzen, H.; Ludwig, B.; Lycko, E.; and Gerlach, D., Z. Rechtsmed., *80*(4), 305-09 (1978).

Organveranderungen bei Ratten and Kaninchen Nach Haschischapplikation [Organic Lesions After Hashish Application in Rats and Rabbits].

Subacute oral administration of cannabis extract to rats and rabbits resulted in brain, liver and kidney lesions. A detailed description of these histological lesions was provided.

4057 Jarbe, T. U. C., Arch. Int. Pharmacodyn. Ther., *227*(1), 118-29 (1977).

Alcohol-Discrimination in Gerbils: Interactions with Bemegride, DH-524, Amphetamine, and $\triangle^9$-THC.

THC, amphetamine, bemegride and DH-524 failed to induce discriminative stimulus properties similar to those produced by alcohol in trained gerbils, and all failed to reverse or antagonize such properties.

4058 Jarbe, T. U. C., Arch. Int. Pharmacodyn. Ther., *231*(1), 49-56 (1978).

$\triangle^9$-Tetrahydrocannabinol: Tolerance After Noncontingent Exposure in Rats.

The THC-induced hypothermia and behavioral depression, under both conditioned and unconditioned settings, subsided after subchronic treatment of rats with 8 mg/kg of the agent.

4059 Jarbe, T. U. C.; Henriksson, B. G.; and Ohlin, G. C., Arch. Int. Pharmacodyn. Ther., *228*(1), 68-72 (1977).

$\triangle^9$-THC as a Discriminative Cue in Pigeons: Effects of $\triangle^8$-THC, CBD, and CBN.

$\triangle^8$-THC and CBN produced stimulus effects similar to those of THC in trained pigeons, while CBD failed to do so. The interactions between cannabinoids were also investigated.

4060 Jarbe, T. U. C.; Johansson, J. O.; and Henriksson, B. G., Pharmacol. Biochem. Behav., *3*(3), 403-10 (1975).

$\triangle^9$-Tetrahydrocannabinol and Pentobarbital as Discriminative Cues in the Mongolian Gerbil (*Meriones unguiculatus*).

This study examines some discrimative properties of $\triangle^9$-THC and pentobarbital in gerbils. A dose response relationship between THC and the formation of drug discrimination in gerbils is indicated. It is suggested that rats are initially more susceptible to THC depressing syndrome than gerbils.

4061 Jarbe, T. U. C.; Johansson, J. O.; and Henriksson, B. G., Psychopharmacologia, *42*, 33-39 (1975).

Drug Discrimination in Rats: The Effects of Phencyclidine and Ditran.

When studying the stimulus properties of phencyclidine and ditran, $\triangle^8$- and $\triangle^9$-THC did not transfer to either agent. The reverse was also true.

4062 Jarbe, T. U. C.; Johansson, J. O.; and Henriksson, B. G., Psychopharmacologia, *48*(2), 181-87 (1976).

Characteristics of Tetrahydrocannabinol (THC)-Produced Discrimination in Rats.

The acquisition rate of Δ^9- or Δ^8-THC discrimination in rats trained in a T-shaped maze was proportional to the dose used. Treatment with AMPT or PCPA failed to alter Δ^9-THC based discrimination.

4063   Jarbe, T. U. C.; and Ohlin, G. C., Psychopharmacology, 54(2), 193-95 (1977).

Stimulus Effects of Δ^9-THC and its Interaction with Naltrexone and Catecholamine Blockers in Rats.

The discriminative effects of THC in trained rats were not blocked by naltrexone, propranolol, phenoxybenzamine or haloperidol. Generalization of test agents to the THC stimulus also did not occur.

4064   Jarvik, M. E., Psychopharmacol. Bull., 12(2), 62-63 (1976).

Behavioral Effects of Drugs in Monkeys (Abstract).

Marihuana was among many psychotropic agents tested for their behavioral effects in monkeys. Behavioral changes due to some hallucinogens were discussed.

4065   Jasso, N. K.; and Wolkon, G. H., Int. J. Addict., 13(2), 317-26 (1978).

Drug Use, Attitudes, and Behaviors of Youth in an Urban Free Clinic.

Among a sample of free clinic users, most have used marihuana and most frequently along with other drugs. Race, age of initial use and first drug used determined the degree of involvement.

4066   Jessor, R., J. Consult. Clin. Psychol., 44(1), 125-34 (1976).

Predicting Time of Onset of Marihuana Use: A Developmental Study of High School Youth.

The youth that is more apt to use marihuana is more independent and critical of social value and more tolerant of deviance. Other predicting attributes were the influence of family and friends. The utility of the theoretical concept of transition proneness or deviance in identifying problem behavior in adolescence was emphasized.

4067   Jessor, R. L.; and Jessor, S. L., pp. 41-71 in Longitudinal Research on Drug Use, edited by D. B. Kandel. Washington, D.C., Hemisphere Publishing Corporation, 1978.

Theory Testing in Longitudinal Research on Marihuana Use.

The longitudinal and cross-sectional study predicted that adolescents more likely to use marihuana are more independent, are not interested in goals of conventional institutions and view society critically. Users are also more likely to be involved in other problem behaviors.

4068   Jochimsen, P. R.; Lawton, R. L.; VerSteeg, K.; and Noyes, R., Clin. Pharmacol. Ther., 24(2), 223-27 (1978).

Effect of Benzopyranoperidine, a Δ^9-THC Congener, on Pain.

Single oral doses of 2 and 4 mg of benzopyranoperidine (BPP) failed to significantly reduce the pain in cancer patients. Indeed, BPP seemed to enhance pain perception in some patients.

4069   Joe, G. W.; and Hudiburg, R. A., Int. J. Addict., 13(4), 627-37 (1978).

Behavioral Correlates of Age at First Marijuana Use.

Age of initial marihuana use may be used as a useful indicator of various concurrent and later deviant behavior.

4070 Johansson, J. O,; Jarbe, T. U. C.; and Henriksson, B. G., T.-I.-T.-J. Life Sci., *5*(1-2), 17-28 (1975).

Acute and Subchronic Influences of Tetrahydrocannabinols on Water and Food Intake, Body Weight, and Temperature in Rats.

Rats were administered Δ^8- and Δ^9-THC i.p. and inhaled hashish. The acute effects on water intake were studied with doses of 0.0, 1.25, 2.5, 5.0 or 10.0 mg/kg. The influence of subchronic treatment of drug on water intake, body weight and temperature was also recorded in deprived and non-deprived rats. Food consumption was decreased in drug groups with tolerance developing after 2 weeks. Water consumption increased. At the lower doses of THC hyperthermia was observed whereas hypothermia was noted at the higher doses. Loss of tolerance occurred when the drug was withdrawn and administered again.

4071 Johnson, C. K., Diss. Abstr. Int. B., *37*(8), 4190 (1977).

The Effects of Δ^9-Tetrahydrocannabinol on the Spontaneous Behavior and Sociability of Nonhuman Primates: A Descriptive Study.

Disruption of normal behavior in monkeys by THC was studied under various conditions. Results indicated that THC may affect males differently than females. Causes of behavioral disruption by THC were discussed.

4072 Johnson, D. D.; McNeil, J. R.; Crawford, R. D.; and Wilcox, W. C., Can. J. Physiol. Pharmacol., *53*(6), 1007-13 (1975).

Epileptiform Seizures in Domestic Fowl. V. The Anticonvulsant Activity of Δ^9-Tetrahydrocannabinol.

Δ^9-THC in doses of 0.5 to 1 mg/kg i.v. reduced the incidence and severity of seizures manifested in epileptic chickens subjected to intermittent photic stimulation. Δ^9-THC did not, however, exert a similar protection against metrazol-induced seizures.

4073 Johnson, K. M., Diss. Abst. Int. B., *35*(11), 5559 (1975).

On the Mechanism and Sites of Action of (-)-Δ^9-*Trans*-Tetrahydrocannabinol in Serotonergic Neurons.

In vivo and *in vitro* studies show that Δ^9-THC can elevate the levels of 5-HT in the brain. The *in vitro* study shows THC blocking uptake of 5-HT, DA, NE and leucine. The release of 5-HT and NE is stimulated. The primary sites of these actions affected by THC are the neuronal membrane and the synaptic vesicle. A common locus of action is found for reserpine and THC.

4074 Johnson, K. M.; and Dewey, W. L., J. Pharmacol. Exp. Ther., *207*(1), 140-50 (1978).

The Effect of Δ^9-Tetrahydrocannabinol on the Conversion of [3_H] Tryptophan to 5-[3_H] Hydroxytryptamine in the Mouse Brain.

After i.v. treatment with 3_H- tryptophan, Δ^9-THC increased the production of mouse brain 3_H-5HT by increasing the availability of the former agent. These THC effects were dose-dependent. THC also increased brain/plasma ratio of labelled tryptophan.

4075 Johnson, K. M.; and Dewey, W. L., Pharmacology, *17*(2), 83-87 (1978).

Effects of $\triangle^9$-THC on the Synaptosomal Uptake of 3_H-Tryptophan and 3_H-Choline.

Addition of THC resulted in non-competitive inhibition of labelled tryptophan and choline uptake by mouse forebrain synaptosomes *in vitro*. Pretreatment with THC, however, did not have any subsequent influence on the above measured parameter.

4076   Johnson, K. M.; and Dewey, W. L., Pharmacologist, *17*(2), 182 (1975).

Structure-Activity-Relationships of the Cannabinoids in Blocking Synaptosomal Serotonin Uptake (Abstract).

Synaptosomal accumulation of 3_H-5-HT was inhibited by $\triangle^9$-THC. The activity of $\triangle^8$- and $\triangle^9$-THC is diminished by 11-OH substitution with no effect if amino or methyl are substituted. Hydroxyl substitution at the 8 position shows less inhibition of activity, whereas in the hexahydrocannabinol, CBN and $\triangle^{10a}$-THC series hydroxyl substitution at the 9 position greatly reduces activity. Loss of activity is seen in $\triangle^8$-THC and CBD by interchanging the phenolic hydroxyl with an aromatic pentyl side chain.

4077   Johnson, K. M.; and Dewey, W. L., Pharmacologist, *19*(2), 221 (1977).

Cannabinoid Induced Elevations in Plasma Endogenous Corticosterone Levels Correlate with Increased Whole Brain Uptake of 3_H-Corticosterone in Adrenalectomized Mice.

11-OH-$\triangle^9$-THC was the most potent cannabinoid in increasing mouse corticosterone plasma levels, followed by THC and CBN. This order of potency correlated well with the behavioral potency of these agents and their in-

duced elevation of corticosterone uptake by adrenalectomized mice brains.

4078   Johnson, K. M.; Dewey, W. L.; and Harris, L. S., Mol. Pharmacol., *12*(3), 345-52 (1976).

Some Structural Requirements for Inhibition of High-Affinity Synaptosomal Serotonin Uptake by Cannabinoids.

$\triangle^9$-THC and 18 related THC's are analyzed *in vitro* for their potential to inhibit the high-affinity uptake of tritiated 5-HT into rat forebrain synaptosomes. With a single exception, all the THC's inhibited 5-HT uptake. Using this *in vitro* parameter, a survey of SAR among the THC is documented.

4079   Johnson, K. M.; Dewey, W. L.; and Ho, B. T., Res. Commun. Chem. Pathol. Pharmacol., *15*(4), 655-71 (1976).

In Vitro Alteration of the Subcellular Distribution of 3_H-Reserpine in the Rat Forebrain by $\triangle^9$-Tetrahydrocannabinol.

Whereas $\triangle^9$-THC increased the binding of reserpine in rat forebrain mitochondrial preparation, the reverse was not true. The greatest increase was in subcellular nerve ending fraction. Other data presented suggest that this phenomenon is rather specific for cannabinoids.

4080   Johnson, K. M.; Dewey, W. L.; Ritter, K. S.; and Beckner, J. S.; Eur. J. Pharmacol., *47*(3), 303-10 (1978).

Cannabinoid Effects on Plasma Corticosterone and Uptake of 3_H-Corticosterone by Mouse Brain.

11-OH-$\triangle^9$-THC, $\triangle^9$-THC and CBN elevated mouse plasma corticosterone levels and resulted in a comparable increase of corticosterone uptake by adrenalectomized mouse brain. The relative order of potency of the three cannabinoids in altering the parameters tested was similar to their behavioral potency.

4081 Johnson, K. M.; Ho, B. T.; and Dewey, W. L., Life Sci., *19*(3), 347-56 (1976).

Effects of Δ^9-Tetrahydrocannabinol on Neurotransmitter Accumulation and Release Mechanisms in Rat Forebrain Synaptosomes.

Δ^9-THC (10-100 μ m) inhibited the uptake of leucine, 5-HT and NE and facilitated the release of the latter two in rat forebrain synaptosomal preparation. Reserpine inhibited THC's release of, but not its more potent inhibition of 5-HT.

4082 Johnson, K. M., Ho, B. T.; Dewey, W. L.; and Harris, L. S., Neurosci. Abstr., *5*, 241 (1975).

In Vitro Induction of 3_H-Reserpine Binding to Subcellular Components of the Rat Forebrain by Δ^9-Tetrahydrocannabinol.

Preincubation of a crude synaptosomal fraction of rat forebrain with Δ^9-THC led to a dose-response increase in the amount of 3_H-reserpine (3_H-R) bound to this fraction. A shift in the localization of 3_H-R from the incubation medium and the microsomal supernatant to the crude mitochondrial pellet was also caused by Δ^9-THC. Other subcellular effects of this cannabinoid and a possible mechanism of its action were discussed.

4083 Johnson, M. H., J. Med. Soc. N.J., *72*(10), 866-68 (1975).

Marihuana - A Political Drug.

The author warns against the move to legalize marihuana and indicates that a 1975 U.N. resolution classified marihuana as harmful and that it should be treated as such.

4084 Johnson, M. R.; and Milne, G. M., Jr., in *Annual Reports in Medicinal Chemistry, Vol. 10*, 1975, pp. 12-20.

Chapter 2. Narcotic Antagonists and Analgesics.

A discussion of the regio- and stereo-specificity of cannabinoids possessing analgesic activity is presented. The 11-OH derivative for Δ^9- and Δ^8-THC were reported to possess the highest activity. In addition, heterocyclic modifications of the cannabinoid nucleus have led to other compounds that are analgetic.

4085 Johnson, W. T.; Petersen, R. E.; and Wells, L. E., Amer. J. Sociol., *83*(3), 681-99 (1977).

Arrest Probabilities for Marijuana Users as Indicators of Selective Law Enforcement.

Arrest rate was the highest in high penalty areas. In the high probability area, males, blacks and persons 25 and under had substantially higher arrest/use ratio than did females, whites and persons over 25. Blue collar group had the highest arrest/use ratio in all jurisdictions.

4086 Johnston, L. D.; Bachman, J. G.; and O'Malley, P. M., eds., *Highlights from Drug Use Among American High School Students, 1975-1977*, NIDA, 1977.

The breadth and depth of the youth involvement in drug abuse was estimated in this cross-sectional national survey of high school seniors. Marihuana was among the eleven separate classes of drugs studied. Attitudes and beliefs of youth toward drug use were also probed.

4087 Johnstone, R. E.; Lief, P. L.; Kulp, R. A.; and Smith, T. C., Anesthesiology, *42*(6), 674-84 (1975).

Combination of Δ^9-Tetrahydrocannabinol with Oxymorphone or Pentobarbital: Effects on Ventilatory Control and Cardiovascular Dynamics.

Oxymorphone (OXM), 1.0 mg/kg; pentobarbital (PBL), 100 mg/kg; and THC, cumulative doses 27, 40, 60, 90 and 134 µg/kg, were administered i.v. through a central venous catheter to adult men. Their physiological and psychological effects were studied. THC combined with OXM increased the sedation properties of OXM but it also increased respiratory depression. THC combined with PBL produced high incidence of anxiety and psychotomimetic effects. Other adverse effects are discussed.

4088 Joneja, M. G., Anat. Rec., *181*(2), 387-88 (1975).

Effects of Δ^9-Tetrahydrocannabinol (THC) on Fetuses of Swiss Webster Mice.

Pregnant mice were treated with Δ^9-THC on various days from the seventh to eleventh day of gestation. All fetuses were examined on the eighteenth day of gestation. The frequency of abnormalities was not significant for any combination of dose plus day of administration except for an intragastric dose of 400 mg/kg on the eleventh day of gestation.

4089 Joneja, M. G., J. Toxicol. Environ. Health, *2*(5), 1031-40 (1977).

Effects of Δ^9-Tetrahydrocannabinol on Hamster Fetuses.

Single or multiple intragastric doses of THC (25-500 mg/kg) administered to hamsters during their gestation period caused minor teratogenic effects. Higher doses increased the incidence of fetal gross internal and external anomalies, growth retardation and mortality, but no clear cut teratogenic responses were observed. Also, hamsters seemed to be less susceptible to the teratogenic effects of THC when compared to other species. Implications of the results were discussed.

4090 Jonja, M. G., Toxicol. Appl. Pharmacol., *36*(1), 151-62 (1976).

A Study of Teratological Effects of Intravenous, Subcutaneous and Intragastric Administration of Δ^9-Tetrahydrocannabinol in Mice.

Mice received a single treatment dose of Δ^9-THC ranging from 3.00 to 400 mg/kg, on days 7 thru 11 of gestation. Fetuses were examined on day 18 of gestation. Injections were ineffective in producing abnormalities and a low frequency of malformations were induced by s.c. administration. Significant teratogenic responses were seen by p.o. administration to Swiss Webster and DBA mice at large doses only. However, no clear dose-response pattern was found.

4091 Joneja, M. G.; and Kaiserman, M. Z., Experientia, *34*(9), 1205-06 (1978).

Cytogenetic Effects of Delta-9-Tetrahydrocannabinol (Δ^9-THC) on Hamster Bone Marrow.

Δ^9-THC treatment did not cause chromosomal aberrations in hamsters, but significantly decreased mitotic indices in their bone marrow. Effects were dose-related.

4092 Jones, A. D., Psychol. Rec., *25*, 329-32 (1975).

Cannabis and Alcohol Usage Among the Plateau Tonga: An Observation Report of the Effects of Cultural Expectation.

The pleasant effect expected after marihuana smoking in the Plateau Tonga,
where marihuana smoking is common,
is similar to the effect of alcohol drinking in Europeans. On the other hand,
the inexperienced drinkers of alcohol in
the Tonga Plateau have something in
common with new marihuana smokers
in Europe.

4093   Jones, B. C., Diss. Abst. Int. B., *36*(8),
        4204 (1976).

Effects of $\triangle^9$-Tetrahydrocannabinol on
Squirrel Monkeys Incentive Competition
Behavior.

In paired monkeys trained to compete
for sweetened water, oral $\triangle^9$-THC
depressed competitive behavior in high
dose and increased it in low dose. The
latter effect depended on baseline performance.

4094   Jones, B. C.; Consroe, P. F.; and Akins,
        F., Bull. Psychon. Soc., *6*(2), 204-06
        (1975).

Physostigmine-Induced Reversal of EEG
and Behavioral Effects of $\triangle^9$-Tetrahy-
drocannabinol.

Doses of 0.5 mg/kg $\triangle^9$-THC and 0.05
mg/kg physostigmine were injected via
ear vein in adult rabbits. The sedative
effect of $\triangle^9$-THC on EEG and behavior
can be reversed by physostigmine. With
the exception of brief periods of retch-
ing, no behavioral indications of toxicity
were observed.

4095   Jones, B. C.; Consroe, P. F.; and Laird,
        H. E., Eur. J. Pharmacol., *38*(2), 253-
        59 (1976).

The Interaction of $\triangle^9$-Tetrahydrocanna-
binol with Cholinomimetic Drugs in an
Agonist-Antagonist Paradigm.

Cholinomimetics transiently reversed the
increased cortical electrogenesis and hippocampal theta rhythm disruption of
THC (0.5 mg/kg, i.v.) in rabbits. Arecoline and physostigmine briefly antagonized the behavioral depression of THC,
while nicotine interacted with THC to
increase behavioral toxicity.

4096   Jones, D. L., N. Z. Vet. J., *26*(5), 135-
        36 (1978).

A Case of Canine Cannabis Ingestion.

The dog experienced a severe case of
intoxication when he ate the neighbor's
discarded hashish cookies.

4097   Jones, H. B., AMA Gazette, *196*, 20-
        25, April 21 (1978).

The Dangers of Cannabis Smoking.

The author stresses that the potential
harmful effects of cannabis ought to be
realized by physicians and others. He
believes that Australian physicians, like
their American colleagues, are unin-
formed about the dangers of cannabis.

4098   Jones, H. B., Executive Health, *14*(1),
        October (1977).

On the Problems Executives Must An-
ticipate with the Growth of Marijuana
Smoking.

The ample evidence indicating the harmful effects of marihuana should be
emphasized publicly so as to deter use.
Executives should not seek pleasure
from the risky marihuana experience
but rather from the challenge and stimulation of their jobs.

4099   Jones, H. B., Private Practice, 35-28,
        January (1976).

What the Practicing Physician Should
Know About Marijuana.

Marihuana-induced harmful effects in users are summarized. Among the many changes physicians can look for in users are withdrawal symptoms, disordered thinking, reduced attention span and ability to concentrate.

4100   Jones, H. B.; and Jones, H., *Sensual Drugs: Deprivation and Rehabilitation of the Mind.* Cambridge University Press, 1977. 383 pp.

A review of the literature on general drug abuse with special emphasis on marihuana.

4101   Jones, J. S., Lancet, *2*(8098), 1053 (1978).

Cannabis and Peptic Ulcer (Letter).

In the past cannabis was prescribed to treat peptic ulcer. Thus, recent reference to this issue is not surprising.

4102   Jones, L. A.; and Foote, R. S., J. Agr. Food Chem., *23*(6), 1129-31 (1975).

Cannabis Smoke Condensate. Identification of Some Acids, Bases, and Phenols.

The smoke condensate of marihuana cigarettes was separated in fractions containing acids (7.5%), bases (4.8%), phenols (4.6%) and neutral compounds (83.1%) respectively. By GC and GC/MS-analysis 8 acids, 7 or 8 bases and 7 or 8 phenols could be identified. All of the identified compounds have also been found in tobacco smoke.

4103   Jones, P. G.; Falvello, L.; Kennard, O.; and Sheldrick, G. M., Acta Crystallogr., Section. B, *B33*(10), 3211-14 (1977).

Cannabidiol.

An x-ray structure determination of CBD was undertaken. The results were compared to structural data received through chemical determinations.

4104   Jones, P. G.; and Kennard, O., J. Pharm. Pharmacol., *30*(12), 815-17 (1978).

Common Stereochemical Features in Anti-Epileptic Drugs: A Reinvestigation.

With the present available data it is not possible to ascertain whether antiepileptics (including CBD) share common stereochemical features.

4105   Jones, P. G.; Kennard, O.; and Sheldrick, G. M., Acta Crystallogr., Sect. B., *B33*, 1982-85 (1977).

3,4,5,6-Tetrahydro-2, 9-Dimethyl-7-Hydroxy-5-Isopropyl-2, 6-Methano-2H-1-Benzoxocin.

The structure of a C_1, -homolog of an iso-HHC was determined by X-ray crystallography.

4106   Jones, R., pp. 128-78 in *Marihuana Research Findings: 1976*, NIDA Research Monograph 14, 1977.

Human Effects.

A review of recent literature pertaining to marihuana effects in humans was undertaken. A wide array of actions is reported including bronchodilation in asthmatic patients and impairment of a variety of cognitive and performance tasks.

4107   Jones, R. T., pp. 373-412 in *Handbook of Psychopharmacology, Vol. 12, Drugs of Abuse*, edited by L. L. Iverson, S. D. Iverson, and S. H. Snyder. New York, Plenum Press, 1978.

Marihuana: Human Effects.

The chapter is a general review of both acute and chronic effects of marihuana use on humans.

4108 Jones, R. T., pp. 118-26 in *Behavioral Tolerance: Research and Treatment Implications*, NIDA Research Monograph 18, 1978.

Behavioral Tolerance: Lessons Learned from Cannabis Research.

The author criticizes the loose use of various terms to describe the different types of tolerance. Based on results of cannabis (Δ^9-THC) studies conducted on hospitalized volunteers, he also questions the concept of distinguishing too sharply between physiologic and behavioral tolerance.

4109 Jones, R. T., pp. 115-20 in *Marijuana and Health Hazards*, edited by J. R. Tinklenberg. NY, Academic Press, 1975.

Effects of Marijuana on the Mind.

Marihuana must have effects on the mind, since people smoke it to change the way they think and feel. The relative inadequacy of methods used to measure brain function and pathology is the major problem in interpreting the effect of marihuana on the mind. The EEG recordings, despite their limitations, can predict brain pathology.

4110 Jones, R. T.; and Benowitz, N., pp. 627-42 in *Pharmacology of Marihuana, Vol. 2*, edited by M. C. Braude and S. Szara. NY, Raven Press, 1976.

The 30-Day Trip: Clinical Studies of Cannabis Tolerance and Dependence.

With the intention of maximizing the development of tolerance and dependence, doses as high as 210 mg of pure THC/24 hrs. were administered orally to 12 marihuana users. A great number of behavioral, subjective, physiological and biochemical tests were then administered. Results indicated that such high doses of THC were very well tolerated by the subjects.

4111 Jones, R. T.; Benowitz, N.; and Backman, J., pp. 221-39 in *Chronic Cannabis Use*, edited by R. L. Dornbush, A. M. Freedman, and M. Fink. NY, Annals of the New York Academy of Sciences, V. 282, 1976.

Clinical Studies of Cannabis Tolerance and Dependence.

Tolerance developed rapidly to most subjective and objective effects experienced by marihuana users consuming Δ^9-THC (10-30 mg), when repeatedly administered. This tolerance was short-lived and possessed characteristics of metabolic, dispositional, and functional adaptations. When treatment ceased, withdrawal symptoms ensued.

4112 Jones, R. T.; Farrell, T. R.; and Herning, R. I., pp. 202-08 in *Self-Administration of Abused Substances: Methods for Study*, NIDA Research Monograph 20, 1978.

Tobacco Smoking and Nicotine Tolerance.

Tolerance to the cardiac and subjective effects of nicotine developed rapidly. Similarities and differences between cannabis and tobacco seeking and self-administration behavior were discussed.

4113 Jordan, V. C.; and Castracane, V. D., Prostaglandins, *12*(6), 1073-81 (1976).

The Effect of Reported Prostaglandin Synthetase Inhibitors on Estradiol-Stimulated Uterine Prostaglandin Biosynthesis *in vivo* in the Ovariectomized Rat.

Aspirin, indomethacin, and naproxen are shown to inhibit the PGE and PGF biosynthesis stimulated by 17-β-estradiol in the progesterone-primed uterus of ovariectomized rats. The compounds did not affect the estrogen-induced increases in uterine wet weights. Δ^9-THC (10 mg/ rat) did not inhibit estradiol-induced synthesis of PG's but increased the effusion of PGE into uterine venous blood.

4114 Joyce, C. R. B., pp. 111-20 in *Cannabis and Health*, edited by J. D. P. Graham. London, Academic Press, 1976.

A Critical Approach to Experiments on Cannabis and the Interpretation of their Results.

Available clinical reports dealing with the effects of psychotropic drugs on humans lack the scientifically sound methodological basis. The author described some of the inadequacies associated with psychopharmacological research and suggested approaches to follow in order to assure quality reports and replicability.

4115 Juneja, R. C.; Nayyar, V. L.; and Mukerji, K. G., Angew. Bot., *50*(1-2), 43-48 (1976).

Further Additions to Plant Diseases of Delhi.

Diseases affecting some Indian plants were reported. *Pseudoperonospora cannabina* is the pathogen infecting cannabis plants.

4116 Jusko, W. J.; Schentag, J. J.; Clark, J. H.; Gardner, M.; and Yurchak, A. M., Clin. Pharmacol. Ther., *24*(4), 406-10 (1978).

Enhanced Biotransformation of Theophylline in Marihuana and Tobacco Smokers.

Chronic marihuana or tobacco users exhibited a more rapid clearance of administered theophylline than did control nonusers. Use of both substances resulted in additive effect.

4117 Just, W. W.; Erdmann, G.; Thel, S.; Werner, G.; and Wiechmann, M., Naunyn-Schmiedebergs Arch. Pharmacol., *287*(2), 219-25 (1975).

Metabolism and Autoradiographic Distribution of Δ^8- and Δ^9-Tetrahydrocannabinol in Some Organs of the Monkey *Callithrix jacchus*.

Thirty minutes following the i.v. injection of labelled Δ^8- and Δ^9-THC, the highest accumulation of radioactivity was measured in the bile, liver and adrenal gland. A marked reduction in the initial metabolic rate of Δ^8-THC was found.

4118 Just, W. W.; Erdmann, G.; Werner, G.; Wiechmann, M.; and Thel, E., pp. 123-36 in *Marihuana: Chemistry, Biochemistry, and Cellular Effects*, edited by G. G. Nahas. NY, Springer-Verlag, 1976.

Forensic, Metabolic and Autoradiographic Studies of Δ^8- and Δ^9-Tetrahydrocannabinol.

Δ^9-THC was detected in the saliva of users by means of fluorescence labeling technique. Correlation between the effects of marihuana in man and its accumulation in the monkey's brain was studied. Highest accumulation of Δ^9- and Δ^8-THC was found in the liver, bile, and adrenal glands after 30 min. of administration.

4119   Just, W. W.; Werner, G.; Erdmann, G.; and Wiechmann, M., Strahlentherapie [Sonderb.] , *74*, 90-97 (1975).

Detection and Identification of Δ^8- and Δ^9-Tetrahydrocannabinol in Saliva of Man and Autoradiographic Investigation of their Distribution in Different Organs of the Monkey.

The metabolism and distribution of Δ^8- and Δ^9-THC was determined using radio-labeled material. THC was specifically concentrated in the salivary glands. Compounds were detected by fluorometry of DANS-derivatives and by autoradiography. Organ distribution of the radio-labeled material after 30 min. and 6 hrs. showed little variation.

K

4120 Kabarity, A.; El-Bayoumi, A.; and Nabib, A., Biologia Plantarum (Praha), *18*(6), 401-407 (1976).

Effect of Cannabis (Hashish) on Mitosis of *Allium cepa L*. Root Tips.

The cytological effect of hashish extracts on root tips of *Allium cepa* is discussed. Data indicated that the chromosomal aberrations are related to dose. Chromosomes may reach the pole but are unable to build normal poles. Also the orientation of the spindle fibre apparatus was slightly disturbed. Data are given on meta-, pro-, ana-, and telophases.

4121 Kaistha, K. K.; Tadrus, R.; and Wojtulewicz, D., J. Pharm. Sci., *67*(8), IV (1978).

Paraquat in Marijuana (Letter).

A new specific method to detect the contamination of marihuana with paraquat was reported. The procedure involved the use of methanol extract which is finally subjected to TLC analysis.

4122 Kajima, M.; Vande Velde, V.; Piraux, M., pp. 163-66 in *IUPAC Int. Symp. Chem. Nat. Prod.*, 11th (1978).

Contribution to the Biosynthesis of Cannabinoids.

Feeding experiments were carried out with 14_C precursors to study the phenolic origin of cannabinoids. The study showed very low incorporation level of 14_C-olivetol, olivetolic acid and olivetolic acid ethyl ester indicating that maybe the monoterpene moiety reacts with a polyketide before aromatization. Synthetic procedures for the 14_C-precursors are given.

4123 Kaklamani, E.; Trichopoulos, D.; Koutselinis, A.; Drouga, M.; and Karalis, D., Arch. Toxicol., *40*(2), 97-101 (1978).

Hashish Smoking and T-Lymphocytes.

Thymidine uptake by T-lymphocytes was slightly higher in hashish users than non-users. This uptake was also elevated in chronic users following smoking sessions.

4124 Kalofoutis, A.; Koutselinis, A.; Dionyssiou-Asteriou, A.; and Miras, C., Acta Pharmacol. Toxicol., *43*(2), 81-85 (1978).

The Significance of Lymphocyte Lipid Changes After Smoking Hashish.

Smoking hashish increased total lipids and phospholipids in lymphocytes of heavy users but not in healthy controls. Alteration of individual phospholipids was pointed out and mechanisms involved were also discussed.

4125 Kamali, K.; and Steer, R. A., Int. J. Addict., *11*(2), 337-43 (1976).

Polydrug Use by High-School Students: Involvement and Correlates.

Predictors of polydrug involvement were sought among the beliefs and desires of 273 high school drug users studied. Marijuana was most frequently used.

4126 Kanakis, C., Clin. Pharmacol. Ther., *19*(1), 94 (1976).

Effects of Marihuana in Coronary Disease (Letter).

The author suggests that although Δ^9-THC causes a deterioration of cardiac performance in patients with angina pectoris, it is inappropriate to attribute the cardiac effects of Δ^9-THC to a direct negative inotropic effect since other mechanisms that might diminish cardiac vigor have not been adequately investigated.

4127   Kanakis, C.; Pouget, J. M.; and Rosen, K. M., Amer. J. Cardiol ,.*35*(1), 147 (1975).

Effects of Delta-9-Tetrahydrocannabinol (Cannabis) on Cardiac Performance Utilizing Systolic Time Intervals.

After i.v. administration of 25 μ g/kg Δ^9-THC, systolic time intervals and BP were measured in supine subjects in a fasting state. Δ^9-THC increases cardiac performance directly or through catecholamine stimulation.

4128   Kanakis, C., Jr.; Pouget, J. M.; and Rosen, K. M., Circulation, *53*(4), 703-07 (1976).

The Effects of Delta-9-Tetrahydrocannabinol (Cannabis) on Cardiac Performance With and Without Beta Blockade.

Male volunteers were monitored for changes in heart rate, BP, and systolic time intervals before and after Δ^9-THC (25 μm/kg, i.v.). A peak response occurred between 5 and 25 mins., and although diastolic and systolic pressures were unchanged, heart rate increased. The cardiovascular responses were attenuated but not abolished by pretreatment with propranolol. Δ^9-THC appears to function through its 11-OH-metabolite.

4129   Kanakis, C.; Pouget, M.; and Rosen, K., Clin. Res., *24*(3), 255A (1976).

Effects of Delta-9-Tetrahydrocannabinol (Cannabis) on Cardiac Performance as Measured by Echocardiography.

In healthy individuals Δ^9-THC (25 μm/kg, i.v.) increased cardiac pre-ejection tension, increased the duration and strength of ventricular contraction, and enhanced the degree of cardiac emptying.

4130   Kanakis, C.; and Rosen, K. M., Chest, *72*(1), 2-3 (1977).

The Cardiovascular Effects of Marihuana in Man.

Although available data, as cited, provide some information on the cardiovascular effects of marihuana in humans, more studies are needed to further clarify the subject.

4131   Kandel, D.; and Faust, R., Arch. Gen. Psychiat., *32*(7), 923-32 (1975).

Sequence and Stages in Patterns of Adolescent Drug Use.

Most youths progress to marihuana use by first using beer and wine and then tobacco and alcohol. Use of marihuana leads to the use of other illicit drugs in most instances.

4132   Kandel, D.; Single, E.; and Kessler, R. C., Amer. J. Pub. Health, *66*(1), 43-53 (1976).

The Epidemiology of Drug Use Among New York State High School Students: Distribution, Trends, and Change in Rates of Use.

Upon questioning, participants reported a high rate of alcohol consumption, cigarette smoking and to a lesser extent drug abuse among high school students. Of these, 29% reported the frequent use of marihuana. Repeated questioning of the same subjects revealed interesting changes over the course of a school year.

4133   Kanter, S. L.; and Hollister, L. E., J. Chromatogr., *151*(2), 225-27 (1978).

Marihuana Metabolites in Urine of Man. IX. Identification of Δ^9-Tetrahydrocannabinol-11-oic Acid by Thin-Layer Chromatography.

A sequential TLC procedure was described which was used to separate THC metabolites into neutrals, alcoholic neutrals and acidics. Extraction of urine at pH8 is indicated to separate the acidics. The process involved the use of multisteps TLC systems. Δ^9-THC-11-oic acid was characterized as a major Δ^9-THC metabolite in the urine of humans.

4134   Kanter, S. L.; and Hollister, L. E., Res. Commun. Chem. Pathol. Pharmacol., *17*(3), 421-31 (1977).

Marihuana Metabolites in Urine of Man. VII. Excretion Patterns of Acidic Metabolites Detected by Sequential Thin-Layer Chromatography.

The 11-oic acid metabolites of Δ^9-THC, CBN, and CBD were presumptively identified via TLC methods alone from human urine samples. TLC spots were compared to those from urine to which standards had been added or from urine of subjects using specific cannabinoids or marihuana. TLC derived excretion patterns are illustrated for the metabolites up to 72 hours after administration.

4135   Kanter, S. L.; Hollister, L. E.; and Loeffler, K. O., J. Chromatogr., *150*(1), 233-37 (1978).

Marihuana Metabolites in the Urine of Man. VIII. Identification and Quantitation of Δ^9-Tetrahydrocannabinol by Thin-Layer Chromatography and High-Pressure Liquid Chromatography.

Urine samples from human subjects were analyzed for THC after oral uptake of 30 mg Δ^9-THC in a cookie. Extraction of urine samples at pH8 with hexane followed by TLC analysis indicated the presence of unchanged Δ^9-THC up to 6 hours. Quantitation was carried out by MPLC using UV detector at 215 nm.

4136   Kanter, S. L.; Hollister, L. E.; and Lombrozo, L., Clin. Chem., *22*(7), 1198 (1976).

Marihuana Metabolites in Urine of Man, VI. Recovery of Acidic Metabolites by Sequential Thin Layer Chromatography (TLC).

The authors report a sequential TLC analysis with two solvents systems after a specific extraction procedure which is said to produce reliable classification of weakly acidic metabolites of marijuana in human urine. These acids are THC-11-oic acids, cannabinol-11-oic acid, and possibly cannabidiol-11-oic acid.

4137   Kanter, S. L.; Hollister, L. E.; and Moore, F., Res. Commun. Chem. Pathol. Pharmacol., *10*(2), 215-19 (1975).

Marihuana Metabolites in Urine of Man, V. Characterization and Separation of Polar Metabolites of Delta-9-Tetrahydrocannabinol.

Extraction of human urine with ether at pH 12 and TLC using two solvent systems permitted separation of several polar metabolites of Δ^9-THC. These metabolites appeared as conjugates and are probably dihydroxy alcohols.

4138   Karacan, I.; Fernandez-Salas, A.; Coggins, W. J.; Carter, W. E.; Williams, R. L.; Thornby, J. I.; Salis, P. J.; Okawa, M.; and Villaume, J. P., pp. 348-74 in *Chronic Cannabis Use*, edited by R. L. Dornbush, A. M. Freedman, and M. Fink. NY, Annals of the New York Academy of Sciences, V. 282, 1976.

Sleep Electroencephalographic-Electro-oculographic Characteristics of Chronic Marijuana Users: Part I.

Available studies on the effect of marihuana on human sleep patterns indicated that marihuana affects REM and slow-wave sleep. EEG-EOG patterns and heart rates assessed in chronic marihuana users demonstrated increased percentage of REM sleep and increased sleep latency.

4139   Karasek, F. W.; Karasek, D. E.; and Kim, S. H., J. Chromatogr., *105*(2), 345-52 (1975).

Detection of Lysergic Acid Diethylamide, $\triangle^9$-Tetrahydrocannabinol and Related Compounds by Plasma Chromatography.

$\triangle^9$-THC, LSD and other related biochemical compounds produced simple and characteristic positive mobility spectra when the plasma chromatographic technique was utilized.

4140   Karbowski, M.; Jagoda, A.; Dewey, W. L.; and Harris, L. S., Pharmacologist, *17*(1), 254 (1975).

Effect of $\triangle^9$-THC on the Level and Turnover of Acetylcholine in Mouse Brain.

Brain acetylcholine levels increased (75%) at 1/2 hr after i.p. administration of 100 mg/kg of $\triangle^9$-THC and remained elevated up to 6 hrs. No significant elevations were observed when $\triangle^9$-THC was administered p.o. up to 100 mg/kg. Other data are presented.

4141   Karbowski, M.; Jagoda, A.; Johnson, K.; Dewey, W. L.; and Harris, L. S., Fed. Proc., *35*(3), 506 (1976).

The Effect of $\triangle^9$-THC on High and Low Affinity Uptake of Choline and its Relationship to Turnover of Acetylcholine in Mouse Brain.

High affinity transport of choline into crude whole brain synaptosomes of male mice with its high conversion to acetylcholine was stimulated by doses of 3, 10, 30, but not 100 mg/kg of $\triangle^9$-THC. The low affinity transport system was essentially unchanged. The highest $\triangle^9$-THC dose has been shown to depress ACh turnover in mouse brain.

4142   Karler, R., pp. 55-66 in *Marihuana Research Findings: 1976*, NIDA Research Monograph, 14, 1977.

Chemistry and Metabolism.

TLC and GC/MS separation techniques are used to isolate new cannabinoids. Research on the chemical elucidation of these cannabis constituents, their pharmacological properties and their biological disposition is continuing.

4143   Karler, R., pp. 67-85 in *Marihuana Research Findings: 1976*, NIDA Research Monograph, 14, 1977.

Toxicological and Pharmacological Effects.

Relevant literature including important contributions to the understanding of the pharmacology and toxicology of marihuana was reviewed. Brain concentrations, anticonvulsant properties and subcellular tissue distribution of cannabinoids were among the many topics discussed.

4144   Karler, R.; Sangdee, P.; Turkanis, S. A.; and Borys, H. K., Fed. Proc., *36*(3), 1026 (1977).

Mechanism of the Inhibition of Hepatic Drug Metabolism by Cannabidiol.

Inhibition of hepatic drug metabolism in mice by CBD is due to unidentified metabolite(s).

4145 Karler, R.; and Turkanis, S., pp. 383-97 in *The Therapeutic Potential of Marihuana*, edited by S. Cohen and R. Stillman. NY, Plenum Medical Book Company, 1976.

The Antiepileptic Potential of the Cannabinoids.

Cannabinoids afforded anticonvulsant activity to mice, rats and frogs (seasonal) depending on the test employed. CBD was found superior to THC in providing protection similar to PB and DPH and in enhancing activities of the latter two. Tolerance developed to THC but not to CBD effects and THC withdrawal precipitated CNS excitability . A potential therapeutic exploration of CBD was suggested.

4146 Karler, R.; and Turkanis, S. A., pp. 299-311 in *Pharmacology of Marihuana, Vol. 1*, edited by M. C. Braude and S. Szara. NY, Raven Press, 1976.

The Development of Tolerance and "Reverse Tolerance" to the Anticonvulsant Activity of Δ^9-Tetrahydrocannabinol and Cannabidiol.

Anticonvulsant properties of Δ^9-THC and CBD were studied in ICR mice and Sprague Dawley rats using several tests. Tolerance developed to the anticonvulsant effects in both species. Δ^9-THC and CBD showed cross tolerance with diphenylhydantoin and phenobarbital The mechanism of tolerance was neither metabolic nor dispositional but decreased sensitivity of the CNS towards these drugs.

4147 Karler, R.; and Turkanis, A., Fed. Proc., *34*(3), 782 (1975).

Hyperexcitability Upon Withdrawal from Marihuana.

Mouse CNS excitability, upon withdrawal of Δ^9-THC, CBD, phenytoin, and phenobarbital was evaluated using 24-hrs post-withdrawal electroshock. Maximal electroshock threshold was unaltered by Δ^9-THC withdrawal, but both 60-Hz and 6-Hz electroshock threshold was decreased. Cessation of chronic marihuana may be associated with CNS hyperexcitability.

4148 Karler, R.; Turkanis, S. A.; and Borys, H., *Seventh International Congress of Pharmacology: Abstracts*, Paris, France, July 16-21, 1978, p. 937.

Human Liver Microsomal Metabolism of Cannabinoids.

Δ^9-THC and CBD were very rapidly metabolized by microsomes from rat, mouse and human livers. 11-OH derivative was the principal metabolite, followed by a dihydroxy metabolite and two other unidentified compounds. Remarkable metabolic similarities were observed among the three species.

4149 Karniol, I. G.; Shirakawa, I.; Takahashi, R. N.; Knobel, E.; and Musty, R. E., Pharmacology, *13*(6), 502-12 (1975).

Effects of Δ^9-Tetrahydroacannabinol and Cannabinol in Man.

In human volunteers, Δ^9-THC increased the heart rate, caused underestimation of time passage and rating of drug reaction and produced a feeling of being drugged. Other physiologic and psychologic effects of THC, alone or in combination with CBN, were also investigated and CBN alteration of some of these effects was discussed.

4150 Kay, E. J.; Lyons, A.; Newman, W.; Mankin, D.; and Loeb, R. C., J. Consult. Clin. Psychol., *46*(3), 470-77 (1978).

A Longitudinal Study of the Personality Correlates of Marijuana Use.

Male college students were initially questioned about their drug use and later requestioned in three consecutive years. Analysis of the study indicated that continuous nonusers measured higher on the scales of socialization, responsibility, self control and conformity to norms, while continuous users were novelty seekers and more adventurous. Nonusers who switched to become users held an intermediate place between the two groups.

4151 Kaymakcalan, S., Int. J. Addict., *10*(4), 721-35 (1975).

Potential Dangers of Cannabis.

Available literature indicating the harmful effects of cannabis to humans is abundant and the legalization of marihuana will benefit neither the individual nor society.

4152 Kaymakcalan, S.; Ayhan, I. H.; and Tulunay, F. C., Psychopharmacology, *55*(3), 243-49 (1977).

Naloxone-Induced or Postwithdrawal Abstinence Signs in $\triangle^9$-Tetrahydrocannabinol-Tolerant Rats.

After chronic dosing of rats with increasing levels of THC until 40 mg/kg (twice daily) was reached and some rats died, the authors either withdrew THC or administered nalozone and then recorded the symptoms of an opiate-like abstinence syndrome.

4153 Kaymakcalan, S.; Ercan, Z. S.; and Turker, R. K., J. Pharm. Pharmacol., *27*(8), 564-68 (1975).

The Evidence of the Release of Prostaglandin-Like Material from Rabbit Kidney and Guinea-Pig Lung by (-)-*Trans*-$\triangle^9$-Tetrahydrocannabinol.

Perfused rabbit kidney and guinea-pig lung preparations were recorded at control dose responses. Then aspirin and SC 19220 (1-acetyl-2-(8-chloro-10,11-dihydrobenz-[b,f] [1,4]-oxazepine-10-carbonyl)-hydrazine) were added to the medium prior to THC and the effects were recorded. Aspirin inhibited the diuretic and vasodilator effects of THC and the production of prostaglandins while SC 19220 inhibited the effects of prostaglandins. Atropine, phenoxybenzamine and mepyramine had no effect on these responses with THC.

4154 Keim, D. A.; Baile, C. A.; Bolton, J. R.; Wangsness, P. J.; and Della Fera, M. A., Fed. Proc., *37*(3), 699 (1978).

Elfazepam and 9-Aza-Cannabinol Suppression of Sheep Abomasal Electromygraphical and Contractile Activities.

I.v. injections of 250 μ g of 9-aza-cannabinol decreased the action potential rate, contraction rate and contraction force of the distal 1/3 of sheep abomasal serosa. Elfazepam was also tested under the same conditions.

4155 Kelley, J. A.; and Arnold, K. P., J. Forensic Sci., *21*(2), 252-62 (1976).

Detection of Urinary Cannabis Metabolites: A Preliminary Investigation.

Purification, detection, and identification of CBN and 11-OH-$\triangle^9$-THC in the urine of professed marihuana users have been achieved. Preparation of urinary samples for GC-MS analysis in the select ion mode necessitated enzymatic hydrolysis with Glusulase[R] followed by organic extractive procedures. CBN and 11-OH-$\triangle^9$-THC existed in the urine as conjugates with the concentrations of CBN substantially higher than those of 11-OH-$\triangle^9$-THC.

4156 Kelly, S. F.; Fisher, S.; and Kelly, R. J., Psychopharmacology, *56*(2), 217-19 (1978).

Effects of Cannabis Intoxication on Primary Suggestibility.

Increased suggestibility and use of psychoactive drugs were discussed. The use of marihuana was said to increase suggestibility in subjects in a manner quite similar to that found with hypnosis, lasting only through the period of intoxication.

4157 Kephalas, T. A.; Kiburis, J.; Michael, C. M.; Miras, C. J.; and Papadakis, D. P., pp. 39-49 in *Marihuana: Chemistry, Biochemistry, and Cellular Effects*, edited by G. G. Nahas. NY, Springer-Verlag, 1976.

Some Aspects of Cannabis Smoke Chemistry.

Using a smoking machine the author investigated the chemical changes in marihuana smoking when the smoke was passed through a water pipe. GC-MS of the neutral fraction, obtained after fractionation of the resulting sublimate, showed the presence of 5 components, one of them identified as cannabinol methylether and the other four as new components formed during smoking. Individual cannabinoids were also examined using CBD as a model.

4158 Kettenes-Van Den Bosch, J. J.; and Salemink, C. A., J. Chromatogr., *131*, 422-24 (1977).

Carnabis. XVI. Constituents of Marihuana Smoke Condensate.

GC-MS was used to characterize the components of marijuana smoke condensate. The condensate was separated into acidic, phenolic, neutral and basic fractions. Many components common in tobacco condensate were identified along with a few cannabinoids.

4159 Kettenes-Van Den Bosch, J. J.; and Salemink, C. A., Recl. Trav. Chim. Pays-Bas, *97*(7-8), 221-22 (1978).

Cannabis XIX. Oxygenated 1,2-Diphenylethanes from Marihuana.

Three 1,2-diphenylethanes (dihydrostilbenes) were isolated from Mexican cannabis. Structures and spectral data were given. However, no structural arguments were presented.

4160 Kettenes-Van Den Bosch, J. J.; Salemink, C. A.; Van Noordwijk, J.; and Khan, I., World Health Organization, Expert Committee on Drug Dependence, Geneva, 26 Sept.-1 Oct., 1977. MNH/ DDC/ 77.7.

Biological Activity of the Tetrahydrocannabinols.

An extensive review of the available literature concerning the pharmacological and toxicological properties of cannabinoids was undertaken in an effort to help the world health organization (WHO) expert committee on drug dependence identify those cannabinoids which must be controlled on the basis of criteria set by WHO.

4161 Khalaf, A. S.; Farag, A.; and Koth, N., Clin. Chem., *21*(7), 972 (1975).

The Effect of Cannabis Intoxication on Serotonin Metabolism.

Plasma and brain levels of 5-HT and urinary excretion of 5-HIAA were evaluated in guinea pigs before and after cannabis extract administration. 5-HT levels were elevated and urinary concentrations of 5-HIAA were depressed. The metabolic effect was attributed to monoamine oxidase inhibition.

4162   Kilbey, M. M.; Johnson, K. M.; and McLendon, D. M., Pharmacol. Biochem. Behav., 7(2), 117-20 (1977).

Time Course of $\triangle^9$-Tetrahydrocannabinol Inhibition of Predatory Aggression.

THC inhibited predatory aggression in rats by elevating their brain 5-HT levels. The 5-HT role in aggressive behavior was discussed.

4163   Kimlicka, T. M.; and Cross, H. J., Int. J. Addict., 13(7), 1145-56 (1978).

A Comparison of Chronic Versus Casual Marijuana Users on Personal Values and Behavioral Orientations.

Heavy users had more heavy users as friends, used more drugs and perceived less risks associated with heavy marihuana use than did casual users. Otherwise, the two groups did not differ in their values and personal orientations.

4164   King, L. J.; Teale, J. D.; and Marks, V., pp. 77-107 in Cannabis and Health, edited by J. D. P. Graham. London, Academic Press, 1976.

Biochemical Aspects of Cannabis.

Rate of THC absorption is fastest when smoking. The 7-hydroxylated derivatives are the major metabolites of THC, CBD and CBN. Tissue distribution studies in animals are difficult to extrapolate to humans. This review article states that concentration of THC in the brain is less than other tissues of the body which were assayed and it is mainly excreted in urine and feces. Detection techniques for THC were described.

4165   King, M. R.; and Manaster, G. J., J. Consult. Clin. Psychol., 43(1), 99 (1975).

Time Perspective Correlates of Collegiate Marihuana Use.

Users and nonusers of marihuana were given demographic data sheets on extent of marihuana use and the time reference inventory. Marihuana users were found to be more past oriented. Little difference was shown in present and future orientation between the groups.

4166   Kirtany, J. K.; and Paknikar, S. K., Chem. Index, 7, 324-25 (1976).

A Synthetic Cannabinoid with a Camphane Moiety.

The authors claim the first report of a cannabinoid with a camphane moiety. This compound is a "by-product" of a photo-oxygenation reaction arising from an acid-catalysed cyclization of the terpenoid moeity of cannabidiolic acid.

4167   Klausner, H. A.; Wilcox, H. G.; and Dingell, J. V., Drug Metab. Dispos., 3(4), 314-19 (1975).

The Use of Zonal Ultracentrifugation in the Investigation of the Binding of $\triangle^9$-Tetrahydrocannabinol by Plasma lipoprotein.

Rate zonal ultracentrifugation was used to compare the binding of ^{14}C-THC (1, 6 and 10 µg/kg) by lipoprotein classes of human and rat plasma. The binding of other lipid-soluble compounds was compared with that of THC. The distribution of THC among the lipoproteins appears to be related to their content of neutral lipid or total lipid rather than that of phospholipids or protein. Binding of THC in plasma is unusual.

4168   Klinge, V.; Vaziri, H., Dis. Nerv. Syst., 38(4), 275-79 (1977).

Characteristics of Drug Abusers in an Adolescent In-Patient Psychiatric Facility.

The population reported on in this study was comprised of 143 adolescents from 12 to 18 years of age who were former in-patients admitted to a psychiatric clinic in Michigan for reasons other than drug addiction or intoxication. Marihuana was the most used drug in this time course study (1969-1971), with 74.1% of the population using it. Seven main social factors were considered and a breakdown of multiple drug use was presented.

4169   Klonoff, H., Int. J. Addict., *11*(1), 71-80 (1976).

Drug Patterns in the Chronic Marijuana User.

Chronic heavy marihuana users use and perceive marihuana differently than do lighter users, tend to ingest multiple drugs, and demonstrate more physiological but less psychological effects to marihuana than do social users. The decrease in psychological effectiveness seen with chronic heavy marihuana consumption may contribute to the propensity to experiment with multiple drug usage.

4170   Klykken, P. C.; Smith, S. H.; Levy, J. A.; Razdan, R.; and Munson, A. E., J. Pharmacol. Exp. Ther., *201*(3), 573-79 (1977).

Immunosuppressive Effects of 8,9-Epoxy-hexahydrocannabinol (EHHC).

Although 8,9-epoxyhexahydrocannabinol suppressed both humoral and cell-mediated immunity in treated mice, its effect on the latter system was much more profound.

4171   Knaus, E. E.; Coutts, R. T.; and Kazakoff, C. W., J. Chromatogr. Sci., *14*(11), 525-30 (1976).

The Separation, Identification, and Quantitation of Cannabinoids and their t-Butyldimethylsilyl, Trimethylsilylacetate and Diethylphosphate Derivatives using High-Pressure Liquid Chromatography, and Mass Spectrometry.

The t-butyldimethylsilyl, trimethylsilylacetate, and diethylphosphate derivatives of CBD, CBN, Δ^9-, and Δ^8-THC were prepared and examined using GLC, HPLC, and MS. Specifics are given with emphasis on stability and ease of separation.

4172   Knight, F., pp. 64-71 in *Chronic Cannabis Use*, edited by R. L. Dornbush, A. M. Freedman, and M. Fink. NY, Annals of the New York Academy of Sciences, V. 282, 1976.

Role of Cannabis in Psychiatric Disturbance.

In clinically controlled studies, Jamaican chronic cannabis users did not differ from non-users with respect to mental health as measured by physical, physiologic, psychometric, and EEG testing. However, a significant percentage of patients admitted to psychiatric wards demonstrated functional psychoses with previous cannabis use as a contributory factor. Clinical experience, but not structured studies, implicate cannabis as a causative agent in the development of certain psychiatric dysfunctions.

4173   Knights, R. M.; and Grenier, M. L., pp. 307-12 in *Chronic Cannabis Use*, edited by R. L. Dornbush, A. M. Freedman, and M. Fink. NY, Annals of the New York Academy of Sciences, V. 282, 1976.

Problems in Studying the Effects of Chronic Cannabis Use on Intellectual Abilities.

Effects of chronic marihuana use on human cognitive functioning were reviewed and studies conducted in several countries having prevalent marihuana use were also cited. The consensus was that chronic marihuana use did not cause overt impairment of cognition, although subtle effects were not excluded.

4174   Kohn, P. M.; and Annis, H. M., J. Consult. Clin. Psychol. *46*(2), 366-67 (1978).

Personality and Social Factors in Adolescent Marijuana Use: A Path-Analytic Study.

A new multivariate model was employed to evaluate the use of marihuana by high school students. Various characteristics of the model were discussed.

4175   Kohn, P. M.; Fox, J.; Barnes, G. E.; Annis, H. M.; Hoffman, F. M.; and Ejchental, B., Represent. Res. Soc. Psychol., *9*(2), 122-39 (1978).

Progressive Development of a Model of Youthful Marijuana Use.

Marihuana use was found to correlate negatively with sociopolitical outlook and positively with internal sensation seeking, peer acceptance, symbolic-protest functions, and favorable attitude toward marihuana use. All of this was part of a model studying the drug use behavior of young people.

4176   Kolansky, H.; and Moore, W. T., J. Amer. Med. Ass., *232*(9), 923-24 (1975).

Marihuana: Can It Hurt Yor?

In marihuana users a correlation of symptoms to duration and frequency of smoking was found. Structural and biochemical changes were found in the brain and CNS after heavy cannabis use. Subjects showed slow judgement, poor time estimation and difficulty in depth perception. THC is lipophilic and has been found to be retained in tissues, especially brain and testicles, as long as 8 days.

4177   Kolodny, R. C., pp. 71-82 in *Marijuana and Health Hazards*, edited by J. R. Tinklenberg. NY, Academic Press, 1975.

Research Issues in the Study of Marijuana and Male Reproductive Physiology in Humans.

A brief summary of androgen production and metabolism, along with RIA used to measure testosterone levels and their limitations, is outlined. In- and outpatient studies on the effect of marihuana use on testosterone levels indicated a significant depression below control values. Animal studies supported such a finding. Oligospermia, changes in secondary sex characteristics, and delays or limitations of normal growth patterns are among several speculations on the outcome of decreased testosterone levels.

4178   Kolodny, R. C.; Lessin, P. J.; Toro, G.; Masters, W. H.; and Cohen, S., pp. 217-29 in *Pharmacology of Marihuana, Vol. 1*, edited by M. C. Braude and S. Szara. NY, Raven Press, 1976.

Depression of Plasma Testosterone with Acute Marihuana Administration.

Acute marihuana use (1 or 3 cigarettes containing 900 mg of natural marihuana, 2.2% Δ^9-THC) in humans resulted in significant depression of plasma testosterone and LH with no effect on FSH or cortisol levels. Decreased testosterone levels may be due to a central effect while disruption in spermatogenesis may be a direct gonadal effect.

4179 Kolodny, R. C.; Toro, G.; and Masters, W. H., New Eng. J. Med., *292*(16), 868 (1975).

Normal Plasma Testosterone Concentrations after Marihuana Smoking.

Replies to the letter of Schaefer *et al.*, (New Eng. J. Med., *292*(16), 867, 1975). The data of the various studies might be consistent since each study examined different periods of marihuana use.

4180 Kopell, B. S.; Roth, W. T.; and Tinklenberg, J. R., Psychopharmacology, *56*(1), 15-20 (1978).

Time Course Effects of Marijuana and Ethanol on Event-Related Potentials.

The effect of marihuana and ethanol intoxication on event-related potentials was studied using twelve male subjects. The contingent negative variation (CNV), auditory evoked potential (EP), heart rate (HR) and subjective measures of intoxication were recorded before the oral administration of the drugs and at regular intervals for 4.5 hours after ingestion. This study shows that CNV and N1-P2 amplitudes and HR are affected differently by marihuana and ethanol intoxication both in timing and pattern.

4181 Kopplin, D. A.; Greenfield, T. K.; and Wong, H. Z., Int. J. Addict., *12*(1), 73-94 (1977).

Changing Patterns of Substance Use on Campus: A Four-Year Follow-Up Study.

Questionnaires were sent to students at one university and answers compared to those of a similar study done four years earlier. Since the questions asked concerned not only substances "ever used," but also when used and frequency of use, certain patterns of changing drug abuse could be seen. Marihuana, hashish and alcohol showed the largest rate of increase in number of users.

4182 Korcok, M., Can. Med. Ass. J., *119*(4), 374-79 (1978).

The Medical Applications of Marihuana and Heroin: High Time the Laws Were Changed.

Some available evidence points to beneficial effects of marihuana and heroin. The author predicts that these agents might become medications of choice and that Canada's laws regarding the two agents will eventually be modified.

4183 Kosersky, D. S., Arch. Int. Pharmacodyn. Ther., *233*(1), 76-81 (1978).

Antihypertensive Effects of Δ^9-Tetrahydrocannabinol.

Δ^9-THC (25 mg/kg, p.o.) lowered systolic BP in hypertensive, but not normotensive, rats. Tolerance did not develop after repeated THC administration for 10 days.

4184 Kostellow, A. B.; Bloch, E.; Morrill, G. A.; and Fujimoto, G. I., Fed. Proc., *37*(3), 858 (1978).

Effects of Cannabinoids on Estrus Cycle, Reproductive Capacity, and Fetal Development in A/J Mice.

Oral subchronic administration of Δ^9-THC (1-25 mg/kg) or crude marihuana extract (3-75 mg/kg) had no effect on the estrus cycle of female mice. Other Δ^9-THC effects included an increase in the incidence of cleft palate and fetal resorption and 50 to 90% reduction in term pregnancy.

4185 Kosviner, A.; pp. 343-77 in *Cannabis and Health*, edited by J. D. P. Graham. London, Academic Press, 1976.

Social Science and Cannabis Use.

The epidemiological analysis of cannabis use is complex. Social, psychological and cultural factors influencing its use are not very well defined, do not have specific boundaries and vary according to given dimensions. Cannabis users are likely to be liberal and permissive; politically, socially and religiously active.

4186   Kosviner, A.; and Hawks, D., Brit. J. Addict., *72*(1), 41-57 (1977).

Cannabis Use Amongst British University Students. II. Patterns of Use and Attitudes to Use.

Factors differentiating light from heavy cannabis users were identified in a sample of British college students in an effort to characterize the motivating factors for starting, continuing or discontinuing cannabis use. Other facets of use patterns and effects experienced were also investigated.

4187   Kosviner, A.; and Hawks, D., Drug Alcohol Depend., *1*(5), 339-48 (1976).

Seven Attitude Scales Used in Assessing Cannabis Use Amongst Students.

A new list of scales useful for studying and understanding the attitude and behavior of young marihuana users was described.

4188   Koukkou, M.; and Lehmann, D., Biol. Psychiat., *11*(6), 663-77 (1976).

Human EEG Spectra Before and During Cannabis Hallucinations.

Changes in the EEG patterns occurring during subjective experiences induced by THC as well as changes in the EEG due to individual disposition to such experiences were studied. Twelve normal volunteers took 200 μg/kg THC p.o. Period analysis was performed on the EEG before and repeatedly after THC ingestion, during resting, attention, eye closure, visual hallucinations, and body

image disturbances. A significant change in EEG frequency spectra was noted between resting, visual hallucinations, and body image disturbances. Such differences indicate functional brain states.

4189   Koukkou, M.; and Lehman, D., *Eleventh Collegium Internationale Neuro-Psychopharmacologicum: Abstracts*, Vienna, Austria, July 9-14, 1978, p. 118.

Experience of Induced Hallucinations Depends on Pre-treatment EEG Spectrum.

THC-treated subjects showed consistency of the pre-treatment EEG differences between high and low hallucinators. Higher alpha modal frequencies, fast alpha and less slow alpha characterized the high hallucinators.

4190   Koukkou, M.; and Lehmann, D., Exp. Brain Res., *23*(5), 112 (1975).

Cannabis Hallucinations and Human EEG Spectra.

Human subjects took 200 μg/kg THC orally. The subjects reported visual hallucinations and body image disturbances which resulted in changes in parietal-occipital EEG theta and alpha frequency bands.

4191   Koukkou, M.; and Lehmann, D., Pharmakopsychiat. Neuro-Psychopharmakol., *11*(5), 220-27 (1978).

Correlations Between Cannabis-Induced Psychopathology and EEG Before and After Drug Ingestion.

Predisposition to marihuana-induced hallucinations would be predicted from initial EEG values. EEG changes after Δ^9-THC (200 μg/kg, p.o.) also correlated well with experienced marihuana effects.

4192 Koukkou, M.; Lehmann, D.; Zimmer, D.; and Wyss, U., Electroencephalogr. Clin. Neurophysiol., *41*(6), 665 (1976).

Tendency to Cannabis-Induced Hallucinations Indicated by Predrug EEG.

Low hallucinators had slower alpha peak frequencies, less fast alpha and less slow theta activity than did high hallucinators after 200 µg/kg oral Δ^9-THC. Spectra of high hallucinators were said to be reminiscent of those of subjects with high neurosis scores.

4193 Koutselinis, A.; Kalofoutis, A.; Dionyssiou-Asteriou, A.; and Miras, C., Forensic Sci., *12*(1), 65-72 (1978).

The Possible Effect of Hashish on Leukocytes and Plasma Lipids.

Smoking hashish increased total lipids and phospholipids and altered the relative ratio of the various types of the latter in plasma and leukocytes of human subjects.

4194 Kozhevnikova, S. K., Bot. Zh., *61*(4), 566-67 (1976).

Additions to the Adventitious Flora of the Crimea.

The author reports expanded wild growth of *Cannabis ruderalis J.* at the bottom of mountains in the regions of Simferopol, Pionerskoe, Dobroe, Russkoe, Donckoe, Zhuia, Krsnogorje, Urozhainoe, Shistenskoe, and Zholotoe. It is found as a weed in fields of sunflowers and roses grown for oil and also in parks.

4195 Kraatz, U.; and Korte, F., Chem. Ber., *109*(7), 2485-89 (1976).

Die Synthese von 8-Methyl-Δ^8-Tetrahydrocannabinolen [The Synthesis of 8-Methyl-Δ^8-Tetrahydrocannabinols.]

In order to study the correlation between structure and pharmacological activity, Δ^8-THC derivatives which had and additional methyl group were synthesized starting from the tetrahydro dibenzo (b,d) pyran-6-ones with C_5, C_3, and C_0 side chains respectively. Iso-THC's were formed depending on reaction conditions. The products were characterized by NMR data. No pharmacological data were reported.

4196 Kraatz, U.; and Korte, F., Tetrahedron Lett., *23*, 1977-78 (1976).

Synthese von 1-Desoxy-Δ^8-Tetrahydrocannabinol - ein Beitrag zur Struktur-Aktivitatsbeziehung am Δ^8-Tetrahydrocannabinol [Synthesis of 1-Desoxy-Δ^8-Tetrahydrocannabinol. A Contribution to the Structure-Activity Relationship of Δ^8-Tetrahydrocannabinol.]

Δ^8-THC was converted into 1-desoxy-Δ^8-THC in order to determine whether the free phenolic hydroxy group is a necessary structural element for pharmacological activity. The structure of 1-desoxy THC was proven by nuclear magnetic resonance, MS and IR spectroscopy.

4197 Kraatz, U.; and Korte, F., Z. Naturforsch [B], *31*(10), 1382-86 (1976).

Oxygen Analogous of Δ^8- and Δ^9-Tetrahydrocannabinols.

The synthesis of Δ^8-THC oxygen analogs and their conversion to Δ^9-analogs were described in detail.

4198 Kraatz, U.; Wolfers, H.; Kraatz, A.; and Korte, F., Chem. Ber., *110*(5), 1776-79 (1977).

Synthesis of Thio Analogs of Δ^9-Tetrahydrocannabinols.

Thio analogs of $\triangle^8$-THC were synthesized using a condensation reaction. Details are given on normal and abnormal derivatives. Isomers were distinguished by their ^{1}H nmr spectra.

4199 Kralik, P. M.; Ho, B. T.; and Matthews, H. R., Experientia, *32*, 723-25 (1976).

Effect of $\triangle^9$-THC on Ethanol Withdrawal in Mice.

Acute $\triangle^9$-THC (10 mg/kg, p.o.) administered to male mice after 3 days of exposure to ethanolic vapor increased the severity and duration of ethanol withdrawal. $\triangle^9$-THC during exposure to ethanolic vapors had no significant effect on ethanol dependence or withdrawal . The author concludes that ethanol addiction and withdrawal are manifestations of distinct biological events.

4200 Kramer, J.; and Ben-David, M., Endocrinology, *103*(2), 452-57 (1978).

Prolactin Suppression by (-)$\triangle^9$-Tetrahydrocannabinol (THC): Involvement of Serotonergic and Dopaminergic Pathways.

$\triangle^9$-THC antagonized the elevation of rat serum prolactin induced by 5-hydroxytryptophan or pimozide (in low dose only), whereas cyproheptadine or pimozide antagonized the THC suppression of prolactin. Results were discussed in the light of dopaminergic and serotonergic interaction.

4201 Krejci, Z.; and Hanus, L., Acta Univ. Palacki. Olomuc. Fac. Med., 76, 145-52 (1976).

Identification of Cannabinoidic Acids by Thin-Layer Chromatography of their Methyl Esters.

A method for the identification of cannabinoidic acids as their methylesters is described. The authors stated that the conversion of the acids to the methylesters followed by GLC analysis is a rapid and simple method for the identification of the acids in mixtures obtained from natural material.

4202 Krejci, Z.; Hanus, L.; Yoshida, T.; and Braenden, O. J., Acta Univ. Palacki. Olomuc. Fac. Med., 74, 147-60 (1975).

The Effect of Climatic and Ecologic Conditions upon the Formation and the Amount of Cannabinoid Substances in Cannabis of Various Provenance.

Climatic and ecologic conditions were related to cannabinoid production of four variants of cannabis; (1) Thailand, UNC-254; (2) South Africa UNC-255; (3) Turkey, UNC-258; and (4) Czechoslovakia. Three cannabinoids (CBD, $\triangle^9$-THC, CBN) with their acids were investigated. Results are given by charts. Analysis was by TLC and GC. No CBD was found in South African samples. $\triangle^9$-THC was found in all variants.

4203 Krimmer, E. C.; and Barry, H., pp. 121-35 in *Discriminative Stimulus Properties of Drugs, Advances in Behavioral Biology 22*, edited by H. Lal., New York, Plenum, 1977.

Discriminable Stimuli Produced by Marihuana Constituents.

The discriminative stimulus properties of marihuana constituents in several animal species are reviewed. Findings suggest that the effects of THC and related substances are highly discriminable from control conditions and that tolerance does not develop to the stimulus properties of THC. A wide range of compound, including stimulants and hallucinogens, failed to elicit the $\triangle^9$-THC response.

194

4204 Krimmer, E. C.; and Barry, H., Psychopharmacol. Comm., *2*(4), 319-22 (1976).

Discriminable Stimuli Produced by Marihuana Constituents.

As a reward-reinforced task associated
with Δ^9-THC drug effects, maintenance
of differential responding (discrimination) has been observed in numerous
animal species by the common routes
of administration, including inhalation.
Generalization of the Δ^9-THC-induced
effects occurs with Δ^8-THC, 11-OH-
Δ^9-THC, cannabis extract, and hashish
smoke but not with non-cannabinoid
compounds. Discrimination of THC
is not antagonized by standard drugs,
and tolerance to the discriminative
stimuli is only partial. Cannabis products do not conform to a single pharmacological category .

4205 Krishnamurty, H. G.; and Kaushal, R.,
Indian J. Chem., Sect. B., *14B*(8), 639-
40 (1976).

Free Sugars and Cyclitols of Indian
Marihuana (*Cannabis sativa Linn.*).

The isolation and characterization of
simple carbohydrates and polyols are
reported. The constituents isolated
from Indian marihuana were compared
with those found in samples from USA,
Thailand and Vietnam . Some note-
worthy differences are shown.

4206 Krishnamurty, H. G.; and Siva Prasad,
J., Tetrahedron Lett., *29*, 2511-12
(1975).

New and Simple Syntheses of Olivetol.

A synthesis of olivetol via the condensation of 3:5 dimethoxy benzaldehyde
with ethyl methyl ketone. Yield of this
key condensation reaction is stated as
65%, overall yield of the synthesis of

olivetol is not given. The method may
also be applicable as a general method
for the synthesis of n-alkyl resorcinols.

4207 Kroll, P., J. Nerv. Ment. Dis., *16*(3),
149-56 (1975).

Psychoses Associated with Marihuana
Use in Thailand.

Extensive marihuana use at an air force
base was noted. However, only 5 out
of 200 psychiatric patients hospitalized
were incapacitated by marihuana use.
These 5 cases are discussed. For the
well-integrated person marihuana usage
did not produce a lasting psychosis.
Marihuana was a hazardous drug to
borderline adolescents.

4208 Kuehnle, J.; Mendelson, J. H.; Davis,
K. R.; and New, P. F. J., J. Amer. Med.
Ass., *237*(12), 1231-32 (1977).

Computed Tomagraphic Examination of
Heavy Marijuana Smokers.

Prior work with patients suffering cerebral
atrophy showed that some of them
were heavy marihuana smokers. Computerized axial tomography examination
of nineteen healthy males who were
known to be heavy marihuana smokers
showed no indication of atrophic changes.

4209 Kuppers, F. J. E. M.; Bercht, C. A. L.;
Salemink, C. A.; Lousberg, R. J. J. Ch.;
Terlouw, J. K.; and Heerma, W., J.
Chromatogr., *108*, 375-79 (1975).

Cannabis. XIV. Pyrolysis of Cannabidiol - Analysis of the Volatile Constituents.

Comparison of the pyrolysis products
of CBD as obtained under an air or
nitrogen gas effluent are reported. Analysis and identification was made by
GC/MS. Considerable similarity is noted

between the thermolytic products and common routes of mass fragmentation. Preliminary pharmacological assays on the volatile constituents of the CBD pyrolyzate indicated no significant effects. The major product was olivetol.

4210   Kuppers, F. J. E. M.; Bercht, C. A. L.; Salemink, C. A.; Lousberg, R. J. J. Ch.; Terlouw, J. K.; and Heerma, W., Tetrahedron, *31*(13/14), 1513-16 (1975).

Cannabis. XV. Pyrolysis of Cannabidiol - Structure Elucidation of Four Pyrolytic Products.

Pyrolysis of CBD was carried out in an air and nitrogen atmosphere. From the N_2-pyrolysate CBN and Δ^8-THC were detected. A compound having m/e 314 and a base peak m/e 108 was structurally assigned (iso-THC) but not named. A compound m/e 314 and base peak m/e 272 was found to be $\Delta^{4(5)}$-CBD.

4211   Kurth, H. -J.; Kraatz, U.; and Korte, F., Chem. Ber., *109*, 2164-74 (1976).

Synthesis of Sulfur Analogs of Cannabis Derivatives.

The tetrahydrocannabinol types of compounds were synthesized in which the pyrone oxygen (^{6}) was replaced with a sulfur, producing the corresponding thio compounds.

4212   Kurth, H. -J.; Kraatz, U.; and Korte, F., Justus Liebigs Ann. Chem., *7/8*, 1313-18 (1976).

Synthese von 1-Mercaptocannabinoiden [Synthesis of 1-Mercapto Cannabinoids].

"Cannabithiols" (with C_5 and C_1 side chains) were synthesized, starting from Δ^8-THC and Δ^8-THC-C_1, respectively. Characteristic spectroscopical and physical data were given for the products as well as for the intermediates.

4213   Kurzman, M. G., J. Amer. Coll. Health Ass., *26*(6), 312-15 (1978).

Decriminalizing Possession of All Controlled Substances.

Upon recommendation of a Blue Ribbon Interdisciplinary Committee, Minnesota relaxed its law on the non-commercial possession of marihuana. The rationale for such a recommendation was discussed.

4214   Kurzman, M. G.; Fullerton, D. S.; and McGuire, M. D., Natl. J. Crim. Defense *1*(2), 487-544 (1975).

Winning Strategies for Defense of Marijuana Cases: Chemical and Botanical Issues.

Criminal statutes that prohibit possession of marihuana are vague and methods used to identify marihuana are non-specific. All this creates legal conflicts that require resolving.

4215   Kutsch, L. J. C., Ned. Tijdschr. Geneeskd., *122*(40), 1509-11 (1978).

Farmacologische Aspecten van Drugs [Pharmacological Aspects of Drugs].

This review paper summarizes the action of several drugs (amphetamines, LSD, mescaline, psi: locybine and cannabis) on the human body. Δ^9-THC accumulates in the liver, lung, pancreas, kidney and fat tissue and also penetrates the cerebrum. No effect has been observed on the metabolism of (*nor*)-adrenaline or dopamine in the brain. The anticholinergic activity of Δ^8-THC and Δ^9-THC has clearly been demonstrated.

4216   Kvalseth, T. O., Ergonomics, *19*(4), 529 (1976).

Marihuana and Human Performance.

The paper presents a review of current research dealing with behavioral effects of marihuana in humans and also presents preliminary results of studies carried out by the author. Data from the author's laboratory show that when chronic users smoke marihuana the behavioral effects are varied, but some of the subjects actually performed temporal motor-responding tasks and reacted to visual stimuli as well as, or better than, they did before taking the drug.

4217   Kvalseth, T. O., Percept. Motor Skills, *45*(3), 935-39 (1977).

Effects of Marijuana on Human Reaction Time and Motor Control.

In six experienced marihuana users, THC (6.5-26 mg) did not affect the reaction time for accurate responses, decreased linear but not rotary arm movement time and increased the rate of error for both types of arm movements.

L

4218   Labrecque, G.; Halle, S.; Berthiaume, A.; Morin, G.; and Morin, P. J., Can. J. Physiol. Pharmacol., *56*(1), 87-96 (1978).

Potentiation of the Epileptogenic Effect of Penicillin G by Marihuana Smoking.

Dogs treated with penicillin G following acute or chronic THC smoking exhibited epileptic episodes not seen in penicillin-treated dogs. Mechanisms by which THC enhances the penicillin-induced neurotoxicity were discussed.

4219   LaDriere, M. L.; Odell, R. E.; and Pesys, E., J. Psychol., *91*(second half), 297-307 (1975).

Marijuana: Its Meaning to a High School Population.

A study designed to ascertain if motivation and meaning of marihuana use in high school corresponded with users and nonusers in a college population. Semantic differentials were administered to find the meaning of the concept of marihuana. Questionnaires provided information on motivation of use and nonuse. The greatest differences were between users and nonusers, rather than sex, age or educational level. Users considered marihuana as pleasant whereas nonusers considered it dangerous to health, unintelligent and bad.

4220   Laird, H. E., II; Consroe, P. F.; Jones, B. C.; and Picchioni, A. L., Fed. Proc., *34*(3), 743 (1975).

Stimulant Drug Antagonism of EEG and Behavioral Effects of Δ^9-Tetrahydrocannabinol.

Unrestrained rabbits receiving THC (0.5 mg/kg, i.v.) demonstrated increased cortical voltage output and sprawling with decreased general activity. The same parameters were then measured after a challenge by cocaine (1 mg/kg, i.v.), apomorphine (1 mg/kg, i.v.), methamphetamine (0.5 mg/kg, i.v.) and caffeine (25 mg/kg, i.v.).

4221   Lander, N.; Ben-Zvi, Z.; Mechoulam, R.; Martin, B.; Nordqvist, M.; and Agurell, S., J. Chem. Soc. [*Perkins Trans. 1*], 8-16 (1976).

Total Synthesis of Cannabidiol and Δ^1-Tetrahydrocannabinol Metabolites.

Three metabolites, 10-hydroxy cannabidiol, 6-α- and 6-β-hydroxy-cannabidiol were synthesized from cannabidiol. A total synthesis of 7-hydroxy-cannabidiol triacetate and 7-acetoxy-Δ^1-THC was achieved. Structural evidence was based on spectrochemical data and by comparison with the isolated metabolites.

4222   Lansky, D.; and Pihl, R. O., Psychol. Rep., *39*(3), 975-82 (1976).

Personality Correlates of Placebo Responsibility and Religiosity.

Various performance comparisons were obtained from persons who responded to marijuana, placebos, or group behavior utilizing meditative techniques. Results show that members of some groups which learn to meditate have similar drug responses when compared to average college students, but have better internal control and less anxiety.

4223   Laporte, J.-R.; Cami, J.; Gutierrez, R.; and Laporte, J., Eur. J. Clin. Pharmacol., *11*(6), 449-53 (1977).

Caffeine, Tobacco, Alcohol and Drug Consumption Among Medical Students in Barcelona.

Since data collection on drug abuse in Spain is very sparse, this report on drug use among medical students in Barcelona may be very useful to Spain's data base. The population tested was limited and showed a lower level of abuse than the overall population. The relative rates of common drug use (e.g., marihuana and hashish) were comparable to most populations.

4224 Larsen, F. F.; and Pryor, G. T., Pharmacol. Biochem. Behav., 7(4), 323-29 (1977).

Factors Influencing Tolerance to the Effects of Δ^9-THC on a Conditioned Avoidance Response.

Upon repeated administration of THC, tolerance to its impairment of conditioned avoidance response in rats was found to develop much sooner and last longer when rats were simultaneously exposed to drug and testing situations than when they were exposed to the drug alone. The type of tolerance developed was discussed.

4225 Latt, S. A.; and Allen, J. W., pp. 40-49 in Interactions of Drug Abuse, edited by E. S. Vesell and M. C. Braude. NY, Annals of the New York Academy of Sciences, V. 281, 1976.

Investigative Approaches for the Analysis of Drug Interactions at the Genetic Level.

The authors present an excellent and comprehensive review of past work in the fields of mutagenesis and teratogenesis with respect to LSD and Δ^9-THC. In most cases of positive mutagenicity or cellular changes caused by Δ^9-THC, another study refuted (or failed to support) the conclusion.

4226 Latta, R. P.; and Eaton, B. J., Econ. Bot., 29, 153-63 (1975).

Seasonal Fluctuations in Cannabinoid Content of Kansas Marijuana.

All parts of domestically grown (Riley County, Kansas) cannabis were assayed for cannabinoids. Data on seasonal fluctuations of cannabinoids are also included.

4227 Lau, R. J.; Lerner, C. B.; Tubergen, D. G.; Benowitz, N.; Domino, R. J.; and Jones, R. T., Fed. Proc., 34(3), 783 (1975).

Non-Inhibition of Phytohemagglutinin (PHA) Induced Lymphocyte Transformation in Humans by Δ^9-Tetrahydrocannabinol (Δ^9-THC).

Lymphocytes from healthy chronic marihuana smokers given Δ^9-THC orally at 210 mg/day for up to 14 days responded no differently than did control lymphocytes when challenged by phytohemagglutinin (0.05-50.0 μ g/ml). Δ^9-THC did not impair either the sensitivity or the maximal rate of lymphocyte transformation.

4228 Lau, R. J.; Tubergen, D. G.; Barr, M., Jr.; and Domino, E. F., Science, 192 (4241), 805-07 (1976).

Phytohemagglutinin-Induced Lymphocyte Transformation in Humans Receiving Δ^9-Tetrahydrocannabinol.

History of chronic marihuana use or its subchronic treatment under controlled hospital conditions did not influence lymphocyte response to phytohemagglutinin.

4229 Lau-Cam, C. A., Clin. Toxicol., 12(5), 535-41 (1978).

Coffee as an Interference in the Duquenois Test: A Differential Test.

Cannabinoids or coffee samples in a vanillin, metaldehyde, methanol and HCl mixture yielded colored products extractable in chloroform. Only cannabinoids, however, will give a positive reaction when para-dioxane is added after HCl to the Meta-Duquenois test.

4230   Lau-Cam, C. A.; and McDonnell, J., Bull. Narcotics, *30*(2), 63-68 (1978).

The Furfural Test for Cannabis: An Evaluation and Modification.

The furfural test was evaluated and compared with Beam's and Meta-Duquenois' tests. A modification was also done to include a chloroform partitioning step. All tests were compared by screening cannabis plant material, pure cannabinoids, as well as other plant materials and chemical compounds. The comparison results are tabulated.

4231   Laurent, B.; and Roy, P. E., Int. J. Clin. Pharmacol. Biopharm., *12*(1/2), 261-66 (1975).

Alteration of Membrane Integrity by Δ^1-Tetrahydrocannabinol.

The microsomal fraction of rat ileum was centrifuged and Na^+K^+-ATPase and Mg-ATPase were collected. THC was added *in vitro* (200 mg/ml) to study the effects on membrane integrity. The membrane-bound enzymes were inhibited by THC yet their structures were not affected. The authors suggest that the *in vivo* effects of marihuana may influence the membrane transport system of various substrates.

4232   Law, F. C. P., Drug Metab. Dispos., *6*(2), 154-63 (1978).

Metabolism and Disposition of Δ^1-Tetrahydrocannabinol by the Isolated Perfused Rabbit Lung.

Data show that the metabolic pathways of THC in the isolated perfused lung vary with the perfusion conditions of the preparation. Radioactive THC was administered i.v. or applied to the trachea of the rabbit lung preparation. The pharmacokinetic data are discussed. Tissue uptake was probably mediated by simple diffusion, drug binding was mainly to nuclei and mitochondria, and elimination half-life was biphasic.

4233   Lawrence, D. K.; and Gill, E. W., Mol. Pharmacol., *11*(5), 595-602 (1975).

The Effects of Δ^1-Tetrahydrocannabinol and Other Cannabinoids on Spin-Labeled Liposomes and Their Relationship to Mechanisms of General Anesthesia.

Δ^1-THC and its two analogs, dimethylheptyl-Δ^1-THC and 7-OH-Δ^1-THC fluidized the lecithin-cholesterol liposome bilayer, whereas CBN and CBD decreased its fluidity. The partial anesthetic properties of the psychoactive cannabinoids were discussed.

4234   Lecorsier, A.; Hoellinger, H.; Nguyen-Hoang-Nam; and Fournier, A., Soc. Biol., Compt. Rend., *285*(15), 1351-53 (1977).

Allergy-Creating Character of Tetrahydrocannabinol (Δ^9-THC) Active Principle of 'Chanvre indien' (*Cannabis sativa var. indica.*) (Fr.)

Results from the maximization test in guinea pigs and the mast cell degranulation test in sensitized guinea pig serum revealed Δ^9-THC produces an allergic response. Antibodies to the circulating Δ^9-THC were also isolated.

4235   Ledbetter, M. C.; and Krikorian, A. D., Phytomorphology, *25*(2), 166-76 (1975).

Trichomes of *Cannabis sativa* as Viewed with Scanning Electron Microscope.

A study of nonglandular and glandular trichomes and sessile globoid, small stalked, and large-stalked globoid glands is reported. Photos are presented. Frequency of occurrence is discussed.

4236 Lee, C.-M.; Michaels, R. J.; Zaugg, H. E.; Dren, A. T.; Plotnikoff, N. P.; and Young, P. R., J. Med. Chem., 20(11), 1508-11 (1977).

Cannabinoids. Synthesis and Central Nervous System Activity of 8-Substituted 10-Hydroxy-5,5-dimethyl-5H-(1) benzo-pyrano (4,3-c) pyridine and Derivatives.

Nitrogen analogs of cannabinoids were synthesized and evaluated for their CNS activity in mice, rats, and dogs.

4237 Lee, G.-M.; Olmsted, C. A., Amer. J. Drug Alcohol Abuse, 3(4), 629-38 (1976).

Effects of Cannabinoids on Synaptic Membrane Enzymes. II. *In vivo* Studies of NaK-ATPase in Synaptic Membranes Isolated from Rat Brain.

THC (1.0 and 2.0 mg/kg, i.p.) inhibited rat brain synaptic membrane Na^+K^+-ATPase activity. Effects of alcohol, used as a THC solvent, were also investigated.

4238 Lee, M. L.; Novotny, M.; and Bartle, K. D., Anal. Chem., 48(2), 405-16 (1976).

Gas Chromatography/Mass Spectrometric and Nuclear Magnetic Resonance Spectrometric Studies of Carcinogenic Polynuclear Aromatic Hydrocarbons in Tobacco and Marihuana Smoke Condensates.

Analysis of the polynuclear hydrocarbon fraction of tobacco and marihuana smoke lead to the identification of 150 components. Separation was accomplished using capillary GC and identification using MS and in some cases NMR. Some confirmation of identity was made by comparisons of GC retention times.

4239 Lefkowitz, S. S.; and Chiang, C. Y., Res. Commun. Chem. Pathol. Pharmacol., 11(4), 659-62 (1975).

Effects of Δ^9-Tetrahydrocannabinol on Mouse Spleens.

THC reduces spleen cellularity and antibody synthesis in mice immunized with sheep erythrocytes. Possible mechanisms involved were discussed.

4240 Lefkowitz, S. S.; and Klager, K., Immunol. Commun., 7(5), 557-66 (1978).

Effect of Δ^9-Tetrahydrocannabinol on *In Vitro* Sensitization of Mouse Splenic Lymphocytes.

Mouse splenic lymphocytes exhibited a decreased immunologic response after *in vivo* or *in vitro* exposure to Δ^9-THC.

4241 Lefkowitz, S. S.; Klager, K.; Nemeth, D.; and Pruess, M., Res. Commun. Chem. Pathol. Pharmacol., 19(1), 101-07 (1978).

Immunosuppression of Mice by Δ^9-Tetrahydrocannabinol.

Daily injections of 25 mg/kg THC into mice immunized with sheep erythrocytes caused a 49% decrease in the formation of Ig-G forming B cells and a 37% decrease in formation of rosette-forming T cells when compared to vehicle controls.

4242 Legator, M. S.; Weber, E.; Connor, T.; and Stoeckel, M., pp. 699-709 in *Pharmacology of Marihuana, Vol. 2*, edited by M. C. Braude and S. Szara. NY, Raven Press, 1976.

Failure to Detect Mutagenic Effects of Δ^9-Tetrahydrocannabinol in the Dominant Lethal Test, Host-Mediated Assay, Blood-Urine Studies, and Cytogenetic Evaluation with Mice.

The mutagenic potential of THC was investigated using several different sophisticated tests, both *in vivo* and *in vitro*. Results showed that, under the experimental designs used, THC did not induce either mutation or cytogenetic aberrations.

4243 Legowska, Z.; Szymkowska, K.; and Zolnierowicz, M., Farm. Pol., *31*(4), 315-17 (1975).

Wykrywanie Haszyszu I Strychniny Obok Siebie Metoda Chromatography Cienkowarstwowej [Detection of Hashish and Strychnine in a Mixture with each Other by Thin-Layered Chromatography].

The recent spread of the use of narcotics justifies this research centering on the identification of deliberately added ingredients used to enhance the hallucinogenic properties of the drug. This simple method will define relative composition of such additives as strychnine combined with hashish. The color bans most clearly defined when added to a benzene-ethanol solution are: strychnine, brownish-red; cannabis, violet, violet rose and rose violet.

4244 Leighty, E. G.; Fentiman, Jr., A.F.; and Foltz, R. L., Res. Commun. Chem. Pathol. Pharmacol., *14*(1), 13-28 (1976).

Long-Retained Metabolites of Δ^9- and Δ^8-Tetrahydrocannabinol Identified as Novel Fatty Acid Conjugates.

The long retained metabolites of Δ^9- and Δ^8-THC in the liver, spleen, fat and bone marrow of rats were identified as fatty acid conjugates of their respective 11-OH-metabolites. Several MS techniques were used to confirm the structures of the *in vitro* products, whereas identification of the *in vivo* metabolites was based mainly on TLC analysis.

4245 Lemberger, L., pp. 405-18 in *The Therapeutic Potential of Marihuana*, edited by S. Cohen and R. Stillman. NY, Plenum Medical Book Company, 1976.

Clinical Pharmacology of Natural and Synthetic Cannabinoids.

Clinical studies employing a newly synthesized cannabinoid (nabilone) indicated that the agent offers the therapeutic potentials of THC without its overt adverse effects or its insolubility. DMHP was also investigated.

4246 Lemberger, L., pp. 169-78 in *Marihuana: Chemistry, Biochemistry, and Cellular Effects*, edited by G. G. Nahas. NY, Springer-Verlag, 1976.

The Pharmacokinetics of Δ^9-Tetrahydrocannabinol and its Metabolites: Importance and Relationship in Developing Methods for Detecting Cannabis in Biologic Fluids.

Pharmacokinetic data of Δ^9-THC and its metabolites are presented using methods involving radioactivity and GC/MS. Different problems are associated with detecting cannabinoids in body fluids. RIA does appear to have the most promise of the newer methods available or under consideration for detecting cannabinoids.

4247 Lemberger, L.; Crabtree, R.; Rowe, H.; and Clemens, J., Life Sci., *16*(8), 1339-43 (1975).

Tetrahydrocannabinols and Serum Prolactin Levels in Man.

Six casual marihuana smokers were administered placebo, Δ^9-THC (1 mg) or 11-OH-Δ^9-THC (1 mg) by continuous infusion. After 2 hr., Δ^9-THC produced a slight increase in prolactin levels but the effect was gone after 4 hr. Both Δ^9- and 11-OH-Δ^9-THC increased heart rate and produced a psychologic "high."

4248 Lemberger, L.; Dalton, B.; Martz, R.; Rodda, B.; and Forney, R., pp. 219-28 in *Interactions of Drug Abuse*, edited by E. S. Vesell and M. C. Braude. NY, Annals of the New York Academy of Sciences, V. 281, 1976.

Clinical Studies on the Interaction of Psychopharmacologic Agents with Marihuana.

In a double blind study, 12 male subjects were given THC in combination with secobarbital. This treatment resulted in additive CNS depressing effects. While CBD (150 or 500 mg/kg) tended to attenuate the response to THC, it did not affect the secobarbital plasma levels or response.

4249 Lemberger, L.; McMahon, R.; and Archer, R., pp. 125-35 in *Pharmacology of Marihuana, Vol. 1*, edited by M. C. Braude and S. Szara. NY, Raven Press, 1976.

The Role of Metabolic Conversion on the Mechanism of Action of Cannabinoids.

Pharmacological and physiological studies after i.v. administration of 1 mg of Δ^9-THC or 11-OH-Δ^9-THC suggest that 11-OH-Δ^9-THC is the active metabolite of Δ^9-THC and may be responsible for its psychological effects. Metabolic studies with a synthetic cannabinoid, DMHP, show it is metabolized differently. The lack of psychological "high" with DMHP when tested in humans is attributed to the inability of the carbon 11 position to be hydroxylated.

4250 Lemberger, L.; and Rowe, H., Clin. Pharmacol. Ther., *18*(6), 720-26 (1975).

Clinical Pharmacology of Nabilone, A Cannabinol Derivative.

Nabilone was administered p.o. to six male volunteers in doses from 1 to 5 mg every 6 to 7 days to study its therapeutic usefulness. At the higher doses euphoria was reported with postural hypotension. Tolerance to these effects occurred rapidly and the effect on heart rate was negligible. At the lower doses nabilone appeared to be an acceptable relaxant.

4251 Lemberger, L.; and Rowe, H., Pharmacologist, *17*(2), 210 (1975).

The Clinical Pharmacology of Lilly Compound 109514 in Normal Volunteers.

A synthetic cannabinoid was tested as a potential anti-anxiety drug. At 1.0 or 2.5 dose, sedation was observed without or with minimal anticholinergic side effects. Marked effects were seen at 5 mg. Chronic use and tolerance were also discussed.

4252 Lemberger, L.; and Rubin, A., Drug Metab. Rev., *8*(1), 59-68 (1978).

Cannabis: The Role of Metabolism in the Development of Tolerance.

Tolerance to cannabis effects seen in animals is most probably not related to altered disposition of the agent. In human studies, this issue is still controversial.

4253 Lemberger, L.; and Rubin, A., pp. 269-310 in *Physiologic Disposition of Drugs of Abuse*. NY, Spectrum Publications, Inc., 1976.

The Cannabinoids.

Literature pertaining to the physiologic disposition and metabolism of marihuana in humans and animals was reviewed. Studies conducted following the introduction of radiolabelled cannabinoids contributed significantly to the understanding of these processes. 11-hydroxylation was found to be an important metabolic pathway for Δ^9- and Δ^8-THC *in vivo* and *in vitro*. The hydroxylated metabolites were as potent, or more potent, than their active precursors.

4254   Lemberger, L.; and Rubin, A., Life Sci., *17*(11), 1637-42 (1975).

The Physiologic Disposition of Marihuana in Man.

Smoking marihuana leads to Δ^9-THC absorption from the lung. Δ^9-THC is then metabolized in the liver and is finally excreted along with its metabolites in feces and urine.

4255   Lessin, P. J.; and Thomas, S. A., pp. 681-83 in *Pharmacology of Marihuana, Vol. 2*, edited by M. C. Braude and S. Szara. NY, Raven Press, 1976.

Assessment of the Chronic Effects of Marihuana on Motivation and Achievement: A Preliminary Report.

Chronic marihuana smoking (at least 900 mg/day for 73 days) did not alter motivation to earn money by task performance in both psychomotor and cognitive tasks. Learning and performance of subjects were also not affected.

4256   Leuchtenberger, C.; and Leuchtenberger, R., pp. 595-616 in *Pharmacology of Marihuana, Vol. 2*, edited by M. C. Braude and S. Szara. NY, Raven Press, 1976.

Cytological and Cytochemical Studies of the Effects of Fresh Marihuana Ciga-

rette Smoke on Growth and DNA Metabolism of Animal and Human Lung Cultures.

Marihuana added to tobacco cigarettes evoked abnormal proliferation at the cellular level, and increased mitotic index and DNA synthesis in mouse lung explants. Atypical growth of human lung cultures occurred and transformation of malignant cells increased in cultures of hamster lungs when exposed to either marihuana or tobacco smoke. Results and implications are discussed.

4257   Leuchtenberger, C.; and Leuchtenberger, R., Brit. J. Exp. Pathol., *58*(6), 625-34 (1977).

Protection of Hamster Lung Cultures by L-Cysteine or Vitamin C against Carcinogenic Effects of Fresh Smoke from Tobacco or Marihuana Cigarettes.

L-cysteine and vitamin C reversed or protected against the atypical growth and malignant transformations induced in hamster lung cultures by repeated exposures to tobacco or marihuana smokes. The possible mechanisms involved were discussed.

4258   Leuchtenberger, C.; Leuchtenberger, R.; Zbinden, J.; and Schleh, E., pp. 243-56 in *Marihuana: Chemistry, Biochemistry, and Cellular Effects*, edited by G. G. Nahas. NY, Springer-Verlag, 1976.

Cytological and Cytochemical Effects of Whole Smoke and of the Gas Vapor Phase from Marihuana Cigarettes on Growth and DNA Metabolism of Cultured Mammalian Cells.

Comparative studies on animal and human lung cultures and on animal testis cultures after exposure to smoke from marihuana or tobacco cigarettes are reported. In the model system developed, cultures are exposed to puffs of fresh smoke under standardized conditions. This proved to be a suitable bioassay to assess simultaneously time sequential alterations in morphology, growth, and DNA metabolism of the various cells and chromosomes after short- and long-term exposure to fresh smoke from tobacco and/or marihuana cigarettes.

4259   Levett, A.; Saayman, G. S.; and Ames, F., Psychopharmacology, 53(1), 79-81 (1977).

The Effects of *Cannabis sativa* on the Behavior of Adult Female Chacma Baboons (*Papio ursinus*) in Captivity.

Oral cannabis administration resulted in a decrease of locomotor activity in one pair of baboons and no change in loco- motion in a second pair. Social inter- action was enhanced in the second pair only.

4260   Levi, R.; Friedlander, M.; Dvilanski, A.; and Livne, A., Isr. T. Med. Sci., 11(4), 401-02 (1975).

Effects of the hashish component Δ^1- Tetrahydrocannabinol on the Ultrastruc- ture of Human Platelets.

The effects of THC (10^{-5} to 10^{-7}M) and the addition of ADP (5×10^{-6}M) to human platelets were studied at the ultrastructural level. This substan- tiated the biphasic effect of THC on

platelet aggregation and indicated that this effect is mediated by the inter- action of the drug with the platelet membrane.

4261   Levy, J. A., Diss. Abstr. Int. B. 37(8), 3903 (1977).

Modifications in Immune Reactivity by Δ^9-Tetrahydrocannabinol.

THC depressed cellular and humoral immune responses but did not signifi- cantly alter reactivity of the reticulo- endothelial system.

4262   Levy, J. A.; and Heppner, G. H., J Immunopharmacol., 1(1), 105-14 (1978- 79).

Alterations in Murine Delayed Type Hypersensitivity Responses by Δ^8-THC and Cannabinol.

Alterations of the development of hyper- sensitivity to sheep red blood cells in mice was evident when Δ^8-THC was given prior to, and when CBN was given after, immunization. Multiple dosing was also required.

4263   Levy, J. A.; Munson, A. E.; Harris, L. S.; and Dewey, W. L., Fed. Proc., 34(3), 782 (1975).

Effects of Δ^9-THC on the Immune Response of Mice.

In vitro preparations from mice receiving

oral THC (50-200 mg/kg) indicate that there is impaired functioning of both the cell-mediated and humoral components of the immune system. *In vivo* THC (25-200 mg/kg, p.o.) transiently suppressed splenic and peripheral nucleated cells and peripheral leucocytes, specifically.

4264   Levy, R.; and Livne, A., Biochem. Pharmacol., *25*(3), 359-60 (1976).

Mode of Action of Hashish Compounds in Reducing Blood Platelet Count.

CBD or Δ^9-THC (1×10^{-6} - 1×10^{-4}) lowered the platelet count of whole human blood. This effect was prevented by platelet centrifugation or by blocking ADP-induced platelet aggregation.

4265   Levy, R.; Schurr, A.; Nathan, I.; Dvilanski, A.; and Livne, A., Thromb. Haemostas., *36*(3), 634-40 (1976).

Impairment of ADP-Induced Platelet Aggregation by Hashish Components.

THC, in low concentrations, was more potent than CBD in inhibiting ADP-induced platelet aggregation whereas higher concentrations enhanced aggregation. Neither THC or CBD was effective against the ADP, collagen or thrombin-induced 5-HT release or irreversible aggregation of platelet rich plasma.

4266   Levy, S.; and McCallum, N. K., Experienta, *31*(11), 1268-69 (1975).

Cannabidiol and its Pharmacokinetic Interaction with Δ^1-Tetrahydrocannabinol.

CBD (1 mg) and Δ^1-THC (1 mg) were administered i.v. in a mixture or separately to male rats. The blood level disappearance rates were the same for CBD + Δ^1-THC as when they were administered separately.

4267   Levy, S.; Yagen, B.; and Mechoulam, R., Science, *200*(4348), 1391-92 (1978).

Identification of a *C*-Glucuronide of Δ^6-Tetrahydrocannabinol as a Mouse Liver Conjugate *in vivo*.

GC-MS analysis revealed that mice treated with Δ^8-THC formed Δ^8-THC-4'-glucuronide in their liver.

4268   Lewis, A., Brit. Med. J., *2*(6192), 56 (1978).

Legalization of Cannabis (Letter).

The author strongly warns against the legalization of cannabis and urges other physicians to reiterate his views.

4269   Lewis, C. R.; and Slavin, R. G., J. Allergy Clin. Immunol., *55*(2), 131-32 (1975).

Allergy to Marijuana: A Clinical and Skin-Testing Study.

In human subjects, allergic reactions to marihuana appear to be rare.

4270 Lewis, E. G.; Dustman, R. E.; and Beck, E. C., pp. 160-74 in *Progress in Clinical Neurophysiology, Vol. 2*, edited by J. E. Desmedt, Basel, Karger, 1977.

The Effect of Alcohol and Marijuana on Cerebral Evoked Potentials.

An up to date review of the authors' and others' work regarding the acute and chronic effects of marihuana and alcohol on the electrophysiological activity of humans and animals was provided. The evoked potential technique was employed to assess the effects of these two agents.

4271 Lewis, G. S.; and Turner, C. E., J. Pharm. Sci., *67*(6), 876-78 (1978).

Constituents of *Cannabis sativa L*. XIII: Stability of Dosage Form Prepared by Impregnating Synthetic (-)-Δ^9-*trans*-Tetrahydrocannabinol on Placebo Cannabis Plant Material.

Synthetic THC, impregnated on cannabis plant material, was stable only when stored under freezing conditions (-18 degrees). Decomposed THC included additional products besides cannabinol.

4272 Lewis, M. F.; Ferraro, D. P.; Mertens, H. W.; and Steen, J. A., Aviat., Space Environ. Med., *47*(2), 121-23 (1976).

Interaction Between Marihuana and Altitude on a Complex Behavioral Task in Baboons.

Female baboons were administered Δ^9-THC orally at doses of 0.25, 0.5, 1.0 or 2.0 mg/kg. They were tested at ground level or 1275 ft, 8,000 ft and 12,000 ft above sea level. At ground level 95% of the matching-to-sample trials were completed at all drug levels. At 8,000 and 12,000 ft, increased doses of THC produced decreases in percentage of complete trials. Altitude and THC interacted to affect total work output rather than just accuracy of performance. Relative to nondrug conditions, low doses of THC increased the response speed. Higher doses decreased response at each higher altitude.

4273 Lewis, M. J., Brit., J. Pharmacol., *54*(2), 277P (1975).

Δ^1-Tetrahydrocannabinol and Adrenergic Mechanisms.

Isotope studies have shown that Δ^9-THC in doses ranging from 1.1×10^{-7}M to 1.4×10^{-5}M inhibited the uptake of 3H-1-NA into the isolated perfused rat heart. Further evidence that Δ^9-THC is taken up into adrenergic neurone was shown. Isolated rat vas deferens, incubated with 3H-Δ^9-THC, retained more tritium prior to treatment of animals with 6-OH dopamine (a dose which destroys adrenergic nerves) than afterwards.

4274 Li, D. M. F.; and Chung, J. P. C., Clin. Exp. Pharmacol. Physiol., *5*(3), 207-13 (1978).

The Effects of Adrenalectomy on the Cardiovascular Responses to Δ^9-Tetrahydrocannabinol in rats.

Δ^9-THC (1 mg/kg, i.v.) induced hypotension and bradycardia in both adrenalectomized and sham-operated rats. Hypotension was more pronounced in the latter group. Hydrocortisone exerted diferential influence on these THC effects.

4275   Liakos, A.; Boulougouris, J. C.; and Stefanis, C., pp. 375-86 in *Chronic Cannabis Use*, edited by R. L. Dornbush, A. M. Freedman, and M. Fink. NY, Annals of the New York Academy of Sciences, V. 282, 1976.

Psychophysiologic Effects of Acute Cannabis Smoking in Long-Term Users.

After inhalation of hashish (2 and 4 gm), marihuana (3 gm) or Δ^9-THC (100 mg), chronic marihuana users exhibited heart rate increase, tendency of finger blood flow to decrease, dilated pupils and diminished basal skin conductance. Respiration rate and body temperature did not change.

4276   Lieber, M., Econ. Bot., *29*, 164-70 (1975).

The Economics and Distribution of *Cannabis sativa* in Urban Trinidad.

Marihuana smoking in Trinidad was found more prevalent among the older generation of Indians than the Creoles and younger Indians. The Indians are the cultivators while the Creoles do the wholesaling. The other sources of marihuana, ways of distribution and price fluctuations are discussed.

4277   Liedgren, S. R. C.; Odkvist, L. M.; Davis, E. R.; and Fredrickson, J. M., J. Otolaryngol., *5*(3), 233-37 (1976).

Effect of Marihuana on Hearing.

Thirty subjects were employed in this study; 15 received placebo, 15 received 0.8 gm THC. A standard group of audiological tests were conducted both prior to smoking and at the peak of the "high," usually 15 to 30 min. after commencement of smoking. No significant differences in the audiologic tests were noted upon comparison of pre- and post-smoking test scores. Conclusions reached

in this study were: Hearing was not improved by THC, and the tests administered may detect subnormal hearing but may not detect supranormal hearing.

4278   Lima-De-Faria, A., Hereditas, *83*(1), 23-34 (1976).

The Chromosome Field II. The Location of "Knobs" in Relation to Telomeres.

This paper describes the distribution chromomeres called "knobs" which appear in the terminal regions of pachytene chromosomes. Of the many species listed, *Cannabis sativa* is reported to have 20 chromosome arms, each with one knob in the telomeric region.

4279   Linton, P. H.; Kuechenmeister, C. A.; and White, H. B., Res. Commun. Psychol. Psychiat. Behav., *1*(5-6), 629-43 (1976).

Drug Preference and Response to Marijuana and Alcohol.

Although physiological changes and psychological task performance depended on the type of treatment (marihuana or alcohol) and the degree of alertness, drug preference was the most influential factor. Implications of personality drug interaction were discussed.

4280   Linton, P. H.; Kuechenmeister, C. A.; White, H. B.; and Travis, R. P., Res. Commun. Chem. Pathol. Pharmacol., *10*(2), 201-14 (1975).

Marijuana: Heart Rate and EEG Response.

Heart rate and EEG were examined under various dose levels of marihuana and Δ^9-THC. Results were significantly influenced by the experimental design; i.e., the nature of the problem task, the state of psychological alertness, and the drug-treatment effect.

4281 List, A.; Nazar, B.; Nyquist, S.; and Harclerode, J., Drug Metab. Dispos., 5(3), 268-72 (1977).

The Effects of Δ^9-Tetrahydrocannabinol and Cannabidiol on the Metabolism of Gonadal Steroids in the Rat.

Steroid Hydroxylase activity increased after THC or CBD (2 or 10 mg/kg, i.p.). Chronic THC or CBD decreased cytochrome P-450 but did not influence cytochrome b_5 levels, while the reverse was true following acute treatment with 10 mg/kg of either agent. Both compounds also depressed microsomal testosterone formation, whereas only chronic THC significantly decreased testicular enzyme activity.

4282 List, A. F.; Bartram, S. F.; Nazar, B. L.; and Harclerode, J., J. Pharm. Pharmacol., 27, 606-07 (1975).

Interactions of Δ^9-Tetrahydrocannabinol, Adrenal Steroids, and Ethanol.

With low levels of corticosterone, Δ^9-THC depressed respiration of mouse brain tissue homogenate. THC increased respiration with high corticosterone levels and ethanol potentiated THC's effects.

4283 Littleton, J. M.; and Maclean, K. I., Brit. J. Pharmacol., 56(3), 370P (1976).

Alterations in Dopamine Uptake in Rat Corpus Striatum Induced by Combinations of Stress and Δ^8-Tetrahydrocannabinol (Δ^8-THC).

Δ^8-THC (10 mg/kg, i.p.) produced a non-significant reduction in DA uptake by striatal tissue from non-stressed rats. In stressed rats, DA uptake was significantly increased.

4284 Llamas, R., Hart, D. R.; and Schneider, N. S., Chest, 73(6), 871-72 (1978).

Allergic Bronchopulmonary Aspergillosis Associated with Smoking Moldy Marihuana.

A case of allergic bronchopulmonary aspergillosis is reported in a chronic marihuana user. The smoked marihuana was the source of aspergillus.

4285 Llewellyn, G. C.; and O'Rear, C. E., pp. 319-23 in Developments in Industrial Microbiology, 1977, 19 (1978).

A Preliminary Evaluation of Illicit Marihuana (Cannabis sp.) for Mycotoxins.

Thirty street samples of marihuana were checked for mycotoxins. Ten showed mold growth and sterigmatocystin (a metabolic product of several species of fungi) was tentatively identified in the range of 20 ppb.

4286 Llewellyn, G. C.; and O'Rear, C. E., Mycopathologia, 62(2), 109-12 (1977).

Examination of Fungal Growth and Aflatoxin Production on Marihuana.

Although tests for aflatoxins on confiscated cannabis samples all proved negative, culturing of cannabis with either Aspergillus flavus or Aspergillus parasiticus produced afatoxins B_1 and G_1.

4287 Lockhart, A. B.; West, M. E.; and Lowe, H. I. C., West Indian Med. J., 26(2), 66-70 (1977).

The Potential Use of Cannabis sativa in Ophthalmology.

Smoking a single marihuana cigarette decreased the IOP of glaucoma patients but did not affect that of normal subjects.

4288 Loeffler, K. O.; Green, D. E.; Chao, F. C.; and Forrest, I. S., Proc. West Pharmacol. Soc., 18, 363-68 (1975).

New Approaches to Assay of Cannabinoids in Biological Extracts.

Biotransformation products of cannabinoids are identified in feces using HPLC and mass fragmentography. The procedures are automated to provide qualitative and quantitative results. The detection limits for Δ^9-THC was determined to be 5 ng. Δ^9-THC and 8-β-OH-Δ^9-THC were identified in the sample.

4289   Lokhandwala, M. F.; Pariani, H. K.; Buckley, J. P.; and Jandhyala, B. S., Eur. J. Pharmacol., 42(2), 107-12 (1977).

Involvement of Central α-Adrenoceptors in the Hypotensive and Bradycardic Effects of (-)-Δ^9-trans-Tetrahydrocannabinol.

Δ^9-THC (0.1 and 0.25 mg/kg, i.v.) decreased BP and heart rate in anesthetized cats. Central perfusion of phentolamine antagonized the lower dose of THC only. It was suggested that these THC effects are mediated in part by a decreased brain α-adrenergic outflow.

4290   Lombrozo, L.; Kanter, S. L.; and Hollister, L. E., Res. Commun. Chem. Pathol. Pharmacol., 15(4), 697-703 (1976).

Marihuana Metabolites in Urine of Man. VI. Separation of Cannabinoid by Sequential Thin Layer Chromatography.

A sequential TLC-system was developed to separate cannabinoid-metabolites. The non-polar system separates the neutral cannabinoids while the basic system separates the hydroxylated cannabinoids; the acidic system separates the acidic-metabolites.

4291   Loscalzo, B., Riv. Tossicol.: Sper. Clin., 5(3-4), 255-59 (1975).

Effects of Hashish (Alcoholic Extract) on the Hypothalamo-Hypophyseal-Adrenal Axis of the Rat.

The oral or i.p. administration of an alcoholic hashish extract caused a marked depletion of adrenal ascorbic acid and cholesterol and elevated plasma corticosterone levels in rats. Stimulation of the hypothalamo-hypophyseal-adrenal axis due to the induction of a stress reaction by hashish is postulated.

4292   Loscalzo, B.; and Di Napoli, T., Riv. Tossicol. : Sper. Clin., 7(3-4), 103-10 (1977).

Hahshis e Reattivita' Ipofiso-Cortico-Surrenalica Nel Ratto Albono [Hashish and Hypophysial-Adrenocortical Reactivity in Albino Rats].

Treatment with hashish extract depleted rat adrenal ascorbic acid and cholesterol levels while increasing the level of plasma corticosterone. Pretreatment with hashish extract also potentiated the physical stress-induced effects.

4293   Lott, P. F.; Lott, J. W.; and Doms, D. J., J. Chromatogr. Sci., 16(9), 390-95 (1978).

The Determination of Paraquat.

A review of different procedures for the determination of paraquat was given. Colorimetric methods using sodium dithionite were described for plant tissues, water and biological fluids. In addition, GC procedures were outlined. Rigorous tests were recommended for determination of paraquat on marihuana.

4294   Lotter, H. L.; Abraham, D. J.; Turner, C. E.; Knapp, J. E.; Schiff, P. L., Jr.; and Slatkin, D. J., Tetrahedron Lett., 33, 2815-18 (1975).

Cannabisativine, A New Alkaloid from Cannabis sativa L. Root.

Cannabisativine obtained from Cannabis sativa L. root was structurally determined by x-ray crystallography. This is the first

210

time a ring system of this nature has been detected in higher plants.

4295   Lotz, F.; Kraatz, U.; and Korte, F., Justus Liebigs Ann. Chem., 7, 1132-40 (1977).

Synthese Stickstoffanaloger Δ^8-Tetrahydrocannabinole [Synthesis of Nitrogen-Analogous Δ^8-Tetrahydrocannabinols.]

The 5-substituted resorcinol derivatives when reacted with menthadienol gave the corresponding Δ^8-tetrahydrocannabinols, which in the presence of dimethyl amine followed by reduction with lithium aluminum hydride ($LiAlH_4$) afforded the nitrogen analogs of Δ^8-THC. ^{1}H-NMR data of these compounds were tabulated.

4296   Lotz, F.; Kraatz, U.; and Korte, F., Z. Naturforsch. B, 33(3), 349-50 (1978).

Zur Synthese Seitenkettenhydroxylierter Tetrahydrocannabinole [Synthesis of Side Chain Hydroxylated Tetrahydrocannabinols].

A procedure was described for the synthesis of 3'-OH-Δ^8-THCV and 5'-OH-Δ^8THCV starting from (+)-trans-p-mentha-2,8-diene-1-01 and the respective resorcyl-alkyl ester.

4297   Lousberg, R. J. J. C.; Bercht, C. A. L.; Van Ooyen, R.; and Spronck, H. J. W., Phytochemistry, 16(5), 595-97 (1977).

Cannabinodiol: Conclusive Identification and Synthesis of a New Cannabinoid from Cannabis sativa.

Cannabinodiol, a new cannabinoid from Lebanese hashish, was identified as 2,6-dihydroxy-6'-isopropenyl-3'-methyl-4-n-pentyl-biphenyl, through synthesis and acid catalyzed conversion into CBN.

4298   Lowry, W. T., J. Forensic Sci., 21(2), 453-56 (1976).

Letter to the Editor.

Although most state legislation and the federal Controlled Substances Act (1970) define marihuana in terms of a single species, Cannabis sativa L., court interpretations include all cannabis species within the scope of the term, marihuana. Rejection of appeals is the rule when appellants base their arguments on the inability of expert witnesses to differentiate between cannabis species. Intent of the law takes precedence over the letter of the law in this instance.

4299   Lowry, W. T.; and Garriott, J. C., J. Forensic Sci., 20(4), 624-29 (1975).

On the Legality of Cannabis: The Responsibility of the Expert Witness.

Marihuana should be legally redefined to include not just Cannabis sativa L. but all other members belonging to the genus. This would facilitate its identification by forensic scientists.

4300   Lucas, W. L., Int. J. Addict., 13(7), 1035-47 (1978).

Predicting Initial Use of Marijuana from Correlates of Marijuana Use: Assessment of Panel and Cross-Sectional Data 1969-1976.

Tolerant attitude, educational attainment and opportunity to use marihuana were among factors predicting initial marihuana use. Factors predicting sustained use may be different than those predicting initial use.

4301   Lucas, W. L.; Grupp, S. E.; and Schmitt, R. L., Int. J. Addict., 10(2), 305-26 (1975).

Predicting Who Will Turn On: A Four-Year Follow-up.

Results from longitudinal study trying to pinpoint factors predicting future marihuana use revealed that favorable attitude toward marihuana and expressed desire to use it were the strongest predictors.

4302   Luteyn, J. M.; Spronck, H. J. W.; and Salemink, C. A., Recl. Trav. Chim. Pays-Bas, *97*(7-8), 187-90 (1978).

Cannabis XVIII. Isolation and Synthesis of Olivetol Derivatives Formed in the Pyrolysis of Cannabidiol.

The pyrolysis of CBD resulted in the formation of different olivetol derivatives and new cannabinoids. Two-substituted olivetols (2-methyl and 2-ethyl derivatives) and others were synthesized for proof of structure. Intermediates 2,6-dimethoxy-4-pentylphenyl-lithium and the cuprates derived thereof were coupled with a variety of compounds to give desired products in good yields.

4303   Luthra, Y. K.; Rosenkrantz, H.; and Braude, M. C.; Toxicol. Appl. Pharmacol., *35*(3), 455-65 (1976).

Cerebral and Cerebellar Neurochemical Changes and Behavioral Manifestations in Rats Chronically Exposed to Marihuana Smoke.

Repeated exposure of rats to marihuana smoke resulted in behavioral inhibition followed by excitation. Tolerance to these behavioral alterations developed. Fighting and involuntary vertical jumping were also manifested. Central neurochemical changes including altered AChE activity and RNA correlated with behavioral changes.

4304   Luthra, Y. K.; Rosenkrantz, H.; Heyman,

I. A.; and Braude, M. C., Toxicol. Appl. Pharmacol., *32*(2), 418-31 (1975).

Differential Neurochemistry and Temporal Pattern in Rats Treated Orally with $\triangle^9$-Tetrahydrocannabinol for Periods up to Six Months.

An extensive study involving behavioral and neurochemical changes observed in both male and female rats after chronic treatment with pure $\triangle^9$-THC. Three dosage levels (2, 10 and 50 mg/kg) were administered orally. Results and implications are discussed.

4305   Lyle, M. A., Diss. Abstr. Int. B., *36*(11), 5440 (1976).

Biotransformation of Cannabinoids by Microorganisms.

A study of the major metabolic transformations of four cannabinoids, $\triangle^9$-THC, $\triangle^8$-THC, CBN and CBD by a fungus, *S. racemosum*, is presented. A number of more polar metabolites containing an additional hydroxyl group were identified using GC-MS. Mass spectral fragmentation pathways are described for the major metabolite which is hydroxylated in the 4' position.

4306   Lyle, M. A.; Pallante, S.; Head, K.; and Fenselau, C., Biomed. Mass Spectrom., *4*(3), 190-96 (1977).

Synthesis and Characterization of Glucuronides of Cannabinol, Cannabidiol, $\triangle^9$-Tetrahydrocannabinol and $\triangle^8$-Tetrahydrocannabinol.

Synthesis of the glucuronide conjugates of THC, $\triangle^8$-THC, CBD and CBN is described. TLC and GC/MS were employed to characterize certain derivatives of these glucuronides.

Mc

4307　McBay, A., pp. 91-99 in *Drugs and Driving*, NIDA Research Monograph, 11, 1977.

Drug Impairment Reviews: Marihuana. Other Drugs.

When reviewed, studies investigating the effects of marihuana on driving were found limited in the sense that plasma concentrations of THC were not always measured. Depending on situation and individual, marihuana may impair or improve performance.

4308　McBay, A. J., J. Forensic Sci., *22*(3), 493-99 (1977).

Marihuana: Current Assessment.

Available scientific knowledge on the effects of marihuana in humans does not justify the rigid sanctions imposed on users. The author proposes that laws should be based on verifying and quantifying the amount of THC present in a sample rather than the commonly utilized gross identification procedure.

4309　McCallum, N. K., Experientia, *31*(8), 957-58 (1975).

Effect of Cannabinol on Δ^1-Tetrahydrocannabinol Clearance from the blood.

The clearance rate of Δ^9-THC from the blood of rats was increased when co-administered with CBN.

4310　McCallum, N. K.; and Cairns, E. R., J. Pharm. Sci., *66*(1), 114-16 (1977).

Simple Device for GLC Separations of Cannabinoids using a Surface-Coated Open Tube Column Without Stream Splitting.

A method to quantitate cannabinoids using a high-resolution capillary column system is reported. An inlet port design is described which reduces solvent vapors from coming in contact with the septum and eliminates dead volumes. Solvent systems are discussed.

4311　McCallum, N. K.; Cairns, E. R.; Ferry, D. G.; and Wong, R. J., J. Anal. Toxicol., *2*(3), 89-93 (1978).

A Simple Gas Chromatographic Method for Routine Δ^1-Tetrahydrocannabinol Analyses of Blood and Brain.

A GC procedure, suitable for use in toxicological laboratories, for determination of Δ^9-THC (I) in blood and brain samples was described. Compounds are detected as their diethylphosphate esters using thermionic or alkali flame ionization detectors. Detection limits of (I) were 0.5 ng/ml blood and 10 ng/g brain.

4312　McCallum, N. K.; and Eastwood, M. E., J. Pharm. Pharmacol., *30*(6), 384-86 (1978).

In Vivo Binding of Δ^1-Tetrahydrocannabinol and Cannabinol to Rat Serum Proteins.

The presence of CBN did not alter THC binding to rat plasma proteins.

4313　McCallum, N. K.; Gugelmann, A.; Brenninkmeijer, C. A. M.; and Mechoulam, R., Experientia, *33*(8), 1012-14 (1977).

Isotope Effect Studies on the Dehydrogenation of Δ^1-Tetrahydrocannabinol in the Rat.

Rapid binding to plasma proteins and rapid conversion to CBN seem to be the most important transformation responsible for lowering THC levels in the blood after i.v injection. Using tritiated THC in a position where it is lost upon conversion of THC to CBN, it was shown that THC was already being cleared from the blood in rats at 40 seconds postinjection (i.v.).

4314   McCallum, N. K.; Yagen, B.; Levy, S.; and Mechoulam, R., Experientia, *31*, 520-21 (1975).

Cannabinol. A Rapidly Formed Metabolite of Δ^1- and Δ^6-Tetrahydrocannabinol.

CBN was identified in the rat blood as a very rapid metabolite of Δ^9- and Δ^8-THC by using GLC and TLC comparison with authentic natural CBN, as well as by the crystallization of metabolic ^{14}C-CBN.

4315   McCarthy, C. R.; Cutting, M. B.; Simmons, G. A.; Pereira, W.; Laguarda, R.; and Huber, G. L., pp. 211-16 in *Pharmacology of Marihuana, Vol. 1*, edited by M. C. Braude and S. Szara. NY, Raven Press, 1976.

The Effect of Marihuana on the *In Vitro* Function of Pulmonary Alveolar Macrophages.

The bactericidal activity of pulmonary alveolar macrophages of CD-albino rats exposed to Δ^9-THC smoke was significantly depressed *in vitro*. Similar depression was observed with tobacco smoke and placebo marihuana cigarettes. Cytotoxin was located in the water soluble fraction of the smoke. 0.1 mg of pure Δ^9-THC *in vitro* did not affect the bactericidal activity of macrophages. The results suggest that chronic marihuana smokers may be more prone to lung infections due to decreased bactericidal activity of alveolar macrophages.

4316   McCarthy, L. E.; and Borison, H. L., The Pharmacologist, *19*, 230 (1977).

Antiemetic Activity of Nabilone, a Cannabinol Derivative, Reversed by Naloxone in Awake Cats.

I.v. administered nabilone antagonized apomorphine-induced emesis in cats. Duration of action was dose-related. Naloxone antagonized nabilone's antiemetic effects.

4317   McChesney, J. D., pp. 417-76 in *GLC and HPLC Determination of Therapeutic Agents, Part 2*, edited by Kiyoshi Tsuji, NY, Marcel Dekker, Inc., 1978.

Drugs of Abuse and Overdose.

A brief summary of analytical procedures for cannabis preparations is given. Limited data on biological fluid analysis are presented. GC and HLPC systems are discussed.

4318   McClean, D. K.; and Zimmerman, A. M., Pharmacology, *14*(4), 307-21 (1976).

Action of Δ^9-Tetrahydrocannabinol on Cell Division and Macromolecular Synthesis in Division Synchronized Protozoa.

The effect of Δ^9-THC on the cellular growth and division in log growth phase and division-synchronized *Tetrahymena pyriformis* GL was studied at concentrations which would not produce irreversible cytotoxic action. Δ^9-THC depressed the incorporation of 5-^{3}H-uridine, 2-^{14}C-thymidine and L-3-^{14}C-phenylalanine into RNA, DNA and proteins respectively in *Tetrahymena* during division I.

4319   McConnell, W. R., Diss. Abstr. Int. B, *37*(8), 3853 (1977).

The Effects of Δ^9-Tetrahydrocannabinol on Submaxillary Salivary Tissue.

In vivo and *in vitro* work with several species of animals helped elucidate possible mechanisms whereby $\triangle^9$-THC causes a reduction in salivary flow. It was shown that electrically stimulated salivary glands released and/or synthesized less acetylcholine in the presence of THC and that blood flow to the gland was depressed by as much as 50%.

4320   McConnell, W. R.; and Borzelleca, J. F., Arch. Int. Pharmacodyn. Ther., *235*(2), 180-86 (1978).

A Study of the Mechanism of Transport of $\triangle^9$-Tetrahydrocannabinol in the Rat Submaxillary Gland *in vitro*.

Metabolic inhibitors or oxygen replacement with nitrogen did not influence the firm binding of incubated 3H-$\triangle^9$-THC to rat submaxillary gland slices.

4321   McConnell, W. R.; Borzelleca, J. F.; and Chambers, J. W., Fed. Proc., *34*(3), 782 (1975).

The Effects of $\triangle^9$-Tetrahydrocannabinol (THC) on Electrically Stimulated Saliva from Cat Submaxillary Gland.

$\triangle^9$-THC decreased salivary flow in stimulated cat submaxillary gland. Effects were dose related and cholinergically mediated.

4322   McConnell, W. R.; Borzelleca, J. F.; and Dewey, W. L., Fed. Proc., *35*(3), 644 (1976).

The Mechanism by Which $\triangle^9$-Tetrahydrocannabinol (THC) Produces a Decrease in Salivary Flow Following Electrical Stimulation.

$\triangle^9$-THC (0.5 and 1.0 mg/kg) produces a 45% decrease in submaxillary gland arterial blood flow in dogs that is correlated with a 50% depression of saliva flow. Neither dosage changed blood or salivary cholinesterase activity in the dog or cat. *In vitro* $\triangle^9$-THC (3 µgm/ml) suppressed, by 37%, acetylcholine (Ach) release from guinea pig ileum electrically stimulated.

4323   McConnell, W. R.; Dewey, W. L.; Harris, L. S.; and Borzelleca, J. F., J. Pharmacol. Exp. Ther., *206*(3), 567-73 (1978).

A Study of the Effect of $\triangle^9$-Tetrahydrocannabinol ($\triangle^9$-THC) on Mammalian Salivary Flow.

$\triangle^9$-THC decreased electrically stimulated salivary flow in cats and dogs. Mechanisms involved were investigated and the possible influence of THC on acetylcholine release was indicated.

4324   McCoy, D. J., Diss. Abst. Int. B, *35*(10), 5030 (1975).

The Combined Effects of Cannabidiol and Delta-9-Tetrahydrocannabinol.

A spectrum of pharmacological tests was employed to assess the activity of CBD alone or in combination with $\triangle^9$-THC. Results indicated that CBD is a pharmacologically active agent which interacts with $\triangle^9$-THC in an unpredictable manner.

4325   McCoy, D. J.; Brown, D. J.; and Forney, R. B., Res. Commun. Psychol. Psychiat. Behav., *1*(5-6), 619-28 (1976).

The Effect of Cannabinoid Mixtures on Methamphetamine-Induced Locomotor Activity, Electroshock Produced Convulsions, and the Lethality of Strychnine and Pentylenetetrazol.

THC altered the methamphetamine-induced increase in mice activity whereas CBD did not. CBD, in turn, increased strychnine lethality and shortened the hind leg extension phase following electroshock-induced convulsions whereas THC failed to do so. Effects of a combination of both THC and CBD on these and other parameters were also investigated.

4326   McCoy, D. J.; Brown, D. J.; and Forney, R. B., Res. Commun. Psychol. Psychiat. Behav., *3*(2), 89-99 (1978).

The Effect of Cannabinoid Mixtures on Induced Sleep Intervals and the Disappearance of Ethanol and Hexobarbital.

In mice, THC potentiated ethanol and hexobarbital sleeping times without altering their metabolism, whereas CBD potentiated hexobarbital effects but blocked its metabolism. A mixture of the two agents also had synergistic effects on hexobarbital sleeping time and metabolism.

4327   McGlothlin, W., pp. 38-54 in *Marihuana Research Findings: 1976*, NIDA Research Monograph, 14, 1977.

Epidemiology of Marihuana Use.

Recent surveys concerning marihuana use by various segments of the population were analyzed. It is concluded that the question of the causal effects relative to marihuana use remains unresolved.

4328   McLendon, D. M.; Harris, R. T.; and Maule, W. F., Psychopharmacology, *50*(2), 159-63 (1976).

Suppression of the Cardiac Conditioned Response by Δ^9-Tetrahydrocannabinol: A Comparison with Other Drugs.

THC (0.2-1.0 mg/kg, i.v.) possesses anti-anxiety properties similar to those of diazepam (0.5-1.5 mg/kg, i.v.) in male rhesus monkeys. Suppression of the cardiac conditioned response (tachycardia or bradycardia due to anxiety) varied in degree from partial to complete and was dose related. Neither anti-anxiety agent altered the ability of the test subjects to differentiate tones.

4329   McMillan, D. E., pp. 1-34 in *Advances in Behavioral Pharmacology, Vol. 1*, edited by Travis Thompson and Peter B. Dews, NY, Academic Press, 1977.

Behavioral Pharmacology of the Tetrahydrocannabinols.

A summary of the available literature concerning the effects of marihuana on both controlled and gross behavioral parameters was presented. Difficulties encountered when studying the behavioral pharmacology of cannabinoids were also discussed.

4330   McMillan, D. E., Fed. Proc., *37*(3), 273 (1978).

Acute and Chronic Interactions Between Δ^9-Tetrahydrocannabinol (Δ^9-THC) and Pentobarbital in the Pigeon.

Pentobarbital produced dose-dependent decreases in the rate of pigeon responding to a multiple FR 30 FI 5 schedule of reinforcement. A single 1.0 mg/kg injection of Δ^9-THC greatly potentiated the rate decreasing effects of pentobarbital. Furthermore, a cross-tolerance between the two agents was demonstrated following the chronic administration of Δ^9-THC.

M

4331 Macavoy, M. G.; and Marks, D. F., Psychopharmacology, *44*(2), 147-52 (1975).

Divided Attention Performance of Cannabis Users and Non-Users Following Cannabis and Alcohol.

A visual divided attention task is used in cannabis-naive and experienced users to assess performance with cannabis (2.62 mg and 5.24 mg Δ^9-THC by inhalation), ETOH, and marihuana-ETOH combinations. Marihuana alone impaired performance while ETOH did not. Combinations resulted in synergistic impairment in non-users, but antagonistic activity in chronic users. Cross-tolerance develops between cannabis and ETOH.

4332 Maccannell, K.; Milstein, S. L.; Karr, G.; and Clark, S., Progr. Neuro-Psychopharmacol., *1*(3-4), 339-43 (1977).

Marijuana-Produced Impairments in Form Perception. Experienced and Non-Experienced Subjects.

A tactual form board was used to measure the form perception ability in human subjects. Results indicated that marihuana smoking impairs form perception in both experienced and naive smokers, with the impairment being greater in the former group.

4333 Maclean, K. I.; and Littleton, J. M., Eur. J. Pharmacol., *41*(2), 171-82 (1977).

Environmental Stress as a Factor in the Response of Rat Brain Catecholamine Metabolism to Δ^8-Tetrahydrocannabinol.

Interactions of Δ^8-THC (10 mg/kg, i.p.), a stressful environment (isolation and food deprivation), and central catecholamine metabolism were assessed in male Wistar rats. THC caused immobilization, hyper-reactivity, and hypothermia under stressful conditions. Biochemically, THC increased striatal uptake of DA *in vivo* and *in vitro* and prevented the AMT-induced (400 mg/kg, i.p.) depletion of striatal DA. Environment directly affected both the behavioral and biochemical responses to THC.

4334 Magence, D. N.; and Petzel, T. P., J. Alter. State. Conscious., *2*(2), 147-60 (1976).

Evaluation of the Reported Effects of Marijuana Use.

The prior knowledge of college students evaluating marihuana effects definitely influenced their rating. This influence, however, was not always negative as Goode hypothesized. Implications of the findings were discussed.

4335 Magour, S.; Coper, H.; and Fahndrich, Ch., Naunyn Schmeidebergs Arch. Pharmacol., *293* (Suppl.), 29 (1976).

The Development of Tolerance to the Depressant Effect of Δ^9-Tetrahydrocannabinol on Motor Activity of Rats. Correlations to its Subcellular Distribution in the Brain.

Tolerance to the duration but not to initial inhibition of rat locomotor activity developed after repeated Δ^9-THC administration. Tolerance was metabolic in nature.

4336 Magour, S.; Coper, H.; and Fahndrich, Ch., Pol. J. Pharmacol. Pharm., *28*(6), 589-92 (1976).

An attempt to Correlate the Development of Tolerance to Δ^9-Tetrahydrocannabinol and D-amphetamine with their Subcellular Distribution in Rat Brain.

Tolerance to the amphetamine-induced increase in motor activity of rats was not due to changes in its brain subcellular accumulation. In contrast, tolerance to the THC depressant effects was found to be metabolically mediated.

4337   Magour, S.; Coper, H.; and Fahndrich, Ch., Psychopharmacol., 51(2), 141-45 (1977).

Is Tolerance to Δ^9-THC Cellular or Metabolic? The Subcellular Distribution of Delta-9-Tetrahydrocannabinol and its Metabolites in Brains of Tolerant and Non-Tolerant Rats.

Parallel studies are directed at correlating the onset of tolerance to the locomotor (LM) depressant effects of Δ^9-THC with the central distribution of cannabinoids in female Wistar rats. Animals receiving i.p. THC (10 mg/kg, b.i.d.) for 4 days demonstrated decreased durations but unchanged intensities of LM depression. Tolerance to the LM depression coincided with the accelerated appearance of polar metabolites in brain subcellular fractions.

4338   Magour, S.; Coper, H.; Fahndrich, Ch.; and Hill, R., Life Sci., 18(6), 575-84 (1976).

Relationship Between the Subcellular Distribution of Delta-9-Tetrahydrocannabinol and its Metabolites in Rat Brain and the Duration of the Effect on Motor Activity.

Female rats were used to study the subcellular distribution of Δ^9-THC and its metabolites in the brain. Both ^{3}H-labelled and unlabelled Δ^9-THC were used (10 mg/kg, i.p.) and the locomotor activity observed every 15

mins. for 12 hrs. The concentration of unchanged Δ^9-THC or 11-OH-Δ^9-THC in brain subcellular fractions were determined by TLC methods. No preferential site of accumulation was observed. The fate of labelled material was also indicated.

4339   Mahfouz, M.; Makar, A. B.; Ghoneim, M. T.; and Mikhail, M. M., Pharmazie, 30(12), 772-74 (1975).

Effect of Hashish on Brain Gamma Aminobutyric Acid System, Blood Fibrinolytic Activity and Glucose and Some Serum Enzymes in the Rat.

Exposure of rats to hashish smoke decreased brain GABA level but left glutamic acid level unchanged. Activity of GABA related enzymes, especially aminobutyrate aminotransferase, along with blood glucose, fibrinolytic activity, SGOT and LDH, were increased.

4340   Maier, R.; and Maitre, L., Biochem. Pharmacol., 24(18), 1695-99 (1975).

Steroidogenic and Lipolytic Effects of Cannabinols in the Rat and the Rabbit.

Δ^9, Δ^8-THC and DMHP were injected i.p. (30 mg/kg) in rats and rabbits. Δ^9-THC was found to still have corticotropic activity after 5 hr. while Δ^8-THC and DMHP no longer had any effects in rats. Δ^9-THC was 3 times more potent than DMHP and 10 times more potent than Δ^8-THC at threshold levels. The same lypolytic activity was found for all 3 cannabinoids and all stimulated release of ACTH.

4341   Malik, O. P., Indian J. Pharm., 38(2), 31-34 (1976).

Synthesis of Substituted Chromenes as Analogs of Tetrahydrocannabinol.

2, 2-dimethyl-6-*n*-propyl-7-hydroxy-chromene (I) and its 6-isopentyl homolog (II) were prepared by base catalysed condensation of 3-hydroxyisovaleraldehyde dimethylacetal (III) and the respective 5-alkyl resorcinol. Reaction of III with methyl, 3,5-dihydroxybenzoate offered two isomeric products. The biological activity of I and II and some of their omega-tertiaryaminoalkyl ethers were reported.

4342 Malik, O. P.; Kapil, R. S.; and Anand, N., Indian J. Chem., *14B*(6), 449-54 (1976).

Studies of Cannabinoids: Part I - Synthesis of 5-Hydroxy-2, 2-dimethyl-7-*n*-pentylchromene, *trans*-3-*n*-Butyl-5-hydroxy-2, 2, 4-trimethyl-7-*n*-pentylchroman and Some Related Compounds.

The condensation of 3,5-dehydroxy-*n*-pentylbenzene or 2,4-dihydroxy-*n*-pentylbenzene with 3, hydroxy-3-methylbutyaldehyde dimethyl acetal resulted in the isolation of different cannabinoid derivatives. None of these compounds were biologically active.

4343 Malik, O. P.; Kapil, R. S.; and Anand, N., Indian J. Chem., *14B*(6), 455-58 (1976).

Studies on Cannabinoids: Part II-Synthesis of *trans*-6a,7,12,12a-Tetrahydro-6, 6-dimethyl-3-*n*-pentyl-6H-benzo [*b*] naphtho [2,3-*d*] pyran-I-ol and Some Related Compounds.

A great number of cannabinoid derivatives having four six membered rings were synthesized. The analogs with i-C_5 and Me_3 side chains were also prepared.

4344 Malik, O. P.; Kapil, R. S.; and Anand, N., Indian J. Chem., *14B*(12), 975-78 (1976).

Studies on Cannabinoids: Part III - Synthesis of 9,10,11,11a-Tetrahydro-6*H*, 8*H*-Pyrido (1,2-*c*) (1,3) Benzoxazine.

A step-by-step description of the methods employed in the synthesis of the heterocyclic cannabinoid-like pyrido (1,2-*c*) (1,3) benzoxazine was provided.

4345 Malingre, Th.; Hendriks, H.; Batterman, S.; Bos, R.; and Visser, J., Planta. Med., *28*(1), 56-61 (1975).

The Essential Oil of *Cannabis sativa*.

Cannabis produced from seeds of an unknown origin (birdseed) was extracted prior to and after steam distillation. The cannabinoid content was determined on both extracts and essential oils from distillate. Approximately 75% of the essential oil is removed by steam distillation. Cannabinoids are present in small amounts in distillate.

4346 Malit, L. A.; Johnstone, R. E.; Bourke, D. I.; Kulp, R. A.; Klein, V.; and Smith, T. C., Anesthesiology, *42*(6), 666-73 (1975).

Intravenous Δ^9-Tetrahydrocannabinol: Effects on Ventilatory Control and Cardiovascular Dynamics.

Ten male subjects (ages 21 to 41 years) received THC i.v. (27, 40, 60, 90, 134, and 201 μg/kg). THC shifted the ventilatory response and a dose related tachycardia was noted. The heart rate increased as did the arterial pressure and cardiac index suggesting β-adrenergic stimulation. Intense mental effects and anxiety prohibited higher THC doses.

4347 Malor, R.; Chesher, G. B.; and Jackson, D. M., J. Pharm. Pharmacol., *28*(8), 652-54 (1976).

The Effect of Δ^9-Tetrahydrocannabinol on Plasma Concentrations of Non-Esterified Fatty Acids in the Mouse.

Like epinephrine, Δ^9-THC increased concentration of mouse plasma non-esterified fatty acids in a dose-dependent fashion. THC's effect had longer duration of action and was not blocked by propranolol.

4348   Malor, R.; Jackson, D. M.; and Chesher, G. B., Biochem. Pharmacol., *27*(4), 407-13 (1978).

Possible Central Dopaminergic Modulation of the Rise in Plasma Concentration of Non-Esterified Fatty Acids Produced in the Mouse by (-)-*trans*-Δ^9-Tetrahydrocannabinol.

In view of recent suggestions that THC may affect the hypothalamic-pituitary-adrenal axis, the authors investigated mechanisms whereby THC produced a dose-dependent rise in mouse plasma free-fatty-acids *in vivo*, but not *in vitro*. Perphenazine or pimozide blocked the action as well as prior adrenalectomy or treatment with α-methyl-*p*-tyrosine but no alteration in response was seen with FLA-63 or phentolamine.

4349   Malor, R.; Jackson, D. M.; and Chesher, G. B., J. Pharm. Pharmacol., *27*(8), 610-12 (1975).

The Effects of Δ^9-Tetrahydrocannabinol, Cannabidiol and Cannabinol on Ether Anaesthesia in Mice.

Δ^9- and CBN prolonged, whereas CBD reversed, ether anesthesia in mice. Combined with either THC or CBN, CBD reversed the latter's effect only.

4350   Malor, R.; Starmer, G. A.; Chesher, G. B.; Jackson, D. M.; and Welburn,

P. J., Abstract 52 of *Southeast Asian/ Western Pacific Regional Meeting of Pharmacologists*, Singapore, May 11-14, 1976.

The Suppression of the Prostaglandin-E_1-Induced Abdominal Constriction Response in the Mouse by Δ^9-Tetrahydrocannabinol: A Kinetic Study.

A kinetic study revealed that Δ^9-THC (0.25-2.0 mg/kg) given orally to female QS strain mice competitively antagonized prostaglandin E_1-induced abdominal constriction. Δ^9-THC also antagonized formic acid-induced abdominal constriction.

4351   Manning, F. J., Pharmacol. Biochem. Behav., *5*(3), 269-73 (1976).

Role of Experience in Acquisition and Loss of Tolerance to the Effect of Δ^9-THC on Spaced Responding.

Trained rats previously exposed to Δ^9-THC did not differ in their behavioral response from Δ^9-THC naive rats when both were tested in the drug state.   Regardless of previous drug history, repeated testing resulted in behavioral tolerance.   Reversal of tolerance resulted after several training sessions.

4352   Manning, F., Pharmacol. Biochem. Behav., *4*(1), 17-21 (1976).

Chronic Delta-9-Tetrahydrocannabinol. Transient and Lasting Effects on Avoidance Behavior.

The effect of Δ^9-THC on conditioned avoidance behavior was examined after 1-6 weeks of treatment with the drug (30 mg/kg/day, i.g.).   Although the effect of THC on shock avoidance was variable in various test animals, tolerance developed to these effects within

6 sessions. Extent and time course of tolerance development was dependent on the degree of detrimental effect on the animal.

4353 Manno, B. R.; and Manno, J. E., Fed. Proc., *35*(3), 504 (1976).

Alterations in Cardiac Inotropism and Coronary Vascular Resistance in Isolated, Perfused Hearts Produced by 11-OH-Δ^9-Tetrahydrocannabinol and Vehicle Components.

The coronary vascular resistance, cardiac contractility and intrinsic rate were measured for Δ^9-THC and 11-OH-Δ^9-THC in isolated perfused rat hearts. 11-OH-Δ^9-THC produced a change in coronary vascular resistance.

4354 Manno, B. R.; and Manno, J. E., Toxicol. Appl. Pharmacol., *33*(1), 159-60 (1975).

11-Hydroxy- Δ^9- Tetrahydrocannabinol Induced Changes in the Perfused Rat Heart.

Perfused rat heart received 11-OH-THC doses ranging from 0.1 to 28 μg infused in a 3 min. period. 11-OH-THC had little direct effect on heart rate but did produce a negative inotropic response on myocardium with subsequent decreased coronary vasculature resistance followed by an increased vasculature resistance.

4355 Manno, B. R.; and Manno, J. E., pp. 129-50 in *Toxicology Annual 1974*, edited by C. L. Winek. New York, Marcel Dekker, Inc., 1975.

The Marihuana Dilemma: Implications of Recent Research into the Pharmacokinetics, Psychomotor Effects and Cardiovascular Actions of THC.

The marihuana-induced decrement in human motor and mental functions constitutes a danger to active individuals when it comes to safety and rapid, accurate decision making. The authors argue that marihuana may be more dangerous than alcohol and suggest ideas to be considered in future marihuana research .

4356 Manno, B. R.; Manno, J. E.; Brown, R. D.; and Wood, C. D., Fed. Proc., *36*(3), 1026 (1977).

Influence of Repeated Low Doses of Δ^9-Tetrahydrocannabinol on Blood Enzymes and Organ Weights of Rats.

Repeated Δ^9-THC (p.o.) altered organ weights of rats. It also modified blood glycerol, SGOT, SGPT and creatinine phosphokinase.

4357 Manno, B. R.; Manno, J. E.; Kaga, C. S.; and Schaller, J. L., Toxicol. Appl. Pharmacol., *45*(1), 314 (1978).

Response of Rats to Repeated Administration of Δ^9-Tetrahydrocannabinol: Serum Protein, Lipoprotein, and LDH-Isozyme Electrophoretic Patterns (Abstract).

Repeated low dosing of rats with Δ^9-THC produced changes in A and pre-β - lipoproteins; α 1-, α 2-, and β proteins; and LDH-1 (heart), LDH-3, LDH-4, and LDH-5 (liver). No other significant changes in relevant fractions were observed.

4358 Manno, J. E.; and Manno, B. R., Toxicol. Appl. Pharmacol., *33*(1), 160 (1975).

Cardiovascular Actions of 11-Hydroxy-Δ^9-Tetrahydrocannabinol in the Rat.

11-OH-Δ^9-THC (s.c. or i.v,. 0.025, 0.05 and 0.15 mg/kg) showed no cardiovascular changes in male rats. With SKF 525A there was a positive change at the 0.05 mg/kg of 11-OH-Δ^9-THC. At the higher dose there was a negative response that returned to normal after the i.v. dose of 11-OH-Δ^9-THC.

4359   Mantilla-Plata, B., Diss. Abstr. Int. B, *37*(1), 174 (1976).

Studies on the Reproductive Toxicology of Delta-9-Tetrahydrocannabinol in Mice.

Chronic treatment with THC produced a distinct antifertility effect, early fetal deaths and teratogenic defects such as cleft palate. Pretreatment with phenobarbital or SKF-525A enhanced the teratogenicity of THC. Levels of Δ^9-THC and its metabolites in maternal and fetal tissue were also changed by phenobarbital and SKF-525A pretreatment.

4360   Mantilla-Plata, B.; Clewe, G. L.; and Harbison, R. D., Toxicol. Appl. Pharmacol., *33*, 333-40 (1975).

Δ^9-Tetrahydrocannabinol-Induced Changes in Prenatal Growth and Development of Mice.

THC increased utero death and reabsorption at levels of 40, 80, and 100 mg/kg (i.p.) on days 6-15 of gestation and other day-dose-effect relations were recorded in mice. Reduced body weight of surviving fetuses was noted after multiple administration of THC. During late organogenesis and part of fetal maturation, anomalies of fetuses (especially cleft palate) were noted.

4361   Mantilla-Plata, B.; and Harbison, R., pp. 469-80 in *Marihuana: Chemistry, Biochemistry, and Cellular Effects,* Edited by G. G. Nahas. NY, Springer-Verlag, 1976.

Alteration of Δ^9-Tetrahydrocannabinol-Induced Prenatal Toxicity by Phenobarbital and SKF-525A.

Δ^9-THC (50 or 200 mg/kg) administered to pregnant mice increased resorption and reduced fetal body weight. SKF-525A potentiated the former two effects whereas phenobarbital antagonized the latter effect only. Also, SKF-525A increased plasma concentration and placental transfer of THC while phenobarbital did the reverse.

4362   Mantilla-Plata, B.; and Harbison, R. D., pp. 733-44 in *Pharmacology of Marihuana, Vol. 2*, edited by M. C. Braude and S. Szara. NY, Raven Press, 1976.

Influence of Alteration of Tetrahydrocannabinol Metabolism on Tetrahydrocannabinol-Induced Teratogenesis.

SKF-525A pretreatment to pregnant mice increased the levels of THC in placenta and fetus compared to values obtained after THC alone (50 mg/kg, i.p.). Phenobarbital pretreatment, on the other hand, produced a significant decrease of THC levels in fetal tissue and a significant increase in plasma levels compared to those obtained with THC treatment alone (200 mg/kg, i.p.). Phenobarbital partly antagonized, while SKF-525A potentiated the THC-induced reduction of fetal body weight.

4363   Mantilla-Plata, B.; and Harbison, R. D., Toxicol. Appl. Pharmacol., *34*(2), 292-300 (1975).

Distribution Studies of [^{14}C] Delta-9-Tetrahydrocannabinol in Mice: Effect of Vehicle, Route of Administration, and Duration of Treatment.

^{14}C-THC, 5 mg/kg was administered to mice i.v., i.p., p.o., and s.c. to study the effects of route of administration and suspending agents. THC administered i.p. was 4 to 6 times higher in plasma concentration than by p.o. or s.c. The highest concentration was found in the liver after i.v. administration. The choice of vehicle and route affected distribution, absorption, and excretion of THC.

4364 Maple, P. J.; Borison, R. L.; and Sabelli, H. C., Fed. Proc., 35(3), 668 (1976).

Possible Mediation of the Euphoriant and Sedative Effect of Marihuana by 2-Phenylthylamine and by Phenylacetic Acid.

The authors defend previous suggestions that THC-behavioral stimulation is mediated by brain α-phenylethylamine. Behavioral sedation is produced by the deaminated metabolites of biogenic amines, and MAO inhibitors prevent THC-sedation in mice. In rabbits, THC pretreatment caused a large rate increase in deamination of phenylethylamine.

4365 Marcotte, J.; Skelton, F. S.; Cote, M. G.; and Witschi, H., Toxicol. Appl. Pharmacol., 33(2), 231-45 (1975).

Introduction of Aryl Hydrocarbon Hydroxylase in Rat Lung by Marihuana Smoke.

Marihuana, administered by placing rats in smoke filled chambers, stimulated the activity of aryl hydrocarbon hydroxylase, which may be the result of de novo synthesis of enzyme molecules. The components of marihuana responsible for the induction are not yet known. Ultrastructural changes in cells of the ciliary epithelium and alveolar macrophages were also noted.

4366 Margolis-Kazan, H. and Blamire, J., Biochem. Biophys. Res. Commun., 76(3), 674-81 (1977).

The Effect of Δ^9-Tetrahydrocannabinol on Cytoplasmic DNA Metabolism.

THC (400 µg/ml) inhibited cytoplasmic DNA synthesis and promoted its degradation while nuclear DNA was unaffected in the Volvox species. Results with prelabeled [^{3}H]-adenine (experiment described) supported these findings and also indicated the degradation of already existing cytoplasmic DNA.

4367 Marin, G., Int. J. Addict., 11(2), 199-207 (1976).

Social-Psychological Correlates of Drug Use Among Colombian University Students.

Psychological profiles were administered to over 2,000 college students in 10 universities in Bogota, Columbia, concerning drug use. The primary reason for using marihuana in this study was for "adventure" and the most common suggestion for marihuana use came from friends. Frequency of answers were further classified as coming from infrequent users or habitual users.

4368 Marini, J. L.; Bridges, C. I.; and Sheard, M. H., Int. J. Addict., 13(3), 493-502 (1978).

Multiple Drug Abuse: Examination of Drug-Abuse Patterns in Male Prisoners.

After alcohol, marihuana was the most commonly used drug in this sample of male prisoners. It was also their drug of choice. Other aspects of drug abuse were also examined.

4369 Marks, V.; Teale, D.; and Fry, D., Brit. Med. J., 3(5979), 348-49 (1975).

Detection of Cannabis Products in Urine by Radioimmunoassay.

Application of a RIA procedure for the 3-ring-fused cannabis nucleus. No cross reaction was observed for any other drugs in the urine of control subjects. Level of detection for a positive THC urine is 10 µg/ml. Cross-reaction of Δ^9-THC and its metabolites is demonstrated.

4370   Marks, V., Teale, J. D.; and King, L. J., pp. 71-85 in *Marihuana: Chemistry, Biochemistry, and Cellular Effects*, edited by G. G. Nahas, NY, Springer-Verlag, 1976.

Radioimmunoassay of Cannabis Products in Blood and Urine.

Cannabis products are measured in blood and urine using RIA. The authors present a technique they have used to produce high-avidity antiserum against Δ^9-THC in sheep. The assay, however, is not specific for THC and it is referred to the material measured in biological fluids as THC cross- reacting cannabinoids (THC-CRC).

4371   Marshman, J. A.; Popham, R. E.; and Yawney, C. D., Bull. Narcotics, *28*(4), 63-68 (1976).

A Note on the Cannabinoid Content of Jamaican Ganja.

Thirty-six samples of Jamaican-grown cannabis were analyzed for Δ^9-THC, CBD, and CBN content by GC. The content ranged from trace amounts to 8% w/w with a mean value of 2.8% w/w. Harvest season and type of fertilizer affected cannabis potency. Plants grown in the spring in an organic fertilizer yielded highest cannabinoid concentrations.

4372   Martens, S., Laekartidningen, *73*(45), 3874-75 (1976).

Internationella Aspekter Pa° Cannabis [International Aspects of Cannabis].

Because of varying opinions on cannabis among different countries, the United Nations has been unable to either change the classification of cannabis as a narcotic (at present it belongs to the same class as heroin) or develop concrete programs to stop the production or illegal transport of cannabis.

4373   Martin, B.; Agurell, S.; Krieglstein, J.; and Rieger, H., Biochem. Pharmacol., *26*(23), 2307-09 (1977).

Perfusion of the Isolated Rat Brain with (^{14}C)-Δ^9-THC.

No *in situ* metabolism of THC was found to occur in rat brains. EEG changes including high amplitude bursts and decreased frequency were evident upon perfusion with THC or its 11-hydroxy metabolite. Implications of findings were discussed.

4374   Martin, B.; Agurell, S.; Nordqvist, M.; and Lindgren, J-E., J. Pharm. Pharmacol., *28*(8), 603-08 (1976).

Dioxygenated Metabolites of Cannabidiol Formed by Rat Liver.

The *in vitro* metabolic conversion of CBD by a cofactor-fortified rat 10,000 xg hepatic soluble fraction is discussed. Using differential elution and extraction techniques and TLC, fractions of the incubation media yield zones predominately associated with unchanged CBD, monohydroxylated metabolites, and various dioxygenated metabolites of which were identified by GLC-MS and NMR. Primary metabolic conversion consisted of 7-hydroxylation and side-chain hydroxylations.

4375 Martin, B., Nordqvst, M.; Agurell, S.; Lindgren, J.-E., Leander, K.; and Binder, M., J. Pharm. Pharmacol., *28*(4), 275-79 (1976).

Identification of Monohydroxylated Metabolites of Cannabidiol Formed by Rat Liver.

Eight metabolites of CBD, formed by rat liver enzymes, were isolated and identified. Hydroxylation occurred in the 6 position (resulting in two isomers -6α and 6β hydroxy CBD) and in all positions of the pentyl side chain. Structure elucidation was based on comparison with authentic compounds and on spectroscopical (NMR, MS) evidence.

4376 Martin, B. R., Diss. Abst. Int. B, *36*(2), 669 (1975).

The Cellular and Subcellular Distribution of Δ^9-Tetrahydrocannabinol in Tolerant, Nontolerant, and Prenatal Dogs.

Signs of Δ^9-THC-altered metabolism were not evident in tolerant dogs, but its specific brain localization and contest of synaptic vesicle subfraction were reduced. THC transfer from pregnant dogs to their offspring was also indicated.

4377 Martin, B. R.; Carney, J. M.; Balster, R. L.; and Harris, L. S., Pharmacologist, *20*(3), 164 (1978).

Behavioral Activity, Distribution and Metabolism of ^{3}H-Δ^9-THC in Monkey Brain Following an Intravenous Injection (Abstract).

11-OH-Δ^9-THC was much more potent than Δ^9-THC in decreased behavioral responses of trained monkeys. Brain levels of both drugs indicated that Δ^9-THC is responsible for behavioral activity.

4378 Martin, B. R.; Dewey, W. L.; Aceto, M. D.; Adams, M. D.; Earnhardt, J. T.; and Carney, J. M., Res. Commun. Chem. Pathol. Pharmacol., *16*(1), 187-90 (1977).

A Potent Antinociceptive Cannabinoid Which Lacks Opiate Substitution Properties in Monkeys.

Given subcutaneously to mice, (-)-9-*nor*-9-β-OH-HHC was more potent than morphine sulfate by the tail flick and *p*-phenylquinone writhing tests. It did not suppress the morphine abstinence syndrome in the single dose suppression test in physically dependent rhesus monkeys. The compound's potential for physical dependence production is not known.

4379 Martin, B. R.; Dewey, W. L.; Harris, L. S.; and Beckner, J. S., J. Pharmacol. Exp. Ther., *196*(1), 128-44 (1976).

^{3}H-Δ^9-Tetrahydrocannabinol Tissue and Subcellular Distribution in the Central Nervous System and Tissue Distribution in Peripheral Organs of Tolerant and Nontolerant Dogs.

Ataxia manifested in dogs acutely treated with tritiated Δ^9-THC (0.5 mg/kg) was not evident after seven daily administrations of THC. Tolerance was not due to altered metabolism or disposition, but tolerant dogs exhibited 4% less radioactivity in their synaptic vesicle fraction.

4380 Martin, B. R.; Dewey, W. L.; Harris, L. S.; and Beckner, J. S., Res. Commun. Chem. Pathol. Pharmacol., *17*(3), 457-70 (1977).

^{3}H-Δ^9-Tetrahydrocannabinol Distribution in Pregnant Dogs and their Fetuses.

The distribution of radioactivity in various brain regions and peripheral tissues was investigated in pregnant dogs and their fetuses 30 min. following an i.v. injection of 0.5 mg/kg of labeled THC. Results were tabulated and discussed.

4381 Martin, B. R.; Dewey, W. L.; Harris, L. S.; Beckner, J.; Wilson, R. S.; and May, E. L., Pharmacol. Biochem. Behav., 3, 849-53 (1975).

Marihuana-like Activity of New Synthetic Tetrahydrocannabinols.

Synthetic analogs of Δ^9- and Δ^8-THC, immune to 11-hydroxylation, produced several cannabinoid-related cardiovascular and behavioral effects in mice and dogs.

4382 Martin, B. R.; Dewey, W. L.; Harris, L. S.; and Munson, A. E., Fed. Proc., 36(3), 1026 (1977).

Alteration in the Pharmacodynamics of ^{3}H-Δ^9-Tetrahydrocannabinol in Mice by Endotoxin.

Pretreatment with endotoxin elevated the level of ^{3}H-Δ^9-THC in various tissues and organs of mice.

4383 Martin, B. R.; Harvey, D. J.; and Paton, W. D. M., Drug Metab. Dispos., 5(3), 259-67 (1977).

Biotransformation of Cannabidiol in Mice. Identification of New Acid Metabolites.

Fourteen new metabolites of CBD, obtained through in vivo metabolism in mice, were detected by GC-MS analyses of their TMS-derivatives. Oxy metabolites were reduced prior to TMS-derivation.

4384 Martin, B. R.; Harvey, D. J.; and Paton, W. D. M., J. Pharm. Pharmacol., 28(10), 773-74 (1976).

Identification of New in vivo Side-Chain Metabolites of Δ^1-Tetrahydrocannabinol.

Three acid metabolites were isolated from animals treated with THC. Various characteristics of these metabolites were reported.

4385 Martin, B. R.; Montgomery, J.; Dewey, W. L.; and Harris, L. S., Drug Metab. Dispos., 6(3), 282-87 (1978).

Alterations in the Pharmacokinetics of ^{3}H-Δ^9-Tetrahydrocannabinol in Mice by Bacterial Endotoxin.

Pretreatment of mice with endotoxin increased the levels of labeled THC and metabolites in plasma, brain and peripheral tissues and also altered THC metabolism. Results were discussed in light of the synergistic lethality between endotoxin and THC.

4386 Martin, P.; and Consroe, P., Pharmacol. Biochem. Behav., 9(6), 753-58 (1978).

Tolerance to Δ^9-Tetrahydrocannabinol in Adapted and Nonadapted Rabbits.

Tolerance to Δ^9-THC-induced behavioral and EEG changes developed in rabbits after 12 days drug administration. These changes varied when rabbits were adapted or nonadapted to experimental environment.

4387 Martin, P.; and Consroe, P., Science, 194, 965-67 (1976).

Cannabinoid Induced Behavioral Convulsions in Rabbits.

A strain of New Zealand white rabbits is shown to be differentially sensitive to the convulsant activity of several cannabinoids via an autosomal recessive mutation. Onset latencies and relative potencies are given with 11-OH-Δ^9-THC exhibiting the shortest onset and greatest potency . CBD (10-20 mg/kg, i.v). caused no behavioral convulsions and possessed anticonvulsant properties exclusively. Tolerance development to the convulsant activity of Δ^9-THC (0.5-2.0 mg/kg, i.v.) and loss of tolerance are reported.

4388 Martin, P.; and Consroe, P., Science, *197*(4310), 1302 (1977).

Marihuana and Epilepsy. Reply to Comments.

The enhancement of EEG seizures induced by THC in cats and CBD in man are noted and the EEG effects are not clear. The authors suggest that EEG spiking in Feeney's epileptic dogs is novel and is probably a strain-specific or strain-sensitive process. With respect to the mechanisms of action of cannabinoid-induced epileptic activity, Feeney's reasoning assumes that cannabinoids and methamphetamines have the same mechanism of action but the authors state that there is not enough data to support this.

4389 Maser, J. D.; Gallup, G. G.; Thorn, W. R.; and Edson, P. H., Pharmacol. Biochem. Behav., *3*(6), 1069-72 (1975).

Relative Potency of Tetrahydrocannabinol Derivatives on Tonic Immobility in Chickens.

Δ^9-THC was more potent than Δ^8-THC or Δ^3-THC in prolonging the duration of fear-induced tonic immobility in chickens.

4390 Maskarinec, M. P., Diss. Abstr. Int. B, *39*(5), 2258 (1978).

Analysis of Steroids by Glass Capillary Gas Chromatography/Mass Spectrometry: Applications to Cannabis Pharmacology.

A procedure was developed for the quantitative analysis of steroids in small plasma samples. The procedure was then used to study the endocrine alterations in rats induced by cannabis extract. Comparison was made with Δ^9-THC. Preliminary studies in humans were performed and marihuana smoke condensate was chemically analyzed.

4391 Maskarinec, M. P.; Alexander, G.; and Novotny, M., J. Chromatogr., *126*, 559-68 (1976).

Analysis of the Acidic Fraction of Marijuana Smoke Condensate by Capillary Gas Chromatography-Mass Spectrometry.

Phenols and organic acids were identified in Mexican and Turkish cannabis and compared to those found in a standard tobacco cigarette. Differences were observed by GLC to be both quantitative and qualitative. Procedures are given for all methods discussed. A silyl procedure was used to derivatize the phenols and organic acids. An identification chart of compounds is given for Mexican cannabis.

4392 Maskarinec, M. P.; Shipley, G.; Novotny, M.; Brown, D. J.; and Forney, R. B., Experientia, *34*(1), 88-89 (1978).

Different Effects of Synthetic Δ^9-Tetrahydrocannabinol and Cannabis Extract on Steroid Metabolism in Male Rats.

After seven days of oral administration, cannabis extracts were much more effective than synthetic cannabinoids in decreasing testosterone and other androgenic steroid levels in rat blood and urine.

4393 Maskarinec, M. P.; Shipley, G.; Novotny, M.; Brown, D. J.; and Forney, R. B., Toxicol. Appl. Pharmacol., *45*(2), 617-28 (1978).

Endrocrine Effects of Cannabis in Male Rats.

THC (1 to 25 mg/kg) elevated rat plasma corticosterone and metabolite levels as indicated by GC/MS analysis. Male rats treated with THC also had considerable amounts of estrogens in their plasma but their testosterone levels were not affected.

4394   Masoud, A. N., J. Pharm. Sci., *64*(5), 841-44 (1975).

Systematic Identification of Drugs of Abuse I: Spot Tests.

Various spot tests and reagents were discussed for use in identification of drugs of abuse. Since many of these tests are run in series, and drugs are often mixed and mislabeled, certain false-positive and false-negative results can be obtained. However, with the use of Duquenois Reagent, only cannabinoids were positive, and cannabinoids did not show positive on any of the tests for other drug classes.

4395   Masoud, A. N., J. Pharm. Sci., *65*(11), 1585-89 (1976).

Systematic Identification of Drugs of Abuse II: TLC.

Five solvent systems and seven spray reagents were used for the systematic identification of 43 drugs of abuse by TLC. Among these drugs were Δ^9-THC, CBN, and CBD.

4396   Matsumoto, K., Stark, P.; and Meister, R. G., J. Med. Chem., *20*(1), 17-24 (1977).

Cannabinoids. 1. 1-Amino- and 1-Mercapto-7,8,9,10-tetrahydro-6H-dibenzo [*b,d*] pyrans.

The synthesis of 1-amino- and 1-mercapto- 7,8,9,10- tetrahydro- 6*H*- dibenzo [*b,d*] pyrans was carried out and CNS evaluation of these compounds and derivatives thereof indicated that substitution of the 1-hydroxy group with an amino function retains the activity of the oxygenated compound while exchange of oxygen with sulphur leads to loss of activity. Other structure activity relationships were presented.

4397   Matsumoto, K.; Stark, P.; and Meister, R. G., J. Med. Chem., *20*(1), 25-30 (1977).

Cannabinoids. 2. Synthesis and Central Nervous System Activities of Some B-Ring Homocannabinoid Derivatives and Related Lactones.

The synthesis of 5 new B-ring homocannabinoid derivatives (6,7,8,9,10,11-hexahydrodibenz [*b,d*] oxepins) was carried out. The CNS activity of these compounds was studied in comparison with the corresponding six membered ring homologues.

4398   Matsuyama, S.; and Jarvik, L., pp. 179-93 in *Marihuana Research Findings: 1976*, NIDA Research Monograph, 14, 1977.

Effects of Marihuana on the Genetic and Immune Systems.

Conclusive evidence pointing to the deleterious effects of marihuana on human immune and genetic systems is still lacking. The need for systematic prospective research with adequate design and methodology is urgent.

4399   Matsuyama, S. S., pp. 17-24 in *Marijuana and Health Hazards*, edited by J. R. Tinklenberg. NY, Academic Press, 1975.

Cytogenetic Studies of Marijuana.

Available *in vitro* studies with THC reported negative results on chromosomal breaks in human leukocyte cultures, whereas *in vivo* studies reported contradictory results. Retrospective studies provide biased findings since they do not account for many uncontrolled prospective studies. An outline of such studies is indicated and a recent technique for the detection of sister chromatid exchanges in lymphocyte culture is described.

4400 Matsuyama, S. S.; Jarvik, L. F.; Fu, T.; and Yen, F.-S., pp. 723-31 in *Pharmacology of Marihuana, Vol. 2*, edited by M. C. Braude and S. Szara. NY, Raven Press, 1976.

Chromosome Studies Before and After Supervised Marihuana Smoking.

Marihuana smoking (approx. 19.8 mg of THC) for 72 out of 94 days in-hospital stay did not increase the frequency of chromosome breaks nor did it change the shape of chromosomes in lymphocyte cultures of male marihuana users.

4401 Matsuyama, S. S.; Yen, F.-S.; Jarvik, L. F.; Sparkes, R. S.; Fu, T.-K.; Fisher, H.; Reccius, N.; and Frank, I. M., Mutat. Res., *48*(2), 255-65 (1977).

Marijuana Exposure *in vivo* and Human Lymphocyte Chromosomes.

Twenty one male volunteers (21-27 years old) smoked one natural blend marihuana cigarette (1%, 2%, or no Δ^9-THC standardized to contain 7 mg/kg body weight) a day for 28 consecutive days. Sequential venous samples were cultured independently in two cytogenetic laboratories for lymphocytes and examined for chromosomal abberations. Neither laboratory recorded a significant increase in chromosomal break frequencies associated with marihuana smoking.

4402 Matte, A. C., Psychopharmacologia, *45*(1), 125-28 (1975).

Effects of Hashish on Isolation Induced Aggression in Wild Mice.

Increased motor activity and intense fighting were observed in wild mice with a 20 mg/kg, i.p. injection of hashish.

4403 Mattox, K. L., J. Amer. Coll. Emerg. Phys., *5*(1), 26-28 (1976).

Pneumomediastinum in Heroin and Marihuana Users.

Marihuana smoking with repeated deep inhalation of smoke and forceful Valsalva's maneuvers for 20-30 secs. is linked in a cause/effect manner to the occurrence of mediastinal and cervical emphysema in patients. Conservative treatment resulted in the recovery of all patients within 2-5 days.

4404 Maugh, T. H., Science, *190*(4217), 865-67 (1975).

Marihuana: New Support for Immune and Reproductive Hazards.

A review of the effects of marihuana on the immune system and the reproductive system and problems associated thereto.

4405 Maybaum, J.; and Perry, D. C., Pharm. Chem. Newsl., *7*(3), 1-8 (1978).

Marihuana and Paraquat.

The article summarizes the development of paraquat spraying of marihuana fields in Mexico with its political ramifications. A summary of the chemistry, mechanisms of action, toxicity and detection of paraquat is also given.

4406 Mechoulam, R., Harefuah, *90*(8), 378-80 (1976).

Medicines Developed from Hashish.

A Hebrew language version of the paper, "Toward Drugs Derived from Cannabis."

4407 Mechoulam, R., Recherche, *7*(73), 1018-26 (1976).

Cannabis.

An overall review of marihuana at the biological, chemical, therapeutic, somatic and psychotropic levels is provided. In aggressive monkeys, the use of THC produces tranquility. The possible promising therapeutic use of hashish is limited by its psychotropic properties.

4408 Mechoulam, R.; and Carlini, E. A., Naturwissenschaften, *65*(4), 174-79 (1978).

Toward Drugs Derived from Cannabis.

Various THC effects (including reduction of IOP, bronchodilatation in asthmatics and antiemesis in cancer chemotherapy) were reviewed. Also, the therapeutic potentials of other cannabinoids were discussed.

4409 Mechoulam, R.; Lander, N.; Dikstein, S.; Carlini, E.; and Blumenthal, M., pp. 35-45 in *The Therapeutic Potential of Marihuana*, edited by S. Cohen and R. Stillman. NY, Plenum Medical Book Company, 1976.

On the Therapeutic Possibilities of Some Cannabinoids.

Several CBD derivatives, namely, CBD aldehyde-diacetate, 6-oxo-CBD diacetate, 6-OH-CBD-triacetate and 9-OH-CBD-triacetate were synthesized. The effects these derivatives on electroshock convulsions, pentobarbital sleeping time,

spontaneous motility in mice and rats and IOP of rabbits with induced stable glaucoma were compared to those of CBD. Results were discussed.

4410 Mechoulam, R.; McCallum, N.; Levy, S.; and Lander, N., pp. 3-14 in *Marihuana: Chemistry, Biochemistry, and Cellular Effects*, edited by G. G. Nahas. NY, Springer-Verlag, 1976.

Cannabinoid Chemistry: An Overview.

Major patterns of research into the chemistry of cannabinoids are discussed. Analytical techniques for the preparation or identification of cannabinoids are outlined with emphasis on established chromatographic methods and on newer, promising methods. The chemical trends in the area of cannabinoid metabolism should be the determination of the ultimate fate of metabolites, quantification of and rate studies on metabolites and natural products in biological tissues, and identification of cannabinoid receptors.

4411 Mechoulam, R.; McCallum, N. K.; and Burstein, S., Chem. Rev., *76*(1), 75-112 (1976).

Recent Advances in the Chemistry and Biochemistry of Cannabis.

This review of literature from 1973 includes the chemistry of new plant constituents, synthesis of various cannabinoids as well as various tehcniques used for the analysis of cannabinoids from natural and metabolic sources. 409 references are given.

4412 Mechoulam, R.; McCallum, N. K.; Lander, N.; Yagen, B.; Ben-Zvi, Z.; and Levy, S., pp. 39-48 in *Pharmacology of Marihuana, Vol. 1*, edited by M. C. Braude and S. Szara. NY, Raven Press, 1976.

Aspects of Cannabis Chemistry and Metabolism.

The primary psychotomimetic compound in hashish is Δ^9-THC. Isolation and identification of hydroxylated THC metabolites have yielded compounds with pharmacological activity. CBD and CBN are discussed as major cannabis components, and their pharmacology and interactions with THC are described. Partial and complete synthetic procedures for the preparation of oxygenated CBD metabolites are presented. CBN accelerates the disappearance of THC from rat plasma while CBD has the opposite effect. A precedence for the *in vivo* conversion of Δ^9-THC and Δ^6-THC to CBN is established in male rats by means of GLC and TLC.

4413   Mechoulam, R.; Yagen, B.; Levy, S.; and Ben-Zvi, Z., pp. 136-40 in *Symp. Pap-UIPAC Int. Symp. Chem. Nat. Prod., 11th*, 4 (Part 2) (1978).

Recent Advances in the Metabolism of Cannabinoids.

Δ^8-THC was found to undergo enzymatic C-glucuronidation both *in vivo* and *in vitro*. Procedures were described.

4414   Medek, A.; Navratil, J.; Hrbek, J.; Komenda, S.; and Krejci, Z., Agressologie, *19D*, 193-95 (1978).

The Influence of Nicotine and Marihuana on Conditioned Alimentary Motor Reflexes in Cats.

Δ^9-THC (0.6 mg/kg, p.o.) administration, 30 and 45 min. prior to nicotine, antagonized the nicotine-induced impairment of fixed motor reactions in cats.

4415   Medek, A.; Navratil, J.; Hrbek, J.; Komenda, S.; Macakova, J.; and Krejci, Z., Acta Univ. Palacki. Olomuc. Fac. Med., *80*, 223-29 (1976).

Effect of Methylbromidatropine and its Interaction with Cannabis on Conditioned Food Motor Reflexes in Cats.

THC (0.6 mg/kg, p.o.) failed to antagonize the atropine methylbromide-induced disruption of lever press behavior for food reinforcement in trained cats.

4416   Mehndiratta, S. S.; and Wig, N. N., Drug Alcohol Depend., *1*, 71-81 (1975).

Psychosocial Effects of Long Term Cannabis Use in India. A Study of Fifty Heavy Users and Controls.

India was a good area for study because cannabis has been used for years without the use of other drugs. Twenty-five hashish smokers, 25 bhang drinkers (a tea from the leaves) and 25 controls were interviewed. Tables are given of amount of cannabis used, age at first use, physical complaints, sexual history, job evaluations, social behavior and psychiatric examinations.

4417   Melges, F. T., Amer. J. Psychiat., *133*(9), 1024-28 (1976).

Tracking Difficulties and Paranoid Ideation During Hashish and Alcohol Intoxication.

The research discussed was based upon and supports the theory that a high dose of hashish causes memory tracking difficulties in the user who consequently loses the ability to analyze interpersonal relationships with those around him, leading to paranoia. Other comparisons are presented, dealing with hashish-vs-alcohol and fast-vs-slow dosing.

4418   Mellinger, G. D.; Somers, R. H.; Davidson, S. T.; and Manheimer, D. I., Ann. NY Acad. Sci., *282*, 37-55 (1976).

The Amotivational Syndrome and the College Student.

The view that marihuana may be directly or indirectly responsible for students dropping out of school is refuted. The role of parents in motivating students is also discussed. In this study marihuana alone does not produce an amotivational syndrome. However, multiple drug use was associated with a motivational syndrome.

4419 Mello, N. K.; and Mendelson, J. H., pp. 133-58 in *The Bases of Addiction*, Life Sciences Research Report 8, edited by J. Fishman. Berlin, Abakon Verlag., 1978.

Behavioral Pharmacology of Human Alcohol, Heroin and Marihuana Use.

Marihuana users working to earn money or marihuana worked harder and longer hours than did alcoholics under analogous conditions. Also, unlike alcohol, marihuana did not disrupt social behavior nor did it produce exaggerated mood changes.

4420 Mello, N. K.; and Mendelson, J. H., pp. 93-127 in *Self-Administration of Abused Substances: Methods for Study*, NIDA Research Monograph 20, 1978.

Marihuana, Alcohol and Polydrug Use: Human Self-Administration Studies.

Studies of marihuana self-administration did not confirm the notion of a marihuana-induced amotivational syndrome. Concurrent access to alcohol and marihuana was not necessarily associated with increased use of these two agents, and their simultaneous availability was associated with a significant decrease in alcohol consumption in comparison to a baseline period when only alcohol was available.

4421 Mello, N. K.; Mendelson, J. H.; and Kuehnle, J. C., in *Committee on Prob-*

lem of Drug Dependence, 1977. Division of Medical Sciences, National Research Council, National Academy of Sciences, Washington, D. C., 1977, pp. 187-203.

Human Polydrug Use: Marihuana, Alcohol and Tobacco.

Under research ward settings, consumption of alcohol decreased whereas that of marihuana increased when both were made available simultaneously. Tobacco use did not correlate well with alcohol availability. Other aspects of polydrug use were also investigated and discussed.

4422 Mello, N. K.; Mendelson, J. H.; Kuehnle, J. C.; and Greenberg, I., in *Committee on Problem of Drug Dependence, 1975*. Division of Medical Sciences, National Research Council, National Academy of Sciences, Washington, D.C., 1975, pp. 407-22.

4423 Mello, N. K.; Mendelson, J. H.; Kuehnle, J. C.; and Greenberg, I., Psychopharmacol. Bull., *12*(4), 7-9 (1976).

Effects of Marihuana Use on Operant Behavior in Man.

Marihuana did not influence the motivation to work for a reward; however, a delayed effect on operant behavior was evident in heavy users.

4424 Mello, N. K.; Mendelson, J. H.; Kuehnle, J. C.; and Sellers, M. L., J. Pharmacol. Exp. Ther., *207*(3), 922-35 (1978).

Human Polydrug Use: Marihuana and Alcohol.

Concurrent users of alcohol and marihuana consumed less alcohol when marihuana was also available, as compared to when alcohol alone was provided. The reverse was not true; rather, marihuana consumption increased over time.

4425 Mellors, A., pp. 283-98 in *Marihuana: Chemistry, Biochemistry, and Cellular Effects*, edited by G. G. Nahas. NY, Springer-Verlag, 1976.

Cannabinoids: Effects on Lysosomes and Lymphocytes.

Experiments were carried out *in vivo* using Δ^9-THC to determine the effects of the latter on lysosomes and lymphocytes. Several mechanisms are proposed to explain cannabinoid impairment of normal cellular function.

4426 Mendelson, J. H., Contemp. Drug Probl., *4*(4), 447-48 (1975).

Marijuana: US. Army Study.

Specific objectives and a progress report of a U.S. Army study completed in 1974 on controlled casual and heavy marihuana use was presented. In general, few adverse reactions to marihuana inhalation were observed in adult volunteers. Specific conclusions were also drawn.

4427 Mendelson, J. H., Med. Aspects Hum. Sex, *10*(11), 23-24 (1976).

Marihuana and Sex.

Various views regarding effects of marihuana on sex are discussed. The author concludes from the available data that marihuana by itself has no effect on sexual behavior.

4428 Mendelson, J. H., Postgrad. Med., *60*(5), 111-15 (1976).

Marihuana Use: Biologic and Behavioral Aspects.

The biological and behavioral effects of marihuana were evaluated in healthy male volunteers under controlled hospital conditions. After 21 days of marihuana use, there was no abnormality in blood tests nor in cardiovascular function. However, pulmonary function was adversely affected by marihuana. Behavioral effects varied between subjects. No change in plasma testosterone levels was found.

4429 Mendelson, J. H.; Babor, T. F.; Kuehnle, J. C.; Rossi, A. M.; Bernstein, J. G.; Mello, N. K.; and Greenberg, I., pp. 186-210 in *Chronic Cannabis Use*, edited by R. L. Dornbush, A. M. Freedman, and M. Fink. NY, Annals of the New York Academy of Sciences, V. 282, 1976.

Behavioral and Biologic Aspects of Marijuana Use.

Marihuana-induced changes in biologic, social and psychologic functions were studied in casual and heavy marihuana users given free access to marihuana cigarettes for 21 days. Parameters measured included behavioral and social reactions to drug use, group interactions, short-term memory and cardiovascular and pulmonary functions. Findings and utility of such longitudinal studies were discussed.

4430 Mendelson, J. H.; Ellingboe, J.; and Kuehnle, J. C., in *Committee on Problem of Drug Dependence, 1976*. Division of Medical Sciences, National Research Council, National Academy of Sciences, Washington, D. C., 1976, pp. 525-37.

Effects of Alcohol and Marihuana on Plasma Luteinizing Hormone and Testosterone.

Circhoral plasma testosterone and LH levels after acute and chronic marihuana exposure in humans were not significantly different from those of control patients. In contrast to this, acute alcohol consumption significantly lowered plasma testosterone levels which were followed by increased levels of LH.

4431 Mendelson, J. H.; Ellingboe, J.; Kuehnle, J. C.; and Mello, N., J. Pharmacol. Exp. Ther., *207*(2), 611-17 (1978).

Effects of Chronic Marihuana Use on Intergrated Plasma Testosterone and Luteinizing Hormone Levels.

Twenty-one days of marihuana use did not significantly alter plasma values for testosterone and LH in male subjects.

4432 Mendelson, J. H.; Kuehnle, J.; Ellingboe, J.; and Babor, T. F., pp. 83-94 in *Marijuana and Health Hazards*, edited by J. R. Tinklenberg. NY, Academic Press, 1975.

Effects of Marijuana on Plasma Testosterone.

The double antibody immunoassay procedures used to measure testosterone levels should be improved. Plasma testosterone levels of chronic marihuana users did not differ from control values either as a function of dose or dose-time relationships. The importance of factors such as intra-subject variability, exogenous vs. endogenous variance and multiple drug use (i.e., alcohol) on the outcome of measuring testosterone levels are emphasized.

4433 Mendelson, J. H.; Kuehnle, J.; Ellingboe, J.; and Babor, T. F., New Eng. J. Med., *292*(16), 868 (1975).

Normal Plasma Testosterone Concentrations after Marihuana Smoking. Comments.

The authors' reply to the letter of Schaefer, Gunn and Dubowski (New Eng. J. Med., *292*(16), 867, (1975).

4434 Mendelson, J. H.; Kuehnle, J. C.; Greenberg, I.; and Mello, N. K., pp. 643-57 in *Pharmacology of Marihuana, Vol. 2*, edited by M. C. Braude and S. Szara. NY, Raven Press, 1976.

The Effects of Marihuana Use on Human Operant Behavior: Individual Data.

Performance of operant work for marihuana or money was analyzed in 27 male volunteers. Results indicated that operant work decreased in a dose-related manner in heavy marihuana smokers only. Evidence of physical withdrawal was not noticed.

4435 Mendelson, J. H.; Kuehnle, J. C.; Greenberg, I.; and Mello, N. K., J. Pharmacol. Exp. Ther., *198*(1), 42-53 (1976).

Operant Acquisition of Marihuana in Man.

Marihuana's ability to alter reward-oriented motivational behavior in adult male marihuana users is explored. Subjects were required to perform a simple operant task. Although performance of the operant task deteriorated to a certain extent, motivation to continue the operant work was apparent in spite of increased marihuana consumption.

4436 Mendhiratta, S. S.; Wig, N. N.; and Verma, S. K., Brit. J. Psychiat., *132*, 482-86 (1978).

Some Psychological Correlates of Long-Term Heavy Cannabis Users.

Several psychological tests revealed the detrimental effects of chronic cannabis use in this sample of Indian users. Smoking Charas was most harmful.

4437 Mendleson, G., Med. J. Aust., *1*(7), 391-92 (1978).

Effect of Cannabis on Driving (Letter).

Cannabis use is detrimental to driving ability.

4438 Mercer, G. W.; Hundleby, J. D.; and Carpenter, R. A., Can. J. Behav. Sci., *10*(1), 79-90 (1978).

Adolescent Drug Use and Attitudes Toward the Family.

Family social environment correlated better with females' than with males' use of marihuana, tobacco and alcohol. Perceived warmth, support and interest was negatively correlated with use of all three drugs by adolescents of both genders.

4439 Mercer, G. W.; and Kohn, P. M., Brit. J. Addict., *72*(2), 151-58 (1977).

Values Associated with Marijuana Use Among College Students.

When undergraduates were surveyed regarding marihuana use, several differences were found between users and non-users. Analysis of responses indicated that users ranked broadmindedness, freedom and imaginativeness higher than non-users. Other differences were also discussed.

4440 Messiha, F. S., Clin. Pharmacol. Ther., *21*(1), 111 (1977).

Dopamine, the Psyche, and Extrapyramidal Disorders.

Cannabis administration to healthy volunteers led to minimal psychic changes and urinary excretion of DA whereas LSD caused significant changes in both parameters. The present results were compared to those obtained in patients with extrapyramidal disorders.

4441 Messiha, F. S.; and Larson, J. W., Proc. West. Pharmacol. Soc., *20*, 297-301 (1977).

Biochemical Changes Associated with Drug-Produced Alterations in Motor Function and the Psyche: A Possible Underlying Mechanism.

Cannabis administration caused a decrease in the excretion of DA and homovanillic acid (HVA) when compared to the excretion of DA and HVA following administration of placebo. LSD also caused a significant decrease in the excretion of DA and an insignificant decrease in the excretion of HVA. Possible correlations between changes in DA turnover and the behavioral effects of cannabis are discussed.

4442 Metzger, M. H., Clin. Toxicol., *8*(4), 465-73 (1975).

Notes on Marijuana Identification in Criminal Cases.

A legalistic quandary is outlined predicated on the fact that federal and state legislation associates illicit marihuana use, possession, and sale with the single botanical source, *Cannabis sativa L*. The author maintains that the botanical sources of marihuana are polytypic, and not monotypic as suggested by current scientific opinion.

4443 Meyer, R. E., pp. 1639-52 in *Psychopharmacology: A Generation of Progress*, edited by M. A. Lipton, A. Dimascio, and K. F. Killam. NY, Raven Press, 1978.

Behavioral Pharmacology of Marihuana.

A very complete and current review of marihuana pharmacology with 116 references.

4444 Meyer, R. E., pp. 133-52 in *Marijuana and Health Hazards*, edited by J. R. Tinklenberg. NY, Academic Press, 1975.

Psychiatric Consequences of Marijuana Use: The State of the Evidence.

The author provides an extensive review of literature relating psychiatric consequences to marihuana. This review supports the concept of acute adverse reactions under the influence of marihuana. Whether or not flashbacks and psychotic reactions are triggered by marihuana use is an unresolved issue. Acute marihuana psychosis in Eastern literature is indicated. Habituation and amotivational syndromes, two examples of marihuana induction of non-psychotic prolonged adverse reactions, are discussed.

4445   Miczek, K. A., Activ. Nerv. Super., *19*(3), 224-25 (1977).

A Behavioral Analysis of Aggressive Behaviors Induced and Modulated by Δ^9-Tetrahydrocannabinol, Pilocarpine, *d*-amphetamine and L-DOPA.

THC did not produce the dose-dependent biphasic effects seen in dominant rats when treated with amphetamine and several CNS drugs; however, it shared with these compounds the pattern of behavioral alteration in submissive rats. Chronic THC administration induced mouse-killing behavior in non-killer rats.

4446   Miczek, K. A., pp. 499-514 in *Pharmacology of Marihuana, Vol. 2*, edited by M. C. Braude and S. Szara. NY, Raven Press, 1976.

Does THC Induce Aggression?: Suppression and Induction of Aggressive Reactions by Chronic and Acute Δ^9-Tetrahydrocannabinol Treatment in Laboratory Rats.

Acute THC treatment (1.0 mg/kg, i.p.) resulted in less frequent attacks and threats in dominant rats and less submissive and defensive behavior in sub-ordinate rats. Chronic THC treatment did not induce intraspecies aggression (rat vs. rat) or peritonitis, but caused interspecies (rat vs. mouse) aggressive behavior. The effect of acute and chronic THC on locomotor and vertical activities of rats was studied.

4447   Miczek, K. A., Psychopharmacology, *47*(1), 59-64 (1976).

Mouse-Killing and Motor Activity: Effects of Chronic Δ^9-Tetrahydrocannabinol and Pilocarpine.

The effect of chronic administration of Δ^9-THC (2, 10, 20, or 50 mg/kg/day for 5-8 weeks) on the induction of mouse killing behavior in "non-killer" rats were compared to those of pilocarpine (12.5 mg and 25 mg/kg/day for 3 weeks). The killing behavior was found to depend on the daily dose and housing conditions. The locomotor effects of the drug were not related to the appearance of muricide behavior.

4448   Miczek, K. A., Science, *199*(4336), 1459-61 (1978).

Δ^9-Tetrahydrocannabinol: Antiaggressive Effects in Mice, Rats, and Squirrel Monkeys.

Aggressive behavior was induced in 3 species of rodents by putting a strange animal into their cages. Low doses of THC reduced the degree and frequency of aggression so induced. This increased rates of self grooming, investigation of intruders, locomotion, etc.

4449   Miczek, K. A.; and Barry, H., pp. 251-64 in *Advances in Experimental Medicine and Biology 85B, Alcohol Intoxication and Withdrawal 3B*, edited by M. M. Gross. New York, Plenum, 1977.

Comparison of the Effects of Alcohol, Chlordiazepoxide, and Δ^9-Tetrahydrocannabinol on Intraspecies Aggression in Rats.

Δ^9-THC (2 and 4 mg/kg, i.p.) suppressed the attack behavior by dominant rats toward nondrugged opponents. In experienced subordinate rats, Δ^9-THC prolonged immobile crouch and submissive-supine reactions and resulted in more wounds. Other effects of Δ^9-THC, alcohol and chlordiazepoxide were also investigated.

4450 Mikuriya, T. H., Clin. Toxicol., 8(2), 233-37 (1975).

Marijuana: Medical, Social, and Moral Aspects.

The author believes that we must face up to the fact that marihuana use does exist and on a continuing basis. Institutions existing to protect the public health and safety should respond appropriately to this new situation.

4451 Mikuriya, T. H., J. Psychedelic Drugs, 10(3), 211-16 (1978).

Cannabis in Western Medicine: An Abbreviated History.

A brief historical review of cannabis use in western medicine is provided. Various therapeutic potentials of cannabis, including analgesia and reduction of IOP, are also discussed. The immediate restoration of cannabis to prescription status is proposed by the author, based on the overwhelming historical evidence of its safety and effectiveness.

4452 Miller, J. D.; Cisin, I. H.; and Harrell, A. V., Eds., Highlights from the National Survey on Drug Abuse: 1977. NIDA, 1978.

Levels of drug abuse in the U. S. was estimated in this survey conducted under the sponsorship of NIDA. In 1977, the upward trend in marihuana use continued and its use spread to larger and more varied segments of the population.

4453 Miller, L.; Cornett, T.; Brightwell, D.; McFarland, D.; Drew, W. G.; and Wikler, A., Pharmacol. Biochem. Behav., 5(6), 639-43 (1976).

Marijuana and Memory Impairment: The Effect of Retrieval Cues on Free Recall.

Marihuana smoking (one gram of 0.94% THC) resulted in a recall deficit which was less severe in the presence than in the absence of cues. Only the number of external intrusions increased under cued conditions.

4454 Miller, L.; Cornett, T.; Drew, W.; McFarland, D.; Brightwell, D.; and Wikler, A., Pharmacology, 15(3), 268-75 (1977).

Marihuana: Dose-Response Effects on Pulse Rate, Subjective Estimates of Potency, Pleasantness, and Recognition Memory.

Subjective high, pleasantness and pulse rate increased with doses of THC (0-15 mg) administered to experienced marihuana users. The recognition memory test was not altered by THC.

4455 Miller, L.; Cornett, T.; and McFarland, D., Pharmacol. Biochem. Behav., 8(4), 327-32 (1978).

Marijuana: An Analysis of Storage and Retrieval Deficits in Memory with the Technique of Restricted Reminding.

Using a restricted reminding procedure in which only words not recalled were presented again, marihuana smoking by experienced users was found not to affect the amount of information stored but rather to result in poorer information retrieval from long-term storage.

4456   Miller, L.; Cornett, T.; and Nallan, G., Psychopharmacology, *58*(3), 297-301 (1978).

Marijuana: Effect on Nonverbal Free Recall as a Function of Field Dependence.

Marihuana intoxication reduced the free recall of nonverbal material and increased intrusion errors. Only the former effect was related to performance on the embedded figures test.

4457   Miller, L. L., pp. 271-92 in *The Therapeutic Potential of Marihuana*, edited by S. Cohen and R. Stillman. NY, Plenum Medical Book Company, 1976.

Marihuana and Human Cognition: A Review of Laboratory Investigations.

Analysis of available data on the cognitive effects of marihuana in humans was made. The cognitive changes following THC seem to be proportionally related to its dose and can progress from minor to severe deficits. Specific actions of marihuana on memory, perception and state-dependent learning were discussed.

4458   Miller, L. L.; and Cornett, T. L., Pharmacol. Biochem. Behav., *9*(5), 573-77 (1978).

Marijuana. Dose Effects on Pulse Rate, Subjective Estimates of Intoxication, Free Recall and Recognition Memory.

Marihuana administered to human subjects resulted in deficit in free recall, but not recognition memory. It also increased intrusion errors, pulse rate and subjective high. Except for intrusion errors, all changes were dose related.

4459   Miller, L. L.; Cornett, T. L.; Brightwell, D. R.; McFarland, D. J.; Drew, W. G.; and Wikler, A., Psychopharmacology, *51* (3), 311-16 (1977).

Marijuana: Effects on Storage and Retrieval of Prose Material.

Marihuana (500 mg cigarette containing 2.1% THC) was found to influence the storage and retrieval processes involved in the free recall of prose in male subjects. Implications of the findings were indicated.

4460   Miller, L. L.; McFarland, D.; Cornett, T. L.; and Brightwell, D., Pharmacol. Biochem. Behav., *7*(2), 99-103 (1977).

Marijuana and Memory Impairment: Effect on Free Recall and Recognition Memory.

Marihuana smoking (14 mg of THC) reduced final and immediate free recall of words and increased internal and external intrusions, but it did not influence the rate of acquisition of repeated list or the long term retention of encoded information.

4461   Miller, L. L.; McFarland, D. J.; Cornett, T. L.; Brightwell, D. R.; and Wikler, A., Psychopharmacology, *55*(3), 257-62 (1977).

Marijuana: Effects on Free Recall and Subjective Organization of Pictures and Words.

The authors measured visual and verbal memory impairment caused by marihuana. Results showed greater impairment in picture recall. The possible causes for this form of memory showing more deficit with THC than did verbal memory are discussed.

4462   Miller, R. A., Diss. Abstr. Int. B, *39*(2), 669-70 (1978).

The Inhibitory Effect of Δ^9-Tetrahydro-cannabinol on Horse Serum Cholinesterase.

Δ^9-THC inhibited the activity of horse serum cholinesterase. This inhibition was not due to altered enzyme ionization.

4463   Miller, R. E.; and Deets, A. C., Psychopharmacology, 48, 53-58 (1976).

Delta-9-THC and Nonverbal Communication in Monkeys.

Δ^9-THC (1 mg/kg, p.o.) altered the performance of monkeys trained to nonverbally communicate via change of facial expression.

4464   Miller, R. H.; Dhingra, R. C.; Kanakis, C.; Amat-y-Leon, F.; and Rosen, K. M., Amer. Heart J., 94(6), 740-47 (1977).

The Electrophysiological Effects of Delta-9-Tetrahydrocannabinol (Cannabis) on Cardiac Conduction in Man.

THC (25 mg/kg, i.v.) increased the sinus automaticity and facilitated conduction of the sinoatrial and A-V nodes in human subjects.

4465   Milman, D. H., Pediatrics, 58(6), 916-17 (1976).

A Cannabis Registry? (Letter).

The author commends the report of the Committee on Drugs concerning marihuana effects on humans but emphasizes that uncontrolled experiments reporting adverse effects should not be discounted. The author also indicates that a registry of instances of adverse psychological reactions to cannabis might provide a practical alternative to controlled studies.

4466   Milner, G., Aust. Fam. Physician, 6(11), 1370-80 (1977).

The Case Against 'Pot.'

The author contends that available literature proves beyond any reasonable doubt that marihuana is a harmful drug for users. Hazardous driving and progression to the use of other drugs are among the many risks associated with marihuana consumption.

4467   Milner, G., Med. J. Aust., 1(7), 208-11 (1977).

Marihuana and Driving Hazards.

After having reviewed pertinent literature on marihuana and driving, both in real life and simulated settings, the author concluded that marihuana use constitutes a definite hazard for those using automobiles.

4468   Milner, G., Med. J. Aust., 2(9), 420-21 (1978).

The "Great" Marihuana Debate.

An Australian account of marihuana use was given. Attention should be placed on hazards involved in driving under the influence of marihuana.

4469   Milstein, S. L.; MacCannel, K.; Karr, G.; and Clark, S., Int. Pharmacopsychiat., 10 (3), 177-82 (1975).

Marijuana-Produced Changes in Pain Tolerance. Experienced and Non-Experienced Subjects.

600 g of 1.3% Δ^9-THC and placebo were compared in cannabis experienced and naive subjects. An increased tolerance to pain was observed in both groups after smoking marihuana. However, there was a trend towards a greater increase in tolerance for the experienced (16%) compared to the naive group (8%).

4470 Milstein, S. L.; MacCannell, K.; Karr, G.; and Clark, S., J. Nerv. Ment. Dis., *161*(1), 26-31 (1975).

Marijuana-Produced Impairments in Co-ordination.

The effects of marihuana (600 mg of 1.3% Δ^9-THC) on perceptualmotor co-ordination, motor ability, and visual perception were compared in experienced marihuana subjects and naive ones. Both groups showed impairments; however, the impairment was greater in the experienced than the naive group.

4471 Mims, R. B.; and Lee, J. H., J. Natl. Med. Ass., *69*(7), 491-95 (1977).

Adverse Effects of Intravenous Cannabis Tea.

Four case reports of subjects administering 'pot tea' i.v. and requiring hospitalization are described. Subjects suffered severe adverse reactions including hypotension, gastrointestinal disturbances, hypovolemic shock and renal failure.

4472 Miras, C. J.; Kyrkou, K. A.; and Markidou, S. G., United Nations ST/SOA/SER.S/56, June 30, 1978.

Scientific Research on Cannabis. 56. Chromosomal Abnormalities in Heavy Hashish Users.

An *in vitro* experiment was initiated to study the effect of hashish on the chromosome complement of 15 heavy male users. Chromosomal preparations were made from cultures of whole blood. Results showed chromosomal abnormalities in all hashish users.

4473 Mirin, S. M.; and McKenna, G. J., Mil. Med., *140*, 482-85 (1975).

Combat Zone Adjustment: The Role of Marihuana Use.

The use of marihuana in a combat area is discussed in terms of composition of group using it, reasons for use, extent of use and time of use. Marihuana was used to decrease anxiety feelings and as a relaxant but rarely during actual combat confrontations.

4474 Mishra, S. S.; and Sahai, I., *Seventh International Congress of Pharmacology: Abstracts*, Paris, France, July 16-21, 1978, p. 168.

Interactions of *Cannabis indica* with Some Neuropharmacological Agents.

A resinous alcoholic extract of *Cannabis indica* leaves potentiated the antipyretic action of aspirin, the analgetic effects of pethidine and pentazocine and the anticonvulsant activity of diphenylhydantion.

4475 Mitra, G.; Poddar, M. K.; and Ghosh, J. J., Toxicol. Appl. Pharmacol., *34*(3), 525-28 (1975).

Effect of Δ^9-Tetrahydrocannabinol on Rat Liver Microsomal Lipid Peroxidation.

Acute or subchronic Δ^9-THC administration decreased lipid peroxide formation in livers of treated rats. Δ^9-THC also significantly inhibited *in vitro* CCl_4-, NADPH- and ascorbate-induced lipid peroxidation.

4476 Mitra, G.; Poddar, M. K.; and Ghosh, J. J., Toxicol. Appl. Pharmacol., *35*(3), 523-30 (1976).

In Vivo and *In Vitro* Effects of Δ^9-Tetrahydrocannabinol on Rat Liver Microsomal Drug-Metabolizing Enzymes.

The effects of Δ^9-THC *in vivo* (10 mg and 50 mg/kg acute and 10 mg/kg chronic for 21 days) and *in vitro* (2, 4 and 8 µg THC/mg enzyme protein) on rat liver microsomal drug-metabolizing enzymes, dimethylamine-N-demethylase, p-nitroanisole-O-demethylase and aniline hydroxylase, activities were investigated. Some inhibition of these enzymes was observed.

4477   Mitra, G.; Poddar, M. K.; and Ghosh, J. J., Toxicol. Appl. Pharmacol., 37(3), 517-24 (1976).

Delta-9-Tetrahydrocannabinol: Effect on Adrenal Catecholamines.

Δ^9-THC (10 and 50 mg/kg, i.p.) exerted an initial rise in rat adrenal NE and Epi followed by a prolonged decrease while producing a long lasting depression of DA levels. Subchronic THC caused a sustained increase in Epi levels, an early decline in DA, and latent depressed levels of NE. Hypotheses for the observed effects were presented.

4478   Mitra, G.; Poddar, M. K.; and Ghosh, J. J., Toxicol. Appl. Pharmacol., 42(3), 505-12 (1977).

Interaction of Δ^9-Tetrahydrocannabinol with Reserpine, Phenobarbital and LSD-25 on Plasma and Adrenal Corticosterone.

THC (10 and 50 mg/kg) or reserpine increased rat corticosterone levels and had addictive effects when administered simultaneously. LSD, however was ineffective, whereas phenobarbital decreased corticosterone levels and antagonized THC effects. Chronic THC administration did not alter any of the results discussed above.

4479   Mitra, M. G.; Poddar, M. K.; and Ghosh, J. J., Indian J. Biochem. Biophys., 12(4), 379-82 (1975).

Interaction of Cannabis Extract with Reserpine, Phenobarbital, Amphetamine and LSD-25 on Activities of Hepatic Enzymes.

Cannabis alone induced tryptophan pyrrolase and tyrosine aminotransferase activities in rats. Neither amphetamine nor LSD had any interactive effects with cannabis, but simultaneously administered reserpine or pentobarbital caused an additive effect or prolonged cannabis effects respectively.

4480   Mobarak, Z.; Bieniek, D.; and Korte, F., Chemosphere, 4(5), 299-300 (1975).

Untersuchung der Inhaltsstoffe der Cannabis sativa Wahrend der Vegetationsperiode [Contents of Cannabis sativa During the Vegetation Period].

Cannabis from Brazilian origin and cultivated in Germany was analyzed for relative changes of hydrocarbon content during the vegetation period. By means of GC and TLC two cannabinoids (THC and CBC) could be detected; this observation may be of significance for the biosynthetic pathway.

4481   Mobarak, Z.; Bieniek, D.; and Korte, F., Forensic Sci., 11(3), 189-93 (1978).

Some Chromatographic Aspects of Hashish Analysis. II.

GC data and TLC data are given on several hash samples. Extraction procedures are described. Mass spectral data were used. Data on pentyl and propyl side chains are discussed.

4482   Moffat, A. C.; Proc. Anal. Div. Chem. Soc., 15(8), 237-39 (1978).

Analytical Chemistry and Drug Metabolism.

In this brief summary, a general discussion is given regarding the different analytical procedures used for studying drug metabolism of LSD and THC. Techniques such as TLC, GC, HPLC, GC/MS, and RIA are briefly discussed.

4483 Mon, M. J.; Jansing, R. L.; Doggett, S.; Stein, J. L.; and Stein, G. S., Biochem. Pharmacol., *27*(13), 1759-65 (1978).

Influence of Δ^9-Tetrahydrocannabinol on Cell Proliferation and Macromolecular Biosynthesis in Human Cells.

Δ^9-THC depressed the growth of HeLa S_3 cells in a dose-dependent fashion. It also depressed cellular RNA, DNA and protein synthesis and concentrated mainly in the cytoplasmic fraction of these cells.

4484 Montagna, M.; Avato, F.; and Crippa, O., Riv. Tossicol. Sper. Clin., *5*(3-4), 207-19 (1975).

Studio Sulla Reperibilita del "Cannabinoli" nei Substrati Organici di Interesse Clinica [Study on the Detectability of Cannabinols in Organic Substrates of Clinical Interest].

TLC and GC procedures are given for the detection of the cannabinoids Δ^9-THC, CBD and CBN in the nasal and finger washings of hemp smokers immediately after smoking. Saliva and blood were also analyzed. The procedure could be used to detect the intake of cannabis.

4485 Montana, E.; and O'Neill, C., Ga. Med. Assoc. J., *67*(3), 211-14 (1978).

Prevalence of Tobacco, Marijuana, and Alcohol Usage Among High School Students: A Local Survey and Comments on Current Patterns of Usage.

Marihuana use among high school students in a middle size Georgia community was evident in 25.47% of males and in 18.18% of females surveyed. Percentages of alcohol consumption among these students were 45.59% and 31.86% for males and females respectively.

The author concludes that small and medium size communities do not greatly differ in the national spectrum of prevalence of drug use.

4486 Montero, J.-L.; and Winternitz, F., C. R. Acad. Sci. (D), *281*(4), 197-99 (1975).

Syntheses d'Analogues des Tetrahydrocannabinols [Synthesis of Some THC Analogs].

The synthesis of THC and other derivatives was accomplished by the condensation of either olivetol or phloroacetophenone with (+)-epoxy-carene-3.

4487 Montgomery, B. J., J. Amer. Med. Ass., *240*(14), 1469-70 (1978).

High Interest in Medical Uses of Marijuana and Synthetic Analogues.

Investigations concerning the use of synthetic cannabinoids to take advantage of the therapeutic benefits of marihuana dissociated from its subjective effects are currently underway.

4488 Monti, J. M., Psychopharmacology, *55*(3), 263-65 (1977).

Hypnoticlike Effects of Cannabidiol in the Rat.

Though THC is thought to decrease slow-wave sleep (SWS) and REM sleep while increasing wakefulness, it is apparent that CBD has the opposite effects upon these parameters. Acute doses (20 mg/kg) of CBD increased onset of SWS in the rat and a dose of 40 mg/kg CBD increased SWS and decreased wakefulness. REM sleep was not significantly decreased.

4489 Monti, J. M.; and Carlini, E. A., Pharmacol. Biochem. Behav., *3*(6), 1025-29 (1975).

242

Spontaneous Behavior and Sleep-Wakefulness Cycle in Isolated and Paired REM Sleep Deprived-Marihuana Treated Rats.

Chronically implanted male Wistar rats received control treatment or 10 mg/kg, i.p. marihuana extract and were evaluated electroencephalographically for changes in their sleep-wakefulness cycle. Marihuana extract did not prevent REM sleep rebound in non-deprived rats nor in deprived rats in isolation; aggressive behavior was also absent. Pairing of sleep-deprived rats resulted in failure of REM sleep rebound and in the appearance of aggressiveness. The authors suggest that marihuana aggressiveness in REM sleep-deprived rats occurs through a catecholaminergic mechanism.

4490   Moore, M. D., J. Police Sci. Admin., 3(4), 387-93 (1975).

The Marijuana Merry-Go-Around.

The author advocates the point of view that legal deterrents have been unsuccessful in curbing marihuana use and that perhaps legalization or decriminalization might be a more rational approach to the problem of marihuana abuse.

4491   Morgan, H. G.; and Hayward, A., Brit. J. Addict., 71(3), 285-88 (1976).

Effects of Drug Talks to School Children.

In attempting to assess the effects of drug education, it was found that most schoolboys were antagonistic to the use of hard drugs, but seemed to be more sympathetic toward such drugs as sedatives, stimulants and

cannabis. The study points out that informal rather than formal talks with adaquate time for discussion are most effective.

4492   Morishima, A.; Henrich, R.; Jou, S.; and Nahas, G., pp. 265-71 in Marihuana: Chemistry, Biochemistry, and Cellular Effects, edited by G. G. Nahas. NY, Springer-Verlag, 1976.

Errors of Chromosome segration Induced by Olivetol, a Compound with the Structure of C-Ring Common to Cannabinoids: Formation of Bridges and Multipolar Division.

In vitro experiments indicated that olivetol induces uneven chromosome segregation including the formation of multipolar cell divisions. Olivetol and cannabinoids may have a unique ability to disturb the formation of microtubules and spindles.

4493   Morishima, A.; Henrich, R. T.; and Nahas, G. G., Pediat. Res., 10(4), 368 (1976).

Segregational Errors of Chromosomes Induced by Tetrahydrocannabinol and Olivetol.

Abnormal cell divisions were found in T-lymphocytes exposed to THC or olivetol. It is suggested that the THC- and olivetol-induced segregational errors of chromosomes may have resulted from effects of both agents on microtubule formation.

4494   Morishima, A.; Milstein, M.; Henrich, R.; and Nahas, G. G., Fed. Proc., 34(3), 782 (1975).

Effects of Delta-9-Tetrahydrocanabinol and Olivetol on Replication of Human Lymphocytes.

Lymphocytes from chronic heavy marihuana smokers showed an increased incidence of metaphase cells with subnormal amounts of chromatin material. A similar situation resulted when lymphocytes from healthy nonsmokers were exposed to THC (6.4 x 10^{-6} M) or olivetol (1.5 x 10^{-4} M) *in vitro*.

4495 Morishima, A.; Milstein, M.; Henrich, R. T.; and Nahas, G. G., pp. 711-22 in *Pharmacology of Marihuana, Vol. 2*, edited by M. C. Braude and S. Szara. NY, Raven Press, 1976.

Effects of Marihuana Smoking, Cannabinoids, and Olivetol on Replication of Human Lymphocytes: Formation of Micronuclei.

A significant increase in the incidence of micronuclei occurred in heavy marihuana smokers. However, when all metaphases were considered no change in the mitotic index was evident in light or heavy smokers. When THC or olivetol were added to lymphocytes or when cultures were exposed to water, a marked increase in micronuclei resulted. Manipulation of blood samples and preparations of cultures are described.

4496 Morishima, A.; Milstein, M.; and Nahas, G. G., Bull. N. Y. Acad. Med., *51*(10), 1177-78 (1975).

Effects of Opium Alkaloids and Cannabinoids on Replication of Lymphocytes.

Lymphocytes from chronic marihuana smokers possess a subnormal number of chromosomes in metaphase cells. Addition of Δ^9-THC and olivetol to lymphocytic cultures from healthy, non-smokers resulted in the same phenomenon.

4497 Moschovakis, A.; Liakopoulos, D.; Armaganidis, A.; Kapsambelis, V.; Papanikolaou, G.; and Petroulakis, G., Psychopharmacology, *58*(2), 181-83 (1978).

Cannabis Interferes with Nest-Building Behavior in Mice.

THC (5 and 10 mg/kg, i.p.) disrupted nest-building behavior in mice. The nonsoluble nonvolatile products and the sublimate fractions of cannabis also induced similar effects to those of THC.

4498 Moskowitz, H., Accid. Anal. Prev., *8*(1), 21-26 (1976).

Marihuana and Driving.

Conclusions from simulator, laboratory and car driving studies suggest that marihuana impairs perceptual functions, tracking and other care control components of driving. An increase in accident probability, therefore, can be expected.

4499 Moskowitz, H., pp. 77-90 in *Drugs and Driving*, NIDA Research Monograph. 11, 1977.

Drug Impairment Reviews: Hallucinogens (General). Marihuana.

Upon reviewing pertinent literature, it was concluded that marihuana does impair several performance skills required for safe driving. Behavioral components affected by marihuana should be better defined.

4500 Moskowitz, H., pp. 283-95 in *Res. Adv. Alcohol and Drug Probl., 3*, edited by Y. Israel; R. J. Gibbins; H. Kalant; R. E. Popham; W. Schmidt; and R. G. Smart. NY, John Wiley and Sons, 1976. 476 pp.

Cannabis and Experimental Studies of Driving Skills.

A discussion of the difficulties encountered in measuring extent and type of impairments of driving skills due to cannabis use is presented. The advantages and disadvantages of various testing methods are presented. Tracking and perceptual ability generally decreased with cannabis use.

4501 Moskowitz, H.; Hulbert, S.; and Mc-Glothlin, W. H., Accid. Anal. Prev., 8(1), 45-50 (1976).

Marihuana: Effects on Simulated Driving Performance.

Marihuana smoking did not influence subjects' control of car and tracking under simulated driving conditions. Marihuana, however, impaired reaction times to subsidiary tasks. It was concluded that marihuana impairs perceptual or attentional-related tasks.

4502 Moskowitz, H.; Ziedman, K.; and Sharma, S., Hum. Factors, 18(5), 417-32 (1976).

Visual Search Behavior While Viewing Driving Scenes Under the Influence of Alcohol and Marihuana.

In the studies concerned with the effects of marihuana on visual searching patterns, 10 male social users of the drug were tested both with a placebo and under the influence of THC (200 mg/kg). Marihuana was shown not to affect any parameter measured to any significant degree. Differences between alcohol and marihuana are discussed.

4503 Moss, D. E.; Peck, P. L.; and Salome, R., Pharmacol. Biochem. Behav., 8(6), 763-65 (1978).

Tetrahydrocannabinol and Acetylcholinesterase.

THC (20 mg/kg, i.g.) induced pronounced hypothermia in rats but did not affect brain acetylcholinesterase (AChE) activity, nor did it influence physostigmine inhibition of AChE.

4504 Moss, I. R.; and Friedman, E., Life Sci., 19(1), 99-104 (1976).

Δ^9-Tetrahydrocannabinol: Depression of Ventilatory Regulation; Other Respiratory and Cardiovascular Effects.

The effects of Δ^9-THC (1.0, 0.5 and 0.25 mg/kg, i.v.) and of CBD (80.5 mg/kg, i.v.) on ventilatory response to carbon dioxide (CO_2) were measured using anesthetized dogs. Other respiratory and cardiovascular effects were measured. Δ^9-THC caused marked decrease of ventilatory response to CO_2, decrease of total pulmonary resistance, bradycardia and transient arterial hypotension.

4505 Mott, J., Bull. Narcotics, 28(1), 43-54 (1976).

The Epidemiology of Self-Reported Drug Misuse in the United Kingdom.

This review lists various sources and types of self-report methods of data collection and uses the derived data to make some generalizations. Most self-confessed drug abusers admit to using cannabis, had favorable attitudes towards drugs and had slightly elevated neuroticism scores. The data reviewed covers people in England between 1968 and 1972.

4506 Muller, P.; Tran Van Ky, P.; and Dumetz, J., Bull. de Med. Leg., Urg. Med., Cent. Anti-Poisons, 20(3), 205-10 (1977).

Interet de la Recherche in Chromatographie in Phase Gazeuse dans Certaenes Expertises Crimenalistiques [Interest in the Study of Gas Chromatography in Certain Criminal Investigations].

TLC and GC techniques were used for the analysis of cannabis samples. Attempts were made to correlate the analytical data and microscopic examination of hashish samples to the geographical origin of confiscated hemp. Positive differentiation between samples was difficult. The use of GC in forensic analysis of other drugs such as alcohol and organic solvents such as butane was also described.

4507 Mullins, C. J.; Vitola, B. M.; and Michelson, A. E., Int. J. Addict., *10*(3), 481-502 (1975).

Variables Related to Cannabis Use.

A survey with Air Force servicemen as subjects. Experimenters with cannabis are a little more likely than nonusers to have used amphetamines, opiates, barbiturates or other illicit drugs at least once. Use of other drugs increases with increasing use of cannabis. Catholics and those with no religious preference are the heaviest cannabis users and Baptist are the least. The more education past 12 years of school, the less tendency to use cannabis. Cannabis users are less likely to get promotions than nonusers.

4508 Munsen, A. E., pp. 39-46 in *Marijuana and Health Hazards*, edited by J. R. Tinklenberg. NY, Academic Press, 1975.

Marijuana and Immunity.

Studies on the susceptibility of marihuana users to disease and the immunosuppressant properties of marihuana are difficult to conduct in humans, whereas animal studies conducted on this subject are discussed along with the description of 5 immunoassays that can be employed.

4509 Munson, A. E.; Harris, L. S.; Friedman, M. A.; Dewey, W. L.; and Carchman, R. A., J. Natl. Cancer Inst., *55* (3), 597-602 (1975).

Antineoplastic Activity of Cannabinoids.

In vivo and *in vitro* studies were performed to test Δ^8- and Δ^9-THC, CBN and CBD effects on different mouse tumor systems. Δ^8-THC, Δ^9-THC and CBN were all inhibitory to Lewis lung tumor growth. Increased survival was also noted in animals. CBD seemed to enhance tumor growth.

4510 Munson, A. E.; Levy, J. A.; Harris, L. S.; and Dewey, W. L., pp. 187-97 in *Pharmacology of Marihuana, Vol. 1*, Edited by M. C. Braude and S. Szara. NY, Raven Press, 1976.

Effects of Δ^9-Tetrahydrocannabinol on the Immune System.

A systemic study of the effects of Δ^9-THC (25-200 mg/kg) in Nylar-A mice on the immune system was made. The phagocytic activity to colloidal carbon taken as an indicator of reticuloendothelial system was unaffected by Δ^9-THC. Both cell-mediated and humoral immunity was depressed by Δ^9-THC treatment both *in vivo* and *in vitro*. In a 16-day study no tolerance developed to this effect of Δ^9-THC.

4511 Munson, A. E.; Sanders, V. M.; Bradley, S. G.; Loveless, S. E.; and Harris, L. S., J. Reticuloendothel. Soc., *24* (6), 647-55 (1978).

Lethal Interaction of Bacterial Lipopolysaccharide and Naturally Occurring Cannabinoids.

Single i.p. doses of *E. coli* lipopolysaccharide (LPS) given to mice simultaneously with or up to 18 hours before sublethal doses of Δ^9-THC, Δ^8-THC or CBN caused mortality within 72 hours. No lethality was observed, however, when Δ^9-THC (100 mg/kg) was administered 3 and 24 hours prior to LPS. Other aspects of this lethal synergism were also investigated and discussed.

4512 Munson, A. E.; Sanders, V. M.; Harris, L. S.; and Loveless, S. E., Res. J. Reticuloendothelial. Soc., *20*(6), 12a (1976).

Lethal Interaction of Bacterial Lipopolysaccharide (LPS) and Naturally Occurring Cannabinoids.

A lethal synergism resulted in mice treated with Δ^9-THC, Δ^8-THC or CBN in combination with one of several bacterial lipopolysaccharides.

4513 Munson, A. E.; White, A. C.; Carchman, R. A.; and Harris, L. S., Pharmacologist, *17*(1), 265 (1975).

Delta-9-THC: Inhibition of DNA Synthesis on Cells in Tissue Culture.

Lewis lung carcinoma cells isolated from mouse tumors and established in tissue cultures were inhibited in a dose-dependent manner by Δ^9-THC (1 x 10^{-5} - 1 x 10^{-4} M). At less than cytocidal concentration, Δ^9-THC had no effect on precursor uptake; however at frank cytocidal concentration, Δ^9-THC inhibited DNA synthesis by 80% while suppressing precursor uptake by only 20%.

4514 Murray, T. F.; and Craigmill, A. L., Proc. West. Pharmacol. Soc., *19*, 362-68 (1976).

Interactions Between Δ^9-THC and Phencyclidine in Rats and Mice.

The PCP induced loss of righting reflex and suppression of operant response was significantly potentiated by Δ^9-THC. Low doses of Δ^9-THC (2.5 mg/kg) produced 66.3% increase and the increase was directly related to dose. LD-50 values were not affected by Δ^9-THC. PCP treated rats had lower brain levels of Δ^9-THC than did the saline control group.

4515 Musty, R. E.; Karniol, I. G.; Shirakawa, I.; Takahashi, R. N.; and Knobel, E., pp. 559-63 in *Pharmacology of Marihuana, Vol. 2*, edited by M. C. Braude and S. Szara. NY, Raven Press, 1976.

Interactions of Δ^9-THC and Cannabinol in Man.

In a double blind study, CBN and THC were given separately or in combination to five male volunteers. Among the several physiological and behavioral tests conducted, THC produced a significant increase in heart rate and underestimation of time only, while CBN did not alter any of the parameters tested. Potentiation of effects was seen when THC and CBN were given in combination.

4516 Musty, R. E.; Lindsey, C. J.; and Carlini, E. A., Psychopharmacology, *48*(2), 175-79 (1976).

6-Hydroxydopamine and the Aggressive Behavior Induced by Marihuana in REM Sleep-Deprived Rats.

Marihuana or 6-OH-DA alone did not induce aggressive behavior although a combination of both or in REM sleep-deprived rats resulted in aggression. I.c.v. administration of NE and DA to REM sleep-deprived rats pretreated with marihuana extract and 6-OH-DA revealed that NE attenuated, while DA enhanced, aggressiveness.

4517   Musty, R. E.; and Sands, R., Pharmacology, *16* (4), 199-205 (1978).

Effects of Marijuana Extract Distillate and Cannabidiol on Variable Interval Performance as a Function of Food Deprivation.

Lever pressing for food reinforcement was depressed by i.p. marihuana extract administration in the 12- and 24-hr. deprived rats only. Although CBD was ineffective when administered alone, it enhanced the marihuana extract-induced depression.

N

4518 Naditch, M. P., J. Personal., *43*(2), 305-20 (1975).

Ego Functioning and Acute Adverse Reactions to Psychoactive Drugs.

Whereas denial and intellectualization protect against, defensive regression contributes to acute adverse reactions experienced after use of marihuana and LSD. Defensive regression may also lead to increased use of LSD.

4519 Naditch, M. P.; Alker, P. C.; and Joffe, P., J. Nerv. Ment. Dis., *161*(5), 326-35 (1975).

Individual Differences and Setting as Determinants of Acute Adverse Reactions to Psychoactive Drugs.

Schizophrenia, regression and maladjustment all contributed to the possible experiencing of adverse reactions to marihuana. Setting variables had minute relations.

4520 Nagle, B.; Tomassone, B. M.; Digregorio, J.; and Piraino, A., Eur. J. Pharmacol., *40*(2), 337-43 (1976).

The Influence of Δ^9-Tetrahydrocannabinol on Pilocarpine-Induced Parotid Secretions of the Rat.

In parotid glands of rats cannulated after single exposures to intravenous Δ^9-THC (1-10 mg/kg), mean salivary flow was minimally affected as were cations while α-amylase was elevated at doses greater than 2.5 mg/kg. Cardiovascular function was depressed with hypotension and bradycardia most apparent at 2.5 mg/kg. THC elevates salivary protein and is a factor in the production of xerostomia in man.

4521 Nagy, C. M.; Furnas, B. E.; Einhorn, L. H.; and Bond, W. H., Proc. AACR. ASCO., *19*, 30 (1978).

Nabilone (N) Anti-Emetic Crossover Study in Cancer Chemotherapy Patients.

As an anti-emetic, nabilone was preferred over prochloperazine in cancer patients undergoing chemotherapy.

4522 Nahas, G., Bull. Narcotics, *30*(3), 23-32 (1978).

Symposium on Marijuana: Rheims, France, 22-23 July 1978.

Recent advances in marihuana-related biological research conducted by several nations, including the U.S.A., were outlined and summaries were provided. Papers presented will be published in a book.

4523 Nahas, G.; Desoize, B.; Armand, J. P.; and Morishima, A., J. Pharmacol. (Paris), *6*(3), 377-78 (1975).

Inhibition par les Cannabinoides Naturels de la Transformation Lymphocytaire et de la Synthese des Acides Nucleiques [Inhibition of Lymphocyte Transformation and Nucleic Acid Synthesis by Natural Cannabinoids].

All cannabinoids inhibit lymphocyte mitosis and synthesis of DNA, RNA and proteins.

4524 Nahas, G.; Desoize, B.; Hsu, J.; and Morishima, A., pp. 299-313 in *Marihuana: Chemistry, Biochemistry, and Cellular Effects*, edited by G. G. Nahas. NY, Springer-Verlag, 1976.

Inhibitory Effects of Δ^9-Tetrahydrocannabinol on Nucleic Acid Synthesis and Proteins in Cultured Lymphocytes.

The inhibitory effects of Δ^9-THC on the uptake and incorporation of thymidine, uridine, and leucine in cultured lymphocytes are studied. Experiments are also performed to study the reversibility of this inhibition, its time course, and the interactions of THC with the culture medium, especially serum.

4525   Nahas, G.; Desoize, B.; and Morishima, A., Nouv. Presse Med., *5*(7), 423-26 (1976).

Le Chanvre Indien. Donnees Physiopathologiques [Indian Hemp. Physiopathological Parameters].

The authors reviewed literature covering the harmful effects associated with the chronic use of hashish. They also warned of the growing popularity of hashish in Europe.

4526   Nahas, G. G., Ed., *Marihuana: Chemistry, Biochemistry, and Cellular Effects.* New York, Springer-Verlag, 1976. 556 pp.

Proceedings of the satellite symposium on marihuana of the Sixth International Congress of Pharmacology held July 26-27, 1975 in Helsinki, Finland. The book contains 16 chapters on the chemistry of marihuana and its constituents. In 26 chapters, the biochemical and cellular effects of cannabis and cannabinoids are discussed. Individual chapters are abstracted under senior author.

4527   Nahas, G. G., pp. 16-36 in *Medical Aspects of Drug Abuse*, edited by R. W. Richter.   Hagerstown, Md., Harper & Row, 1975.

Marihuana.   Toxicity and Tolerance.

A review of available literature indicated that marihuana use is associated with a substantial toxicity and that

tolerance to its psychological and physiological effects develops after its chronic use.

4528   Nahas, G. G., Bull. Narcotics, *29*(2), 13-27 (1977).

Biomedical Aspects of Cannabis Usage.

A synopsis of the biological effects of THC is presented. Toxic effects of THC include (1) disruption of DNA, RNA, and protein synthesis, (2) decreased cell division, (3) impairment of spermatogenesis in the production of abnormal sperm cells, (4) abnormal discharges recorded from the limbic area of the brain, and (5) decreased conception and increased resorption effects due to accumulation in the tissues. THC can be used for treatment of asthma and glaucoma while CBD can be used to treat epilepsy.

4529   Nahas, G. G., J. Amer. Med. Ass., *233*(1), 79-80 (1975).

Marihuana.

A summary of the effects of marihuana ranging from cellular abnormalities to personality changes.

4530   Nahas, G. G., *Keep Off the Grass.* NY, Reader's Digest Press, 1976.   205 pp.

Dr. Nahas has written an account (directed toward the layman) of the history of marihuana use and of his interest and research in the field. He defends his position on the marihuana issue and warns of the possible dangers associated with the use of marihuana.

4531   Nahas, G. G., *Marihuana - Deceptive Weed.*   Rev. Ed.   NY, Raven Press, 1975. 334 pp.

Dr. Nahas takes a hard stand on the use of marihuana and warns against its legalization, indicating the dangerous consequences of adding an extra burden to an already toxicomanic society.

4532   Nahas, G. G., pp. 47-54 in *Marijuana and Health Hazards*, edited by J. R. Tinklenberg. NY, Academic Press, 1975.

Effects of Marijuana Smoking and Natural Cannabinoids on the Replication of Human Lymphocytes and the Formation of Hypodiploid Cells.

T-lymphocytes taken from marihuana smokers possess decreased ability to form rosettes to incorporate 3-H-thymidine and increased number of hypodiploid cells. The latter two findings are supported by *in vitro* studies. While a clinical manifestation of immunological incompetence is not apparent in marihuana users, the author still warns against any weakening of immune defenses.

4533   Nahas, G. G.; Desoize, B.; Armand, J. P.; Hsu, J.; and Morishima, A., pp. 177-86 in *Pharmacology of Marihuana, Vol. 1*, edited by M. C. Braude and S. Szara. NY, Raven Press, 1976.

Natural Cannabinoids: Apparent Depression of Nucleic Acids and Protein Synthesis in Cultured Human Lymphocytes.

Δ^9-THC (0.00001 to 0.0001 M) was shown to inhibit DNA synthesis as inhibition of DNA synthesis was seen with Δ^9- and Δ^8-THC, their 11-hydroxyl metabolites CBD, CBC, CBL and olivetol, all of which have a common C-ring. Thus, inhibition of DNA may be a two-fold action - by inhibition of precursor uptake and by inhibition of protein and RNA synthesis.

4534   Nahas, G. G.; Morishima, A.; and Desoize, B., Fed. Proc., *36*(5), 1748-52 (1977).

Effects of Cannabinoids on Macromolecular Synthesis and Replication of Cultured Lymphocytes.

Uptake of radio labeled thymidine, uridine and leucine was measured. Cannabinoids produced an inhibition of thymidine uptake. Olivetol, aspirin and caffeine also inhibited uptake at high doses whereas alcohol did not. Inhibition of all three precursors occurred within 15 minutes after addition of THC.

4535   Nail, R. L.; and Dean, L. M., Drug Alcohol Depend., *1*(6), 429-34 (1976).

Drug Abuse: A Manifestation of the Cyclic Nature of Human Behavior.

From a study of 903 Navy men, most of whom returned from Viet Nam with a history of drug use, the authors concluded that a cyclic pattern of drug abuse continues among populations. For the most part, marihuana was the first drug used by the test group, and the least likely drug for multiple-drug users to quit using. A short discussion of marihuana dependence and functional impairments was presented.

4536   Nakano, S.; Gillespie, H. K.; and Hollister, L. E., Clin. Pharmacol. Ther., *23*(1), 54-62 (1978).

A Model for Evaluation of Antianxiety Drugs with the Use of Experimentally Induced Stress: Comparison of Nabilone and Diazepam.

Nabilone (2 mg single doses) was less effective than diazepam (5 mg single doses) in reducing experimentally-induced stress in subjects with high levels of trait anxiety.

4537 Naliboff, B. D.; Rickles, W. H.; Cohen, M. J.; and Naimark, R. S., Psychophysiology, *13*(6), 517-22 (1976).

Interactions of Marihuana and Induced Stress: Forearm Blood Flow, Heart Rate, and Skin Conductance.

Stress/marihuana (14 mg THC by inhalation) interactions are evaluated in social marihuana users drawn from a college population. Forearm blood flow (FBF), skin conductance (SC), and heart rate (HR) are reactive to stress, but only increased FBF and HR correlated with marihuana use during stress. Subjective effects and SC are associated with significant habituation between test sessions.

4538 Nalin, D. R.; Rhead, J.; Rennels, M.; O'Donnell, S.; Levine, M. M.; Bergquist, E.; Hughes, T.; and Hornick, R. B., Lancet, *2*(8095), 859-62 (1978).

Cannabis, Hypochlorhydria, and Cholera.

Stomach acid output in human subjects increased after beer consumption and decreased after cannabis. Association of cannabis use with severe diarrhea was suggested.

4539 Narayanaswami, K.; Golani, H. C.; and Bami, H. L., Forensic Sci., *5*(2), 153-54 (1975).

Stability of Cannabis (Resin) Charas Samples Under Tropical Conditions.

Legal samples, stored for up to 6 years, were analyzed for CBN, THC and CBD. THC and CBN can be used to determine approximate age of sample. Data are given for charas, ganja and mano samples.

4540 Narayanaswami, K.; Golani, H. C.; Bami, H. L.; and Dua, R. D., Bull. Narcotics, *30*(4), 57-69 (1978).

Stability of *Cannabis sativa L.* Samples and their Extracts on Prolonged Storage in Delhi.

Data are presented on the decomposition of cannabinoids in cannabis preparations over time. Graphic data cover a five year period.

4541 Navaratnam, V.; and Spencer, C. P., Bull. Narcotics, *30*(1), 1-7 (1978).

A Study on Socio-Medical Variables of Drug-Dependent Persons Volunteering for Treatment in Penang, Malaysia.

Hospitalization due to drug use among Malaysian youth is increasing. Cannabis was the second ranked drug of choice and was used on a daily basis by 37% of those sampled.

4542 Navratil, J.; Medek, A.; Hrbek, J.; Komenda, S.; and Krejci, Z., Activ. Nerv. Super., *17*(1), 66 (1975).

The Effect of Interaction of Synostigmine and Cannabis upon the Alimentary Motor Reflexes in Cats.

Synostigmine, physostigmine and THC (0.6 mg/kg) were administered s.c. to cats trained to lever press for food. It was concluded that a central anticholenergic effect, more than a peripheral effect, is seen from cannabis.

4543 Nazar, B.; Kairys, D. J.; Fowler, R.; and Harclerode, J., J. Pharm. Pharmacol., *29*(12), 778-79 (1977).

Effects of Δ^9-Tetrahydrocannabinol on Serum Thyroxine Concentrations in the Rat.

Acute and chronic THC administration (10 mg/kg, i.p.) decreased serum thyroxine levels in rats. The possible mechanisms involved were discussed.

252

4544 Neu, C.; DiMascio, A.; and Zwilling, G., pp. 153-60 in *The Therapeutic Potential of Marihuana*, edited by S. Cohen and R. Stillman. NY, Plenum Medical Book Company, 1976.

Hypnotic Properties of THC: Experimental Comparison of THC, Chloral Hydrate, and Placebo.

Compared to placebo, THC (10, 20 and 30 mg/kg, p.o.) significantly lowered the "total time to fall asleep" in human subjects. In a second study, both THC and chloral hydrate failed to exhibit any hypnotic properties.

4545 Nichols, D. E.; Mason, D. L.; and Jacobsen, L. B., Life Sci., *21*(9), 1245-47 (1977).

Allylbenzene Analogs of Δ^9-Tetrahydrocannabinol as Tumor Growth Inhibitors.

Δ^9-THC has previously been shown to inhibit tumor growth. In an attempt to investigate the possibility of the allylbenzene moiety being the active entity, a long list of allylbenzene derivatives were synthesized. None, however, exhibited *in vitro* activity comparable to that of Δ^9-THC.

4546 Nicolau, M.; Lapa, A. J.; and Valle, J. R., Arch. Int. Pharmacodyn. Ther., *236*(1), 131-36 (1978).

The Inhibitory Effects Induced by Δ^9-Tetrahydrocannabinol on the Contractions of the Isolated Rat Vas Deferens.

Δ^9-THC, in ethanol, and SP-111 antagonized the response of the rat vas deferens to NE and ACh. THC alone somewhat antagonized ethanol potentiated-barium effect.

4547 Nieburg, H. A.; Margolin, F.; and Seligman, B. R., New Eng. J. Med., *294*(3), 168 (1976).

Tetrahydrocannabinol and Chemotherapy.

Two case histories of patients suffering from cancer and related bone pain are cited. In both instances marihuana smoking subjectively lowered pain thresholds during periods of patient highs. Use of marihuana or Δ^9-THC ingestion for cancer must be on an individual basis.

4548 Nishimura, H.; and Tanimura, T., pp. 225-30 in *Clinical Aspects of the Teratogenicity of Drugs*. NY, Elsevier Publishing Company, 1976.

Psychotomimetic Drugs.

The teratogenicity of cannabis and LSD in the offspring of human users is still a debatable issue. More thorough epidemiological studies are needed.

4549 Nitake, M.; and Davis, L. J., Drug Intell. Clin. Pharm., *12*(9), 544, 568 (1978).

Paraquat Toxicity (Response to Request).

A brief summary is given on the toxicity of paraquat. Data from NIDA are presented for marihuana contaminated with paraquat.

4550 Noirfalise, A.; and Lambert, J., Bull. Narcotics, *30*(3), 65-67 (1978).

Proof of the Consumption of Cannabis.

Proof of cannabis consumption could be done by examining the dental deposits for cannabinoids. Mechanical removal of the deposits was done with a sharp toothpick covered with cotton soaked with petroleum ether or chloroform.

Extraction of the swab with benzene and TLC analysis of the extract revealed the presence of cannabinoids in deposits obtained from users.

4551   Nordqvist, M.; Agurell, S.; Falk, L.; Lindgren, J.-E.; and Ryman, T., Acta Pharm. Suecica, *14*(suppl.), 60 (1977).

Acidic Metabolites of Δ^1-Tetrahydrocannabinol Isolated from Rabbit Urine.

Nineteen acidic metabolites of THC were isolated from rabbit urine: 17 were identified and their structures established by GC-MS and NMR. Thirteen of the metabolites have not been previously reported in any species.

4552   Nordqvist, M.; Lindgren, J.-E.; and Agurell, S., pp. 64-69 in *Cannabinoid Assays in Humans*, NIDA Research Monograph Series, 7, 1976.

A Method for the Identification of Acid Metabolites of Tetrahydrocannabinol (THC) by Mass Fragmentation.

Mass fragmentography may be a useful tool in the determination of acidic metabolites of THC. However, a clean up procedure (methylation column chromatography, silylation) is necessary. The identification of Δ^1-THC-oic acid (a major metabolite) may be a practical method to identify cannabis users. The sensitivity of the method (ng/ml range) needs further investigation.

4553   Nordqvist, M.; Lindgren, J.-E.; and Agurell, S., pp. 441-48 in *Mass Spectrom Drug Metab.*, (Proc. Int. Symp., 1976) edited by A. Frigerio and E. L. Ghisalberti. NY, Plenum, 1977.

Identification of a Major Metabolite of Tetrahydrocannabinol in Plasma and Urine from Cannabis Smokers.

An identification method for Δ^1-THC-7-oic acid in urine and plasma of cannabis smokers was described. The use of this procedure in identifying users was advocated.

4554   Nosal, G.; Lapointe, G.; and Lin, K. N., Vie Med. Can. Fr., *4*(2), 109-29 (1975).

Alterations Neuronales Induites par le LSD-25 et le Δ^1-THC chez les Petits Rongeurs en Developpement Neonatal et Postnatal [Neuronal Alterations Induced by LSD-25 and Δ^1-THC in Small Rodents During Neonatal and Postnatal Development].

Daily injections, from the first to the eighth day after birth of mice and rats, of LSD-25 and Δ^1-THC (25, 50, 75 and 150 mg/kg) caused defects in the maturation of Purkinje neurons. The stage of neuronal development at the time of treatment determined the changes observed. The interactions of hallucinogenic drugs with nucleic acids and synthesis of proteins is discussed in relation to CNS development.

4555   Novotny, M.; Lee, M. L.; and Bartle, K. D., Experientia, *32*(3), 280-82 (1976).

A Possible Chemical Basis for the Higher Mutagenicity of Marijuana Smoke as Compared to Tobacco Smoke.

Marihuana smoke condensate (MSC) and tobacco smoke condensate (TSC) were analyzed and compared for their content of known and suspected carcinogens. MSC was found to be higher in polynuclear aromatic hydrocarbons. Pyrolysis of THC's and/or non-polar higher terpenes was concluded to be the source of the difference.

4556   Novotny, M.; Lee, M. L.; C.-E.; and Maskarinec, M. P., Steroids, *27*(5), 665-73 (1976).

254

High-Resolution Gas Chromatography Mass Spectrometric Analysis of Tobacco and Marijuana Sterols.

Silyl derivatives of sterols isolated from tobacco and marihuana are compared. Several sterols present in tobacco are not present in cannabis and *vice versa*. A SE-52 capillary column was used. GC-MS was used to tentatively identify some sterols.

4557   Novotny, M.; Lee, M. L.; Low, C.-E.; and Raymond, A., Anal. Chem., *48*(1), 24-29 (1976).

Analysis of Marijuana Samples from Different Origins by High-Resolution Gas-Liquid Chromatography for Forensic Application.

Glass capillary GC columns are used to obtain characteristic profiles of non-polar marihuana components. Thirty-eight of these components have been identified using GC/MS procedures. Data are presented to draw some correlation between GC analysis and geographical origin of the sample.

4558   Novotny, M.; and Maskarinec, M. P., pp. 95-106 in *Mass Spectrom. Comb. Tech. Med., Clin. Chem. Clin. Biochem.*, Symp., 1977.

Studies of Cannabis-Induced Changes in Steroid Metabolism by Capillary GC-MS.

Δ^9-THC (1 to 50 mg/kg) caused a dose-dependent increase in estrogens, corticosterone and metabolites in plasma of treated rats. Increased urinary excretion of androgen metabolites was also measured.

4559   Nowlan, R.; and Cohen, S., Clin. Pharmacol. Ther., *22*(5, pt. 1), 550-56 (1977).

Tolerance to Marijuana: Heart Rate and Subjective "High."

Tolerance to the psychotropic and cardiac effects of THC developed after 2-3 weeks of daily marihuana smoking. Dose-related changes were also noted in the above parameters.

4560   Noyes, R.; Brunk, S. F.; Avery, D. H.; and Canter, A., Compr. Psychiat., *17*(5), 641-46 (1976).

Psychologic Effects of Oral Delta-9-Tetrahydrocannabinol in Advanced Cancer Patients.

THC produced analgesia, appetite stimulation, relaxation and mild mood elevation in cancer patients. Pulse rate and BP changes were absent while few undesirable effects such as dizziness, blurred vision and impaired thinking were observed.

4561   Noyes, R.; Brunk, S. F.; Baram, D. A.; and Canter, A., pp. 833-36 in *Pharmacology of Marihuana, Vol. 2*, edited by M. C. Braude and S. Szara. NY, Raven Press, 1976.

Analgesic Effects of Delta-9-Tetrahydrocannabinol.

Increasing doses of THC (5-20 mg, p.o.) resulted in progressive relief of pain in advanced cancer patients. Undesirable side-effects were also experienced.

4562   Noyes, R., Jr.; Brunk, S. F.; Avery, D. H.; and Canter, A., Clin. Pharmacol. Ther., *18*(1), 84-89 (1975).

The Analgesic Properties of Delta-9-Tetrahydrocannabinol and Codeine.

The set and setting were important determinants of THC's depressant effects. At a dose of 20 mg, THC induced side effects that would prohibit its therapeutic use. THC at 10 mg was well tolerated though somewhat sedating.

4563   Noyes, R., Jr.; Brunk, S. F.; Baram, D. A.; and Canter, A., J. Clin. Pharmacol., 15(2), 139-43 (1975).

Analgesic Effect of Delta-9-Tetrahydrocannabinol.

In ten advanced cancer patients, relief of pain was demonstrated at 15 and 20 mg Δ^9-THC dose levels. At the highest dose levels, sedation and mental clouding were reported. The reduction in pain appears to be independent of the euphoric and anti-anxiety effects of Δ^9-THC.

O

4564   Ohlsson, A.; Agurell, S.; Lindgren, J.-E.; and Leander, K., Acta Pharm. Suecica, *14*(suppl.), 60-61 (1977).

Quantification of Tetrahydrocannabinol in Human Blood Plasma by Mass Fragmentography.

The authors discussed their publications dealing with mass fragmentographic methods for quantitative determination of Δ^9-THC and Δ^8-THC in the blood of cannabis smokers.

4565   Ohlsson, A.; Lindgren, J.-E.; Leander, K.; and Agurell, S., pp. 48-63 in *Cannabinoid Assays in Humans*, NIDA Research Monograph Series, 7, 1976.

Detection and Quantification of Tetrahydrocannabinol in Blood Plasma.

A procedure is reported for quantitating cannabinoids in biological fluids using GC/MS. Synthesis of radiolabelled standards is reported. Method has sensitivity of 0.3 ng/ml. Mass fragmentograms of several cannabinoids are reported.

4566   Ohlsson, A.; Lindgren, J.-E.; Leander, K.; and Agurell, S., pp. 429-40 in *Mass Spectrom. Drug Metab.*, (Proc. Int. Symp., 1976) edited by A. Frigerio and E. L. Ghisalberti. NY, Plenum, 1977.

Detection and Quantification of Cannabinoids in Human Blood Plasma.

Discussion of synthesis of deuterated internal standards, handling of blood samples, extraction and purification of samples, silylation and mass fragmentography was included in this paper. Advantages and disadvantages of the techniques described were given, as were the expected plasma levels over time in humans after smoking marihuana.

4567   Okey, A. B.; and Bondy, G. P., Science, *200*(4339), 312-14 (1978).

Δ^9-Tetrahydrocannabinol and 17 β-Estradiol Bind to Different Macromolecules in Estrogen Target Tissues.

THC did not reduce the high-affinity of estradiol to its binding sites in mouse mammary and uterine cytosols. Binding of THC was nonspecific and of low-affinity. Implications of the findings were discussed.

4568   Okey, A. B.; and Bondy, G. P., Science, *195*(4281), 904-05 (1977).

Is Delta-9-Tetrahydrocannabinol Estrogenic? Comments.

The authors argue that data presented by Solomon *et al.* (Science, *192*:559, 1976) does not provide enough support to their claim of an estrogenic activity for THC.

4569   Okey, A. B.; and Truant, G. S., Life Sci., *17*(7), 1113-18 (1975).

Cannabis Demasculinizes Rats But is Not Estrogenic.

During the sexual maturation period, male rats were fed cannabis resin in chow. The testes, prostrate and seminal vesicles showed a dose-related decrease in development. In females cannabis resin also caused a decrease in uterine weight and did not compete with diethylstilbestrol for estrogen receptor sites.

4570   Olmsted, C. A., Amer. J. Drug Alcohol Abuse, *3*(3), 485-505 (1976).

Effects of Cannabinoids on Synaptic Membrane Enzymes. I. *In Vitro* Studies on Synaptic Membranes Isolated from Rat Brain.

The effects of Δ^9-THC, 11-OH-Δ^9-THC, CBN and olivetol on synaptic membrane bound enzymes were examined. Δ^9-THC (1×10^{-7} M) showed significant inhibition of Na-K-ATPase and Mg-ATPase. Other cannabinoids also showed some inhibition. Δ^9-THC was also bound to synaptic membrane irreversibly. It is postulated that the psychoactive effects of Δ^9-THC may be mediated through inhibition of Na-K-ATPase which would affect biochemical gradients in brain.

4571   Olmsted, C. A.; and Lee, G. M., Fed. Proc., *35*(3), 644 (1976).

Brain Synaptic Membrane Na-K-ATPase Following Chronic Injection of Δ^9-Tetrahydrocannabinol (THC).

Δ^9-THC inhibits the specific activity of brain synaptic membrane Na-K-ATPase *in vitro* (90% inhibition) and *in vivo* (65% inhibition) 20 mins post injection. Rats were given 2.0 mg/kg Δ^9-THC/day for 5 days. Accumulated Δ^9-THC is not mobilized sufficiently in fasted animals to permit recovery of Na-K-ATPase specific activity to levels exceeding those seen in non-fasted animals.

4572   Olsen, J. L.; Lodge, J. W.; Shapiro, B. J.; and Tashkin, D. P., J. Pharm. Pharmacol., *28*(1), 86 (1976).

An Inhalation Aerosol of Δ^9-Tetrahydrocannabinol.

Sorbitan trioleate was used as a detacifier in a high pressure solvent system container to administer Δ^9-THC in an aerosol. Human studies showed an increase in specific airway conductance without marked heart rate increase. This method was more easily quantitated than pyrolysis, where other compounds may be formed besides Δ^9-THC.

4573   Orcutt, J. D., Int. J. Addict., *10*(6), 1021-33 (1975).

Social Determinants of Alcohol and Marijuana Effects: A Systematic Theory.

A systematic psychosocial theory of recreational drug effects is formulated. The theory stresses research on the normal use of marihuana and ETOH to define an effect-orientation continuum from the experiential effect of marihuana (internally oriented) to the behavioral effect of ETOH (externally oriented).

4574   Orcutt, J. D., Soc. Probl., *22*(3), 346-56 (1975).

Deviance as a Situated Phenomenon: Variations in the Social Interpretation of Marijuana and Alcohol Use.

The situational context dictates the social acceptability or non-acceptability of marihuana or alcohol use. Also, marihuana use was especially viewed as deviant in those situations involving task goals.

4575   Orcutt, J. D.; and Biggs, D. A., Int. J. Addict., *10*(2), 229-39 (1975).

Recreational Effects of Marijuana and Alcohol: Some Descriptive Dimensions.

Large sociable groups and small intimate groups were the settings studied, using the data from questionnaires submitted to college students who had used both drugs in both settings. Specific attention was given to external/internal effects-orientation and relaxation. Marihuana and alcohol produced comparable relaxation, but differed with regard to effects-orientation.

4576   Osgood, P. F.; and Howes, J. F., Fed. Proc., *34*(3), 744 (1975).

The Cardiovascular Effects of Cannabinoid Compounds in the Unanesthetized Rat.

I.p. Δ^9-THC and SP-111 (0.1-20 mg/kg, and 0.2-40 mg/kg, respectfully) yielded a similar transient increase in heart rate. After an initial increase, BP went to a minimum at 60 min.

4577   Osgood, P. F.; and Howes, J. F., Life Sci., *21*(9), 1329-35 (1977).

Δ^9-Tetrahydrocannabinol and Dimethylheptylpyran Induced Tachycardia in the Conscious Rat.

An animal model for the study of cannabinoid-induced tachycardia in humans is described.

4578   Osgood, P. F.; Howes, J. F.; Razdan, R. K.; and Pars, H. G., J. Med. Chem., *21*(8), 809-11 (1978).

Drugs Derived from Cannabinoids. 7. Tachycardia and Analgesia Structure-Activity Relationships in Δ^9-Tetrahydrocannabinol and Some Synthetic Analogues.

Δ^9-THC and eight other synthetic analogs were tested for analgesia and tachycardia using conscious Wister rats. The water soluble esters of DMHP showed the most analgesic and least tachycardiac effects.

4579   Osgood, P. F.; and Pars, H. G., Fed. Proc., *35*(3), 643 (1976).

Structure Activity Relationships in Analogs of Δ^9-Tetrahydrocannabinol: Tachycardia vs. Analgesia.

In benzopyrans previously assayed for analgesic potency, tachycardia potency was diminished and analgesic potency was elevated by changing the n-amyl side chain of Δ^9-THC's aromatic ring to a 1,2 dimethyl heptyl constituent and by substitution of an heterocyclic ring system for the alicyclic ring of Δ^9-THC. Greatest analgesic potency and least tachycardia is exhibited by an esterified 2-methyl piperidine ring substitution.

4580   Ottersen, R.; Aasen, A.; El-Feraly, F. S.; and Turner, C. E., J. Chem. Soc. Chem. Commun. *15*, 580-81 (1976).

X-Ray Structure of Cannabispiran: A Novel Cannabis Constitutent.

Cannabispiran, a new constituent from an ethanol extract of cannabis, is reported. Its structure is determined by X-ray. Physical constants are also given.

4581   Ottersen, T.; and Rosenqvist, E., Acta Chem. Scand., Ser. B, *31*(9), 749-55 (1977).

Crystal and Molecular Structure at -165 °C of the 1:1 Molecular Complex Formed by 8-βHydroxy-Δ^9-Tetrahydrocannabinol and N,N-Dimethylformamide.

Structural details of a 1:1 molecular complex of 8-β-OH-Δ^9-THC and N,N-dimethylformamide were reported using X-ray crystallography as the analytical tool.

4582   Ottersen, T.; Rosenqvist, E.; Turner, C. E.; and El-Feraly, F. S., Acta Chem. Scand., Ser. B, *31*(9), 781-87 (1977).

Crystal and Molecular Structure of Cannabinol.

Structural details of crystalline CBN were reported using X-ray crystallography as the analytical tool.

4583   Ottersen, T.; Rosenqvist, E.; Turner, C. E.; and El-Feraly, F. S., Acta Chem. Scand., Ser. B, *31*(9), 807-12 (1977).

Crystal and Molecular Structure of Cannabidiol.

Structural details of crystalline CBD were reported using X-ray crystallography as the analytical tool.

P

4584 Pack, A. T.; Brill, N. G.; and Christie, R. L., Dis. Nerv. Syst., *37*(4), 205-09 (1976).

Quitting Marijuana.

Profiles of marihuana quitters, never-users or continuous users differed significantly from each other. Never-users stick more to traditional social values and behavior, continuous users have counter cultural beliefs and behavior, and quitters hold an in-between position.

4585 Page, J. G.; and West, L. E., Pharmacology, *15*(3), 233-41 (1977).

Hypothermia in Rats Produced by Nabilone, a Synthetic Cannabinoid.

A dose-related hypothermia was produced by nabilone (1-25 mg/kg). The magnitude of this response was independent of factors such as age, sex, depth of probe, and time of acclimation, but was influenced by the ambient temperature and route of administration. Tolerance developed to the hypothermic effect.

4586 Page, J. G.; and West, L. E., Pharmacologist, *17*(2), 211 (1975).

Acute Tolerance to Hypothermia in Rats Produced by dl-3-(1,1-Dimethylheptyl)-6a-β ,7,8,10,10a-α Hexahydro-1-Hydroxy-6,5-Dimethyl-9H-Dibenzo b,d Pyran-9-One (Lilly Compound 109514).

Oral doses of a synthetic cannabinoid in rats produced hypothermic responses. The hypothermia was dependent on ambient temperature, potentiated by pretreatment with beverage xanthines, and not reproducible with successive doses until at least 72 hours after the first dose. A cross-tolerance was demonstrated between compound 109514 and dimethylheptylpyran which has similar hypothermic effects.

4587 Pagel, M. L.; and Sanders, M. G., *USAARL Report No. 76-17*, U. S. Army Aeromedical Research Laboratory, Fort Rucker, Alabama, March 1976. (Avail. Defense Documentation Center (DDC), Cameron Station, Alexandria, Virginia.)

Marijuana and Human Performance: An Annotated Bibliography (1970-1975).

This bibliography is chiefly concerned with information regarding the effects of marihuana on psychomotor, cognitive, and physiological factors affecting flight performance and consists of 199 references which are indexed.

4588 Palermo Neto, J. P.; Nunes, J. F.; and Carvalho, F. V., Psychopharmacologia, *42*(2), 4195-200 (1975).

The Effects of Chronic Cannabis Treatment upon Brain-5-Hydroxytryptamine, Plasma Corticosterone and Aggressive Behavior in Female Rats with Different Hormonal Status.

Ovariectomized rats treated with estrogen or Δ^9-THC (20 mg/kg, i.p.) for 25 days exhibited more aggressive behavior than controls. The combined treatment of Δ^9-THC, estrogen and progesterone resulted in diminished aggressiveness. Levels and turnover rates of brain 5-HT were lower and plasma corticosterone levels were higher in aggressive estrogen- or Δ^9-THC treated animals.

4589 Pallante, S.; Lyle, M. A.; and Fenselau, C., Drug. Metab. Dispos., *6*(4), 389-95 (1978).

Synthesis and Characterization of Glucuronides of 5'-Hydroxy-Δ^9-Tetrahydrocannabinol and 11-Hydroxy-Δ^9-Tetrahydrocannabinol.

Glucuronides of 11-OH-Δ^9-THC and 5'-

OH-Δ^9-THC were synthesized by incubation of each compound with rabbit liver. Characterization of the glucuronides was carried out by GC/MS analysis of the TMS-methyl esters of the TMS derivatives themselves. EI and CI mass spectra were used and important fragments discussed.

4590   Pandina, R. J.; and Musty, R. E., Pharmacology, *13*(4), 297-08 (1975).

Effects of Δ^9-Tetrahydrocannabinol on Active Avoidance Acquisition and Passive Avoidance Retention in Rats with Amygdaloid Lesions.

Male rats with basolateral amygdaloid lesions, were administered Δ^9-THC (0.75, 1.5, and 3.0 mg/kg, i.v.). The basolateral amygdaloid lesions did not affect performance on two-way active avoidance learning tasks or passive avoidance retention.

4591   Pang, K.-Y. Y.; and Miller, K. W., Biochim. Biophys. Acta, *511*(1), 1-9 (1978).

Cholesterol Modulates the Effects of Membrane Perturbers in Phospholipid Vesicles and Biomembranes.

CBN increased the order of spin-labeled phosphatidylcholine vesicles but was less effective than cholesterol. CBN also decreased the order of erythrocyte membranes and increased that of mitochondrial membranes. Effects of other membrane perturbers were also investigated.

4592   Parad, R.; Calihan, M.; Pollack, C.; Middleton, B.; Sornberger, C.; and Huber, G., Amer. Rev. Resp. Dis., *113*(4), 73 (1976).

The Combined Effects of Alcohol and Marijuana or Tobacco on the Anti-Bacterial Defenses of the Lung.

In vivo testing in rats of radiolabeled (^{32}P) *S. aureus* cultures in their lungs showed that anti-staphylococcal activity is independently impaired by either smoking marihuana, smoking tobacco, or drinking alcohol. In some combinations these adverse effects were additive.

4593   Parfrey, P. S., Brit. J. Addict., *72*(1), 59-65 (1977).

Factors Associated with Undergraduate Marijuana Use in Cork.

In a sample of college students, 23% of the males and 13% of the females admitted using marihuana at least once. Users in this Irish sample were characterized as being more liberal and less religious than nonusers. Also peer pressure was found to be more important than family related factors in influencing marihuana use.

4594   Parfrey, P. S., Scand. J. Soc. Med., *4*(3), 135-40 (1976).

The Effect of Religious Factors on Intoxicant Use.

A negative association between religious belief, religious practice and marihuana use was evident among a sample of Irish undergraduates. Also, the lack of religious belief and church attendance were better determinants of alcohol use than was Roman Catholicism.

4595   Paris, M.; Boucher, F.; and Cosson, L., Econ. Bot., *29*(3), 245-53 (1975).

The Constituents of *Cannabis sativa* Pollen.

Cannabis pollen from plants grown in a phytotron was assayed for cannabinoids, flavonoids and alkaloid type compounds. TLC and GLC were used. Alkaloidal type compounds were detected. Pollen was found to be rich in THC and THC acids.

4596 Paris, M.; Boucher, F.; and Cosson, L., Plant Med. Phytother., 9(2), 136-39 (1975).

Importance des Composes Propyliques dans le Cannabis Originaire d'Afrique du Sud [Importance of Propyl Compounds in Cannabis of South African Origin].

Cannabis from South African origin grown in France contained mainly tetrahydrocannabivarolic acid as shown by TLC and GC-MS. Data are given for TLC procedures etc. The propyl homologs of cannabinoids are reported to be independent of geographical locations.

4597 Paris, M.; and Lenicque, P.-M., Therapie, 30, 97-102 (1975).

Effets du Tetrahydrocannabinol et du Cannabidiol sur la Cicatrisation et la Regeneration de la Planaire Dugesia Tigrina [The Effects of Tetrahydrocannabinol and Cannabidiol on the Cicatrization and Regeneration of the Planarian Worm, *Dugesia tigrina*].

The effect of THC and CBD on the ability of the planarian worm to heal and regenerate itself rapidly when it is cut was studied. THC was found to effect the morphogenetic actions of 5-HT. The outcome of such experimentation is discussed.

4598 Paris, R. R.; Henri, E.; and Paris, M., Arh. Farm., 25(5-6), 319-28 (1975).

O C-Flavonoidima *Cannabis sativa L.* [C-Flavonoids of *Cannabis sativa L.*].

Ten flavonoid glycosides were isolated from the leaves of the cannabis plant by column and paper chromatographic techniques. One of these glycosides was found to be an O-glucoside of acyl apigenol. The remaining flavonoids are O- and C-glycosides of vitexin, isovitexin, and orientin.

4599 Paris, R. R.; Henri, E.; and Paris, M., Plant Med. Phytother., 10(2), 144-54 (1976).

Sur Les C-Flavonoides du *Cannabis sativa L.* [C-Flavonoids of *Cannabis sativa L.*].

Ten flavonoids are isolated from the leaves of *Cannabis sativa L.* using chromatographic techniques. These are C- and O-flavone glycosides related to apigenol and luteolol.

4600 Pars, H. G.; Granchelli, F. E.; Razdan, R. K.; Keller, J. K.; Teiger, D. G.; Rosenberg, F. J.; and Harris, L. S., J. Med. Chem., 19(4), 445-54 (1976).

Drugs Derived from Cannabinoids. 1. Nitrogen Analogs, Benzopyranopyridines and Benzopyranopyrroles.

Various nitrogen analogs of $\Delta^{6a(10a)}$-tetrahydrocannabinol were prepared including pyridine, quinuclidine and pyrrolo analogs and derivatives thereof. Pharmacologic evaluation of these compounds in mouse, cat, dog and monkey was carried out and comparison was made with DMHP.

4601 Pars, H. G.; Osgood, P. F.; Howes, J. F.; and Razdan, R. K., in *Committee on Problem of Drug Dependence, 1976*. Division of Medical Sciences, National Research Council, National Academy of Sciences, Washington, D. C., 1976, pp. 332-41.

Benzopyranopyridines: Analgesic Chemically Related to Cannabinoids and Narcotics.

The possible therapeutic application of the nitrogen-containing cannabinoid-like benzopyranopyridines as analgesics was explored and results are presented.

4602 Pars, H. G.; and Razdan, R., pp. 419-37 in *The Therapeutic Potential of Marihuana*, edited by S. Cohen and R. Stillman. NY, Plenum Medical Book Company, 1976.

Heterocyclic Analogs of the Cannabinoids.

The SAR of several cannabis related nitrogen or sulfur-containing benzopyrans along with the influence of alkyl substitution on the alicyclic ring of some of these analogs were investigated and the results discussed. Of these analogs, a special reference was made to compound *26* which is the most potent nitrogen analog of DMHP. Comparisons across several animal species indicated a similarity between the pharmacological profiles of these two agents.

4603 Pars, H. G.; Razdan, R. K.; and Howes, J. F., pp. 97-189 in *Advances in Drug Research, 11*, edited by A. B. Simmonds. NY, Academic Press, 1977.

Potential Therapeutic Agents Derived from the Cannabinoid Nucleus.

A review of the SAR relationships of the carboxylic and heterocyclic analogs of THC is presented. The review also includes not only the pharmacological effects of THC and other natural cannabinoid constituents of *Cannabis sativa* but also the pharmacology of the carboxylic and heterocyclic analogs. Various therapeutic uses of these compounds are also discussed.

4604 Passatore, M.; Perinetti Casoni, R.; Chiarotti, M.; and Giusti, G. V., Acta Med. Rom., *13*(6), 427-31 (1975).

Muscular Dystrophy in Adult Mice Chronically Treated with Cannabinoids at Behavioral Doses. III-Functional Tests on Muscle.

Mouse gastrocnemius muscles were isolated (along with sciatic nerve) from animals pretreated with THC, CBD, and CBN. When responses to electrical stimulation were compared to vehicle controls, it was seen that Δ^9-THC caused a significant decrease of twitch tension and maximal tetanic tension. CBD also produced some decrement in both tensions; whereas CBN induced an enhancement of contractile strength.

4605 Patel, A. R.; and Gori, G. B., Bull. Narcotics, *27*(3), 47-54 (1975).

Preparation and Monitoring of Marijuana Smoke Condensate Samples.

Procedures are described which will transform crude marihuana plant material, i.e., stems, seeds, leaves, into cigarettes. Moisture content of the plant material was a crucial factor in the packing of the cigarettes. The designs of a cigarette smoking machine and trapping mechanism for smoke condensate are also described.

4606 Paton, S. M.; and Kandel, D. B., Adolescence, *13*(50), 187-200 (1978).

Psychological Factors and Adolescent Illicit Drug Use: Ethnicity and Sex Differences.

Positive correlation between youths' use of drugs and psychological factors was found. Marihuana use did not, however, relate to any psychological factors studied.

4607 Paton, W. D. M., Ann. Rev. Pharmacol., *15*, 191-220 (1975).

Pharmacology of Marijuana.

The new developments in the biochemical effects of cannabis metabolites and the cellular and toxicological effects of marihuana are reviewed. The composition of cannabis, the relation between structure-action and site of action, neuro-physiology and human studies are presented. 268 references are cited.

4608 Paton, W. D. M., pp. 617-18 in *Pharmacology of Marihuana, Vol. 2*, edited by M. C. Braude and S. Szara. NY, Raven Press, 1976.

Additional Remarks on the Chronic Toxicity of Cannabis.

Dietary effects should be considered when studying the cause of weight loss in chronic cannabis-treated animals. In mice treated with labeled THC (1 mg/kg by gavage) for 5-7 days, radioactivity was found mainly in fat, liver, spleen, skin and heart. Body regions involved in cannabis toxicity have physico-chemical properties different from those involved in its central effects.

4609 Paton, W. D. M., pp. 569-70 in *Pharmacology of Marihuana, Vol. 2*, edited by M. C. Braude and S. Szara. NY, Raven Press, 1976.

Preclinical Studies: An Introduction. Long-Term Studies in Animals.

Chronic toxicity studies are controversial issues, but their importance cannot be underestimated. A question of what constitutes a relevant dose of cannabis is raised. Research in the area of pre-clinical studies should be more general and less strictly cannabis-centered.

4610 Patwardan, G. M.; Pundlik, M. D.; and Meghal, S. K., Indian J. Pharm. Sci., *40*(5), 166-67 (1978).

Gas-Chromatographic Detection of Resins in Cannabis Seeds.

Brief data are presented on the cannabinoids present in cannabis fruits. GLC was used.

4611 Patwardan, G. M.; Pundlik, M. G.; and Meghal, S. K., Arch. Kriminol., *159*(1-2), 36-39 (1977).

Dunnschichtchromatographischer Nachweis von Haschischwirkstoffen in Cannabis-Samen [A Thin-Layer Chromatographic Method for the Detection of Resins in Cannabis Seeds].

A procedure for the extraction and TLC identification of cannabinoids from cannabis seeds was described. Extraction with simple organic solvents was not as efficient as pretreatment of the seeds with NAOH followed by acidification and extraction with chloroform. TLC of the extracts using different solvent systems showed the presence of both CBN and THC in the seeds.

4612 Paul, M. K., J. Drug Educ., *7*(4), 323-35 (1978).

Comparative Attitudes of University Students and School Teachers on the Use and Legalization of Marijuana.

University students in Canada were shown to have more permissive attitudes towards marihuana use than did school teachers. Of the teachers, 95.3% did not use marihuana but 28.2% of the students did. About as many students started smoking marihuana in high school as started in college (13%) but only 1.2% of the teachers started in high school. Attitudes towards legalization and a discussion of other social aspects were presented.

4613 Payne, R. J.; and Brand, S. N., J. Amer. Med. Ass., *233*(4), 351-54 (1975).

The Toxicity of Intravenously Used Marihuana.

Four case histories are reported that indicate the danger of i.v. use of marihuana extracts. The severity of the toxic reactions was dose-related. Initial examination showed toxic hepatitis, acute renal failure, electrolyte inbalance, hypoalbuminemia, leukocytosis, and a relative thrombocytopenia.

4614   Peeke, S. C.; Jones, R. T.; and Stone, G. C., Psychopharmacology, *48*(2), 159-63 (1976).

Effects of Practice on Marijuana-Induced Changes in Reaction Time.

The effect of marihuana (0.9 marihuana cigarette containing 20% Δ^9-THC) on the two phases of a reaction time of task performance was examined. Marihuana affected only the attention-demanding phase. Effects of marihuana on pulse rate, salivary flow and subjective response were also examined.

4615   Perec, C. J.; Di Cuneo, F.; and Tocci, A. A., *Seventh International Congress of Pharmacology: Abstracts*, Paris, France, July 16-21, 1978, p. 788.

Buccal State of Patients who Make Improper Use of Drugs.

Except for injuries similar to leucoplasia, the study of six buccal parameters, including the D.P.O. index and the state of soft tissue, did not show much difference in marihuana users and controls.

4616   Pereira, W.; McLaughlin, T.; Baranano, M. T.; Dudley, S.; O'Connell, D., Cutting, M.; and Huber, G., Clin. Res., *23*(3), 351A (1975).

The Acute Effect of Marijuana Smoke on Antibacterial Defense Mechanisms of the Lung.

Marihuana smoke impairs the ability of rat lung to deactivate aerosolized *S. aureus*. *In vivo* exposure resulted in suppression of bacterial inactivation and increased carboxyhemoglobin levels. *In vitro* alveolar macrophagic bactericidal activity is decreased in a dose-dependent manner by a H_2O-soluble cytotoxin not associated with purified THC.

4617   Perez-Reyes, M.; Brine, D.; and Wall, M. E., pp. 173-79 in *Chronic Cannabis Use*, edited by R. L. Dornbush, A. M. Freedman, and M. Fink. NY, Annals of the New York Academy of Sciences, V. 282, 1976.

Clincial Study of Frequent Marijuana Use: Adrenal Cortical Reserve Metabolism of a Contraceptive Agent, and Development of Tolerance.

Frequent marihuana use was not associated with altered adrenal cortical reserve, did not accelerate the disappearance of the contraceptive agent, norethynodiel, from plasma and did not produce tolerance or sensitization to drug-induced effects.

4618   Perez-Reyes, M.; Simmon, J.; Brine, D.; Kimmel, G. L.; Davis, K. H.; and Wall, M. E., pp. 179-84 in *Marihuana: Chemistry, Biochemistry, and Cellular Effects*, edited by G. G. Nahas. NY, Springer-Verlag, 1976.

Rate of Penetration of Δ^9-Tetrahydrocannabinol and 11-OH-Δ^9-Tetrahydrocannabinol to the Brain of Mice.

Studies on the rate of penetration of Δ^9-THC and 11-OH-Δ^9-THC to the brain using human volunteers and mice are presented. Results obtained in man and mice are in agreement, and they suggest that the 11-OH-Δ^9-THC penetrates to the brain of humans at a faster rate than Δ^9-THC.

4619   Perez-Peyes, M.; Wagner, D.; Brine, D. R.; Christensen, D. H.; Davis, K. H.;

and Wall, M. E., pp. 117-23 in *Pharmacology of Marihuana, Vol. 1*, edited by M. C. Braude and S. Szara. NY, Raven Press, 1976.

Tetrahydrocannabinols: Plasma Disappearance in Man and Rate of Penetration to Mouse Brain.

Infusion of radiolabelled Δ^9-THC or 11-OH-Δ^9-THC in humans resulted in higher plasma levels of the forms, where 4-5 times greater quantities of 11-OH-Δ^9-THC were found in the mouse brain after i.v. injection. Both cannabinoids are equipotent. Thus Δ^9-THC seems to have greater affinity for receptors.

4620 Perez-Reyes, M.; Wagner, D.; Wall, M. E.; and Davis, K. H., pp. 829-32 in *Pharmacology of Marihuana, Vol. 2*, edited by M. C. Braude and S. Szara. NY, Raven Press, 1976.

Intravenous Administration of Cannabinoids and Intraocular Pressure.

Among the several cannabinoids infused i.v. to 12 normal paid subjects, only Δ^8-THC, Δ^9-THC and 11-OH-Δ^9-THC resulted in a significant reduction of IOP.

4621 Perez-Vitoria, C., Rev. Iber. Endocrinol., *23*(137), 437-44 (1976).

Gynecomastia and Marihuana (Editorial).

Three cases of gynecomastia have been reported in 3 patients who were heavy marihuana users (3 to 6 years). Thorough examinations ruled out the predominant causes of gynecomastia. The author classifies THC as an estrogenic substance. Chronic use of THC may therefore lead to testicular dysfunction and the appearance of gynecomastia.

4622 Permutt, M. A.; Goodwin, D. W.; Schwin, R.; and Hill, S. Y., Amer. J. Psychiat., *133*(2), 220-21 (1976).

The Effect of Marijuana on Carbohydrate Metabolism.

After the ingestion of 1 gm of marihuana (1.5% Δ^9-THC) by means of a spirometer, no hypoglycemia occurs in fasted individuals, and exaggerated rebound stimulation of insulin release in response to a glucose load does not occur. No effect on carbohydrate is discerned after marihuana smoking.

4623 Persaud, T. V. N., Anat. Anz., *140*(4), 345-71 (1976).

Zu Problemen der Angsborenen Mibilduugen in Raum der Englisch Sprechenden Karibien [Congenital Abnormalities in the English-Speaking Caribbean Area].

The teratogenic effects of cannabis are reviewed along with the effect of other known teratogens: Hypoglycin A, leucine, and carnitine.

4624 Pertwee, R. G.; and Tavendale, R., Brit. J. Pharmacol., *60*(4), 559-68 (1977).

Effects of Δ^9-Tetrahydrocannabinol on the Rates of Oxygen Consumption of Mice.

The THC-induced hypothermia in mice is directly related to the dose and inversely related to the ambient temperature. A fall in the rate of oxygen consumption always accompanied this hypothermia. Relationships of stress and THC-induced hypothermia to the oxygen utilizing process were discussed.

4625 Pet, D., Conn. Med., *41*(2), 91-94 (1977).

Marihuana: Current and Recurrent Issues in Connecticut.

Findings of a study conducted by the Ad Hoc Committee to investigate the issue of marihuana use in Connecticut are discussed. The committee recommended no change in present statutes regarding the sale of marihuana but requested that present penalties, with respect to possession of less than 30 g. of the natural plant for age 16 and over for the first offense, be diminished, making it a civil offense subject to a fine.

4626 Peters, B. A.; Lewis, E. G.; Dustman, R. E.; Straight, R. C.; and Beck, E. G., Psychopharmacology, *47*(2), 141-48 (1976).

Sensory, Perceptual, Motor and Cognitive Functioning and Subjective Reports Following Oral Administration of Δ^9-Tetrahydrocannabinol.

Performance during sensory, motor, and cognitive tests was minimally affected by the oral administration of THC (0.2, 0.4, and 0.6 mg/kg) in human subjects. Subjects experienced euphoria and dysphoria after THC administration with dysphoria prominent at the high doses. Autonomic function was severely affected.

4627 Petersen, B. H.; Graham, J.; and Lemberger, L., Clin. Res., *23*(4), 477A (1975).

Marihuana, Tetrahydrocannabinol, and T-Cell Function.

THC either stimulated or reduced T-cell rosette formation in chronic users. Effects were transient.

4628 Petersen, B. H.; Graham, J.; and Lemberger, L., Life Sci., *19*(3), 395-400 (1976).

Marihuana, Tetrahydrocannabinol and T-Cell Function.

The effect of "street" marihuana or Δ^9-THC smoking on T-lymphocytes was examined. Test subjects were chronic marihuana users with a one-month drug free period prior to the experiment. Results showed that the effect on T-lymphocytes was variable, transient and probably related to factors other than marihuana.

4629 Petersen, B. H.; and Lemberger, L., Fed. Proc., *35*(3), 333 (1976).

Effect of Delta-9-Tetrahydrocannabinol Administration of Antibody Production in Mice.

Δ^9-THC (100 mg/kg) significantly lowered the number of splenic antibody-forming cells within 2-5 days following Srbc injection, but within 6-8 days the number of active cells had increased to above control levels. Δ^9-THC retards the initiation of the T-cell immune response without directly affecting the production/release of antibody.

4630 Petersen, B. H.; Lemberger, L.; Graham, L.; and Dalton, B., Psychopharmacol. Commun., *1*(1), 67-74 (1975).

Alterations in the Cellular-Mediated Immune Responsiveness of Chronic Marihuana Smokers.

Chronic marihuana smokers were contrasted with matched non-smokers with respect to the functioning of their humoral and cellular immune systems. The percentage of peripheral T-lymphocytes was lower in marihuana smokers, their lymphocytes responded sluggishly to mitogenic stimulation, and their polymorphonuclear leukocytes were less efficient at phagocytizing yeast cells. The clinical significance of these data is unknown.

268

4631 Petersen, R. C., ed., *Marihuana Research Findings: 1976*, NIDA Research Monograph, 14, 1977. 261 pp.

This report provided the basis for the shorter sixth edition of the *Marihuana and Health Report*. It is intended for those with a need for more specialized information. Each chapter is abstracted according to individual author.

4632 Petersen, R. C., pp. 1-37 in *Marihuana Research Findings: 1976*, NIDA Research Monograph, 14, 1977.

Summary.

Although a lot of research has been conducted, more work is needed in the area of chronic marihuana effects. The author also stresses that the inadequately designed studies indicating the harmless effects of marihuana are overemphasized.

4633 Petersen, R. C., pp. 416-21 in *Chronic Cannabis Use*, edited by R. L. Dornbush, A. M. Freedman, and M. Fink. NY, Annals of the New York Academy of Sciences, V. 282, 1976.

Discussion Paper: Toward a Rationally Based Social Policy on Marijuana Usage.

Social implications of marihuana use are discussed. Emphasis is placed on decriminalization of marihuana, the role of the researcher in shaping drug use social policy, the limitations of current knowledge about persistent use, and areas requiring additional research. Elimination of drug usage appears impractical and social policy should be formulated to minimize drug risks to the individual and society.

4634 Petersen, R. C., pp. 13-18 in *Pharmacology of Marihuana, Vol. 1*, edited by M. C. Braude and S. Szara. NY, Raven Press, 1976.

The Psychosocial Context of Cannabis Research.

A discussion of the beginnings of marihuana research, some psychosocial difficulties of such experimentation, and the relevance of the findings to society are given. The observations represent the progress of the NIMH's marihuana program as summarized in the periodic "Marihuana and Health Reports."

4635 Petit, L.; and Pichon, J., Eur. J. Toxicol. Environ. Hyg., *9*(7), 442-45 (1976).

Sur une Nouvelle Synthese du Δ^9-Tetrahydrocannabinol [A Novel Method for the Synthesis of Δ^9-Tetrahydrocannabinol].

A method for the synthesis of Δ^9-Tetrahydrocannabinol is described. Preparation of the starting materials olivetol (I) and *p*-menthadiene-2,8-ol-1 (II) was first carried out. Then (I) and (II) were reacted together in the presence of *p*-toulene sulfonic acid to give Δ^8-THC which was converted to the isomeric Δ^9-THC.

4636 Petrizilka, T.; Prasad, K. K.; and Schmid, G., Helv. Chim. Acta, *59*(6), 1963-68 (1976).

Transformations of 9-α, 10-α, Epoxy-Hexahydrocannabinol Acetate.

The transformation of 9-α, 10-α, epoxy-hexahydrocannabinol acetate to 9-β-fluoro-10-α -acetoxy-hexahydro-cannabinol, 10-oxo-hexahydrocannabinol acetate and 9-α hydroxy, 10-β -acetoxy-hexahydrocannabinol was carried out. In addition, Δ^8-THC acetate was converted to 9-α -hydroxy-hexahydrocannabinol.

4637 Pfefferbaum, A.; Darley, C. F.; Tinklenberg, J. R.; Roth, W. T.; and Kopell,

B. S., J. Nerv. Ment. Dis., *165*(6), 381-86 (1977).

Marijuana and Memory Intrusions.

During a recall task, marihuana (0.3 mg of THC, p.o.) reduced the number of correct list items recalled and increased the number of intrusions made. These marihuana effects were viewed as "psychological disinhibition" and their implications were discussed.

4638   Piemme, T. E., Med. Aspects Hum. Sex., *10*(1), 85-86 (1976).

Sex and Illicit Drugs.

The effects and possible mechanisms of various drugs on human sexual behavior were presented.   The often reported enhancement of the act by marihuana was explained by the sensation of time expansion and intensified concentration on the sex act.

4639   Pieper, W. A., Fed. Proc., *35*(11), 2254-57 (1976).

Great Apes and Rhesus Monkeys as Subjects for Psychopharmacological Studies   of Stimulants and Depressants.

Experiments involving the use of non-human primates for the evaluation of CNS drugs were described.   THC was among the agents tested and was found to impair spaced responding behavior in chimpanzees.

4640   Pihl, R. O.; Hickcox, P.; and Costa, L., J. Clin. Psychol., *33*(3), 908-11 (1977).

The Discrimination of Marijuana Intoxication.

While users reported experiencing marihuana intoxication at low and high doses, experienced and non-experienced observers detected such an intoxication only after high doses.

4641   Pihl, R. O.; Segal, Z.; and Shea, D., J. Clin. Psychol., *34*(4), 978-82 (1978).

Negative Expectancy as a Mediating Variable in Marihuana Intoxication.

As compared to non-threatened controls, subjects smoking marihuana under the threat of shock experienced attenuated "subjective high," less pleasant environment, and increased pulse rate.

4642   Pihl, R. O.; and Shea, D., J. Clin. Psychol., *34*(4), 982-87 (1978).

Voluntary Heart Rate Changes and the Marihuana "High."

Subjects trained to increase pulse rate experienced "subjective high" in response to marihuana in a similar fashion to that of non-trained subjects.   These results suggested the dissociation of marihuana's psychological and physiological effects.

4643   Pihl, R. O.; Shea, D.; and Caron, P., J. Clin. Psychol., *34*(2), 569-70 (1978).

The Effect of Marihuana Intoxication on Blood Pressure.

Smoking marihuana resulted in "subjective high," increased pulse rate and reduced BP in experienced users.

4644   Pihl, R. O.; Shea, D.; and Costa, L., J. Clin. Psychol., *34*(3), 775-79 (1978).

Odor   and   Marijuana   Intoxication.

Aversive odorous stimulus (burning hair) added to marihuana cigarettes increased "subjective high" and decreased heart rate in previously informed subjects.

4645   Pihl, R. O.; and Sigal, H., J. Abnorm. Psychol., *87*(2), 280-85 (1978).

Motivation Levels and the Marihuana High.

Marihuana resulted in overestimated time perception, increased reaction times and more deficit of paired associate learning task. Under drug influence, subject did not show significant variation of performance as a result of motivation levels.

4646 Pihl, R. O.; and Spiers, P., pp. 93-95 in *Progress in Experimental Personality Research, Vol. 8*, edited by B. A. Maher, NY, Academic Press, 1978.

Individual Characteristics in the Etiology of Drug Abuse.

Research methods investigating personality correlates of drug abusers are complicated and flawed by many factors. Objective and projective personality tests do not discriminate between marihuana users and non-users. Also all marihuana users do not suffer internal anxiety and conflict states. Important issues to consider in studying the addictive personality were also discussed.

4647 Pihl, R. O.; Spiers, P.; and Shea, D., Psychopharmacology, *52*(3), 227-30 (1977).

The Disruption of Marijuana Intoxication.

The disruptive effects of certain extra-pharmacological factors such as aversive noise or music on human marihuana intoxication were investigated. Measures employed, treatment combinations, results and their significance were also discussed.

4648 Pitt, C. G.; Fowler, M. S.; Sathe, S.; Srivastava, S. C.; and Williams, D. L., J. Amer. Chem. Soc., 97(13), 3798-3802 (1975).

Synthesis of Metabolites of Δ^9-Tetrahydrocannabinol.

Synthetic routes are reported for metabolites of Δ^9-THC which have been positively identified in man. 11-OH-Δ^9-THC was obtained in 20% yield from Δ^9-THC. Yield and physical data are reported for other mono- and di-hydroxylated metabolites.

4649 Pitt, C. G.; Hobbs, D. T.; Schran, H.; Twine, C. E., Jr.; and Williams, D. L., J. Label. Compd. Radiopharm., *11*(4), 551-75 (1975).

The synthesis of Deuterium, Carbon-14, and Carrier-Free Tritium Labeled Cannabinoids.

The following labeled cannabinoids, metabolites and novel heptans were prepared using 1',2'-dehydroolivetol and its monomethyl ether, 5'-bromoolivetol, and olivetol-5'-^{2}H$_3$: 5'-bromo-Δ^8-THC, Δ^9-THC-5'-^{2}H$_3$, 4',5'-dehydro-Δ^8 and Δ^9-THC, 4' and 5' OH-Δ^8-THC, Δ^9-THC-11-^{2}H$_3$, Δ^9-THC-11-^{14}C and cannabinol-5'-^{2}H$_3$. The availability of these compounds assists in making detection improvement from nanogram to picogram range and they are especially useful in RIA.

4650 Pitt, C. G.; Seltzman, H. H.; Sayed, Y.; Twine, C. E.; and Willaims, D. L., Tetrahedron Lett., *1*, 37-40 (1978).

A General Synthesis of Side Chain Derivatives of Δ^9-THC.

Side chain derivatives of Δ^9-THC including 1', 2', 3', and 4'-OH-Δ^9-THC were synthesized through the intermediate (6aR, 10aR)-*trans*-3-[1',3'-dithian-2',-yl]-6a, 7, 8, 10a-tetrahydro-6, 6,9-trimethyl-6*H*-dibenzo[b,d] pyran-1-ol t-butyl dimethylsilyl ether. The intermediate compound was used to prepare CBN derivatives. CBD analog of this intermediate was also prepared.

4651 Plotnikoff, N. P., pp. 475-93 in *The Therapeutic Potential of Marihuana*, edited by S. Cohen and R. Stillman. NY, Plenum Medical Book Company, 1976.

New Benzopyrans: Anticonvulsant Activities.

The anticonvulsant activity of benzopyrans SP-141, SP-143 and SP-175 was demonstrated against audiogenic, electroshock and chemically-induced seizures in mice. These DMHP analogs were more protective than DPH against MES seizures in rats. Tolerance to audiogenic seizures only did not occur under any drug treatment.

4652 Poddar, M. K.; Biswas, B.; and Ghosh, J. J., pp. 193-99 in *Drugs Central Synaptic Transmission, (Pap. Symp.) 1974*, edited by P. B. Bradley and B. N. Dhawan. Baltimore, University Park Press, 1976.

Delta-9-Tetrahydrocannabinol and Brain Biogenic Amines.

THC was shown to increase rat whole-brain 5-HT levels at low and high doses while no change was noted in 5-HIAA levels. THC increased DA levels at both dose ranges, but increased or decreased NE levels, depending on dose. Time to maximum change values were given for the above mentioned parameters, as well as a comparison of the effects of chronic versus acute dosing.

4653 Poddar, M. K.; Dewey, W. L.; and Harris, L. S., Fed. Proc., *37*(3), 273 (1978).

The Biphasic Effect of Δ^9-Tetrahydrocannabinol (Δ^9-THC) on the Uptake of Catecholamines into Synaptosomes from Rat Hypothalamus and Corpus Striatum.

Concentrations of 0.05, 0.1 and 0.2 μm Δ^9-THC caused significant increases in the uptake of DA into the rat corpus striatum, but only the middle concentration increased NE uptake. DA and NE uptake into the hypothalamus were increased by 0.1 and 0.2 μm Δ^9-THC. Higher concentrations of this cannabinoid, however, significantly reduced NE and DA uptake into both brain regions.

4654 Poddar, M. K.; Dewey, W. L.; and Harris, L. S., Pharmacologist, *20*(3), 164 (1978).

Cannabinoids: Effects on the Release of Catecholamines from Synaptosomes of Brain Striatum (S) and Hypothalamus (H) (Abstract).

At low concentrations, only Δ^9- and Δ^8-THC inhibited the release of NE and DA in brain striatum and hypothalamus. At higher concentrations, the reverse was true for the above cannabinoids and for CBD and CBN. 11-OH-Δ^9-THC was unique in its effects.

4655 Poddar, M. K.; and Ghosh, J. J., Indian J. Biochem. Biophys., *13*(3), 267-72 (1976).

Effect of Cannabis Extract and Delta-9-Tetrahydrocannabinol on Brain Adenosine Triphosphatase Activity.

In vivo exposure to i.p. cannabis extract (CE) (10 and 50 mg/kg) or Δ^9-THC (10 and 100 mg/kg) inhibited the Na^{++}-K^{++} ATPase of synaptosomes, but stimulated ATPases of microsomes. Direct exposure to either substance inhibited ATPase activity, an effect that was enhanced by prior treatment with deoxycholate. Chronic treatment (10 mg/kg/day for 25 days) resulted in tolerance development.

4656 Poddar, M. K.; and Ghosh, J. J., Indian J. Biochem. Biophys., *13*(3), 273-77 (1976).

Effect of Cannabis Extract and Delta-9-Tetrahydrocannabinol on Rat Brain Catecholamines.

Brains from male rats treated acutely with cannabis extract or Δ^9-THC (10 mg/kg, i.p.) had elevated DA levels, but decreased NE levels. Whole brain increases of both DA and NE were observed after higher doses. Chronic administration (24 days) of each cannabinoid resulted in no change.

4657 Poddar, M. K.; and Ghosh, J. J., pp. 157-76 in *Pharmacology of Marihuana, Vol. 1*, edited by M. C. Braude and S. Szara. NY, Raven Press, 1976.

Neuronal Membrane as the Site of Action of Delta-9-Tetrahydrocannabinol.

The effect of Δ^9-THC on membrane bound enzymes like Na^+-K^+ ATPase, Mg^{++} ATPase, acetylcholinesterase (AChe) and glutamate synthetase (GS) of synaptosomal, mitochondrial and microsomal fractions were examined. Both *in vitro* and *in vivo* THC affected the activities of the above enzymes, probably by changes in phospholipid content. Pretreatment with deoxycholate *in vitro* enhanced the effects of THC. These subcellular changes may help to explain the mechanism of action of THC.

4658 Poddar, M. K.; Ghosh, J. J.; and Datta, J., Sci. Cult., *41*(10), 492-95 (1975).

A Micromethod for the Estimation of Cannabis Components.

Reports a colorimetric method useful for the quantitation of THC, CBN, and CBD. Extracts are separated using TLC, zone scraped, treated with a chromogenic reagent, and the optical density of the complex is then determined at specific wavelengths.

4659 Poddar, M. K.; Mitra, G.; and Ghosh, J. J., Toxicol. Appl. Pharmacol., *46*(3), 737-57 (1978).

Δ^9 - Tetrahydrocannabinol Induced Changes in Brain Ribosomes.

Δ^9-THC, in low doses, stabilized rat brain ribosomes and increased the hydrogen bonded structure in cortical and hypothalamic total RNA. After higher doses or subacute treatment, the reverse was true.

4660 Pohl, K. D., pp. 137-52 in *Themen zur Chemie, Toxikologie and Analytik der Rauschaifte*, edited by K. Maas. Heidelberg, Huethig, 1975.

Forensisch-Toxikologische Aspekte des Erkennens and Identifizierens Naturlicher Rauschmittel, Insbesondere von Cannabis-Praparaten [Forensic-Toxicological Aspects of the Detection and Identification of Natural Intoxicants, Particularly Cannabis Preparations].

A forensic review of natural intoxicants with special attention to cannabis was given. Methods of identification and detection were discussed.

4661 Pomazol, R. J.; and Brown, J. D., J. Health Soc. Behav., *18*(2), 212-22 (1977).

Understanding Drug Use Motivation: A New Look at a Current Problem.

The authors theorize that the tendency to abuse a drug such as marihuana is based on the person's attitude towards the drug and the social and moral norms. A study conducted among 101 university students revealed significant correlation between this theory and occurrence of marihuana abuse. The study also showed that most students who abused marihuana believed that it was good for them and had no harmful effects.

4662 Powell, K. E., Nat'l. Clgh. Poison Control Cent. Bull., *Spring*, 1-4 (1978).

A Summary of Pertinent Medical Information about Paraquat in Marijuana.

It is unlikely for small amounts of paraquat in marihuana to cause adverse pulmonary effects. Such a possibility, however, cannot be guaranteed after chronic use.

4663 Pradhan, S. N., pp. 148-73 in *Drug Abuse 1977*, edited by S. N. Pradhan and S. N. Dutta. St. Louis, Mo., C. V. Mosby Company, 1977.

Marijuana.

A review which includes history, extent and pattern of use in the United States, different preparations and their source, the chemistry of cannabinoids and their SAR. Also, the different pharmacologic effects and pharmacokinetics were discussed. Tolerance, drug interaction and toxicity, both acute and chronic, were reviewed. In addition, comparison of marihuana with other drugs (ethanol and LSD) was made.

4664 Prakash, R.; and Aronow, W. S., Clin. Pharmacol. Ther., *19*(1), 94-95 (1976).

Letter to the Editor.

Reply to the editor maintains that Δ^9-THC per se may cause deterioration of cardiac performance based on the precedence that *in vitro* the cardiac contractility of guinea pig and rat hearts is directly suppressed. Increased heart rate with an elevated afterload in patients with coronary disease also cannot be dismissed from consideration as a cause of inefficient cardiac output in the presence of Δ^9-THC.

4665 Prakash, R.; Aronow, W. S.; Warren, M.; Laverty, W.; and Gottschalk, L. A., Clin. Pharmacol. Ther., *18*(1), 90-95 (1975).

Effects of Marihuana and Placebo Marihuana Smoking on Hemodynamics in Coronary Disease.

Ten patients with classic stable angina pectoris due to coronary artery disease smoked either a marihuana cigarette (18 mg Δ^9-THC) on one morning, or a placebo marihuana cigarette (0.05 mg of Δ^9-THC) on the other morning. Echocardiograms and heart rates were recorded and BP determined immediately and at 10, 15, 20, 30, 60, 90 and 120 min. after smoking.

4666 Prather, J. E.; and Fidell, L. S., Int. J. Addict., *13*(6), 863-85 (1978).

Drug Use and Abuse Among Women: An Overview.

The use and abuse of drugs by females is an understudied research area. Characteristics of female users and factors influencing their use of marihuana are not much different than are those of their male counterparts.

4667 Preston, J., J. Health Soc. Behav., *17*(3), 314-16 (1976).

On Student Marijuana Use and Societal Alienation. Comments.

The author discusses a behavioral study with high school students using marihuana and how the results correlate well with those of a prior study with college students. The major point of agreement is that students who use marihuana tend to alienate themselves from society without personal alienation.

274

4668   Pringle, H. L.; and Bradley, S. G., Fed. Proc., *37*(6), 1651 (1978).

Mechanism of Action of Immunosuppressive Cannabinoids.

In vitro proliferation of *Naegleria fowleri* was effectively inhibited by cannabinoids including Δ^9-THC. Uptake of labeled adenine, uridine, thymidine and leucine by cannabinoid-treated *Naegleria* was inhibited, as was RNA, DNA and protein synthesis. SAR and implications of findings were discussed.

4669   Prioreschi, P., Med. Hypotheses, *3*(6), 265-66 (1977).

On the Abuse of Marihuana and Other Drugs.

The author believes that marihuana should remain forbidden but questions the possible enforcement of its prohibition.

4670   Pruess, M. M.; and Lefkowitz, S. S., Proc. Soc. Exp. Biol. Med., *158*(3), 350-53 (1978).

Influence of Maturity on Immunosuppression by Δ^9-Tetrahydrocannabinol.

Short-term exposure of young mice to Δ^9-THC reduced splenic and body weight. Younger mice were also found to be more sensitive to the immunosuppressive effect of THC than were mature mice.

4671   Pryor, G. T., pp. 543-58 in *Pharmacology of Marihuana, Vol. 2*, edited by M. C. Braude and S. Szara. NY, Raven Press, 1976.

Acute and Subacute Behavioral and Pharmacological Interactions of Δ^9-Tetrahydrocannabinol with Other Drugs.

Acute and subacute administration of Δ^9-THC (5 and 10 mg/kg, i.g.) attenuated the effects of stimulants and potentiated the actions of depressants. None of the 13 drugs tested was able to offset the depressant properties of Δ^9-THC, but tolerance to either Δ^9-THC or the interacting drugs did.

4672   Pryor, G. T.; and Braude, M. C., Pharmacologist, *17*(2), 182 (1975).

Interactions between Δ^9-Tetrahydrocannabinol (THC) and Phencyclidine (PC).

PC (1.25, 2.5, or 5.0 mg/kg, i.p.) had no photocell activity effect at the lower doses. Yet when combined with THC (2.5, 5.0 or 10.0 mg/kg, p.o.) depression was potentiated in the rat. PC alone did not affect heart rate or body temperature but increased these effects with THC.

4673   Pryor, G. T.; Husain, S.; Larsen, F.; McKenzie, C. E.; Carr, J. D.; and Braude, M. C., Pharmacol. Biochem. Behav., *6*(1), 123-36 (1977).

Interactions between Δ^9-Tetrahydrocannabinol and Phencyclidine Hydrochloride in Rats.

THC and phencyclidine (PCP) were found to interact by potentiating the depressant and antagonizing the stimulatory effects of each other. Impairment of conditioned avoidance response performance was greater when the two agents were combined. Subacute treatment with either agent caused tolerance to THC, reverse tolerance to PCP and attenuated their combined effects. Changes in brain or plasma concentrations of either agent were not related to their functional interactions.

4674   Pryor, G. T.; Husain, S.; and Mitoma, C., Pharmacol. Biochem. Behav., *6*(3), 331-41 (1977).

Influence of Fasting on the Absorption and Effects of $\triangle^9$-Tetrahydrocannabinol after Oral Administration in Sesame Oil.

An elaborate study of the absorption and pharmacological effects of THC (10 mg/kg/day) under different conditions of feeding, fasting, vehicles and routes of administration was undertaken. Correlations between tissue levels and certain behavioral responses were made. The possible mechanisms involved were discussed in detail.

4675   Pryor, G. T.; Husain, S.; Mitoma, C.; and Braude, M. C., pp. 171-89 in *Interactions of Drug Abuse*, edited by E. S. Vessell and M. C. Braude. NY, Annals of the New York Academy of Sciences, V. 281, 1976.

Acute and Subacute Interactions Between $\triangle^9$-Tetrahydrocannabinol and Other Drugs in the Rat.

An extensive study utilizing several different behavioral and pharmacological tests was conducted in rats to determine the interactive effects of THC and other classes of compounds both at the acute and subacute levels. Types of tests conducted, experimental designs and results were discussed. The major finding was that the depressing properties of THC predominated most of the time.

4676   Pryor, G. T.; Husain, S.; and Siemens, A. J., Life Sci., *21*(3), 441-49 (1977).

A Comparison of the Disposition of ^{14}C-$\triangle^9$-Tetrahydrocannabinol and ^3H-$\triangle^9$-Tetrahydrocannabinol.

When excretion rates and blood levels in male rat of ^3H-$\triangle^9$-THC were compared with those of ^{14}C-THC given by the same route (intragastric), it was

seen that total blood levels of radio-activity declined faster with the carbon-14 compound. Additional experimentation and consultation led to the theory that tritiated water from metabolism of ^3H-THC was the cause of the problem.

4677   Pryor, G. T.; Larsen, F. F.; Carr, J. D.; and Braude, M. C., Pharmacol. Biochem. Behav., *7*(4), 331-45 (1977).

Interactions of $\triangle^9$-Tetrahydrocannabinol with Phenobarbital, Ethanol and Chlordiazepoxide.

THC (2.5-10 mg/kg) depressed all the pharmacological parameters tested in rats, whereas ethanol, chlordiazepoxide and phenobarbital depressed some but not all of these parameters. When combined with other agents, THC effects were potentiated in some cases, and tolerance to its effects developed after its repeated administration. Other results were also discussed.

4678   Pryor, G. T.; Larsen, F. F.; Husain, S.; and Braude, M. C., Pharmacol. Biochem. Behav., *8*(3), 295-318 (1978).

Interactions of $\triangle^9$-Tetrahydrocannabinol with *d*-Amphetamine, Cocaine and Nicotine in Rats.

The acute reciprocal dose-response interactions between THC and either *d*-amphetamine, cocaine, or nicotine were studied. Parameters compared were: change in conditioned avoidance response, photocell activity, heart rate, temperature and rotarod performance. THC-induced bradycardia and hypothermia seemed to be uniformly augmented by all of the stimulants but the other parameters underwent mixed reactions which were drug dependent. Pharmacokinetics and tolerance were also discussed, as was a 6-day subacute study.

4679   Purnell, W. D.; and Gregg, J. M., Ann. Ophthalmol., 7(7), 921-23 (1975).

Δ^9-Tetrahydrocannabinol, Euphoria and Intraocular Pressure in Man.

Two male volunteers were administered THC i.v. in increments of 1 mg at a rate of 0.2 mg/min. to study the effects on IOP and length of euphoria. IOP was decreased and the effects outlasted the euphoria suggesting that THC may be used clinically.

Q

4680   Quimby, M. W.; and Doorenbos, N. J., J. Miss. Acad. Sci., 22, 82-88 (1977).

Botany of Cannabis sativa L.

The botanical classification of the monotypic genus, cannabis, is outlined. The pattern of growth of this plant in different types of soil is described. The authors also noted that, although the vegetative portion of the plant may show wide variation, the reproductive structures are remarkably alike.

R

4681   Rachelefsky, G. S.; and Opelz, G., Clin. Pharmacol. Ther., *21*(1), 44-46 (1977).

Normal Lymphocyte Function in the Presence of Delta-9-Tetrahydrocannabinol.

Purified Δ^9-THC dissolved in 96% ethanol (20 mg/ml) was added to normal human AB plasma at dilutions ranging from 1:5 to 1:1000. Peripheral blood lymphocytes obtained from heparinized blood were cultured for 4 days at 37°, ^{3}H-thymidine (0.8 µ Ci per culture) was added and the cells incubated overnight, harvested and counted. The inhibitory effect of THC was tested by addition to cultures containing 25 µg or 12. 5 µg phytohemagglutin (PHA), or to one-way mixed lymphocyte cultures of 5 x 10^4 responding cells and 5 x 10^4 irradiated allogeneic cells. Concentrations of THC in the cultures ranged from 0.6 x 10^4 to 10.6 x 10^{-4} M. It was demonstrated that THC had no effect on DNA synthesis or on the response to PHA or on allogeneic lymphocytes.

4682   Rachelefsky, G. S.; Opelz, G.; Mickey, M. R.; Lessin, P.; Kiuchi, M.; Silverstein, M. J.; and Stiehm, E. R., J. Allergy Clin. Immunol., *58*(4), 483-90 (1976).

Intact Humoral and Cell-Mediated Immunity in Chronic Marijuana Smoking.

Chronic THC smoking did not cause appreciable changes in humoral and cell-mediated immunity under controlled experimental conditions.

4683   Radouco-Thomas, S.; Magnan, F.; Grove, R. N.; Singh, P.; Garcin, F.; and Radouco-Thomas, G., pp. 487-98 in *Pharmacology of Marihuana, Vol. 2*, edited by M. C. Braude and S. Szara. NY, Raven Press, 1976.

Effect of Chronic Administration of Delta-1-Tetrahydrocannabinol on Learning and Memory in Developing Mice.

Chronic daily doses (10 mg/kg, i.p.) of THC were administered to young mice in order to study the effects of such treatment on the shuttle box performance in the adult period. Results indicated that such a prolonged treatment in young age induces long-term changes in behavior.

4684   Radouco-Thomas, S.; Magnan, F.; and Radouco-Thomas, C., pp. 481-94 in *Marihuana: Chemistry, Biochemistry, and Cellular Effects*, edited by G. G. Nahas. NY, Springer-Verlag, 1976.

Pharmacogenetic Studies on Cannabis and Narcotics: Effects of Delta-1-Tetrahydrocannabinol and Morphine in Developing Mice.

This work describes acute and chronic behavioral effects of THC in young mice of three highly inbred strains which differ markedly in general arousal level, emotionality and avoidance learning. Comparative data concerning the effect of morphine in the same experimental conditions are also presented.

4685   Radwan, S. S.; and Moore, H. K., Adv. Lipid Res., *14*, 171-211 (1976).

The Lipids of Plant Tissue Culture.

This review presents evidence of the fact that while sterylesters, triglycerides, steroids, phospholipids and glycolipids have been isolated from tissue cultures of *Cannabis sativa*, no traces of squalene or fatty acids have been isolated.

4686   Raft, D.; Gregg, J.; Ghia, J.; and Harris, L., Clin. Pharmacol. Ther., *21*(1), 26-33 (1977).

Effects of Intravenous THC on Experimental and Surgical Pain.

THC (0.022 and 0.044 mg/kg, i.v.) increased the pain detection threshold in dental patients. Its analgesic effects on surgical pain were dose and subject dependent. Implications of the results were discussed.

4687   Ragonese, R. R., Diss. Abstr. Int. B, *37*(10), 5014-15 (1977).

Evaluation of the Effect of Delta-9-Tetrahydrocannabinol on Fetal Development in the Rat.

THC induced weight loss in pregnant rats and their offspring in addition to causing brain damage, poor learning ability in male offspring and hyperactivity in both sexes. These effects also persisted in the second generation. The possible mechanisms involved were further investigated and discussed.

4688   Raifman, M. A.; and Berant, M., Amer. J. Dis. Child., *132*(4), 432-33 (1978).

Flying High with Angel Dust (Letter).

Street marihuana is being diluted with phencyclidine hydrochloride to lower cost. Users and physicians should be aware of this.

4689   Raine, J. M.; Wing, D. R.; and Paton, W. D. M., Eur. J. Pharmacol., *51*(1), 11-17 (1978).

The Effects of Δ^1-Tetrahydrocannabinol on Mammary Gland Growth, Enzyme Activity and Plasma Prolactin Levels in the Mouse.

Δ^9-THC (25 mg/kg, s.c.) administered to pregnant mice suppressed mammary gland growth and lipoprotein lipase activity. It also delayed the rise of plasma prolactin. The latter effect preceeded the former two effects.

4690   Rao, N. G. S.; Poklis, A.; Khalil, S. K. W.; and Schermeister, L. J., Quart. J. Crude Drug Res., *16*(1), 22-28 (1978).

Examination of North Dakota Plants by a Thin Layer Chromatographic Method Used to Identify Cannabis.

Petroleum ether extracts of different plant parts of 118 species of North Dakota plants were examined by TLC using chloroformpetroleum ether (6:4) system and Fast Blue salt B spray reagent. None of the extracts tested showed any colors that could be confused with cannabis. A table of the plants analyzed, parts used and their families is presented.

4691   Rao, N. V. R., Curr. Sci. India, *46*(5), 140 (1977).

1-Nitroso 2-Naphthol as a Spray Reagent for the Detection of Cannabis on Thin Layer Plates.

A spray reagent (1-nitroso-2-napthol), which is specific for phenols, was used for the detection of the phenolic compounds in cannabis.

4692   Rao, S. M.; Swonger, A. K.; and Smith, N., Res. Commun. Psychol. Psychiat. Behav., *1*(3), 381-90 (1976).

The Effects of Δ^8- and Δ^9-Tetrahydrocannabinol (THC) on the Performance of the Rat Shuttle-Box Avoidance Behavior.

Both Δ^9-THC (3.2 to 32 mg/kg) and Δ^8-THC (10 to 100 mg/kg) impaired the acquisition of shock-avoidance behavior and later suppressed avoidance responding in a dose-related fashion with the former being more potent than the latter. Retention tests indicated that only animals treated with the highest dose of $\triangle^8$-THC differed significantly from controls.

4693   Rasmussen, K. E., J. Chromatogr., *109*, 175-76 (1975).

Analysis of Cannabinoids in Cannabis by Means of Gas-Liquid Chromatography and Solid Injection. Improvements to the Method.

Flash evaporation of cannabis plant material in the injector part of a GC may lead to interference of cannabinoid quantitation by the alkanes. A non-polar liquid phase lessens this problem, hence SE-30 is recommended. Column temperature is kept low to hold the compounds on the column during inlet heating. After a fixed time, GC analysis is carried out by heating the column.

4694   Rasmussen, K. E., J. Chromatogr., *114*, 250-54 (1975).

On-Column Silylation of Cannabinoids after Injection of Solid Plant Material and Cold Trapping.

The author describes a method by which a solid injector is used to introduce a sample of plant material into flash heater of a GC. The Volatile components are then flushed onto the column. The volatility of cannabinoid components is enhanced by the formation of TMS derivatives.

4695   Rasmussen, K. E., Medd. Nor. Farm. Selsk., *37*(2), 128-35 (1975).

Quantitative Determination of Heptacosane and Nonacosane in Norwegien-Grown Cannabis Plants.

A method is presented for the determination of the major alkanes in cannabis plant material free from interference by cannabinoids. The alkanes are separated by preparative TLC on silica gel coated glass fiber plates. Squalane is used as an internal standard for the GC analysis on a 3% OV-17 column. Interference of cannabinoids is observed with the OV-17 column but is less of a problem if a OV-1 column is used.

4696   Rasmussen, K. E.; and Aaro, B., Medd. Nor. Farm. Selsk., *39*(1), 22-31 (1977).

A Combination of TLC and GLC Using Direct Transfer of the TLC Spot into Gas Chromatograph.

A technique is described in which materials could be separated on TLC and then the spots transferred with a piece of solid support onto the injector part of the GC for analysis. THC, phenobarbital and aprobarbital were used as test compounds. The volatile substances were trapped on the cold column and the column temperature was raised 2 minutes after application of sample.

4697   Rasmussen, K. E.; Brugaard, G.; and Toennesen, F., Medd. Nor. Farm. Selsk., *39*(1), 12-15 (1977).

The Content of Tetrahydrocannabinol in Cannabis Plants Grown from Birdseeds.

Cannabis plants were cultivated from hemp seeds accessible to the public in Norway. THC content was found to vary depending on the kind of seed employed.

4698   Rasmussen, K. E.; and Herweijer, J. J., Pharm. Weekbl., *110*(5), 91-93 (1975).

Examination of the Cannabinoids in Young Cannabis Plants.

Several variants of greenhouse grown cannabis were assayed at 1, 3, 7, 14, 18, and 21 days of growth. Cannabi-

280

noids were observed only in foliage leaves. Alkanes C^{27} and C^{29} were dominant in cotyledons.

4699   Rawitch, A. B.; Schultz, G. S.; Ebner, K. E.; and Vardaris, R. M., Science, 197(4309), 1189-91 (1977).

Competition of Δ^9-Tetrahydrocannabinol with Estrogen in Rat Uterine Estrogen Receptor Binding.

Radiolabeled Δ^9-THC competitively inhibited the binding of ^{3}H-estradiol to the estrogen receptor in the *in vitro* rat uterine preparation. This data suggests that Δ^9-THC has direct estrogenic activity at least at the molecular level.

4700   Ray, R.; Mohan, D.; Prabhu, G. G.; Nath, L. M.; and Neki, J. S., Drug Alcohol Depend., 3(4), 235-41 (1978).

Psychosocial Correlates of Chronic Cannabis Use.

No adverse psychosocial effects were observed in long-term heavy cannabis users when compared to a matched sample of nonusers. The authors concluded that no cause-effect relationship between cannabis use and social dysfunctioning can be established.

4701   Ray, R.; Prabhu, G. G.; Mohan, D.; Nath, L. M.; and Neki, J. S., Drug Alcohol Depend., 3(5), 365-68 (1978).

The Association Between Chronic Cannabis Use and Cognitive Functions.

Attention, concentration, visual-motor coordination and memory functions of chronic cannabis users did not differ from those of non-users.

4702   Raz, A.; and Goldman, R., Lab. Invest., 34(1), 69-76 (1976).

Effect of Hashish Compounds on Mouse Peritoneal Macrophages.

Peritoneal macrophages were collected from male mice and exposed to either Δ^9-THC or CBD for various time intervals. 15 to 30 μg/ml THC or CBD for 60 to 90 min. caused collapse of cytoplasmic structure. Once exposed to THC or CBD for 15 to 30 min. the effects could not be reversed by washing the cells.

4703   Razdan, R. K.; and Dalzell, H. C., J. Med. Chem., 19(5), 719-21 (1976).

Drugs Derived from Cannabinoids. 6. Synthesis of Cyclic Analogues of Dimethylheptylpyran.

The synthesis of 2 cyclic analogues of DMHP is outlined and some of their pharmacology is described. Unlike DMHP which is very active centrally by the dog ataxia test and is prominently antihypertensive, both cyclic derivatives are essentially inactive on both parameters.

4704   Razdan, R. K.; Dalzell, H. C.; and Herlihy, P., J. Heterocycl. Chem., 13(5), 1101-102 (1976).

Hashish (1): Ceric Ammonium Nitrate Oxidation of $\Delta^{6a,10a}$-Tetrahydrocannabinols (THC's).

Ceric ammonium nitrate oxidation of $\Delta^{6a(10a)}$-THC's was studied and results showed that 10-23% of these were converted to 7-oxo-derivatives, while the 10-oxo-isomers were absent. The biological activities of the 7-oxo-derivatives are given.

4705   Razdan, R. K.; Dalzell, H. C.; Herlihy, P.; and Howes, J. F., J. Med. Chem., 19(11), 1328-30 (1976).

Hashish.   Unsaturated Side-Chain Analogues of Δ^8-Tetrahydrocannabinol with Potent Biological Activity.

Two Δ^8-THC's with modification in the side chain were synthesized starting from 3,5 diacetoxy benzaldehyde. One compound was more active than Δ^9-THC when tested in mice for ataxia and sensory stimuli reactivity. The second compound was less active in both the tests. The MED of those compounds was tested and the results were compared with those of Δ^8-THC and Δ^9-THC.

4706   Razdan, R. K.; Handrick, G. R.; and Dalzell, H. C., Experientia, *31*(1), 16-17 (1975).

A One-Step Synthesis of (-)-Δ^1-Tetrahydrocannabinol from Chrysanthenol.

A single step synthesis of Δ^9-THC is reported using chrysanthenol and olivetol. The intermediate product, which could possibly produce CBC, is described.

4707   Razdan, R. K.; Handrick, G. R.; Dalzell, H. C.; Howes, J. F.; Winn, M.; Plotnikoff, N. P.; Dodge, P. W.; and Dren, A. T., J. Med. Chem., *19*(4), 552-54 (1976).

Drugs Derived from Cannabinoids.   4. Effect of Alkyl Substitution in Sulfur and Carbocyclic Analogs.

Different cannabinoids with the alicyclic ring thiopheno, cyclopenteno, or cyclohexeno were synthesized with the alkyl substituent in various positions. Selected pharmacologic tests in mice, rats, dogs and cats were used for comparing these compounds. These tests included Dopa potentiation, audiogenic seizure activity, mouse fighting, analgesia, sedative-hypnotic and dog ataxia.

4708   Razdan, R. K.; Howes, J. F.; Uliss, D. B.; Dalzell, H. C.; Handrick, G. R.; and Dewey, W. L., Experientia, *32*(4), 416-17 (1976).

(-) - 8-βHydroxymethyl-Δ^1-Tetrahydrocannabinol: A Novel Physiologically Active Analog of Δ^1-Tetrahydrocannabinol.

The (-)-8-β-hydroxmethyl derivative of Δ^1-THC was found to be physiologically active in the dog ataxia test. Its activity was equivalent to that of Δ^1-THC. These results are in contrast to earlier predictions based on SAR which required a methyl group in position 8 for optimal activity.

4709   Razdan, R. K.; Terris, B. Z.; Handrick, G. R.; Dalzell, H. C.; Pars, H. G.; Howes, J. F.; Plotnikoff, N.; Dodge, P.; Dren, A.; Kyncl, J.; Shoer, L.; and Thompson, W. R., J. Med. Chem., *19*(4), 549-51 (1976).

Drugs Derived from Cannabinoids.   3. Sulfur Analogs, Thiopyranobenzopyrans and Thienobenzopyrans.

Sulfur analogs of cannabinoids corresponding to DMHP with various structure types (different ring size and position of the sulfur atom) were prepared and their pharmacologic effects evaluated. The synthesis involved Pechmann condensation between the appropriate keto ester and 5-(1,2-dimethylheptyl) resorcinol. The basic esters of some derivatives were also prepared and tested.

4710   Razdan, R. K.; Terris, B. Z.; Pars, H. G.; Plotnikoff, N. P.; Dodge, P. W.; Dren, A. T.; Kyncl, J.; and Somani, P., J. Med. Chem., *19*(4), 454-61 (1976).

Drugs Derived from Cannabinoids.   2. Basic Esters of Nitrogen and Carbocyclic Analogs.

This paper describes the synthesis of various basic esters of nitrogen and carbocyclic analogs of THC. All compounds synthesized were tested in various species for CNS depression and antinociceptive activity and were found to be pharmacologically active.

4711 Reed, Jr., H. B. C., pp. 121-24 in *Marijuana and Health Hazards*, edited by J. R. Tinklenberg. NY, Academic Press, 1975.

Marijuana and Brain Dysfunction: Selected Research Issues.

Studies conducted to determine the CNS effects of marihuana should be well-planned and should utilize the best measures available. Analysis of data should take into consideration intra-individual effects and should utilize expert opinion. The Halstead battery of tests is the most sensitive method for studying brain dysfunction.

4712 Regelson, W.; Butler, J. R.; Schulz, J.; Kirk, T.; Peek, L.; Green, M. L.; and Zalis, M. O., pp. 763-76 in *Pharmacology of Marihuana, Vol. 2*, edited by M. C. Braude and S. Szara. NY, Raven Press, 1976.

Delta-9-Tetrahydrocannabinol as an Effective Antidepressant and Appetite Stimulating Agent in Advanced Cancer Patients.

The psychological and toxicological effects of chronic administration (0.1-0.34 mg/kg, p.o., q.i.d.) were studied in cancer patients on in- and out-patient basis. Results indicated that THC may be of value as an antidepressant without any psychological side-effects. The clinical observations demonstrated that THC slows or reverses weight loss and possesses some antiemetic and analgesic properties.

4713 Reid, L. D.; and Ibrahim, M. F. K., IEEE Trans. Syst. Man Cybernet., *5*(5), 506-19 (1975).

The Application of Human Operator Describing Functions to Studies on the Effects of Alcohol and Marijuana on Human Performance.

The influence of marihuana and alcohol on some manual tracking tasks was assessed in human subjects using linear mathematical models. Both marihuana and ethanol impaired tracking behavior, increased noise injection and reduced crossover frequency. Interaction between the two agents was also investigated.

4714 Repetto, M.; Lopez-Artiquez, M.; and Martinez, D., Bull. Narcotics, *28*(4), 69-74 (1976).

Separation of Cannabinoids.

A preparative GC technique is described that can be used to separate THC, CBN, and CBD in high yield and purity. The method involves the use of a Perkins-Elmer F-21 GC that is programmed to sense fractions of cannabis resin oil containing the cannabinoid of interest which is then trapped. Details of GC operating conditions are included.

4715 Revuelta, A. V.; Moroni, F.; Cheney, D. L.; and Costa, E., Fed. Proc., *37*(3), 737 (1978).

Effect of Cannabinoids on the Turnover Rate of Acetylcholine and GABA in Rat Brain Areas.

Δ^9-THC and CBD (5 and 20 mg/kg, i.v., respectively) reduced the turnover rate of ACh in rat striatum but not in parietal cortex. Δ^9-THC also decreased hippocampal ACh turnover in a dose-related manner, whereas CBD had no effect. Neither cannabinoid exerted any effect on GABA and glutamate levels.

4716 Revuelta, A. V.; Moroni, F.; Cheney, D. L.; and Costa, E., Naunyn Schmiedebergs Arch. Pharmakol. Exp. Pathol., *304*(2), 107-10 (1978).

Effect of Cannabinoids on the Turn-over Rate of Acetylcholine in Rat Hippocampus, Striatum and Cortex.

Δ^9-THC and CBD at high doses reduced striatal turnover rate of ACh whereas only THC decreased it in the hippocampus in a dose-related manner. Neither agent influenced the turnover rate of ACh in the parietal cortex nor affected its concentrations in all regions studied.

4717 Rickles, W. H.; Cohen, M. J.; Naliboff, B. D.; Klitzner, M. D.; and McIntyre, K. E., Brit. J. Addict., *73*(1), 69-74 (1978).

Measures of Heart Rate and Skin Conductance to Orienting Stimuli During Repetitive Administration of Marijuana.

Smoking marihuana cigarettes (5 or 10 mg of THC/day) for 28 days did not appreciably alter basic and phasic skin conductance or heart rate of male subjects.

4718 Rinder, I. D., Psychiatry, *41*(2), 202-06 (1978).

The Effects of Marijuana: A Social Psychological Interpretation.

A marihuana trip, whether good or bad, depends on the social and psychological status of the user. The well-adjusted person enjoys it as a recreation, while the ill-adjusted does not.

4719 Robertson, L. W.; Koh, S.-W.; Huff, S. R.; Malhotra, R. K.; and Ghosh, A., Experientia, *34*(8), 1020-22 (1978).

Microbiological Oxidation of the Pentyl Side Chain of Cannabinoids.

Microbial transformation products of Δ^8-THC, Δ^9-THC, CBD and CBN were identified when these cannabinoids were incubated with *Syncephalastrum rancemosum* (fungus) and *Mycobacterium rhodochrous* (bacterium) grown on yeast malt extract broth. The cannabinoid metabolites produced by these organisms involve formation of C_3 alcohols or acids as the major products with removal of the two terminal carbons of the pentyl side chain. Other metabolites were also identified.

4720 Robertson, L. W.; Lyle, M. A.; and Billets, S., Biochem. Mass Spectrom., *2*, 266-71 (1975).

Biotransformation of Cannabinoids by *Syncephalastrum racemosum*.

Metabolic transformation by a micro organism of Δ^9-THC, Δ^8-THC, CBN, and CBD was studied. All were shown to lead to a common product. The 4'-OH compound of each of these parent compounds was identified by GC/MS techniques. An analysis of the key ions in the mass spectral fragmentation pattern of these compounds allowed for identification. Other unidentified metabolic products were detected.

4721 Rock, N. L.; and Moore, R. J., Int. J. Addict., *11*(2), 237-44 (1976).

Methaqualone (Mandrax) Abuse, Urine Testing, and Identification: Clinical Correlation Between a New Mass Urinalysis Test and a Military Drug Abuse Program.

Of forty American soldiers showing positive urine tests for methoqualone while stationed in Europe, 14 said they preferred to use hashish with methoqualone and 39 admitted to using hashish.

4722 Rodgers, R.; Crowl, C. P.; Eimstad, W. M.; Hu, M. W.; Kam, J. K.; Ronald, R. C.; Rowley, G. L.; and Ullman, E. F., Clin. Chem., 24(1), 95-100 (1978).

Homogeneous Enzyme Immunoassay for Cannabinoids in Urine.

Using a THC derivative as a hapten and covalently bonding it to pigheart malate dehydrogenase, the authors developed an immunoassay for detection of cannabinoids in urine. The antibodies were raised in sheep following injection of a bovine gamma globulin conjugate of the THC derivative. Details of procedures, calibration, and sensitivities are given.

4723 Roffman, R. A., Contemp. Drug Probl., 6(4), 533-51 (1977).

Marijuana and its Control in the Late 1970's.

Marihuana use is a hotly debated issue. Therefore, the battle between those advocating the status quo and those in favor of reform continues.

4724 Rogers, C.; pp. 154-57 in A Multicultural View of Drug Abuse, Proc. Natl. Drug Abuse Conf., 1977, edited by D. E. Smith, S. M. Anderson, M. Buxton, N. Gottlieb, W. Harvey, and T. Chung. Cambridge, Massachusetts, Schenkman Publishing Co., Inc., 1978.

Drug Use or Abuse? Differential Perceptions of Marijuana in Jamaica.

Jamaicans use "ganja" (cannabis) leaves in three ways: for tea, for tonic, and for smoking. The tea and tonic are mainly used for medicinal purposes such as headache, fever and asthma. With few exceptions, smokers are male and members of the lowest socioeconomic stratum.

4725 Rose, R. M., pp. 63-70 in Marijuana and Health Hazards, edited by J. R. Tinklenberg. NY, Academic Press, 1975.

Background Paper on Testosterone and Marijuana.

Techniques such as competitive protein binding or RIA are used to assay free plasma steroids. Some factors increase, whereas stress, phenothiazines and some opiates decrease the secretion of testosterone. Human data cited did not definitely conclude whether or not marihuana depresses testosterone levels.

4726 Rose, S. E., Diss. Abstr. Int. B., 37(11), 5876-77 (1977).

The Effect of Delta-9-Tetrahydrocannabinol on the Absolute Visual Threshold of the Albino Rabbit.

By the method of limits, dosages of THC were shown to cause significant temporary elevation of visual threshold in the albino rabbit. In connection with this effect, the possibility of THC changing 5-HT levels in the lateral geniculate nucleus or the superior colliculus was discussed.

4727 Rosell, S., Lakartidningen, 73(45), 3864-66 (1976). (Swedish).

Pharmacology of the Cannabinoids.

This review of the pharmacology of cannabis discusses the several pharmacologic activities. In particular it is pointed out that cannabis use can cause a decline in testosterone. (25 references).

4728 Rosell, S.; and Agurell, S., Acta Physiol. Scand., 94, 142-44 (1975).

Effects of 7-Hydroxy-Δ^6-Tetrahydrocannabinol and Some Related Cannabinoids on the Guinea Pig Isolated Ileum.

Δ^8-THC inhibited the electrically induced twitches in the guinea pig isolated ileum, but was 10 times less potent than 11-OH-Δ^6-THC. This inhibition of the twitch is of presynaptic origin. Up to 100 ng/ml, CBD and CBN were without any effect.

4729 Rosell, S.; Agurell, S.; and Martin, B., pp. 397-406 in *Marihuana: Chemistry, Biochemistry, and Cellular Effects*, edited by G. G. Nahas. NY, Springer-Verlag, 1976.

Effects of Cannabinoids on Isolated Smooth Muscle Preparations.

Different cannabinoids were tested for their effects on isolated smooth muscle preparations. The isolated guinea pig ileum appears to be very sensitive to cannabinoids, especially to the 7-hydroxy derivatives. In low concentrations they inhibit the twitch responses produced by electric field stimulation.

4730 Rosenberg, C. M., pp. 173-82 in *The Therapeutic Potential of Marihuana*, edited by S. Cohen and R. Stillman. NY, Plenum Medical Book Company, 1976.

The Use of Marihuana in the Treatment of Alcoholism.

The use of marihuana as a reinforcer for disulfiram in treating alcoholics was investigated. Experiments conducted on humans indicated that such a possibility is feasible.

4731 Rosenberg, C. M.; Gerrein, J. R.; and Schnell, C., J. Stud. Alcohol, *39*(11), 1955-58 (1978).

Cannabis in the Treatment of Alcoholism.

Compared to disulfiram, cannabis did not prove effective in treating alcoholism in human subjects.

4732 Rosenblum, I., in *Committee on Problems of Drug Dependence, 1975.*, Division of Medical Sciences, National Research Council, National Academy of Sciences, Washington, D.C., 1975, pp. 1051-54.

Pharmacologic Actions of a New Series of Tetrahydrocannabinoids.

The cardiovascular and behavioral effects of various synthetic cannabinoids were studied in dogs and monkeys respectively. These synthetic cannabinoids had the basic tetrahydrocannabinol skeleton and only the side chain of carbon 5 was modified. One of the compounds synthesized had the hypotensive effect of Δ^8-THC but had only minimal behavioral effects.

4733 Rosenfeld, J., Anal. Lett., *10*(12), 917-30 (1977).

The Simultaneous Determination of Δ^9-Tetrahydrocannabinol and 11-OH-Δ^9-Tetrahydrocannabinol in Plasma.

A method based on the reactivity of phenolic groups and involving derivatization of the cannabinoids prior to GC-MS analysis, was utilized. Sensitivities were reported to be 5 ng/ml for THC and 1 ng/ml for 11-OH-THC. Since plasma proteins may interfere with this process, extraction efficiencies for 3 solvents were given.

4734 Rosenfeld, J., pp. 87-92 in *Marihuana: Chemistry, Biochemistry, and Cellular Effects*, edited by G. G. Nahas. NY, Springer-Verlag, 1976.

Mass Fragmentographic Assays for the Cannabinoids and their Metabolites.

A mass fragmentographic assay for Δ^9-THC, 11-OH-Δ^9-THC in blood, and for Δ^9-THC metabolites in urine was presented. Derivatization of the different cannabinoids through the formation of their predeuterated methyl ethers as internal standard was developed. An on column methylation procedure for Δ^9-THC and an alkylative extraction procedure for 11-OH-Δ^9-THC were given.

4735   Rosenfeld, J. M.; and Taguchi, V. Y., Anal. Chem., *48*(4), 726-28 (1976).

Mass Fragmentographic Assay for 11-Hydroxy-Δ^9-Tetrahydrocannabinol from Plasma.

Multiple ion monitoring of the molecular ions of $1\text{-}OC_2H_5\text{-}11\text{-}OTMS\text{-}\Delta^9$-THC was used to relate the quantitative determination of 11-OH-Δ^9-THC in plasma. The derivative (*O*-ethylether) is formed with all phenolic compounds in the plasma; this metabolite was not detected in dogs given oral or i.v. doses of Δ^9-THC.

4736   Rosenkrantz, H., pp. 441-56 in *Marihuana: Chemistry, Biochemistry, and Cellular Effects*, edited by G. G. Nahas. NY, Springer-Verlag, 1976.

The Immune Response and Marihuana.

Immunosuppression of the humoral response was observed after oral administration of Δ^9-THC. The present investigation evaluated also this potential interaction of marihuana with the humoral immune pathway under conditions simulating marihuana smoking in man using automatic inhalator. The immunosuppression obtained by the inhalation route was similar to that obtained by corresponding oral doses of Δ^9-THC in the same strain of rat.

4737   Rosenkrantz, H., pp. 141-46 in *Pharmacology of Marihuana, Vol. 1*, edited by M. C. Braude and S. Szara. NY, Raven Press, 1976.

Cellular, Immunological, and Hormonal Effects. Introduction.

The mechanism of cell-mediated and humoral immunity is described, along with the possible points of attack on the defense mechanism. A review of the literature of effects of cannabinoids on immunity and hormonal balance is also presented. Thymus atrophy may be responsible for the lymphocytic and hormonal disturbances seen with cannabinoids.

4738   Rosenkrantz, H.; and Bruade, M. C., Pharmacologist, *17*(2), 181 (1975).

Rat Inhalation Toxicity of Turkish Marihuana.

Turkish marihuana, high in CBD and CBC, was administered to rats daily, 5 days/wk. for 25 days with the doses of CBD + CBC, 1, 1.5 or 2 mg/kg in a 50 ml puff. Cumulative toxicity was noted in both sexes; however, respiratory arrest appeared sooner for the males than the females. At the higher doses in both sexes transaminases and relative organ weights increased.

4739   Rosenkrantz, H.; and Braude, M. C., pp. 571-84 in *Pharmacology of Marihuana, Vol. 2*, edited by M. C. Braude and S. Szara. NY, Raven Press, 1976.

Comparative Chronic Toxicities of Δ^9-Tetrahydrocannabinol Administered Orally or by Inhalation in the Rat

The present study indicates the parallelism of THC effects upon its inhalation or intragastric administration in comparable doses, in inducing changes in several parameters tested. Such a parallelism substantiates the applicability of the oral findings which are generally more practical for use in humans.

4740 Rosenkrantz, H.; Fleischman, R. W.; and Baker, J. R., Toxicol. Appl. Pharmacol., *45*(1), 288 (1978).

Pulmonary Pathology in Rats Exposed to Marijuana Smoke for One Year (Abstract).

Rats exposed to daily marihuana smoke for a year exhibited CNS inhibition followed by stimulation. THC induced pulmonary toxicity that was not reversed for 30 days post-drug exposure.

4741 Rosenkrantz, H.; Fleischman, R. W.; and Baker, J. R., Fed. Proc., *37*(3), 737 (1978).

Embryotoxicity of Marihuana by Inhalation.

No adverse effects on conception rate, dam growth rate, litter size and weight and sex ratio were detected in rats and mice exposed to 0.9, 2.6 and 3.5 mg/kg of Δ^9-THC in marihuana smoke during gestation days 6-15. A significant increase in early resorptions was seen in marihuana-treated mice, and fetal mortality increased in both species.

4742 Rosenkrantz, H.; Hayden, D.; and Braude, M. C., Fed. Proc., *35*(3), 643 (1976).

Inhalation Toxicity of Turkish Marihuana, Cannabichromene (CBCH) and Cannabidiol (CBD) in Rats.

Toxicity of Turkish marihuana was found to be dose related. Acute inhalation LD 50 values for Turkish marihuana, CBD, or CBC were found to be 10, 34, and 32 mg/kg respectively. Tolerance occurred but CNS-stimulation was absent.

4743 Rosenkrantz, H.; Miller, A. J.; and Esber, H. J., J. Toxicol. Environ. Health, *1*(1), 119-25 (1975).

Δ^9-Tetrahydrocannabinol Suppression of the Primary Immune Response in Rats.

Δ^9-THC (1 to 10 mg/kg, p.o.) suppressed both the inductive and productive phases of the primary immune response of rats to an i.p. injection of sheep red blood cells. Implications of the findings were discussed.

4744 Rosenkrantz, H.; Sprague, R. A.; Fleischman, R. W.; and Braude, M. C., Toxicol. Appl. Pharmacol., *32*(2), 399-417 (1975).

Oral Δ^9-Tetrahydrocannabinol Toxicity in Rats Treated for Periods Up to Six Months.

The chronic toxicity of Δ^9-THC given orally 28, 90 and 180 days to Fischer rats at doses of 2, 10 and 50 mg/kg was investigated. Behavioral changes were noted; fighting, aggression, convulsive activity and lethal cumulative toxicity. The ratios of organ/FBW at 50 mg/kg THC increased in most of the vital organs.

4745 Rosenqvist, E.; and Ottersen, T., Acta Chem. Scand. B, *29*(3), 379-84 (1975).

The Crystal and Molecular Structure of Δ^9-Tetrahydrocannabinolic Acid B.

The crystal structure of the cyclohexene and pyran portion of the molecule is found in the half-chair conformation. The bond distances and angles and twist of the benzene ring indicate considerable strain in the aromatic system. Both the phenolic and carboxylic groups are significantly out of the plane through the benzene ring. Hydrogen bonding (intra-molecular) is observed between the carboxylic acid and the pyran oxygen.

288

4746 Rosenthal, D.; Harvey, T. M.; Bursey, J. T.; Brine, D. R.; and Wall, M. E., Biomed. Mass Spectrom., *5*(4), 312-16 (1978).

Comparison of Gas Chromatography Mass Spectrometry Methods for the Determination of Δ^9-Tetrahydrocannabinol in Plasma.

A GC-MS procedure for the detection of Δ^9-THC in plasma is compared with other detection methods.

4747 Rosenthal, M. P., J. Drug Issues, *7*(1), 61-77 (1977).

The Legislative Response to Marihuana: When the Shoe Pinches Enough.

One of the reasons given for the rapid marihuana decriminalization law was the fact that many white American children were convicted. Involved legislative changes were discussed.

4748 Rossi, A. M.; Kuehnle, J. C.; and Mendelson, J. H., Pharmacol. Biochem. Behav., *6*(1), 73-77 (1977).

Effects of Marihuana on Reaction Time and Short-Term Memory in Human Volunteers.

The study was conducted in a hospital research ward for a period of 31 days. There were no statistically significant differences between control and marihuana performance in reaction time, choice reaction time or short-term memory. However, subject performances were significantly correlated from test session to test session during control conditions but not during marihuana smoking conditions.

4749 Rossi, A. M.; Kuehnle, J. C.; and Mendelson, J. H., Pharmacol. Biochem. Behav., *8*(4), 447-53 (1978).

Marihuana and Mood in Human Volunteers.

In a subacute in-hospital study, euphoria increased right before and after marihuana smoking by experienced users while no linear correlation was found between euphoric mood ratings and level of intoxication. Influence of the prevailing mood of other subjects on mood rating of intoxicated subjects was also indicated.

4750 Roth, S. H., Can. J. Physiol. Pharmacol., *56*(6), 968-75 (1978).

Stereospecific Presynaptic Inhibitory Effect of Δ^9-Tetrahydrocannabinol on Cholinergic Transmission in the Myenteric Plexus of the Guinea Pig.

Both Δ^9-THC isomers were effective in depressing the force of contraction of the electrically stimulated longitudinal muscle strip of guinea pig ileum. The (-) isomer was 24.6 times more active than the (+) isomer and maximal effect was reached in approximately 20 min. A presynaptic site of action was proposed due to the failure to depress responses to ACh.

4751 Roth, W. T.; Rosenbloom, M. J.; Darley, C. F.; Tinklenberg, J. R.; and Kopell, B. S., Psychopharmacologia, *43*, 261-66 (1975).

Marihuana Effects on TAT Form and Content.

Seventy-two males with a prior experience with marihuana were administered 20 mg Δ^9-THC orally. A Thematic Apperception Test was given. Intoxicated subjects showed timelessness, discontinuity, non-narrativeness and the stories were shorter. The authors found no correlation between marihuana and increased hostile or sexual thoughts.

4752   Roth, W. T.; Tinklenberg, J.; and Ko-
        pell, B., pp. 255-69 in *The Therapeutic
        Potential of Marihuana*, edited by S.
        Cohen and R. Stillman. NY, Plenum
        Medical Book Company, 1976.

Subjective Benefits and Drawbacks of
Marihuana and Alcohol.

Results of a questionnaire answered by
a sample of professionals indicated that
people use marihuana for its induced
sensory changes and alteration of state
of consciousness, while alcohol is consumed to relieve anxiety and tension.
The major drawback in both cases is the
inability to work.

4753   Roth, W. T.; Tinklenberg, J. R.; and
        Kopell, B. S., Electroencephlogr. Clin.
        Neurophysiol., *42*(3), 381-88 (1977).

Ethanol and Marihuana Effects on
Event-Related Potentials in a Memory
Retrieval Paradigm.

The Sternberg memory retrieval task
was performed by 12 subjects following
THC (0.7 mg/kg) or alcohol administration. Specific changes in performance,
caused by these two agents, were compared to performance under placebo
conditions.

4754   Roth, W. T.; Tinklenberg, J. R.; and
        Kopell, B. S., Psychophysiology, *13*(2),
        168 (1976).

Ethanol and Δ^9-THC Effects on Event-
Related Potentials in a Memory Retrieval Paradigm.

The Sternberg memory retrieval paradigm is used to evaluate the effects of
(0.7 mg/kg, Δ^9-THC or 1.0 ml/kg 95%
ethanol), on event-related potentials
recorded by EEG and EOG leads in 12
men. Δ^9-THC did not alter potential
evoked by a warning tone, nor did it

change the degree of preparedness for
task performance. Δ^9-THC did pro-
long the interval required to recognize
the digit as in or out of a set of digits
and increased reaction time.

4755   Rothschild, M.; Rowan, M. G.; and
        Fairbairn, J. W., Nature, *266*(5603),
        650-51 (1977).

Storage of Cannabinoids by *Arctia
caja* and *Zonocerus elegans* fed on Chemically Distinct Strains of *Cannabis sativa*.

When fed cannabis, *Arctia caja* (moth)
and *Zonocerus elegans* (grasshopper)
were found to store more THC than
CBD in the cuticle and frass, respectively.

4756   Rowan, M. G.; and Fairbairn, J. W.,
        J. Pharm. Pharmacol., *29*(8), 491-94
        (1977).

Cannabinoid Patterns in Seedlings of
Cannabis sativa L. and their Use in the
Determination of Chemical Race.

Seedlings of 12 strains of cannabis
were examined for cannabinoid content. These strains were known to be
either of the THC or the CBD type.
Differentiation of the types could best
be performed at 14 days post-emergence.
The features of a Chinese type were
also discussed.

4757   Rowley, G. L.; Armstrong, T. A.; Crowl,
        C. P.; Eimstad, W. M.; Hu, W. M.; Kam,
        J. K.; Rodgers, R.; Ronald, R. C.; Ruben-
        stein, K. E.; Sheldon, B. G.; and Ullman,
        E. F., pp. 28-32 in *Cannabinoid Assays
        in Humans*, NIDA Research Monograph
        Series, 7, 1976.

Determination of THC and its Metabolites by Emit (Trademark) Homogeneous
Enzyme Immunoassay.

Chemical preparations for a THC hapten and conjugate to produce antibodies are discussed. Percent native enzyme activity was determined according to conjugated THC residues per enzyme. Data are presented for the lowest detectable level of Δ^9-THC and 11-*nor*-Δ^9-THC acid. Usable range was 0.5 ng to 10 ng/ml. Enzyme immunoassays should be possible for Δ^9-THC metabolites in urine with this procedure.

4758   Roy, P. E.; Magnan-Lapointe, F.; Huy, N. D.; and Boutet, M., Res. Commun. Chem. Pathol. Pharmacol., *14*(2), 305-17 (1976).

Chronic Inhalation of Marijuana and Tobacco in Dogs: Pulmonary Pathology.

Pulmonary pathology induced by chronic tobacco (3.2 gm/dog/day) and marihuana (3.0 gm/dog/day) inhalation for 900 days is documented in female beagles relative to non-surgical controls and tracheostomized controls. All treatments caused bronchiolitis with the greatest severity seen in marihuana-treated dogs. Tobacco inhalation decreased pulmonary volume and alveolar surface area to a greater degree than did tracheostomy and marihuana treatments which did not differ.

4759   Rubin, A.; Lemberger, L.; Warrick, P.; Crabtree, R. E.; Sullivan, H.; Rowe, H.; and Obermeyer, B. D., Clin. Pharmacol. Ther., *22*(1), 85-91 (1977).

Physiologic Disposition of Nabilone, a Cannabinol Derivative, in Man.

The distribution of radiolabeled nabilone in man was investigated after i.v. and oral administration. Elimination is via feces (65%) and urine (20%). Nabilone has few of the undesirable effects of cannabinoids. Half life of nabilone is estimated at 1.7 hours; total radioac-tivity half-life is 20.6 hours. Nabilone is rapidly distributed and metabolized by reduction of the 9 keto group plus oxidation at the terminal C_5 on the side chain. Metabolites do not appear to be sulfate or glucuronide conjugates.

4760   Rubin, V., pp. 1-14 in *The Therapeutic Potential of Marihuana*, edited by S. Cohen and R. Stillman. NY, Plenum Medical Book Company, 1976.

Cross-Cultural Perspectives on Therapeutic Uses of Cannabis.

Traditional uses of cannabis in different cultures over the millennia have been very diverse and interesting. Since cannabis has been used therapeutically for such a long time, the possibility of its therapeutic potentials should not be underestimated.

4761   Rubin, V., ed., *Cannabis and Culture*. The Hague and Paris, Mouton Publishers, 1975. 598 pp.

This book is a volume in the World Anthropology series and consists of 35 papers presented at a 1973 conference on Cross-Cultural Perspectives on Cannabis, which was chiefly concerned with social science data on cannabis use.

4762   Rubin, V.; and Comitas, L., Ganja in Jamaica: A Medical Anthropologic Study of Chronic Marihuana Use, The Hague, Paris, Mouton and Co., 1975. 205 pp.

A cultural, physiological and psychological study of cannabis in Jamaica where cannabis is not only smoked for its "high" but used medicinally in other forms. Laborers smoke it before going to work to give themselves more energy.

4763 Russell, G. K., *Proceedings: The Myrin Institute, Inc. for Adult Education, No. 29*, September 1975, 61 pp.

Marihuana Today.

A thorough summary of marihuana is presented including a brief history, a review of pertinent literature and a study of psychological, pharmacological and physiological aspects, in an attempt to bridge the gap between scientific knowledge and public beliefs.

4764 Russell, R. D., J. Stud. Alcohol, *37*(3), 365-74 (1976).

Philosophies for Educating about Alcohol and Other Mood-Modifying Substances. Personal or Social Controls.

Various groups of people of all ages were given a choice of three philosophies and objectives for education about several mood-modifying substances. Overall, the groups tested agreed upon general philosophies pertaining to the various drugs. With respect to marihuana, however, it was seen that high school students differed significantly in their philosophies, as did college students and teachers.

S

4765　Sa, L. M.; Mansur, E.; Aucelio, J. G.; and Valle, J. R., Rev. Brasil. Biol., *38*(4), 863-64 (1978).

Cannabinoid Content of Samples of Marijuana Confiscated in Sao Paulo, Brazil.

A total of 129 confiscated marihuana samples were analyzed by TLC and GC methods for their cannabinoid content. THC and CBN were the major cannabinoids with only traces of CBD. The THC content ranged from 0.16 to 2.45% and CBN from 0.9 to 7.8%.

4766　Sadava, S. W.; and Forsyte, R., Psychol. Rep., *38*, 1119-33 (1976).

Decisions About Drug Use: An Application of the Choice-Shifts Paradigm.

Marihuana tended to cause a greater number of risky decisions in individuals and groups before and after homogeneous group discussions. Males in general and non-users, after discussion in heterogeneous groups, also tended to make riskier decisions.

4767　Sadava, S. W.; and Forsyth, R., Int. J. Addict., *12*(4), 509-28 (1977).

Turning On, Turning Off, and Relapse: Social Psychological Determinants of Status Change in Cannabis Use.

Canadian college students (374) answered two questionnaires on cannabis use six months apart. Data were used to compare new-smokers with nonusers, ex-users with continued users, and non-users with those who continued as ex-users. Personal and social attributes were shown to have considerable predictive utility with respect to status transition.

4768　Salemink, C., pp. 31-38 in *Marihuana: Chemistry, Biochemistry, and Cellular Effects*, edited by G. G. Nahas. NY, Springer-Verlag, 1976.

Pyrolysis of Cannabinoids.

Cannabis produces more immediate and stronger effects when smoked than when taken orally. As a result, the author is interested in studying the products of pyrolysis of CBD under air and then under air and nitrogen using combined GC and MS to identify pyrolytic products.

4769　Salemink, C., pp. 541 in *Pharmacology of Marihuana, Vol. 2*, edited by M. C. Braude and S. Szara. NY, Raven Press, 1976.

Behavioral Interactions: An Introduction.

Research on the interactions between cannabinoids and other substances such as alcohol, along with good analytical methods, are of utmost importance in terms of public health and legal issues.

4770　Salemink, C. A., J. Pharm. Belg., *33*(4), 213-26 (1978).

Developpements Recents dans le Domaine du Cannabis: Aspects Chimiques, Pharmacologiques et Therapeutiques [Recent Developments in the Field of Cannabis: Chemical, Pharmacological and Therapeutic Aspects].

A general survey of the different natural constituents of cannabis (marihuana and hashish) is presented. Interest is directed to the pyrolytic products of CBD, Δ^9-THC, Δ^8-THC and CBN, and where possible their pharmacology is discussed.

4771　Salemink, C. A., Pharm. Weekbl., *112*, 54-59 (1977).

Cannabis.

This paper presents a review of new cannabis constituents and of the pyrolysis products of CBD.

4772   Sallan, S. E.; Zinberg, N.; and Frei, E., pp. 329-35 in *The Therapeutic Potential of Marihuana*, edited by S. Cohen and R. Stillman. NY, Plenum Medical Book Company, 1976.

Antiemetic Effect of Delta-9-Tetrahydrocannabinol in Patients Receiving Cancer Chemotherapy.

THC was found to successfully reduce emesis in cancer patients under chemotherapy.

4773   Sallan, S. E.; Zinberg, N. E.; and Frei, E., III, New Eng. J. Med., *293*(16), 795-97 (1975).

Antiemetic Effect of Delta-9-Tetrahydrocannabinol in Patients Receiving Cancer Chemotherapy.

Twenty-two cancer patients received THC, 10 mg/sq meter body-surface, p.o. before and after chemotherapy. Nausea and vomiting were controlled in all but 19% of the subjects.

4774   Sallan, S. E.; Zinberg, N. E.; and Frei, E., New Eng. J. Med., *294*(3), 168 (1976).

Tetrahydrocannabinol and Chemotherapy (Reply to Comments).

Letter to the editor indicates the equivocal positions of Δ^9-THC as an analgesic agent. Analgesia attributed to Δ^9-THC probably is vastly influenced by set and setting.

4775   Salvendy, G.; and McCabe, G. P., Jr., Hum. Factors, *17*(3), 229-35 (1975).

Marijuana and Human Performance.

Subjects were challenged to perform a manipulative skill task (One-hole test) and a hand-eye coordination task (Rotary Pursuit test) thirty minutes after smoking marihuana. Results demonstrated that marihuana significantly impairs task performance.

4776   Salzman, C., pp. 30-35 in *Side Effects of Drugs Annual 2*, 1978, edited by M. N. G. Dukes. Amsterdam/Oxford, Excerpta Medica, 1978.

Social Drugs.

The respiratory, immunological, hematological, endocrine, cytogenetic, ophthalmological, neurological, and psychiatric side effects of marihuana use were briefly reviewed. The impairment of driving, verbal concentration and other perceptual-motor functions by marihuana was also discussed. 68 references are given.

4777   Salzman, C.; Kochansky, G. E.; Van Der Kolk, B. A.; and Shader, R. I., Amer. J. Drug Alcohol Abuse, *4*(2), 251-55 (1977).

The Effect of Marihuana on Small Group Process.

Although marihuana smoking increased friendliness in small group settings and decreased attention to consensus tasks, subjects were able to control their intoxication and collaborated to solve a problem after a frustration stimulus. Marihuana, however, did not improve creativity.

4778   Salzman, C.; Van Der Kolk, B. A.; Shader, R. I., Amer. J. Psychiat., *133*(9), 1029-33 (1976).

Marijuana and Hostility in a Small-Group Setting.

Data from current research show that marihuana decreases hostile feelings and hostile verbal expressions in human subjects. Suggestions for future improvements in aggression research is presented.

4779 Sarkar, C.; and Ghosh, J. J., J. Neurochem., 24(2), 381-85 (1975).

Effect of Delta-9-Tetrahydrocannabinol Administration on the Lipid Constituents of Rat Brain Subcellular Fractions.

The composition and content of lipids in the mitochondrial, synaptosomal and myeline fractions are significantly decreased in rats treated with an acute dose of Δ^9-THC (10 mg/kg, i.p.). The decrease of the lipid content in all 3 subfractions was less after chronic administration of Δ^9-THC. In the microsomal fraction, Δ^9-THC (acute treatment) increased all lipid components and under chronic treatment there was a tendency towards normalization.

4780 Sarkar, C.; and Ghosh, J. J., J. Neurochem., 26(4), 721-23 (1976).

Effect of Delta-9-Tetrahydrocannabinol on Gangliosides and Sialoglycoproteins in Subcellular Fractions of Rat Brain.

Acute Δ^9-THC (10 and 50 mg/kg) elevated rat brain microsomal and synaptosomal sialoglycoproteins and ganglioside levels while decreasing their mitochondrial levels. Repeated low dose-treatment for 15 days increased synaptosomal levels of gangliosides and sialoglycoproteins.

4781 Sarma, N. P.; Samba Murty, A. V. S. S.; and Mohan Ram, H. Y., J. Cytol. Genetics, 11, 91-93 (1976).

Sex and Chiasma Variance in *Cannabis*.

The influence of sex genotype on chiasma frequency was studied in female cannabis plants treated with gibberellin to produce male flowers. Lower chiasma frequency for male than female genotypes was indicated.

4782 Sassenrath, E. N.; and Chapman, L. F., Fed. Proc., 34(8), 1666-70 (1975).

Tetrahydrocannabinol-Induced Manifestations of the "Marihuana Syndrome" in Group-Living Macaques.

In chronic marihuana administration to primates at a drug level comparable to heavy use in man, no testosterone depression in males nor derangement in the reproductive system of the females were noticed. Initial short term use of the drug mimicked many aspects of "marihuana high" in man, while chronic administration did not produce any effects comparable to chronic marihuana syndrome in humans.

4783 Sassenrath, E. N.; and Chapman, L. F., Fed. Proc., 35(11), 2238-44 (1976).

Primate Social Behavior as a Method of Analysis of Drug Action: Studies with THC in Monkeys.

Acute administration of Δ^9-THC (0.6-2.4 mg/kg, p.o.) to group-caged rhesus monkeys produced sedation, excitation and a tendency toward decreased social interaction, although some dominant animals became excessively belligerent. Chronic Δ^9-THC administration (2.4 mg/kg), however, traced its psychoactive effects from acute intoxication through behavioral tolerance to the stage of irritable aggressiveness.

4784 Satz, P.; Fletcher, J. M.; and Sutker, L. S., pp. 266-306 in *Chronic Cannabis Use*, edited by R. L. Dornbush, A. M. Freedman, and M. Fink. NY, Annals of the New York Academy of Sciences, V. 282, 1976.

Neuropsychologic, Intellectual, and Personality Correlates of Chronic Marijuana Use in Native Costa Ricans.

The neuropsychologic functions, intelligence and personality of Costa Rican chronic marihuana users did not differ significantly from those of matched non-users. Chronic marihuana use did not impair intelligence or cause irreversible brain damage.

4785 Savaki, H. E.; Cunha, J.; Carlini, E. A.; and Kephalas, T. A., Bull. Narcotics, *28*(2), 49-56 (1976).

Pharmacological Activity of Three Fractions Obtained by Smoking Cannabis Through a Water Pipe.

The pharmacological activity of the six chemical fractions obtained by smoking cannabis through a water pipe was determined. The most active fraction of cannabis smoke was water-insoluble and was condensed on top of the water phase. The highly volatile fraction which probably reaches the human lung was moderately active.

4786 Saxena, K. K.; Tayal, G.; Srivastava, R. K.; and Srivastava, V. K., Indian J. Physiol. Pharmacol., *20*(2), 116 (1976).

Analgesic Activity of Cannabis.

Δ^9-THC caused significant analgesic activity as tested by analgesiometer, clip method and aconitine-induced writhing in mice.

4787 Schaefer, C. F.; Gunn, C. G.; and Dubowski, K. M., New Eng. J. Med., *292*(16), 867 (1975).

Normal Plasma Testosterone Concentrations After Marihuana Smoking.

Placebo, 10 mg and 20 mg of THC in cigarettes were administered to men for 4 days. 30 to 90 minutes after smoking, blood samples were taken and no significant decrease in testosterone levels was found.

4788 Schaefer, C. F.; Gunn, C. G.; and Dubowski, K. M., New Eng. J. Med., *293*(2), 101 (1975).

Marihuana Dosage Control Through Heart Rate.

To better control the amount of THC a subject smokes, continuous monitoring of the heart rate is suggested. Heart rate already verifies the presence of THC in the plasma.

4789 Schaefer, C. F.; Gunn, C. G.; and Dubowski, K. M., Percept. Motor Skills, *44*(1), 3-16 (1977).

Dose-Related Heart-Rate, Perceptual, and Decisional Changes in Man Following Marihuana Smoking.

Marihuana smoking, in doses evoking strong subjective high effects in humans, caused an increase in the heart rate, impaired circle-counting performance and slowed complex reaction times. No effect on field-dependence was detected.

4790 Schaeffer, G. M.; Schuckit, M. A.; and Morrissey, E. R., Psychol. Rep., *39*(3), 915-19 (1976).

Correlation Between Two Measures of Self-Esteem and Drug Use in a College Sample.

Marihuana or light alcohol users showed no difference in self-esteem. Heavy alcohol use was however, associated with low self-esteem.

4791   Schenk, J., Int. J. Addict., *12*(4), 459-69 (1977).

Structure of Drug Use and Drug Definition Among Youth.

The results of a study of drug abuse in Germany by young men is presented. The population tested rated marihuana health hazards equal to cigarette smoking, but less than hallucinogens and opiates. Most opiate users and young men smoked marihuana.

4792   Scherrman, J. M.; Hoellinger, H.; Nguyen-Hoang-Nam; Bourdon, R.; and Fournier, E., Clin. Chim. Acta, *79*(2), 401-409 (1977).

Method for the Detection and Quantitation of Delta-9-Tetrahydrocannabinol in Plasma by Dansylation and Double Labeling.

A method is reported for quantitating Δ^9-THC when added to plasma. Dansylation of Δ^9-THC with a tagged [^{14}C] atom is discussed in detail. Labeled Δ^9-THC, [^{3}H], is the internal standard. Purification is by TLC. Sensitivity is 2.5 ng and reproducibility is 10%.

4793   Schlegel, R. P., Can. J. Behav. Sci., *7*(4), 387-96 (1975).

Multidimensional Measurement of Attitude Towards Smoking Marijuana.

A multidimensional approach to measuring attitudes toward smoking marihuana was described. This system may be predictive to behavioral types predisposed to marihuana use and may aid in programs to dissuade drug use.

4794   Schmeling, W. T.; and Hosko, M. J., Arch Int. Pharmacdyn. Ther., *227*(2), 302-08 (1977).

Blockade of Δ^9-THC Induced Hypothermia in Rats.

Both 6-hydroxydopamine and hexamethonium blocked Δ^9-THC (10 mg/kg, i.p.) induced hypothermia in rats.

4795   Schmeling, W. T.; and Hosko, M. J., Fed. Proc., *34*(3), 782 (1975).

The Effect of Tetrahydrocannabinols on Thermoregulatory Response of Hypothalamus and Spinal Cord.

Unanesthetized cats, given 100 μgm of either Δ^9-THC, 11-OH-Δ^9-THC, or the dimethyl-heptyl analogue of THC (DMHP) intracerebrally into the anterior hypothalamus, exhibited no changes in body temperature. I.v. administration of all three cannabinoids (0.5-2.0 mg/kg) depressed body temperatures by 2-7°. By the same route Δ^9-THC (0.25-2.0 mg/kg, i.v.) blocked shivering of anteriod hypothalamic and spinal cord origin.

4796   Schmeling, W. T.; and Hosko, M. J., Fed. Proc., *36*(3), 1026 (1977).

Tetrahydrocannabinol (THC) Induced Hypothermia: Evidence for a Caudal-Brain Stem Site of Action.

Microinjection of Δ^9-THC into the cisterna magna of cats resulted in maximum hypothermia. Evidence suggested a medullary site of action.

4797   Schmeling, W. T.; and Hosko, M. J., Fed. Proc., *37*(3), 737 (1978).

The Effect of Δ^9-Tetrahydrocannabinol (Δ^9-THC) on Centrally Mediated Homeostatic Cardiovascular Reflexes.

Δ^9-THC (1-2 mg/kg, i.v.) attenuated the pressor response to carotid occlusion as well as the depressor response elicited by carotid sinus nerve stimulation in cats. These and other findings suggested an alteration of autonomic outflow from central cardiovascular control centers by Δ^9-THC.

4798 Schmeling, W. T.; and Hosko, M. J., Pharmacol. Biochem. Behav., 5(1), 79-83 (1976).

Hypothermia Induced by Δ^9-Tetrahydrocannabinol in Rats With Electrolytic Lesions of Preoptic Region.

Δ^9-THC (5 and 10 mg/kg, i.p.) induced hypothermia in sham-operated and preoptic region-lesioned rats. Such an effect, however, was nore intense and lasted longer in lesioned rats.

4799 Schmeling, W. T.; and Hosko, M. J., Pharmacologist, 17(2), 181 (1975).

Δ^9-Tetrahydrocannabinol (THC) and Regio Pre Optica (RPO) Thermoregulation in Rats.

The site of action of THC, a potent poikilothermic agent does not appear to be at RPO. However, this area does modify the duration and magnitude of the hypothermia induced by THC as shown by administering THC i.p. (5 and 10 mg/kg).

4800 Schneider, R. J.; Sangsingkeo, P.; Panpanya, B.; Tumrongrachaniti, S.; and Witayarut, C., Int. J. Addict., 11(1), 175-85 (1976).

Incidence of Daily Drug Use as Reported by a Population of Thai Partners Working Near United States Military Installations: A Preliminary Study.

497 Thai prostitutes who reported to a V.D. clinic for examination were interviewed about their drug habits and those of their American soldier partners. Of the 82 subjects reporting current drug use, 22% admitted using marihuana.

4801 Schoenfeld, R. I., Science, 192(4241), 801-03 (1976).

Lysergic Acid Diethylamide- and Mescaling-Induced Attenuation of the Effect of Punishment in the Rat.

While LSD and mescaline attenuated the effect of electric shock on rat licking behavior, both THC and dimethyltryptamine were ineffective. The possible mechanisms involved were discussed.

4802 Schoolar, J. C.; Ho, B. T.; and Estevez, V. S., pp. 63-70 in Marihuana: Chemistry, Biochemistry, and Cellular Effects, edited by G. G. Nahas. NY, Springer-Verlag, 1976.

Comparison of Various Solvent Extractions for the Chromatographic Analysis of Delta-9-Tetrahydrocannabinol and its Metabolites.

Methanol compared to iso-amylalcohol in n-heptane followed by diethyl ether and petroleum ether followed by ether, with methanol. Methanol appears to be the solvent of choice if total recovery of metabolites from biological systems is desired.

4803 Schou, J.; Prockop, L. D.; Dahlstrom, G.; and Rohde, C., Acta Pharmacol. Toxicol., 41(1), 33-38 (1977).

Penetration of Delta-9-Tetrahydrocannabinol and 11-OH-Delta-9-Tetrahydrocannabinol Through the Blood-Brain Barrier.

Unlike 11-OH-THC, the uptake of THC by rat brain decreased when plasma was used as a vehicle instead of saline. Implications of the findings were discussed.

4804   Schultes, R. E., J. Psychedelic Drugs, 9(3), 247-63 (1977).

The Botanical and Chemical Distribution of Hallucinogens.

The author gives a brief and general discussion of cannabis covering origin, botany, early chemistry, early biodynamic activity, and legal aspects.

4805   Schultes, R. E., pp. 41-70 in *Principles of Psychopharmacology*, 2nd ed., edited by W. G. Clark and J. del Giudice. New York, Academic Press, 1978.

Ethnopharmacological Significance of Psychotropic Drugs of Vegetal Origin.

The multipurpose use of cannabis is abundant in both the new and old world. Knowledge about the plant is, however, still lacking.

4806   Schurr, A.; and Livne, A., Biochem. Pharmacol., 25(10), 1201-03 (1976).

Differential Inhibition of Mitochondrial Monoamine Oxidase from Brain By Hashish Components.

Preincubation with Δ^9-THC and hashish extract (HE), but not with CBD, inhibited brain MAO. CBD did diminish the inhibitory actions of Δ^9-THC and HE when administered concurrently. None of the three components affected hepatic MAO activity in spite of prolonged preincubations with each. Differential sensitivity between two MAO's is observed.

4807   Schurr, A.; and Livne, A., Isr. J. Med. Sci., 12(2), 176 (1976).

Inhibition of Mitochondrial Monoamine Oxidase by Hashish Components, Showing Tissue Selectivity.

Brain MAO is inhibited noncompetitively by both Δ^9-THC and CBD although the magnitude of Δ^9-THC inhibition is greater. Neither compound inhibited liver MAO.

4808   Schurr, A.; Porath, O.; Krup, M.; and Livne, A., Biochem. Pharmacol., 27(21), 2513-17 (1978).

The Effects of Hashish Components and Their Mode of Action on Monoamine Oxidase from the Brain.

Δ^9-THC was a much more potent inhibitor of MAO activity of brain mitochodria than was CBD. The degree of inhibition varied with types of substrates used and was completely dependent upon the presence of the enzymes' phospholipids.

4809   Schut, J.; and Steer, R. A., in *Committee on Problem of Drug Dependence, 1976*. Division of Medical Sciences, National Research Council, National Academy of Sciences, Washington, D. C., 1976, pp. 655-66.

Differentiation of Heroin Addicts by Marijuana Use.

The background characteristics of a large number of heroin addicts were investigated. Addicts reporting the use of marihuana in addition to heroin had a different background from non-marijuana users. Implications of the findings were discussed.

4810   Schwam, J. S.; Stein, J. I.; and Winn, F. J., Compr. Psychiat., 17(1), 125-33 (1976).

A Drug-Abuse Program at a U.S. Army Post.

This paper is a report on the results and significance of a pilot program for contacting and helping drug abusers in the U.S. Army. Only four patients presented marihuana problems.

4811 Schwarz, S.; Harclerode, J.; and Nyquist, S. E., Life Sci., *22*(1), 7-13 (1978).

Effects of Δ^9-Tetrahydrocannabinol Administration on Marker Proteins of Rat Testicular Cells.

Effects of THC on various cell types of testicular tissues were investigated in rats. THC induced a substantial reduction of microsomal cytochrome P-450 along with a significant reduction of gamma glutamyl transpeptidase activity. Other protein markers were also studied.

4812 Schweitzer, G.; and Levin, A., S. Afr. J. Med. Sci., *50*(34), 1311 (1976).

Cannabis Related Acute Brain Syndrome Following Major Trauma.

Cessation of dagga consumption because of surgical intervention precipitates an abstinence syndrome in man. Citations for tolerance to and physical dependence on cannabis are given.

4813 Seffrin, J. R.; and Seehafer, R. W., J. Sch. Health, *46*(5), 263-68 (1976).

A Survey of Drug Use Beliefs, Opinions and Behaviors Among Junior and Senior High School Students. Part One: Group Data.

Among this sample of high school students, alcohol rather than marihuana, was the most frequently used substance. Reasons for drug use were mainly the desire for fun and recreation and knowledge of the particular drug.

4814 Seffrin, J. R.; and Seehafer, R. W., J. Sch. Health, *46*(7), 413-16 (1976).

Multiple Drug-Use Patterns Among a Group of High School Students: Regular Users vs. Nonusers of Specific Drug Types.

Marihuana users, among this sample of high school students, also used barbiturates and amphetamines in roughly 50% of the cases. Patterns of drug use were pointed out and, in general, users of one drug were more likely to use other drugs.

4815 Segal, B., J. Alcohol Drug Educ., *22*(3), 64-69 (1977).

Reasons for Marijuana Use and Personality: A Canonical Analysis.

The relationship between personality variables and marihuana use was studied by means of canonical analysis. More than one interrelated factor was found to exist. Implications of findings were discussed.

4816 Segal, M., Brain Res., *139*, 263-75 (1978).

The Effects of SP-111, A Water-Soluble THC Derivative, on Neuronal Activity in the Rat Brain.

SP-111 (10-20 mg/kg, i.p.) induced a behavioral syndrome similar to that caused by Δ^9-THC. Unlike CBD, both SP-111 and THC reduced the spontaneous activity of cells in the hippocampus with a single-spike firing pattern without affecting firing of bursting neurons. Other aspects of SP-111 effects on neuronal activity in the rat brain were also investigated.

4817 Segal, M.; Edelstein, E. L.; and Lerer, B., Experientia, *34*(5), 629 (1978).

Interaction Between Delta-6-Tetrahydrocannabinol (Δ^6-THC) and Lithium at the Blood Brain Barrier in Rats.

Treatment of rats with Δ^6-THC acutely (10 mg/kg, i.p.) or subacutely (1 mg/kg/day for 7 days) did not alter blood or brain lithium concentrations.

4818 Segawa, T.; Bando, S.; and Hosokawa, M., Jap. J. Pharmacol., *27*(4), 581-82 (1977).

Brain Serotonin Metabolism and Δ^9-Tetrahydrocannabinol-Induced Muricide Behavior in Rats.

The muricidal behavior induced in rats by THC was found to be associated with decreased central serotonergic activity.

4819 Segawa, T.; Takeuchi, S.; and Nakano, M., Jap. J. Pharmacol., *26*(3), 377-79 (1976).

Mechanism for the Increase of Brain 5-Hydroxy-Tryptamine and 5-Hydroxyindoleacetic Acid Following Δ^9-THC Administration to Rats.

Δ^9-THC (10 mg/kg, i.p.) increased whole brain 5-HT and 5-HIAA. THC also antagonized tetrabenazine-induced release of 5-HT but not its elevation of 5-HIAA, all in Wistar rats. S-D rats treated with THC (20 mg/kg) or probenecid had elevated 5-HIAA levels, but their combined administration did not produce additive effects.

4820 Segelman, A. B.; and Segelman, F. P., J. Chromatogr., *123*(1), 79-100 (1976).

Cannabis sativa L. (Marijuana). VII. The Relative Specificity of the RIM Test.

In order to test the specificity of the RIM testing procedure a total of 526 non-marihuana plants are investigated for cannabinoid content. Those which give positive tests for the Fast Blue B reagent can be distinguished from cannabinoids on the basis of TLC chromatography retention indices.

4821 Segelman, A. B.; Segelman, F. P.; Star, A. E.; Wagner, H.; and Seligmann, O., Phytochemistry, *17*(4), 824-26 (1978).

Structure of Two *C*-Diglycosylflavones from *Cannabis sativa*.

The isolation of orientin, 2"-*O*-glucopyranosylorientin and 2"-*O*-glucopyranosylvitexin from cannabis leaves was described. The structure identification was done by spectral means, hydrolysis and preparation of permethylethers and peracetates.

4822 Segelman, A. B.; Segelman, F. P.; Varma, S. D.; Wagner, H.; and Seligmann, O., J. Pharm. Sci., *66*(9), 1358-59 (1977).

Cannabis sativa L. (Marijuana) IX: Lens Aldose Reductase Inhibitory Activity of Marijuana Flavone *C*-Glycosides.

Three flavone *C*-glycosides from *Cannabis sativa* were isolated and checked for possible inhibition of an enzyme thought to be involved in some kinds of cataracts, lens aldose reductase. Although two of these glycosides were relatively weak inhibitors of the *in vitro* enzyme system from the rat, one was a powerful inhibitor. Structures are given.

4823 Seiden, R. H.; Tomlinson, K. R.; and O'Carroll, M., Amer. J. Pub. Health, *65*(6), 613-21 (1975).

Patterns of Marijuana Use Among Public Health Students.

Graduate public health students were surveyed via a questionnaire to discover their patterns of marihuana use, their beliefs about use, knowledge of effects and opinions on legalization of marihuana. The degree and pattern of marihuana use were similar to a survey administered to Boalt Law School students in 1969.

4824   Senchenko, G. I.; Sazhko, M. M.; and Gorshkova, L., Tr.-Vses. Nauchno-Issled. Inst. Lub. Kul't., *38*, 39-44 (1975).

Method for Determining the Cannabinoid Content of Cannabis. (Rus.)

Δ^9-THC and CBD contents increased upon heating hemp samples. CBN content tended to decline.

4825   Sengupta, D.; Chakravarty, I.; Datta, S. C.; and Ghosh, J. J., Indian J. Biochem. Biophys., *14*(1), 93-94 (1977).

Effect of Delta-9-Tetrahydrocannabinol on Rat Intestinal ATPases.

After 10 days of daily administration, Δ^9-THC (10 and 20 mg/kg, s.c.) inhibited ATPase activity in the gastrointestinal tract of rat.

4826   Sethi, V. K.; Jain, M. P.; and Thakur, R. S., Planta Med., *32*(4), 378-79 (1977).

Chemical Investigation of Wild *Cannabis sativa L.* Roots.

Studies on petrol and benzene extracts of the roots of *Cannabis sativa L.* resulted in isolation and characterization of friedelin, epifriedelinol, β-sitosterol, carvone and dihydrocarvone. The chloroform extract of the ammoniacal water treated roots led to the isolation of some basic constituents.

4827   Seyfeddinipur, N., Munch. Med. Wochenschr., *117*(12), 477-82 (1975).

Klinische und Elektroenzephalographische Beobachtungen bei Akuter Haschisch-Wirkung [Clinical and Electroencephalographic Observations During the Acute Action of Hashish].

Thirty volunteers (21 to 36 yrs.) who had never smoked hashish before, were tested before and after smoking hashish (25-50 μg/kg). The electroencephalogram showed no pathological changes, but the heart rate was raised and the BP decreased. A reaction of fear occurred after acute hashish intoxication.

4828   Shanahan, M. G., Police Chief, *45*(11), 44-45 (1978).

Comments on Decriminalizing Marijuana.

Decriminalization of marihuana contradicts the fundamental rules of law and order, limits police officers and tampers with justice mechanisms.

4829   Shanker, R.; Dogra, R. K. S.; Gupta, B. N.; and Clerk, S. H., Indian J. Exp. Biol., *16*(6), 671-74 (1978).

Effect of Hemp Dust (*Cannabis sativa Linn.*) on Lungs and Lymph Nodes of Guinea Pigs.

Intratracheal cannabis dust administered to guinea pigs on days 1, 7 and 15 resulted in allergic responses consisting of acute pulmonary inflammatory reactions which were reversible with time. The paracortical areas of the tracheobronchial lymph nodes, however, developed immunoblasts and later the nodes became markedly swollen and exhibited a pronounced increase in lymphocytes.

4830   Shannon, H. E.; Martin, W. R.; and Silcox, D., Life Sci., *23*(1), 49-54 (1978).

302

Lack of Antiemetic Effects of Δ^9-Tetrahydrocannabinol in Apomorphine-Induced Emesis in the Dog.

Δ^9-THC (0.003-0.3 mg/kg, i.v.) had no effect on the total dose of apomorphine required to produce emesis in dogs and on the apomorphine-induced stimulation of pulse rate. Dose-related increases in the duration of emesis were also observed following Δ^9-THC administration.

4831   Shapiro, B. J.; Reiss, S.; Sullivan, S. F.; Tashkin, D. P.; Simmons, M. S.; and Smith, R. T., Chest, 70(3), 441 (1976).

Cardiopulmonary Effects of Marihuana Smoking During Exercise.

Various cardiovascular and pulmonary parameters were monitored in exercising subjects who had just smoked marihuana. A decrease in exercise tolerance in some of the marihuana group was found.

4832   Shapiro, B. J.; and Tashkin, D. P., pp. 277-89 in *Pharmacology of Marihuana, Vol. 1*, edited by M. C. Braude and S. Szara. NY, Raven Press, 1976.

Effects of β-Adrenergic Blockage and Muscarinic Stimulation on Cannabis Bronchodilation.

Smoking of Δ^9-THC (0.07-0.14 mg/kg) and oral administration (10-20 mg) of Δ^9-THC produced significant dose-related bronchodilation in normal humans. Evidence is also presented to show that this bronchodilation is mediated neither by antimuscarinic action nor by β-adrenergic agonist action.

4833   Shapiro, B. J.; Tashkin, D. P.; McLatchie, C. C.; and Rosenthal, D. L., pp. 685-88 in *Pharmacology of Marihuana, Vol. 2*, edited by M. C. Braude and S. Szara. NY, Raven Press, 1976.

Sputum Cytology Following Subacute Marihuana Smoking in Healthy Males.

Sputum specimens were collected from 17 male subjects before smoking, on days 10 and 25 of smoking cigarettes containing 0, 1 or 2% THC and 3 days post-smoking. No correlation was found between the number of cigarettes smoked and scores for sputum characteristics.

4834   Shapiro, B. J.; Tashkin, D. P.; and Vachon, L., Chest, 71(4), 558-59 (1977).

Tetrahydrocannabinol as a Bronchodilator. Why Bother?

Despite several disadvantages of THC use as a bronchodilator, the potential therapeutic application of other cannabinoids should be explored.

4835   Shapiro, C. M.; Orlina, A. R.; Unger, P. J.; Telfer, M.; and Billings, A. A., Clin. Res., 23(4), 488A (1975).

Marihuana Induced Antibody Response and Laboratory Correlates.

The indirect Coombs' test was found positive in 167 out of 170 tests performed on 34 habitual marihuana smokers. Abnormal liver function tests, depressed IgA and elevated reticulocyte count were also detected in these subjects. It is concluded that marihuana is antigenic and capable of eliciting an antibody response.

4836   Shapiro, C. M.; Orlina, A. R.; Unger, P. J.; Telfer, M.; and Billings, A. A., J. Lab. Clin. Med., 88(2), 194-201 (1976).

Marihuana-Induced Antibody Response.

Human subjects who had previously been exposed to marihuana were shown to have humoral antibodies to marijuana,

Δ^9-THC, CBN, CBD and Δ^8-THC by an indirect Coomb's technique. Routine laboratory tests revealed an abnormally high rate of reticulocytosis in marihuana users.

4837   Sharma, B. P., Brit. J. Psychiat., *127*, 550-52 (1975).

Cannabis and its Users in Nepal.

The groups studied were graduates, undergraduates, high school students, barely literates and illiterates. The users who had jobs were irregular or unpunctual in attendance and were dominated by superiors and subordinates. Users felt no need for a job. All the controls were employed. Conversation of cannabis users was full of unnecessary details and monotonous. Their personal appearance was unkempt, they had a passive, docile nature, and family relations were poor. No difference was seen between the groups in crime rate.

4838   Sharma, G. K., A. S. B. Bull., *25*(2), 83 (1978).

Ecotypic Variations in Cannabis (Cannabinaceae). (Abstract)

A description of the morphological features and habitat of cannabis grown in the Himalayas is given.

4839   Sharma, G. K., Bot. Mus. Leafl., *25*(7), 203-15 (1977).

Cannabis Folklore in the Himalayas.

The author gives an account of his investigation of cannabis use in the northern and central Himalayas and urges others to investigate the remaining Himalayan niches.

4840   Sharma, G. K., Bull. Torrey Bot. Club, *102*(4), 199-200 (1975).

Altitudinal Variation in Leaf Epidermal Patterns of *Cannabis sativa*.

Two marihuana populations in diverse environments of India were used. Plants in a hot climate (40° C) were slender and dusty to dull green in color; whereas, plants in a cool climate (15° C) were stout and had a shiny, bright green appearance. All epidermal features are presented to illustrate differences due to altitudinal variations.

4841   Sharma, G. K., J. Psychedelic Drugs, *9*(4), 337-39 (1977).

Ethnobotany and Its Significance for Cannabis Studies in the Himalayas.

Cannabis serves as a source of fiber, oil, fruit, narcotic, and folk medicine in the Himalayas. A discussion of the benefits which may be derived from an ethnobotanical study of the remote populations of the world is presented.

4842   Shevin, R. L., J. Drug Issues, *8*(3), 297-301 (1978).

Marijuana and Florida Law.

The author stresses that although Florida has made some steps toward the development of a comprehensive public policy regarding the use of drugs, these steps remain fragmented and do not address the overall issues that are involved. Possible future trends in marihuana possession and trafficking are discussed.

4843   Shick, J. F. E.; Dorus, W.; and Hughes, P. H., Drug Alcohol Depend., *3*(3), 199-210 (1978).

Adolescent Drug Using Groups in Chicago Parks.

Distinctive drug use, age, socio-economic profile and demographic characteristics of adolescent users in Chicago parks were studied. Patterns of use and purchase of marihuana and other abused drugs, along with implications of findings concerning intervention and prevention strategies, were discussed.

4844 Shimomura, H.; Kuriyama, E.; and Tomizawa, A., Yakugaku Zasshi (J. Pharm. Soc. Japan), 96(1), 75-81 (1976).

Studies on Cannabis. III. Young Plants From the Seed Irradiated with 60-Co-γ Rays for Inhibiting Their Development after Seedling.

Cannabis plants were grown from seeds irradiated with gamma rays from cobalt 60. Results of morphological and histological changes are reported.

4845 Shinogi, M.; and Mori, I., Yakugaku Zasshi (J. Pharm. Soc. Japan), 96(11), 1282-87 (1976).

Determination of Phosphorus in Cannabis by Neutron Activation Analysis Measurement of 32-P Cerenkov Radiation by Liquid Scintillation Spectrometer.

The amount of phosphorus in the upper and middle leaves as well as in the (male) flowers was determined by neutron activation analysis. A comparison was made between this method and the Molybdenum Blue method. Research was done on optimal experimental conditions and detection limit.

4846 Shinogi, M.; and Mori, I., Yakugaku Zasshi (J. Pharm. Soc. Japan), 98(11), 1466-71 (1978).

Multielement Determination in Cannabis Leaves by Instrumental Neutron Activation Analysis. A comparison of Cannabis of Various Geographical Origins in Japan.

Cannabis leaves from 9 different locations in Japan were collected and analyzed for 35 trace elements. The analysis was carried out by the instrumental neutron activation method. Discussion was given as to the correlation between relative concentration of these elements and the geographic locations and the soil used for cultivation.

4847 Shinogi, M.; and Mori, I., Yakugaku Zasshi (J. Pharm. Soc. Japan), 98(5), 569-76 (1978).

The Study of the Trace Element in Organisms by Neutron Activation Analysis. II. The Elemental Distribution in Each Parts of Cultivated Cannabis.

Twenty-nine elements were identified in cannabis samples using the neutron activation analysis technique. Male and female plants along with parts of the plants were employed for this purpose. The types of elemental distribution obtained were discussed.

4848 Shoemaker, R. H.; and Harmon, J. W., Fed. Proc., 36(3), 345 (1977).

Suggested Mechanisms for the Demasculinizing Effect of Marijuana.

Δ^9-THC and 11-OH-Δ^9-THC competitively inhibited the binding of 17-β-estradiol to the estrogenic receptors of rat uterine and mammary tissues in vitro. THC-receptor complexes had sedimentation characteristics identical to the 4-5 S component of the estrogenic receptor complex. THC causes demasculinization via an interaction with estrogenic receptors.

4849 Shoyama, Y.; Hirano, H.; Makino, H.; Umekita, N.; and Nishioka, I., Chem. Pharm. Bull., 25(9), 2306-11 (1977).

Cannabis. X. The Isolation and Structures of Four New Propyl Cannabinoid Acids, Tetrahydrocannabivarinic Acid, Cannabidivarinic Acid, Cannabichromevarinic Acid and Cannabigerovarinic Acid, from Thai Cannabis, 'Meao Variant.'

Propyl homologs of THC-acid, CBD-acid, CBC-acid, and CBG-acid were isolated. Their structure was proven by spectroscopy (IR, NMR, MS, UV) and by correlation with known cannabinoids.

4850   Shoyama, Y.; Hirano, H.; and Nishioka, I., J. Label. Compd. Radiopharm., *14*(6), 835-42 (1978).

Cannabis. XI. Synthesis of Cannabigerorcinic-*Carboxyl*-^{14}C Acid, Cannabigerovarinic *Carboxyl*-^{14}C Acid, Cannabidivarinic-*Carboxyl*-^{14}C Acid and *dl*-Cannabichromevarinic-*Carboxyl*-^{14}C Acid.

The synthesis of the title compounds was carried out by reacting the respective neutral cannabinoid with methylmagnesium carbonate-^{14}C, except for racemic-CBCVA which was prepared by cyclization of the radiolabeled CBGVA. A specially designed apparatus was used for the carboxylation reaction.

4851   Shoyama, Y.; Hirano, H.; Oda, M.; Somehara, T.; and Nishioka, I., Chem. Pharm. Bull., *23*(8), 1894-95 (1975).

Cannabichromevarin and Cannabigerovarin, Two New Propyl Homologues of Cannabichromene and Cannabigerol.

The propyl homologs of CBC and CBG were isolated from a Thailand variant of cannabis. Trivial names of cannabichromevarin (CBCV) and cannabigerovarin (CBGV) were assigned. Physical data are included.

4852   Shoyama, Y.; and Nishioka, I., Chem. Pharm. Bull., *26*(12), 3641-46 (1978).

Cannabis XIII. Two New Spiro-Compounds, Cannabispirol and Acetyl Cannabispirol.

Cannabispirol and its acetate were isolated from Japanese cannabis and their structures determined and spectral data given. A proposed relationship was given between the biosynthetic route of these spiro-compounds and the cannabinoids.

4853   Shoyama, Y.; Yagi, M.; Nishioka, I.; and Yamauchi, T., Phytochemistry, *14*(10), 2189-92 (1975).

Biosynthesis of Cannabinoid Acids.

Labeled malonic and mevalonic acid, geraniol and nerol were fed to four strains of Cannabis sativa. Data obtained from these feeding experiments indicated a biosynthetic pathway which produces CBG, CBGM, CBC, CBD and THC as their carboxylic acid derivatives.

4854   Sidorenko, N. M., Tsitol. Genet., *12*(2), 115-17 (1978).

(Anatomo-Cytological Characteristics of Tetraploid Monoecious Hemp.)

A Russian paper with nine references.

4855   Sieber, M.; and Angst, J., Schweiz. Med. Wochenschr., *107*(51), 1912-20 (1977).

Zur Epidemiologie des Drogen-, Zigaretten- und Alkoholkonsums bei Jungen Mannern [On the Epidemical Use of Drugs, Cigarettes and Alcohol by Young Males].

Males of 19 years old in the county of Zurich were selected at random and questioned about their drug, cigarette and alcohol consumption. Three years later they were questioned again. It was shown that drug consumption had dropped, cigarette smoking had remained constant and alcohol use had increased.

4856 Sieber, M.; Angst, J.; and Baumann, U., Schweiz. Med. Wochenschr., *106*(1), 1-7 (1976).

Development of Drug, Alcohol and Tobacco Consumption. Comparison Between 2 Studies from 1971 and 1974 in the Canton Zurich.

See above abstract.

4857 Siegel, P.; Siegel, M. I.; Krimmer, E. C.; Doyle, W. J.; and Barry, H., Toxicol. Appl. Pharmacol., *42*(2), 339-44 (1977).

Fluctuating Dental Asymmetry as an Indicator of the Stressful Prenatal Effects of Δ^9-Tetrahydrocannabinol in the Laboratory Rat.

Treatment of pregnant rats with Δ^9-THC resulted in increased fluctuating dental asymmetry in their offspring. These results indicate the stressful effects of THC.

4858 Siemens, A. J., Fed. Proc., *37*(3), 318 (1978).

Cross-Tolerance Between Ethanol and Δ^9-Tetrahydrocannabinol: The Contribution of Changes in Drug Disposition. (Abstract)

Tolerance to Δ^9-THC (10.1 mg/kg, p.o.) effects on rotarod performance developed in female rats following repeated administration. A cross-tolerance was also detected between Δ^9-THC and ethanol. Other findings indicated that tolerance and cross-tolerance to these two agents were not of dispositional origin.

4859 Siemens, A. J., Life Sci., *20*(11), 1891-1904 (1977).

Effects of Δ^9-Tetrahydrocannabinol on the Disposition of *d*-Amphetamine in the Rat.

Possible drug interactions between THC and *d*-amphetamine are described. When THC was administered 2 hours prior to amphetamine dosing, the disappearance of labeled ^{14}C amphetamine from the blood of rats was slowed. If the dosings were closer in time, there was no effect. Fasted rats also provided different results than did fed rats.

4860 Siemens, A. J.; De Nie, L. C.; Kalant, H.; and Khanna, J. M., Eur. J. Pharmacol., *31*(1), 136-47 (1975).

Effects of Various Psychoactive Drugs on the Metabolism of Δ^9-Tetrahydrocannabinol by Rats *In Vitro* and *In Vivo*.

Barbiturates, amphetamine and meprobamate, at relatively high concentrations, inhibit the metabolism of THC *in vivo*. The interaction of these agents with THC is not primarily based on inhibition of THC metabolism.

4861 Siemens, A. J.; and Kalant, H., Biochem. Pharmacol., *24*(7), 755-62 (1975).

Metabolism of Δ^1-Tetrahydrocannabinol by the Rat *In Vivo* and *In Vitro*.

6,7-di-OH-Δ^9-THC, along with six other major metabolites, was identified when Δ^9-THC was incubated in rat liver homogenates. The duration of incubation had a dramatic influence on the quantitative pattern of the metabolites which were highly polar and were eliminated mainly in the bile.

4862 Siemens, A. J.; Kalant, H.; and Denie, J. C., pp. 77-92 in *Pharmacology of Marihuana, Vol. 1,* edited by M. C. Braude and S. Szara. NY, Raven Press, 1976.

Metabolic Interactions Between Δ^9-Tetrahydrocannabinol and Other Cannabinoids in Rats.

CBD (1.67, 6 or 18 mg/kg, i.v.), CBN (18 mg/kg, i.v.), CBG and SKF-525 (30 mg/kg, i.p.) inhibited the metabolism of THC. However, plasma disappearance of ^{14}C-THC was unaffected. Disposition studies also showed unusually high concentrations of THC in the lung after CBD and CBN.

4863   Siemens, A. J.; and Khanna, J. M., Alcoholism, *1*(4), 343-48 (1977).

Acute Metabolic Interactions Between Ethanol and Cannabis.

While THC (10 mg/kg) potentiated the hypnotic effect of ethanol in rats without interfering with its metabolism, CBD was inactive and failed to alter the THC-ethanol interaction. Ethanol, however, decreased THC distribution in blood and brain.

4864   Silva, M. T. A.; and Calil, H. M., Psychopharmacologia, *42*(2), 163-71 (1975).

Screening Hallucinogenic Drugs: Systematic Study of Three Behavioral Tests.

Increased head twitching (mice), decreased fecal bolus formation in an open field (rats) and suppression of bar pressing (rats) as a manifestation of differential reinforcement of low food-water reward rates (DRL) are tested as to their utility for the screening of hallucinogenic drugs. None of the 3 depressed activities except nursing.

4865   Silverman, P. B.; and Ho, B. T., Psychopharmacology, *58*(2), 10 (1978).

Stimulus Properties of DOM: Commonality with Other Hallucinogens (Abstract).

Low doses of Δ^9-THC, phencyclidine, and amphetamine generated saline responses in rats trained to discriminate DOM in a 2 lever operant procedure. After high doses, responding was eliminated completely. Psilocybin, DOET, LSD or mescaline generated DOM responses.

4866   Silverstein, M. J.; and Lessin, P. J., pp. 199-205 in *Pharmacology of Marihuana, Vol. 1*, edited by M. C. Braude and S. Szara. NY, Raven Press, 1976.

DNCB Skin Testing in Chronic Marihuana Users.

2,4-dinitrochlorobenzene skin testing was carried out in chronic marihuana users. 100% of the test subjects showed a positive response; however, in age-matched cancer patients only 80% showed a positive response. Results of this test showed no suppression of cell-mediated immunity present in human marihuana users.

4867   Simon, W. E.; and Primavera, L. H., Int. J. Addict., *11*(1), 71-80 (1976).

The Personality of the Cigarette Smoker: Some Empirical Data.

Findings presented are consistent with those of previous studies dealing with various parameters that make up the personality of the cigarette smoker. Population was 199 single, white, middle class, female, under-graduate, Catholic students at one college. A significantly higher number of smokers used marihuana, as compared to non-smokers.

4868   Simpson, D. D., J. Drug Educ., *6*(1), 53-71 (1976).

Pretreatment Drug Use by Patients Entering Drug Treatment Programs During 1971-1973.

4869   Simpson, D. D.; Curtis, B.; Butler, M. C., Amer. J. Drug Alcohol Abuse, *2*(1), 15-28 (1975).

Description of Drug Users in Treatment: 1971-1972 DARP Admissions.

Fifty-seven percent of contemporary American drug users started their drug taking habits by using marihuana. Drug use is more prevalent among males than females and in blacks than whites. This information was extracted from the population of drug abuse reporting programs (DARP).

4870   Singh, N., Indian J. Physiol. Pharmacol., *22*(2), 176-77 (1978).

Effect of Cannabinol on Human Behavior (Abstract).

CBN (5 mg orally) caused a wide range of changes in the general behavior of humans including partial forgetfulness, depraved appetite, sex depression and blurred vision.

4871   Singh, P.; and Das, P. K., Indian J. Exp. Biol., *16*(1), 82-85 (1978).

Effect of *Cannabis indica* on Locomotor Activity.

Depending on the doses used and on individual animals, cannabis induced either excitatory or inhibitory effects on locomotor activity of mice. Cannabis also induced a stereotyped behavior and antagonized the psychomotor stimulation caused by amphetamine.

4872   Singh, P. P.; Bhattacharya, S. K.; and Das, P. K., Indian J. Exp. Biol., *16*(3), 326-29 (1978).

Interaction of Cannabis, Reserpine and Chlorpromazine on Body Temperature and Mechanism of Hyperthermic Response to Cannabis in Tolerant Albino Rats.

Pretreatment with chlorpromazine (CPZ) or reserpine blocked the development of tolerance to THC-induced hypothermia in rats. CPZ pretreatment also resulted in an initial blockade of reserpine and THC-induced hypothermia while the latter two agents caused a pronounced blockade of CPZ effects. Other treatments were also investigated.

4873   Singh, P. P.; and Das, P. K., Indian J. Exp. Biol., *15*(4), 280-84 (1977).

Tolerance to Cannabis in Albino Rats.

Repeated administration of cannabis to rats resulted in tolerance to its hypothermic, analgesic, anticonvulsive and pentobarbital hypnosis-potentiating effects. Tolerance, however, did not develop to the hyperthermic- or locomotor activity-induced changes in tolerant rats. Other behavioral parameters were also investigated.

4874   Singh, P. P.; and Das, P. K., Ind. J. Pharmac., *7*(3), 51-57 (1975).

A Neuro-Psychopharmacological Study of *Cannabis indica*.

While establishing a neuropsychopharmacological profile of the *Cannabis indica*, it was found that the resin produced hypothermia, analgesia, both depressant and excitory behavior in mice and rats. Other pharmacological properties of this compound include: anticonvulsant activity, anti-inflammatory action and an antipyretic effect.

4875   Singh, P. P.; and Das, P. K., Psychopharmacology, *50*(2), 199-204 (1976).

Role of Catecholamines in the Hypothermic Activity of Cannabis in Albino Rats.

Agents which altered monoamine levels (such as reserpine) had the same hypothermic effects as cannabis in rat but acted differently at the adrenergic synapse. Some brain amines were not involved in the hypothermic response.

4876 Singh, P. P.; and Das, P. K., Psychopharmacology, 56(3), 309-16 (1978).

Studies on the Interactions of Copper and Cannabis.

The development of tolerance to hypothermic activity of cannabis was markedly delayed by single doses of copper. Tolerance to barbiturate hypnosis-potentiating activity of cannabis was also partially inhibited. The actions of copper on tolerance could be antagonized by the specific chelator penicillamine, and are possibly hypothalamic in nature.

4877 Sklenovsky, A., Acta Univ. Palacki. Olomuc. Fac. Med., 80, 175-82 (1976).

The Mechanism of Effect of Delta-9-Tetrahydrocannabinol.

Δ^9-THC (10 mg/kg, i.p.) activates rat brain phospholipase A. The resulting lysoderivatives and free fatty acids exhibit a biphasic effect whereby small amounts stabilize the synaptic membrane with subsequent inhibition of neurotransmitter release and large amounts produce exactly opposite effects.

4878 Sklenovsky, A.; Navratil, J.; Hrbek, J.; Chmela, Z.; and Krejci, Z., Acta Univ. Palacki. Olomuc. Fac. Med., 80, 183-88 (1976).

The Effect of Delta-9-Tetrahydrocannabinol (Δ^9-THC) upon the Release of Unesterified Fatty Acids in the Brain.

Δ^9-THC (10 mg/kg, i.p.) increased the levels of rat brain fatty acid in the cortical, hypothalamic and brain stem regions.

4879 Sklenovsky, A.; Navratil, J.; Hrbek, J.; and Skrabal, J., Activ. Nerv. Super., 17(1), 67 (1975).

Effect of Delta-9-Tetrahydrocannabinol (THC) on the "Labilization" of Phospholipoid Complexes of Brain Tissue.

In Wistar rats given 10 mg/kg THC, i.p., fatty acids increased in the extracts of the cortex and hypothalamus but were greatest in the brain stem. Breakdown of the phospholipoid complexes as the "labilization" of membranes, possibly increases their permeability.

4880 Slatkin, D. J.; Knapp, J. E.; Schiff, P. L.; Turner, C. E.; and Mole, M. L., Phytochemistry, 14, 580-81 (1975).

Steroids of Cannabis sativa Root.

Sitosterol, campesterol, stigmasterol, stigmast-4-en-3-one (sitost-4-en-3-one), campest-4-en-3-one, stigmast-4,22-dien-3-one, stigmast-5-en-3β-ol-7-one, and stigmast-5, 22-dien-3β-ol-7-one were isolated from cannabis roots.

4881 Small, E., Bull. Narcotics, 27(3), 1-20 (1975).

American Law and the Species Problem in Cannabis: Science and Semantics.

An exhaustive review of the botanical aspects of cannabis is presented. The specific species C. sativa, C. indica and C. ruderalis are discussed as to their origin in botanical journals. The author gives data to support only one species of cannabis which is sativa.

4882 Small, E., Can. J. Bot., 53(10), 978-87 (1975).

Morphological Variation of Achenes of Cannabis.

Morphological variation of cultivated and wild cannabis achenes (fruit "seed") were compared macroscopically, microscopically and according to geographical distribution. From data obtained, no basis for the separate recognition of the putative species *C. ruderalis* or *C. indica* was determined. It was hypothesized that degree of development of characteristics in uncultivated plants is indicative of departure or independence from the effects of domestication.

4883   Small, E., Econ. Bot., *29*(3), 254 (1975).

The Case of the Curious "Cannabis."

An unusual plant previously reported as *Cannabis sativa L*. was found to be *Datisca cannabina L*.

4884   Small, E., J. Forensic Sci., *21*(2), 239-51 (1976).

The Forensic Taxonomic Debate on Cannabis: Semantic Hokum.

A review of legal species of marihuana plants. Emphasis is placed on subjectivity of classification phase of taxonomy and ambiguities of biological names.

4885   Small, E., J. Forensic Sc., *20*(4), 739-41 (1975).

Cannabis sativa L. (Letter to the Editor).

Taxonomic studies on cannabis were discussed. The forensic issue of cannabis is logically resolvable as a scientific problem investigating how many species of cannabis should be recongized; and as a semantic problem bearing on how widely understood is the name *C. sativa*.

4886   Small, E., Plant Sci. Bull., *21*(3), 34-39 (1975).

On Toadstool Soup and Legal Species of Marihuana.

Misunderstandings concerning biological nomenclature are discussed. The role of CBD and Δ^9-THC are discussed as the two most important cannabinoids present in cannabis. Discussions and photographs are used to explain differences between drug and fiber types. A proposal that cannabis is one species with two subspecies is presented. *C. indica* and *C. ruderalis* are discussed.

4887   Small, E.; Beckstead, H. D.; and Chan, A., Econ. Bot., *29*(3), 219-32 (1975).

The Evolution of Cannabinoid Phenotypes in Cannabis.

The results of a Canadian cannabis research program are presented. The entire plant is discussed from a structural point of view. A historical distribution profile is also given. Cannabis is divided into three phenotypes according to chemical analysis. These three phenotypes are discussed regarding country of origin.

4888   Small, E.; and Cronquist, A., Taxon., *25*(4), 405-35 (1976).

A Practical and Natural Taxonomy for Cannabis.

A thorough review of the taxonomy of cannabis is presented. The authors concluded that cannabis consists of a single highly variable species, namely *C. sativa*. Two subspecies of cannabis (subsp. *sativa* and subsp. *indica*) and four varieties (*sativa, spontanea, indica* and *kafiristanica*) are recognized by the authors.

4889   Small, E.; Jui, P. Y.; and Lefkovitch, L. P., Syst. Bot., *1*(1), 67-84 (1976).

A Numerical Taxonomic Analysis of Cannabis with Special Reference to Species Delimitation.

A detailed discussion on numerical taxonomic analysis is presented for cannabis. Cannabis is only one species according to these analyses. Morphological, chemical, wild, domesticated, intoxicating, and nonintoxicating data are given.

4890   Smart, R. G., Bull. Narcotics, *28*(1), 55-65 (1976).

Effects of Legal Restraint on the Use of Drugs: A Review of Empirical Studies.

This is a review of studies on the effectiveness of legal restraints related to the use of narcotics, marihuana, and prescription drugs. The data base consists of only those studies which show evidence of increasing or decreasing drug use. The cannabis studies were judged not to have adequate controls.

4891   Smart, R. G., Bull. Narcotics, *29*(4), 59-63 (1977).

Perceived Availability and the Use of Drugs.

The availability of several abused drugs, including cannabis, was associated with their use in a representative sample of high school students.

4892   Smiley, K. A., Diss. Abstr. Int. B, *39*(6), 2768-69 (1978).

An Electrophysiological Analysis of the Antiseizure Action of Cannabidiol on Limbic Seizures in Conscious Rats.

CBD was more effective than Δ^9-THC, phenytoin or ethosuximide in protecting rats against limbic seizures. CBD was also the only agent lacking CNS excitatory effects.

4893   Smiley, K. A.; Karler, R.; and Turkanis, S. A., Fed. Proc., *35*(3), 506 (1976).

Effects of Cannabinoids on the *In Vitro* Perfused Rat Heart (Abstract).

The chronotropic and inotropic effects of Δ^9-THC, CBN and CBD were observed. All cannabinoids markedly reduced contraction force. Δ^9-THC and CBN increased cardiac rate, CBD decreased, and Δ^8-THC produced arrythmias. All cannabinoids accumulated in heart tissue.

4894   Smiley, K. A.; Karler, R.; and Turkanis, S. A., Res. Commun. Chem. Pathol. Pharmacol., *14*(4), 659-75 (1976).

Effects of Cannabinoids on the Perfused Rat Heart.

THC, Δ^8-THC, CBD, and CBN depressed the contractility of isolated rat hearts, while having variable effects on the heart rate. The relationship between tissue concentrations and cardiac effects was discussed.

4895   Smiley, K. A.; Turkanis, S. A.; and Karler, R., Fed. Proc., *37*(3), 738 (1978).

Cannabidion- and Δ^9-Tetrahydrocannabinol-Caused Increase in Hippocampal Seizure Threshold (Abstract).

Δ^9-THC and CBD, in doses ranging from 0.3-15 mg/kg, i.p., raised the hippocampal seizure threshold in conscious rats. An increase in amplitude and duration of the electrical seizure was also induced by Δ^9-THC but not by CBD.

4896   Smith, C. G.; Asch, R. H.; and Fernandez, E., Pharmacologist, *20*(3), 165 (1978).

The effect of short-term administration of Delta-9-Tetrahydrocannabinol on the Reproductive Tissues in the Ovariectomized Rhesus Monkey (Abstract).

Evidence presented suggested that Δ^9-THC does not exert a direct estrogenic activity on reproductive tissues of ovariectomized monkeys.

4897 Smith, C. G.; Besch, N. F.; and Besch, P. K., Fed. Proc., *36*(3), 223 (1977).

The Effect of Tetrahydrocannabinol (THC) on the Secretion of Follicle Stimulating Hormone (FSH) in the Female Rhesus Monkey (Abstract).

In female, ovariectomized rhesus monkeys, THC (1.25-5.00 mg/kg, i.m.) depressed FSH secretion by 36-80%. FSH remained suppressed for 6-24 hrs. and recovered to control levels within 18-48 hrs.

4898 Smith, C. G.; Besch, N. F.; Smith, R. G.; and Besch, P. K., Fed. Proc., *37*(3), 724 (1978).

Mechanism for the Anti-Gonadotrophic Action of Tetrahydrocannabinol (THC) (Abstract).

Effects of THC administration (2.5 mg/kg, i.m.) 6 hours prior to LH releasing factor (LHRF) injection were examined in ovariectomized monkeys. LH and FSH levels were significantly increased.

4899 Smith, C. G.; Moore, C. E.; Besch, N. F.; and Besch, P. K., Clin. Chem., *22*(7), 1184 (1976).

The Effect of Marihuana (Delta-9-Tetrahydrocannabinol) on the Secretion of Sex Hormones in the Mature Male Rhesus Monkey.

Data obtained from a single male rhesus monkey suggests that acute THC administration depresses LH and testosterone levels, which recover within three days. Data suggests CNS mediation in hormonal control by THC.

4900 Smith, C. M., pp. 384-92 in *Interactions of Drugs of Abuse*, edited by E. S. Vesell and M. C. Braude. NY, Annals of the New York Academy of Sciences, V, 281, 1976.

Interactions of Drugs of Abuse with Alcohol.

The author points out the need for concern about possible drug interactions with alcohol, considering the high frequency with which alcohol is ingested; the possible enlightenment as to mechanisms of action that could derive from such study; and possibilities of the use of one drug predisposing a person to use of another. Interactions of alcohol and cannabis are discussed.

4901 Smith, G. M.; and Fogg, C. P., pp. 101-13 in *Longitudinal Research on Drug Use*, edited by D. B. Kandel. Washington, D. C., Hemisphere Publishing Corporation, 1978.

Psychological Predictors of Early Use, Late Use, and Nonuse of Marihuana Among Teenage Students.

A five-year longitudinal study revealed that nonusers were more personally competent and socially responsible than were early marihuana users. Late users held an intermediate position between the two teenage groups.

4902 Smith, G. M.; and Fogg, C. P., Fed. Proc., *35*(3), 564 (1976).

High School Performance and Behavior Before and After Initiation of Illicit Drug Use (Abstract).

Students were measured as to grade point average, attendance, suspension rate, and graduation. Apparent non-drug users measured highest in grades and graduations and lowest in absences and suspensions. Marihuana users measured poorly in all four categories and "hard drug" users measured poorest of all.

4903 Smith, H. W., Soc. Sci. Med., *12*(2A), 107-09 (1978).

Effects of Set on Subject's Interpretation of Placebo Marihuana Effects.

Heavy marihuana users experienced and perceived partners to experience marihuana high under placebo conditions when placed in a mixed sex dyad only. Behavioral performance of subjects also changed accordingly. The importance of social setting in perceiving marihuana effects was emphasized.

4904 Smith, J. P., pp. 9-11 in *Pharmacology of Marihuana, Vol. 1*, edited by M. C. Braude and S. Szara. NY, Raven Press, 1976.

International Cooperation in Cannabis Research.

The international dissemination and exchange of information relevant to all aspects of cannabis use is emphasized. Two organizations - WHO's Office of Mental Health and the U. N. Narcotics Laboratory - are coordinating worldwide research efforts into drugs of abuse. In close collaboration with the U. N. Narcotics Laboratory, the NIDA's division of research distributes standardized cannabis materials to licensed researchers.

4905 Smith, R. J., Science, *199*(4331), 861-64 (1978).

Spraying of Herbicides on Mexican Marijuana Backfires on U. S.

The political ramifications of controlling marihuana by spraying Mexican fields with the herbicide paraquat are discussed.

4906 Smith, R. J., Science, *200*(4340), 417-18 (1978).

Poisoned Pot Becomes Burning Issue in High Places.

A short, but comprehensive summary of the recent governmental and industrial activities related to paraquat contamination of marihuana.

4907 Smith, R. J., Science, *201*(4354), 427 (1978).

Efforts to Stop Paraquat Set Back.

NORML and some members of Congress are continuing to fight the State Department program helping Mexico spray marihuana with paraquat.

4908 Smith, R. M.; and Kempfert, K. D., Phytochemistry, *16*(7), 1088-89 (1977).

Δ^1-*Cis*-Tetrahydrocannabinol in *Cannabis sativa*.

The isolation and characterization of Δ^1-3,4-*cis*-THC from confiscated marihuana samples is reported. A correlation between the CBD content of marihuana and the relative amount of Δ^1-3,4-*cis* to that of Δ^1-3,4-*trans*-THC was made based on GLC analysis of the cannabinoids of numerous samples.

4909 Smith, R. N., J. Chromatogr., *115*(1), 101-06 (1975).

High-Pressure Liquid Chromatography of Cannabis. Identification of Separated Constituents.

A number of the neutral and acidic cannabinoids were detected using HPLC. The components were eluted via LC and their identities confirmed using GC/MS techniques. The optimum UV detector wavelength for observing

314

the greatest number of peaks was determined to be between 250-260 nm. Acid components were eluted and decarboxylated prior to GC/MS analysis.

4910   Smith, R. N.; Jones, L. V.; Brennan, J. S.; and Vaughan, C. G., J. Pharm. Pharmacol., 29(2), 126-27 (1977).

Identification of Hexadecanamide in Cannabis Resin.

Hexadecanamide was detected in cannabis resin thought to be of Pakistan origin. Identification was based on GC/MS data.

4911   Smith, R. N.; and Vaughan, C. G., J. Chromatogr., 129, 347-54 (1976).

High-Pressure Liquid Chromatography of Cannabis. Quantitative Analysis of Acidic and Neutral Cannabinoids.

HBLC method for the quantitation of cannabinoids at $26 \pm 0.5°$ was discussed. The separation of different cannabinoids and some cannabinoid acids was shown. Interference of CBGA with CBN was discussed and two methods for overcoming that problem were given. The method offered simultaneous analysis of neutral and acidic cannabinoids.

4912   Smith, R. N.; and Vaughan, C. G., J. Pharm. Pharmacol., 29(5), 286-90 (1977).

The Decomposition of Acidic and Neutral Cannabinoids in Organic Solvents.

Methanol and ethanol were found to be very efficient extracting solvents for removing neutral and acidic cannabinoids from cannabis resin. Chloroform or petroleum ether or methanolchloroform (9:1) were less efficient. Acidic and neutral compounds were found to be unstable to light while in solution.

Dark storage prevented decomposition of neutral cannabinoids to a large extent but the acid compounds decomposed by varying amounts.

4913   Smith, S. H.; Harris, L. S.; Uwaydah, I. M.; and Munson, A. E., J. Pharmacol. Exp. Ther., 207(1), 165-70 (1978).

Structure-Activity Relationships of Natural and Synthetic Cannabinoids in Suppression of Humoral and Cell-Mediated Immunity.

Δ^8-THC, its 1-methyl- or abnormal analogs were more potent inhibitors than was Δ^9-THC in reducing humoral immune response. Also, all cannabinoids inhibited cell-mediated immunity to varying degrees without exerting any anti-inflammatory activity. Implications of the findings were discussed.

4914   Smith, S. H.; Munson, A. E.; and Bowman, F. J., Fed. Proc., 37(3), 829 (1978).

Immunosuppressant Effects of Cannabinoids on Humoral and Cell-Mediated Immunity (Abstract).

Results of a series of immunological experiments showed that 1-methyl Δ^8-THC, a non-psychoactive cannabinoid, suppressed humoral and cellular immune responses dependent on T-lymphocytes. Δ^9- and Δ^8-THC were also effective immunosuppressants under the same conditions.

4915   Smith, T. C.; and Kulp, R., pp. 123-32 in The Therapeutic Potential of Marihuana, edited by S. Cohen and R. Stillman. NY, Plenum Medical Book Company, 1976.

Respiratory and Cardiovascular Effects of Delta-9-Tetrahydrocannabinol Alone and in Combination with Oxymorphone, Pentobarbital and Diazepam.

As a drug suggested for use in anesthesiology because of its subjective effects, THC did not cause any alarming changes in respiration or cardiovascular parameters but did induce psychic effects when administered i.v. in large doses to human subjects. Of the depressants tested, pentobarbital worsened the THC-induced psychosis while diazepam was superior to oxymorphone in alleviating such a psychosis with less side effects.

4916 Soares, J. R.; and Gross, S. J., Life Sci., *19*(11), 1711-18 (1976).

Separate Radioimmune Measurements of Body Fluid Δ^9-THC and 11-*Nor*-9-Carboxy-Δ^9-THC.

Δ^9-THC and 11-*nor*-9-carboxy-Δ^9-THC (C-THC) were measured by a RIA technique in body fluids. Both could be measured with a 2-(4'-carboxyphenyl 230)-Δ^9-THC antiserum. Plasma, urine, and saliva samples were used. Δ^9-THC peaked in plasma between 15-30 min and C-THC between 30-60 min. Other relationships between Δ^9-THC and C-THC are discussed.

4917 Sobrino Lazaro, G.; and Macias, G.-S., G., Salud Publica Mex., *19*(3), 431-35 (1977).

Farmacodependencia for Mariguana en Quintana Roo [Pathological Drugs by Marihuana in Quintana Roo State, Mexico].

Drug dependence problems stemming from marihuana use in Quintana Roo State, Mexico, are described.

4918 Sofia, R. D., pp. 319-71 in *Handbook of Psychopharmacology, Vol. 12, Drugs of Abuse*, edited by L. L. Iverson, S. D. Iverson, and S. H. Snyder. NY, Plenum Press, 1978.

Cannabis: Structure Activity Relationships.

A general review of the chemistry, metabolism and pharmacology of cannabis with particular emphasis on the effects of changes in the cannabinoids structure on the different pharmacologic properties. Natural, as well as synthetic cannabinoids, were discussed.

4919 Sofia, R. D.; and Barry, H., Arch. Int. Pharmacodyn. Ther., *228*(1), 73-78 (1977).

Comparative Activity of Δ^9-Tetrahydrocannabinol, Diphenylhydantoin, Phenobarbital and Chlordiazepoxide on Electrochock Seizure Threshold in Mice.

THC, phenobarbital and diphenylhydantoin raised the electroshock seizure threshold (EST) in mice but only chlordiazepoxide reached the established significant criterion. All agents tested reversed the hyponatremia-induced lowering of EST, but THC offered the most protection.

4920 Sofia, R. D.; Diamantis, W.; and Edelson, J., Pharmacology, *17*(2), 79-82 (1978).

Effect of Δ^9-Tetrahydrocannabinol on the Gastrointestinal Tract of the Rat.

Δ^9-THC caused neither gastrointestinal bleeding nor ulceration nor did it promote fecal blood loss in the fasted rat at a dose of 200 mg/kg using ^{51}Cr-labeled erythrocyte test). Results are compared with acetylsalicylic acid as a reference agent.

4921 Sofia, R. D.; Diamantis, W.; Harrison, J. E.; and Melton, J., Pharmacology, *17*(3), 173-77 (1978).

Evaluation of Antiulcer Activity of Δ^9-Tetrahydrocannabinol in the Shay Rat Test.

Δ^9-THC (100 mg/kg) was not as potent as tridihexethyl chloride in protecting rats against pyloric-ligation-induced gastric ulcer.

4922   Sofia, R. D.; Dixit, B. N.; and Barry, H., Arch. Int. Pharmacodyn. Ther., *229*(1), 52-58 (1977).

The Effect of Repeated Administration of Δ^9-Tetrahydrocannabinol on Serotonin Metabolism in the Rat Brain.

THC administration (20 mg/kg, i.p.) to rats for 6 days elevated brain 5-HT levels and reduced its turnover rate.

4923   Sofia, R. D.; and Knobloch, L. C., Pharmacol. Biochem. Behav., *4*(5), 591-99 (1976).

Comparative Effects of Various Naturally Occurring Cannabinoids on Food, Sucrose and Water Consumption by Rats.

The effects of i.p. administration of Δ^9-THC, CBN and CBD on food, sucrose and water consumption in rats were compared to those of *d*-amphetamine sulfate (*d*-AMP). All drugs produced a significant reduction in food and water consumption immediately after dosing. However, sugar consumption was not affected in rats receiving Δ^9-THC, CBN and CBD, whereas *d*-AMP had an equal anorexic action on both food and sucrose intake.

4924   Sofia, R. D.; Knobloch, L. C.; Harakal, J. J.; and Erikson, D. J., Arch. Int. Pharmacodyn. Ther., *225*(1), 77-87 (1977).

Comparative Diuretic Activity of Δ^9-Tetrahydrocannabinol, Cannabidiol, Cannabinol and Hydrochlorothiazide in the Rat.

CBD and CBN had no diuretic activity, whereas THC had dose dependent diuretic activity comparable to hydrochlorothiazide (HCT). The mechanism of diuresis by THC was judged to be different than that of the thiazides due to differing electrolyte excretion rates and hypothalamic control. The THC-induced diuresis disappeared with time as tolerance developed.

4925   Sofia, R. D.; Solomon, T. A.; and Barry, H., Eur. J. Pharmacol., *35*(1), 7-16 (1976).

Anticonvulsant Activity of Δ^9-Tetrahydrocannabinol Compared with Three Other Drugs.

Nicotine seizures were not prevented by Δ^9-THC, diphenylhydantoin (DPH), phenobarbital or chlordiazepoxide. Δ^9-THC (40 mg/kg) and DPH, however, antagonized electroshock seizures and potentiated strychnine- and pentylenetetrazol-induced seizures and mortality.

4926   Sofia, R. D.; Vassar, H. B.; and Knoblock, L. C., Psychopharmacologia, *40*(4), 285-95 (1975).

Comparative Analgesic Activity of Various Naturally Occurring Cannabinoids in Mice and Rats.

Two screening procedures in mice (acetic acid-induced writhing and hot plate) and one in rats (Randell-Selitto paw pressure) are used to describe the patterns and potencies of analgesia for oral Δ^9-THC, crude marihuana extract, CBN, and CBD relative to two standard analgesics - morphine and aspirin.

4927   Solomon, J.; and Cocchia, M. A., Science, *195*(4281), 905-06 (1977).

Is Delta-9-Tetrahydrocannabinol Estrogenic? (Reply to Comments).

In responding to Okey and Bondy criticism, the authors cited few differences including the route of administration, doses used, duration of experiments and *in vivo* vs. *in vitro* techniques between them and their critics' studies of the estrogenic effects of THC.

4928 Solomon, J.; Cocchia, M. A.; and Di-Martino, R., Science, *195*(4281), 875-77 (1977).

Effect of Delta-9-Tetrahydrocannabinol on Uterine and Vaginal Cytology of Ovariectomized Rats.

THC (1, 2.5 and 10 mg/kg) increased the uterine weight and induced vaginal changes indicative of estrogenic-like activity in ovariectomized rats. The intermediate dose was the most effective.

4929 Solomon, J.; Cocchia, M. A.; Gray, R.; Shattuck, D.; and Vossmer, A., Science, *192*(4239), 559-61 (1976).

Uterotrophic Effect of Delta-9-Tetrahydrocannabinol in Ovariectomized Rats.

Neither Δ^9-THC (1 to 10 mg/kg, i.p. for 14 days) nor estradiol benzoate increased adrenal weight in ovariectomized rats although a combination of the two did. Both agents, however, yielded significant uterotrophic effects in all instances.

4930 Soni, C. M.; and Gupta, M. L., Indian J. Physiol. Pharmacol., *22*(2), 152-54 (1978).

Effect of Cannabis (Bhang) Extract on Blood Glucose and Liver Glycogen in Albino Rats.

Cannabis extract increased blood glucose and concomitantly decreased liver glycogen of treated rats. Effects were dose-related.

4931 Sorfleet, P., Can. J. Criminol. Corrections, *18*(2), 123-51 (1976).

Dealing Hashish: Sociological Notes on Trafficking and Use.

Cultivation and preparation of hashish and its market structure, along with background and lifestyles of dealers in Ottawa were described. Marginal profit from hashish trafficking and great disparity between hashish and marihuana made the former's market shrink considerably.

4932 Sorosiak, F. M.; Thomas, L. E.; and Balet, F. N., Psychol. Rep., *38*(1), 211-21 (1976).

Adolescent Drug Use: An Analysis.

Tobacco and marihuana followed alcohol as the favorite drugs used by a sample of students in grades 8 to 12. Also, legal and illegal drug use increased proportionally to age and, except for tobacco, was always higher in males than in females. Perception of drug use by peers and poor communications with parents were important factors in drug use and abuse.

4933 Soueif, M. I., Bull. Narcotics, *27*(4), 1-26 (1975).

Chronic Cannabis Users: Further Analysis of Objective Test Results.

Eight hundred and fifty chronic cannabis users and 839 nonusers, all Egyptian males incarcerated in prison, were administered general aptitude, time estimation, digit span, Bender Gestalt visual motor and recall tests in order to generate 16 test variables. Defective visual-motor coordination, impaired memory and psychomotor performance were all noted in cannabis users.

4934 Soueif, M. I., Bull Narcotics, *28*(1), 25-42 (1976).

Some Determinants of Psychological Deficits Associated with Chronic Cannabis Consumption.

In Egyptian cannabis users, cannabis use caused the least disruption of cognitive and psychomotor tasks performance in those persons with low, non-drug baseline proficiency. Literates, urban dwellers and young people exhibited best non-drug performance.

4935 Soueif, M. I., Bull. Narcotics, *29*(2), 35-43 (1977).

The Egyptian Study of Chronic Cannabis Use: A Reply to Fletcher and Satz.

Dr. Soueif objected to the critical comments of Fletcher and Satz on his study concerning the chronic use of hashish in Egypt and labeled the comments as either unconvincing or irrelevant. He suggested that criticism should only come after a proper replication of the study is undertaken.

4936 Soueif, M. I., pp. 121-25 in *Chronic Cannabis Use*, edited by R. L. Dornbush, A. M. Freedman, and M. Fink. NY, Annals of the New York Academy of Sciences, V. 282, 1976.

Cannabis-Type Dependence: The Psychology of Chronic Heavy Consumption.

Heavy and moderate hashish users in Egypt are characterized and contrasted by means of standardized interviewing schedules. Factors such as the high degree of drug attachment, cannabis reinforcement of drug-taking behavior, and the high degree of multiple-drug usage in heavy user population indicate the powerful influence of cannabis on such users.

4937 Soueif, M. I., pp. 323-43 in Chronic Cannabis Use, edited by R. L. Dornbush, A. M. Freedman, and M. Fink. NY, Annals of the New York Academy of Sciences, V. 282, 1976.

Differential Association Between Chronic Use and Brain Function Deficits.

Monitoring psychomotor performance, distance and time estimation, immediate memory and visuomotor coordination revealed that chronic cannabis users differed from non-users on most parameters measured. Use of cannabis and related deficits correlated with literacy, urbanism and age. Functional deficits were also dependent on baseline levels of cortical arousal and test proficiency.

4938 Soueif, M. I., Drug Alcohol Depend., *1*, 125-54 (1975/1976).

Chronic Cannabis Takers: Some Temperamental Characteristics.

The author presents a study of the reasons for use and the background of cannabis users and nonusers in Egypt. The sociocultural factors vary among countries therefore making comparisons of cannabis users difficult.

4939 Spaulding, T. C.; and Dewey, W. L., Res. Commun. Chem. Pathol. Pharmacol., *11*(3), 503-06 (1975).

Some Effects of the Behaviorally Active Drug, Phenitrone, a Purported Hashish and LSD Antagonist, on Brain Noradrenergic and Serotonergic Systems.

The bizarre behavioral effects of phenitrone (which is reported to be a hashhish antagonist) in cats and dogs and its general depressant action are suggested to be mediated through its effects on brain 5-HT levels.

4940   Sprague, C. L., Diss. Abstr. Int. B, *37*(8), 3909-10 (1977).

Pharmacological Interaction of Ethanol and $\triangle^9$-Tetrahydrocannabinol.

THC metabolism was not affected by prior treatment with THC but was influenced by ethanol. Pretreatment with either ethanol or THC, however, did not alter ethanol elimination in mice. Severity of handling convulsions during ethanol withdrawal was increased by THC or nabilone and attenuated by ethanol, diazepam or phenytoin. Other aspects of the physical dependence upon ethanol were also investigated.

4941   Sprague, G. L.; and Craigmill, A. L., Fed. Proc., *36*(3), 1027 (1977).

Effect of $\triangle^9$-Tetrahydrocannabinol in Ethanol-Dependent Mice.

$\triangle^9$-THC resulted in handling-induced convulsions in normal mice and potentiated those in ethanol-dependent mice. Both agents abolished the hyperreactive startle reflex in dependent mice.

4942   Sprague, G. L.; and Craigmill, A. L., Pharmacologist, *17*(1), 198 (1975).

Development of Cross-Tolerance Between $\triangle^9$-THC and Ethanol.

The authors speculate that the cross-tolerance they report may involve both tissue and metabolic components. Propylene glycol was the vehicle.

4943   Sprague, G. L.; and Craigmill, A. L., Pharmacol. Biochem. Behav., *5*(4), 409-15 (1976).

Ethanol and Delta-9-Tetrahydrocannabinol: Mechanism for Cross-Tolerance in Mice.

Neither alcohol nor THC pretreatment affected alcohol elimination in mice. Alcohol pretreatment, on the other hand, was effective in altering THC metabolism and distribution. Tolerance to the impairment of mouse rotarod performance by either agent and also to the resulting cross-tolerance between THC and alcohol is not due to lower brain concentrations.

4944   Sprague, G. L.; and Craigmill, A. L., Pharmacol. Biochem. Behav., *9*(1), 11-15 (1978).

Effects of Two Cannabinoids Upon Abstinence Signs in Ethanol-Dependent Mice.

Nabilone and $\triangle^9$-THC resulted in handling-induced convulsions in normal mice and intensified convulsions resulting from alcohol abstinence in dependent mice. Both, however, antagonized the increased responsiveness to electric foot shock seen during ethanol withdrawal.

4945   Sprague, G.; and Craigmill, A., Res. Commun. Chem. Pathol. Pharmacol., *14*(4), 739-42 (1976).

Behavioral and Metabolic Interaction of Propylene Glycol Vehicle and Delta-9-Tetrahydrocannabinol.

Several daily treatments with propylene glycol (PG), used in a $\triangle^9$-THC vehicle, attenuated the impairment of rotarod performance manifested in mice treated with $\triangle^9$-THC but not with alcohol. PG, however, inhibited metabolism of both agents.

4946   Spronck, H. J. W., Pharm. Weekbl., *110*(21), 441-45 (1975).

Pyrolyse Van Cannabinoiden ['Pyrolysis of Cannabinoids].

320

The main pyrolytic product formed on pyrolysis of CBD in air is cannabielsoin (CBE). The structure elucidation was based on IR, NMR, and MS. CBE was also isolated from hashish and has no pharmacological activity.

4947 Spronck, H. J. W.; and Lousberg, R. J. J. C., Experientia, *33*(6), 705-06 (1977).

Pyrolysis of Cannabidiol. Structure Elucidation of a Major Pyrolytic Conversion Product.

Pyrolysis of CBD yielded (1*R*, 4a*S*, 9b*R*) - 1,2,3,4,4a,9b-hexahydro-9-OH-4-isopropylidene-1-methyl-7-pentyldibenzofuran, among other products. The structure determination was based on NMR, MS, and IR data; the stereospecific route leading to the new cannabinoid was discussed.

4948 Spronck, H. J. W.; Luteijn, J. M.; Salemink, C. A. L.; and Nugteren, D. H., Biochem. Pharmacol., *27*(4), 607-08 (1978).

Inhibition of Prostaglandin Biosynthesis by Derivatives of Olivetol Formed under Pyrolysis of Cannabidiol.

Some prolytic products of CBD were identified. These included olivetol and 2-alkyl derivatives, thereof, chromene derivative, benzofuran derivative and benzopyran derivative, as well as several rearrangement products. The activity of the major components as inhibitors of prostaglandin biosynthesis was studied. All compounds tested were active.

4949 Spronck, H. J. W.; and Salemink, C. A., Recl. Trav. Chim. Pays-Bas, *97*(7-8), 185-86 (1978).

Cannabis XVII. Pyrolysis of Cannabidiol. Structure Elucidation of Two Pyrolytic Conversion Products.

CBD was pyrolyzed under N_2, a process found to be a good model for smoking cannabinoids, and the pyrolytic products examined. Two new products were isolated and their structures determined by spectral evidence and synthesis. The products indicated rearrangement in carbon skeleton of CBD during pyrolysis.

4950 Spronck, H. J. W.; Salemink, C. A.; Alikaridis, F.; and Papadakis, D., Bull. Narcotics, *30*(3), 55-59 (1978).

Pyrolysis of Cannabinoids: A Model Experiment in the Study of Cannabis Smoking.

Experimental devices were used to study water pipe smoking and pyrolysis of cannabinoids and to measure the O_2 content in a cigarette. The model cannabinoid used was CBD and the pyrolysates were analyzed by GC, MS and TLC. Comparison was made between water pipe and cigarette smoking and pyrolysis.

4951 Staab, R. J.; and Lynch, V. D., Pharmacologist, *19*(2), 179 (1977).

Cannabis Induced Teratogenesis in the CF_1 Mouse.

Exposure of pregnant mice to cannabis smoke on days 8-11 of gestation caused increased mortality and runting in the first and second generations. Hydronephrosis was also evident in the first generation.

4952 Staak, M.; Moosmayer, A.; and Besserer, K., Beitr. Gerichtl. Med., *36*, 443-49 (1978).

Die Rechtsmedizinische Beurteilung van Dosis-Wirkungs-Beziehungen bei Cannabis-Missbrauch [Forensic Medicine Evaluation of Dose-Effect Relationship in Cannabis Abuse].

Different methods for cannabis analysis including microscopic examination, TLC and GC are discussed. Along with these methods, the psychopharmacological effects of small doses of THC provice better grounds for forensic studies. A dose-activity relationship is given for THC using different routes of administration.

4953 Staats, G. R., Brit. J. Addict., *73*(4), 391-98 (1978).

An Empirical Assessment of Controls Affecting Marijuana Usage.

Supply, rather than secrecy or immorality, is the most important determinant of marihuana use.

4954 Staats, G. R., Contemp. Drug Probl., *6*(3), 437-49 (1977).

Effects of Supply, Secrecy, and Immorality on Marijuana Use: An Examination of the Becker Hypothesis.

Surveyed users indicated that the crucial factors influencing their marihuana use were drug access and supply, followed by secrecy of use. The immorality issue, however, was the least important determinant.

4955 Stahl, E.; and Brombeer, J., Deut. Apth. -Ztg., *118*(41), 1527-34 (1978).

Schnellnachweis von Rauschgiften mit der Dunnschicht-Chromatographie im Apothekenlaboratorium [TLC for the Rapid Identification of Some Hallucinogenic Drugs in the Pharmacy Laboratory].

A TLC procedure for hashish is presented. Comparison of DMF impregnated TLC plate with non-impregnated plates is given.

4956 Stanton, M. D., Amer. J. Drug Alcohol Abuse, *3*(4), 557-70 (1976).

Drugs, Vietnam, and the Vietnam Veteran: An Overview.

Marihuana use by military men was high during the Vietnam war. Whereas its use started before Vietnam, heroin use which replaced marihuana's in the early 70s, was clearly a "Vietnam phenomenon." What the military did to cope with illicit drug use was reviewed.

4957 Stanton, M. D.; Mintz, J.; and Franklin, R. M., Int. J. Addict., *11*(1), 53-69 (1976).

Drug Flashbacks. II. Some Additional Findings.

A review of several past studies relating to drug flashbacks is presented. One set of sample data was drawn from a survey of 2001 army personnel entering and leaving Vietnam. Statistical analysis of these data correlated marihuana use to LSD flashbacks, regardless of dose or frequency of use of either drug.

4958 Staquet, M.; Gantt, C.; and Machin. D., Clin. Pharmacol. Ther., *23*(4), 397-401 (1978).

Effect of a Nitrogen Analog of Tetrahydrocannabinol on Cancer Pain.

A study planned to examine the analgesic effect of a nitrogen-containing benzopyran derivative (NIB) related to delta-1-*trans*-THC was carried out using two consecutive, randomized, double-blind experiments. In each trial, NIB was found to be superior to placebo and 50 mg of secobarbital, but was equivalent to 50 mg of codeine phosphate. NIB is not usable in current medical practice due to side effects.

4959 Stark, P.; and Archer, R. A., Pharmacologist, *17*(2), 210 (1975).

Preclinical Pharmacologic Profile of a Psychoactive Cannabinoid.

Nabilone is shown to possess significant behavior altering effects orally and parenterally as determined by standard behavior assays in rats, dogs, and mice. Minimal effects on the cardiovascular systems of unanesthetized rabbit and dogs are detected at less than incapacitating doses.

4960 Stark, P.; Fabre, L. F.; Newell, F. W.; and Einhorn, L., Eleventh Collegium Internationale Neuro-Psychopharmacologicum: Abstracts, Vienna, Austria, July 9-14, 1978, p. 100.

Clinical and Pre-Clinical Pharmacology of a Synthetic Cannabinoid, Nabilone (Lilly Compound 109514).

Oral nabilone (1 mg t.i.d. for 28 days) induced a sustained improvement of anxiety symptomatology in patients with a generalized anxiety state. It also lowered IOP in glaucoma patients and blocked the emesis and nausea caused by various antineoplastic agents.

4961 Starks, M., *Marijuana Potency*. Berkeley, California, And/Or Press, 1977. 174 pp.

By knowing the potency of marihuana preparations, users will be able to estimate the degree of high from a given sample. Factors and ways to determine such a potency were discussed.

4962 Steadward, R. D.; and Singh, M., Med. Sci. Sports, 7(4), 309-11 (1975).

The Effects of Smoking Marihuana on Physical Performance.

Twenty male marihuana smokers were given 1.4 g marihuana cigarettes containing 18.2 mg Δ^9-THC or placebo cigarettes. An increase in heart rate was shown from control to marihuana and from placebo to marihuana. Hand grip strength showed no difference. However physical work capacity was reduced with placebo but significantly less with marihuana.

4963 Stefanis, C., pp. 149-78 in *The International Challenge of Drug Abuse*, edited by R. C. Petersen. NIDA Research Monograph 19, 1978.

Biological Aspects of Cannabis Use.

No significant differences in most of the investigated parameters were detected among hashish users and non-users. Chronic cannabis use was found to affect cell-nuclear metabolism, whereas its acute effects are correlated with changes in metabolism directly related to biogenic amine biosynthesis and function.

4964 Stefanis, C.; Boulougouris, J.; and Liakos, A., pp. 659-65 in *Pharmacology of Marihuana, Vol. 2*, edited by M. C. Braude and S. Szara. NY, Raven Press, 1976.

Clinical and Psychophysiological Effects of Cannabis in Long-Term Users.

To compare the effects of chronic marihuana use on physical and mental health, 47 male marihuana users and 40 non-users were examined clinically. Results showed that in most of the parameters tested, chronic users did not differ from controls. On the psycho-physiologic tests, only a few could discriminate between active substances and placebo.

4965 Stefanis, C.; Dornbush, R.; and Fink, M., eds., *Hashish: Studies of Long-Term Use*. New York, Raven Press, 181 (1977).

Aside from a higher incidence of psychopathic diagnosis and enlarged liver, extensive testing did not reveal any difference between this sample of Greek chronic cannabis users and their matched controls. Relationships to other major cross-cultural studies were also reviewed.

4966 Stefanis, C.; Liakos, A.; Boulougouris, J.; Fink, M.; and Freedman, A. M., Amer. J. Psychiat., *133*(2), 225-27 (1976).

Chronic Hashish Use and Mental Disorder.

Chronic hashish users were more likely to have prison records and unemployment than nonusers. Psychopathology was prevalent and included antisocial personality disorders, neuroses, and paranoid schiozophrenia.

4967 Stefanis, C.; Liakos, A.; and Boulougouris, J. C., pp. 58-63 in *Chronic Cannabis Use*, edited by R. L. Dornbush, A. M. Freedman, and M. Fink. NY, Annals of the New York Academy of Sciences, V. 282, 1976.

Incidence of Mental Illness in Hashish Users and Controls.

Greek cannabis users had a higher incidence of psychopathology (antisocial type) than did controls although the degree of use did not correlate with the incidence of such disturbances. Personality type predisposes to cannabis use, but cannabis use does not necessarily cause psychiatric disease.

4968 Stefanis, C.; Liakos, A.; Boulougouris, J. C.; Dornbush, R. L.; and Ballas, C., pp. 113-20 in *Chronic Cannabis Use*, edited by R. L. Dornbush, A. M. Freedman, and M. Fink. NY, Annals of the New York Academy of Sciences, V. 282, 1976.

Experimental Observations of a 3-Day Hashish Abstinence Period and Reintroduction.

In a 6-day, double-blind study chronic cannabis users did not develop tolerance to cannabis effects and did not evidence withdrawal symptoms upon cessation of use.

4969 Stefanis, C. N., *Eleventh Collegium Internationale Neuro-Psychopharmacologicum: Abstracts*, Vienna, Austria, July 9-14, 1978, p. 145.

Biological Effects of Cannabis Chronic Use in Man.

Chronic cannabis smoking affected human plasma nucleotide levels as well as plasma dopa-β-hydroxylase activity. Changes in nuclear metabolism and membrane of blood cells were also observed.

4970 Stefanis, C. N.; and Issidorides, M. R., pp. 533-50 in *Marihuana: Chemistry, Biochemistry, and Cellular Effects*, edited by G. G. Nahas. NY, Springer-Verlag, 1976.

Cellular Effects of Chronic Cannabis Use in Man.

This work presents findings obtained by the morphological, histochemical and ultrastructural investigation of blood cells and spermatozoa of chronic cannabis users.

4971 Stefanis, C. N.; and Issidorides, M. R., Science, *191*(4233), 1217 (1976).

Marihuana Effects.

The authors correct misinformation on sperm of men who were chronic users of cannabis. They found low arginine-rich protein (protamine) content in sperm nuclei indicating deviant maturation. However, sperm heads were normal which is necessary for normal condensation and reproductive capacity.

4972   Steffenhagen, R. A.; McCann, H. G.; and Merriam, G., J. Drug Educ., 8(2), 93-99 (1978).

A Case Against Decriminalization of Pot.

Using a questionnaire of 23 questions and 514 students (358 females and 156 males), patterns of drug use among undergraduates were investigated. The authors conclude that marihuana should be legalized.

4973   Steffenhagen, R. A.; Polich, J. M.; and Lash, S., Int. J. Soc. Psychiat., 24(2), 125-37 (1978).

Alienation, Delinquency and Patterns of Drug Use.

Alcohol was most commonly used by a surveyed sample of high school students, followed by marihuana and cigarette smoking. Also patterns of alcohol and cigarette use were established before, while those of marihuana and other illicit drugs were established during, the high school period. The increase in alcohol use was associated with a high level of marihuana consumption.

4974   Steinberg, S.; Offermeier, J.; Field, B. T.; and Jansen Van Ryssen, F. W., S. Afr. Med. J., 49, 279 (1975).

Investigation of the Influence of Soil Types, Environmental Conditions, Age and Morphological Plant Parts on the Chemical Composition of *Cannabis sativa* (Dagga) Plants.

The THC contents of several cannabis chemovariants is discussed. Dagga from South Africa is more potent than sam-

ples from British, American, Canadian, or Swiss seed. THCV is the major cannabinoid in one South African variant.

4975   Stenchever, M. A., pp. 25-30 in *Marijuana and Health Hazards*, edited by J. R. Tinklenberg. NY, Academic Press, 1975.

Observations on the Cytogenetic Effects of Marijuana.

Implications of the presence of a chromosome damaging agent in marihuana makes the issue worth pursuing. The use of newer techniques in assessing such an effect is important and follow-up studies are complicated. Whether THC is the marihuana component responsible for the chromosomal damage or not is a serious question. Carefully planned teratogenic studies and animal experiments should be undertaken.

4976   Stenchever, M. A.; Parks, K. J.; and Stenchever, M. R., pp. 257-63 in *Marihuana: Chemistry, Biochemistry, and Cellular Effects*, edited by G. G. Nahas. NY, Springer-Verlag, 1976.

Effects of Δ^8-Tetrahydrocannabinol, Δ^9-Tetrahydrocannabinol and Crude Marihuana on Human Cells in Tissue Culture.

Possible chromosome damage and aneuploidy in human leukocytes pretreated in tissue culture for 4 hrs with Δ^8-THC, Δ^9-THC, and crude marihuana extract in varying amounts was investigated.

4977   Stepanov, G. S., Tsitol. Genet., 10(5), 458-61 (1977).

Inheritability of the Basic Elements of Productivity and the Expected Gain on Account of Them in a Population of Different Types of Interspecies Hemp Hybrids (Rus.).

The number and weight of seeds in hemp hybrids depend on growth condition. Plant height and stem fiber content are highly inheritable regardless of crossing types.

4978   Stepanov, G. S., Tsitol. Genet., *10*(4), 326-30 (1977).

Relationship Between Crossing Type and Character of Variability and Inheritability of Plant Height in Populations of Intervarietal Hemp Hybrids (Rus.).

The law of basic elements of productivity in interspecies hemp hybrids was studied and the genetic acquisition of each of these hybrids for practical work was predicted. Results indicated that influence of genotype on phenotype is best observed during simple and complicated interspecies crossing. Height of plant and content of fiber in stalk were the best index of reproducibility.

4979   Stewart, J.; Nielson, P. J.; and Neidig, P. H., Int. J. Addict., *13*(5), 831-37 (1978).

An Investigation of Procedures Reported to Increase Potency of Marijuana: A Chemical Analysis and Psychological Interpretation.

Three procedures reported to enhance the drug quality of marihuana were investigated. No chemical basis was found to justify these reports. No Δ^9-THC was produced from other cannabinoids.

4980   Stillman, R.; Eich, J. E.; Weingartner, H.; and Wyatt, R. J., pp. 453-56 in *Pharmacology of Marihuana, Vol. 1*, edited by M. C. Braude and S. Szara. NY, Raven Press, 1976.

Marihuana-Induced State-Dependent Amnesia and its Reversal by Cueing.

Male human volunteers under the influence of marihuana (10 mg THC/ cigarette) showed state dependent loss of memory. However, cueing helped the subjects to recall most of the words they had missed earlier.

4981   Stillman, R.; Galanter, M.; Lemberger, L.; Fox, S.; Weingartner, H.; and Wyatt, R. J., Life Sci., *19*, 569-76 (1976).

Tetrahydrocannabinol (THC): Metabolism and Subjective Effects.

Both subjective "high" and blood concentration of THC peaked rapidly in human users after smoking marihuana cigarettes (10 mg of Δ^9-THC). The former THC effects lasted longer under non-stressful conditions. Standardized natural inhalation techniques, used in the present study, resulted in reproducible levels of Δ^9-THC.

4982   Stillman, R. C.; Wolkowitz, O.; Weingartner, H.; Waldman, I.; Derenzo, E. V.; and Wyatt, R. J., Life Sci., *21*(12), 1793-99 (1977).

Marijuana: Differential Effects on Right and Left Hemisphere Functions in Man.

The effect of marihuana on cerebral dominance to verbal and pictorial stimuli was examined in right handed males. Marihuana slowed the reaction to pictorial stimuli in both cerebral hemispheres but the left hemisphere was significantly slower than the right hemisphere. Reaction time to verbal stimuli was equally affected.

4983   Stillman, R. C., Wyatt, R. J.; Murphy, D. L.; and Rauscher, F. P., Life Sci., *23*(15), 1577-81 (1978).

Low Platelet Monoamine Oxidase Activity and Chronic Marijuana Use.

Marihuana users had lower MAO activity than nonusers and an inverse relationship existed between this activity and current use of marihuana. Also acute marihuana smoking did not reduce MAO activity *in vivo* and THC concentrations above 1×10^{-5} were required to induce significant *in vitro* inhibition of this enzyme.

4984 Stoeckel, M.; Weber, E.; Connor, T.; and Legator, M. S., *Sixth Annual Meeting, Environmental Mutagen Society*, May 9-12, 1975, Miami Beach, Florida.

Failure to Detect Mutagenic Effects of Delta-9-Tetrahydrocannabinol in *in vitro* and *in vivo* Studies with Mice.

Tester strains, TA 1535 and TA 1538, of the histidine auxotrophs of *S. typhimurium* were used to determine if Δ^9-THC induced gene mutations. Mice also were administered by gavage, 200 mg/kg/day THC for seven days and their blood, urine and tissues were examined. No mutations were observed in either situation or in a dominant lethal study.

4985 Stoller, K.; Swanson, G. D.; and Bellville, J. W., J. Clin. Pharmacol., *16*(5,6), 271-75 (1976).

Effects on Visual Tracking of Δ^9-Tetrahydrocannabinol and Pentobarbital.

Δ^9-THC (22.5 mg, p.o.) or pentobarbital impaired performance of subjects under a critical tracking task, the impairment being significant in the former case only.

4986 Stoller, K. P.; Swanson, G. D.; and Bellville, J. W., Pharmacologist, *17*(2), 181 (1975).

Effects on Visual Tracking of Δ^9-Tetrahydrocannabinol and Pentobarbital.

22.5 mg Δ^9-THC, 150 mg pentobarbital or placebo was administered to five subjects. The mean score of a tracking test decreased with THC and pentobarbital. THC was found significantly different from placebo; however, pentobarbital was not.

4987 Stone, C. J.; and Forney, R. B., Toxicol. Lett., *1*(5,6), 331-35 (1978).

The Effects of Cannabidiol or Delta-9-Tetrahydrocannabinol on Phencyclidine-Induced Activity in Mice.

Treatment of mice with 20 mg/kg of THC or CBD in combination with phencyclidine significantly lowered their activity counts below those of phencyclidine alone. CBD also prolonged phencyclidine half-life in whole mouse homogenates.

4988 Stone, C. J.; McCoy, D. J.; and Forney, R. B., J. Forensic Sci., *21*(1), 108-11 (1976).

Combined Effect of Methaqualone and Two Cannabinoids.

Male mice pretreated with CBD and Δ^9-THC (10-30 mg/kg, i.p.) prior to methaqualone slept longer than control mice. THC was more potent than CBD with respect to sleeptime prolongation. Changes in absorption, distribution, or excretion of MQ as well as metabolism may contribute to the effects elicited by the cannabinoids.

4989 Strichartz, G. R.; Chiu, S. Y.; and Ritchie, J. M., J. Pharmacol. Exp. Ther., *207*(3), 801-09 (1978).

The Effect of Δ^9-Tetrahydrocannabinol on the Activation of Sodium Conductance in Node of Ranvier.

Δ^9-THC reduced voltage-dependent sodium conductance in frog nerve fibers.

This was accomplished by inhibiting activation of sodium channels and reducing maximum sodium conductance.

4990 Stromberg, L., J. Chromatogr., *12*(2), 313-22 (1976).

Minor Components of Cannabis Resin. VI. Mass Spectrometric Data and Gas Chromatographic Retention Times of Components Eluted after Cannabinol.

Thirty components of cannabis resin were detected by means of GC/MS. Many of the detected compounds were found to be (poly)-hydroxylated cannabinoids but they are not fully characterized.

4991 Stuart, R. B.; Guire, K.; and Krell, M., Contemp. Drug Probl., *5*(4), 553-63 (1976).

Penalty for the Possession of Marijuana: An Analysis of Some of its Concomitants.

Although the legal issues dealing with marihuana use proved quite controversial, the pattern of its use by high school students was not greatly influenced by these issues.

4992 Sulkowski, A.; and Vachon, L., Amer. J. Psychiat., *134*(6), 691-92 (1977).

Side Effects of Simultaneous Alcohol and Marijuana Use.

Nausea and vomiting were experienced in 4 of 7 subjects given both alcohol and marihuana. Autonomic and behavioral disturbances were also evident.

4993 Sulkowski, A.; Vachon, L.; and Rich, E. S., Psychopharmacology, *52*(1), 47-53 (1977).

Propranolol Effects on Acute Marihuana Intoxication in Man.

Propranolol antagonized the marihuana (10 mg/kg of THC)-induced subjective "high," learning impairment, and heart rate and BP increases in experienced subjects. Propranolol alone, however, affected only the heart rate and BP.

4994 Sullivan, H. R.; Kau, D. L. K.; and Wood, P. G., Proc. Int. Conf. Stable Isot., 2nd, 1975, 196-76 (1976).

Plasma Levels of *dl*-3-(1,1-Dimethylheptyl)-6, 6 β, 7, 8, 10, 10a α-Hexahyro-1-Hydroxy-6, 6-Dimethyl-9H-Dibenzo [b, d] Pyran-9-One (Lilly 109514) by Quantitative Mass Fragmentography.

An analytical method for the quantitation of nabilone using quantitative MS is discussed. Standard curves, accuracy, precision and sensitivity are discussed. Half life of nabilone and its major metabolite are compared and pharmacokinetics of nabilone and metabolites are investigated.

4995 Sullivan, H. R.; Kau, D. L. K.; and Wood, P. G., Biomed. Mass Spectrom., *5*(4), 296-301 (1978).

Pharmacokinetics of Nabilone, a Psychotropically Active 9-Ketocannabinoid, in the Dog. Utilization of Quantitative Selected Ion Monitoring and Deuterium Labeling.

A new sensitive and specific selected ion monitoring method was used to determine plasma concentration of nabilone and two metabolites in treated dogs. The method was described and results were detailed.

4996 Sullivan, M. F.; and Willard, D. H., Fed. Proc., *35*(3), 643 (1976).

The Effect of Chronic Marihuana Smoking on the Beagle Dog (Abstract).

4997 Sullivan, M. F.; and Willard, D. H., Toxicol. Appl. Pharmacol., *45*(2), 445-62 (1978).

The Beagle Dog as an Animal Model for Marihuana Smoking Studies.

Marihuana decreased the respiration and heart rate of Beagle dogs trained to smoke it. Tolerance developed to the induced heart rate decrease but failed to develop to marihuana-induced muscular weakness and loss of reflexes. Chronic effects of marihuana were also studied.

4998 Symons, A. M.; Teale, J. D.; and Marks, V., J. Endocrinol., *68*(3), 43P-44P (1976).

Effect of Δ^9-Tetrahydrocannabinol on the Hypothalamic-Pituitary-Gonadal System in the Maturing Male Rat.

Acute or subchronic treatment of male rats with Δ^9-THC (5 mg/kg, i.v.) suppressed plasma LH and testosterone levels and lowered the pituitary response to LH-releasing hormone. Such a response was more pronounced under acute conditions.

4999 Szara, S., pp. 27-33 in *Pharmacology of Marihuana, Vol. 1*, edited by M. C. Braude and S. Szara. NY, Raven Press, 1976.

Clinical Pharmacology of Cannabis: Scientific and Nonscientific Constraints.

Chemical and psychopharmacological peculiarities of cannabis products are listed along with an enumeration of marihuana's potential as a health hazard and as a therapeutic agent. Increasing constraints on the accumulation of knowledge about marihuana arise due to the illicit status of marihuana use and social opprobrium, difficulties of obtaining a research license, and the diminishing availability of funding.

5000 Szepsenwol, J.; Fletcher, J.; and Toro-Goyco, E., Fed. Proc., *37*(3), 450 (1978).

Effects of Δ^9-Tetrahydrocannabinol in Mice (Abstract).

Neonatal mice treated weekly with 20 μg of Δ^9-THC reproduced, but their offspring died of starvation unless foster nursed by lactating females. One animal developed fibrosarcoma at the injection site. Transplants of the tumor grew faster and were detected earlier in Δ^9-THC-treated mice.

T

5001 Taboada, M. E.; and Monti, J. M., *Seventh International Congress of Pharmacology: Abstracts*, Paris, France, July 16-21, 1978, p. 195.

The Effects of the Combined Administration of *Cannabis sativa* Derivatives on the Sleep-Wakefulness Cycle of the Rat.

While Δ^9-THC (2.5-10 mg/kg) increased wakefulness and decreased slow wave sleep in a dose-related manner, CBD (10-40 mg/kg) had opposite actions. REM sleep was depressed by both cannabinoids and by CBN (10-40 mg/kg). Effects of combinations of the three cannabinoids on the different sleep parameters were also investigated and discussed.

5002 Takahashi, R. N.; and Karniol, I. G., Psychopharmacologia, *41*, 277-84 (1975).

Pharmacological Interaction Between Cannabinol and Δ^9-Tetrahydrocannabinol.

When comparing the effects of CBN to those of Δ^9-THC on rats, mice and rabbits by using several pharmacological tests, CBN was less potent. The depressant effect of Δ^9-THC was potentiated when given concomitantly with CBN. In assessing the effects of cannabis, attention should be paid not only to the amount of Δ^9-THC present, but also to the content of CBN in the sample.

5003 Takahashi, R. N.; Zuardi, A. W.; and Karniol, I. G., Rev. Bras. Pesqui. Med. Biol., *10*(6), 379-85 (1977).

Composicao Quimica E Importanica Dos Diversos Constituintes Na Atividade Farmacologica de Amostras de *Cannabis sativa* Brasileiras [Chemical Composition of Brazilian Marihuana Samples and the Importance of Several Constituents to the Pharmacological Activity of the Plant].

Analysis of seized Brazilian marihuana samples by GC showed the presence of Δ^9-THC and CBN in high concentration, whereas the amounts of Δ^8-THC and CBD were low. Comparison of the levels of Δ^9-THC in these samples with samples used in other countries is made. Pharmacological studies of a natural marihuana extract and a synthetic one having the same proportions of cannabinoids were found not to be identical in all animal tests used.

5004 Takeya, K.; and Itokawa, H., Chem. Pharm. Bull., *25*(8), 1947-51 (1977).

Stereochemistry in the Oxidation of Allylic Alcohols by a Cell-Free System of Callus Induced from *Cannabis sativa L.*

A cell free system of callus induced from *Cannabis sativa* was used to study the stereochemistry involved in the bio-oxidation of secondary allylic alcohols.

5005 Talbott, J. A., pp. 153-61 in *Acute Drug Abuse Emergencies: A Treatment Manual*, edited by R. G. Bourne. NY, Academic Press, 1976.

Emergency Management of Marihuana Psychosis.

Patients manifesting marihuana-induced psychotic reactions should be treated with reassuring, positive words. Drug treatment, however, should not be exercised unless severe reactions are encountered.

5006 Tamir, I.; Lichtenberg, D.; and Mechoulam, R., pp. 405-22 in *Nuclear Magnetic Resonance Spectroscopy in Molecular Biology (Jerusalem Symp.*

Quantum Chem. Biochem.), edited by B. Pullman. Dordrecht, Holland, D. Reidel Publishing Company, 1978.

Interaction of Cannabinoids with Model Membranes - NMP Studies.

A comparison was made between the effects of Δ^9-THC and CBD on the physical properties of model membranes (sonicated dispersions of egg yolk lecithine), using LH and ^{31}P NMR determinations. The drug-induced changes in the size of the vesicle, the cation binding capacity of the membrane surface and the motional state of the hydrocarbon chain of the phospholipids were studied. A mechanism for psychoactivity of Δ^9-THC is postulated.

5007   Tashkin, D. P.; Calvarese, B.; and Simmons, M., Amer. Rev. Resp. Dis., *117*(4, pt. 2), 261 (1978).

Respiratory Status of 75 Chronic Marijuana Smokers: Comparison with Matched Controls (Abstract).

Chronic marihuana smoking by human subjects was more detrimental to respiratory functions than was tobacco smoking.

5008   Tashkin, D. P.; Levisman, J. A.; Abbasi, A. S.; Shapiro, B. J.; and Ellis, N. M., Chest, *72*(1), 20-26 (1977).

Short-Term Effects of Smoked Marihuana on Left Ventricular Function in Man.

Marihuana smoking increased the heart rate and cardiac output of experienced users tested in an in-hospital stay condition. It also slightly decreased the stroke volume while it did not change the BP or left ventricular function.

5009   Tashkin, D. P.; Reiss, S.; Shapiro, B. J.; Calvarese, B.; Olsen, J. L.; and Lodge, J. W., Amer. Rev. Resp. Dis., *115*(1), 57-65 (1977).

Bronchial Effects of Aerosolized Δ^9-Tetrahydrocannabinol in Healthy and Asthmatic Subjects.

Δ^9-THC as an aerosol or p.o., produced bronchodilatation in normal and asthmatic subjects. This therapeutic potential is, however, limited by local irritation or psychophysiologic effects depending on route of administration.

5010   Tashkin, D. P.; Shapiro, B.; Reiss, S.; Olsen, J.; and Lodge, J., pp. 97-109 in *The Therapeutic Potential of Marihuana*, edited by S. Cohen and R. Stillman. NY, Plenum Medical Book Company, 1976.

Bronchial Effects of Aerosolized Δ^9-Tetrahydrocannabinol.

Experiments conducted on healthy subjects suggested that THC administered as an aerosol was more beneficial than oral or smoked THC in inducing bronchodilatation with less side effects.

5011   Tashkin, D. P.; Shapiro, B. J.; and Frank, I. M., pp. 785-801 in *Pharmacology of Marihuana, Vol. 2*, edited by M. C. Braude and S. Szara. NY, Raven Press, 1976.

Acute Effects of Marihuana on Airway Dynamics in Spontaneous and Experimentally Induced Bronchial Asthma.

Marihuana, either inhaled or administered orally to asthmatic patients, resulted in a long lasting bronchial dilatation. Comparison between THC and isoproterenol reversal of bronchoconstriction induced by methacholine or exercise was studied.

5012   Tashkin, D. P.; Shapiro, B. J.; Lee, Y. E.; and Harper, C. E., Amer. Rev. Resp. Dis., *112*(3), 377-86 (1975).

Effects of Smoked Marihuana in Experimentally Induced Asthma.

Both isoproterenol and 500 mg of smoked marihuana containing 2% Δ^9-THC reversed the methacholine- or exercise-induced bronchospasm in asthmatic patients.

5013 Tashkin, D. P.; Shapiro, B. J.; Lee, Y. E.; and Harper, C. E., New Eng. J. Med., *294*, 125-29 (1976).

Subacute Effects of Heavy Marihuana Smoking on Pulmonary Function in Healthy Men.

Experienced cannabis smokers were tested for pulmonary function after 7 to 9 weeks of ad-libitum marihuana smoking (averaged 5.2 cigarettes/day, 900 mg marihuana at 2.2% THC/cigarette). Significant differences in the acute effects of one cigarette on maximal mid-expiratory flow rate, airway resistance and specific airway conductance were observed between early intoxication (beginning of study) and late intoxication. Tolerance was said to develop to the broncodilation effects. After 1 week and 1 month of no smoking reversal of the airway impairment occurred.

5014 Tashkin, D. P.; Shapiro, B. J.; Ramanna, L.; Taplin, G. V.; Lee, Y. E.; and Harper, C. E., pp. 291-95 in *Pharmacology of Marihuana*, edited by M. C. Braude and S. Szara. NY, Raven Press, 1976.

Chronic Effects of Heavy Marihuana Smoking on Pulmonary Function in Healthy Young Males.

Chronically, unlimited access to Δ^9-THC resulted in slight constriction of both large and small airways of the lungs. Acutely, however, bronchodilation was observed in the early and late period of intoxication, although the amount of bronchodilation in the late period of intoxication decreased slightly.

5015 Tashkin, D. P.; Shapiro, B. J.; Reiss, S.; Olsen, J. L.; and Lodge, J. W., Amer. Rev. Resp. Dis., *113*(4) 167 (1976).

Bronchial Effects of Aerosolized Δ^9-Tetrahydrocannabinol (THC).

Aerosolized Δ^9-THC was found to be more efficacious than oral THC (20 mg) or smoking marihuana (20 mg THC) in producing bronchodilation. Not only did it have a shorter onset and longer duration, but it also produced fewer side effects. THC was also compared to nebulized isoproterenol.

5016 Tashkin, D. P.; Shapiro, B. J.; Rosenthal, D.; and McLatchie, C., Amer. Rev. Resp. Dis., *111*(6), 895 (1975).

Chronic Effects of Heavy Marihuana Smoking on Pulmonary Function and Sputum Cytology in Healthy, Young Men (Abstract).

Smoking marihuana by healthy users resulted in airway narrowing without any changes in sputum cytologic features.

5017 Tashkin, D. P., Soares, J. R.; Hepler, R. S.; Shapiro, B. J.; and Rachelefsky, G. S., Ann. Intern. Med., *89*(4), 539-49 (1978).

Cannabis, 1977: UCLA Conference.

The therapeutic potentials of cannabis are worth further investigation. Marihuana increases heart rate and diminishes peak exercise performance, but its effects on the immunologic system are still a debatable issue.

5018 Tassinari, C. A.; Ambrosetto, G.; Peraita-Adrados, M. R.; and Gastaut, H., pp. 357-82 in *Pharmacology of Marihuana, Vol. 1*, edited by M. C. Braude and S. Szara. NY, Raven Press, 1976.

The Neuropsychiatric Syndrome of Δ^9-Tetrahydrocannabinol and Cannabis Intoxication in Naive Subjects: A Clinical and Polygraphic Study During Wakefulness and Sleep.

Acute oral administration of Δ^9-THC (0.7 to 1.0 mg/kg) to naive subjects induced similar effects to those caused by a 10 g dose of hashish containing equivalent amounts of Δ^9-THC. Effects included severe intoxication leading to significant changes in nocturnal sleep and a typical psychic and neurological syndrome. Tolerance to the actions of this cannabinoid could account for the differences between these effects and the ones observed in chronic cannabis users.

5019   Tayal, G.; Goel, S.; Srivastava, V. K.; and Srivastava, R. K., Indian J. Physiol. Pharmacol., 20(2), 117-18 (1976).

Anti-Inflammatory Activity of Δ^9-Tetrahydrocannabinol.

THC was found to be an effective anti-inflammatory agent in rats. Possible site of action was indicated.

5020   Tayal, G.; Sinha, J. N.; Srivastava, R. K.; Srivastava, V. K.; and Bhargava, K. P., Indian J. Physiol. Pharmacol., 20(2), 118 (1976).

Some Behavioral Studies with Cannabis.

Results of several behavioral measures in rats, mice and rabbits indicated that cannabis has definite tranquilizing properties.

5021   Taylor, D. A.; and Fennessy, M. R., Eur. J. Pharmacol., 46(2), 93-99 (1977).

Biphasic Nature of the Effects of Δ^9-Tetrahydrocannabinol on Body Temperature and Brain Amines of the Rat.

Administration of THC resulted in a biphasic effect on body temperature of rats, i.e., hyperthermia in low doses and hypothermia in doses greater than 0.5 mg/kg. This biphasic effect correlated inversely with 5-HIAA levels and no changes in brain catecholamines were noted. THC also caused biphasic changes in rat behavior.

5022   Taylor, D. A.; and Fennessy, M. R., J. Pharm. Pharmacol., 30(10), 654-56 (1978).

'Antagonist'-Precipitated Withdrawal in the Rat after Chronic Δ^9-Tetrahydrocannabinol Treatment.

Behavioral changes suggestive of withdrawal symptoms were observed in rats treated with Δ^9-THC when challenged with clorimipramine. THC reduced body weight and food intake in the treated rats.

5023   Taylor, D. A.; and Fennessy, M. R., Psychopharmacology, 56(3), 279-85 (1978).

Relationship Between Body Temperature and Brain Monoamines During the Development of Tolerance to Δ^9-Tetrahydrocannabinol in the Rat.

The results of this 10-day study show that THC induced tolerance to hypothermia, while inducing elevation of 5-HIAA levels in a linear manner. THC did not markedly affect brain levels of NE or DA.

5024   Taylor, D. A.; Lewis, S. J.; and Fennessy, M. R., Proc. Aust. Physiol. Pharmacol. Soc., 9(2), 182 (1978).

The Effect of Acute Δ^9-Tetrahydrocannabinol on Central and Peripheral Histamine in the Rat.

Δ^9-THC (2 mg/kg, i.v.) decreased the histamine levels in brain, heart, liver and ileum of rats, but increased them in the lungs. A biphasic effect of Δ^9-THC on brain histamine was also noted and implications of the findings were discussed.

5025   Taylor, S. P.; Vardaris, R. M.; Rawtich, A. B.; Gammon, C. B.; Cranston, J. W.; and Lubetkin, A. I., Aggress. Behav., *2*(2), 153-61 (1976).

The Effects of Alcohol and Delta-9-Tetrahydrocannabinol on Human Physical Aggression.

By allowing subjects to shock other volunteers before and after provocation, researchers probed the effects of THC and alcohol on the degree of aggressiveness produced by the same unpleasant stimuli. The higher the dose of alcohol consumed, the more aggressive was the response. Conversely, higher doses of THC caused a decrement in aggressive responding.

5026   Teale, J. D.; Clough, J. M.; Fry, D.; Backhouse, C.; and Marks, V., Proc. Eur. Soc. Toxicol., *18*(Clin. Toxicol.), 252-54 (1977).

The Use of Radioimmunoassay in the Detection of Urinary Cannabinoids.

RIA was used for the detection of Δ^9-THC and other cross-reactive cannabinoids in urine. The procedure was used to screen 1002 urine specimens collected from various sources with the advantages of sensitivity, ease and speed.

5027   Teale, J. D.; Clough, J. M.; King, L. J.; Marks, V.; Williams, P. L.; and Moffat, A. C., J. Forensic Sci. Soc., *17*(2-3), 177-83 (1977).

The Incidence of Cannabinoids in Fatally Injured Drivers: An Investigation by Radioimmunoassay and High Pressure Liquid Chromatography.

Postmortem blood analysis, by RIA, of fatally injured drivers revealed cannabis use in 6 out of 66 subjects. However, when detection techniques combined the above method with HPLC, three more cannabis use cases were identified.

5028   Teale, J. D.; Clough, J. M.; Piall, E. M.; King, L. J.; and Marks, V., Res. Commun. Pathol. Pharmacol., *11*(2), 339-42 (1975).

Plasma Cannabinoids Measured by Radioimmunoassay in Rabbits after Intravenous Injection of Tetrahydrocannabinol, 11-Hydroxy-Tetrahydrocannabinol, Cannabinol and Cannabidiol.

In vivo testing by RIA using sheep antiserum, when THC, 11-OH-THC, CBN or CBD were injected (80 µg/kg), rabbits showed: CBN and its metabolites are not cross-reacting cannabinoids (CRC), CBN is a CRC but its metabolites are not CRC, and THC and 11-OH-THC are CRC and are additive.

5029   Teale, J. D.; Forman, E. J.; King, L. J.; Piall, E. M.; and Marks, V., J. Pharm. Pharmacol., *27*(7), 465-72 (1975).

The Development of a Radioimmunoassay for Cannabinoids in Blood and Urine.

A discussion of the experimental considerations required for the use of a RIA for Δ^9-THC. The assay is designed for three-ringed cannabinoids and shows cross-reaction among members of this class. THC binding to plasma precluded a direct analysis from serum while no such problem was encountered in urine analysis.

5030   Teal, D.; and Marks, V., Lancet, *1*(7965), 884-85 (1976).

A Fatal Motor-Car Accident and Cannabis Use.

This is a case report of a 19 year old crashing into a truck. At postmortem examination blood and urine were checked for alcohol and THC-cross-reacting cannabinoids using RIA. No alcohol was found but plasma contained THC-CRC at a concentration of 315 ng/ml and urine at a concentration of 1210 ng/ml.

5031   Teitel, B., Amer. J. Psychiat., *134*(5), 587 (1977).

Observations on Marijuana Withdrawal (Letter).

The author, a private practitioner, had noticed a manic-depressive type of illness among patients believed to have withdrawn from prolonged use of marihuana.

5032   Ten Ham, M., Pharmacol. Biochem. Behav., *6*(2), 183-85 (1977).

Tolerance to the Effects of Δ^9-THC on Shuttle-Box Performance and Body Temperature.

Tolerance to the behavioral inhibiting effect of THC (20 mg/kg, i.p.) developed in trained rats regardless of whether the drug was administered before or after the shuttle-box test. Tolerance also developed to the THC-induced hypothermia.

5033   Ten Ham, M.; and De Jong, Y., New Eng. J. Med., *298*(14), 798-99 (1978).

"Anti-Emetic" Activity of Tetrahydrocannabinol in Rats and Pigeons (Letter).

The possible antiemetic properties of THC were investigated. THC was found to antagonize the apomorphine-induced behavioral symptoms in pigeons and, to a lesser extent, in rats.

5034   Ten Ham, M.; and De Jong, Y., Pharm. Weekbl., *110*(47), 1157-61 (1975).

Effects of Δ^9-Tetrahydrocannabinol and Cannabidiol on Blood Glucose Concentrations in Rabbits and Rats.

Rabbits were injected i.v. with THC (1 or 5 mg/kg) and insulin s.c. An increase in blood sugar was found after the THC injection. Adrenalectomized rats were administered THC and a decrease in blood glucose developed. CBD was found to antagonize the action of insulin.

5035   Ten Ham, M.; and De Jong, Y., Psychopharmacologia, *41*(2), 169-74 (1975).

Absence of Interaction Between Δ^9-Tetrahydrocannabinol (Δ^9-THC) and Cannabidiol (CBD) in Aggression, Muscle Control and Body Temperature Experiments in Mice.

Male Swiss mice, after 6 weeks of tactile and visual isolation, received Δ^9-THC and/or CBD. THC administration produced a dose-related depression of aggression and body temperature. THC did not alter motor coordination. CBD appeared to depress aggression but did not influence motor coordination or body temperature. No interaction between THC and CBD was noted.

5036   Ten Ham, M.; Loskota, W. J.; and Lomax, P., Eur. J. Pharmacol., *31*(3), 148-52 (1975).

Acute and Chronic Effects of Δ^9-Tetrahydrocannabinol on Seizures in the Gerbil.

20 mg/kg of Δ^9-THC did not offer any protection when given i.p. to seizure sensitive gerbils while a dose of 50 mg/kg of the agent protected the animals from spontaneous seizures. Tolerance to the anticonvulsive effect developed by the sixth day, while the toxic syndrome appeared to increase in severity.

5037   Tennant, F. S.; and Detels, R., Prev. Med., 5(1), 70-77 (1976).

Relationship of Alcohol, Cigarette, and Drug Abuse in Adulthood with Alcohol, Cigarette and Coffee Consumption in Childhood.

An epidemiological survey carried out among American soldiers based in Germany revealed that people who started drinking coffee and alcohol or smoking cigarettes before twelve years of age were more prone to abuse hashish and other commonly abused drugs including alcohol. Thus, if the use of alcohol, tobacco and coffee could be curbed in children below 13 years, perhaps the number of people abusing drugs and alcohol could be lowered.

5038   Tennant, F. S., Jr.; and Detels, R., in Committee on Problem of Drug Dependence, 1976. Division of Medical Sciences, National Research Council, National Academy of Sciences, Washington, D. C., 1976, pp. 667-78.

Relationship of Alcohol, Cigarette, and Drug Abuse in Adulthood with Alcohol, Cigarette, and Coffee Consumption in Childhood.

See above abstract.

5039   Thacore, V. R.; and Shukla, S. R. P., Arch. Gen. Psychiat., 33(3), 383-86 (1976).

Cannabis Psychosis and Paranoid Schizophrenia.

A clinical contrast between long-term cannabis paranoia and paranoid schizophrenia is given. Psychoses of cannabis origin are associated with some insight into the disease process while paranoid schizophrenia usually implies complete loss of contact with reality. In contrast to paranoid schizophrenics, cannabis-induced psychotics tend to demonstrate rapid and flighty patterns of ideation intermingled with elation-panic episodes.

5040   Thakkar, A. L.; Hirsch, C. A.; and Page, J. G., J. Pharm. Pharmacol., 29(12), 783-84 (1977).

Solid Dispersion Approach for Overcoming Bioavailability Problems Due to Polymorphism of Nabilone, A Cannabinoid Derivative.

Nabilone, is a potential anti-anxiety agent, and is essentially insoluble in water. Recrystallizations of the compound on some dry medium for capsular administration result in gradual decreases in bioavailability of the drug. Dispersion of nabilone in a polyvinylpyrrolidone matrix maintains the compound in a bioavailable form for at least 2 years.

5041   Thomas, R. J., Toxicol. Appl. Pharmacol., 32, 184-90 (1975).

The Toxicologic and Teratologic Effects of Δ^9-Tetrahydrocannabinol in the Zebrafish Embryo.

When using embryos of Zebrafish at late high blastula, exposure to THC (up to 10 ppm concentration) cannot be considered cytotoxic.

5042   Thompson, G.; and Yang, C., pp. 457-73 in The Therapeutic Potential of Marihuana, edited by S. Cohen and R. Stillman. NY, Plenum Medical Book Company, 1976.

336

Comparative Toxicities of Tetrahydro-pyridobenzopyrans.

Toxicity evaluation of the three tetra-hydropyridobenzopyrans, SP-1, SP-106 and SPA-80 in rats, dogs and monkeys indicated behavioral and physiological effects similar to the ones produced by cannabinoids under acute and subacute conditions. These results seem to warrant the initiation of human efficacy studies.

5043   Thompson, G. R.; and Ford, T. M., Pharmacologist, *17*(2), 181 (1975).

Ophthalmic Toxicity of **ABBOTT**-41988, A Synthetic Cannabinoid Congener, in Dogs.

ABBOTT-41988 at 1.0, 2.8 and 80 mg/kg was administered p.o. to 40 beagles for 30 days and the effects were compared to those of Δ^9-THC. Ophthalmic effects were less for THC than for **ABBOTT**-41988. The other effects studied were similar.

5044   Thompson, G. R.; and Levin, S., Toxicol. Appl. Pharmacol., *33*(1), 160 (1975).

Subacute Oral Toxicity of **ABBOTT**-41988, A Synthetic Cannabinoid Congener.

In a study of 50 male and 50 female rats administered 2, 10, and 50 mg/kg/day of **ABBOTT**-41988, female rats were more sensitive. Both sexes showed toxicity similar to other cannabinoids although pharmacological effects differed.

5045   Thompson, G. R.; Rosenkrantz, H.; Fleischman, R. W.; and Braude, M. C., Toxicology, *4*, 41-51 (1975).

Effects of Δ^9-Tetrahydrocannabinol Administered Subcutaneously to Rabbits for 28 Days.

Administration of Δ^9-THC for 28 days resulted in several manifestations of dermal toxicity and hemochemical changes in rabbits. Decreased body and liver weight along with decreased liver glycogen were also evident.

5046   Thorn, W. R., Diss. Abst. Int. B, *35*(8), 3843 (1975).

Synthetic Approaches to (-)-Δ^8-*Trans*-Tetrahydrocannabinol and Related Compounds.

Δ^8-*trans*-THC was synthesized through the condensation of (-)-Verbenol, *cis*-pin-3-en-2-o1, and olivetol. A base catalysed approach using dihydro-olivetol yielded fewer isomeric products. Other techniques using various derivatized starting reagents is also discussed with the need to minimize the number of side-products.

5047   Tiess, D., Krim. Forensische Wiss., *25*, 93-105 (1976).

Beitrag zur Systematischen Chemisch-Analytischen Bestimmung and Differenzierung von Cannabis-Praparaten Mittels Dunnschicht- und Gaschromatographie [Systematic Thin-Layer and Gas Chromatography Chemico-Analytical Determination and Differentiation of Cannabis].

Confiscated cannabis preparations (hashish, marihuana) of various geographical sources were extracted with chloroform. The extracts were studied by GC and TLC. Turkish, Indian, Lebanese, Arabian, Afghanistanian and Mexican samples were examined. The method of analysis was described in detail and the test results as well as the desirable interpretations and conclusions were presented and explained in 8 figures.

5048 Tinklenberg, J. R., ed., *Marihuana and Health Hazards: Methodological Issues in Current Research*. NY, Academic Press, Inc., 1975. 178 pp.

This book summarizes the issues investigated at the Drug Abuse Council Inc. meeting at Washington, D. C. The areas of concern were the effect of marihuana on immunity, genetics, testosterone, psychiatric problems, and the central nervous system.

5049 Tinklenberg, J. R., Ration. Drug Ther., 9(7), 1-6 (1975).

What a Physician Should Know About Marihuana.

The author summarizes the metabolism, cardiovascular effects, DNA synthesis, altered susceptibility and other physio-pharmacological and psychological effects of marihuana.

5050 Tinklenberg, J. R.; and Darley, C. F., pp. 429-43 in *Pharmacology of Marihuana, Vol. 1*, edited by M. C. Braude and S. Szara. NY, Raven Press, 1976.

A Model of Marihuana's Cognitive Effects.

A new model of human memory is described. There is constant exchange between short and long term memory. This model is used to explain the effects of marihuana on the memory process. It is suggested that under cannabis intoxication the input into the conceptual store is increased, and this limits the relevant information stored in the short term memory.

5051 Tinklenberg, J. R.; Darley, C. F.; Roth, W. T.; Pfefferbaum, A.; and Kopell, B. S., J. Nerv. Ment. Dis., 166(5), 362-64 (1978).

Marijuana Effects on Associations to Novel Stimuli.

THC (0.3 mg/kg, p.o.) did not enhance creativity in male subjects given an object description task.

5052 Tinklenberg, J. R.; Roth, W. T.; and Kopell, B. S., Psychopharmacology, 49(3), 275-79 (1976).

Marijuana and Ethanol: Differential Effects on Time Perception, Heart Rate, and Subjective Response.

Marihuana extract (0.7 mg Δ^9-THC/ kg, p.o.) and ethanol (1.0 ml/kg, p.o.) are compared to each other and to baseline responses in adult human males. THC accelerates perceived time relative to actual elapsed time concurrent with increased heart rates and subjective intoxication. In conjunction, the 3 parameters are sensitive to marihuana intoxication.

5053 Tinklenberg, J. R.; Roth, W. T.; Kopell, B. S.; and Murphy, P., Ann. NY Acad. Sci., 282, 85-94 (1976).

Cannabis and Alcohol Effects on Assaultiveness in Adolescent Delinquents.

The relationships of assaultive behavior and cannabis on ETOH consumption are assessed in adolescent delinquents experienced with a wide variety of drugs and convicted of serious crimes. ETOH increased the tendency toward aggressive, violent behavior while cannabis produced a subjective lessening of aggression and was the illicit drug of choice to this end. Both ETOH and secobarbital were disproportionately involved in violent behavior patterns.

5054 Titus, H. W., J. Drug Issues, 7(1), 23-34 (1977).

Oregon Marijuana Decriminalization: The Moral Question.

The author criticizes two Oregon laws, "marihuana decriminalization" and the "bottle bill," by pointing out their past and present consequences. He also strongly urges reconsideration.

5055   Todd, J.; Goldstein, R.; and Whitehouse, A., Psychol. Rep., *40*(3, pt. 1), 990 (1977).

Personality and Attitudes of British Marijuana Users.

British marihuana users have common features with U. S. users. The differences between users and nonusers among college students were indicated.

5056   Toohey, J. V., Bull. Narcotics, *30*(3), 61-64 (1978).

Non-Medical Drug Use Among Intercollegiate Athletes at Five American Universities.

Marihuana and other drug use behavior in students classified as athlete and nonathlete did not differ.

5057   Toohey, J. V.; and Dezelsky, T. L., J. Sch. Health, *48*(1), 672-79 (1978).

A Six-Year Analysis of Patterns in Non-Medical Drug Use Behavior.

Marihuana use is prevalent among students of five universities sampled in 1970, 1973, and 1976. Recent trends included a less hostile attitude toward marihuana laws and a decline in the percent getting high or encouraging others to use marihuana. Patterns of other drugs were also examined.

5058   Topp, G.; Dallmer, J.; and Schou, J., pp. 187-94 in *Marihuana: Chemistry,*

Biochemistry, and Cellular Effects, edited by G. G. Nahas. NY, Springer-Verlag, 1976.

Changes in the Metabolism of Δ^9-Tetrahydrocannabinol Caused by Other Cannabis Constituents.

A comparison between the changes in the metabolism of Δ^9-THC caused by other cannabis constituents in man and experimental animals is given. Effects of specie difference on the rate of metabolism of Δ^9-THC is shown. Biotransformations seem to occur mainly in liver and lung. Metabolites found in brain had to gain access through blood-brain barrier.

5059   Toro-Goyco, E.; and Rodriguez, M. B., Fed. Proc., *36*(3), 3028 (1977).

Δ^9-THC is an Inhibitor of Brain ($Na^+ + K^+$) ATPases.

($Na^+ - K^+$) ATPases of rat brain homogenates are competitively inhibited by Δ^9-THC (3×10^{-2} mm). THC is primarily inhibitory to the Na^+-dependent phosphorylation involved in ATP hydrolysis. THC binds irreversibly to the lipid portion of ATPase rather than at an active site.

5060   Toro-Goyco, E.; Rodriguez, M. B.; and Preston, A. M., Mol. Pharmacol., *14*(1), 130-37 (1978).

On the Action of Δ^9-Tetrahydrocannabinol as an Inhibitor of Sodium- and Potassium-Dependent Adenosine Triphosphatase.

THC is inhibitory to ($Na^+ + K^+$)-ATPases irrespective of their source. Ouabain-insensitive ATPases from rat brain were also inhibited by THC. Inhibition of electric eel ATPases (oubain-sensitive) was noncompetitive with respect to ATP. Whereas, inhibition of oubain-insensitive ATPases is competitive in nature.

5061 Tran Van Ky, P.; and Dumetz, J., Lille Med., *23*(3), 181-83 (1978).

Contribution a l'etude Chimique et Toxicologique du Chanvre Indien (*Cannabis sativa L.*, variete Indica): Application Medico-Legale [Chemical and Toxicological Studies of Indian Hemp (*Cannabis sativa L.*, Indica Variety): Forensic Applications].

A brief description of the different methods used for the detection of cannabis and its preparations is given. Detection of cannabinoids in biological fluids and samples from finger nails, nose and mouth as evidence of cannabis use is indicated.

5062 Traub, S. H., Brit. J. Addict., *72*(1), 67-74 (1977).

Perceptions of Marijuana and its Effects: A Comparison of Users and Nonusers.

College students were questioned concerning marihuana use and effects. Both groups differed in their polydrug use and regarded the mass media as a primary influential source in the campaign against marihuana use. While no demographic differences were found between these two groups, nonusers seemed to have very little knowledge of the behavioral patterns of marihuana-intoxicated persons as well as the effects experienced when high.

5063 Traub, S. H., Int. J. Addict., *12*(4), 583-90 (1977).

Rural High School Student Drug Use and the Effect of "Summer Jam, 1973" on Drug Use Patterns: The Watkins Glen Case.

School children 14-18 years of age were the population studied in this report which concludes that a rock concert in their area had no effect on marihuana use patterns.

5064 Treffert, D. A., Amer. J. Psychiat., *135*(10), 1213-15 (1978).

Marijuana Use in Schizophrenia: A Clear Hazard.

Cases of psychotic episodes precipitated by marihuana use in clinically controlled schizophrenics were reported.

5065 Treich, I.; Pastier, D.; Ayrault-Jarrier, M., Toxicol. Eur. Res. *1*(6), 347-54 (1978).

Dissociation *in vitro* des HDL de Serum Humain en Presence de Δ^9-THC [*In vitro* Dissociation of Human Serum HDL in the Presence of Δ^9-THC].

Incubation of high density lipoproteins (HDL) with Δ^9-THC resulted in their dissociation into three separate and distinct fractions.

5066 Trice, H. M.; and Beyer, J. M., J. Stud. Alcohol, *38*(1), 58-74 (1977).

A Sociological Property of Drugs. Acceptance of Users of Alcohol and Other Drugs Among University Undergraduates.

In this study of the strength of peer acceptance accorded drug users in a university setting, it was shown that a higher degree of acceptance of alcohol and nicotine use was found. Marihuana users were accepted by peers more often than users of any other drugs (except nicotine and alcohol), and moderate marihuana users were more acceptable than heavy users or nonusers.

5067 True, W. R.; and True, J. H., J. Psychedelic Drugs, *10*(2), 129-32 (1978).

Chronic Cannabis Use Among Working Class Men in Costa Rica.

Cannabis use is an integral behavioral process incorporated into the normal life style of working-class Costa Ricans. The life style of users was no different from that of nonusers.

5068 Truitt, E. B.; Kinzer, G. W.; and Berlo, J. M., pp. 463-74 in *Pharmacology of Marihuana, Vol. 2*, edited by M. C. Braude and S. Szara. NY, Raven Press, 1976.

Behavioral Activity in Various Fractions of Marihuana Smoke Condensate in the Rat.

Smoke condensate containing various amounts of THC (0.04-1 mg/ml) were given i.v. to male rats in order to determine the significance of the non-cannabinoids present in marihuana in inducing behavioral changes. Results indicated that some of the fractions produced behavioral symptoms disproportionate to the amounts of THC available.

5069 Truitt, E. B., Jr., Adv. Exp. Med. Biol., *56*, 291-309 (1975).

Marihuana vs. Alcohol: A Pharmacologic Comparison.

Similarities and differences between alcohol and marihuana on several toxicological, behavioral and pharmacological parameters were reviewed. Marihuana, like alcohol, should be classified as a sedative.

5070 Truitt, E. B., Jr.; Kinzer, G. W.; and Berlo, J. M., Fed. Proc., *34*(3), 743 (1975).

Behavioral Activity in Various Fractions of Marihuana Smoke Condensate in the Rat. (Abstract)

Marihuana whole smoke condensate was solvent fractionated with pentane, ethanol, ether, and methylene chloride. The ability of these fractions to modify rat's behavior is related to Δ^9-THC. Separation of behavioral effects from THC potentiation with the ether and methylene chloride fractions implies that marihuana smoke contains non-cannabinoid behaviorally active components.

5071 Tucker, A. N.; and Freidman, M. A., Res. Commun. Chem. Pathol. Pharmacol., *17*(4), 703-14 (1977).

Effects of Cannabinoids on L1210 Murine Leukemia. 1. Inhibition of DNA Synthesis.

Among several cannabinoids tested, Δ^8-THC was the most effective, whereas Δ^9-THC was the least effective, inhibitor of *in vivo* thymidine uptake by L1210 murine leukemia. Tolerance to Δ^9-THC, but not to Δ^8-THC, inhibitory effects developed after repeated administration. Uptake of cytidine and leucine was also inhibited by the two cannabinoids.

5072 Tunving, K., Lakartidningen, *73*(45), 3867-73 (1976).

Cannabis: Bruk och Missbruk [Cannabis: Use and Misuse].

The clinical psychological problems arising from cannabis intoxication are discussed and the reasons why people become habituated to cannabis are presented. The adverse effects of chronic cannabis use along with possible treatments are discussed.

5073 Turkanis, S. A.; Chiu, P.; Borys, H. K.; and Karler, R., Psychopharmacology, *52*(2), 207-12 (1977).

Influence of Δ^9-Tetrahydrocannabinol and Cannabidiol on Photically Evoked After-Discharge Potentials.

THC and CBD both have anticonvulsant properties similar to diphenylhydantoin (DPH), except in pentylenetetrazol minimal seizures in which CBD has no effect and THC enhances seizure activity. This report discusses CBD and THC in a test system that measures after-discharge potentials of the visually evoked response of the conscious rat. The results produced are consistent with those of past work.

5074   Turkanis, S. A.; Chiu, P.; and Karler, R., Fed. Proc., *36*(3), 1026 (1977).

Effects of Cannabidiol and Δ^9-Tetrahydrocannabinol on the After-Discharge Potentials of the Visually Evoked Response.

Trimethadione and ethosuximide decreased the after-discharge potentials of visually-evoked response in the rat. CBD and diphenylhydantoin had minimal effects, whereas Δ^9-THC and pentylenetetrazol enhanced activity.

5075   Turkanis, S. A.; and Karler, R., Fed. Proc., *34*(3), 782 (1975).

Influence of Cannabinoids on Posttetanic Potentiation (PTP) at a Bullfrog Paravertebral Ganglion (Abstract).

In a curarized bullfrom paravertebral ganglion X, 11-OH-Δ^9-THC and phenytoin depressed posttetanic potentiation but Δ^9-THC did not. Eleven hydroxylation of Δ^9-THC appears essential for anti-convulsant activity.

5076   Turkanis, S. A.; and Karler, R., Life Sci., *17*(4), 569-78 (1975).

Influence of Anticonvulsant Cannabinoids on Posttetanic Potentiation at Isolated Bullfrog Ganglia.

Δ^9-THC and CBD were tested for their anticonvulsant properties of posttetanic potentiation. The findings show that the metabolites 11-OH- and 8 α, 11-diOH-Δ^9-THC may account for Δ^9-THC's anticonvulsant properties.

.5077   Turkanis, S. A.; and Karler, R., pp. 331-34 in *Pharmacology of Marihuana, Vol. 1*, edited by M. C. Braude and S. Szara. NY, Raven Press, 1976.

The Influence of Δ^9-Tetrahydrocannabinol and its 11-Hydroxy Metabolite on Posttetanic Potentiation at Bullfrog Symphathetic Ganglia.

Anticonvulsant activity of Δ^9-THC (10 μm) and 11-OH-Δ^9-THC (0.1 μm) on a paravertibral ganlia X from a bullfrog was examined. Only 11-OH-Δ^9-THC reduced posttetanic potentiation. Thus, hydroxylation may be necessary for the anticonvulsant properties of THC.

5078   Turker, R. K.; Kaymakcalan, S.; and Ercan, Z. S., Arch. Int. Pharmacodyn. Ther., *214*(2), 254-62 (1975).

Antihistaminic Action of (-)-*Trans*-Delta-9-Tetrahydrocannabinol.

THC has an antispasmodic effect against different antagonists on the isolated guinea pig ileum without affecting the contractile action of bradykinin. In rabbit's aortic strips, 100 percent relaxation is obtained by THC when a maximum contraction is induced by histamine but not by angiotensin II and NE. Similar inhibition of histamine by THC was obtained in both the isolated perfused guinea pig lung and rabbit kidney. THC has a protecting effect against histamine aerosol in guinea pigs.

5079   Turner, C. E., *Eleventh Collegium Internationale Neuro-Psychopharmacologicum: Abstracts*, Vienna, Austria, July 9-14, 1978, p. 142.

Natural Chemical Constituents in *Cannabis sativa* (Marihuana) and Their Significance.

A detailed account of the 250 known natural chemical compounds present in *Cannabis sativa* was provided. Cannabinoids, with a total of 54, constitute one of the largest chemical types and are exceeded only by the 63 terpenes.

5080   Turner, C. E.; Cheng, P. C.; Torres, L. M.; and ElSohly, M. A., Bull. Narcotics, *30*(4), 47-56 (1978).

Detection and Analysis of Paraquat in Confiscated Marijuana Samples.

Confiscated marihuana samples (160) were analyzed for paraquat and cannabinoids. Twenty samples tested positive for paraquat. All samples were seized in the southwestern United States.

5081   Turner, C. E.; ElSohly, M. A.; Cheng, F. P.; and Torres, L. M., J. Amer. Med. Ass., *240*(17), 1857 (1978).

Marihuana and Paraquat (Letter).

A rapid review of the history of marihuana and paraquat was given. Data are shown for the level and frequency of paraquat contamination of confiscated samples with the herbicide.

5082   Turner, C. E.; Fetterman, P. S.; Hadley, K. W.; and Urbanek, J. E., Acta Pharm. Jugoslav., *25*(1), 7-16 (1975).

Constituents of *Cannabis sativa L*. X. Cannabinoid Profile of a Mexican Variant and its Possible Correlation to Pharmacological Activity.

The quantitation of the following cannabinoids: Δ^9-THC, combined with CBD + CBC, CBN and Δ^8-THC was conducted in cannabis to show the rhythmic fluctuation with regard to age of the plant. The importance of cannabinoid profiles was discussed. Also discussed was how the fluctuation of cannabinoids may cause conflicts in pharmacological data when inaccurate analytical data are given.

5083   Turner, C. E.; Hadley, K. W.; Holley, J. H.; Billets, S.; and Mole, M. K., J. Pharm. Sci., *64*(5), 810-14 (1975).

Constituents of *Cannabis sativa L*. VIII. Possible Biological Application of a New Method to Separate Cannabidiol and Cannabichromene.

A description of a new method that provides for the quantitation of CBD and CBC without preparing derivatives is presented. Since CBC is present in drug type cannabis and misidentified as CBD, previous data on crude drugs from cannabis is obviously incomplete. A complete analysis might prevent conflicts in cannabis research.

5084   Turner, C. E.; and Henry, J. T., J. Pharm. Sci., *64*(2), 357-59 (1975).

Constituents of *Cannabis sativa L*. IX: Stability of Synthetic and Naturally Occurring Cannabinoids in Chloroform.

Synthetic and naturally occurring cannabinoids were found to be stable in chloroform for at least 21 days and do not decompose as previously thought. Chloroform is solvent of choice for extracting cannabinoids from cannabis plant material.

5085   Turner, C. E.; Hsu, M. H.; Knapp, J. E.; Schiff, P. L.; and Slatkin, D. J., J. Pharm. Sci., *65*(7), 1084-85 (1976).

Isolation of Cannabisativine, an Alkaloid, from *Cannabis sativa L*. Root.

The isolation procedure for cannabisativine, a new spermidine alkaloid from cannabis roots is reported. Physical constants, structure, and TLC procedures are also reported.

5086   Turner, J. C.; Hemphill, J. K.; and Mahlberg, P. G., Amer. J. Bot., *64*(6), 687-93 (1977).

Gland Distribution and Cannabinoid Content in Clones of *Cannabis sativa L.*

A negative correlation was found to exist when the CBD content in three phenotypically different strains of cannabis was compared to the number of glands present in different plant organs. Implications of findings were discussed.

5087   Turner, J. C.; Hemphill, J. K.; and Mahlberg, P. G., Amer. J. Bot., *65*(10), 1103-06 (1978).

Quantitative Determination of Cannabinoids in Individual Glandular Trichomes of *Cannabis sativa L.* (Cannabaceae).

The principal cannabinoid content of both capitate-stalked and capitate-sessile glandular hairs of two strains (drug and fiber) and two clones of *Cannabis sativa L.* was determined. Qualitative and quantitative cannabinoid profiles of each type of hair in each strain were compared. Sampling of the glandular hairs was done from vein and non-vein areas of pistillate bracts and leaves.

5088   Turner, J. C.; Hemphill, J. K.; and Mahlberg, P. G., Bull Narcotics, *30*(1), 55-65 (1978).

Cannabinoid Composition and Gland Distribution in Clones of *Cannabis sativa L.* (Cannabiceae).

Three strains of *Cannabis sativa L.* (drug, nondrug and fiber) were cloned to provide genetically uniform material. The number and type of glands was determined for several organs at different ages of the pistillate plants and the relationship between the glandular trichomes and cannabinoid content was investigated. A negative correlation was observed in the three clones, suggesting that cannabinoids may exist in plant cells other than trichomes.

5089   Twitchett, P. J.; Williams, P. L.; and Moffat, A. C., J. Chromatogr., *149*, 683-91 (1978).

Photochemical Detection in High Performance Liquid Chromatography and its Application to Cannabinoid Analysis.

A procedure is described for detection and quantitation of CBN in urine samples with sensitivity of less than 1 ng. A photochemical reactor was used for on-line irradiation of the HPLC column eluent which is then passed to the detector. Both UV and fluorimetric detectors were used with advantages.

5090   Tyrey, L., Endocrinology, *102*(6), 1808-14 (1978).

Δ^9-Tetrahydrocannabinol Suppression of Episodic Luteinizing Hormone Secretion in the Ovariectomized Rat.

THC (0.5 to 8.0 mg/kg, i.v.) prevented the episodic fluctuation of serum LH in ovariectomized rats. The duration of THC-induced decrease in LH secretion was dose-dependent.

U

5091 Ueki, S., and Fujiwara, M., Farumashia, *13*(1), 54-57 (1977).

Pharmacological Properties of Tetrahydrocannabinol and its Applications.

Low doses of THC (4 mg/kg, i.p.) increased, whereas higher doses decreased, the spontaneous movements of rats. The THC-induced catalepsy and muricidal behavior were suggested as methods for the evaluation of new antidepressants and antiparkinsonian drugs. Results supporting such a concept were indicated.

5092 Ueki, S.; Fujiwara, M.; Yamamoto, T.; and Ibii, N., *Seventh International Congress of Pharmacology: Abstracts.* Paris, France, July 16-21, 1978.

Effects of Psychotropic Drugs on Muricide Induced by Δ^9-Tetrahydrocannabinol in Rats.

Δ^9-THC-induced muricide disappeared in grouped rats but was recovered when Δ^9-THC was given again in an isolated condition. Effects of various psychotropic drugs, including antidepressants and tranquilizers, on reversible and irreversible muricide were also investigated and discussed.

5093 Ueki, S.; and Michihiro, F., Kagaku (Tokyo), *47*(9), 530-36 (1977).

Peculiar Effects of Marihuana on the Behavior of Rats.

A review of marihuana and Δ^9-THC is presented with emphasis on the historical background and pharmacological effects of these two drugs.

5094 Uliss, D. B.; Dalzell, G. R.; Handrick, G. R.; Howes, J. F.; and Razdan, R. K., J. Med. Chem., *18*(2), 213-15 (1975).

Hashish. Importance of the Phenolic Hydroxyl Group in Tetrahydrocannabinols.

The phenolic hydroxyl group was found to be important for Δ^9-THC's activity. Δ^9-*cis* THC is less active than *trans*, thus the *trans* isomer also has structural specificity for activity. Specific structural data were given for compounds reported for the first time and no anticonvulsant activity was observed using the antimetrazole test.

5095 Uliss, D. B.; Handrick, G. R.; Dalzell, H. C.; and Razdan, R. K., Experientia, *33*(5), 577-78 (1977).

A Novel Cannabinoid Containing a 1,8-Cineol Moiety.

An intramolecular cyclization was observed to occur when cannabielson was refluxed under certain conditions. On the basis of NMR and MS data, the novel cannabinoid is described as having a 1,8-cineol moiety. The structure of this compound is shown.

5096 Uliss, D. B.; Handrick, G. R.; Dalzell, H. C.; and Razdan, R. K., J. Amer. Chem. Soc., *100*(9), 2929-30 (1978).

A Terpenic Synthon for Δ^1-Cannabinoids.

The synthesis of a monoterpene with a dithiane masking group is described. The monoterpene is described as intermediate in the synthesis of metabolites of Δ^9-THC oxygenated at C-11. The isomerization of the double bond to Δ^8-THC was inhibited in this procedure.

5097 Uliss, D. B.; Handrick, G. R.; Dalzell, H. C.; and Razdan, R. K., Tetrahedron, *34*(13), 1885-88 (1978).

The Conversion of 3,4-*cis*- to 3,4-*trans*-Cannabinoids.

The conversion of Δ^1-3,4-*cis*-THC to Δ^6-3,4-*trans*-THC was accomplished with BBr$_3$. The main epimerization occurred at C-4 with the small loss of optical purity explained by competitive epimerization at C-3 or racemization. Exclusive C-4-epimerization was observed in the hexahydroderivative. The effect of BF$_3$ was also studied and no *trans* products were obtained. Mechanisms are presented.

5098   Uliss, D. B.; Razdan, R. K.; Dalzell, H. C.; and Handrick, G. R., Tetrahedron, *33*(16), 2055-59 (1977).

Synthesis of Racemic and Optically Active Δ^1- and Δ^6-3,4-*cis*- Tetrahydrocannabinols.

A step by step description of several methods utilized to synthesize (±)-Δ^6-3,4-*cis*-THC and the optically active Δ^1- and Δ^6-*cis*-THC's was presented.

5099   Uliss, D. B.; Razdan, R. K.; Dalzell, H. C.; and Handrick, G. R., Tetrahedron Lett., *49*, 4369-72 (1975).

Hashish: Synthesis of dl-$\Delta^{1,6}$-*cis*-Tetrahydrocannabinol (THC).

dl-$\Delta^{1,6}$-*cis*-THC was synthesized through three different routes. Equilibrium constants and free energy differences (Δ G) are given for *cis* and *trans* THC. The differences in equilibrium constants may be due to steric factors.

5100   Uyeno, E. T., in *Committee on Problems of Drug Dependence, 1975*. Division of Medical Sciences, National Research Council, National Academy of Sciences, Washington, D. C., 1975, pp. 1033-44.

Δ^9-Tetrahydrocannabinol, Lysergic Acid Diethylamide, and Reproduction of the Rat.

The effects on offspring of rats treated with Δ^9-THC (30-120 mg/kg) on day 4 of gestation were examined. No gross teratogenic effects were observed, but reproduction was adversely affected and abnormal offspring were found. Prenatal exposure of Δ^9-THC had little effect on learning ability as shown by the maze test. A comparison of the effects of LSD and Δ^9-THC on reproduction is also presented.

5101   Uyeno, E. T., Pharmacologist, *17*(2), 181 (1975).

Δ^9-Tetrahydrocannabinol Administered to Pregnant Rats (Abstract).

Acute doses of THC (30, 60 and 120 mg/kg, s.e.) and LSD (2, 4 and 6 mg/kg) were administered to pregnant rats. LSD was more potent than THC in producing abnormal pregnancies. However, THC produced more still births. No gross teratogenic or behavioral effects were observed with either drug.

5102   Uyeno, E. T., Proc. West. Pharmacol. Soc., *19*, 369-72 (1976).

Effects of Δ^9-THC and 2, 5-Dimethoxy-4-methylamphetamine on Rat Sexual Dominance Behavior.

Sexual dominance behavior in treated male rats was inhibited by i.p. Δ^9-THC and 2, 5-dimethoxy-4 methylamphetamine, at 0.5 mg/kg each. Time of peak inhibitory effect was 120 and 45 min. respectively.

V

5103 Vachon, L., New Eng. J. Med., *294*, 160-61 (1976).

The Smoke in Marihuana Smoking.

Certain beneficial and deleterious effects of marihuana were cited. Analogies drawn between tobacco and marihuana smoking suggested that the former is more of a public health hazard because of its more frequent use by a larger population.

5104 Vachon, L.; Mathe, A. A.; and Weissman, B., Res. Commun. Chem. Pathol. Pharmacol., *13*(2), 345-48 (1976).

Effect of Δ^9-THC on the Catecholamine Content of the Guinea Pig Lung.

Guinea pigs were sacrificed 30 min. after i.p. injection of 100 and 200 mg/kg THC or 50 mg of atropine. The lungs were removed and the homogenates were assayed for catecholamines. DA and EPI levels were altered by 200 mg/kg THC, and by 100 mg/kg THC and atropine. Atropine was slightly higher than 100 mg/kg of THC.

5105 Vachon, L.; Mikus, P.; Morrissey, W.; FitzGerald, M.; and Gaensler, E., pp. 777-84 in *Pharmacology of Marihuana, Vol. 2*, edited by M. C. Braude and S. Szara. NY, Raven Press, 1976.

Bronchial Effect of Marihuana Smoke in Asthma.

Inhalation of marihuana smoke (containing 29 or 64 mg/kg of THC before combustion) by asthmatic patients was monitored clinically. Results showed that THC, even in low doses, is a bronchodilator and has a brief tachycardiac effect.

5106 Vachon, L.; Robins, A.; and Gaensler, E., pp. 111-21 in *The Therapeutic Potential of Marihuana*, edited by S. Cohen and R. Stillman. NY, Plenum Medical Book Company, 1976.

Airways Response to Aerosolized Delta-9-Tetrahydrocannabinol: Preliminary Report.

The therapeutic effectiveness of THC as a bronchodilator in humans was improved by its microaerosol administration. THC was found to be comparable to isoproterenol in producing airflow changes.

5107 Vachon, L.; Robins, A. G.; and Gaensler, E. A., Chest, *70*(3), 444 (1976).

Airways Response to Micro-Aerosolized Delta-9-Tetrahydrocannabinol.

THC (0.7 mg) micro-aerosol proved to be an effective bronchodilator with minimal side effects.

5108 Vachon, L.; and Sulkowski, A., pp. 161-71 in *The Therapeutic Potential of Marihuana*, edited by S. Cohen and R. Stillman. NY, Plenum Medical Book Company, 1976.

The Effect of Beta-Adrenergic Blockade on Acute Marihuana Intoxication.

In human subjects, propranolol antagonized the THC-induced tachycardia and B.P. increase while reducing its subjective "high." The adrenergic involvement in THC-induced behavioral changes was also suggested.

5109 Vachon, L.; and Sulkowski, A., pp. 449-52 in *Pharmacology of Marihuana, Vol. 1*, edited by M. C. Braude and S. Szara. NY, Raven Press, 1976.

Attention, Learning, and Speed in Psychomotor Performance After Marihuana Smoking.

Using sophisticated tests it was shown that attention, learning and psychomotor speed of human volunteers smoking marihuana (25 mg Δ^9-THC) was unaffected. Although short term memory was also not affected, the assimilation of information was decreased.

5110 Vaille, C., Nouv. Presse Med., *5*(17), 1149-50 (1976).

Cannabis et Khat [Cannabis and Khat].

Factors used in assessing the physical and psychological effects of cannabis are discussed. Phytochemical studies of khat showed that, in addition to the presence of the stimulant alkaloid cathine, several alkaloids have been isolated and their pharmacologic actions remain to be studied.

5111 Valentine, J. L.; Bryant, P. J.; Gutshall, P. L.; Gan, O. H. M.; and Driscoll, P., pp. 291-96 in *Trace Substances in Environmental Health,* Proceedings of the Annual Conference, 9, University of Missouri, 1975.

Quantification of Trace Substances in Biological Samples Using HPLC-MS Techniques.

A procedure consisting of combined HPLC-MS techniques for the quantitation of trace amounts of substances in biological samples was presented. The method is based on the use of a stable isotope of the substance to be analyzed as internal standard, separation on HPLC and analyzing the mixture by MS using peak matching and ion counting techniques.

5112 Valentine, J. L.; Bryant, P. J.; Gutshall, P. L.; Gan, O. H. M.; Lovegreen, P. D.; Thompson, E. D.; and Niu, H. C., J. Pharm. Sci., *66*(9), 1263-66 (1977).

High-Pressure Liquid Chromatographic-Mass Spectrometric Determination of Δ^9-Tetrahydrocannabinol in Human Plasma Following Marihuana Smoking.

HPLC was used for the detection of Δ^9-THC in marihuana smoke. A MS quantification method had to be developed to analyze the eluants.

5113 Valentine, J. L.; Bryant, P. J.; Gutshall, P. L.; Gan, O. H. M.; Thompson, E. D.; and Niu, H. C., pp. 96-106 in *Cannabinoid Assays in Humans*, NIDA Research Monograph Series, 7, 1976.

HPLC-MS Determination of Δ^9-Tetrahydrocannabinol in Human Body Samples.

HPLC was shown to be useful in the quantitative analysis of Δ^9-THC. Level was higher in brain and bile than in blood plasma.

5114 Valle, J. R.; Vieira, J. E. V.; Aucello, J. G.; and Valio, I. F. M., Bull. Narcotics, *30*(1), 67-68 (1978).

Influence of Photoperiodism on Cannabinoid Content of *Cannabis sativa L.*

Increased exposure of cannabis plants to natural light from 10 to 12 hrs./day more than doubled THC content and decreased CBC level but did not significantly change the level of CBN.

5115 Vallejo, E.; Piga, A.; and Tena, G., Aktuel. Probl. Intensivmed., *1*, 303-07 (1975).

Identification des Cannabinols dans des Plantes Cultivees en Espagne [Identification of the Cannabinols in Some Plants Grown in Spain].

The CBD, THC, and CBN content of cannabis plants of different origins grown in Spain was determined by GC, TLC, and color reactions.

5116 Van Boven, M.; Bruneel, N.; and Daenens, P., J. Pharm. Belg., *31*(2), 215-19 (1976).

Determination des Cannabinoides dans le *Cannabis sativa* D'Origine Belge [Determination of Cannabinoids in *Cannabis sativa* from Belgian Origin] .

Twenty samples of cannabis from Belgian origin were examined and most of them contained only CBD; 30% of the samples contained THC-acid and showed some euphoric activity.

5117 van den Broek, G.; Robertson, J.; Keim, D. A.; and Baile, C. A., Fed. Proc., *37*(3), 699 (1978).

Elfazepam and 9-Aza-Cannabinol Depression of Abomasal Secretion in Sheep.

9-Aza-cannabinol (5.5 μg/kg, i.v.) and elfazepam increased sheep feed intake for 3 hours, but severely depressed abomasal secretion between 0.5 and 2 hours post-injection.

5118 van Klingeren, B.; and ten Ham, M., Anton. Leeuwenhoek J. Microbiol., *42* (1-2), 9-12 (1976).

Antibacterial Activity of Δ^9-Tetrahydro-cannabinol and Cannabidiol.

Δ^9-THC and CBD effectively inhibited and killed G (+) staphylococci and streptococci in the concentration range of 1-5 μ gm/ml of nutrient broth agar, but the additio of horse serum or blood to the agar decreased these activities 10 fold. G (-) bacteria are unaffected by both compounds.

5119 van Ree, J. M.; Slangen, J. L.; and de Wied, D., J. Pharmacol. Exp. Ther., *204*(3), 547-57 (1978).

Intravenous Self-Administration of Drugs in Rats.

Although Δ^9-THC induced a low incidence of i.v. self-administration in rats, the unit dose required to elicit this behavior in a majority of the animals (ED 50 or 400 μg/kg/injection) caused severe toxicity. Other drugs, including narcotics and *d*-amphetamine, were also tested.

5120 Van Went, G. F., Experientia, *43*(3), 324-25 (1978).

Mutagenicity Testing of 3 Hallucinogens: LSD, Psilocybin and Δ^9-THC, Using the Micronucleus Test.

No significant increase in the number of micronuclei was detected when mice were injected twice with Δ^9-THC (5, 10 and 20 mg/kg, i.p.), LSD or psilocybin. The micronucleus test was employed to screen these agents for mutagenic activity.

5121 Vardaris, R. M.; and Weisz, D. J., Brain Res. Bull., *2*(3), 181-87 (1977).

Δ^9-Tetrahydrocannabinol and the Hippocampus: Effects of CA1 Field Potentials in Rats.

In unanesthetized paralyzed rats, THC (2 mg/kg, i.p.) substantially increased the amplitudes of orthodromic, antidromic and EPSP population spikes from pyramidal cells. THC also prolonged latencies to peak amplitudes for these tested potentials and attenuated recurrent inhibition mediated by basket cells. These responses were also compared to those obtained in anesthetized animals.

5122 Vardaris, R. M.; Weisz, D. J.; Fazel, A.; and Rawitch, A. B., Pharmacol. Biochem. Behav., *4*(3), 249-54 (1976).

Chronic Administration of Delta-9-Tetrahydrocannabinol to Pregnant Rats: Studies of Pup Behavior and Placental Transfer.

Chronic oral administration of Δ^9-THC in pregnant rats resulted in its placental transfer to offspring. Although no overt teratogenicity was evident, the study revealed increased competitive behavior and initial deficit in passive avoidance response in pups.

5123 Varma, D. R.; and Goldbaum, D., J. Pharm. Pharmacol., 27(10), 790-91 (1975).

Effect of Δ^9-Tetrahydrocannabinol on Experimental Hypertension in Rats.

Rats injected (Δ^9-THC, 1 or 2 mg kg-1, s.c.) daily for 3 to 5 weeks after induced hypertension showed no systolic pressure or heart rate change, thus demonstrating tolerance.

5124 Vazquez, A. J.; Borison, R.; May, J.; and Sabelli, H. C., Pharmacologist, 17(1), 258 (1975).

Evidence for 2-Phenylethylamine (PEA) as a Mediator for the Central Stimulant and Anti-Tremorgenic Actions of Δ^9-THC.

Data suggest that Δ^9-THC inhibits the conversion of 2-phenylethylamine to a major unidentified metabolite. Euphoriant and central anti-tremorgenic effects of Δ^9-THC may be partially mediated by an increase in brain 2-phenylethylamine. Sedative effect may depend on formation of the deaminated metabolite.

5125 Vega-Franco, L.; Romo-Quitanar, G.; and Jimenez-Cardosa, E., Rev. Invest. Salud Publica (Mexico), 36(1), 19-27 (1976).

Efecto de la Mariguana sobre el Crecimiento del Sistema Nervioso Central durante la Etapa Embriofetal (Modelo Exerimental) [Effect of Marihuana on the Central Nervous System During the Embryofetal State (Experimental Model)].

Levels of brain nucleic acids of pregnant rats exposed to marihuana smoke did not differ significantly from control values. Those of their litters were, however, depressed.

5126 Velazquez y Cols, G. F., Salud Publica Mex., 17(4), 487-92 (1975).

Valoracion Clinica de Enfermos Adictos a la Marihuana en Baja California [Clinical Evaluation of Patients Addicted to Marihuana in Baja, California].

This Spanish paper depicts the seriousness of marihuana and heroine addiction in Baja, Calif. Major emphasis was placed on the psychological problems of marihuana users.

5127 Verbeke, R.; and Corin, E., Brit. J. Addict., 71(2), 167-74 (1976).

Use of Indian Hemp in Zaire: A Formulation of Hypotheses on the Basis of an Inquiry Using a Written Questionnaire.

Certain aspects of cannabis use in Zaire were investigated via a questionnaire administered to university students. Information obtained and conclusions drawn were reported.

5128 Verin, P. H.; Vildy, A.; Maurin, J. F.; and Hubert, G., Ann. D'Oculist., 210(6), 453-75 (1977).

Les Hallucinogenes: Incidences Ophtalmologiques [Hallucinogenic Agents: Ophthalmologic Incidences].

The various effects of some main hallucinogenic drugs such as hashish, amphetamines, lysergic acid (LSD), mescaline and psilocybine have been individually discussed. The effects, as expected, vary with the substance, persons and doses involved and remain within the limits of several characteristic syndromes. The most important of the sensorial changes are those that are visual. Hallucinogenic substance can lead to serious ophthamological complications.

5129   Vidic, H. J.; Hoyer, G. A.; Kieslich, K.; and Rosenberg, D., Chem. Ber., *109*(11), 3606-14 (1976).

Mikrobiologische Umwandlungen Nichtsteroider Strukturen, IX. Mikrobiligische Hydroxylierung Von Δ^8-Tetrahydrocannabinol [Microbiological Transformations of Nonsteroidal Structures. IX. Microbiological Hydroxylation of Δ^8-Tetrahydrocannabinol].

Hydroxylated derivatives of Δ^8-THC are formed on fermentation by *Pellicularia filamentosa* and *Streptomyces lavendulae*. The structures of these hydroxy cannabinoids were determined by NMR, MS, IR, and UV.

5130   Vidic, H. J.; Kieslich, K.; and Petzoldt, K. (Schering A.-G.), Ger. Offen. (Ger. Patent) 2,335,136, 16 Jan 1975, 9 pp.

Microbiological Preparation of 7-Hydroxy-Δ^8-Tetrahydrocannabinols.

The use of *Pellicularia filamentosa saskii* and *Streptomyces lavendulae* in the microbiological transformation of cannabinoids leading to the production of side-chain hydroxylated metabolites is presented.

5131   Vieira, J. E. V.; Nicolau, M.; Aucelio, J. G.; and Valle, J. R., Bull. Narcotics, *29*(3), 75-76 (1977).

Vegetative Growth of *Cannabis sativa* and Presence of Cannabinoids.

The appearance of THC, CBC and CBN are examined during the vegetative growth period (38 to 60 days) using TLC and GLC.

5132   Vijay, K. K.; and Manocha, S. L., Baroda J. Nutr., *3*, 197-216 (1976).

Pharmaco-Physiological Implications of Marihuana Use.

An extensive review of the available knowledge concerning the properties of marihuana was conducted. In spite of the tremendous bulk of research, questions such as the amount ingested, dose-response, and chronic and subchronic effects remain to be answered.

5133   Vijayalakshmy, G.; and Singh, S., Anat. Soc. India J., *24*(2), 71-74 (1975).

Effect of Cannabis Resin on Human Mitotic Chromosomes.

Peripheral lymphocytic cultures were made from 10 subjects. Cannabis resin was added in doses of 0.5, 0.75 and 1 mg/ml of media 24 hrs. before termination of culture. Cultures with 1 mg/ml had no metaphase plates - showing complete inhibition of cell division. 0.5 and 0.75 inhibited the mitotic rate.

5134   Vinson, J. A.; and Hooyman, J. E., J. Chromatogr., *106*, 196-99 (1975).

Studies in Laboratory-Use Reagents. III. Simple Thin-Layer Chromatographic System for the Separation of Cannabinoids.

Detection and identification of the constituents of marihuana can be easily accomplished by the described method.

5135   Vinson, J. A.; Patel, D. D.; and Patel, A. H., Anal. Chem., *49*(1), 163-65 (1977).

Detection of Tetrahydrocannabinol in Blood and Serum Using a Fluorescent Derivative and Thin-Layer Chromatography.

A TLC procedure for the detection of cannabinoids and their metabolites in biological fluids is described. Detection level for Δ^9-THC was 0.4 ng/ml. The derivative is prepared with a 2-p-chlorosulfophenol-3-phenylindone and occurs as a yellow-green fluorescent spot under long-wave UV light.

5136   Volavka, J.; Fink, M.; Stefanis, C.; Panayiotopoulos, C.; and Dornbush, R., Electroencephalogr. Clin. Neurophysiol., *42*(5), 730 (1977).

EEG Effects of Cannabis in Chronic Hashish Users.

The immediate EEG changes following marihuana smoking by chronic users were an increase in alpha percent time and a decrease of the average frequency. Examination of the EEG records of chronic users revealed no association between brain damage and cannabis use.

5137   Vree, T. B., J. Pharm. Sci., *66*(10), 1444-50 (1977).

Mass Spectrometry of Cannabinoids.

A review (with 7 references) is given on the formation of the major ions in the mass spectra of CBD, CBN, CBC, CBL, Δ^9-THC, and Δ^8-THC, their homologs and derivatives.

5138   Vree, T. B., T. Alc. Drugs, *2*(2), 67-73 (1976).

Wat is Kwaliteit van Hashish? [What is the Quality of Hashish?].

Due to the high number of xenobiotics circulating in the body following marihuana ingestion and due to variation in the constituents of marihuana depending on its origin, the exact composition of the marihuana sample should be known when correlating its effects with its concentration.

5139   Vyas, D. K.; and Singh, R., Indian J. Exp. Biol., *14*(1), 22-25 (1976).

Effect of Cannabis and Opium on the Testis of the Pigeon *Columba livia* Gmelin.

A significant decrease in the gross weight of both testes was noted in cannabis-treated pigeons and could be associated with a considerable reduction in the size of the seminiferous tubules. Treatment with cannabis led to a histologic picture which resembles that seen in sexually inactive pigeons. Possible mechanisms of action are discussed.

W

5140 Wada, J. A.; Osawa, T.; and Corcoran, M. E., Epilepsia, *16*(3), 439-48 (1975).

Effects of Tetrahydrocannabinols on Kindled Amygdaloid Seizures and Photogenic Seizures in Senegalese Baboons, *Papio papio*.

Δ^8-THC and Δ^9-THC protected baboons against established kindled seizures caused by electrical stimulation of amygdala but not against photic stimulation-induced convulsions. Higher doses of Δ^8-THC than of Δ^9-THC were required to produce these effects.

5141 Wada, J. A.; Wake, A.; Sato, M.; and Corcoran, M. E., Epilepsia, *16*, 503-10 (1975).

Antiepileptic and Prophylactic Effects of Tetrahydrocannabinols in Amygdaloid Kindled Cats.

Δ^9- and Δ^8-THC failed to protect cats against already established kindled amygdaloid convulsions. Full protection against seizure development was seen only following chronic Δ^9-THC treatment.

5142 Wada, J. A.; Wake, A.; and Corcoran, M. E., Electroencephalogr. Clin. Neurophysiol., *39*(2), 206 (1975).

Anticonvulsive and Prophylactic Potency of Cannabis: Successful Prevention of Amygdaloid Seizure Development by Δ^9-Tetrahydrocannabinol.

In testing the antiepileptic property of Δ^8- and Δ^9-THC, only Δ^9-THC showed a complete protective effect in 2 out of 4 cats, and partial protection in one. One month after Δ^9-THC treatment, the protected cats required greater stimulation for development of seizures.

5143 Wagner, E. E.; and Romanik, D. G., Percept. Motor Skills, *43*, 1303-06 (1976).

Hand Test Characteristics of Marihuana-Experienced and Multiple Drug-Using College Students.

Marihuana users demonstrated the highest degree of behavior directed at interpersonal approval ("showing off"), scored lower on those parameters associated with environmental interaction (amotivation), but were normal in all other respects. Multiple-drug use was associated with decreased motivation which was not specific for marihuana use.

5144 Wall, M. E., Recent Advances in Phytochemistry, *9*, 29-61 (1975).

Recent Advances in the Chemistry and Metabolism of the Cannabinoids.

A review article on recent cannabinoid research, discussing such topics as: origin, activity, and nomenclature of cannabinoids; analysis of natural and synthetic cannabinoids; and metabolism of cannabis constituents in animals. Standard methods are given for blood, urine, and fecal analyses. Various synthetic preparations are outlined and 28 references are given.

5145 Wall, M. E., *Eleventh Collegium Internationale Neuro-Psychopharmacologicum: Abstracts*, Vienna, Austria, July 9-14, 1978, p. 144.

The Metabolism of Cannabinoids in Man.

Liver microsomal oxidation rapidly converted labeled Δ^9-THC to 11-OH-Δ^9-THC (active) which was then converted to 11-*nor*-Δ^9-THC-9-carboxylic acid (11-*nor*-acid). Other polar acids were also found and predominance of these metabolites in urine and feces, as well as their metabolism, were discussed.

5146   Wall, M. E.; and Brine, D. R., *Seventh International Congress of Pharmacology: Abstracts*, Paris, France, July 16-21, 1978, p. 836.

Blood-Brain Levels of Δ^9-Tetrahydrocannabinol and Metabolites.

A relationship exists between brain levels and the structure of Δ^9-THC and four of its major metabolites. Maximal levels were observed 0.5 min. after an i.v. injection of each compound and remained constant for almost 30 min., then dropped rapidly. The brain levels of these compounds varied considerably. Higher levels of the more psychomimetic compounds were seen.

5147   Wall, M. E., and Brine, D. R., pp. 51-62 in *Marihuana: Chemistry, Biochemistry, and Cellular Effects*, edited by G. G. Nahas. NY, Springer-Verlag, 1976.

Identification of Cannabinoids and Metabolites in Biological Materials by Combined Gas-Liquid Chromatography-Mass Spectrometry.

Major metabolic route of Δ^9-THC and related cannabinoids such as CBN and CBD involves rapid hydroxylation at carbon 11 followed by further oxidation of the carboxylic acids. Minor routes involve hydroxylation at the 8-α or 8-β positions or in the side chain alone or in combination with the major routes. Combined GLC-MS can be used to identify many of the metabolites present in biological systems.

5148   Wall, M. E.; Brine, D. R.; and Perez-Reyes, M., pp. 93-116 in *Pharmacology of Marihuana, Vol. 1*, edited by M. C. Braude and S. Szara. NY, Raven Press, 1976.

Metabolism of Cannabinoids in Man.

Metabolism of 3-H-labeled Δ^9-THC (4.6 mg i.v. and 4.5 mg smoking), 11-OH-Δ^9-THC (4.8 mg, i.v.), CBN (18 mg, i.v.), and CBD (20 mg, i.v.) was studied in human volunteers. A novel extraction procedure for the cannabinoids and their metabolites from plasma, urine and feces is described. The pattern of metabolism of the compounds was similar. Contrary to expected results, the 11-hydroxy metabolite was not the major metabolite.

5149   Wall, M. E.; Harvey, T. M.; Bursey, J. T.; Brine, D. R.; and Rosenthal, D., *Proc. Int. Conf. Stable Isot., 2nd, 1975*, 105-16 (1976).

Quantitative Gas Chromatographic-Mass Spectral Analysis of Cannabinoids Using Deuterium Labeled Carriers and Internal Standards.

A pharmacokinetic study of blood plasma levels over 23 hrs. in man of THC, 11-OH-THC and CBN was performed by GC/MS analysis. Samples were either subjected to chemical ionization mode or pre-cleaned on a sephadex column and subjected to the electron impact mode. Deuterium labeled carrriers and internal standards were used. A biphasic elimination of THC was observed.

5150   Wall, M. E.; Harvey, T. M.; Bursey, J. T.; Brine, D. R.; and Rosenthal, D., pp. 107-17 in *Cannabinoid Assays in Humans*, NIDA Research Monograph Series, 7, 1976.

Analytical Methods for the Determination of Cannabinoids in Biological Materials.

A comparison of analytical methods for quantitating cannabinoids in human biological fluids is presented. Metabolic and pharmacokinetic data are presented and compared. Δ^9-THC, 11-OH-Δ^9-THC and CBN levels were determined using human plasma after i.v. administration of Δ^9-THC only. Level of reliability was 1 ng/ml.

5151   Wallace, L., Amer. J. Psychiat., *135*(8), 990-91 (1978).

Psychoanalytic Observations on Marijuana Use.

Psychoanalysis of a marihuana user revealed that the immediate consequence of marihuana use is to provide temporary escape from internal conflict with subsequent fatigue and lethargy and finally a tranquilizing effect.

5152   Waller, C. W., *Eleventh Collegium Internationale   Neuro-Psychopharmacologicum: Abstracts*, Vienna, Austria, July 9-14, 1978, p. 143.

A Decade of Marihuana Research at the University of Mississippi.

Establishing a good marihuana drug type, developing a routine analytical technique and studying the pharmacology and toxicology of crude marihuana were the goals set forth and accomplished at the University of Mississippi. The discovery that CBC is more abundant in nature than previously thought and the isolation and identification of new cannabinoids are among the many achievements of this research program.

5153   Waller, C. W., pp. 19-20 in *Pharmacology of Marihuana, Vol. 1*, edited by M. C. Braude and S. Szara. NY, Raven Press, 1976.

Standardized Sources of Supply for Marijuana Research.

Standardized cannabinoids and their metabolites are available through the NIMH and the supply program of the National Institute of Drug Abuse (NIDA). Sources of current marihuana information are mentioned.

5154   Waller, C.; Hadley, K.; and Turner, C. E., pp. 15-30 in *Marihuana: Chemistry, Biochemistry, and Cellular Effects*, edited by G. G. Nahas. NY, Springer-Verlag, 1976.

Detection and Identification of Compounds in Cannabis.

The authors discuss the basic analytical developments applicable to synthetic cannabinoids and extracts from cannabis preparations, application of electron voltage-mass fragment graphs as a potential tool in identifying cannabinoids and their metabolites in body fluids and fermentation process, and new alkaloids that have been isolated and identified from *Cannabis sativa L*.

5155   Waller, C. W.; Johnson, J. J.; Buelke, J.; and Turner, C. E., *Marihuana: An Annotated Bibliography*. NY, Macmillan Information, 1976. 560 pp.

This bibliography contains entries for 3045 papers or books on marihuana published from 1964 through 1974, arranged alphabetically by senior author. Included are structural tables of known cannabinoids and metabolites and author and subject indexes.

5156   Walsh, J. M.; and Burch, L. S., Pharmacol. Biochem. Behav., 7(2), 111-16 (1977).

Reduction of the Behavioral Effects of Δ^9-Tetrahydrocannabinol by Hyperbaric Pressure.

The behavioral toxicity of THC (0.5-4 mg/kg) observed in trained rats under normal barometric pressure was reduced when the atmospheric pressure was increased.

5157 Warner, A. M.; and Pierozynski, G.; Postgrad. Med., *61*(1), 275-77 (1977).

Pseudocatationia Associated with Abuse of Amphetamine and Cannabis.

A case report of an amphetamine user who consumed marihuana and developed symptoms of catatonia is presented.

5158 Warner, W.; Carchman, R. A.; Harris, L. S.; and Watts, D. T., Fed. Proc., *35*(3), 643 (1976).

Inhibition of Corticosteroidogenesis by Cannabinoids.

Δ^9-THC inhibited ACTH-induced corticosteroidogenesis in mouse adrenal tumor cells and in normal cat adrenal cell suspensions and effectively blocked that induced by cholera toxin and CAMP. Differentiation of steroidogenesis from behavioral and anti-tumor activity was achieved with CBN and CBD, respectively.

5159 Warner, W.; Harris, L. S.; and Carchman, R. A., Endocrinology, *101*(6), 1815-20 (1977).

Inhibition of Cortiocosteroidogenesis by Delta-9-Tetrahydrocannabinol.

THC exerted a direct inhibitory effect on the mouse steroid-secreting tissues. The possible site of steroidogenesis inhibition was indicated.

5160 Warnock, G. R.; and Shalla, C. L., J. Dental Res., *54*(Special Issue A), 173 (1975).

Effects of Marijuana Smoking on Maturation of Oral Epithelium (Abstract).

Oral exfoliative smears of buccal mucosa, dorsum of the tongue, soft palate and attached gingiva were obtained from both smokers of marihuana and non-smokers to determine its effects on maturation of oral epithelium.

5161 Waser, P. G.; and Frischknecht, H. R., *Seventh International Congress of Pharmacology: Abstracts*, Paris, France, July 16-21, 1978, p. 106.

Social Behavior of Ants Under Hallucinogenic Drugs.

The frequencies of aggressive elements, social grooming and food-sharing or the number of interactions per meeting were not significantly altered in Δ^9-THC-treated ants compared to controls. No distinct behavioral changes were observed due to repeated Δ^9-THC administration.

5162 Waser, P. G.; and Martin, A., pp. 313-29 in *Pharmacology of Marihuana, Vol. 1*, edited by M. C. Braude and S. Szara. NY, Raven Press, 1976.

Barbiturate Potentiating, Temperature Reducing, Analgesic, and Behavioral Effects of Some Synthetic Tetrahydrocannabinol Derivatives in Comparison with Δ^9-Tetrahydrocannabinol.

Pharmacological properties of 4 synthetic cannabinoids, $\Delta^{9,11}$-8-OH-THC (25-100 mg/kg), $\Delta^{7,8}$-9-OH-THC (25-100 mg/kg), $\Delta^{8,9}$-3-(1-dimethyl-3'-aza-4'keto) THC (25-100 mg/kg) and $\Delta^{8,9}$-dimethyl-THC (0.1-5.0 mg/kg) and Δ^9-THC (5-100 mg/kg) were studied in mice. Qualitatively similar responses were present. Behaviorally, initial excitation followed by sedation was observed. $\Delta^{8,9}$-dimethyl-THC was consistently most active and also showed cross-tolerance to Δ^9-THC.

5163 Waser, P. G.; Martin, A.; and Heer-Carcano, L., Psychopharmacologia, *46*(3), 249-54 (1976).

The effect of Δ^9-Tetrahydrocannabinol and LSD on the Acquisition of an Active Avoidance Response in the Rat.

The effect of Δ^9-THC (1.0, 3.0, and 9.0 mg/kg) on conditioned avoidance behabior in 6 week old male rats was examined. At the two higher doses used, higher avoidance rates were observed. The animals also showed different gross behavioral changes at the three doses examined. LSD, on the other hand, suppressed avoidance rates in these animals.

5164 Watanabe, K., Japan (Patent). 75 20, 873 (Cl. GolN), 18 Jul 1975, 3 pp.

Detecting a Small Amount of Hemp Quickly and Simply in the Field.

Plant material is extracted with chloroform or dichloromethane which in turn contains some tetrazotized di-*O*-anisidine. The extract is made basic by the addition of NaOH or KOH. A positive test is determined by formation of a red color in the organic layer.

5165 Watts, R. J., Nurs. Forum, *17*(2), 169-83 (1978).

The Physiological Interrelationships Between Depression, Drugs, and Sexuality.

Depression and alcohol decrease sexual behavior. The effect of marihuana on sex is a controversial issue. Other drugs, licit and illicit, have variable effects.

5166 Way, E. L., pp. 619-20 in *Pharmacology of Marihuana, Vol. 2*, edited by M. C. Braude and S. Szara. NY, Raven Press, 1976.

Clinical Studies: An Introduction.

Penalties imposed for drug misuse should be based on the degree of consequent misbehavior rather than on the drug itself. The fact that a substance causes physical dependence should not be an excuse for enacting punitive legislation.

5167 Wechsler, H., J. Stud. Alcohol, *37*(11), 1672-77 (1976).

Alcohol Intoxication and Drug Use Among Teen-Agers.

In a study of drug abuse in two communities, a strong relationship was found in junior and senior high school students between the extent of drinking and the use of marihuana and other drugs.

5168 Wechsler, H.; and McFadden, M., J. Stud. Alcohol, *37*(9), 1291-1301 (1976).

Sex Differences in Adolescent Alcohol and Drug Use: A Disappearing Phenomenon.

Results of this study showed that although there are still sex differences in the types of drugs used at the high school level, these differences are eliminated with age. Even at the high school level, rate of marihuana use is the same in both sexes.

5169 Weckowicz, T. E.; Collier, G.; and Spreng, L., Psychol. Rep., *41*(1), 291-302 (1977).

Field Dependence, Cognitive Functions, Personality Traits, and Social Values in Heavy Cannabis Users and Nonuser Controls.

An extended cross-validation of a previous study comparing marihuana users with non-users was conducted. Findings indicated that drug users were more field independent and introverted and more radical and critical of social systems. The lack of apparent intellectual deterioration resulting from chronic marihuana use was also indicated.

5170   Weckowicz, T. E.; Fedora, O.; Mason, J.; Radstaak, D.; Bay, K. S.; and Yonge, K. A., J. Abnorm. Psychol., *84*(4), 386-98 (1975).

Effect of Marijuana on Divergent and Convergent Production Cognitive Tests.

Marihuana smoking (3 mg of Δ^9-THC) improved performance of subjects under several divergent production and oral fluency measuring cognitive tests. A higher dose of THC (6 mg), however, impaired such performance. The possibility of THC acting as a stimulant in low doses was discussed.

5171   Weinberg, A. D.; Dimen, E.; Brozelleca, J. F.; and Harris, L. S., J. Pharm. Pharmacol., *29*(8), 477-81 (1977).

Weight and Activity in Male Mice After Daily Inhalation of Cannabis Smoke in an Automated Smoke Exposure Chamber.

Marihuana smoke (0.123 mg/litter THC concentration) decreased the activity of mice significantly by the sixth day of treatment over both air and placebo controls but had no effect on weight gain. A detailed description of the automated smoking apparatus is also given.

5172   Weinberg, A. D.; Dimen, E. M.; Simon, G. S.; Harris, L. S.; and Borzelleca, J. F., Toxicol. Appl. Pharmacol., *42*(2), 301-07 (1977).

Measurements of Weight and Activity in Male Mice Following Inhalation of Cannabis Smoke in a Controlled Smoke Exposure Chamber.

Repeated exposure to cannabis smoke resulted in decreased motor activity and body weight in mice. The latter effect depended on dosing regimen. Detailed description of exposure chamber was also given.

5173   Weiner, B.-Z.; and Zilkha, A., Chim. Ther., *10*(1), 79-83 (1975).

Monomers and Polymers of $\Delta^{1(6)}$-Tetrahydrocannabinol and Cannabidiol.

Synthesis of the *O*-methacryloyl derivatives of $\Delta^{1(6)}$-THC and of CBD and free radical polymerization of these compounds was presented. The parent compounds were also linked with the terminal carbons of polyethylene oxide (PEO) of different molecular weights by carbonate bonds. Carbonate dimers of $\Delta^{1(6)}$-THC and polycarbonates of CBD as well as carbamate derivatives with amines and amino acids were also prepared. The psychomimetic activity of some $\Delta^{1(6)}$-THC derivatives was similar to that of the parent compound.

5174   Weinstein, M., Int. J. Addict., *13*(4), 683-88 (1978).

Changes in Drug Usage and Associated Personality Traits Among College Students.

A survey of 419 university students indicated that drug use, except that of marihuana, has leveled off. Four out of six personality factors continued to be moderately good predictors of drug use.

5175   Weinstein, R. M., Int. J. Addict., *11*(4), 571-95 (1976).

The Imputation of Motives for Marijuana Behavior.

In users, former users, and non-users, response patterns toward marihuana use were most biased by the frequency of marihuana use and by attitudes favorable to drug use. Imputation of motives for marihuana use varies with historical epoch and societal conditions as suggested by Mills.

5176 Weinstein, R. M., Int. J. Addict., *12*(1), 121-36 (1977).

Interpersonal Expections for Marijuana Behavior.

When questioned, current marihuana users indicated that social improvement follows marihuana use, whereas former users and non-users believed social impairment to be the consequence. Research methodology and other findings of the study were discussed.

5177 Weinstein, R. M., Int. J. Addict., *13*(6), 887-910 (1978).

The Avowal of Motives for Marijuana Behavior.

Curiosity or search for a new knowledge were the motives behind initial marihuana use, whereas self-fulfillment accounted for continued use. Subjects who never used marihuana were influenced by legal, moral and psychological implications of marihuana use, whereas discontinued users simply lost interest.

5178 Weisman, R.; and Asher, J., Sci. News, *114*(6), 94 (1978).

Marijuana's Synthetic Cousin.

Nabilone possesses the therapeutic potentials of THC but lacks its mind-altering properties.

5179 Weiss, G. K.; Fenney, D. M.; and Spiker, M., Fed. Proc., *35*(3), 644 1976).

Effect of Δ^9-THC on Physical Symptoms and EEG in the Naturally Epileptic Beagle.

Naturally epileptic beagles, receiving CBD or Δ^9-THC for 20 days, demonstrated myoclonic jerks and generalized seizures only in the presence of high doses of Δ^9-THC (3.0 and 5.0 mg/kg, p.o.). Δ^9-THC also unmasked reliably existing epileptic pathology in animals implanted with cortical and subcortical electrodes.

5180 Weissman, A., Psycopharmacology, *58*(2), 12 (1978).

Generalization of the Discriminative Stimulus Properties of Δ^9-Tetrahydrocannabinol to Cannabinoids with Therapeutic Potential (Abstract).

In rats trained to discriminate Δ^9-THC, generalization to THC, HHC, CBN, CBD, 11-OH-Δ^9-THC and nabilone resulted. ED_{50} values were given. Nabilone and HHC were not discriminated as diazepam and morphine, respectively.

5181 Weissman, A., pp. 122 in *Stimulus Properties of Drugs: Ten Years of Progress,* edited by F. C. Colpaert and J. A. Rosecrans. New York, Elsevier North-Holland, 1978.

Generalization of the Discriminative Stimulus Properties of Δ^9-Tetrahydrocannabinol to Cannabinoids with Therapeutic Potential.

In rats trained to discriminate Δ^9-THC, generalization to 11-OH-Δ^9-THC, Δ^8-THC, HHC, CBN and nabilone, but not to CBD, resulted. Implications of the findings were discussed.

5182 Weisz, D. J., Diss. Abstr. Int. B, *38*(9), 4526 (1978).

Effects of Delta-9-THC on CAl Pyramidal Cell Activity in Rat Hippocampus.

THC (2 to 16 mg/kg) increased spike latencies and recurrent inhibition of the CAl cell field in the rat hippocampus. THC also lowered and increased the seizure threshold at 4 and 16 mg/kg, respectively, and resulted in a biphasic effect on low frequency potentiation.

5183   Weisz, D. J.; and Vardaris, R. M., Physiol. Psychol., *4*(2), 145-48 (1976).

Effects of Δ^9-Tetrahydrocannabinol on the Slope of Auditory Generalization Gradients in Rats.

Δ^9-THC (2 to 6 mg/kg, p.o.) did not affect the acquisition of shuttle avoidance behavior in rats, but interesting results were obtained during extinction trials. Results were interpreted in terms of motivational processes.

5184   Welburn, P. J.; Starmer, G. A.; Chesher, G. B.; and Jackson, D. M., Psychopharmacologia, *46*(1), 83-85 (1976).

Effect of Cannabinoids on the Abdominal Construction Response in Mice: Within Cannabinoid Interactions.

Δ^9-THC and CBN exhibited analgesic activity in mice with ED_{50} of 1.25 and 61.8 mg/kg, p.o., respectively. The analgesic effects of these two cannabinoids were additive. CBD failed to demonstrate any activity and antagonized that of Δ^9-THC and CBN

5185   Wells, B.; and Stacey, B., Brit. J. Addict., *71*(2), 161-65 (1976).

Further Comparison of Cannabis (Marijuana) Users and Non-Users.

Cannabis was the most frequently used drug among this Scottish sample. Social and psychological patterns of disruption were associated with cannabis use. Polydrug use was also common.

5186   Weppner, R. S.; and Inciardi, J. A., Int. J. Offend. Ther. Comp. Criminol., *22*(2), 115-26 (1978).

Decriminalizing Marijuana.

The authors used data taken from drug treatment, crime and hospital statistics of Dade County, Florida, to argue that the reluctance of some states to decriminalize marihuana may be a costly process from both social and financial perspectives.

5187   Wesson, D. R.; and Smith, D. E., Curr. Psychiat. Ther., *16*, 203-08 (1976).

Psychoactive Drug Crisis Intervention.

Adverse reactions to marihuana were often said to be paranoia, anxiety and panic. Due to the generally brief time spans of "crisis" usually encountered, treatment suggested is supportive and conservative, with medication rarely being necessary. The article lists diazepam as the drug of choice and phencyclidine as the common adulterant in street THC.

5188   West, M. E.; and Lockhart, A. B., *Seventh International Congress of Pharmacology: Abstracts*, Paris, France, July 16-21, 1978, p. 916.

The Cardiovascular Responses to Intravenous Injection of a Non-Narcotic Preparation from *Cannabis sativa*.

A non-narcotic, water-soluble fraction of *Cannabis sativa* induced a fall in BP and heart rate, an inversion of the T-wave and a decrease in the left ventricular contractile force when injected i.v. into anesthetized dogs. The existence of a potent cardiac depressant, which may not be related to the psychoactive principles, is suggested.

5189   West, M. E.; and Lockhart, A. B., West Indian Med. J., 27(1), 16-25 (1978).

The Treatment of Glaucoma Using a Non-Psychoactive Preparation of *Cannabis sativa*.

A non-psychotropic, non-toxic principle of *Cannabis sativa* was separated, formulated in an ophthalmic preparation and used topically in dogs as well as in the eyes of 26 human glaucoma patients. This preparation, which compared favorably with pilocarpine in the dog, caused significant lowering of IOP in all subjects tested.

5190   Whalen, R. P., N. Y. State J. Med., 78(8), 1308 (1978).

Paraquat Toxicity: Background Report.

A brief report on paraquat and marihuana.   Clinical symptoms are listed. These symptoms seem likely to be absent in marihuana smokers at current levels of contamination.

5191   Wheals, B. B., J. Chromatogr., 122, 85-105 (1976).

Forensic Aspects of High-Pressure Liquid Chromatography.

HPLC is particularly useful in discriminating between samples of cannabis of different origins and in providing a simple means of analysis for the acidic cannabinoids.   Methods and references are given for the application of HPLC techniques in analyzing other drugs as well.

5192   Wheals, B. B.; and Smith, R. N., J. Chromatogr., 105, 396-400 (1975).

Comparative Cannabis Analysis: A Comparison of High-Pressure Liquid Chromatography with Other Chromatographic Techniques.

A favorable comparison of HPLC to GC or TLC techniques is given.   Cannabis samples of different geographical origin showed greater diversity by HPLC than by GLC.

5193   White, A.; Carchman, R.; and Funderburk, W., Fed. Proc., 35(3), 644 (1976).

Cellular Mediated Decreases in Sensitivity to the Inhibitory Effects of Delta-9-Tetrahydrocannabinol (Δ^9-THC).   (abstract)

In the intact mouse, Lewis lung adenocarcinoma cells developed cellular resistance to the antitumor effects of chronically administered Δ^9-THC. Acute pulses of Δ^9-THC (10^{-4} M for 2.5 hrs) produced additive inhibitor effects of DNA synthesis in acutely treated cells, but failed to alter the DNA synthesis of chronically treated cells.   Tolerance derives from chronically administered Δ^9-THC.

5194   White, A. C.; Munson, J. A.; Munson, A. E.; and Carchman, R. A., J. Natl. Cancer Inst., 56(3), 655-58 (1976).

Brief Communication: Effects of Δ^9-Tetrahydrocannabinol in Lewis Lung Adenocarcinoma Cells in Tissue Culture.

THC (0.00001 m) reduced Lewis lung cultured cell number immediately.   Ara-C and actinomycin-D had similar cytotoxicity.   THC also caused a dose-related decrease in acid soluble radioactivity.   THC inhibited replication after the incorporation of thymidine.

5195   White, E. R., Diss. Abst. Int. B, 35(8), 4080-01 (1975).

Metabolism of I-Δ^9-Tetrahydrocannabinol.

Methodology is described which permits a determination of the degree of interaction between Δ^9-THC and hepatic microsomal cytochrome P-450. The spectral association constant is determined to be 0.083 ($\pm$) 0.012 mm. The sole metabolic conversion product is determined to be 11-OH-THC.

5196   White, S. C.; Brin, S. C.; and Janicki, B. W., Science, *187*, 71-72 (1975).

Mitogen-Induced Blastogenic Responses of Lymphocytes from Marihuana Smokers.

Mitogen-induced blastogenic responses of lymphocytes from healthy, long-term marihuana smokers did not differ from those of matched control subjects.

5197   Whitehead, P. C.; and Cabral, R. M., Drug Forum, *5*(1), 45-54 1975/1976).

Scaling the Sequence of Drug Using Behaviours: A Test of the Stepping-Stone Hypothesis.

The authors describe a method for determining the "best fit" order of drug use for high school students. From the results of this method used on 902 drug using high school students in Halifax, it was ascertained that the average user first used tobacco, then alcohol, then solvents, then marihuana. The list continues through opiates and LSD but with less consistency than for the first four drugs mentioned.

5198   Wiberg, D. M.; Swanson, G. D.; and Bellville, J. W., Pharmacologist, *17*(2), 180 (1975).

Respiratory Effects of Marijuana Characterized by Dynamic End-Tidal Forcing.

The respiratory effects of placebo cigarette, two 900 mg cigarettes of 2.2% Δ^9-THC and 30 mg pentazocine i.m.

were studied using the dynamic end-tidal forcing method. The depressant effect of marihuana and pentazocine were demonstrated and a quantitative relationship was observed.

5199   Widman, M., Laekartidningen, *73*(45), 3857-59 (1976).

Chemistry and Metabolism of the Cannabinoids.

This review of the metabolism of THC discusses the activity of the metabolites and includes 20 references.

5200   Widman, M.; Dahmen, J.; Leander, K.; and Petersson, K., Acta Pharm. Suecia, *12*(4), 385-92 (1975).

In Vitro Metabolism of Cannabinol in Rat and Rabbit Liver: Syntheses of 2"-, 3"-, and 5"-Hydroxycannabinol.

Metabolism of CBN *in vitro* by supernatant from rat and rabbit liver provided side chain hydroxylated compounds. The side chain metabolites were, 2"-, 3"-, 4"-, 5"-hydroxylated-CBN. The known metabolite 7-OH-CBN was also isolated. Isolation and synthetic procedures are discussed. Physical data are given for metabolites.

5201   Widman, M.; Nordqvist, M.; Dollery, C. T.; and Briant, R. H., J. Pharm. Pharmacol., *27*(11), 842-48 (1975).

Metabolism of Δ^1-Tetrahydrocannabinol by the Isolated Perfused Dog Lung. Comparison with *In Vitro* Liver Metabolism.

In the perfused dog lung Δ^1-THC is metabolized to two new major metabolites, 3"-OH-Δ^1-THC and 4"-OH-Δ^1-THC. Small amounts of 7-OH, 6 α and 6 β-OH-Δ^1-THC were formed.

With liver microsomal metabolism, traces of these new side chain hydroxylate metabolites were found along with the previously reported major metabolites, 7-OH-Δ^1-THC, 6 α and 6 β-OH-Δ^1-THC.

5202   Wig, N. N.; and Varma, V. K., Drug Alcohol Depend., *2*(3), 211-19 (1977).

Patterns of Long-Term Heavy Cannabis Use in North India and its Effect on Cognitive Functions: A Preliminary Report.

Long-term cannabis users were found to have lower intellectual, memory and concentration abilities when compared with controls. The question of whether the impairment of the above parameters was related to drug use or existed prior to drug use is raised.

5203   Wikler, A., pp. 126-47 in *Chronic Cannabis Use*, edited by R. L. Dornbush, A. M. Freedman, and M. Fink. NY, Annals of the New York Academy of Sciences, V. 282, 1976.

Aspects of Tolerance to and Dependence on Cannabis.

Data pertinent to the development of pharmacologic or learned tolerance to cannabis along with reverse tolerance phenomenon were reviewed. Tissue and dispositional tolerance are probable components of such tolerance development. It was reported that behavioral but not physiologic dependence on cannabis is seen in man.

5204   Willette, R. E., ed., *Cannabinoid Assays in Humans*, NIDA Research Monograph 7, 1976.

The editor includes twelve review articles contributed by various research groups describing methodologies for the detection and quantitation of cannabinoids in humans.

5205   Willette, R. E., ed., *Drugs and Driving*, NIDA Research Monograph, 11, 1977.

This review is conducted by a panel of nationally recognized experts on the behavioral effects of drug use. See McBay, A. and Moskowitz, H.

5206   Williams, P. L.; Moffat, A. C.; and King, L. J., J. Chromatogr., *155*, 273-83 (1978).

Combined High-Pressure Liquid Chromatography and Radioimmunoassay Method for the Quantitation of Δ^9-Tetrahydrocannabinol and Some of its Metabolites in Human Plasma.

The procedure depends on the separation of cannabinoids from methanol extracts of plasma by HPLC followed by RIA of the separated fractions. The plasma concentrations of cannabinoids with retention volumes equivalent to Δ^9-THC, CBN and mono-hydroxylated metabolites were measured in volunteers who smoked tobacco cigarettes impregnated with 8-10 mg of Δ^9-THC. The sensitivity was 0.1 ng/ml.

5207   Williams, S. J.; Hartler, J. P. R.; and Graham, J. D. P., Thorax, *31*(6), 720-23 (1976).

Bronchodilator Effect of Δ^1-THC Administered by Aerosol to Asthmatic Patients.

Δ^9-THC as an aerosol (200 µg in 62 ml) was as effective as salbutamol in treatment of bronchial asthma patients. Forced expiratory volume increased rapidly with salbutamol but after one hour the increase was equivalent to that with THC. At this dose of THC there was neither a change in cardiovascular function nor any behavioral side effects.

5208   Willinsky, M. D.; Loizzo, A.; and Longo, V. G., Psychopharmacologia, *41*(2), 123-26 (1975).

EEG Spectral Analysis for the Evaluation of the Central Effects of Δ^6-Tetrahydrocannabinol in Rabbits.

Once every 7 days rabbits were administered 10, 50, 100, 250 and 1000 µg/kg Δ^9-THC, i.v. Dose related changes were found in the hippocampal EEG. Even small amounts of drug produced changes with no observable behavioral changes.

5209   Wilson, P. R., pp. 67-77 in *Two Faces of Deviance: Crimes of the Powerless and the Powerful*, edited by P. R. Wilson and J. Braithwaite. St. Lucia, Queensland, Australia, University of Queensland Press, 1978.

Cannabis, Witches, and Social Scapegoats.

Australian marihuana laws are too harsh and biased since marihuana is no more harmful than alcohol, tobacco or even the legally prescribed drugs. Australia should learn from the American experience with decriminalization laws.

5210   Wilson, R. S.; and May, E. L., J. Med. Chem., *18*(7), 700-03 (1975).

Analgesic Properties of the Tetrahydrocannabinols, their Metabolites, and Analogs.

The metabolites of Δ^8-THC and Δ^9-THC were given s.c. to mice to determine the analgesic effects. The 11-hydroxy compounds were found to be more potent than their parent compounds. The effects of pretreatment with naloxone and SKF-525A are discussed.

5211   Wilson, R. S.; and May, E. L., pp. 137-38 in *Pharmacology of Marihuana, Vol. 1*, edited by M. C. Braude and S. Szara. NY, Raven Press, 1976.

The role of 11-Hydroxylation in Tetrahydrocannabinol Activity.

The pharmacological properties of 9-*nor*-Δ^8-THC and 9-*nor*-Δ^9-THC were studied. These compounds were found to be equipotent to Δ^8- and Δ^9-THC in all tests except for analgesia where they were comparitively inactive. The 11-OH metabolites of Δ^8- and Δ^9-THC were considerably more potent.

5212   Wilson, R. S.; May, E. L.; Martin, B. R.; and Dewey, W. L., J. Med. Chem., *19*(9), 1165-67 (1976).

9-*nor* - 9-Hydroxyhexahydrocannabinols. Synthesis, Some Behavioral and Analgesic Properties, and Comparison with the Tetrahydrocannabinols.

When compared to Δ^8-THC and their 11-OH metabolites, 9-*nor*-9-α-HHC and its 9-β-OH isomer also produced ataxia in dogs and decreased locomotor activity in mice. Only the latter agent, however, produced morphine-like potency of analgesia in mice.

5213   Win Pe, U., Forensic Sci., *10*(3), 261-64 (1977).

Demonstration of Marijuana and Coca Leaf in Illicit Cigarette Sample.

Marihuana and coca leaves were tested for in 32 samples of cigarettes obtained from the illicit market in different parts of Burma. Microscopical examination and TLC were used for identification of both drugs. Thirteen brands contained marihuana and six contained coca leaves.

5214   Win Pe, U., Forensic Sci., *8*(2), 203 (1976).

A Rapid Method for Testing Marihuana (Letter).

364

KaKo Blue Salt B (Naphthol color, Sanyo Japan) can be mixed with a petroleum-ether extract of marijuana to yield a bright red color. A 0.1% solution of the salt can be used as a spray reagent to develop thin-layer chromatograms of various cannabinoids and derivatives.

5215 Win Pe, U., Forensic Sci., *11*(2), 165 (1978).

Simplified Method for Testing Marijuana, Tetrahydrocannabinol, Hashish and Derivatives.

A paper chromatographic procedure is given with two different systems. The systems gave separation of THC, CBD and CBN. The time needed for one development was 5 hours.

5216 Winek, C. L., Clin. Toxicol., *10*(2), 243-53 (1977).

Some Historical Aspects of Marijuana.

A group of references obtained from older Materia Medica texts and journals is presented. The references deal with the medicinal uses of the plant and its products such as: extractum cannabis, cannabinaceae, *Cannabis indica*, extractum cannabis purificatum, and tinctura cannabis indicae.

5217 Wing, D. R.; and Paton, W. D. M., J. Pharm. Pharmacol., *30*(12), 802-03 (1978).

An Effect of Cannabis Treatment *In Vivo* on Noradrenaline-Stimulated Lipolysis in Rat Adipocytes.

Fat cells from cannabis-treated rats (5.4 mg/kg for 2 days) exerted higher

lipolytic rate than did those of control animals in the presence of NE and the absence of albumin from incubation medium. The mechanisms involved were further investigated.

5218 Winn, M.; Arendsen, D.; Dodge, P.; Dren, A.; Dunnigan, D.; Hallas, R.; Hwang, K.; Kyncl, J.; Lee, Y.-H.; Plotnikoff, N.; Young, P.; and Zaugg, H., J. Med. Chem., *19* 4), 461-71 1976).

Drugs Derived from Cannabinoids. 5. $\Delta^{6a,10a}$-Tetrahydrocannabinol and Heterocyclic Analogs Containing Aromatic Side Chains.

Various arylalkyl side chains were introduced into $\Delta^{6a,10a}$-THC and its nitrogen, sulfur and carbocyclic analogs. The synthesis of these compounds is described. The pharmacological activities tested include: analgesic, tranquilizer, antipsychotic, hypnotic, antisecretary, antidiarrheal, and antiulcer activity. Compounds having activity in the above tests invariably contained 1-methyl 4-(4 flurophenyl) butyl or 1,2 dimethyl 4-(4 flurophenyl) butyl side chains. These compounds have a relatively high margin of safety.

5219 Wold, J. K.; and Hillestad, A., Phytochemistry, *15*, 325-26 (1976).

The Demonstration of Galactosamine in a Higher Plant: *Cannabis sativa*.

Galactosamine is reported for the first time in a higher plant and glucosamine is reported for the first time in cannabis. Separation techniques and analytical data are given.

5220 Woodhouse, E. J., U.S. NTIS Report PB-250431, 1975. 121 pp.

Marihuana Contact Test Evaluation and Development.

For detecting human contact with marihuana, the colorimetric swab test is found to be most effective on the lip area. However, there are natural and cosmetic interferences. A new method using TLC was developed in which the cannabinoids are extracted from the swab. MS and RIA are more sensitive.

5221 Woodside, A. G.; Bearden, W. O.; and Ronkainen, I., J. Psychol., 96(1), 11-14 (1977).

Images on Serving Marijuana, Alcoholic Beverages, and Soft Drinks.

The kind of image marihuana serving reflects depends in part on the using habits of the questioned persons. Also, people are more likely to judge a person based on the type of products he offers.

5222 Wrenn, J. M.; and Friedman, M. A., Arch. Int. Pharmacodyn. Ther., 235(1), 4-8 (1978).

Effects of Chronic Administration of Δ^8- and Δ^9-Tetrahydrocannabinol on Hepatic Tyrosine Aminotransferase Activity in Mice.

Tolerance to the stimulation of hepatic tyrosine aminotransferase activity caused by Δ^8- and Δ^9-THC developed after 12 weeks of treatment.

5223 Wrenn, J. M.; and Friedman, M. A., Toxicol. Appl. Pharmacol., 41(1), 186 (1977).

Evidence for a Highly Specific Interaction Between Δ^8-Tetrahydrocannabinol and Hydrocortisone in the Liver Tyrosine-Aminotransferase System (Abstract).

Δ^8-THC (12.5-200 mg/kg, i.p.) produced a dose-dependent stimulation of mouse liver tyrosine aminotransferase (TAT). Δ^8-THC enhanced the induction of TAT elicited by both hydrocortisone Ac and glucagon, but was without effect on tryptophan-induced TAT activity. Δ^8-THC and Δ^9-THC differ with respect to effects on TAT.

5224 Wrenn, J M.; and Friedman, M. A., Toxicol. Appl. Pharmacol., 43(3), 569-76 (1978).

Evidence for Highly Specific Interactions Between Δ^8- and Δ^9-Tetrahydrocannabinol and Hydrocortisone in the Rodent Tyrosine Aminotransferase System.

Both an acute and a subacute study of Δ^8- and Δ^9-THC in mice produced a stimulation of basal tyrosin aminotransferase (TAT) activity and inhibition of steroid mediated induction. Rat liver TAT activity (enhanced by glucagon) was further enhanced by pretreatment with either cannabinoid, but adrenalectomized rats showed no change from pretreatment w/cannabinoids on TAT induction by tryptophan.

5225 Wrenn, J. M.; Friedman, M. A.; and Harris, L. S., Toxicol. Appl. Pharmacol., 45(1), 263 (1978).

Effects of Δ^8- and Δ^9-Tetrahydrocannabinol on Murine Hepatic RNA Polymerase Systems (Abstract).

Both Δ^9- and Δ^8-THC stimulated basal activity of murine hepatic RNA polymerase systems. The two cannabinoids, however, acted at different sites to inhibit steroid-mediated induction of tyrosine aminotransferase activity.

5226   Wright, P. L.; Smith, S. H.; Keplinger, M. L.; Calandra, J. C.; and Braude, M. C., Toxicol. Appl. Pharmacol., *38*, 223-35 (1976).

Reproductive and Teratologic Studies with Δ^9-Tetrahydrocannabinol and Crude Marijuana Extract.

The effect of Δ^9-THC (0.5-1.5 mg/kg) and crude marihuana extract (CME) on the reproductive system were examined in rats and rabbits. In addition, the teratogenic potential of Δ^9-THC and CME in the above two species was studied. In rabbits both Δ^9-THC and CME decreased survival time in pups at the highest dose.

Y

5227 Yagen, B.; Levy, S.; Mechoulam, B.; and Ben-Zvi, Z., J. Amer. Chem. Soc., 99(19), 6444-46 (1977).

Synthesis and Enzymatic Formation of a C-Glucuronide of Δ^6-THC.

Δ^6-THC-C-4'-glucuronide (3a) was synthesized in 20% yield by condensation of Δ^6-THC (1a) with equimolar amount of methyl (tetra-O-acetyl)-β-D-gludopyranurmate (2) in presence of boron trifluoride etherate. When (1a) and (2) were used in a molar ratio (3:1) and in presence of para-toulene sulfonic acid, 3 compounds were obtained: Δ^6-THC-O-glucuronide methyl ester triacetate (4) (10% yield), (3a) (10% yield), and Δ^6-THC-C-6'-glucuronide (5a) (1% yield). Δ^6-THC-C-4'-glucuronide (3a) was also prepared enzymatically.

5228 Yisak, W.; Agurell, S.; Lindgren, J. E.; and Widman, M., J. Pharm. Pharmacol., 30(7), 462-63 (1978).

In Vivo Metabolites of Cannabinol Identified as Fatty Acid Conjugates.

Fatty acid conjugates of various metabolites of CBN were identified by combined GC and MS.

5229 Yisak, W.; Widman, M.; and Agurell, S., J. Pharm. Pharmacol., 30(9), 554-57 (1978).

Acidic In Vivo Metabolites of Cannabinol Isolated from Rat Faeces.

After six days of daily CBN administration, acidic metabolites were isolated from rat faeces by GC/MS analysis. Major metabolite was CBN-7-oic acid.

5230 Yisak, W.; Widman, M.; Lindgren, J.-E.; and Agurell, S., Acta Pharm. Suecica, 14(Suppl.), 59 (1977).

In Vivo Metabolism of Cannabinol.

The authors used radioactive labeling studies to investigate the metabolism of CBN in rats, isolating and characterizing several urinary and fecal metabolites.

5231 Yisak, W. A., Widman, M., Agurell, S., and Lindgren, J. E., West Afr. J. Pharmaco., Drug Res., 4(1), 83-84 (1977).

In Vivo Neutral Metabolites of Cannabinol from Rat Faeces (Abstract).

Free CBN, 2 conjugated metabolites, and nine free neutral mono and dioxygenated metabolites were identified in the analysis of faeces collected for six days after the i.v. administration of ^{14}C-CBN to male rats.

5232 Yisak, W. A.; Widman, M.; Lindgren, J. E.; and Agurell, S., J. Pharm. Pharmacol., 29(8), 487-90 (1977).

Neutral In Vivo Metabolites of Cannabinol Isolated from Rat Faeces.

^{14}C-CBN was used in the rat and neutral radioactive-labeled metabolites were recovered from the feces and identified. Nine mono- and di-oxygenated metabolites were characterized. A metabolism chart was constructed from this data and the relative percentages of each pathway used in the rat were given.

5233 Yoshida, A., Nippon Yakuzaishikai Zasshi, 30(5), 407-13 (1978).

Pharmacological Actions of Cannabis.

The pharmacology of cannabis in humans and laboratory animals is reviewed. Special emphasis is placed on the major psychoactive constituent, Δ^9-THC.

5234   Yoshimura, H.; Watanabe, K.; Oguri, K.; Fujiwara, M.; and Ueki, S., J. Med. Chem., 21(10), 1079-81 (1978).

Synthesis and Pharmacological Activity of a Phosphate Ester of Δ^8-Tetrahydrocannabinol.

Synthetized water soluble phosphate ester of Δ^8-THC was less active than Δ^8-THC in the cataleptogenic and thiopental sleep-potentiating effect, but showed almost the same potency and longer duration of hypothermic effect. The phosphate ester was also found to be difficult to hydrolyze by alkaline phasphatase or mouse liver homogenate *in vitro*.

5235   Youngs, D. D.; Niebyl, J. R.; Blake, D. A.; Shipp, D. A.; Stanley, J.; and King, T. M., Obstet. Gynecol., 50(2), 212-16 (1977).

Experience with an Adolescent Pregnancy Program: *A Preliminary Report*.

From results of interviews and urinalyses of pregnant adolescents admitted to a program, it was found that half used nicotine, 23% used alcohol, 17% used aspirin and 10% used marihuana, with all other drugs being used by less than 4% of the patients. Of the 202 patients in the study, 89% were black and all were 17 years of age or younger.

Z

5236 Zaugg, H. E.; and Dunnigan, D. A., J. Org. Chem., *41*(21), 3415-19 (1976).

2,4-Dihydroxyphenanthrenes and Derived Ethers. Regioselective Etherification of Acetates.

An improved synthetic route for preparing certain cannabinoids is discussed. Some 2,4-disubstituted phenanthrenes and corresponding 9,10-dihydro derivatives were prepared as carbocyclic analogues of some cannabinoids. The analogues were not psychoactive but the synthetic route may prove useful in future research.

5237 Zavala, D. C.; and Rhodes, M. L., Chest, *74*(4), 418-20 (1978).

An Effect of Paraquat on the Lungs of Rabbits: Its Implications in Smoking Contaminated Marihuana.

Intrabronchial instillation of paraquat in rabbits resulted in lung damage. That suggested possible hazards to marihuana users.

5238 Zeidenberg, P.; Bourdon, R.; and Nahas, G. G., Amer. J. Psychiat., *134*(1) 76-78 (1977).

Marihuana Intoxication by Passive Inhalation.

A placebo smoker and staff members experienced "contact highs" because of their close proximity to subjects using marihuana heavily. The subjective complaints consisted of dizziness and nausea, tachycardia, and conjunctivitis. Passive inhalation of marihuana also resulted in urinary metabolites of the cannabinoids.

5239 Zimmer, B. D.; Bickel, P.; and Dittrich, A., Arzneim Forsch., *26*(8), 1614-16 (1976).

Changes of Simple Somatic Parameters by Δ^9-*trans*-Tetrahydrocannabinol (Δ^9-THC) in a Double-Blind Study.

Of the objective parameters tested, only the pulse rate was found to increase in THC (250 mg/kg) treated subjects. A positive correlation existed between the "anxiety-depression," "euphoria-agitation" scales and the increase of eosinophilic granulocytes. Increase in pulse rate and eosinophilic granulocytes were the only significantly different parameters as compared to controls.

5240 Zimmerman, A. M.; Stich, H.; and San, R., Pharmacology, *16*(6), 333-43 (1978).

Nonmutagenic Action of Cannabinoids *In Vitro*.

THC and a few other cannabinoids produced no mutagenic effects when tested in several microbial and mammalian *in vitro* systems. Implications of the findings were discussed.

5241 Zimmerman, A. M.; and Zimmerman, S. B., pp. 195-205 in *Marihuana: Chemistry, Biochemistry, and Cellular Effects*, edited by G. G. Nahas. NY, Springer-Verlag, 1976.

The Influence of Marihuana on Eukaryote Cell Growth and Development.

The action of THC on all growth and development was studied using the protozoan, *Tetrahymena pyriformis,* as a model cellular system. These studies show that THC depresses the exponential growth of tetrahymena, delays the onset of the first synchronous division in heat-synchronized cultures, and causes a reduction of DNA and RNA and protein synthesis.

370

5242   Zimmerman, D. H.; and Wieder, D. L., Soc. Probl., *25*(2), 198-207 (1977).

You Can't Help but Get Stoned. Notes on the Social Organization of Marijuana Smoking.

Informants' description of the social factors leading to marihuana use indicated that group planning provided for marihuana use but they insisted that such a use was not planned, "it just happened." These contradictory statements were discussed.

5243   Zimmerman, S.; Zimmerman, A. M.; Cameron, I. L.; and Laurence, H. L., Pharmacology, *15*(1), 10-23 (1977).

Δ^1-Tetrahydrocannabinol, Cannabidiol and Cannabinol Effects on the Immune Response of Mice.

All drugs were given in 0.1 ml of vehicle (i.p. for 4 consecutive days) and sacrificed on day 5. Mice which received antigen were given a single injection of sheep red blood cells (0.25 ml, i.p.) on day 1. Suppression of the humoral immune response was specific for THC (1.5 or 10 mg/kg) but not for CBN (25 mg/kg) or CBD (25 mg/kg). This suppression was reflected by a reduction of splenic weight, reduction in the number of splenic antibody-forming cells, lowered hemaglutination titer and reduction in the percentage of splenic white pulp to total spleen volume.

5244   Zinberg, N. E., Psychol. Today, *10*(7), 45-52, 102-06 (1976).

The War Over Marijuana.

The author refutes charges of the harmful effects of marihuana and concludes that "marihuana is a remarkably innocuous substance."

5245   Zwillich, C.; Doekel, R.; Hammill, S.; and Weil, J., Clin. Res., *25*(2) 136A (1977).

Does Smoked Marijuana Depress Respiration?

Various respiratory parameters were measured before and at certain intervals after smoking marihuana with 0% and 2% THC content. Marihuana devoid of THC affected none of the variables, while smoked marihuana with 2% THC had transient stimulatory effects on metabolic rate (oxygen consumption), resting ventilation, and the ventilatory response to carbon dioxide, but was not a respiratory depressant.

5246   Zwillich, C. W.; Doekel, R.; Hammill, S.; and Weil, J. V., Amer. Rev. Resp. Dis., *115*(4, part 2), 392 (1977).

Does Smoked Marijuana Depress Respiration?

See above abstract.

5247   Zwillich, C. W.; Doekel, R.; Hammill, S.; and Weil, J. V., Amer. Rev. Resp. Dis., *118* (5), 885-91 (1978).

The Effects of Smoked Marihuana on Metabolism and Respiratory Control.

Smoking marihuana increased resting minute ventilation, hypercapnic ventilatory response and heart rate in human subjects. Elevated metabolic rate accompanied the increased ventilation.

ADDENDUM II

5248   Annonymous, Bull. Narcotics, *28*(3), 11-29 (1976).

Drug Dependence Among Secondary School Students at Bogota, Barranquilla and Bucaramanga (Columbia).

This survey characterizes the incidence of use or experimentation of psychoactive substances by factors such as socioeconomic class, sex, age, religion, type of school, type and source of substance, home situation and level of parental education.

5249   Blumenthal, M.; Yankelev, S.; and Dikstein, S., Ophthal. Res., *8*, 259-61 (1976).

Method for Antiglaucoma Drug Screening on Rabbits.

Delta-8-THC was found to be an effective antiglaucoma agent in rabbits with pharmacologically-induced elevation of IOP.

5250   Carchman, R. A.; End, D.; Thourson, K.; Dewey, W. L.; and Harris, L. S., Pharmacologist, *18*(2), 166 (1976).

The Inhibition of Growth and Macromolecular Synthesis in Neural Cells in Tissue Culture by Delta-9-Tetrahydrocannabinol (Δ^9-THC) (Abstract).

Rat glial and mouse neuroblastoma cell cultures treated with Δ^9-THC demonstrated a reversible growth inhibition characterized by inhibition of DNA synthesis, ^{3}H-uridine uptake and incorporation, protein synthesis, and altered cell morphology.

5251   Clarke, E. G. C., ed. *Isolation and Identification of Drugs in Pharmaceuticals, Body Fluids, and Post-Mortem Materials, Vol. 2*, London, The Pharmaceutical Press, 1975.

In this book, cannabis and its cannabinoids were briefly discussed in different chapters. The information provided includes the definition of cannabis, absorption and excretion of Δ^9-THC, a brief summary of some chromatographic data on CBD, CBN and Δ^9-THC and IR spectra of these cannabinoids and Δ^8-THC.

5252   Collins, F. G.; Haavik, C. O.; and Skibba, J. L., Pharmacologist, *18*(2), 167 (1976).

Depression of Oxygen Consumption by Δ^9-Tetrahydrocannabinol (Δ^9-THC): Whole Body and Perfused Liver (Abstract).

Intravenous administration of Δ^9-THC to mice resulted in a decrease in whole body O_2 consumption and a decrease in O_2 consumption of the isolated perfused rat liver as measured by arteriovenous differences. These results indicate a possible decrease in heat production as the mechanism for Δ^9-THC induced hypothermia.

5253   Cook, C. E.; Hawes, M. L.; Amerson, E. W.; Pitt, C. G.; Williams, D. L.; and Willette, R. G., Pharmacologist, *18*(2), 166 (1976).

Tetrahydrocannabinol (THC) Radioimmunoassay: Immunogen and Novel ^{125}I-Radioligand Based on 5'-Substituted Δ^8-THC (Abstract).

5'-carboxy-Δ^8-THC coupled to BSA was given to rabbits and resulted in the production of antibodies which would bind Δ^9-THC or Δ^8-THC preferentially over other cannabinoids or metabolites. In addition, it was demonstrated that ^{125}I exchange with 5'-iodo-Δ^8-THC produced a novel iodinated radioligand.

5254 End, D.; Carchman, R. A.; Thoursen, K.; Dewey, W. L.; and Harris, L. S., Pharmacologist, *18*(2), 166 (1976).

The Uptake and Distribution of (^{3}H)-Δ^9-Tetrahydrocannabinol (^{3}H-Δ^9-THC) in Cultured Neural and Glial Cells (Abstract).

Uptake of ^{3}H-Δ^9-THC into rat glial (C6) and mouse neuroblastoma (NB2A) tissue culture cells was rapid with the NB2A cells accumulating twice as much as the C6 cells. The largest concentration of Δ^9-THC within the cell was in the nucleus indicating the nucleus may be the site of cytotoxicity.

5255 Fournier, G.; Lenicque, P. M.; and Paris, M. R., Toxicol. Eur. Res., *ISS6*, 385-89 (1978).

Etude de la Toxicite de l'Huile Essentielle de *Cannabis sativa L.* et de ses Principaux Constituants sur la Planaire (*Dugesia tigrina G*) [Toxic Effects of the Essential Oil of *Cannabis sativa L.* and its Main Constituents on Planarian (*Dugesia tigrina G*)].

Tissue regeneration in the planaria was used as a model to compare the toxic effects of the constituents of *Cannabis sativa* extract. Seratonin protected against the lethal effects of Δ^9-THC, CBN and CBD but not against caryophyllene oxide.

5256 Friedman, M. A.; and Testa, T., Pharmacologist, *18*(2), 167 (1976).

Effects of Cannabinoids on L1210 Murine Leukemia Oxygen Consumption (Abstract).

Delta-9-THC induced a decrease in O_2 consumption of L1210 leukemia cells; however, other cannabinoids (*abn* Δ^8-THC, *abn*, CBN, 9-*nor*-9-α-OH-HHC, 9-*nor*-9-β-OH-HHC) were shown to be more active. *In vivo* studies revealed similar results. These results do not correlate with inhibition of DNA synthesis in L1210 cells on CNS activity.

5257 Gagliardi, L.; Amato, A.; Profili, M.; Ricciardi, G.; and Chiavarelli, S., Riv. Tossicol.; Sper. Clin., *8*(3), 227-36 (1978).

Reattivi Di Colorazoine Dei Principi Attivi Della *Cannabis indica*: Aldeidi Aromatiche. Nota I [Color Reagents of the Active Principles of *Cannabis indica*: Aromatic Aldehydes. Part 1].

A series of reagents containing aromatic aldehydes in 1% sulfuric acid solutions are recommended as spray color reagents for TLC of cannabis extracts. Δ^9-THC can be identified also in traces and Δ^9-THC and CBN can be differentiated as they give different colors.

5258 Haavik, C. O.; and Hardman, H. F., Pharmacologist, *18*(2), 167 (1976).

Effect of Delta-9-Tetrahydrocannabinol (Δ^9-THC) on Tail and Rectal Temperature in the Mouse (Abstract).

Δ^9-THC induced decreases in both tail (TT) and rectal (TR) temperature. Since TT did not increase, the hypothermina is not mediated primarily by heat loss but is proposed to be a central decrease in heat production. Adrenergic antagonists potentiated the hypothermia by increasing heat loss.

5259 Haertzen, C. A.; Hooks, N. T.; and Pross, M., J. Nerv. Ment. Dis., *158*(3), 189-97 (1974).

Drug Associations as a Measure of Habit Strength for Specific Drugs.

In this study opiate addicts associated more words with heroin than with benzedrine, alcohol, "goof balls," or "reefers." Reefers were the second most associated drug differing significantly from heroin only on drug-relevant words. Brief mention of this observation is made in the discussion.

5260 Hanus, L., Scripta Med. (Brno), *51*(2), 124 (1978).

Soucasny Stav A Smery Vyzkumu Chemie Cannabinoidu [The Present State and Trends in the Research of Cannabinoids].

The paper discusses chemistry and pharmacology of cannabis research at present. The author worked on capillary gas chromatography cannabinoids and compared content of basic cannabinoids of fresh and dried flowering tops. More than 200 substances were detected in fresh flowering tops.

5261 Hirom, P. C.; and Smith, R. L., pp. 990-91 in *Isolation and Identification of Drugs in Pharmaceuticals, Body Fluids, and Post-Mortem Material, Vol. 2*, edited by E. G. C. Clark, London, The Pharmaceutical Press, 1975.

The Metabolism of Drugs.

The absorption and excretion of delta-9-THC are briefly discussed in this chapter. 11-OH-delta-9-THC is the only metabolite mentioned.

5262 Johnson, K. M.; Dewey, W. L.; and Harris, L. S., Pharmacologist, *18*(2), 166 (1976).

Δ^9-THC Induced Elevations of Mouse Brain Tryptophan and Consequent Increased Serotonin Production (Abstract).

Δ^9-THC was shown to induce an increase in ^{3}H-tryptophan and ^{3}H-5HT levels in whole mouse brain with no change in specific activity. The authors postulate that increased 5HT levels result from greater substrate availability rather than an increase in synthesis rate.

5263 Klykken, P.; Levy, J.; Razdan, R.; and Munson, A., Fed. Proc., *35*(3), 333 (1976).

Inhibition of Hemolytic Plaque Forming Cells (PFC) by 8,9-Epoxy-Hexahydrocannabinol (SIR-69).

8,9-Epoxy-hexahydrocannabinol is slightly less active than Δ^9-THC in the inhibition of IgM antibody production.

5264 Krejci, Z.; and Hanus, L., Scripta Med. (Brno), *51*(2), 123-24 (1978).

Nektere Vysledky Vyzkumu Cannabis Na Lekarske Fakulte Up V Olomouci [Some Results of Cannabis Research at Medical Faculty, Palacky University in Olomouc].

The work presents a survey of some results of cannabis research at the Medical Faculty in Olomouc from 1950 to present date concerning chemical and pharmacological research.

5265 Law, F. C. P., Pharmacologist, *18*(2), 166 (1976).

Metabolism of Δ^1-Tetrahydrocannabinol (Δ^1-THC) by the Isolated Perfused Rabbit Lung (IPL): Comparison with Lung (LUM) and Liver (LIM) Microsomal Incubations (Abstract).

LIM exhibited a different pattern of metabolites for Δ^1-THC and was more active when compared to IPL and LUM. These results indicate that liver may have a different metabolic pathway for Δ^1-THC than IPL and LUM.

5266   Leighty, E. G.; Fentiman, A. F.; and Foltz, R. L., Pharmacologist, *18*(2), 166 (1976).

Δ^9- and Δ^8-Tetrahydrocannabinols Long-Retained Metabolites Identified as Novel Fatty Acid Conjugates.

Metabolites of Δ^8-THC and Δ^9-THC detected in several tissues after acute and chronic administration appeared to be less polar than the parent drugs. MS indicated that these metabolites were conjugated primarily to palmitic and stearic acids.

5267   Malloy, K. P.; Buckley, J. P.; and Jandhyala, B. S., Pharmacologist, *18*(2), 167 (1976).

Influence of Several Anesthetic Agents on the Effects of Δ^9-Tetrahydrocannabinol (Δ^9-THC) on Heart Rate (HR) in Mongrel Dogs (Abstract).

Δ^9-THC induced a significantly greater decrease in heart rate in dogs anesthetized with pentobarbital when compared to those treated with chlorolose, or morphine or conscious dogs. A tachycardia was induced in dogs treated with both morphine and chlorolose apparently mediated by different vagi and adrenal medullary release of epinephrine.

5268   Marozzi, E.; and Gambaro, V., Zacchia, *11*(2), 153-87 (1975).

Operational Scheme for General Methods of Extraction and Identification of Narcotics in Non-Biological Material.

GLC and TLC conditions used by the authors for routine analysis of cannabis materials are reported and compared with those used by others.

5269   Nordqvist, M., Metabolic Studies on Cannabinoids. Ph.D. Dissertation, Uppsala University, 1977. (Unpubl.)

The metabolites were studied from CBN with rat liver *in vitro*, from Δ^9-THC with dog liver and lung *in vitro*, from Δ^9-THC with rabbits *in vivo* in the urine, and from Δ^9-THC with rats *in vivo* in the bile. Hydroxylation of the pentyl side chain and β-oxidation to carboxylic acid as well as hydroxylation of the allylic positions of the terpenoid ring were found with these cannabinoids.

5270   Oskoui, M.; and Hofmann, S., Pharmacologist, *18*(2), 167 (1976).

Mechanism of Cardiovascular Action of Δ^1-Tetrahydrocannabinol (Δ^1-THC) (Abstract).

Δ^1-THC and propanolol exhibited additive decreases in heart rate, blood pressure, and myocardial force of contraction in chlorolose-anesthetized cats. Isoproterenol was blocked by propanolol and enhanced by Δ^1-THC. In addition, Δ^1-THC decreased the ability of propanolol to block isoproterenol.

5271   Tashkin, D. P.; Shapiro, B. J.; Frank, I. M., Clin. Res., *22*(3), 512A (1974).

Acute Bronchial Effects of Smoked Marijuana (MJ) and Oral Δ^9-Tetrahydrocannabinol (THC) in Asthmatic Subjects.

Results obtained with asthmatic subjects showed that smoked marihuana (7 mg/kg) and oral Δ^9-THC (15 mg) both produced a significant degree of bronchodilation. This increase in specific airway conductance persisted for at least two hrs. Furthermore, smoked marihuana reversed exercise on methacholine-induced bronchospasm.

5272   Wrenn, J. M.; Friedman, M. A., Pharmacologist, *18*(2), 167 (1976).

Inhibition of Hydrocortisone Induction of Mouse Liver Tyrosine Aminotransferase (TAT) Activity by Δ^9-Tetrahydrocannabinol (Δ^9-THC) (Abstract).

Although Δ^9-THC alone does not inhibit TAT activity, treatment with Δ^9-THC prior to or after hydrocortisone caused a dose-related decrease in hydrocortisone induction of TAT in mice.

1979 SUPPLEMENT

A

5273 Abbott, S. R., Berg, J. R.; Loeffler, K. O.; Kanter, S.; Hollister, L. E.; Abrams, J. H.; Baras, H. L.; and Jones, R. T., pp. 115-36 in *Cannabinoid Analysis in Physiological Fluids*, ACS Symposium Series 98, edited by J. A. Vinson. Washington, D. C., American Chemical Society, 1979.

HPLC Analysis of Δ^9-Tetrahydrocannabinol and Metabolites in Biological Fluids.

The authors describe an HPLC method for the direct analysis of cannabinoids in human urine and breast milk. It involves the use of a simultaneous dual wave length (215 nm, 280 nm) absorbance detection. The A215/A280 absorbance ratio is determined as it acts as a valuable check on extract peaks having retention times coincident with cannabinoid standards. The A215/A280 absorbance ratio of certain cannabinoids is tabulated.

5274 Abel, E. L., *A Comprehensive Guide to the Cannabis Literature*, Westport, Connecticut, Greenwood Press, 1979. 699 pp.

This bibliography, with citations through 1977, includes popular as well as scientific literature.

5275 Abel, E. L., Neurobehav. Toxicol., *1*, 285-87 (1979).

Behavioral Teratology of Marihuana Extract in Rats.

In utero exposure to cannabis extract impaired Rotarod performance in female rats only. Other behavioral measures were not affected.

5276 Abel, E. L., Day, N.; Dintcheff, B. A.; and Ernst, C. A. S., Bull. Psychon. Soc., *14*(5), 353-54 (1979).

Inhibition of Postnatal Maternal Performance in Rats Treated with Marijuana Extract During Pregnancy.

Pups raised by surrogate mothers treated with marihuana extract while pregnant, exhibited less weight gain and behavioral deficit.

5277 Agurel, S.; Edward, C.; Halldin, M.; Leander, K.; Levy, S.; Lindgren, J.-E.; Mechoulam, R.; Nordqvist, M.; and Ohlsson, A., Drug Metab. Dispos., *7*(3), 155-61 (1979).

Chemical Synthesis and Biological Occurrence of Carboxylic Acid Metabolites of $\Delta^{1,6}$-Tetrahydrocannabinol.

Metabolism of $\Delta^{1,6}$-THC was examined in the mouse, guinea pig and rabbit. The distribution of radioactive $\Delta^{1,6}$-THC in tissue was determined two hrs. after i.p. administration. High concentrations were in liver, kidney, spleen, lung and bile; low concentrations were in brain and blood. Seven new metabolites were identified and characterized by spectral means. Synthesis of compounds is reported.

5278 Agurell, S.; Lindgren, J.-E.; and Ohlsson, A., pp. 3-13 in *Marihuana: Biological Effects*, Advances in the Biosciences Vols. 22-23, edited by G. G. Nahas and W. D. M. Paton. NY, Pergamon Press, 1979.

Introduction to Quantification of Cannabinoids and Their Metabolites in Biological Fluids.

Δ^9-THC, the main active cannabinoid, is rapidly distributed and protein bound. Methods of its determination in biological fluids were reviewed. Included are: TLC, GC, RIA and GC-MS methods. Plasma levels were highest and lowest after i.v. and p.o. routes, respectively.

5279 Alikaridis, P.; Armaganidis, A.; Kephalas, T. A.; Kiburis, J.; Michael, C. M.; Moschovakis, A.; and Papadakis, D. P., United Nations Document, ST/SOA/Ser. S/57, January 29, 1979.

Scientific Research on Cannabis. 57. Water Pipe Cannabis Smoking: Chemical and Pharmacological Aspects.

Cannabis was smoked using a water pipe. Fractions of the smoke were collected and analyzed. Δ^9-THC, CBD and CBN were found to be most abundant in the smoke. Some hydroxylated cannabinoids were detected. Pharmacological activity of fractions was carried out. Δ^9-THC was found not to be solely responsible for hallucinations when other compounds were present.

5280 Altman, J. L.; Appel, J. B.; and McGowan, W. T., Psychopharmacology, 60(2), 183-88 (1979).

Drugs and the Discrimination of Duration.

LSD increased latency of response in pigeons trained to discriminate visual stimuli but did not affect accuracy of response. Δ^9-THC and chlorpromazine lowered both behavioral parameters, while d-amphetamine increased spatial bias.

5281 Ames, F. R.; Brownell, B.; and Zuurmond, T. J., S. Afr. Med. J., 55(27), 1127-32 (1979).

Effects of the Oral Administration of Cannabis sativa (Dagga) on Chacma Baboons (Papio ursinus).

Chronic ingestion of cannabis increased lethargy in baboons in a dose-related manner. Neuropathological examination of the brain did not reveal any gross abnormality.

5282 Anderson-Baker, W. C.; McLaughlin, C. L.; and Baile, C. A., Pharmacol. Biochem. Behav., 11(5), 487-91 (1979).

Oral and Hypothalamic Injections of Barbiturates, Benzodiazepines and Cannabinoids and Food Intake in Rats.

The effects of oral and hypothalamic injections, namely ventromedial hypothalmic (VMH) and lateral hypothalamic (LH), of barbiturates, benzodiazepines and d- and 1-isomers of Δ^9-THC on the food intake were studied in rats. Intragastric administration of 4 mg/kg of 1-Δ^9-THC increased the food intake at 1 and 2 hrs., while the d-isomer had no effect. VMH injection of 1-Δ^9-THC (0.25 µg) caused a 24-hr increase in intake. The d-isomer (0.25 µg) when injected at the same site caused a decrease in feeding at 0.5 hr but not 24-hr. The effect of the latter was reversed upon LH injection.

5283 Andrysiak, T.; Carroll, R.; and Ungerleider, J. T., Amer. J. Nurs., 79(8), 1396-98 (1979).

Marijuana for the Oncology Patient.

Marihuana is currently being investigated as an antiemetic in cancer patients. THC is compared to compazine.

5284 Anonymous, Amer. Fam. Physician, 19(1), 84, 86 (1979).

Paraquat in Marijuana (Editorial).

A brief report on paraquat-contaminated marihuana which notes the Center for Disease Control wants to study patients suspected of having lung problems from smoking marihuana.

5285   Anonymous, Congressional Digest *58*(2), 33-64 (1979).

Controversy over Policy Controlling Marihuana Use.

Entire issue is devoted to this topic. It includes an overview of marihuana usage, federal enforcement operations, summary of federal and state laws, and action in the Congress.   A separate section (Pros-Cons: Should Penalties for Possession of Small Amounts of Marihuana be Decriminalized?) includes statements from Senator Jacob Javits, the National Organization for the Reform of Marijuana Laws (NORML), and Lester Grinspoon, M. D., supporting decriminalization and from the International Assn. of Chiefs of Police, the International Narcotics Enforcement Officers Association, and Robert W. Baird, M. D., opposing decriminalization.

5286   Anonymous,   JAMA   *242*(18),   1962 (1979).

Reports of Marihuana for Glaucoma Treatment are Misleading; Researchers Will Study.

The National Eye Institute is sponsoring scientific research in order to have definitive clinical evidence to the appropriateness of using marihuana for glaucoma.

5287   Anonymous, Lancet, *1*(8110), 279-80 (1979).

Conflicting Views on Cannabis (Commentary).

The British Advisory Council on the Misuse of Drugs voted to transfer cannabis to the least dangerous controlled drug list and to reduce penalties for its illegal possession.

5288   Anonymous, Lancet, *1*(8131),. 1417 (1979).

Cannabis Possession as an Offence.

The British Advisory Council on the Misuse of Drugs voted to recommend the reclassification of cannabis and its resin to class C (least harmful) drugs. Custodial sentence for unlawful possession was also revoked.

5289   Anonymous, Sightsaving Review, *48*(4), 146 (1978-79).

Editorial   (Experimental   Marihuana Therapy for Glaucoma).

A cautious optimism regarding the potential therapeutic effects of marihuana for glaucoma was voiced.

5290   Anonymous, R. N., Am. J. Nursing, *79*(12), 2100 (1979).

"Relief   Obtained   from   Marijuana" (Letter).

A wife, who is also a registered nurse, talks about the relief obtained from smoking marihuana by her cancer stricken husband.

5291   Archer, J.; and Lopata, A., Pers. Guid. J., *57*(5), 244-50 (1979).

Marijuana Revisited.

Data pointing to the deleterious effects of marihuana are inconclusive and evidence to the contrary is lacking. Regardless of these limitations however, the public must be given accurate rather than biased information.

5292   Archer, R. A.; Fukuda, D. S.; Kossoy, A. D.; and Abbott, B. J., Appl. Environ. Microbiol., 37(5), 965-71 (1979).

Microbiological Transformations of Nabilone, a Synthetic Cannabinoid.

Nabilone was subjected to 362 microorganisms for possible metabolism. There were 113 molds, 43 bacterial isolates and 206 actinomycetes used. Yields were 2 to 5% (w/wt). Details on hydroxylation and stereo-selectivity are presented. PMR data were used along with exact mass determinations.

5293   Armaganidis, A.; Moschovakis, A.; Papanikolaou, G.; Kapsabelis, G.; Petroulakis, G.; Liakopoulos, D.; and Lazaratou, H., Separatum Experientia, 35, 894 (1979).

Hashish Smoke Interfers with Sidman Avoidance in Mice.

The sublimate of marihuana smoke disrupted behavior in trained mice in a manner similar to hallucinogens.

5294   Asch, R. H., Fert. Sterl., 32(5), 571-75 (1979).

Acute Decreases in Serum Prolactin Concentrations Caused by Δ^9-Tetrahydrocannabinol in Nonhuman Primates.

Administration of thyrotropin-releasing hormone before or simultaneously with Δ^9-THC antagonized the latter suppression of serum prolactin levels in monkeys.

5295   Asch, R. H.; Fernandez, E. O.; Smith, C. G.; and Pauerstein, C. J., Fertil. Steril., 31(3), 331-34 (1979).

Precoital Single Doses of Δ^9-Tetrahydrocannabinol Block Ovulation in the Rabbit.

Δ^9-THC blocked ovulation in rabbits. Lack of plasma LH was also found. Effects were dose-related.

5296   Asch, R. H.; Smith, C. B.; Siler-Kohdr, T. M.; and Pauerstein, C. J., Fertil. Steril., 32(5), 576-82 (1979).

Effects of Δ^9-Tetrahydrocannabinol Administration of Gonadal Steroidogenic Activity In Vivo.

Δ^9-THC did not influence gonadal steroidogenic activity in rabbits or monkeys.

5297   Asch, R. H.; Smith, C. G.; Siler-Khodr, T. M.; and Pauerstein, C. J., Fertil. Steril., 32(4), 497 (1979).

Effects of Δ^9-Tetrahydrocannabinol, the Principle Psychoactive Component of Marihuana, in Gonadal Steroidogenesis in Primates and Rodents (Abstract).

Effects of Δ^9-THC on gonadal steroidogenesis in vivo are not direct but rather are mediated through inhibition of the secretion or release of gonadotropins.

5298   Avakian, E. V.; Horvath, S. M.; Michael, E. D.; and Jacobs, S., Clin. Pharmacol. Ther., 26(6), 777-81 (1979).

Effect of Marihuana on Cardiorespiratory Responses to Submaximal Exercise.

Of several cardiorespiratory variables measured, smoking marihuana by chronic users only resulted in a persistent increase in heart rate and also elevated the systolic index values.

5299 Ayhan, I. H.; Kaymakcalan, S.; and
Tulunay, F. C., Psychopharmacology,
63 2), 169-72 (1979).

Interaction Between Δ^9-Tetrahydrocan-
nabinol and Morphine on the Motor
Activity of Mice.

Doses of 5 to 20 mg/kg of Δ^9-THC
potentiated whereas higher doses attenuated morphine induced locomotor
stimulation in mice. Also THC (10
mg/kg) shifted the dose-response curve
of morphine to the left.

B

5300 Bachmann, E. W.; Hofmann, A. A.;
and Waser, P. G., J. Chromatogr., *178*(1),
320-23 (1979).

Identification of Δ^9-Tetrahydrocannabi-
nol in Human Plasma by Gas Chromatography.

A new GC method to identify Δ^9-
THC following derivatization with hepta-
fluorobutyric anhydride in human plasma
was described.

5301 Bachman, J., Addict. Behav., *4*(4),
361-71 (1979).

Personality Correlates of Cannabis Dependence.

Experiments conducted on cannabis
users indicated that frequent users
possess personality traits that predict
their greater propensity toward experiencing withdrawal symptoms and
dependence.

5302 Bachman, J. A.; Benowitz, N. L.; Herning,
R. I.; and Jones, R. T., Psychopharmacology, *61*(2), 171-75 (1979).

Dissociation of Autonomic and Cognitive Effects of THC in Man.

Propranolol and atropine blocked THC-
induced tachycardia, but failed to
alter its induced subjective and EEG
changes in human subjects.

5303 Baloh, R. W.; Sharma, S.; Moskowitz,
H.; and Griffith, R., Aviat., Space Environ. Med., *50*(1), 18-23 (1979).

Effect of Alcohol and Marijuana on
Eye Movements.

Alcohol, but not marihuana, impaired
tracking eye movements in humans.
Combined treatment with the two
agents resulted in additive effects.

5304 Banchereau, J.; Desoize, B.; Leger, C.;
and Nahas, G., pp. 129-44 in *Marihuana:
Biological Effects,*. Advances in the
Biosciences, Vols. 22-23, edited by
G. G. Nahas and W. D. M. Paton. NY,
Pergamon Press, 1979.

Inhibitory Effects of Delta-9-Tetrahy-
drocannabinol and Other Psychotropic
Drugs on Cultured Lymphocytes.

Incorporation of thymidine and uridine
by cultured lymphocytes was inhibited
by Δ^9-THC. Degree of inhibition was
inversely related to concentration of
serum protein in the medium. THC
was compared to psychotropic agents
and the technique followed was described.

5305 Barreuther, A., Drug Intell. Clin. Pharm.,
13(1), 43 (1979).

Paraquat Contaminated Marijuana
(Letter).

The author questions the validity of
current paraquat toxicity treatment and
actual paraquat content of marihuana
samples.

5306 Bearden, W. G.; Woodside, A. G.; and
Jones, J. J., Precept. Motor Skills, *48*,
743-51 (1979).

Beliefs and Anticipated Situations Influencing Intentions to Use Drugs.

A modified version of Fishbein's extended behavioral model was used to explain and predict motivation to use marihuana. Drug use was not hindered by restrictive or prohibitive external factors.

5307 Bedell, S. E., Ann. Intern Med., *90*(2), 276 (1979).

Cannabis and Cancer Chemotherapy (Letter).

The clinical use of cannabis to alleviate the side effects of cancer chemotherapy is an important issue that is very much alive.

5308 Belgrave, B. E.; Bird, K. D., Chesher, G. B.; Jackson, D. M.; Lubbe, K. E.; Starmer, G. A.; and Teo, R. K. C., Psychopharmacology, *62*(1), 53-60 (1979).

The Effect of (-) *Trans*-Δ^9-Tetrahydrocannabinol, Alone and in Combination with Ethanol, on Human Performance.

(-) *Trans*-Δ^9-THC (320 μg/kg) or ethanol caused significant decrement on several aspects of human performance. Combined treatment resulted in additive rather than synergistic effects.

5309 Belgrave, B. E.; Bird, K. D.; Chesher, G. B.; Jackson, D. M.; Lubbe, K. E.; Starmer, G. A.; and Teo, R. K. C., Psychopharmacology, *64*(2), 243-46 (1979).

The Effect of Cannabidiol, Alone and in Combination with Ethanol, on Human Performance.

CBD (320 μg/kg, p.o.) alone or in combination with ethanol did not result in decrement in human performance. Ethanol alone did.

5310 Benowitz, N. L.; Rosenberg, J.; Rogers, W.; Bachman, J.; and Jones, R. T., Clinical Pharmacol. Ther., *25*(4), 440-46 (1979).

Cardiovascular Effects of Intravenous Delta-9-Tetrahydrocannabinol: Autonomic Nervous Mechanisms.

A combination of propranolol and atropine was more effective than either agent alone in antagonizing Δ^9-THC-induced vascular changes in human subjects. These agents did not influence Δ^9-THC-induced hypothermia.

5311 Beutler, J. A.; and Der Marderosian, A. H., Econ. Bot., *32*(4), 387-94, 1978 (Pub. 1979).

Chemotaxonomy of Cannabis I. Cross-breeding Between *Cannabis sativa* and *C. ruderalis*, with Analysis of Cannabinoid Content.

A breeding experiment between alleged Mexican (*sativa*) and known Russian cannabis labeled (*ruderalis J*) was carried out. Analytical, genetic, and morphological data indicate cannabis is a monotypic genus.

5312 Beutler, J. A.; Varano, A.; and Der Marderosian, A., J. Forensic Sci., *24*(4), 808-13 (1979).

Pyrolysis Analysis of the Herbicide Paraquat on Cannabis by Coupled Gas Chromatography-Infrared Spectroscopy.

Pyrolysis of marijuana contaminated with paraquat showed two peaks which are difficult to detect at lower limits. Data on experimental design are given. Pure paraquat was pyrolyzed and studied.

5313 Binder, M.; Edery, H.; and Porath, G., pp. 71-80 in *Marihuana: Biological Effects*, Advances in the Biosciences,

Vols. 22-23, edited by G. G. Nahas and W. D. M. Paton. NY, Pergamon Press, 1979.

Δ^7-Tetrahydrocannabinol, A Non-Psychotropic Cannabinoid: Structure-Activity Considerations in the Cannabinoid Series.

Δ^7-THC was synthesized and structural conformations were determined. This cannabinoid did not antagonize the behavioral effects of Δ^1-THC nor produce any of its own. SAR of cannabinoids were discussed in relation to a possible THC receptor theory.

5314 Boeren, E. G.; Elsohly, M. A.; and Turner, C. E., Experientia, 35, 1278 (1979).

Cannabiripsol: A Novel Cannabis Constituent.

A new polyhydroxylated cannabinoid was isolated from the polar fraction of a South African cannabis variant. The new compound contained a hydroxyl group in the 9 and 10 position. Stereochemistry assignments were made. The new compound was named cannabiripsol.

5315 Bohlmann, F.; and Hoffmann, E., Phytochemistry, 18(8), 1371-74 (1979).

Cannabigerol-Ahnliche Verbindungen Aus *Helichrysum Umbraculigerum*.

A compound similar to cannabigerol was isolated from a South African *Helichrysum* species. Biogenetic pathway was through resorcinol.

5316 Bonuccelli, C. M., J. Pharm. Sci., 68(2), 262-63 (1979).

Stable Solutions for Marijuana Analysis (Letter to the Editor).

The stability of cannabinoid solution: (especially CBD and Δ^9-THC) in either chloroform or ethanol was studied under different conditions. It was found that chloroform solutions are relatively unstable, should be used within one hour or kept refrigerated at all times. Addition of stabilizers to chloroform solutions of cannabinoids was discussed.

5317 Borys, H. K.; Ingall, G. B.; and Karler, R., Brit. J. Pharmacol., 67(1), 93-101 (1979).

Development of Tolerance to the Prolongation of Hexobarbitone Sleeping Time Caused by Cannabidiol.

CBD's effects on hexobarbitone sleeping time in mice are due to changes in drug metabolism. Evidence suggests these changes involve cytochrome P-450.

5318 Borys, H. K.; and Karler, R., Biochem. Pharmacol., 28(9), 1553-59 (1979).

Cannabidiol and Δ^9-Tetrahydrocannabinol Metabolism: *In Vitro* Comparison of Mouse and Rat Liver Crude Microsome Preparations.

Hepatic metabolism of Δ^9-THC and CBD is faster in mice than rats. Although their metabolic patterns are similar, Δ^9-THC was more rapidly metabolized than CBD. Metabolites of CBD limit the metabolism of both cannabinoids.

5319 Bourn, W. M.; Keller, W. J.; and Bonfiglio, J. F., Life Sci., 25(12), 1043-54 (1979).

Comparisons of Mescal Bean Alkaloids with Mescaline, Δ^9-THC and other Psychotogens.

Mescal bean alkaloids induced behavioral effects in rats similar to those of mescaline, DMT or psilocybin and different from those of THC, amphetamine or pentobarbital.

5320   Braut-Boucher, F.; Paris, M.; Hoellinger, H.; Nguyen-Hoang-Nam, and Fournier, E., Toxicol. Eur. Res., 2(4), 175-80 (1979).

Isolation and Toxicological Study of Tetrahydrocannibivarol, A Homolog of Tetrahydrocannabinol (Δ^9-THC).

Δ^1-Tetrahydrocannabivarol and Δ^1-THC were isolated from a South African variant of cannabis. Both compounds were evaluated for allergenicity and were found to be very potent allergens.

5321   Burstein, S., pp. 1-12 in *Cannabinoid Analysis in Physiological Fluids*, ACS Symposium Series 98, edited by J. A. Vinson. Washington, D. C., American Chemical Society, 1979.

A Survey of Metabolic Transformations of Δ^1-Tetrahydrocannabinol.

A survey of the metabolic transformations of Δ^1-THC in dog, mouse, rat and man is discussed. The resulting oxygenated and polyoxygenated metabolites are presented. It is concluded that the composition of the metabolite mixture shows a quantitative dependence on species.

5322   Burstein, S.; Hunter, S. A.; and Shoupe, T. S., Mol. Pharmacol., 15(3), 633-40 (1979).

Site of Inhibition of Leydig Cell Testosterone Synthesis by Δ^1-Tetrahydrocannabinol.

Δ^1-THC inhibited the synthesis of testosterone in isolated Leydig cells by blocking cleavage of cholesterol ester.

5323   Burstein, S.; Hunter, S. A.; and Shoupe, T. S., Res. Commun. Chem. Pathol. Pharmacol., 24(2), 413-16 (1979).

Cannabinoid Inhibition of Rat Luteal Cell Progesterone Synthesis.

Δ^9-THC, CBN and their 11-OH- metabolites inhibited progesterone synthesis in rat luteal cells. This was accomplished by blocking cleavage of cholesterol esters.

5324   Burton, T. A., J. Amer. Med. Ass., 242(4), 351 (1979).

Urinary Retention Following Cannabis Ingestion.

An older man (previously an alcoholic) experienced urinary retention and constipation after eating leftover cannabis butts.

5325   Busch, F. W.; Seid, D. A.; and Wei, E. T., Cancer Lett., 6(6), 319-24 (1979).

Mutagenic Activity of Marihuana Smoke Condensates.

Both marihuana and tobacco smoke condensates possessed mutagenic activity. Assay followed was described.

C

5326   Candela, R. G.; and Marino, C., Boll.-Soc. Ital. Biol. Sper., 55(1), 32-37 (1979).

Determinazione Dei Cannabinoli Nei Liquidi Biologici [Determination of Cannabinols in Biological Fluids].

The presence of 3 cannabinoids was detected in urine using TLC and Fast Blue B Salt and GC up to 12 hrs after contact with hashish and in saliva for 4 hrs. Washing the hands with 1.5% isoamyly alc. in petroleum ether also provide positive test for cannabinoids.

5327 Caolo, M. A.; and Stermitz, F. R., Tetrahedron, *35*(12), 1487-92 (1979).

Alfileramine. A New Zanthoxylum Alkaloid Structurally Related to Tetrahydrocannabinol.

A product called alfileramine was isolated from a plant. The structure of alfileramine contains a three ring system in the same spacial relationship as Δ^9-THC. Mass fragmentation yielded a chromene type with m/e 231.

5328 Carchman, R. A.; End, D. W.; Dewey, W. L.; and Warner, W., pp. 237-52 in *Membrane Mechanisms of Drugs of Abuse*, Prog. Clin. Biol. Res., Vol. *27*, edited by C. W. Sharp and L. G. Abood. New York, Alan R. Liss, Inc., 1979.

Marihuana and Opiate Interactions with Hormonal Induced Systems in Cell Culture.

Δ^9-THC inhibited macromolecular synthesis and growth of neuroblastoma cells of the mouse. Effects were attenuated in rat glioma cells. Condensation of chromatin after THC treatment was evident. Also, morphine altered Ca^{++} induced effects in neuroblastoma cells.

5329 Carchman, R. A.; End, D. W.; and Parker, M. R., pp. 219-28 in *Marihuana: Biological Effects*. Advances in the Biosciences, Vols. 22-23, edited by G. G. Nahas and W. D. M. Paton. NY, Pergamon Press, 1979.

Marihuana and Cell Function.

In the steroid sensitive HTC cells, Δ^8-THC and dexamethasone inhibited macromolecular synthesis alone and synergistically when combined. Both Δ^8- and Δ^9-THC enhanced the uptake and distribution of dexamethasone. Other

cell cultures were used and a model for the THC/cell interaction was proposed.

5330 Carlini, E. A.; Masur, J.; and Magalhaes, C. C. P. B., Cienc. Cult. (Sao Paulo), *31*(3), 315-22 (1979).

Possivel Efeito Hipnotico Do Canabidiol No Ser Humano. Estudo Preliminar [Possible Hypnotic Effect of Cannabidiol on Human Beings. Preliminary Study].

CBD induced sleep in insomniac patients. Subjects experienced fewer dreams and no side effects.

5331 Carney, J. M.; Balster, R. L.; Martin, B. R.; and Harris, L. S., J. Pharmacol. Exp. Ther., *210*(3), 399-404 (1979).

Effects of Systemic and Intraventricular Administration of Cannabinoids on Schedule-Controlled Responding in the Squirrel Monkey.

Cannabinoids decreased responding in monkeys trained under FI-FR schedule of food presentation. B-HHC was the most potent cannabinoid tested. Although the order of potency of the cannabinoids tested remained the same after i.p. or i.v.t. administration, pronounced differences in the i.v.t./i.p. potencies were detected.

5332 Castro, M. E.; and Valencia, M., Bull. Narcotics, *31*(1), pp. 41-48 (1979).

Drug and Alcohol Use, Problems and Availability Among Students in Mexico and Canada.

This survey reports that Canadian students show a greater frequency of drinking and drug problems, police arrests and family problems, and greater drug availability than Mexican students. In Canada there seems to be greater use of cannabis, heroin and cocaine and about equal use of alcohol and tobacco when compared to Mexico.

5333 Chakravarty, I.; Shah, G.; Sheth, A. R.; and Ghosh, J. J., J. Biosci., *1*(3), 289-93 (1979).

Delta-9-Tetrahydrocannabinol and Human Spermatozoa.

Δ^9-THC induced biphasic dose-related changes in metabolism of human sperm.

5334 Chakravarty, I.; Shah, P. G.; Sheth, A. R.; and Ghosh, J. J., J. Reprod. Fertil., *57*(1), 113-15 (1979).

Mode of Action of Delta-9-Tetrahydrocannabinol on Hypothalamo-Pituitary Function in Adult Female Rats.

Δ^9-THC (5 and 10 mg/kg, i.p.) for 10 days decreased levels of LH-RH and serum prolactin in proestrous rats. LH and FSH levels were not depressed.

5335 Chang, A. E.; Shiling, D. J.; Stillman, R. C.; Goldberg, N. H.; Seipp, C. A.; Barofsky, I.; Simon, R. M.; and Rosenberg, S. A., Ann. Intern. Med., *91*, 819-24 (1979).

Delta-9-Tetrahydrocannabinol as an Antiemetic in Cancer Patients Receiving High-Dose Methotrexate.

Δ^9-THC afforded significant antiemetic activity in patients with osteogenic sarcoma undergoing chemotherapy.

5336 Chapman, L. F.; Sassenrath, E. N.; and Goo, G. P., pp. 693-712 in *Marihuana: Biological Effects*. Advances in the Biosciences, Vols. 22-23, edited by G. G. Nahas and W. D. M. Paton. NY, Pergamon Press, 1979.

Social Behavior of Rhesus Monkeys Chronically Exposed to Moderate

Amounts of Delta-9-Tetrahydrocannabinol.

Δ^9-THC, under acute and subacute conditions, resulted in depressive states and social withdrawal in treated monkeys. After chronic (2.4 mg/kg Δ^9-THC, p.o.) treatment for 3 to 4 years, initial sedation was replaced by irritability and aggression. The hierarchy of social order was also disturbed.

5337 Chari-Bitron, A.; and Shahar, A., Experientia, *35*(3), 365-66 (1979).

Changes in Rat Erythrocyte Membrane Induced by Δ^1-Tetrahydrocannabinol, Scanning Electron Microscope Study.

Rat erythrocyte membrane exhibited significant morphological changes when incubated with Δ^9-THC. Effects were prominent only when concentration exceeded 15 µm.

5338 Charles, R.; Holt, S.; and Kirkham, N., Clinical Toxicol., *14*(4), 433-38 (1979).

Myocardial Infarction and Marijuana.

A case report of a 25 year old male who developed acute subendocardial infarction after smoking marihuana is given.

5339 Check, W. A., J. Amer. Med. Ass., *241*(23), 2476 (1979).

Marijuana May Lessen Spasticity of MS.

Δ^9-THC decreased spasticity in multiple sclerosis patients. This effect, albeit limited, calls for future investigation.

5340 Chesher, G. B.; Malor, R.; and Scheelings, P., *Some Recent Advances in the Study of Cannabis. Research Paper 6.* Royal Commission into the Non-Medical Use of Drugs, South Australia, 1979. 142 pp.

This is an eloquent presentation of the relevant and recent findings in marihuana research. Both animal and human studies were reviewed. Pharmacological, botanical, chemical and biochemical aspects were considered.

5341 Chesher, G. B.; Zaluzny, S. G.; Jackson, D. M.; and Malor, R., pp. 605-18 in *Marihuana: Biological Effects*. Advances in the Biosciences, Vols. 22-23, edited by G. G. Nahas and W. D. M. Paton. NY, Pergamon Press, 1979.

Δ^9-Tetrahydrocannabinol and the Quasi Morphine Withdrawal Syndrome.

Morphine (5.0 to 10.0 mg/kg) and Δ^9-THC (1.25 to 10.0 mg/kg) attenuated chemically induced morphine-like withdrawal. Haloperidol (0.1 to 0.8 mg/kg) was partially effective whereas chlordiazepoxide (5.0 to 10.0 mg/kg) and naloxone (3.0 mg/kg) were ineffective in attenuating the quasi morphine withdrawal.

5342 Chiarotti, M.; and Giusti, G. V., Experientia, *35*(1), 90-91 (1979).

Decrease of Serum Alpha-Tocopherol Levels in Rabbits After Acute Treatment with Δ^9-Tetrahydrocannabinol.

Δ^9-THC (10 mg/kg, i.v.) significantly reduced serum alpha-tocopherol level in treated rabbits.

5343 Chiu, P.; Olsen, D. M.; Borys, H. K.; Karler, R.; and Turkanis, S. A., Epilepsia, *20*(4), 365-76 (1979).

The Influence of Cannabidiol and Δ^9-Tetrahydrocannabinol on Cobalt Epilepsy in Rats.

Δ^9-THC induced CNS excitation and exacerbated cobalt-induced epilepsy in the rat parietal cortex. These effects

were attributed mainly to THC rather than metabolites. CBD, on the contrary, exerted anticonvulsive properties.

5344 Choisy, H.; Choisy, G.; Millart, H.; and Legris, H., pp. 265-71 in *Marihuana: Biological Effects*. Advances in the Biosciences, Vols. 22-23, edited by G. G. Nahas and W. D. M. Paton. NY, Pergamon Press, 1979.

Influence of Delta-9-Tetrahydrocannabinol on Contraction Rate and Enzymatic Activity of Embryonic Heart Cells.

Exposure of myocardial cells to Δ^9-THC resulted in a decreased rate of contraction and slowing in glucose consumption and lactate production. Activities of several relevant enzymes were also altered.

5345 Choulis, N. H., J. Chromatogr., *168*(2), 562 (1979).

Thin-Layer Chromatography and Spot Test of Paraquat-Contaminated Marihuana.

The procedure involves extraction of the plant material with methanol and TLC analysis on silica plates using chloroform-dioxane-ethyl acetate-conc.-ammonia (25:60:10:5) or chloroform-acetone (9:1) as solvent systems. In both cases paraquat stayed at the origin and visualized with iodine vapors or sodium carbonate and sodium hydrosulfite.

5346 Clark, M. N.; and Bohm, B. A., Bot. J. Linn. Soc., *79*(3), 249-50 (1979).

Flavonoid Variation in *Cannabis L.*

Flavonoids in cannabis plants were isolated and identified. Results were tabulated according to plant variety and country of origin of the seeds used.

5347 Clark, W. C.; Goetz, R. R.; McCarthy, R. H.; Bemporad, B.; and Zeidenberg, P., pp. 665-80 in *Marihuana: Biological Effects*. Advances in the Biosciences, Vols. 22-23, edited by G. G. Nahas and W. D. M. Paton. NY, Pergamon Press, 1979.

Effects of Marihuana on Pain and Verbal Memory; A Sensory Decision Theory Analysis.

Smoking marihuana for several weeks under inpatient conditions resulted in enhancement of pain and impairment of recall but not recognition memory in experienced users. Analysis in light of a proposed sensory decision theory suggests moderate use of marihuana does not affect memory storage.

5348 Clopton, P. L.; Janowsky, D. S.; Clopton, J. M.; Judd, L. L.; and Huey, L., Psychopharmacology, *61*(2), 203-06 (1979).

Marijuana and the Perception of Affect.

The ability to perceive emotions in others declined after marihuana smoking. Perceived decrease in vigor and increased subjective high were also reported.

5349 Collins, F. G.; and Haavik, C. O., Biochem. Pharmacol., *28*(15), 2303-06 (1979).

Effects of Cannabinoids on Cardiac Microsomal CaATPase Activity and Calcium Uptake.

In the following order of potency, CBD, Δ^9-THC and DMHP all inhibited cardiac microsomal CaATPase. Vehicle used (ethanol) also inhibited activity.

5350 Consroe, P.; Carlini, E. A.; Zwicker, A. P.; and Lacerda, L. A., Psychopharmacology, *66*(1), 45-50 (1979).

Interaction of Cannabidiol and Alcohol in Humans.

CBD (200 mg, p.o.) did not effect motor and psychomotor performance or subjective responses in human subjects. Also, CBD did not alter alcohol induced impairment.

5351 Cook, C. E., pp. 137-54 in *Cannabinoid Analysis in Physiological Fluids*. ACS Symposium Series 98, edited by J. A. Vinson, Washington, D. C., American Chemical Society, 1979.

Radioimmunoassay of Cannabinoid Compounds.

The general principles of radioimmunoassay (RIA) and its application for the analysis of cannabinoids are discussed in detail.

5352 Coutts, R. T.; and Jones, G. R., J. Forensic Sci., *24*(2), 291-302 (1979).

A Comparative Analysis of Cannabis Material.

One hundred forensic cannabis samples were analyzed. Seven of these contained no cannabinoids. Many samples did not contain CBD but did contain CBC. Column conditions for various column packing are given. Two new columns not previously used in cannabinoid analyses were reported as being compromises. Data on what is needed for a positive identification is given.

5353 Cozens, D. D.; Clark, R.; Palmer, A. K.; Hardy, N.; Nahas, G. G.; and Harvey, D. J., pp. 469-77 in *Marihuana: Biological Effects*. Advances in the Biosciences, Vols. 22-23, edited by G. G. Nahas and W. D. M. Paton. NY, Pergamon Press, 1979.

The Effect of a Crude Marihuana Extract on Embryonic and Foetal Development of the Rabbit.

Repeated daily administration (days 6-18 of gestation) of 1 ml/kg of CME resulted in decreased weight gain in treated female rabbits and their offspring. Offspring also showed a slight reduction in ossification.

5354   Craigmill, A. L., Res. Commun. Psychol. Psychiatry Behav., *4*(1), 51-63 (1979).

Cannabinoids and Handling-Induced Convulsions.

Δ^9-THC and nabilone produced handling-induced convulsions in mice. These convulsions were modified by ethanol, diazepam and phenobarbital. Rapid tolerance to THC-convulsive effects developed.

5355   Crawford, W. J.; and Merritt, J. C., Int. J. Clin. Pharmacol. Biopharm., *17*(5), 191-96 (1979).

Effects of Tetrahydrocannabinol on Arterial and Intraocular Hypertension.

Δ^9-THC increased heart rate and decreased arterial and intraocular pressures in glaucoma patients. The former effect was greater in normotensive, while the latter two were greater in hypertensive patients.

5356   Crombie, L.; Crombie, W. M. L.; and Jamieson, S. V., Tetrahedron Lett., *7*, 661-64 (1979).

Isolation of Cannabispiradienone andCannabidihydrophenanthrene. Biosynthetic Relationships Between the Spirans and Dihydrostilbenes of Thailand Cannabis.

Two new compounds were isolated from Thailand cannabis. Cannabispiradienone

is a key product which would be formed by initial oxidative phenol coupling of the dihydrostilbene derivative. Cannabidihydrophenanthrene (a new 9,10 dihydrophenanthrene) could be related to cannabispiradienone by a dienone-phenol rearrangement.

5357   Crombie, L.; Crombie, W. M. L.; Kilbee, G. W.; and Tuchinda, P., Tetrahedron Lett., *49*, 4773-76 (1979).

Synthesis of 4"-Carboxylated Cannabinoids: Stereospecific Processes Involving Ethylidenemalonic Ester.

The synthesis of 4"-carboxylated Δ^1-, $\Delta^{1,6}$-THC, CBD and CBN was described. The key step was the condensation of 3, 5- dimethoxybenzylexybenzaldehyde with diethyl ethylidinemalonate in methanolic benzyltrimethyl ammonium hydroxide. Hydrogenation and decarboxylation of the product gave the starting material which was then condensed with (+)-*p*-menthadienol in acid medium.

D

5358   Dadisch, G. L.; and Machata, G., Beitr. Gerichtl. Med., *37*, 35-38 (1979).

Bewertung von Suchtgift aus Heimischem Anbau [Evaluation of Drugs of Abuse from Domestic Cultivation].

Austrian grown hashish and opium were not different from Asian plants in their contents of Δ^9-THC or morphine, respectively.

5359   Dalterio, S.; and Bartke, A., Science, *205*(4413), 1420-22 (1979).

Perinatal Exposure to Cannabinoids Alters Male Reproductive Function in Mice.

388

Δ^9-THC (50 mg/kg, p.o.) decreased testes weight and increased body weight and plasma LH levels in male mice after perinatal exposure. CBN resulted in an apparent decrease in plasma FSH. Both cannabinoids decreased copulatory behavior.

5360 Daniel, S. A., Diss. Abstr. Int. B., *39*(9), 4610 (1979).

Effects of Chronic Methadone and Tetrahydrocannabinol (THC) on Temporal Discrimination Performance in the Pigeon.

THC altered the temporal discriminative behavior in pigeons maintained on methadone. Magnitude of alteration was inversely related to the methadone dose. Effects of each agent alone were also studied.

5361 Dassel, P. M.; and Punjabi, E., Gastroenterology, *76*(1), 166-69 (1979).

Ingested Marihuana-Filled Balloons.

Ingestion of marihuana-filled balloons, as a means of smuggling, resulted in hazardous complications. Three such cases were reported.

5362 Davies, P.; Sornberger, G. C.; and Huber, G. L., Lab. Invest., *41*(3), 220-23 (1979).

Effects of Experimental Marijuana and Tobacco Smoke Inhalation on Alveolar Macrophages.

Significant subcellular morphological changes were observed in the rat alveolar macrophages after repeated exposure to tobacco but not marihuana smoke.

5363 Davis, G. S.; Brody, A. R.; and Adler, K. B., Chest, *75*(2, Suppl.), 280-82 (1979).

Functional and Physiologic Correlates of Human Alveolar Macrophage Cell Shape and Surface Morphology.

Cigarette smoking caused the appearance of abnormal human pulmonary alveolar macrophages and increased the number of flat (active) cells. Marihuana smoking caused the former effect only.

5364 Dawley, H. H.; Baxter, A. S.; Winstead, D. K.; and Gay, J. R., J. Clin. Psychol., *35*(1), 212-17 (1979).

An Attitude Survey of the Effects of Marijuana on Sexual Enjoyment.

Subjects who experienced sex under the influence of marihuana indicated that its use enhanced their sexual experiences and pleasures. They also considered it to be an aphrodisiac.

5365 De Pasquale, A.; Tumino, G.; Ragusa, S.; and Moschonas, D., Il Farmaco, *34*(10), 841-53 (1979).

Influenza Del Trattamento Concolchicina Sulla Produzione Di Cannabinoidi Delle Infiorescenze Femminili Della *Cannabis sativa L*. [Influence of Colchicine Treatment on the Production of Cannabinoids in Female Fluorescences of *Cannabis sativa L*.] .

The total and relative cannabinoid content of *Cannabis sativa L*. female plants treated with colchicine were determined. Plants treated with 0.25% colchicine solution showed higher total cannabinoids and the highest increase in Δ^9-THC content.

5366 Desoize, B.; Leger, C.; Jardillier, J. C.; and Nahas, G.; pp. 145-59 in *Marihuana: Biological Effects*. Advances in the Biosciences, Vols. 22-23, edited by G. G. Nahas and W. D. M. Paton. NY, Pergamon Press, 1979.

Inhibition by THC of Thymidine Transport: A Plasma Membrane Effect.

Δ^9-THC and other olivetol derivatives inhibited thymidine uptake by lymphocyte cultures. Effects were positively related to the degree of liposolubility. THC weakens the activity of membrane transport of thymidine.

5367 Desoize, B.; Leger, C.; and Nahas, G., Biochem. Pharmacol., _28_(7), 1113-18 (1979).

Plasma Membrane inhibition of Macromolecular Precursor Transport by THC.

Δ^9-THC and other cannabinoids with C-ring olivetol inhibited thymidine uptake in lymphocytes culture. Inhibition was correalted with lipid solubility and was not explained by increased "leakage" of the membrane.

5368 Dewey, W. L.; Poddar, M. K.; and Johnson, K. M., pp. 343-49 in _Marihuana: Biological Effects_. Advances in the Biosciences, Vols. 22-23, edited by G. G. Nahas and W. D. M. Paton. NY, Pergamon Press, 1979.

The Effect of Cannabinoids on Rat Brain Synaptosomes.

Δ^9- and Δ^8-THC exerted biphasic effects on uptake and release of brain DA and NE whereas CBN and CBD exerted only inhibitory effect in the former, and facilitation in the latter case. Δ^9-THC inhibited uptake and enhanced the release of 5-HT. It's 11-OH-metabolite differered from it in its action.

5369 Diamantis, W.; Melton, J.; and Sofia, R. D., Pharmacology, _18_(5), 251-56 (1979).

Comparative Effects of Δ^9-Tetrahydrocannabinol, Tetrabenazine and Chlorpromazine on Rectal Temperature in the Rat.

Δ^9-THC and tetrabenazine had a biphasic effect on rectal temperature of rats. Chlorpromazine administration resulted in hypothermia only.

5370 Drath, D. B.; Shorey, J. M.; Price, L.; and Huber, G. L., Infec. Immun., _25_(1), 268-72 (1979).

Metabolic and Functional Characteristics of Alveolar Macrophages Recovered from Rats Exposed to Marijuana Smoke.

Alveolar macrophages obtained from rats repeatedly exposed to tobacco or marihuana smoke differed from those of control rats only with regard to metabolic alterations. Treated rats experienced reduction in weight gain.

5371 Driessen, R. A., Deuterium Labeled Cannabinoids. Synthesis and Mass Spectrometry. Ph. D. Dissertation, State Univ. of Utrecht (Netherlands), 1979 (Unpubl.).

The synthesis and identification by MS of cannabinoids were studied and reported for the following compounds and their deuterium labeled derivatives: CBC, Δ^9-THC, $\Delta^{9,11}$-THC, CBG and CBD. Δ^9-THC and Δ^8-THC fragment without appreciable intraconversion.

5372 Duncan, G. E.; and Dagirmanjian, R., Psychopharmacology, _60_(3), 237-40 (1979).

Δ^9-Tetrahydrocannabinol Sensitization of the Rat Brain to Direct Cholinergic Stimulation.

$\triangle^9$-THC significantly augmented drinking and abnormal behaviors of rats treated with carbachol. Atropine antagonized the effect of carbachol alone but had no effect on the combined treatment.

5373 DuPont, R. L., pp. 279-84 in *Youth Drug Abuse: Problems, Issues and Treatment,* edited by G. M. Beschner and A. S. Friedman. Lexington, Mass., Lexington Books, 1979.

Marihuana: A Review of the Issues Regarding Decriminalization and Legalization.

The authors discuss reasons why decriminalization of marihuana would be more desirable than the drug's current legal status. Possible economic, sociological and medical consequences of legalized marihuana use are discussed including incidence of adolescent drug use and adverse effects on public health.

E

5374 Ekert, H.; Waters, K. D.; Jurk, I. H.; Mobilia, J.; and Loughnan, P., Med. J. Australia, *2*(12), 657-59 (1979).

Amelioration of Cancer Chemotherapy-Induced Nausea and Vomiting by Delta-9-Tetrahydrocannabinol.

$\triangle^9$-THC was found superior to either metoclopramide or prochlorperazine as an antiemetic in pediatric cancer patients. An increase in drowsiness, appetite and experiencing "high" were reported for the THC group.

5375 El-Feraly, F. S.; Chan, Y. M.; El-Sohly, M. A.; and Turner, C. E., Experientia, *35*, 1131 (1979).

Biomimetic Synthesis of Cannabispiran.

The total synthesis of cannabispiran was reported. The crucial step in the synthesis involved oxidative phenol coupling of 3,4'-di-hydroxy-5 methoxy-bi-benzyl using potassium ferricyanide in a biphasic system followed by catalystic reduction of the resulting dienone.

5376 Ellis, G. J.; and Stone, L. H., Youth and Society, *10*(4), 323-33 (1979).

Marijuana Use in College: An Evaluation of a Modeling Explanation.

The use of marihuana by college students correlated best with use by their peer group. Parental use of alcohol and psychoactive drugs had only marginal influence.

5377 Erickson, P. G.; and Goodstadt, M. S., Criminology, *17*(2), 208-16 (1979).

Legal Stigma for Marijuana Possession.

According to employers, criminal records pertaining to marihuana use make employment difficult regardless of the degree of offense.

5378 Etevenon, P., pp. 659-63 in *Marihuana: Biological Effects.* Advances in the Biosciences, Vols. 22-23, edited by G. G. Nahas and W. D. M. Paton. NY, Pergamon Press, 1979.

Effects of Cannabis on Human EEG.

In humans, EEG records indicated that $\triangle^9$-THC (5-30 mg, p.o.) resulted in both euphoria and dysphoria. Initial arousal was followed by depression.

5379 Etevenon, P., pp. 731-34 in *Marihuana: Biological Effects.* Advances in the Biosciences, Vols. 22-23, edited by G. G. Nahas and W. D. M. Paton. NY, Pergamon Press, 1979.

Cannabis and the Brain: A Summary.

A summary of cannabis effects on the CNS was provided. Effects on central neurotransmitters, EEG, behavior and tolerance were highlighted.

F

5380 Fairbairn, J. W.; and Pickens, Joan T., Brit. J. Pharmacol, *67*(3), 379-85 (1979).

The Oral Activity of Δ^1-Tetrahydrocannabinol and its Dependence on Prostaglandin E_2.

Δ^9-THC was equipotent to chlorpromazine in inducing catalepsy in mice. Inhibitors of prostaglandin biosynthesis blocked the effects of THC only. After 4 hours of dosing, oral THC was 200 times as active as i.p. THC.

5381 Feeney, D. M., pp. 643-57 in *Marihuana: Biological Effects*. Advances in the Biosciences, Vols. 22-23, edited by G. G. Nahas and W. D. M. Paton. NY, Pergamon Press, 1979.

Marihuana and Epilepsy: Paradoxical Anticonvulsant and Convulsant Effects.

The effects of Δ^9-THC on seizure activity in man and animals very depending on tests and conditions. THC may protect against or provoke seizure activity. CBD, however, protects against seizures but lacks psychoactivity and convulsive effects. Mechanisms for these effects were postulated.

5382 Fehr, K. O'B.; Kalant, H.; and Knox, G. V., pp. 681-91 in *Marihuana: Biological Effects*. Advances in the Biosciences, Vols. 22-23, edited by G. G. Nahas and W. D. M. Paton. NY, Pergamon Press, 1979.

Residual Effects of High-Dose Cannabis Treatment on Learning, Muricidal Behavior and Neurophysiological Correlates in Rats.

Male rats were administered ethanol or cannabis extract containing 20.0 mg/kg Δ^9-THC, 1.3 mg/kg CBD and 0.65 mg/kg CBN daily for six months and then tested 30 days post-treatment for ability to learn a complicated motor task. The rats learned at a slower rate and also displayed muricidal behavior. EEG and brain histology of treated rats were also discussed.

5383 Fleischman, R. W.; Baker, J. R.; and Rosenkrantz, H., Toxicol. Appl. Pharmacol., *47*(3), 557-66 (1979).

Pulmonary Pathologic Changes in Rats Exposed to Marihuana Smoke for 1 Year.

In rats exposed to marihuana smoke, 25, 3 and 17 percent died after doses of 0.0, 0.4 and 1.5 mg/kg of THC, respectively. Focal alveolitis or pneumonitis resulted. Pulmonary irritation turned into pronounced inflammatory and focal proliferative changes. A 30-day recovery period did not reverse these pathological lesions.

5384 Foltz, R. L.; Clarke, P. A.; Hidy, B. J.; Lin, D. C. K.; Graffeo, A. P.; and Petersen, B. A., pp. 59-71 in *Cannabinoid Analysis in Physiological Fluids*. ACS Symposium Series 98, edited by J. A. Vinson. Washington, D. C., American Chemical Society, 1979.

Quantitation of Δ^9-Tetrahydrocannabinol and 11-*Nor*-Δ^9-Tetrahydrocannabinol-9-Carboxylic Acid in Body Fluids by GC/CI-MS.

A method is described for the analysis of Δ^9-THC and 11-*nor*-Δ^9-THC-9-carboxylic acid in body fluids. Deuterium labeled Δ^9-THC is added to the plasma sample. The ratio of labeled to unlabeled Δ^9-THC was measured by GC/CI-MS using the technique of selected ion monitoring. Chemical ionization mass spectrometry (CI-MS) was used instead of electron impact (EI) as it affords a better sensitivity. A procedure was also developed for the simultaneous quantitation of Δ^9-THC, 11-OH-Δ^9-THC, and 11-nor-Δ^9-THC-9-carboxylic acid at concentrations as low as 10 pg/ml of body fluid.

5385   Fournier, G. and Paris, M. R., Plant. Med. Phyto., *13*(2), 116-21 (1979).

Le Chanvre Papetier (*Cannabis sativa L.*) Cultive en France: Le Point Sur Ses Constituants [Hemp (*Cannabis sativa L.*) used for Paper Manufacture and Cultivated in France: The Point is Based on the Constituents].

This study on *Cannabis sativa* cultivated in France for use in paper and cloth industry demonstrates the existence of two separate chemo-types: a drug type and a fiber type. The plant may be classified as a drug or fiber type depending on the ratio of Δ^9-THC/CBD it contains.

5386   Fowler, R.; Gilhooley, R. A.; and Baker, P. B., J. Chromatogr., *171*, 509-11 (1979).

Thin-Layer Chromatography of Cannabinoids.

A two dimensional TLC procedure was described for the screening of cannabis extracts. Fifteen cannabinoids were resolved. The two systems were chloroform- 1,1-dichloroethane (15:10) and xylene-1,4-dioxane (19:1). The plates were sprayed with diethylamine before developing in the second system. The potential of the method in comparing samples is indicated.

5387   Fox, F. J., New Eng. J. Med., *301*(13), 728 (1979).

Nabilone as an Antiemetic. (Letter to the Editor)

The author disputed claims that nabilone is superior to prochlorperazine as an antiemetic.

5388   Freedman, D. X., pp. 77-102 in *Ethnopharmacologic Search for Psychoactive Drugs*, edited by D. H. Efron, B. Holmstedt and N. S. Kline. NY, Raven Press, 1979.

Perspectives on the Use and Abuse of Psychedelic Drugs.

The author attempts to describe the drug experience relative to the use of psychotomimetics, in particular LSD, while addressing some of the problems associated with drug use and the study thereof. He proposes that observation of behavior during drugged states will give us a clue as to the chemical organization of the brain and how it relates to the dimensions of the mind. Brief mention of cannabis and its relation to these topics is made.

5389   Fried, P. A.; and Charlebois, A. T., Can. J. Psychol./Rev. Can. Psychol., *33*(3), 125-32 (1979).

Effects upon Rat Offspring Following Cannabis Inhalation Before and/or After Mating.

Female rats exposed to marihuana smoke after mating had litters with lower body weight and slower physiological development. Exposure before mating and/or continued after mating did not induce pronounced effects.

5390   Fried, P. A.; and Charlebois, A. T., Physiol. Psychol., *7*(3), 307-10 (1979).

Cannabis Administered During Pregnancy: First- and Second-Generation Effects in Rats.

Pre-natal exposure of rats to cannabis smoke reduced their fertility and reproductive organ weights. Their offspring also experienced a retarded physiological development.

5391 Frytak, S.; Moertel, C. G.; O'Fallon, J. R.; Rubin, J.; Creagan, E. T.; O'Connell, M. J.; Schutt, A. J.; and Schwartau, N. W., Ann. Intern. Med., *91*(6), 825-30 (1979).

Delta-9-Tetrahydrocannabinol as an Antiemetic for Patients Receiving Cancer Chemotherapy.

Δ^9-THC was not found superior to prochlorperazine as an antiemetic in cancer patients receiving chemotherapy.

5392 Fujimoto, G. I.; Kostellow, A. B.; Rosenbaum, R.; Morrill, G. A.; and Bloche, E., pp. 441-47 in *Marihuana: Biological Effects*. Advances in the Biosciences, Vols. 22-23, edited by G. G. Nahas and W. D. M. Paton. NY, Pergamon Press, 1979.

Effects of Cannabinoids on Reproductive Organs in the Female Fischer Rat.

Seventy-two daily treatments with crude marihuana extract (CME) or Δ^9-THC (1, 5 and 25 mg/kg, p.o.) decreased uterine and ovarian weights and increased estrous cycle irregularities of female rats.

5393 Fujiwara, M.; and Ueki, S., Physiol. Behav., *22*(3), 535-39 (1979).

The Course of Aggressive Behavior Induced by a Single Injection of Δ^9-Tetrahydrocannabinol and its Characteristics.

Isolation plus Δ^9-THC (6 mg/kg, i.p.) induced aggression in treated rats. When rats were group-housed, aggression disappeared but reappeared when rats were re-isolated.

G

5394 Garrett, E. R., pp. 105-21 in *Marihuana: Biological Effects*. Advances in the Biosciences, Vols. 22-23, edited by G. G. Nahas and W. D. M. Paton. NY, Pergamon Press, 1979.

Pharmacokinetics and Disposition of Δ^9-Tetrahydrocannabinol and Its Metabolites.

A pharmacokinetic profile for Δ^9-THC was established. Δ^9-THC is rapidly distributed and metabolized after its administration. THC and its metabolites are tightly bound to tissues, especially fatty ones. The metabolites are slowly eliminated primarily by biliary excretion.

5395 Garrett, E. R.; Gouyette, A. J.; and Hunt, C. A., pp. 13-37 in *Cannabinoid Analysis in Physiological Fluids*. ACS Symposium Series 98, edited by J. A. Vinson. Washington, D. C., American Chemical Society, 1979.

GCL and HPLC Analyses of Cannabinoids in Biological Fluids and Applications.

The advantages of the use of HPLC and GLC for the determination of cannabinoids in biological fluids are discussed in detail. Application of this technique in the (1) study of the stability of tetrahydrocannabinol in agueous solution and in (2) pharmacokinetic studies in dogs is presented.

5396 Georgotas, A.; and Zeindenberg, P., Compr. Psychiat., *20*(5), 427-32 (1979).

Observations on the Effects of Four Weeks of Heavy Marihuana Smoking on Group Interaction and Individual Behavior.

Initially, marihuana smoking increased group interaction. After two weeks of use, apathy gradually developed. Increased irritability was observed after cessation of use.

5397   Ghoneim, M. T.; Mikhail, M. M.; Mahfouz, M.; and Makar, A. B., Pharmazie, *34*(10), 666 (1979).

Effect of Hashish on Some Brain, Liver and Serum Oxidases in Rabbits.

Rabbits exposed to hashish smoke exhibited a doubling of brain and liver monoamine oxidase activity, a reduction in brain and liver cytochrome oxidase and a decrease in hepatic catalase.

5398   Ghosh, P.; and Bhattacharya, S. K., Indian J. Med. Res., *70*(2), 275-80 (1979).

Cannabis-Induced Potentiation of Morphine Analgesia in Rat-Role of Brain Monoamines.

Cannabis extract (25 to 75 mg/kg, i.p.) potentiated morphine induced analgesia in rats. These effects are mediated by 5-HT rather than catecholamines.

5399   Giacoia, G. P.; and Catz, C. S., Clin. Perinatol., *6*(1), 181-96 (1979).

Drugs and Pollutants in Breast Milk.

The transfer of foreign agents from lactating mothers to their nursing infants is an unresolved issue in need of further investigation. Marihuana was among agents discussed.

5400   Giusti, G. V.; Carnevale, A.; Gentile, V.; and Chiarotti, M., Acta Med. Rom., *17*, 12-18 (1979).

Effect of Alfa-Tocopherol in the Δ^9-Tetrahydrocannabinol-Dystrophy of Mice.

Simultaneous treatment of alfa-tocopherol with Δ^9-THC antagonized Δ^9-THC (1 mg/kg, s.c., for 30 days) induced muscular dystrophy in mice.

5401   Glass, R. M.; Uhlenhuth, E. H.; and Hartel, F. W., Psychopharmacol. Bull., *15*(2), 88-90 (1979).

The Effects of Nabilone, a Synthetic Cannabinoid, on Anxious Human Volunteers (Abstract).

Nabilone (1 and 2 mg, p.o.) did not relieve anxiety in anxious subjects. At high doses (4 and 5 mg), adverse effects were experienced.

5402   Glatt, H.; Ohlsson, A.; Agurell, S.; and Oesch, F., Mutat. Res., *66*, 329-35 (1979).

Δ^1-Tetrahydrocannabinol and 1 α, 2 α- Epoxyhexahydrocannabinol: Mutagenicity Investigation in the Ames Test.

The mutagenicity of Δ^9-THC and 1 α, 2 α -epoxyhexahydrocannabinol was studied using different strains of *Salmonella typhimurium*. Both compounds were found to be nonmutagenic.

5403   Godbold, J. C.; Hawkins, B. J.; Woodward, M. G., J. Amer. Vet. Med. Assn., *175*(10), 1101-02 (1979).

Acute Oral Marijuana Poisoning in the Dog.

Three cases of accidental poisoning of dogs with marihuana were reported. Toxicity was slowly reversible.

5404   Goett, J. M., Diss. Abstr. Int. B, *40*(3), 1399-400 (1979).

The Development of Conditioned Aversions in Pigeons: Lithium Chloride and Delta-9-Tetrahydrocannabinol.

$\triangle^9$-THC (2 mg/kg) substituting for lithium chloride, produced conditioned aversion in pigeons.

5405 Goldberg, I.; Kass, M. A.; and Becker, B., Sightsaving Review, *48*(4), 147-55 (1978-79).

Marijuana as a Treatment for Glaucoma.

Research pertaining to marihuana use in glaucoma was summarized. Suggestions for future research were also provided.

5406 Goldfrank, L.; and Melinek, M., Hosp. Phys., *5*, 28-36 (1979).

Toxicologic Emergencies: Marihuana.

Marihuana induced toxic reactions were discussed from a clinical perspective. Management of intoxicated patients was also discussed.

5407 Golub, M. S., Pharmacol., Biochem. Behav., *11*(Suppl.), 47-50 (1979).

A Primate Model for Detecting Behavioral Impairment in Offspring after Chronic Parental Drug Exposure.

Chronic maternal exposure to $\triangle^9$-THC somewhat altered the visual attention of the monkey's offspring. Mother-infant relationship was not altered.

5408 Goode, M., *Drugs and the Law*. Research Paper 7. Royal Commission into the Non-Medical Use of Drugs, South Australia, 1979. 198 pp.

The South Australian laws governing marihuana and other non-medically used drugs were discussed. Thorough analysis of all legal aspects was conducted.

5409 Gossop, M. and Eysenck, S., The Magistrate, *35*, 117-19 (1979).

A Fresh Look at Cannabis.

The author points out some misconceptions about marihuana use, such as its association with stronger drug use and leading to crime, and suggests taking marihuana use out of the "hard crime" category.

5410 Gouvier, W. D.; and Yehle, A. L., Bull. Psychon. Soc., *13*(4), 261-62 (1979).

Delta-9-Tetrahydrocannabinol Induced Response Suppression in Pigeons.

The extent of the depressive effect of $\triangle^9$-THC in trained pigeons was species- and dose-related.

5411 Green, D. E.; Chao, F.-C.; Loeffler, K. O.; and Kanter, S. L., pp. 93-113 in *Cannabinoid Analysis in Physiological Fluids*. ACS Symposium Series 98, edited by J. A. Vinson. Washington, D.C., American Chemical Society, 1979.

Quantitation of $\triangle^9$-Tetrahydrocannabinol and its Metabolites in Human Urine by Probability Based Matching GC/MS.

Probability based matching GC/MS using selected ion monitoring is described. After the correct intensity ratios for selected ions in the pure state are measured, selected ions in an unknown state are measured. Background corrections are made and the absolute intensity pattern is allowed to decrease until it coincides with a single ion that represents a target compound. Crude fractions of biological fluids can be assayed this way. A computer system designated tolerance "window" aids in the identification of unknowns. Limits are restricted to cases where pure knowns are available for data base.

5412 Green, K., Ann Ophthalmol., *11*(2), 203-05 (1979).

Marihuana in Ophthalmology: Past, Present, and Future (Glaucoma Editorial).

Careful evaluation of marihuana's effect on IOP is needed before deciding on whether or not it is therapeutically beneficial.

5413   Green, K., pp. 175-215 in *Current Topics in Eye Research*, edited by J. A. Zadunaisky and H. Davson. New York, Academic Press, 1979.

The Ocular Effects of Cannabinoids.

The effectiveness of cannabinoids in reducing IOP in man and animals has been proven. With the new synthetic cannabinoids, it seems possible to dissociate the subjective effects of cannabis from its potential therapeutic effects.

5414   Green, K., pp. 37-49 in *Symposium on Ocular Therapy, Vol. II*, edited by I. H. Leopold and R. P. Burns. NY, John Wiley & Sons, Inc., 1979.

Current Status of Basic and Clinical Marijuana Research in Ophthalmology.

Although IOP reduction in man and animals is a well established property of cannabis, no simple explanation of such a pharmacologic action is as yet available. Further exploration of this promising therapeutic potential is needed.

5415   Gylys, J. A.; Doran, K. M.; and Buyniski, J. P., Res. Commun. Pathol. Pharmacol., *23*(1), 61-67 (1979).

Antagonism of Cisplatin Induced Emesis in the Dog.

Nabilone did not antagonize cisplatin-induced emesis in dogs whereas metoclopramide did. Cisplatin and apomorphine-induced emeses were compared.

H

5416   Haavik, C. O.; Hardman, H. F., pp. 499-529 in *Body Temperature: Regulation, Drug Effects, Therapeutic Implications*, Vol. 16, Mod. Pharmacol.-Toxicol., edited by Peter Lomax and Eduard Schonbaum. NY, Marcel Dekker, Inc., 1979.

Cannabinoids.

This chapter reviews the effects of cannabinoids on body temperature and the studies that characterize that effect. The sites of Δ^9-THC induced hypothermia and its mechanism of action were discussed.

5417   Halldin, M.; and Widman, M., Acta Pharm. Suecica, *16*(1), 34-40 (1979).

The Importance of Side-Chain Hydroxylated Metabolites of Δ^6-Tetrahydrocannabinol in Rhesus Monkey.

The *in vitro* metabolism of Δ^6-THC by liver microsomal preparation of rhesus monkey was studied. Metabolites were characterized by mass spectrometry and comparison with reference samples. Hydroxylation in the 5 and 7 positions as well as on carbons 1 to 4 of the side chains was common.

5418   Handrick, G. R.; Uliss, D. B.; Dalzell, H. C.; and Razdan, R. K., Tetrahedron Lett., *8*, 681-84 (1979).

Hashish: Synthesis of (-)-Δ^9-Tetrahydrocannabinol (THC) and its Biologically Potent Metabolite 3'-Hydroxy-Δ^9-THC.

The synthesis of Δ^9-THC and its 3'-OH metabolite was performed via condensation of *p*-menth-2-ene-1,8-diol and olivetol or 3'-acetoxy-olivetol respectively. Zinc chloride was used as the catalyst. Less abnormal products were formed compared to the use of *p*-menth-2, 8-dien-1-ol.

5419 Harclerode, J.; Nyquist, S. E.; Nazar, B.; and Lowe, D., pp. 395-405 in *Marihuana: Biological Effects*. Advances in the Biosciences, Vols. 22-23, edited by G. G. Nahas and W. D. M. Paton. NY, Pergamon Press, 1979.

Effects of Cannabis on Sex Hormones and Testicular Enzymes of the Rodent.

Δ^9-THC or CBD at 10 mg/kg lowered testicular production of testosterone. Subacute THC (2 mg/kg) depressed levels of testicular cytochrome P-450 and gamma-glutamyl transpeptidase. Gonadotropin treatment restored the level of both enzymes.

5420 Harris, L. S., pp. 467-73 in *Mechanisms of Pain and Analgesic Compounds*, edited by R. F. Beers and E. G. Bassett, NY, Raven Press, 1979.

Cannabinoids as Analgesics.

SP-106, unlike Δ^9-THC, induces analgesia at doses that do not cause serious and unpleasant side effects.

5421 Harvey, D. J.; and Bourdon, R., pp. 123-26 in *Marihuana: Biological Effects*. Advances in the Biosciences, edited by G. G. Nahas and W. D. M. Paton. NY, Pergamon Press, 1979.

Summary of Session 1.

Summary of the pharmacokinetics and measurement of cannabinoids and metabolites was provided along with advantages and limitations. In terms of reliable plasma level, the i.v. route is the most preferred.

5422 Harvey, D. J.; Martin, B. R.; and Paton, W. D. M., pp. 45-62 in *Marihuana: Biological Effects*. Advances in the Biosciences, Vols. 22-23, edited by G. G. Nahas and W. D. M. Paton. NY, Pergamon Press, 1979.

Identification and Measurement of Cannabinoids and Their *In Vivo* Metabolites in Liver by Gas Chromatography-Mass Spectrometry.

Δ^9-THC, CBN, CBD and their metabolites were identified and quantitated in the liver of mouse, rat and guinea pig. Major metabolic pathways were discussed along with technical difficulties encountered.

5423 Heath, R. G.; Fitzjarrell, A. T.; Garey, R. E. and Myers, W. A., pp. 713-30 in *Marihuana: Biological Effects*. Advances in the Biosciences, Vols. 22-23, edited by G. G. Nahas and W. D. M. Paton. NY, Pergamon Press, 1979.

Chronic Marihuana Smoking: Its Effect on Function and Structure of the Primate Brain.

Chronic exposure of monkeys to cannabinoids or marihuana smoke resulted in significant changes in EEG recording. Only Δ^9-THC (0.69 mg/kg, i.v.) induced changes at brain sites involved with emotional expression. EM studies revealed ultrastructural changes at the septal region.

5424 Hein, K.; Cohen, M. I.; and Litt, I. F., Amer. J. Dis. Child., *133*(1), 38-40 (1979).

Illicit Drug Use Among Urban Adolescents.

Among youth, marihuana use increased whereas opiate use decreased in the second half of this 10-year study. Data were obtained from 76,000 adolescents treated by the Division of Adolescent Medicine.

5425 Hembree, W. C., III; Nahas, G. G.; Zeidenberg, P.; and Huang, H. F. S., pp. 429-39 in *Marihuana: Biological Effects*. Advances in the Biosciences, Vols. 22-23, edited by G. G. Nahas and W. D. M. Paton. NY, Pergamon Press, 1979.

Changes in Human Spermatozoa Associated with High Dose Marihuana Smoking.

In human users, marihuana smoking resulted in decreased sperm concentration and motility and abnormal sperm morphology. Effects were reversible.

5426 Herman, T. S.; Einhorn, L. H.; Jones, S. E.; Nagy, C.; Chester, A. B.; Dean, J. C.; Furnas, B.; Williams, S. D.; Leigh, S. A.; Dorr, R. T.; and Moon, T. E., New Eng. J. Med., *300*(23), 1295-97 (1979).

Superiority of Nabilone over Prochlorperazine as an Antiemetic in Patients Receiving Cancer Chemotherapy.

Although nabilone was found superior to prochlorperazine in cancer patients, its side effects were more severe and included hallucination.

5427 Herning, R. I.; Jones, R. T.; and Peltzman, D. J., Electroencephalogr. Clin. Neurophysiol., *47*(5), 556-70 (1979).

Changes in Human Event Related Potentials with Prolonged Delta-9-Tetrahydrocannabinol (THC) Use.

The depressive effects of Δ^9-THC on human auditory-evoked responses and the contingent negative variation were varied and dose-related. Degree of depression also depended on degree of task complexity.

5428 Hershkowitz, M., pp. 351-58 in *Marihuana: Biological Effects*. Advances in the Biosciences, Vols. 22-23, edited by G. G. Nahas and W. D. M. Paton. NY, Pergamon Press, 1979.

The Effect of *In Vivo* Treatment With (-) Δ^1-Tetrahydrocannabinol, and Other Psychoactive Drugs on the *In Vitro* Uptake of Biogenic Amines.

Δ^9-THC (5 and 10 mg/kg, i.v.) was more potent than CBD in stimulating DA - uptake by cortical synaptosomes obtained from pretreated mice. THC's effect is both stereospecific and brain region specific. THC also potentiated the cortical uptake of NE, 5-HT and GABA.

5429 Hershkowitz, M.; and Szechtman, H., Eur. J. Pharmacol., *59*(3-4), 267-76 (1979).

Pretreatment with Δ^1-Tetrahydrocannabinol and Psychoactive Drugs: Effects on Uptake of Biogenic Amines and on Behavior.

Biogenic amine uptake by mouse brain synaptosomes was stimulated by i.v. administration of cannabinoids. This effect was stereospecific, closely associated with psychoactivity and tolerance to it developed. Mechanisms involved were further analyzed.

5430 Hollister, L. E., pp. 585-89 in *Marihuana: Biological Effects*. Advances in the Biosciences, Vols. 22-23, edited by G. G. Nahas and W. D. M. Paton. NY, Pergamon Press, 1979.

Cannabis and the Development of Tolerance.

Tolerance to the effects of marihuana develops in humans only after high doses. Tolerance also takes place in animals.

5431 Huang, H. F. S.; Nahas, G. G.; and Hembree, W. C., III, pp. 419-27 in *Marihuana: Biological Effects*. Advances in the Biosciences, Vols. 22-23, edited by G. G. Nahas and W. D. M. Paton. NY, Pergamon Press, 1979.

Effects of Marihuana Inhalation on Spermatogenesis of the Rat.

Rats inhaling marihuana smoke (3 mg/kg Δ^9-THC/day) exhibited slight retardation in weight gain and reduction in size of testes, seminal vesicles and sperm counts. Histologic changes in sperm morphology and testicular abnormalities were also observed.

5432   Huber, G. L.; Pochay, V. E.; Shea, J. W.; Hinds, W. C.; Weker, R. R.; First, M. W.; and Sornberger, G. C., pp. 301-28 in *Marihuana: Biological Effects*. Advances in the Biosciences, Vols. 22-23, edited by G. G. Nahas and W. D. M. Paton. NY, Pergamon Press, 1979.

An Experimental Animal Model for Quantifying the Biologic Effects of Marihuana on the Defense System of the Lung.

A smoke generator and animal inhalation system were described. Also described were ways to monitor smoke delivery, dosimetry and an animal model for bioassay of the effects of marihuana on the lung defense system. Finally, chronic exposure to marihuana and tobacco smoke was evaluated in rats.

5433   Huber, G. L.; Shea, J. W.; Hinds, W. C.; Pochay, V. E.; Weker, R. T.; First, M. W.; and Sornberger, G. C., Bull. Eur. Physiopathol. Resp., *15*(3), 491-503 (1979).

Effet de la Phase Gazeuse de la Fumee de Marijuana sur les Defenses Bacteriennes Intrapulmonaires [The Gas Phase of Marihuana Smoke and Intrapulmonary Bactericidal Defenses].

The effect of the gas phase of marihuana smoke on lung antibacterial defenses was examined. The study showed that cytotoxins in the gas phase of the smoke impaired, to some degree, the alveolar antibacterial defenses.

5434   Hughes, R. B.; and Kessler, R. R., J. Forensic Sci., *24*(4), 842-46 (1979).

Increased Safety and Specificity in the Thin-Layer Chromatographic Identification of Marihuana.

The use of Fast Blue 2B and ether/hexane system for the TLC identification of marihuana provides a safer alternative to already existing systems.

5435   Humphries, S. V., Cent. Afr. J. Med., *25*(1), 19-20 (1979).

Cannabis: Its Merits and Hazards. Part 1.

Some of the sociological and psychological aspects of smoking cannabis are discussed.

5436   Humphries, S. V., Cent. Afr. J. Med., *25*(2), 37-38 (1979).

Cannabis: Its Merits and Hazards. Part 2.

The harmful effects of marihuana have been exaggerated. The author wonders why a drug used therapeutically for centuries is being discredited.

5437   Husain, S.; Lame, M.; and DeBoer, B., Proc. West Pharmacol. Soc., *22*, 355-58 (1979).

Rat Testicular Tissue Glucose Metabolism in the Presence of Delta-9-Cannabinol.

Δ^9-THC inhibited testicular tissue glucose metabolism. Inhibition was concentration-dependent and occurred at an early stage of glycolysis.

I

5438   Innemee, H. C.; Hermans, A. J. M.; and Van Zwieten, P. A., Doc. Ophthalmol., *48* 2), 235-41 (1979).

The Influence of Δ^9-Tetrahydrocannabinol on Intraocular Pressure in the Anaesthetized Cat.

Unlike clonidine, the central administration of Δ^9-THC did not produce enhancement of the decrease in IOP encountered after its i.v. administration to cats. It was concluded that the two agents do not share similar mechanisms of action.

5439   Issidorides, M. R., pp. 377-88 in *Marihuana: Biological Effects*. Advances in the Biosciences, Vols. 22-23, edited by G. G. Nahas and W. D. M. Paton. NY, Pergamon Press, 1979.

Observations in Chronic Hashish Users: Nuclear Aberrations in Blood and Sperm and Abnormal Acrosomes in Spermatozoa.

The ultrastructure of blood cell nuclei taken from chronic marihuana users exhibited aberrant condensation of chromatin and altered nuclear boundaries. Incomplete condensation of chromatin in sperm heads lacking acrosomes along with abnormal acrosomal morphogenesis were seen in users.

J

5440   Jacobs, J. A.; Dellarco, A. J.; Manfredi, R. A.; and Harclerode, J., J. Pharm. Pharmacol., *31*(5), 341-42 (1979).

The Effects of Δ^9-Tetrahydrocannabinol, Cannabidiol, and Shock on Plasma Corticosterone Concentrations in Rats.

Δ^9-THC (5 mg/kg, i.p.) and shock increased plasma corticosterone levels in treated rats, more so than either treatment alone. CBD in a similar dose depressed corticosterone levels. Shock reversed such a depression.

5441   Jaerbe, T. U. C.; and McMillan, D. E.; Neuropharmacology, 18(12), 1023-24 (1979).

Discriminative Stimulus Properties of Tetrahydrocannabinols and Related Drugs in Rats and Pigeons.

Generalization to 8 β, 11-di-OH- and 11-OH- metabolites of Δ^9-THC and also to 11-OH-Δ^8-THC resulted in rats and pigeons trained to discriminate the stimulus properties.

5442   Jakubovic, A.; McGeer, E. G.; and Mc-Geer, P. L., pp. 251-64 in *Marihuana: Biological Effects*. Advances in the Biosciences, edited by G. G. Nahas and W. D. M. Paton. NY, Pergamon Press, 1979.

Biochemical Alterations Induced by Cannabinoids in the Leydig Cells of the Rat Testis *In Vitro*: Effects on Testosterone and Protein Synthesis.

SP-111A, Δ^9-THC and the metabolites CBN, CBD, CBG and Δ^8-THC all inhibited testosterone production in isolated leydig cells of rat testis under stimulated but not basal conditions. The cannabinoids, however, caused concentration-dependent inhibition of protein synthesis under both conditions. Further mechanisms were investigated.

5443   Jakubovic, A.; McGeer, E. G.; and Mc-Geer, P. L., Mol. Cell Endocrinol., *15*(1), 41-50 (1979).

Effects of Cannabinoids on Testosterone and Protein Synthesis in Rat Testis Leydig Cells *In Vitro*.

Cannabinoids tested inhibited testosterone synthesis in rat testes under stimulated but not basal conditions. Protein synthesis was inhibited under both conditions. 11-OH- and 8-β-OH-Δ^9-THC were the most potent inhibitors.

5444   Janowsky, D. S.; Clopton, P. L.; Leichner, P. P.; Abrams, A. A.; Judd, L. L.; and Pechnick, R., Arch. Gen. Psychiat., *36*(7), 781-85 (1979).

Interpersonal Effects of Marijuana.

Marihuana intoxication resulted in a decrement of interpersonal skills of human subjects.

5445   Jarbe, T. U. C.; and Ohlin, G. C., Psychopharmacology, 63(3), 233-39 (1979).

Discriminative Effects of Combinations of Δ^9-Tetrahydrocannabinol and Pentobarbital in Pigeons.

Δ^9-THC (0.25 mg/kg, i.m.) or pentobarbital were effective discriminative stimuli in trained pigeons. Both were, however, more discriminable from each other than from nondrug conditions. Combined drug treatment did not enhance their respective responding.

5446   Jardillier, J.-C., pp. 389-91 in Marihuana: Biological Effects.   Advances in the Biosciences, Vols. 22-23, edited by G. G. Nahas and W. D. M. Paton. NY, Pergamon Press, 1979.

Cannabinoids and Cellular Responses: A Summary.

Highlights of the studies on the cellular effects of cannabinoids were summarized. Cannabinoids inhibit the biosynthesis of membrane phospholipids and macromolecular and testosterone synthesis. They also induce biochemical changes in the heart and brain.

5447   Jarvik, M. E., New Eng. J. Med., 300(23), 1330 (1979).

Necessary Risks. (Editorial)

The benefits of nabilone used as an antiemetic may outweigh the risks suggested by chronic toxicity studies in dogs.

5448   Jering, H.; and Toro-Goyco, E.; pp. 161-69 in Marihuana: Biological Effects.   Advances in the Biosciences, Vols. 22-23, edited by G. G. Nahas and W. D. M. Paton. NY, Pergamon Press, 1979.

Effect of Δ^9-Tetrahydrocannabinol in Nucleoside and Amino Acid Uptake in Reuber H-35 Hepatoma Cells.

Δ^9-THC inhibited the uptake of several nucleosides by hepatoma cells.   While the levels of intracellular thymidine nucleotides were depressed, thymidine kinase activity was not altered.

5449   Jering, H.; and Toro-Goyco, E., Mol. Pharmacol., 15(3), 627-32 (1979).

Effect of (-)-Δ^9-Tetrahydrocannabinol on Nucleoside and Amino Acid Uptake in Reuber H-35 Hepatoma Cells.

The uptake of several nucleosides by hepatoma cells was inhibited by Δ^9-THC.   THC also suppressed the level of intracellular thymidine nucleotides but did not inhibit thymidine kinase activity.

5450   Jessor, R., pp. 337-55 in Handbook on Drug Abuse, edited by R. L. Dupont, A. Goldstein, and J. O'Donnell, NIDA, 1979.

Marihuana: A Review of Recent Psychosocial Research.

The author cites references covering the epidemiology of marihuana use as well as factors associated with marihuana use such as social environment, personality, behavior and psychosocial development.

5451   Johnston, L. D.; Bachman, J. G.; and O'Malley, P. M., Drugs and the Class of '78: Behaviors, Attitudes, and Recent National Trends. NIDA, 1979. 335 p.

402

Sampling high school seniors revealed that frequent use of marihuana is becoming prevalent and is on the rise. This is especially true among males in the Northeast and the more urban areas. A high proportion experienced a "high" and about one third perceived marihuana to be harmful, condemned its daily use and believed parents to do the same. In general, more liberal stance toward marihuana use was shown in 1978 compared to 1975. Trends in use of other drugs were also reported.

5452   Jusko, W. J.; Gardner, M. J.; Mangione, A.; Schentag, J. J.; Koup, J. R.; and Vance, J. W., J. Pharm. Sci., *68*(11), 1358-66 (1979).

Factors Affecting Theophylline Clearances: Age, Tobacco, Marijuana, Cirrhosis, Congestive Heart Failure, Obesity, Oral Contraceptives, Benzodiazepines, Barbiturates, and Ethanol.

Marihuana users resulted in the highest values of total body clearance of theophylline. Marihuana use was one of several conditions under which theophylline clearance was studied.

K

5453   Kalofoutis, A.; and Koutselinis, A., Pharmacol. Biochem. Behav., *11*(4), 383-85 (1979).

Changes Induced by Hashish Constituents on Human Erythrocyte Phospholipids.

Smoking hashish by chronic users resulted in lower concentrations of erythrocyte phosphatidylcholine, phosphatidylinositol and phosphatidylserine. Concentration of lysophosphatidylcholine was increased.

5454   Kanakis, C.; Pouget, J. M.; and Rosen, K. M., Ann. Intern. Med., *91*(4), 571-74 (1979).

Lack of Cardiovascular Effects of Delta-9-Tetrahydrocannabinol in Chemically Denervated Men.

Pretreatment with propranolol and atropine blocked Δ^9-THC (25 µg/kg, i.v.) induced cardiovascular changes in human subjects.

5455   Kanter, S. L., Musumeci, M. R.; and Hollister, L. E., J. Chromatogr., *171*, 504-08 (1979).

Quantitative Determination of Δ^9-Tetrahydrocannabinol and Δ^9-Tetrahydrocannabinolic Acid in Marihuana by High-Pressure Liquid Chromatography.

Determination of the total Δ^9-THC (neutral and acid) was carried out on the plant extract which was decarboxylated by heating in a closed tube under N_2 at 200° using sand bath. Analysis of undecarboxylated extract from a second sample was necessary to determine both acid and neutral Δ^9-THC. Normal phase HPLC was used (5 µm Spherisorb silica column and heptane-1% iso-propanol in heptane 70:30 as the solvent).

5456   Kaplan, J. N., Pharmacol. Biochem. Behav., *11*(5), 539-43 (1979).

Maternal Responsiveness in the Squirrel Monkey Following Chronic Administration of Δ^9-THC.

Gradual exposure of mother monkeys to Δ^9-THC (0.5 to 5 mg/kg, p.o.) resulted in less discriminative behavior toward own versus unrelated offspring.

5457   Karler, R.; Sangdee, P.; Turkanis, S. A.; and Borys, H. K., Biochem. Pharmacol., *28*(6), 777-84 (1979).

The Pharmacokinetic Fate of Cannabidiol and its Relationship to Barbiturate Sleep Time.

Prolongation of barbiturate sleep time was not due to CBD, which was rapidly metabolized and eliminated from the mouse liver, but rather to an unidentified metabolite of CBD.

5458 Karler, R.; and Turkanis, S. A., pp. 619-41 in *Marihuana: Biological Effects.* Advances in the Biosciences, Vols. 22-23, edited by G. G. Nahas and W. D. M. Paton. NY, Pergamon Press, 1979.

Cannabis and Epilepsy.

CBD is a prime example of the dissociation between the anticonvulsant activity of cannabis and its psychotropic effects. By establishing and presenting an extensive profile for the cannabinoids and especially CBD, the authors suggested CBD had therapeutic potential that puts it ahead of already established anticonvulsants.

5459 Kaymakcalan, S., Dev. Psychiatry, *2* (Biol. Psychiatry Today, Vol. B), 1633-35 (1979).

Similarities Between Cannabis and Opium.

THC exhibited several pharmacological properties akin to those of morphine. Classifying it with narcotics is, therefore, appropriate.

5460 Kaymakcalan, S., pp. 591-604 in *Marihuana: Biological Effects.* Advances in the Biosciences, Vols. 22-23, edited by G. G. Nahas and W. D. M. Paton. NY, Pergamon Press, 1979.

Pharmacological Similarities and Interactions Between Cannabis and Opioids.

THC is compared to morphine in its ability to produce analgesia, tolerance and dependence in laboratory animals and humans. Drug interaction between THC and opiates is discussed along with the question of whether THC is truly a narcotic.

5461 Keim, D. A.; Baile, C. A.; Bolton, J. R.; Wangsness, P. J.; and Della Fera, M. A., Pharmacol. Biochem. Behav., *10*(1), 63-70 (1979).

Abomasal Function Following Injections of Elfazepam and 9-Aza-Cannabinol.

In the sheep abomasum, elfazepam did not influence electromyographic or contractile activities but decreased pH of abomasal content. 9-Aza-cannabinol (i.v.) only decreased the action potential and contractile activities.

5462 Kelly, L. A.; and Butcher, R. W., J. Cyclic Nucl. Res., *5*(4), 303-13 (1979).

Effects of Δ^1-Tetrahydrocannabinol on Cyclic AMP in Cultured Human Diploid Fibroblasts.

At high concentration, Δ^9-THC reduced both cellular accumulation and escape of cyclic AMP to the medium. Preincubation with THC altered c-AMP response to PGE_1. Further analysis of cannabinoids' mechanisms of action was also carried out.

5463 Kelly, L. A.; and Butcher, R. W., pp. 227-36 in *Membrane Mechanisms of Drugs of Abuse.* Prog. Clin. Biol. Res., Vol. 27, edited by C. W. Sharp and L. G. Abood. New York, Alan R. Liss, Inc., 1979.

Effects of Δ^1-Tetrahydrocannabinol (THC) on Cyclic AMP Metabolism in Cultured Human Fibroblasts.

Δ^9-THC, at low concentration, reduced cyclic nucleotide escape to the medium in cultured human lung cells and activated c-AMP-dependent protein kinase.

404

Combined with PGE_1, THC produced dose-dependent biphasic effects.

5464   Kemal, M.; Khalil, S. K. W.; Rao, N. G. S.; and Woolsey, N. F., J. Nat. Prod.-Lloydia, *42*(5), 463-68 (1979).

Isolation and Identification of a Cannabinoid-Like Compound from *Amorpha* Species.

A phenolic stilbene terpenoid was isolated from *Amorpha* which had some structural features similar to CBG.

5465   Khryanin, V. N.; and Chailakhyan, M. Kh., Fiziol. Rast., *26*(5), 1008-15 (1979).

Biological Activity of Cytokinins and Gibberellins in Roots and Leaves in Expressing Sex in Dioecious Plants.

Two cannabis cultivars were examined for cytokinin and gibberellin activity. Male plants had more cytokinin- and female plants had more gibberellin-like activity. Differences were noted in the roots.

5466   Khyranin, V. N.; and Chailakhyan, M. Kh., Fiziol. Rast. (Moscow), *26*(2), 455-58 (1979).

Separate and Joint Action of Growth Regulators on Manifestation of Sex in Hemp.

The effects of plant hormones, when used separately and in combination with growth inhibitors and retardants, on the manifestation of sex in hemp are studied.

5467   Kielholz, P., Deut. Med. Wochenscr., *104*(1), 10 (1979).

Netzhautblutungen Nach Haschischgebrauch? [Retinal Hemorrhage from Hashish?]

Recent long-term studies and available literature are devoid of any information regarding retinal hemorrhage or detached retina due to chronic hashish use.

5468   Kielholz, P.; Ladewig, D.; and Uchtenhagen, A., Schweiz. Rundsch. Med. Prax., *68*(51), 1687-93 (1979).

Zur Frage der Gesundheitsschadlichkeit des Haschischkonsums [Can Health be Damaged by Consuming Cannabis?].

The health hazards associated with cannabis use are not that grave compared to those associated with heroin use.

5469   Klipec, W. D.; Akins, F. R.; and Koerner, A., Physiol. Psychol., *7*(2), 153-55 (1979).

The Effects of Δ^9-THC on Wavelength Generalization in the Pigeon.

Following generalization tests in pigeons trained to discriminate wavelength stimuli, Δ^9-THC did not affect the peak shift. Rather, it decreased the area shift and increased responding to + with no effect on S-.

5470   Kluin-Neleman, J. C.; Neleman, F. A.; Meuwissen, O. J. A.; and Maes, R. A. A., Veterinary and Human Toxicology, *21*(5), 338-40 (1979).

Delta-9-Tetrahydrocannabinol (THC) as an Antiemetic in Patients Treated with Cancerchemotherapy: A Double-Blind Cross-Over Trial Against Placebo.

In cancer patients undergoing chemotherapy, the side effects of Δ^9-THC by far outweighed its beneficial effects as an antiemetic.

5471   Korcok, M., US J. Drug Alcohol Depend., *3*(7), 1-2 (1979).

Pot for Therapy.

Objective discussion of marihuana does not necessarily imply endorsement of use.

5472 Krakowiak, P. A.; and Cross, H. J., Int. J. Addict., *14*(6), 789-96 (1979).

A Social-Learning Approach to Student Marijuana Use.

Among social and psychological factors, positive experience with marihuana was the best predictor of marihuana use by students. Users also believed that marihuana is harmless. Family modeling for use was also important.

L

5473 Lach, E.; and Schachter, E. N., New Eng. J. Med., *301*(8), 438 (1979).

Marihuana and Exercise Testing (Letter).

Marihuana blocked exercise-induced bronchoconstriction in asthmatic patients.

5474 Lall, B.; and Lall, G., *Marijuana: Friend or Foe?* Nashville, Tennessee, Southern Publishing Association, 1979. 30 pp.

Marihuana is detrimental to physical and mental states of humans. Hence, youth are urged not to use it and society is urged to assume a more responsible role.

5475 Laszlo, J., Ann. Intern. Med., *91*(6), 916-18 (1979).

Tetrahydrocannabinol: From Pot to Prescription?

Although some cannabinoids were proven effective antiemetics in cancer patients, prescribing THC for these purposes is still impeded by many obstacles. Some of these obstacles were discussed.

5476 Lau-Cam, C. A.; and Pizzitola, V., J. Pharm. Sci., *68*(8), 976-78 (1979).

Simple Field Test for Marijuana.

A fast and accurate field test for marijuana is proposed. No interferences were reported. The test involved one solvent and a dry microcolumn formulation of Fast Blue B on alumina.

5477 Law, B.; Williams, P. L.; and Moffat, A. C., Vet. Hum. Toxicol., *21*(Suppl.) 144-47 (1979).

The Detection and Quantification of Cannabinoids in Blood and Urine by RIA, HPLC/RIA and GC/MS.

A sensitive method to identify and quantify cannabinoids in biological fluids was described. Method was applied in forensic analysis.

5478 Leighty, E. G., Res. Commun. Chem. Pathol. Pharmacol., *24*(2), 393-96 (1979).

Hydrolysis of 11-Palmitoyloxy-Δ^9-Tetrahydrocannabinol to 11-Hydroxy-Δ^9-Tetrahydrocannabinol by Cholesterol Esterase and a Lipase.

A metabolite of Δ^9-THC identified in the rat, 11-Palmitoyloxy-Δ^9-Tetrahydrocannabinol (11-palm-Δ^9-THC), can be hydrolyzed to 11-OH-Δ^9-THC by cholesterol esterase and a lipase *in vitro*. This raises possibilities that long-retained metabolites may play an active role in the psychoactivity of Δ^9-THC even though they are nonpsychoactive.

5479 Leighty, E. G., Res. Commun. Chem. Pathol. Pharmacol., *25*(3), 525-35 (1979).

Comparison of the Effects of 11-Palmitoyloxy - Δ^9-Tetrahydrocannabinol with Δ^9-Tetrahydrocannabinol and 11-Hydroxy-Δ^9-Tetrahydrocannabinol on the Hepatic Microsomal Drug-Metabolizing Enzyme System.

In vivo, Δ^9-THC and its 11-OH-metabolite inhibited the microsomal metabolism of aminopyrene and aniline but induced the metabolism of benzo (α) pyrene. 11-Palmitoyloxy-Δ^9-THC caused the latter effect only.

5480   Leighty, E. G., Res. Commun. Pathol. Pharmacol., *23*(3), 483-92 (1979).

An *In Vitro* Rat Liver Microsomal System for Conjugating Fatty Acids to 11-Hydroxy-Delta-9-Tetrahydrocannabinol.

Long retained metabolites of cannabinoids were located in the liver, spleen, fat and bone marrow. These metabolites were identified as palmitic and stearic acid congugates of 11-OH-Δ^9-THC. This study suggests that the same metabolic pathway in microsomes is involved in both the esterification of cholesterol and 11-OH-Δ^9-THC. Methods are discussed.

5481   Leuchtenberger, C.; Leuchtenberger, R.; and Chapuis, L., pp. 209-18 in *Marihuana: Biological Effects*. Advances in the Biosciences, Vols. 22-23, edited by G. G. Nahas and W. D. M. Paton. NY, Pergamon Press, 1979.

Difference in Response to Vitamin C Between Marihuana and Tobacco Smoke Exposed Human Cell Cultures.

Compared to tobacco smoke, exposure of human lung and breast cancer cultures to marihuana smoke resulted in elevated mitotic abnormalities. The ability of vitamin C to block cell de-differentiation and anaplasia after breast cancer cell exposure to tobacco smoke but not marihuana smoke was apparent. Vitamin C accelerates de-differentiation and abnormal growth of breast cancer cells exposed to marihuana smoke.

5482   Levy, J. A.; and Heppner, G. H., J. Immunopharmacology, *1*(1), 105-14 (1978-79).

Alterations in Murine Delayed Type Hypersensitivity Responses by Delta-8-THC and Cannabinol.

Multiple daily postimmunization administration but not single postimmunization or multiple preimmunization doses of cannabinol resulted in a reduction in the delayed-type hypersensitivity to sheep red blood cells in mice. Only multiple preimmunization doses of Δ^8-THC produced a reduction in reactivity.

5483   Liu, J. H.; Fitzgerald, M. P.; and Smith, G. V., Anal. Chem., *51*(11), 1875-77 (1979).

Mass Spectrometric Characterization of Cannabinoids in Raw *Cannabis sativa L.*

A procedure is described for the qualitative determination of cannabinoids in cannabis samples and thus for identification of marihuana. Direct probe insertion of 0.2 mg plant material into the mass spectrometer was utilized. The major cannabinoids CBN, CBD, Δ^1-THC and Δ^6-THC were monitored at different temperatures and ionization energies through their characteristic peaks and a correlation was made.

5484   Liu, J. H.; Lin, W.-F.; Fitzgerald, M. P.; Saxena, S. C.; and Shieh, Y. N., J. Forensic Sci., *24*(4), 814-16 (1979).

Possible Characterization of Samples of *Cannabis sativa L.* by their Carbon Isotopic Distributions.

Carbon isotope distribution varied in cannabis plants of different origins and in different parts of the same plant.

5485   London, S. W.; McCarthy, L. E.; and Borison, H. L., Proc. Soc. Exp. Biol. Med., *160*(4), 437-40 (1979).

Suppression of Cancer Chemotherapy-Induced Vomiting in the Cat by Nabilone, a Synthetic Cannabinoid.

Nabilone antagonized emesis induced in cats by anticancer drugs, apomorphine or deslanoside. Effective doses, however, produced prominent behavioral disturbances.

5486 Lotz, F.; Kraatz, U.; and Korte, F., Z. Naturforsch. B, *34*(2), 306-12 (1979).

Synthese Pyridin-Analoger Tetrahydrocannabinole [Synthesis of Pyridine-Analogous Tetrahydrocannabinols].

The synthesis of different aza-cannabinoids including Benzopyranopyridines and the new ring system 6H-benzo (4,5)-pyrano (2,3-c)-pyridin-6-one was discussed. Structures were proposed and spectroscopic data given.

5487 Luteijn, J. M.; and Spronck, H. J. W., J. Chem. Soc., London, *1*, 201-03 (1979).

Condensation Reactions of Olivetol Bis (Tetrahydropyranyl Ether) Homocuprate with Propargylic Substrates. A Convenient Synthesis of (±)-3,4-*cis*-$\Delta^{1,2}$-Tetrahydrocannabinol and (±)-3,4-*trans*-$\Delta^{1,2}$-Cannabidiol.

A procedure was developed for the synthesis of two pyrolytic products of CBD and for (±)-*cis*-THC starting from olivetol bis (tetrahydropyranyl ether) homocuprate with the appropriate propargylic substrate. In addition the authors showed that (±)-3,4-*trans*-CBD and (±)-3,4-*trans*-Δ^1-THC could be prepared in good yield from citral and olivetol when two-fold excess of citral is used at BF_3 concentration of 0.05%.

5488 Luthra, Y. K., pp. 531-37 in *Marihuana: Biological Effects*. Advances in the Biosciences, Vols. 22-23, edited by G. G. Nahas and W. D. M. Paton. NY, Pergamon Press, 1979.

Brain Biochemical Alterations in Neonates of Dams Treated Orally with Δ^9-Tetrahydrocannabinol During Gestation and Lactation.

Oral Δ^9-THC treatment to pregnant and lactating rats (5 and 10 mg/kg) did not affect them, but depressed brain macromolecular synthesis of their offspring. Therefore, neurological functional deficits would be anticipated.

5489 Lutz, E. G., J. Med. Soc. N. J., *76*(4), 253-59 (1979).

Marihuana and Paranoid Disperception.

Chronic marihuana use may lead to personality changes and perceptual cognitive impairment. Paranoid behavior disappeared after treatment regimen was instituted.

Mc

5490 McGeer, P. L. and Jakubovic, A., pp. 519-30 in *Marihuana: Biological Effects*. Advances in the Biosciences, Vols. 22-23, edited by G. G. Nahas and W. D. M. Paton. NY, Pergamon Press, 1979.

Ultrastructural and Biochemical Changes in CNS Induced by Marihuana.

Δ^9-THC did not affect the rate of respiration or amount of radioactive substrate in the soluble fraction of rat brain slices but inhibited radioactive substrate incorporation into protein. Inhibition was inversely related to age. Uridine incorporation into protein followed a similar pattern but less radioactive substrate was found in the soluble fraction. *In vivo*, Δ^9-THC also reduced the number of nuclear membrane-attached ribosomes both in lactating mothers and their sucklings.

408

5491   McLaughlin, C. L.; Baile, C. A.; and Bender, P. E., Psychopharmacology, *64*(3), 321-23 (1979).

Cannabinols and Feeding in Sheep.

Initially, i.v. 9-Aza-CBN and *l*-but not *d*-$\triangle^9$-THC increased food intake in treated sheep. After 24 hrs, all cannabinoids decreased such behavior.

M

5492   Malor, R.; Jackson, D. M.; and Chesher, G. B., pp. 243-50 in *Marihuana: Biological Effects*. Advances in the Biosciences, Vols. 22-23, edited by G. G. Nahas and W. D. M. Paton. NY, Pergamon Press, 1979.

(-)*Trans*-$\triangle^9$-Tetrahydrocannabinol: Synaptosomal Phospholipids, Synaptosomal Plasma Membrane (Na^+-K^+) -ATPase, and Thiopentone Anaesthesia in Mice.

In vivo, treatment of mice with $\triangle^9$-THC (10 mg/kg, i.p.) did not affect the kinetic behavior of synaptosomal (Na^+-K^+) -ATPase nor did it change the distribution of major synaptosomal phospholipids.

5493   Manatt, M., *Parents, Peers and Pot*, NIDA, 1979. 98 pp.

The author details and illustrates specific ways in which parents can curtail the use of marihuana in their teenage children. She points out the adverse physiological and psychological effects of marihuana use especially in young children. In addition, she emphasizes that parents must become aware and involved using means within the family and community to control marihuana use rather than leaving it up to other institutions such as the schools.

5494   Margolis-Kazan, H.; and Blamire, J., Cytobios, *26*(102), 75-95 (1979).

Effect of Tetrahydrocannabinol and Ethidium Bromide on DNA Metabolism and Embryogenesis in *Volvox*.

The administration of $\triangle^9$-THC or ethidium bromide to *Volvox* spheroids results in changes in the ratio of cytoplasmic DNA to total DNA which are paralleled by morphological changes. A model is proposed for the role that cytoplasmic and nuclear DNA may play in the regulation of embryogenesis of this organism.

5495   Margolis-Kazan, H.; and Blamire, J., Microbios Letters, *11*, 7-13 (1979).

Effect of $\triangle^9$-Tetrahydrocannabinol on Cytoplasmic DNA Metabolism in a Somatic Cell Regenerator Mutant of *Volvox*.

$\triangle^9$-THC has been shown to preferentially inhibit cytoplasmic DNA synthesis seen in the *Volvox* mutant as well as the rapid cell division seen after dedifferentiation. Implications in the study of embryogenesis and carcinogenesis are noted.

5496   Marks, V.; and Teale, J. D., pp. 81-88 in *Marihuana: Biological Effects*. Advances in the Biosciences, Vols. 22-23, edited by G. G. Nahas and W. D. M. Paton. NY, Pergamon Press, 1979.

The Radioimmunoassay of Cannabinoids: Its Clinical Pharmacological and Forensic Applications.

RIA of cannabinoids using antisera produced from immunized sheep was described. The method is useful for identifying cannabis users by detecting cannabinoids present in their urine and blood.

497   Masoud, A. N.; and Wingard, D. W., J. High Resolut. Chromatogr. Chromatogr. Commun., *2*(3), 118-22 (1979).

High Performance Liquid Chromatography with Electrochemical Detection.

Three samples of cannabis including an alcoholic extract of Mexican female leaves and flowering tops, street hashish and street cannabis were analyzed by high performance liquid chromatography with electrochemical detection (HPLC-EC). A total of eleven constituents were obtained of which Δ^9-, Δ^8-THC and CBD were identified. The standard curve for Δ^9-THC was linear, with a correlation coefficient (r) of 0.989 and a slope of 0.021. The detection limits for Δ^9-THC and other cannabinoids were in 2-20 ng range.

498   Medek, A., Hrbek, J., Navratil, J. and Komenda, S., pp. 520-21 in *Progress in Pathophysiology. Proceedings of the International Congress on Pathological Physiology. 2nd.* Prague, July 11-15, 1975. (Pub. 1979)

The Effect of Some Drugs on the Recall of Firmly Established Conditioned Alimentary Motor Reflexes in Cats.

Cannabis, containing 4% Δ^9-THC, was shown to interact with atropine and physotigmine to reverse performance deficits induced by those substances. Lack of interaction of cannabis with the quaternal bases indicates a central mechanism.

5499   Mehrotra, N. K.; and Saxena, A. K., Toxicol Lett., *4*(4), pp. 307-11 (1979).

Haemolytic Activity of Hemp Dust and Crude Hemp Antigen *in vitro*.

Hemp dust was found to be a mild hemolytic in human and sheep RBC. Degree of hemolysis increased with pH. Crude hemp antigen did not possess such an activity at clinically used concentration.

5500   Mellors, A., pp. 329-42 in *Marihuana: Biological Effects.* Advances in the Biosciences, Vols. 22-23, edited by G. G. Nahas and W. D. M. Paton. NY, Pergamon Press, 1979.

Cannabinoids and Membrane-Bound Enzymes.

Δ^9-THC inhibited lipid metabolism in mouse brain synaptosomes and spleen lymphocytes. Effects were evident at contrations of 10^{-5} M *in vitro* and 15-70 mg/kg, i.v. doses *in vivo*. The inhibitory effect of cannabinoids on membrane-bound acyltransferase is related to psychoactive properties.

5501   Miczek, K. A., Psychopharmacology, *60*(2), 137-46 (1979).

Chronic Δ^9-Tetrahydrocannabinol in Rats: Effect on Social Interactions, Mouse Killing, Motor Activity, Consummatory Behavior, and Body Temperature.

Rats treated with Δ^9-THC exhibited bizarre behavior and depressed vertical and locomotor activities, as well as lowered temperature and food and water uptake. Aggressive behavior was also manifested under specific experimental conditions. Tolerance developed to some, but not all, effects.

5502   Miller de Paiva, L., Int. J. Addct., *14*(5), 729-34 (1979).

Psychoanalytical Studies on the Causes of Intoxication by Marihuana.

Psychoanalysis conducted on marihuana users suggested that parents' behavior during upbringing predisposes these subjects to marihuana use.

410

5503   Miller, J. D.; and Cisin, I. H., *Highlights from the National Survey on Drug Abuse: 1979*. NIDA, U. S. Dept. of Health and Human Services, Rockville, MD., 34 pp.

This survey reports on lifetime and current experience with marihuana and other illicit drugs according to age, sex, frequency of use and demographic characteristics. Other aspects of drug abuse reported on include family influences, perceived effects on driving and motivation, and trends in marihuana use as well as use of stronger drugs.

5504   Miller, L. L., pp. 539-66 in *Marihuana: Biological Effects*. Advances in the Biosciences, Vols. 22-23, edited by G. G. Nahas and W. D. M. Paton. NY, Pergamon Press, 1979.

Cannabis and the Brain with Special Reference to the Limbic System.

Cannabinoids alter the overall functioning of the brain including subjective, cognitive and perceptual functions. The limbic system involvement in these functions was explained. Alterations of neurotransmitters and EEG patterns were also discussed.

5505   Miller, L. L.; Cornett, T. L.; and Wikler, A., Life Sciences, *25*(15), 1325-30 (1979).

Marijuana: Effects on Pulse Rate, Subjective Estimates of Intoxication and Multiple Measures of Memory.

After smoking marihuana, short and long term - but not recognition - memory were impaired in users. Subjective high and pulse rate were increased.

5506   Milman, D. H., Amer. J. Psychiat., *136*(2), 240 (1979).

A Cannabis Caveat Reinforced. (Letter)

Concerned psychiatrists are helped by published data confirming the deleterious effects of marihuana on the human mind.

5507   Milne, G. M.; Koe, B. K.; and Johnson, M. R., pp. 84-92 in *Problems of Drug Dependence: 1979*. NIDA Research Monograph 27, 1979.

Stereospecific and Potent Analgetic Activity for Nantradol - a Structurally Novel, Cannabinoid-Related Analgetic.

This study demonstrates that nantradol exhibits two to seven times greater potency than morphine in a battery of analgetic tests. Though this compound does not interact with the opiate receptor, it does exhibit stereospecific activity with the levorotatory isomer being more active.

5508   Miranne, A. C., J. Health. Soc. Behav., *20*(2), 194-99 (1979).

Marihuana Use and Achievement Orientations of College Students.

Achievement orientation of marihuana users did not differ from that of nonusers in this college sample.

5509   Mon, M. J., Diss. Abstr. Int. B, *39*(10), 4870-71 (1979).

Effects of Cannabinoids on Cell Proliferation and Gene Expression in Cultured Human Cells.

Cannabinoids depressed the proliferative process and the associated macromolecular biosynthesis in HeLa S_3 cells.

5510   Morahan, P. S.; Klykken, P. C.; Smith, S. H.; Harris, L. S.; and Munson, A. E., Infec. Immunol., *23*(3), 670-74 (1979).

Effects of Cannabinoids on Host Resistance to *Listeria monocytogenes* and Herpes Simplex Virus.

Resistance of mice to infections dramatically decreased after treatment with Δ^9-THC and, to a lesser extent, marihuana extract. Effects were dose-dependent.

511 Morishima, A.; Henrich, R. T.; Jayaraman, J.; and Nahas, G. G., pp. 371-76 in *Marihuana: Biological Effects.* Advances in the Biosciences, Vols. 22-23, edited by G. G. Nahas and W. D. M. Paton. NY, Pergamon Press, 1979.

Hypoploid Metaphases in Cultured Lymphocytes of Marihuana Smokers.

The frequency of hypoploid cells in lymphocyte cultures of heavy marihuana users was higher after smoking marihuana than during periods of abstinence from marihuana. Effects were reversible.

512 Myers, W. A.; and Heath, R. G., J. Neurosci. Res., *4*(1), 9-17 (1979).

Cannabis sativa: Ultrastructural Changes in Organelles of Neurons in Brain Septal Region of Monkeys.

Fragmentation and disorganization of pattern along with low volume density characterized the brain rough endoplasmic reticulum of Δ^9-THC treated monkeys.

N

513 Nahas, G., pp. xv-xix in *Marihuana: Biological Effects.* Advances in the Biosciences, Vols. 22-23, edited by G. G. Nahas and W. D. M. Paton. NY, Pergamon Press, 1979.

Introduction: Marihuana and the Cell.

The cellular effects of Δ^9-THC were summarized. The plasma membrane seems to be the prime target for the multiple effects of marihuana.

5514 Nahas, G., Nouv. Presse Med., *8*(11), 873-76 (1979).

La Toxicomanie: Symptome ou Syndrome Encephalique [Drug Addiction: Symptom or Encephalic Syndrome].

Abuse of drugs, including cannabis, is not just a symptom of troubled individuals trying to escape. Rather, it is a clinical syndrome resulting from drug-induced brain biochemical alterations.

5515 Nahas, G. G., J. Amer. Med. Ass., *242*(12), 1299 (1979).

Marijuana, Pregnancy, and Breast-Feeding (Questions and Answers).

Female users who plan to become pregnant and breast-feed their child should abstain from using marihuana before and during pregnancy and during lactation.

5516 Nahas, G. G., J. Amer. Med. Assoc., *242*(25), 2775-78 (1979).

Current Status of Marijuana Research.

Highlights of the progress in the field of marihuana research as presented in an international symposium on marihuana (1978) were reported.

5517 Nahas, G. C., *Keep Off the Grass. A Scientific Enquiry into the Biological Effects of Marijuana.* NY, Pergamon Press, 1979. 259 pp.

This is a revised edition of the 1976 book. See previous abstract No. 4530.

5518　Nahas, G. G.; and Paton, W. J. M., Eds., *Marihuana: Biological Effects. Analysis, Metabolism, Cellular Responses, Reproduction and Brain.* Advances in the Biosciences, Vols. 22-23. NY, Pergamon Press, 1979. 777 pp.

Proceedings of the Satellite Symposium on marihuana of the Seventh International Congress of Pharmacology held July 22-23, 1978, in Paris, France. The 56 chapters are divided into four major areas: quantification of cannabinoids and their metabolites in body fluids and tissues, cannabinoids and cellular metabolism, cannabis and reproduction, and cannabis and the brain. Individual chapters are abstracted under senior author.

5519　Natale, M.; Zeidenberg, P.; and Jaffe, J., Int. J. Addict., *14*(7), 877-89 (1979).

Δ^9-Tetrahydrocannabinol: Acute Effects on Defensive and Primary-Process Language.

Under the influence of marihuana, subjects used less defensive speech habits, talked more freely and were more direct. Secondary process language use increased whereas the primary one was not altered.

5520　Needham, L.; Paschal, D.; Rollen, Z. J.; Liddle, J.; and Bayse, D., J. Chromatogr. Sci., *17*(2), 87-90 (1979).

Determination of Paraquat in Marijuana by Reversed-Phase Paired-Ion High Performance Liquid Chromatography.

An HPLC method is described for the analysis of paraquat in marihuana using a reverse phase column C-18 SEP PAK TM and an ion-pairing reagent in the mobile phase. The recovery of paraquat in laboratory spiked material was 90-97%. The limit of detection was 2 ng of paraquat.

5521　Newell, F. W.; Jay, W. M.; and Sternberg, P., Trans. Ophthalmol. Soc. UK, *99*, P2, 269-71 (1979).

Use of Cannabinoid Derivatives in Glaucoma.

This brief review points out the beneficial as well as psychotropic and cardiovascular effects of synthetic and naturally occurring cannabinoids, and the search for congeners of Δ^9-THC which will decrease intraocular pressure without producing other side effects. In particular, the animal studies and clinical trials with nabilone are reviewed.

5522　Newell, F. W.; Stark, P.; Jay, W. M.; and Schanzlin, D. J., Ophthalmology, *86*(1), 156-60 (1979).

Nabilone: A Pressure-Reducing Synthetic Benzopyran in Open-Angle Glaucoma.

Nabilone (0.5-2 mg/kg, p.o.) reduced IOP in glaucoma patients. Topical administration to the eyes of rabbits resulted in similar effects. Tolerance in the latter case developed after one week.

5523　Nicar, M. J., Chemistry, *52*(1), 17-21 (1979).

Marijuana: Use and Abuse.

The issue of whether the effects of marihuana are harmful or harmless will remain unresolved until more conclusive evidence is presented.

5524　Nicolau, M.; Lapa, A. J.; and Valle, J. R., Rev. Bras. Biol., *39*(2), 281-90 (1979).

Peripheral Effects of Δ^9-Tetrahydrocannabinol: Antagonism to Noradrenaline, Acetylcholine and Barium Chloride on the Isolated Rat Vas Deferens

Preincubation of vas deferens with Δ^9-THC reduced maximum contractility after NE, ACh or barium chloride. SP-111 was an effective inhibitor after the first two agents only. Ethanol, used as a vehicle, was also tested.

5525   Niemi, W. D., Res. Commun. Chem. Pathol. Pharmacol., 25(3), 537-46 (1979).

Effect of Δ^9-Tetrahydrocannabinol on Synaptic Transmission in the Electric Eel Electroplaque.

Δ^9-THC blocked synaptic transmission of the electric eel electroplaque. This blockade was not due to influence on ACh-mediated membrane changes.

5526   Nightingale, S. L.; and Perry, S., J. Amer. Med. Ass., 241(4), 373-75 (1979).

Marijuana and Heroin by Prescription?

At present, federal and state health regulatory bodies are doing their best to facilitate the clinical research on heroin and marihuana. The state-by-state substance-specific legislations are therefore unnecessary.

5527   Nordqvist, M.; Agurell, S.; Rydberg, M.; Falk, L.; and Ryman, T., J. Pharm. Pharmacol., 31(4), 238-43 (1979).

More Acidic Metabolites of Δ^1-Tetrahydrocannabinol Isolated from Rabbit Urine.

Nine polar metabolites of Δ^1-THC were isolated from rabbit urine and their structures determined by GC-MS of their TMS derivatives and by ^{1}H NMR. These are side chain hydroxylated monocarboxylic acids and monocarboxylic acids hydroxylated in the allylic positions. In addition, an O-glucuronide of Δ^1-THC was unambiguously established as an in vivo urinary metabolite using MS and ^{1}H NMR.

5528   Nordqvist, M.; Lindgren, J. E.; and Agurell, S., J. Pharm. Pharmacol., 31(4), 231-37 (1979).

Acidic Metabolites of Δ^1-Tetrahydrocannabinol Isolated from Rabbit Urine.

Thirteen metabolites of Δ^1-THC were isolated from rabbit urine following i.v. administration. These are acidic, polar metabolites identified by GC-MS and ^{1}H NMR, as dicarboxylic acids, monocarboxylic acids and mono and dihydroxylated derivatives.

O

5529   O'Donnell, J. A.; pp. 30-43 in Cigarette Smoking as a Dependence Process. NIDA Research Monograph 23, 1979.

Cigarette Smoking as a Precursor of Illicit Drug Use.

Unlike marihuana or alcohol use, cigarette smoking cannot be used as a significant predictor of later illicit drug use.

5530   O'Donnell, J. A.; and Clayton, R. R., pp. 63-110 in Youth Drug Abuse: Problems, Issues and Treatment, edited by G. M. Beschner and A. S. Friedman. Lexington, Mass., Lexington Books, 1979.

Determinants of Early Marihuana Use.

Using path analysis, this study shows a significant correlation between the age at first use of marihuana and the extent of heroin use. "Age at first use" differs for blacks and whites and could be predicted from items related to behavior, family, peers, drug availability, and labeling by others as a potential delinquent. Other studies on predicting early marihuana use are reviewed.

414

5531   O'Neil, J. D.; Dalton, W. S.; and Forney, R. B., Toxicol. Appl. Pharmacol., *49*(2), 265-70 (1979).

The Effect of Cannabichromene on Mean Blood Pressure, Heart Rate, and Respiration Rate Responses to Tetrahydrocannabinol in the Anesthetized Rat.

CBC (10 mg/kg) alone decreased BP and respiration rate but had no effect on heart rate in anesthetized rats. Δ^9-THC (2 mg/kg) on the other hand, decreased BP, respiration rate and heart rate. When CBC was given along with Δ^9-THC, only the latter effect was changed.

5532   Ohlsson, A.; Agurell, S.; Leander, K.; Dahmen, J.; Edery, H.; Porath, G.; Levy, S.; and Mechoulam, R., Acta Pharm. Suecica, *16*(1), 21-33 (1979).

Synthesis and Psychotropic Activity of Side-Chain Hydroxylated Δ^6-Tetrahydrocannabinol Metabolites.

Five side chain mono-hydroxylated Δ^6-THC derivatives were synthesized and evaluated for psychotropic activity in adult rhesus monkeys. All side chain metabolites are (psychotropically) active. Pharmacokinetic profiles are discussed.

5533   Ohlsson, A.; Agurell, S.; Lindgren, J.-E; and Leander, K., pp. 73-79 in *Cannabinoid Analysis in Physiological Fluids*. ACS Symposium Series 98, edited by J. A. Vinson. Washington, D. C., American Chemical Society, 1979.

Improvement of the Mass Fragmentographic Technique for Quantification of Tetrahydrocannabinol in Human Blood Plasma.

A mass fragmentographic method was described for the determination of Δ^1-THC and Δ^6-THC in nanogram amounts in blood samples obtained from human subjects after smoking cannabis samples containing 5-20 mg/Δ^1-THC or Δ^6-THC or given oral doses of up to 50 mg Δ^1-THC. Sensitivity for underivatized THC is 0.3 ng/ml plasma. Increased sensitivity (0.1 ng/ml plasma) was attained by silylation which eliminates compounds interfering with mass fragmentography. The method can also be used for the determination of both underivatized or silylated CBD and CBN.

5534   Ohlsson, A.; and Emanuelson, I., Acta. Pharm. Suecica, *16*, 396-407 (1979).

Metabolism of 1 α, 2 α-Epoxyhexahydrocannabinol.

Metabolism of 1 α, 2 α-epoxyhexahydrocannabinol (EHHC) *in vitro* is discussed. Distribution of *in vivo* metabolites is given. Concentrations were liver > kidney > spleen > lung > brain. Six hydroxylated metabolites were isolated. Structure determination was by spectral data. In the case of EHHC, metabolic routes were not by epoxide deactivating enzymes and oxidizing enzymes but possibly by conjugation reactions.

P

5535   Paton, W. D. M., pp. 735-38 in *Marihuana: Biological Effects*. Advances in the Biosciences, Vols. 22-23, edited by G. G. Nahas and W. D. M. Paton. NY, Pergamon Press, 1979.

Concluding Summary.

Although the present state of the art, as evident in this symposium, indicates that knowledge on cannabis has improved tremendously in recent years, lots of intriguing questions remain unanswered.

5536   Pertwee, R. G.; and Tavendale, R., Brit. J. Pharmacol., *66*(1), 39-50 (1979).

Effects of Δ^9-Tetrahydrocannabinol, 2-4-Dinitrophenol and Pentolinium Tartrate on Behavioral Thermoregulation in Mice.

Initially, rats treated with Δ^9-THC (20 mg/kg, i.p. or 2 mg/kg, i.v.) did not move to a warm compartment to overcome the drug-induced hypothermia. Fifteen to thirty min. after drug injection, rats spent more time in the warm compartment. A useful apparatus to measure behavioral thermoregulation of drugs was described.

5537   Petersen, R. C., Lancet, *1*(8118), 727-28 (1979).

Importance of Inhalation Patterns in Determining Effects of Marihuana Use (Letter).

Importance of variations in the inhalation patterns with respect to tobacco smoking has been confirmed. If the same applies to cannabis use, then health implications (especially for the lung) would be expected to vary considerably. Suggestions for future cannabis inhalation studies are discussed.

5538   Pihl, R. O.; Shea, D.; and Costa, L., Int. J. Addict., *14*(1), 63-71 (1979).

Dimensions of the Subjective Marijuana Experience.

Compared to earlier data, marihuana use seems to occur at an earlier age, is used more frequently and is associated with multiple drug use. The subjective high is a relatively stable and well defined phenomenon.

5539   Pirl, J. N.; Papa, V. M.; and Spikes, J. J., J. Anal. Toxicol., *3*(4), 129-32 (1979).

The detection of Delta-9-Tetrahydrocannabinol in Postmortem Blood Samples.

The authors report on a detection method for Δ^9-THC from blood samples. Data on case samples are presented with a breakdown of positive/negative THC samples. All samples were select postmortem.

5540   Pitt, C. G.; Seltzman, H. H.; Sayed, Y.; Twine, C. E.; and Williams, D. L., J. Org. Chem., *44*(5), 677-83 (1979).

General Synthesis of Side Chain Derivatives of Cannabinoids.

General synthetic schemes for side chain hydroxylation of cannabinoids are presented and discussed. Methods are applicable to hydroxylation at all side chain positions. Data are presented for all compounds synthesized.

5541   Pradhan, S. N.; Bhattacharyya, A. K.; Aulakh, C. S.; Pradhan, S.; and Bailey, P. T., pp. 567-83 in *Marihuana: Biological Effects*. Advances in the Biosciences, Vols. 22-23, edited by G. G. Nahas and W. D. M. Paton. NY, Pergamon Press, 1979.

Cannabis and Brain-Stimulation Reward.

Δ^9-THC in one group of rats inhibited self-stimulation behavior. In another group, initial depression was followed by stimulation and then depression once again. Time-related biphasic effects on spontaneous motor activity were observed in aroused and non-aroused rats whereas hypothermia and potentiation of barbiturate-sleep time persisted. Behavioral activity corresponded to changes in the levels of brain 5-HT and DA.

5542   Prakash, N.; Bohm, L. R.; and Maze, J., Can. J. Bot., *57*(11), 1243-51 (1979).

416

Development Anatomy of the Achene in Cannabis.

The authors examined the anatomy of the achene of four varieties of *Cannabis sativa* at various stages of development. They found little evidence to indicate that there is more than one species.

5543   Pringle, H. L.; Bradley, S. G.; and Harris, L. S., Antimicrobial Agents and Chemother., *16*(5), 674-79 (1979).

Susceptibility of *Naegleria fowleri* to Δ^9-Tetrahydrocannabinol.

Δ^9-THC and 15 other cannabinoids were found to possess antiamoeba activity. THC also partially protected mice against naeglerial infection. SAR's were also investigated.

5544   Purohit, V.; Sihgh, H. H.; and Ahluwalia, B. S., Biol. Reprod., *20*(5), 1039-44 (1979).

Evidence that the Effects of Methadone and Marihuana on Male Reproductive Organs are Mediated at Different Sites in Rats.

Δ^9-THC and CBN decreased the weight of ventral prostates and seminal vesicles in sham operated rats and inhibited the stimulatory action of HCG in hypophysectomized rats. The effect of either cannabinoid, in combination with HCG, on plasma testosterone (T) and dihydrotestosterone (DHT) differed, whereas both blocked the stimulation of sex organ weight induced by T and DHT in castrated rats.

R

5545   Ram, H. Y. M.; and Sett, R., Indian Acad. Sci., *88B*(Pt. 2, No. 4), 303-08 (1979).

Sex Reversal in the Female Plants of *Cannabis sativa* by Cobalt Ion.

Co Cl_2 caused masculinization of flowers of cannabis female plants. These effects may be due to blockade of ethylene synthesis.

5546   Rawitch, A. B.; Rohrer, R.; and Vardaris, R. M., Gen. Pharmacol., *10*(6), 525-29 (1979).

Delta-9-Tetrahydrocannabinol Uptake by Adipose Tissue: Preferential Accumulation in Gonadal Fat Organs.

Substantial accumulation of Δ^9-THC was observed in mice gonadal but not inguinal fat tissues. THC in gonadal tissue is very slowly metabolized.

5547   Ray, R.; Prabhu, G. G.; Mohan, D.; Nath, L. M.; and Neki, J. S., Indian J. Med. Res., *69*, 996-1000 (1979).

Chronic Cannabis Use and Cognitive Functions.

A comparison of chronic cannabis users with non-user controls revealed no significant difference on objective tests for memory, attention, concentration and perceptomotor function.

5548   Repetto, M.; Martinez, D.; Sanz, P.; Giminez, Ma P.; Rodriquez, Ma A., Vet. Hum. Toxicol., *21*(Suppl.), 148-50 (1979).

Potential Carcinogenicity of Cannabis.

Benzypyrene content of marihuana smoke condensate was carcinogenic in newborn rats. It also resulted in spontaneous death in the offspring of chronically treated females.

5549   Revuelta, A. V.; Cheney, D. L.; Wood, P. L.; and Costa, E., Neuropharmacology, *18*(6), 525-30 (1979).

GABAergic Mediation in the Inhibition of Hippocampal Acetylcholine Turnover Rate Elicited by $\triangle^9$-Tetrahydrocannabinol.

$\triangle^9$-THC reduced the turnover rate of acetylcholine in the hippocampus by increasing the release of GABA from septal interneurons. Dopaminergic or endophinergic involvement was ruled out.

5550   Richter, J. A.; and Werling, L. L., J. Neurochem., *32*(3), 935-41 (1979).

K-Stimulated Acetylcholine Release: Inhibition by Several Barbiturates and Chloral Hydrate but not by Ethanol, Chlordiazepoxide or 11-OH-$\triangle^9$-Tetrahydrocannabinol.

The ability of bariturates to inhibit the stimulated release of ACh in rat midbrain was not shown by 11-OH-$\triangle^9$-THC, chlordiazepoxide or ethanol.

5551   Rittenhouse, J. D., Ed., *Consequences of Alcohol and Marihuana Use*. NIDA, 1979. 227 pp.

The importance of the study of consequences of the use of marihuana or alcohol was emphasized. A list of relevant items for the measurement of perception and beliefs of these consequences, based on responses of sample users, was provided. A guide to survey research in this area was outlined.

5552   Ritzlin, R. S.; Gupta, R. C.; and Lundberg, G. D., Clin. Toxicol., *15*(1), 45-53 (1979).

Delta-9-Tetrahydrocannabinol Levels in Street Samples of Marijuana and Hashish: Correlation to User Reactions.

Bad reaction was the major reason for voluntarily submitting marihuana samples for analysis. High $\triangle^9$-THC content,

rather than adulterants, was associated with stronger reaction.

5553   Roffman, R. A., *Using Marijuana in the Reduction of Nausea Associated with Chemotherapy*. Seattle, Washington, Murray Publishing Company, Inc., 1979.

This manuscript represents a handy manual for advanced cancer patients anticipating the use of marihuana to alleviate nausea and vomiting associated with chemotherapy.

5554   Rootman, I., Drug Alcohol Depend., *4*(5), 425-34 (1979).

Recent Trends in Cannabis Use in Canada.

Approximately 1 of 6 Canadians sampled had used marihuana. Use was more prevalent in males and younger people. Education, community size and the native language were significant factors in patterns of use.

5555   Rose, S. E.; Dwyer, W. O.; and Yehle, A. L., Pharmacol. Biochem. Behav., *10*(6), 851-53 (1979).

Delta-9-Tetrahydrocannabinol: Elevation of Absolute Visual Thresholds of Rabbits.

$\triangle^9$-THC 0.025 and 0.5 mg/kg increased visual threshold to lights (conditioned stimulus) in trained rabbits. This occurred without affecting the unconditioned response or the latency to respond to the conditioned stimulus.

5556   Rosell, S.; Bjorkroth, U.; Agurell, S.; Leander, K.; Ohlsson, A.; Martin, B.; and Mechoulam, R., pp. 63-70 in *Marihuana: Biological Effects*. Advances in the Biosciences, Vols. 22-23, edited by G. G. Nahas and W. D. M. Paton. NY, Pergamon Press, 1979.

Relation Between Effects of Cannabinoid Derivatives on the Twitch Response of the Isolated Guinea-Pig Ileum and Their Psychotropic Properties.

Of the side-chain Δ^6-THC hydroxylated metabolites tested, (-)-3''-OH-one was the most potent inhibitor of the twitch response of stimulated guinea-pig ileum. Correlation between the above cited response and psychotropic activity of cannabinoids was also investigated.

5557   Rosenfeld, J., pp. 81-91 in *Cannabinoid Analysis in Physiological Fluids*. ACS Symposium Series 98, edited by J. A. Vinson. Washington, D. C., American Chemical Society, 1979.

A General Approach to the Analysis of Cannabinoids from Physiological Sources.

A general approach for the estimation of Δ^9-THC and metabolites from plasma is presented. Problems involving analysis of nanogram amounts in lipophilic media are discussed. Δ^9-THC and its major metabolite 11-OH-Δ^9-THC were analyzed by GC-MS after suitable derivatization.

5558   Rosenfeld, J.; Crocco, J.; and Ting, T. L., Prepr.-Can. Symp. Catal., *6*, 52-59 (1979).

Biphasic Alkylation Reactions.

Δ^9-THC and 11-OH-Δ^9-THC were converted to their pentafluorbenzyl ethers. The reaction involved the use of a biphasic system and alkylation was affected without any phase transfer catalyst. Other phenols and carboxylic acids were used and the system was found to be specific for phenols over straight chain carboxylic acids.

5559   Rosenkrantz, H., pp. 479-99 in *Marihuana: Biological Effects*. Advances in the Biosciences, Vols. 22-23, edited by G. G. Nahas and W. D. M. Paton. NY, Pergamon Press, 1979.

Effects of Cannabis on Fetal Development of Rodents.

Rats and mice were treated orally or by inhalation with Δ^9-THC at varying doses and at different times during gestation. Dosimetry was carefully monitored. Embryotoxicity but not teratogenicity resulted. Correlation between embryotoxicity and vaginal bleeding was observed.

5560   Rosenkrantz, H.; and Fleischman, R. W., pp. 279-99 in *Marihuana: Biological Effects*. Advances in the Biosciences, Vols. 22-23, edited by G. G. Nahas and W. D. M. Paton. NY, Pergamon Press, 1979.

Effects of Cannabis on Lungs.

A rat model was developed to demonstrate the pulmonary effects of chronic marihuana smoke exposure. Doses of marihuana-smoke administered were correlated to those used by humans by monitoring plasma carboxy-hemoglobin and Δ^9-THC levels. Sub-chronic and chronic exposure to marihuana smoke produce pathological alterations in the rat lungs of greater magnitude than placebo or tobacco smoke.

5561   Rosenkrantz, H.; and Hayden, D. W., Toxicol. Appl. Pharmacol., *48*(3), 375-86 (1979).

Acute and Subacute Inhalation Toxicity of Turkish Marihuana, Cannabichromene, and Cannabidiol in Rats.

Turkish marihuana smoke, which had high CBC and CBD content, was more toxic to exposed rats than was either cannabinoid alone. All agents tested except Δ^9-THC caused testicular damage.

5562   Rosenthal, D.; and Brine, D., J. Forensic Sci., *24*(2), 282-90 (1979).

Quantitative Determination of Δ^9-Tetrahydrocannabinol in Cadaver Blood.

GC/MS procedure was used to determine Δ^9-THC in blood collected in a manner which simulates autopsy situations. 11-d_3-Δ^9-THC was used as internal standard. Extraction was carried out with acetone, followed by hexane and the extract chromatographed Sephadex LH-20 column. The fraction containing Δ^9-THC was then analyzed by GC/MS.

5563   Rosenthal, F., pp. 739-45 in *Marihuana: Biological Effects*. Advances in the Biosciences, Vols. 22-23, edited by G. G. Nahas and W. D. M. Paton. NY, Pergamon Press, 1979.

Appendix-Cannabis and Alcohol: The Green and the Red.

The social debate over use of alcohol and marihuana is no different now than it was during ancient civilizations. It is however, hoped that the objective scientific ability of modern man will aid society in taking the right course of action.

5564   Roth, S. H.; and Williams, P. J., J. Pharm. Pharmacol. *31*(4), 224-30 (1979).

The Non-Specific Membrane Binding Properties of Δ^9-Tetrahydrocannabinol and the Effects of Various Solubilizers.

Binding of 3H-Δ^9-THC was similar in both crude or synaptosomal membranes of rat brains. Cremophor E. L., Tween 80 and, to a lesser extent, ethanol decreased membrane binding. Mechanisms involved were further investigated.

5565   Rubenstein, K. E., pp. 89-99 in *Marihuana: Biological Effects*. Advances in the Biosciences, Vols. 22-23, edited by G. G. Nahas and W. D. M. Paton. NY, Pergamon Press, 1979.

Determination of Cannabinoids in Urine by Emit^R Homogenous Enzyme Immunoassay.

Δ^9-THC and metabolites were positively identified in the urine of users using this described immunoassay. The method utilized THC - antibodies and conjugates of THC with malate dehydrogenase.

5566   Russell, J. A.; and Bond, C. R., Int. J. Addict., *14*(7), 977-86 (1979).

Beliefs Among College Students on Settings and Emotions Conducive to Alcohol and Marijuana Use.

Marihuana and alcohol are more likely used by experienced college students under pleasant rather than adverse circumstances. These results support the amplification rather than the compensation hypotheses.

S

5567   Sallan, S. E.; Zinberg, N. E.; and Frei, E., Hosp. Phys., *5*, 21-24 (1979).

Drug Treatment: THC and Oncology (Was it Serendipity or Science?).

Serendipity rather than science led to the use of marihuana in cancer patients. Social and Legal obstacles would constrain similar research on illicit drugs.

5568   Salzman, C., pp. 26-28 in *Side Effects of Drugs Annual 3, 1979*, edited by M. N. G. Dukes. Amsterdam/Oxford, Excerpte Medica, 1979.

Social Drugs: Cannabis.

Marihuana and alcohol produce more decrement of performance than either agent alone. Marihuana may also induce psychosis. Acute administration decreases IOP in glaucoma patients but chronic use may increase IOP.

5569   Sanders, J.; Jackson, D. M.; and Starmer, G. A., Psychopharmacology, *61*(3), 281-85 (1979).

Interactions Among the Cannabinoids in the Antagonism of the Abdominal Constriction Response in the Mouse.

Δ^9-THC was a more effective analgesic than CBN, while CBD was ineffective. Naloxone did not antagonize THC-induced analgesia. Two metabolites of Δ^9-THC were also tested.

5570   Sarath, G.; and Mohan Ram, H. Y., Experientia, *35*(3), 333-34 (1979).

Comparative Effect of Silver Ion and Gibberellic Acid on the Induction of Male Flowers on Female Cannabis Plants.

Cannabis plants were treated with $AgNO_3$ and gibberellic acid and tested for sex inversion. $AgNO_3$ induced male flowers in female plants. Gibberellic acid was only ½ as effective as $AgNO_3$. The role of endogenous ethylene is discussed.

5571   Sassenrath, E. N.; Chapman, L. F.; and Goo, G. P., pp. 501-12 in *Marihuana: Biological Effects*. Advances in the Biosciences, Vols. 22-23, edited by G. G. Nahas and W. D. M. Paton. NY, Pergamon Press, 1979.

Reproduction in Rhesus Monkeys Chronically Exposed to Delta-9-THC.

Monkeys treated with Δ^9-THC (2.4 or 4.8 mg/kg, p.o.) daily for 5 breeding seasons exhibited normal sexual function. The number of viable offspring

was lower in THC-treated females mated with untreated males than that of the reverse order. Also, weight gain for treated females and their male offspring was lower than control.

5572   Scherrmann, J. M.; Bourdon, R.; Hoellinger, H.; Nguyen-Hoang-Nam; and Fournier, E., pp. 207-23 in *Cannabinoid Analysis in Physiological Fluids*. ACS Symposium Series 98, edited by J. A. Vinson. Washington, D. C., American Chemical Society, 1979.

Detection and Quantitation of Δ^9-Tetrahydrocannabinol in Plasma by Dansylation and Double Labeling.

A method has been developed for the detection and quantitation of Δ^9-THC in plasma using dansyl technology. It involves the use of ^{14}C-DANS-Cl and $^3H_2$-Δ^9-THC as an internal standard. The method involves 3 steps: (1) extraction, (2) esterification and (3) TLC purification of dansyl derivatives.

5573   Schultes, R. E., J. Psychedelic Drugs, *11*(1-2), 13-24 (1979).

Hallucinogenic Plants: Their Earliest Botanical Descriptions.

A bibliographic list of hallucinogenic plants in the fungi and angiosperms categories is presented. Date and place of first publication of a species concept, cannabis included, are reported.

5574   Shiomi, H.; Nakahara, H.; Segawa, M.; and Takagi, H., Jap. J. Pharmacol., *29*(5), 803-06 (1979).

Relationship Between Δ^9-Tetrahydrocannabinol-Induced Mouse Killing Behavior on the Rat and the Metabolism of Monoamines in the Brain, Particularly the Olfactory Bulb.

Δ^9-THC (20 mg/kg, i.p.) induced muricidal behavior in rats, coincided with decreased noradrenergic activity in the olfactory bulb and diencephalon.

5575 Siemens, A. J.; and Doyle, O. L., Pharmacol. Biochem. Behav., 10(1), 49-55 (1979).

Cross-Tolerance Between Δ^9-Tetrahydrocannabinol and Ethanol: The Role of Drug Disposition.

Tolerance and cross-tolerance to impairment of rotarod performance, induced by alcohol or Δ^9-THC, developed in rats after repeated administration. The rate of disappearance of either drug was not, however, influenced by differing treatment regimens.

5576 Siemens, A. J.; Doyle, O. L.; and Pryor, G. T., Life. Sci., 24(14), 1261-74 (1979).

Determinants of the Disposition of ^{14}C-Δ^9-Tetrahydrocannabinol and ^{3}H-Δ^9-Tetrahydrocannabinol.

^{14}C-Δ^9-THC disappeared more rapidly than did ^{3}H-Δ^9-THC from blood or plasma of rats treated with both isotopes. Absorption of both was faster in fed and young versus fasted and older rats. Dried organ distribution was similar in all rats and the gut was the site where tritiated water was formed.

5577 Silvestro, J. R.; and Vacc, N. A., J. Psychedelic Drugs, 11(4), 351-53 (1979).

College Students and Alcohol, Marijuana and Tobacco: A Comparison Survey Between 1967 and 1978.

Compared to 1967, students of 1978 consumed more alcohol and marihuana, had favorable attitude toward marihuana but consumed less tobacco. Authors note that student sample represents western New York State.

5578 Singh, K.; Knezek, L. D.; and Adams, L. D., J. Drug Issues, 9(4), 499-510 (1979).

Changes in Reactions to Deviance: The Issue of Legalization of Marijuana.

An increased trend towards approving marihuana legalization was found in in 1976 as compared to 1973. Education, age and religion are among several demographic variables influencing societal reactions to such an issue.

5579 Siqueira, S. W.; Lapa, A. J.; and Valle, J. R. D., Eur. J. Pharmacol., 58(4), 351-57 (1979).

The Triple Effect Induced Δ^9-Tetrahydrocannabinol on the Rat Blood Pressure.

Δ^9-THC (5 mg/kg, i.v.) resulted in an initial rapid decrease in rat BP, followed by an increase and then a decrease whereas bradycardia persisted throughout. Results indicated that early and late decreases were centrally mediated, while the increase was due to direct effects.

5580 Skinner, W. A.; Rackur, G.; and Uyeno, E., J. Pharm. Sci., 68(3), 330-31 (1979).

Structure-Activity Studies on Tetrahydro- and Hexahydrocannabinol Derivatives.

Five tetrahydro- and hexahydrocannabinols were synthesized with variable substituents at C-9. The activities of these compounds in mice were determined on muscle tone, locomotor, body temperature and analgesia. Comparison was made with Δ^9-THC.

5581 Smith, C. G.; Besch, N. F.; Smith, R. G.; and Besch, P. K., Fertil. Steril., 31(3), 335-39 (1979).

Effect of Tetrahydrocannabinol on the Hypothalamic-Pituitary Axis in the Ovariectomized Rhesus Monkey.

Δ^9-THC (0.625 to 5.0 mg/kg) depressed the level of luteinizing and follicle stimulating hormones in ovariectomized monkeys. THC acts at the level of hypothalamic control.

5582   Smith C. G.; Smith, M. T.; Besch, N. F.; Smith, R. G.; and Asch, R. H.; pp. 449-67 in *Marihuana: Biological Effects.* Advances in the Biosciences, Vols. 22-23, edited by G. G. Nahas and W. D. M. Paton.   NY, Pergamon Press, 1979.

Effect of Δ^9-Tetrahydrocannabinol (THC) on Female Reproductive Function.

Δ^9-THC (0.625 to 5 mg/kg, i.m.) inhibited gonadotropins in ovariectomized monkeys at the hypothalamic level. Treatment with THC during menstrual luteal phase inhibited subsequent cycle ovulation.   No estrogenic activity of THC could be documented.

5583   Smith, R. G.; Besch, N. F.; Besch, P. K.; and Smith, C. G., Science, *204*(4390), 325-27 (1979).

Inhibition of Gonadotropin by Δ^9-Tetrahydrocannabinol: Mediation of Steroid Receptors?

Δ^9-THC did not bind to intracellular receptors for steroid hormones in cytosol preparations of monkey and human uterus.

5584   Smith, S. H., Diss. Abstr. Int. B, *40*(5), 2150 (1979).

Immunosuppressant Activity of Naturally Occurring and Synthetic Cannabinoids.

Among several cannabinoids studied, 1-methyl-Δ^8-THC was found to possess immunosuppressant activity with minimal CNS effects.

5585   Sofia, R. D.; Strasbaugh, J. E.; and Banerjee, B. N., Teratology, *19*(3), 361-66 (1979).

Teratologic Evaluation of Synthetic Δ^9-Tetrahydrocannabinol in Rabbits.

Treatment of pregnant rabbits with Δ^9-THC (15 to 60 mg/kg, s.c.) for several days decreased food consumption and weight gain.   Litter weight and number of fetuses were also reduced but no teratogenic effects were evident.

5586   Srivastava, S. L.; and Naithani, S. C., Curr. Sci. India, *48*(22), 1004-05 (1979).

Cannabis sativa Linn., A New Host for *Phoma* sp.

Examination of diseased leaves of a cannabis plant revealed the pathogen to be an unusual species of *Phoma.*

5587   Staats, G. R., Int. J. Addict., *14*(8), 1163-69 (1979).

Sexual Differentiation Among Marijuana Users: Reality or Inaccuracy.

Self-administered questionnaires indicated minimal sex differences between female and male marihuana users.   Males were more active in acquiring marihuana whereas females were more on the receiving side.

5588   Stein, G. S.; Mon, M. J.; Haas, A. E.; and Jansing, R. L., pp. 171-208 in *Marihuana: Biological Effects.* Advances in the Biosciences, Vols 22-23, edited by G. G. Nahas and W. D. M. Paton. NY, Pergamon Press, 1979.

Cannabinoids: The Influence on Cell Proliferation and Macromolecular Biosynthesis.

In order of potency, Δ^8-THC, 11-OH-Δ^9-THC, CBN and Δ^9-THC all inhibited division of HeLa S_3 cultured cells. Effects were dose-related and reversible. The rates of DNA and RNA syntheses appeared inhibited. Further analysis suggested that cannabinoids alter the functional and structural characteristics of the genomes by affecting chromosomal proteins.

5589   Stimmel, B., pp. 167-78 in *Cardiovascular Effects of Mood-Altering Drugs.* New York, Raven Press, 1979.

Marihuana.

The cardiovascular effects of marihuana vary with the dose, duration of administration and presence or absence of coronary artery disease. Tachycardia is commonly seen in healthy persons following its acute administration, whereas its chronic use leads to a fall in the heart rate and BP in addition to orthostatic changes. Deleterious physiologic responses usually accompany marihuana use in persons with coronary disease.

5590   Stone, L. H.; Miranne, A. C.; Ellis, G. J., Adolescence, *14*(53), 115-22 (1979).

Parent-Peer Influence as a Predictor of Marijuana Use.

Negative relationship between parent orientation and use of marihuana was found for this college sample. The reverse was true for peer-oriented subjects.

5591   Stueck, G. S., Can. Pharm. J., *112*(7), 126-27, 134 (1979).

Marijuana: A Review.

Marihuana is a widely used but still poorly understood substance.

5592   Sugerman, A. A., J. Med. Soc. N. J., *76*(4), 302-03 (1979).

How Dangerous is Marihuana? (Commentary)

A concrete answer to the above question is not as yet available. More objective research is needed.

5593   Szepsenwol, J.; Fletcher, J.; Murison, G. L.; and Toro- Goyco, E., pp. 359-70 in *Marihuana: Biological Effects.* Advances in the Biosciences, Vols. 22-23, edited by G. G. Nahas and W. D. M. Paton. NY, Pergamon Press, 1979.

Long-Term Effects of Delta-9-Tetrahydrocannabinol in Mice.

Unlike estrogen, repeated treatment with Δ^9-THC (20 mg/kg, s.c.) did not inhibit growth or reproduction of treated female mice but a high incidence of malignant tumors was found. Neonatal mortality of THC-treated females was high except when foster nursing took place.

T

5594   Takahashi, R. N.; and Singer, G., Pharmacol. Biochem. Behav., *11*(6), 737-40 (1979).

Self-Administration of Δ^9-Tetrahydrocannabinol by Rats.

Under FI schedule of food presentation, the rate of Δ^9-THC (6.25 and 12.5 μ g/kg) self-administration increased in food-deprived rats only. This effect did not take place when the FI schedule was not included.

5595   Tashkin, D. P., Ann. Intern. Med., *90*(2), 276 (1979).

Cannabis and Cancer Chemotherapy. (Comments)

The author agreed that Δ^9-THC holds a potential therapeutic effect as an antiemetic in cancer patients.

5596 Taylor, D. A.; and Fennessy, M. R., Clin. Exp. Pharmacol., 6, 327-34 (1979).

The Effect of Δ^9-Tetrahydrocannabinol (Δ^9-THC) on the Turnover Rate of Brain Serotonin of the Rat.

Using 3 methods, this study indicates that Δ^9-THC does not alter the turnover rate of rat brain serotonin. The authors suggest that changes in body temperature may be mediated by interference with vesicular binding of serotonin.

5597 Taylor, D. A.; and Fennessy, M. R., Clin. Exp. Pharmacol. Physiol., 6(5), 541-48 (1979).

The Effect of (-)-Trans-Δ^9-Tetrahydrocannabinol on Regional Brain Levels and Subcellular Distribution of Monoamines in the Rat.

In rats, Δ^9-THC (2 mg/kg, i.v.) reduced whole brain levels of NE and increased levels of 5-HT and 5-HIAA in the medulla and hypothalamus, respectively. THC altered subcellular distribution and ratio of DA and 5-HIAA only.

5598 Teale, J. D.; Clough, J. M.; King, L. J.; Marks, V.; Williams, P. L.; and Moffat, A. C., pp. 155-73 in *Cannabinoid Analysis in Physiological Fluids*. ACS Symposium Series 98, edited by J. A. Vinson. Washington, D. C., American Chemical Society, 1979.

Antisera Raised Against Tetrahydrocannabinol in the Radioimmunoassay of Cannabinoids.

The authors discuss the use of RIA for cannabinoid analysis in urine and plasma. Direct analysis of a sample gives an indication of the presence of cannabinoids on a semi-quantitative basis. Quantitation may then be expanded further and more specifically following HPLC separation. Different THC-protein conjugates have been produced. Antisera were obtained from sheep which have been injected with THC-hemisuccinate-albumin conjugate and sera were collected at peaks in titre. Although raised against THC, the assay antiserum is not specific for THC but binds several cannabinoids to varying degrees.

5599 Tennant, F. S., pp. 309-15 in *Problems of Drug Dependence: 1979*, NIDA Research Monograph 27, 1979.

Histopathologic and Clinical Abnormalities of the Respiratory System in Chronic Hashish Smokers.

Subjects who were chronic hashish smokers and smoked cigarettes show a greater incidence of basal cell hyperplasia than those who smoked hashish or cigarettes alone. The types of lesions observed are often associated with emphysema or carcinoma of the lung.

5600 Tewari, S. N.; and Sharma, J. D., Pharmazie, 34(1), 54 (1979).

Separation and Identification of Cannabinoids from *Cannabis indica* L. by Thin Layer Chromatography.

Different samples of Bhang, Ganja and Charas were analyzed by a TLC procedure. Extraction was carried out with chloroform and the extracts spotted on silica gel plates using 13% acetone in hexane. Visualization was with 0.1% Fast Blue salt B in 45% ethanolic solution.

5601 Tewari, S. N.; and Sharma, J. D., Pharmazie, 34(3), 196-97 (1979).

Specific Color Reactions for the Detection and Identification of Microquantities of Cannabis Preparations.

A procedure is reported for characterization of different cannabis preparations (Bang, Ganja and Charas). Extraction was done with chloroform and the extracts were decolorized with charcoal in acetone and evaporated. Eight different reagents were then added to the dried extracts which resulted in characteristic colors. Tables are given for reagents and results.

5602 Toro-Goyco, E.; Rodriquez, M. B.; Preston, A.; and Jering, H., pp. 229-42 in *Marihuana: Biological Effects*. Advances in the Biosciences, Vols. 22-23, edited by G. G. Nahas and W. D. M. Paton. NY, Pergamon Press, 1979.

Effect of (-) $\triangle^9$-THC on ATPase Systems from Various Sources.

In vitro, $\triangle^9$-THC inhibited NA^+- and K^+-ATPases by blocking Na^+-dependent phosphorylation. Such an inhibition was reversed by phosphatidyl ethanolamine. An attempt to correlate *in vitro* and *in situ* effects was undertaken.

5603 Tuchmann-Duplessis, H., pp. 513-15 in *Marihuana: Biological Effects*. Advances in the Biosciences, Vols. 22-23, edited by G. G. Nahas and W. D. M. Paton. NY, Pergamon Press, 1979.

Summary of Session III.

Summary of the preceding nine papers was provided. $\triangle^9$-THC decreases testosterone and inhibits spermatogenesis and ovarian functions. The reproductive functions in man are depressed and embryotoxicity is also evident after $\triangle^9$-THC.

5604 Tucker, A. N.; and Friedman, M. A., Res. Commun. Chem. Pathol. Pharmacol., *23*(2), 327-32 (1979).

Effects of Cannabinoids on L1210 Murine Leukemia. III. Inhibition of Respiration.

CBD, $\triangle^8$- and $\triangle^9$-THC (10^{-4} M concentration) had no effect on respiration by L1210 murine leukemia cells, whereas six other cannabinoids, including CBN, were effective *in vitro* inhibitors. No relationship seems to exist between respiration and the anticancer activity of these cannabinoids.

5605 Tucker, L., Amer. Pharm., *NS19*(10), 25-28 (1979).

Marijuana by Prescription.

Although therapeutic uses for marihuana may be promising, it is still a long way from being available by prescription.

5606 Tucker, L., Amer. Pharm., *NS19*(10), 32-33 (1979).

Legal Grass Farm Supplies Government Pot.

NIDA acts as the pharmaceutical supplier of marihuana. The Research Institute of Pharmaceutical Sciences at The University of Mississippi generates the standard grade of marihuana.

5607 Tucker, L., Amer. Pharm., *NS19*(10), 29 (1979).

Marijuana's Health Effects Probed by Congress.

The special task force on marihuana reported its findings to the Congress. More conclusive research is needed.

5608　Tucker, R. B.; Graham, B. F., Can. Soc. Forensic Sci. J., *12*(4), 163-72 (1979).

Cannabinoid Content of a Stand of Cannabis Grown Clandestinely in Nova Scotia.

Canadian illicitly grown cannabis plants were found to have high contents of $\triangle^9$-THC. Packaging in plastic bags reduced cannabinolic acid content drastically.

5609　Turkanis, S. A.; Smiley, K. A.; Borys, H. K.; Olsen, D. M.; and Karler, R., Epilepsia, *20*(4), 351-64 (1979).

An Electrophysiological Analysis of the Anticonvulsant Action of Cannabidiol on Limbic Seizures in Conscious Rats.

CBD increased the afterdischarge threshold while decreasing amplitude and duration of limbic seizures evoked in rats. CBD, as compared to $\triangle^9$-THC and anticonvulsants, was the most efficacious and was devoid of CNS excitatory effects.

5610　Turner, C. E.; Cheng, P. C.; Lewis, G. S.; Russell, M. H.; and Sharma, G. K., Planta Med., *37*(3), 217-25 (1979).

Constituents of *Cannabis sativa*. XV: Botanical and Chemical Profile of Indian Variants.

Studies were conducted on Indian Cannabis plants collected in India as well as plants grown in Mississippi from fruits taken from the samples collected in India. No classification on cannabinoid content was consistent. No subspecies classification could be made. Leaf cannabinoid content was variable. Analytical data and botanical observations are given.

5611　Turner, C. E.; and Elsohly, M. A., J. Heterocyl. Chem., *16*(8), 1667-68 (1979).

Constituents of *Cannabis sativa L*. XVI. A Possible Decomposition Pathway of $\triangle^9$-Tetrahydrocannabinol to Cannabinol.

From isolated intermediates, a decomposition pathway for $\triangle^9$-THC to CBN was proposed. A flow chart is provided. Data on intermediates are given.

5612　Turner, C. E.; Elsohly, M. A.; Cheng, P. C.; and Lewis, G., J. Nat. Prod., *42*(3), 317-19 (1979).

Constituents of *Cannabis sativa L*. XIV: Intrinsic Problems in Classifying Cannabis Based on A Single Cannabinoid Analysis.

A new method to evaluate phenotypes based on 10 cannabinoids was proposed. The system separates homologs and ring systems. It was shown that present classification systems are not valid for variants but only for each sample. Cannabinoid fluctuations are discussed.

5613　Turner, C. J. and Willis, R. J., J. Drug Educ., *9*(1), 67-78 (1979).

The Relationship Between Self-Reported Religiosity and Drug Use by College Students.

In this survey self-reported religious students differed from non-religious students in that they reported less frequent use of marihuana and alcohol, abstention based on lack of curiosity, less willingness to refer to drug-wise friends in case of drug problems, and more willingness to discuss drug attitudes with their parents.

U

5614　Unnikrishnan, P.; Chandrasekharan, V.;

Shah, G. D.; and Bhattacharyya, S. C., Indian J. Chem., Sect. B, *17B*(3), 250-52 (1979).

Synthesis of Tetrahydrocannabinol Analogues: Effect of Aryl Side Chain on Activity of Tetrahydrocannabinol.

SARs were established for a series of synthetic cannabinoid analogs and homologs. $\Delta^{1,6}$-THC was found to be more "active" than analogs and homologs synthesized. Synthesis techniques are presented.

V

5615 Valentine, J. L.; Bryant, P. J.; Gutshall, P. L.; Gan, O. H. M.; and Niu, H. C., Anal. Lett., *12*(B8), 867-80 (1979).

Detection of Δ^9-Tetrahydrocannabinol in Human Breath Following Marijuana Smoking.

This study demonstrated the ability of 2 methods in enhancing human breath samples following marihuana smoking. The two methods, polyethylene foam water and a cryogenic trap containing ethanol, were followed by HPLC-MS analysis and demonstrated differences in efficiency and usefulness in the field.

5616 Valentine, J. L.; Gan, O. H. M.; Nio, H. C.; and Thompson, E. D., pp. 175-205 in *Cannabinoid Analysis in Physiological Fluids*. ACS Symposium Series 98, edited by J. A. Vinson. Washington, D. C., American Chemical Society, 1979.

HPLC Analysis of Δ^9-Tetrahydrocannabinol and 11-*Nor*-Δ^9-Tetrahydrocannabinol-9-Carboxylic Acid in Human Plasma.

HPLC methods involving the use of both normal and reverse phases were used for the analysis of Δ^9-THC (I)

and 11-*nor*-Δ^9-THC-9-carboxylic acid (II) in human plasma. Normal phase was found satisfactory for the separation of Δ^9-THC from plasma constituents when 0.3% isopropanol in heptane was used as mobile phase to get rid of endogenous plasma constituents that can interfere with the assay. Tandem alkylamine-alkylnitrile columns were used. Reverse phase was the choice for detection and quantitation of (II) using a mixture of water-acetonitrile as mobile phase.

5617 Valentine, J. L.; and Psaltis, P., Anal. Lett., *12*(B8), 855-66 (1979).

Detection of Marijuana Use in Human Saliva Using a Fluorometric Assay Based on Cannabinol Decomposition.

A fluorometric method to detect photolytic decomposition products of CBN is described. Decomposition of CBN in human saliva under air and nitrogen is discussed. Highest concentrations of CBN products were observed at 30 min.

5618 Van Den Broek, G. W.; Robertson, J.; Keim, D. A.; and Baile, C. A., Pharmacol. Biochem. Behav., *11*(1), 51-56 (1979).

Feeding and Depression of Abomasal Secretion in Sheep Elicited by Elfazepam and 9-Aza-Cannabinol.

Both i.v. 9-aza-CBN and Elfazepam concomitantly increased food intake and decreased abomasal acid secretion in treated sheep.

5619 Vinson, J. A., ed., *Cannabinoid Analysis in Physiological Fluids*. ACS Symposium Series, Vol. 98 (Proc. Symp. 173rd Meeting of American Chemical Society, New Orleans, La., March 20-25, 1977). Washington, D. C., American Chemical Society, 1979. 242 pp.

These twelve chapters, the proceedings of a symposium, examine the analytical techniques used in identifying and isolating tetrahydrocannabinol. An abstract of each chapter is given under individual author.

5620   Virgo, B. B., Res. Commun. Chem. Pathol. Pharmacol., 25(1), 65-77 (1979).

The Estrogenicity of Delta-9-Tetrahydrocannabinol (THC): THC Neither Blocks nor Induces Ovum Implantation, nor Does it Effect Uterine Growth.

Δ^9-THC (3 to 12 mg/kg) did not possess any estrogenic activity in mice.

W

5621   Wall, M. E.; and Brine, D. R., pp. 15-43 in *Marihuana: Biological Effects*. Advances in the Biosciences, Vols. 22-23, edited by G. G. Nahas and W. D. M. Paton. NY, Pergamon Press, 1979.

Applications of Mass Spectrometry in Cannabinoid Research.

Sensitive GLC-MS methods for the determination of CBN, Δ^9-THC and its 11-OH-metabolite in the same blood sample and 11-*nor*-Δ^9-THC-7-oic acid in blood or urine samples were detailed. Samples used were from experienced users.

5622   Wall, M. E.; Brine, D. R.; Brine, G. A.; Tomer, K.; Davis, K. H.; and Parker, C. J., pp. 129-37 in *Stable Isotopes: Proceedings Third International Conference, 1978*, edited by E. R. Klein and P. D. Klein. NY, Academic Press, 1979.

Determination of Paraquat in Marihuana Pyrolysis Products.

Paraquat, present in marihuana pyrolysis products, was partitioned in the aqueous layer of a water chloroform system. It was then purified by HPLC and quantitated using GLC-MS.

5623   Wall, M. E.; Brine, D. R.; Bursey, J. T.; and Rosenthal, D., pp. 39-57 in *Cannabinoid Analysis in Physiological Fluids*. ACS Symposium Series 98, edited by J. A. Vinson. Washington, D. C., American Chemical Society, 1979.

Detection and Quantitation of Tetrahydrocannabinol in Physiological Fluids.

Gas-liquid chromatography combined with mass spectrometry (GLC-MS) is used in this study for the quantitative analysis of Δ^9-THC, 11-OH-Δ^9-THC and CBN in blood of human volunteers using one extraction. Detection limits for Δ^9-THC and CBN were found to be 0.5 ng and 0.1 ng, respectively. Details for the determination of 11-*nor*-Δ^9-THC-9-carboxylic acid in blood and urine are presented.

5624   Watanabe, K.; Oguri, K.; and Yoshimura, H., Chem. Phar. Bull., 27(12), 3009-14 (1979).

Synthesis of Δ^8-Tetrahydrocannabinol Glucuronide and Sulfate, and Their Metabolic Disposition in Rats.

Δ^8-THC glucuronide but not sulfate was immune to hydrolysis. After i.v. injection in rats, some biliary but not urinary excretion of these conjugates was observed.

5625   Watanabe, K.; Yamamoto, I.; Oguri, K.; and Yoshimura, H., Biochem. Biophys. Res. Commun., 88(1), 178-82 (1979).

Microsomal Oxygenase Catalyzed Oxidation of 11-Hydroxy-Δ^8-Tetrahydrocannabinol to 11-Oxo-Δ^9-Tetrahydrocannabinol.

Oxidation of 11-OH-Δ^8-THC to 11-oxo-Δ^8-THC was carried out using rabbit liver microsomes. The reaction was found to need NADPH and molecular oxygen. A mixed function oxidase enzyme is thought to be involved.

5626   Weil, A. T., pp. 188-201 in *Ethnopharmacologic Search for Psychoactive Drugs*, edited by D. H. Efron, B. Holmstedt, and N. S. Kline. NY, Raven Press, 1979.

Nutmeg as a Psychoactive Drug.

This review of the source and history of the use of nutmeg points out its use as a substitute for cannabis in situations where drug availability has been restricted or as a first drug experience prior to cannabis or other drugs. Its subjective effects are similar to cannabis; however, it has unpleasant side effects.

5627   Weissman, A.; and Milne, G. M., Neurosci. Biobehav. Rev., *3*(3), 171-73 (1979).

Cannabinoids: Definitional Ambiguities and a Proposal.

The authors discuss ambiguities of the botanical, structural and pharmacological definitions of the term cannabinoid. The term cannabimimetic was introduced to describe natural or synthetic compounds which produce subjective effects and have an abuse potential similar to Δ^9-THC regardless of their structure or possible therapeutic potential.

5628   Widman, M.; Halldin, M.; and Martin, B., pp. 101-03 in *Marihuana: Biological Effects*. Advances in the Biosciences, edited by G. G. Nahas and W. D. M. Paton. NY, Pergamon Press, 1979.

In Vitro Metabolism of Tetrahydrocannabinol by Rhesus Monkey Liver and Human Liver.

Unlike monkey liver, human liver does not biotransform THC to side chain hydroxy metabolites.

5629   Williams, P. L.; and Moffat, A. C., J. Chromatogr., *186*, 595-603 (1979).

Combined High-Performance Liquid Chromatography and Radioimmunoassay Method for the Analysis of Δ^9-Tetrahydrocannabinol Metabolites in Human Urine.

A method to determine polar metabolites in urine is described. Cross-reacting cannabinoid-like materials are reported. Hydrolysis of the acids as esters are described. Subjects (3) smoked Δ^9-THC in tobacco cigarettes. Cross-reactivity was lowest in non-cannabis users. Details on antiserum etc. are given for the RIA analysis.

5630   Wilson, R. S.; Martin, B. R.; and Dewey, W. L., J. Med. Chem., *22*(7), 879-82 (1979).

Some 11-Substituted Tetrahydrocannabinols. Synthesis and Comparison with the Potent Cannabinoid Metabolites 11-Hydroxytetrahydrocannabinols.

The analgesic and behavioral effects of cannabinoids where a hydrogen on the 11 methyl group was replaced by a methyl, methoxy or amino group were evaluated. SAR was discussed. Replacement of the groups mentioned resulted in less analgesic and behavioral effects than Δ^8-THC. Reasons are discussed.

5631   Wilson, R. S.; May, E. L.; and Dewey, W. L., J. Med. Chem., *22*(7), 886-88 (1979).

Some 9-Hydroxycannabinoid-like Compounds. Synthesis and Evaluation of Analgesic and Behavioral Properties.

Substitution of an OH group for the 9-methyl group and a carbonyl group for the *gem*-dimethyl resulted in biological activity unlike other cannabinoids. SARs of OH groups in the 9 position were carried out. Analgesic and behavioral properties were measured. Some of these compounds may represent a new class of CNS depressants.

5632 Wing, D. R.; and Paton, W. D. M., Biochem. Pharmacol., *28*(2), 253-60 (1979).

Effects of Acute Δ^1-Tetrahydrocannabinol Treatment, of Hypothermia and of Ambient Temperature on Choline Incorporation into Mouse Brain.

Δ^9-THC and phenobarbital depressed choline uptake by mouse brain. Manipulation of ambient temperature revealed that hypothermia played a key role for the above mentioned effects.

Y

5633 Yount, R., J. Amer. Med. Ass., *242*(23), 2558 (1979).

Methaqualone Sprinkled on Marijuana. (Letter)

Incidence of methaqualone smoking, alone or over marihuana, was reported.

Z

5634 Zaluzny, S. G.; Chesher, G. B.; Jackson, D. M.; and Malor, R., Psychopharmacology, *61*(2), 207-16 (1979).

The Attenuation by Δ^9-Tetrahydrocannabinol and Morphine of the Quasi-Morphine Withdrawal Syndrome in Rats.

Phosphodiesterase inhibitor and naloxone treatment precipitated morphine-like withdrawal syndrome. Syndrome was significantly antagonized by Δ^9-THC and morphine.

5635 Zimmerman, A. M.; Bruce, W. R.; and Zimmerman, S., Pharmacology, *18*(3), 143-38 (1979).

Effects of Cannabinoids on Sperm Morphology.

Mice treated with CBN and Δ^9-THC had a significantly higher number of abnormal sperm as compared to control values. CBD had no effect.

5636 Zimmerman, A. M.; Zimmerman, S.; and Raj, A. Y., pp. 407-18 in *Marihuana: Biological Effects*. Advances in the Biosciences, Vols. 22-23, edited by G. G. Nahas and W. D. M. Paton. NY, Pergamon Press, 1979.

Effects of Cannabinoids on Spermatogenesis in Mice.

Long term effects of 5 daily treatments with Δ^9-THC (5 and 10 mg/kg) or CBN (10 and 25 mg/kg) included a higher percentage of abnormally shaped sperm heads. Cytological evaluation revealed increased ring and chain translocation.

5637 Zinberg, N. E., J. Psychedelic Drugs, *11*(1-2), 135-44 (1979).

On Cannabis and Health.

The author criticizes the American abstinence-oriented culture in relation to marihuana and other drugs used. Social forces should be realistic and reasonable in dealing with the issue.

U. S. PATENTS

5638   Aaron, Herbert S.; and Ferguson, C. P., Jr. (United States Dept. of the Army) 1-Acetoxy-3-(substituted alkyl)-6, 6, 9-trimethyl-7, 8, 9, 10-tetrahydro-6H-dibenzo [b,d] pyran isomers. U. S. 3,694,464, September 26, 1972.

The synthesis of the title compound is described and claimed as an incapacitating agent (in monkeys).

5639   Adams, Roger, Optically Active Tetrahydrodibenzopyrans Having Marihuana Activity and Process for Making Same. U. S. 2,419,934, May 6, 1947.

The use of pulegone with resorcinols is patented in the preparation of 3-alkyl $\Delta^{6a,10a}$-THC's.

5640   Adams, Roger, Marihuana Active Compounds. U. S. 2,419,935, May 6, 1947.

The process of using cyclohexanone-2-carboxylate with resorcinols is patented in the preparation of 3-alkyl $\Delta^{6a,10a}$-THC's.

5641   Adams, Roger, Preparation of Compounds with Marihuana Activity. U. S. 2,419,936, May 6, 1947.

The process of converting CBD to THC with various acid catalyists is patented. Also the products, Δ^{8}- and Δ^{9}-THC are claimed.

5642   Adams, Roger, Marihuana Active Compounds. U. S. 2,419,937, May 6, 1947.

Hexahydrocannabinols with varying groups at the 3-position are patented. The reduction product of Δ^{9}-THC is claimed.

5643   Adams, Roger, Dibenzopyran Marihuana-Like Compounds. U. S. 2,509,386, May 30, 1950.

The $\Delta^{6a,10a}$-THC with branched 3-alkyl groups are claimed.

5644   Adams, Roger, Dibenzopyran Marihuana-Like Compounds. U. S. 2,509,387, May 30, 1950.

The $\Delta^{6a,10a}$-THC with multi-alkyl substituents on the 3-alkyl side chain are claimed.

5645   Anonymous (Brit. 1,165,025; Sterling Drug) Psychotropic 8-alkyl-10-hydroxy-5, 5-dimethyl-1, 2, 3, 4-tetrahydro-5H-[1] benzopyrano [4, 3-c] pyridines. U. S. 3,535,327; 3,576,798; 3,632,595. September 24, 1969.

The subject compound is a 9-aza-$\Delta^{6a,10a}$-THC type derivative.

5646   Archer, Robert A. (Eli Lilly and Co.) Hexahydrodibenzo [b,d] pyran-9-ones. U. S. 3,953,603, April 27, 1976.

The synthesis of dl-trans-nabilone was described.

5647   Archer, Robert A. (Eli Lilly and Co.) Hexahydrodibenzo [b,d] pyran-9-ones as an Anti-Anxiety Drug. U. S. 3,928,598, December 23, 1975.

Nabilone synthesis and use is described.

5648   Archer, Robert A. (Eli Lilly and Co.) Hexahydrodibenzo [b,d] pyran-9-ones as Analgesic Drugs. U. S. 3,944,673, March 16, 1976.

Nabilone as an analgesic is described.

5649   Archer, Robert A. (Eli Lilly and Co.) Dihydroxyhexahydrodibenzo- [b,d] pyrans. U. S. 3,968,125, July 6, 1979.

The compounds of the nabilone class in which the 9-keto group is reduced to a 9-hydroxyl group are patented. These new compounds are analgesic, sedative, antidepressant and anti-anxietic agents.

5650 Archer, Robert A. (Eli Lilly and Co.) Hexahydrodibenzo [b,d] pyran-9-ones as Sedative Drugs. U.S. 3,987,188, October 19, 1976.

Nabilone was prepared and described as an analgesic and sedative. See also U.S. 3,928,598.

5651 Archer, Robert A. (Eli Lilly and Co.) Reducing Elevated Blood Pressure with Dihydroxyhexahydrodibenzo [b,d] pyrans. U.S. 4,024,275, May 17, 1977.

Nabilone and its metabolite which is the reduced ketone to 9-hydroxy compound were synthesized and described as an antihypertensive agent. See U.S. 3,968,125.

5652 Archer, Robert A.; and Day, William A. (Eli Lilly and Co.) Preparation of Optically Active *trans*-Hexahydrodibenzopyranones. U.S. 4,075,230, February 21, 1978.

Apoverbenone was used to prepare optically active nabilone.

5653 Archer, Robert A.; and Day, William A. (Eli Lilly and Co.) Stereoselective Preparation of Hexahydro Dibenzopyranones and Intermediates Therefor. U.S. 4,102,902, July 25, 1978.

A process is patented for the preparation of optically active *cis*-nabilone and related compounds by reacting norpinanone with a resorcinol followed by cylization to give the product.

5654 Archer, Robert A.; and Lemberger, Louis (Eli Lilly and Co.) Hexahydrodibenzo [b,d] pyran-9-ones as Antiemetic Drugs U.S. 4,087,545, May 2, 1978.

A therapeutic process is claimed for the use of nabilone as an antiemetic drug.

5655 Archer, Robert A.; and Lemberger, Louis (Eli Lilly and Co.) Hexahydrodibenzo [b,d] pyran-9-ones as Antiemetic Drugs. U.S. 4,087,546, May 2, 1978.

A therapeutic process is claimed for the use of nabilone as a drug to relieve asthma.

5656 Archer, Robert A.; and Lemberger, Louis (Eli Lilly and Co.) Hexahydrodibenzo [b,d] pyran-9-ones in Treatment of Glaucoma. U.S. 4,087,547, May 2, 1978.

A therapeutic claim is made for the use of nabilone in the treatment of glaucoma.

5657 Archer, Robert A.; and Lemberger, Louis (Eli Lilly and Co.) Hexahydrodibenzo [b,d] pyran-9-ones as Anticonvulsant Drugs. U.S. 4,088,777, May 9, 1978.

A therapeutic process claim is made for the use of nabilone as an anticonvulsant agent.

5658 Archer, Robert A.; and McMillan, Moses W. (Eli Lilly and Co.) Benzocycloheptapyrans, Compositions, and Method of Treatment. U.S. 4,152,451, May 1, 1979.

The claimed compounds are those in which the ring C of the cannabinoids are expended one carbon to a 7-membered ring.

5659 Bindra, Jasjit S. (Pfizer Inc.) 9-Hydroxydibenzo [b,d] pyrans and Intermediates. U.S. 4,143,139, March 6, 1979.

The claimed compounds are 9-hydroxy or 9-keto-dibenzopyrans with the 3-substituent being connected directly or through an O,S,SO, or SO_2. Another variation in the 3-substituent may have the foregoing elements in the alkylene group.

5660   Blanchard, William B.; and Ryan, Charles W. (Eli Lilly and Co.) Process for Converting *cis*-Hexahydrodibenzo [*b,d*] pyran-9-ones to *trans*-Hexahydrodibenzo [*b,d*]-pyran-9-ones. U.S. 4,054,582, October 18, 1977.

A process for the conversion of a *cis*-6*a*, 10*a* dibenzopyran-9-one to the *trans* using aluminum halide is described. More specifically the process converts *cis*-nabilone to the more active *trans*-nabilone.

5661   Bolger, James W. (Rexall Drug and Chemical Co.) Substituted 3-Hydroxydibenzopyrans. U.S. 3,325,489, June 13, 1967.

The Mannich reaction is used to prepare $\Delta^{6a,10a}$-THC's with alkyl amino methyl groups on the 4 position. There are 14 such compounds claimed.

5662   Bolger, James W. (Rexall Drug and Chemical Co.) Substituted 1-Hydroxydibenzopyrans. U.S. 3,325,490, June 13, 1957.

The Mannich reaction is used to prepare a series of $\Delta^{6a,10a}$-THC's in which the mono and dialkylaminomethyl group is at position 2. There are 16 such compounds claimed.

5663   Bullock, Francis J. (Arthur D. Little, Inc.) Method for Detecting and Quantitating the Presence of Cannabinoids and Analogs Thereof in Biological Materials and Resulting Products. U.S. 3,656,906 April 18, 1972.

The cannabinoids are condensed with malic acid so as to form an additional lactone ring from the 2-carbon and the phenolic hydroxyl with fluorescenes so that the detection of as little as 0.6 micrograms of the cannabinoid is possible.

5664   Day, William A.; and Lavagnino, Edward R. (Eli Lilly and Co.) *dl-cis*-1-Hydroxy-3-substituted-6, 6-dimethyl-6, 6a, 7, 8, 10, 10a-hexahydro-9H-dibenzo [*b,d*] pyran-9-ones. U. S. 4,148,809, April 10, 1979.

See U. S. Patent No. 4,131,614 for the synthesis of the subject compound. This patent claims the process of converting it to the *trans* compound or nabilone.

5665   Day, William A.; and Lavagnino, Edward R. (Eli Lilly and Co.) 9-Amino-Dibenzopyrans. U. S. 4,152,450, May 1, 1979.

The 9-amino compounds are prepared from the 9-keto derivatives by reacting with hydroxylamine to give the oximes which on reduction give the amines.

5666   Dren, Anthony Thomas; and Ebert, Donn Myron (Abbott Laboratories) Anesthesia Methods Using Benzopyrans and Esters Thereof as Pre-Anesthesia Medication. U. S. 4,025,630, May 24, 1977.

The benzopyranopyridines or 9-aza-type cannabinoids as the amino esters are claimed as adjuvants for halothane in general anesthesia. The therapeutic claims are very narrow but the disclosure is extensive with 119 examples. See patent No. 3,941,782.

5667   Elsohly, Mahmoud A.; and Turner, Carlton E., Paraquat Detection in Marihuana. U. S. 4,187,076, February 5, 1980.

Paraquat in marihuana was converted to 4,4-bipyridine by pyrolysis and detected as a dark reddish-orange color with Dragendorff reagent.

5668   Eschenmoser, Albert; Petrzilka, Theodor, Manufacture of 2-Substituted Resorcinol Derivatives. U. S. 3,562,312, February

434

9, 1971.

cis and *trans*-Cannabidiol were prepared without acid catalyst by reacting mentha-2,8-dien-1-ol with olivetol in the presence of dimethylforamide dineopentyl acetal.

5669   Fager, Earl E.; and Wideburg, Norman E. (Abbott Laboratories) 1,4'-Dihydroxy-3-*n*-pentyl-6, 6, 9-trimmethyl-6a, 7, 10, 10a-tetrahydrodibenzo [*b,d*] pyran. U. S. 3,808,234, April 30, 1974.

The compound 4'-OH-Δ^8-THC was produced by microbial transformation of Δ^8-THC. See U. S. 3,822,188.

5670   Fager, Earl Elmer; and Wideburg, Norman Earl (Abbott Laboratories) Method of Producing 1,4'-Dihydroxy-3-*n*-pentyl-6,6, 9-trimethyl-6a, 7, 10, 10a-tetrahydro-dibenzo [*b,d*] pyran. U. S. 3,822,188, July 2, 1974.

The method is claimed for the synthesis of 4'-OH-Δ^8-THC using microorganisms.

5671   Fahrenholtz, Kenneth E. (Hoffmann-La Roche Inc.) 7, 10-Dihydro-3-alkyl-6H-dibenzo[*b,d*] pyran-6, 9-(8H)-diones and 5-hydroxy-7-alkyl-4-chromanones. U. S. 3,636,058, January 18, 1972.

This is a division of U. S. 3,507,885 and describes the synthesis of the subject compounds and their conversion to *dl*-Δ^8- and *dl*-Δ^9-THC.

5672   Fahrenholtz, Kenneth Earl (Hoffmann-La Roche Inc.) 3-Alkyl-6H-dibenzo [*b,d*] pyrans. U. S. 3,507,885, April 21, 1970.

The synthesis of Δ^8-, Δ^9-, $\Delta^{9,11}$-THC is described. Also the 9-keto and 9-chloro-9-methyl derivatives are claimed. The total synthesis used gives racemic compounds.

5673   Fukuda, David S.; Abbott, Bernard J.; and Archer, Robert A. (Eli Lilly and Co.) Novel 3-(Oxygenated alkyl)-1, 9-dihydroxy and 1-Hydroxy-9-keto dibenzo [*b,d*] pyrans. U. S. 4,064,009, December 20, 1977.

Nabilone or its metabolite is oxygenated using the micro-organism, *Bacillus cereus*, to give a hydroxyl or keto group on the carbon next to the terminal methyl group in the 3-alkyl side chain.

5674   Harris, Louis Selig; Pars, Harry G.; Razdan, Raj K.; and Sheehan, John Clark (Sharps Associates) Heterocyclic Esters of Benzopyrans. U. S. 3,941,782, March 2, 1976.

The basic amino esters of a large number of synthetic benzopyrans were prepared and their water soluble salt described as pharmaceutically acceptable forms.

5675   Hughes, Gordon A.; Jen, Timothy Y.; and Smith, Herchel (American Home Products Corp.) Oxaphenanthrenes and their Intermediates. U. S. 3,576,887, April 27, 1971.

The total synthesis *dl*-Δ^8-THC and its resolution to give (-), *trans*-Δ^8-THC is claimed.

5676   Johnson, M. Ross (Pfizer Inc.) Hexahydro-1-hydroxy-9-hydroxymethyl-3-substituted-6H-dibenzo [*b,d*] pyrans. U. S. 4,209,520, June 24, 1980.

The synthesis of the subject compound in which the 3-phenyl-alkoxy groups were related to the mantradol type.

5677   Johnson, Michael R. (Pfizer Inc.) Hexahydro-1-hydroxy-9-hydroxymethyl-3-substituted-6H-dibenzo [*b,d*] pyrans as Analgesic Agents. U. S. 4,133,819, January 9, 1979.

A series of hexahydro-9-hydroxymethyl dibenzopyrans were prepared with varying 3-substitments. These new compounds were patented and had analgesic activity.

5678 Korte, Friedrich-Wilhelm A. G. K.; and Coulston, Frederick (Abbott Laboratories) Tri-Cyclic Compounds Derived from Thiaphloroglucinol Ethers. U. S. 4,025,536, May 24, 1977.

Both Δ^8- and Δ^9-THC compounds in which the 3-alkyl is replaced with RS-group are claimed.

5679 Lee, Cheuk Man (Abbott Laboratories) 5H[1] Benzopyrano [3,4-d] pyridines. U. S. 3,878,219, Appl. July 13, 1973.

The synthesis is described for the 9-azo CBN types with various 3-alkyl groups. These compounds have analgesic activity.

5680 Lee, Cheuk Man; Michaels, Raymond John; and Harris, Louis Selig (Abbott Laboratories) 9-Hydroxy-7, 8, 9, 10-tetrahydro-6H, dibenzo[b] [d] pyrans and pyranones. U. S. 4,066,667, January 3, 1978.

The subject compounds were synthesized and claimed. The side chain in position 3 is varied.

5681 Lee, Cheuk Man; and Zaugg, Harold Elmer (Abbott Laboratories) 10-Amino-5b-[1] benzopyrano [4, 3-c] pyridines. U. S. 4,111,942, September 5, 1978.

The phenolic hydroxy group is replaced with an amino group in the 9-azo type compound. See patent No. 3,886,184.

5682 Loev, Bernard (Smith Kline Corporation) Dibenzo [b,d] pyran Compounds. U. S. 3,799,946, March 26, 1974.

A number of cannabinols are claimed which are prepared by dehydrogenation of $\Delta^{6a,10a}$-THC derivatives such as DMHP.

5683 Loev, Bernard (Smith Kline Corporation) 2-Aminomethyl Dibenzo [b,d] pyrans. U. S. 3,856,820, December 24, 1974.

A large number of compounds were prepared by treating various cannabinols or $\Delta^{6a,10a}$- or Δ^8- or Δ^9-THC with formaldehyde and an amine (Mannich reaction) to introduce a group in the 2-position such as 2-dimethylamino-methyl-Δ^8-THC or 2-dimethylamino-methyl-DMHP.

5684 Loev, Bernard (Smith Kline Corporation) Alkoxy Dibenzo [b,d] pyrans. U. S. 3,856,821, December 24, 1974.

Compounds were prepared and claimed in which the 3-alkyl group is replaced with a 3-alkoxy group of CBN, $\Delta^{6a,10a}$-THC, Δ^8-THC and/or Δ^9-THC.

5685 Loev, Bernard (Smith Kline Corporation) Dibenzo [b,d] pyrans. U. S. 3,856,823, December 24, 1974.

Compounds were prepared and claimed in which the 3-alkyl groups were varied but more importantly the phenolic hydroxyl (1-OH) was removed or replaced by hydrogen. Removal of the hydroxyl group was by reduction of 1-dimethylthionecarbamate derivative.

5686 Lyle, Robert E., Jr.; Razdan Raj K.; Granchelli, Felix E.; and Pars, Harry G. (Arthur D. Little, Inc.) 1,4-Ethano-5H-[1] benzopyrano[3,4-b] pyridines. U. S. 3,493,579, February 3, 1970.

The condensation of ethyl 3-quinu-clidinone-2-carboxylate with resorcinols gives the subject compound. These compounds are 7-aza-$\Delta^{6a,10a}$-THC types.

5687 Matsumoto, Ken; and Archer, Robert A. (Eli Lilly and Co.) Aminodibenzo[*b,d*] pyrans. U. S. 3,886,184, May 27, 1975.

An amino group of $\Delta^{6a,10a}$-THC and hexahydro compounds with various 3-alkyl side chains were prepared by replacing the phenolic hydroxyl group with an amino group.

5688 Pars, Harry G.; and Granchelli Felix E. (Arthur D. Little, Inc.) Novel 6-Oxo-7, 8, 9, 10-tetrahydro-6H-dibenzo[*b,d*] pyrans. U. S. 3,654,312, April 4, 1972.

The subject compounds are claimed in which the 3-position carries an alkyl group with an amino substitution thereon. These are useful in the synthesis of water soluble salts of $\Delta^{6a,10a}$-THC.

5689 Pars, Harry G.; and Granchelli, Felix E. (Arthur D. Little, Inc.) 7, 8, 9, 10-Tetrahydro-6H-dibenzo [*b,d*] pyrans. U. S. 3,676,462, July 11, 1972.

The synthesis of $\Delta^{6a,10a}$-THC in which the 3-alkyl group is dimethylamino-ethyl. See U. S. 3,654,312 for the patent on the intermediates.

5690 Pars, Harry G.; Granchelli, Felix E.; and Razdan Raj K. (Arthur D. Little, Inc.) Psychotropic 5-Oxo-1, 2, 3, 4-tetrahydro-5H-[1] benzopyrano [3,4-*c*] pyridine Cardiovascular Agents. U. S. 3,514,464, May 26, 1970.

The subject compound is an 8-aza-$\Delta^{6a,10a}$-THC type derivative.

5691 Pars, Harry G.; Granchelli, Felix E.; and Razdan Raj K. (Arthur D. Little, Inc.) 1, 2, 3, 4-Tetrahydro-5H-[1]-benzopyranol [3,4-*c*] pyridines. U. S. 3,635,993, January 18, 1972.

The claimed subject compound is an 8-aza-$\Delta^{6a,10a}$-THC type derivative.

5692 Pars, Harry G. and Razdan, Raj K. (Arthur D. Little, Inc.) 4, 4-Dimethyl-9-Hydroxy-7-(3-methyl-2-octyl)-1, 2, 3, 4-Tetrahydrobenzopyrano [3,4-*c*] pyrroles. U. S. 3,888,946, Appl. July 17, 1969.

Compounds in which a pyrrol ring replaced one of the benzo rings were synthesized and were central depressant, psychotropic and antihypertensive agents.

5693 Petrzilka, Theodor, 6a,10a-*trans*-6a, 7, 10, 10a-Tetrahydrodibenzo[*b,d*]-pyran Production. U. S. 3,560,528, February 2, 1971.

cis or *trans* (+) Menth-2, 8-dien-1-ol gave (-) *trans* Δ^8-THC when reacted with olivetol. The reaction of olivetol with (d,1) *p*-menth-1, 5, 8-triene gave d,1-Δ^8-THC.

5694 Petrzilka, Theodor, Process of Producing 6a, 10a-*trans*-6a, 7, 8, 10a-Tetrahydro-dibenzo[*b,d*]-pyrans. U. S. 3,668,224, June 6, 1972.

The process is claimed for the synthesis of Δ^9-THC by converting Δ^8-THC to the 9-chloro and then using potassium *t*-amylate.

5695 Petrzilka, Theodor (Swiss 497,416) Dibenzo[*b,d*] pyrans. U. S. 3,833,616, November 30, 1970.

The synthesis of both Δ^8- and Δ^9-THC in which the 3-alkyl group is replaced by a chloro group is covered.

5696 Petrzilka, Theodor, Tetrahydrodibenzo-pyrans. U. S. 3,873,576, March 25, 1975.

From Δ^8-THC was prepared the diacetate of 8-OH-$\Delta^{9,11}$-THC which was rearranged with heat and hydrolyzed to 11-OH-Δ^8-THC, a metabolite.

5697 Petrzilka, Theodor, 6a,10a-*trans*-6a, 10, 10a-Tetrahydrodibenzo[*b,d*]-pyrans. U.S. 3,920,705, November 18, 1975.

The synthesis of Δ^8-THC with various alkyl groups in the 3-position is described using menthadienol.

5698 Razdan, Raj K.; Dalzell, Haldean C.; and Pars, Harry G. (SISA Inc.) Composition for Treating Glaucoma. U.S. 4,126,694, November 21, 1978.

A method of treatment of wide angle glaucoma with the dialkylamino butyric acid ester of $\Delta^{6a,10a}$-THC in which the 3-alkyl group is methyl.

5699 Razdan, Raj K.; and Dalzell, Haldean Cloyce (The John C. Sheehan Institute for Research, Inc.) Process for the Preparation of (-)-6a, 10a-*trans*-6a, 7, 8, 10a-Tetrahydrodibenzo[*b,d*] pyrans. U.S. 4,025,516, May 24, 1977.

The Petrzilka method (U. S. 3,560,224) is modified and anhydrous magnesium sulfate is added to give Δ^9-THC in a one-step process.

5700 Razdan, Raj K.; and Dalzell, Haldean Cloyce (Sharps Associates) Benzopyrans Having an Unsaturated Side Chain. U. S. 4,036,857, July 19, 1971.

The claimed compounds are Δ^8-THC type in which the side chain in position 3 is unsaturated. The 3-formyl-Δ^8-THC synthesis is described.

5701 Razdan, Raj K.; and Dalzell, Haldean Cloyce (Sheehan Institute for Research, Inc.) Process for the Preparation of (-)-6a, 10a-*trans*-6a, 7, 8, 10a-Tetrahydrodibenzo[*b,d*]-pyrans. U. S. 4,116,979, September 26, 1978.

A process is patented for the conversion of iso-CBD, 4-(*p*-mentha-1, 8-dien-3-yl)

olivetol, to Δ^9-THC. See patent No. 4,025,516.

5702 Razdan, Raj K.; Dalzell, Haldean Cloyce; and Herlihy, Patricia (Sharps Associates) Oxo C-Ring Benzopyrans. U. S. 4,051,152, September 27, 1977.

The patent involves the oxidation of $\Delta^{6a,10a}$, benzopyran with ceric ammonium nitrate to give 7-oxo-$\Delta^{6a,10a}$-benzopyrans.

5703 Razdan, Raj K.; Dalzell, Haldean C.; Terris, Barbara Z.; and Pars, Harry G. (SISA Incorporated) Anti-Glaucoma Composition and Method. U. S. 4,126,695, November 21, 1978.

The method of treating wide angle glaucoma with topical preparation of Δ^9-, Δ^8, and $\Delta^{6a,10a}$-THC in which the 3-alkyl group is from 1 to 4-carbon atoms.

5704 Razdan, Raj K.; Granchelli, Felix E.; and Pars, Harry G. (Arthur D. Little, Inc.) 1, 2, 3, 4-Tetrahydro- and 1, 2, 3, 4, 12, 13-hexahydrocyclopenta[*c*] [1] benzopyrans. U. S. 3,639,427, February 1, 1972.

The claimed subject compound with a 5 membered ring is a $\Delta^{6a,9a}$ type derivative.

5705 Razdan, Raj K.; and Handrick, Richard (The United States of America as Represented by the Secretary of the Department of Health, Education and Welfare) Direct Synthesis of (-)-*trans*-Δ^9-Tetrahydrocannabinol from Olivetol and (+)-*trans*-Δ^2-Carene Oxide. U. S. 3,734,930, May 22, 1973.

A method is claimed for the synthesis of (-) *trans*-Δ^9-THC, *cis*-Δ^9-THC, and Δ^8-THC and the separation by vapor phase chromatography.

5706   Razdan, Raj K.; and Pars, Harry G. (Arthur D. Little, Inc.) Novel Derivatives of Tetrahydrocannabinol. U. S. 3,649,650, March 14, 1972.

Phenolic ethers are claimed in which the 1-hydroxy group is replaced with 1-dialkylaminoalkoxy group of Δ^9-, Δ^8- and $\Delta^{6a,10a}$-THC. Acid addition salts and quaternary ammonium salts are claimed.

5707   Razdan, Raj K.; and Pars, Harry G. (Arthur D. Little, Inc.) Thienobenzopyrans and Thiopyranobenzopyrans. U.S. 3,883,551, May 13, 1975.

The subject compounds in which sulfur replaces various carbon atoms were prepared.

5708   Ryan, Charles W. (Eli Lilly and Co.) Process for Preparing cis-Hexahydrodibenzopyranones. U. S. 4,131,614, December 26, 1978.

The claimed subject compounds encompass the "cis" form of nabilone to the more active nabilone ("trans" form). See U. S. patent No. 4,054,582.

5709   Ryan, Charles W. (Eli Lilly and Co.) 2,6-Methano-2H-1-benzoxocins. U. S. 4,140,701, February 20, 1979.

The preparation of 1-alkoxy-4-(1-hydroxy-1-methylethyl) 1,4-cyclohexadiene and condensation with various 5-substituted resorcinols was described. See U. S. patent No. 4,131,614.

5710   Taylor, Edward C.; and Lenard, Katherine, Dibenzo[b,d]pyrans and Process. U. S. 3,388,136, June 11, 1968.

A process for the preparation of Δ^8- and Δ^9-THC with varying size side chain at the 3 position is claimed in which citral is reacted with the resorcinols. Both cis and trans isomers at 6a, 10a position are claimed.

5711   Twitchett, Peter J.; and Williams, Peter L. (National Research Development Corp.) Methods and Apparatus for Liquid Chromatography. U. S. 4,233,030, November 11, 1980.

Substances (as cannabinol) are subjected to photolysis in the translucent tube during HPLC to produce compounds detectable by conventional fluorescence.

5712.   Winn, Martin (Abbott Laboratories) Heterocyclic Esters of Alkylphenyl Benzopyrans. U. S. 4,049,653, September 20, 1977.

The claimed compounds are amino esters that form water soluble hydrochlorides but more distinctive are the substituted phenyl groups in the 3-alkyl side chain.

5713   Winn, Martin; Lynn, Kathleen R.; Martin, Yvonne Connolly (Abbott Laboratories) Aralkylbenzopyrans. U. S. 3,901,926, October 17, 1974.

Claimed herein are compounds of $\Delta^{6a,10a}$-THC type compounds with larger alkyl groups in the 3-position which encompass a fluorophenyl group.

5714   Winn, Martin; Razdan, Raj k.; Dalzell Haldean Cloyce; and Krei, Joyce Ruth (Sharps Associates) Alkyl Substituted Cyclopenta Benzopyrans. U. S. 3,929,835, December 30, 1975.

The five membered ring compounds of the subject compounds were prepared

5715   Zaugg, Harold E.; and Lee, Cheuk M. (Abbott Laboratories) 2,8-Disubstituted-10-hydroxy-5, 5-dimethyl-1, 2, 3, 4 tetrahydro-5H-[1] benzopyrano [4,3-c] pyridine. U. S. 4,137,232, January 30, 1979.

The claimed compounds are the 9-aza $\Delta^{6a,10a}$THC types.

AUTHOR INDEX

Referenced by annotation number.

Aaro, B., 4696
Aaron, Herbert S., 5638
Aasen, A., 3671, 4580
Abbasi, A. S., 5008
Abbott, B. J., 3178, 3786, 5292
Abbott, Bernard J., 5673
Abbott, S. R., 3179, 5273
Abboud, R. T., 3180
Abel, E. L., 3181, 3182, 3183, 3184, 3185, 3186, 3187, 5274, 5275, 5276
Abraham, D. J., 4294
Abrams, A. A., 5444
Abrams, J. H., 5273
Abruzzi, W., 3188
Abu-Shumays, A., 3179
Aceto, M. D., 4378
Ackerman, M. J., 3386
Ackerman, N. R., 3189
Acosta-Urquidi, J., 3190
Adamec, C., 3191
Adamec, C. S., 3192
Adams, A. J., 3193, 3194, 3195, 3196, 3403, 3404, 3746, 3747
Adams, L. D., 5578
Adams, M. D., 3197, 3198, 3199, 3663, 3664, 4378
Adams, P. M., 3046, 3200, 3201, 3202
Adams, Roger, 5639, 5640, 5641, 5642, 5643, 5644
Adams, T. C., Jr., 3203
Adler, K. B., 5363
Agarwal, S. S., 3092
Agnew, W. F., 3204
Agrawal, M. 3622
Agrell, J., 3205
Agurell, S., 3206, 3207, 3208, 3209, 4221, 4373, 4374, 4375, 4551, 4552, 4553, 4564, 4565, 4566, 4728, 4729, 5228, 5229, 5230, 5231, 5232, 5277, 5278, 5402, 5527, 5528, 5532, 5533, 5556
Ahluwalia, B. S., 5544
Aiken, J. W., 3765
Akasu, M., 4037

Akins, F., 3515, 4094
Akins, F. R., 5469
Al-Marashi, M. S. H., 3767
Albert, J.-M., 3218
Albrecht, S. L., 3047
Aldinger, G., 3715
Aldrich, M. R., 3210
Aldridge, J. W., 3211
Alessandro, A., 3212
Alexander, G., 4391
Alexander, P. C., 3213, 3533, 3534
Aliapoulios, M. A., 3094, 3915
Alikaridis, F., 4950
Alikaridis, P., 3214, 5279
Alker, P. C., 4519
Allen, J. W., 4225
Allen, L. V., 3215
Allen, T., 3216
Alli, B. A., 3217
Alpert, M., 3367
Altman, J. L., 3218, 5280
Alvares, A. P., 3219
Amat-y-Leon, F., 4464
Amato, A., 5257
Ambrose, A. M., 3441
Ambrosetto, G., 5018
Amerson, E. W., 3520, 5253
Ames, F., 4259
Ames, F. R., 5281
Amit, Z., 3220
Anand, N., 4342, 4343, 4344
Anderson, E., 3221
Anderson, M., 3598
Anderson, P. F., 3222
Anderson, W. A., 3108
Anderson-Baker, W. C., 5282
Andouze, A. L., 3533
Andrassy, E., 3711
Andre, C., 3223
Andrews, J., 3224
Andrysiak, T., 5283
Angst, J., 4855, 4856
Annis, H. M., 3048, 4174, 4175

Anokhina, I. P., 3225

Anonymous, 3049, 3226, 3227, 3228, 3229, 3230, 3231, 3232, 3233, 3234, 3235, 3236, 3237, 3238, 3239, 3240, 3241, 3242, 3243, 3244, 3245, 3246, 3247, 3248, 3249, 3250, 3251, 3252, 3253, 3254, 3255, 3256, 3257, 3258, 5248, 5284, 5285, 5286, 5287, 5288, 5289, 5645

Anonymous, R. N., 5290

Antypos, E., 3372

Appel, J. B., 3869, 5280

Aqleh, K., 3309, 3310

Aqleh, K. A., 3311

Archer, J., 5291

Archer, R., 4249

Archer, R. A., 3178, 3259, 3260, 3786, 4959, 5292

Archer, Robert A., 5646, 5647, 5648, 5649, 5650, 5651, 5652, 5653, 5654, 5655, 5656, 5657, 5658, 5673, 5687

Arendsen, D., 5218

Armaganidis, A., 4497, 5279, 5293

Armand, J.-P., 3132, 4523

Armand, J. P., 4533

Armstrong, T. A., 4757

Arnold, K. P., 4155

Arnone, A., 3261, 3262

Aronow, W. S., 3263, 3837, 4664, 4665

Arora, S., 3889

Arrigo Reina, R., 3264

Arya, M., 3620, 3621

Asch, R. H., 3265, 3729, 4896, 5294, 5295, 5296, 5297, 5582

Asher, J., 5178

Askew, W. E., 3050

Atrault-Jarrier, M., 3438

Aucelio, J. G., 4765, 5114, 5131

Aulakh, C. S., 5541

Auld, J., 3266

Aust, M., 3650

Austin, G. A., 3267, 3268

Avakian, E. V., 5298

Avato, F., 4484

Avery, D. H., 3409, 4560, 4562

Ayalon, D., 3269

Aye, U. T., 3270

Ayhan, I. H., 4152, 5299

Ayrault-Jarrier, M., 5065

Babor, T. F., 3271, 3272, 3273, 3274, 32 3276, 3277, 3870, 4429, 4432, 4433

Babst, D. V., 3278

Babu, R., 3279

Bach, D., 3280, 3281, 3282

Bachman, J., 5301, 5310

Bachman, J. A., 5302

Bachman, J. G., 4086, 5451

Bachmann, E. W., 5300

Backhouse, C., 5026

Backhouse, C. I., 3283

Backman, J., 4111

Bader-Bartfai, A., 3208

Bahr, R., 3284

Baile, C. A., 4154, 5117, 5282, 5461, 5491, 5

Bailey, K., 3285, 3286

Bailey, P. T., 3140, 5541

Bailey, R., 4039

Baker, B., 3287

Baker, J. R., 4740, 4741, 5383

Baker, P. B., 3288, 5386

Bakkenist, N., 3055

Balet, F. N., 4932

Ballas, C., 4968

Baloh, R. W., 5303

Balster, R. L., 3289, 3384, 3452, 3753, 3 3755, 4377, 5331

Bami, H. L., 4539, 4540

Banchereau, J., 5304

Bando, S., 4818

Banerjee, A., 3290

Banerjee, B. N., 3291, 3292, 5585

Banerjee, S. P., 3293

Banerji, A., 3294

Bannerjee, A., 3809

Baram, D. A., 3134, 4561, 4563

Baranano, M. T., 4616

Barnes, B. O., 3213

Barnes, G. E., 4175

Barofsky, I., 5335

Barr, M., Jr., 4228

Barratt, E. S., 3046, 3200, 3201, 3202

Barreuther, A., 5305

Barry, G. T., 4003

Barry, H., 3295, 3296, 3297, 4203, 4204, 4 4857, 4919, 4922, 4925

Bartke, A., 3568, 3569, 5359

Bartl, K., 3298

Bartle, K. D., 3299, 4238, 4555
Bartova, A., 3300, 3342
Bartram, S. F., 4282
Batra, S. W. T., 3301
Batterman, S., 3960, 3961, 3962, 3963, 4345
Battistich, V. A., 3302
Baumann, P. A., 3115
Baumann, U., 4856
Bauminger, S., 3269
Baxter, A. S., 5364
Bay, K. S., 5170
Bayse, D., 5520
Baytop, T., 3303
Bazzaz, F. A., 3304
Beaconsfield, P., 3051
Beahrs, J. O., 3052
Bearden, W. G., 5306
Bearden, W. O., 3305, 3306, 5221
Beautrais, A. L., 3307
Beck, E. C., 4270, 4626
Becker, B., 5405
Becker, B. M., 3308
Beckner, J., 4381
Beckner, J. S., 3610, 3754, 4080, 4379, 4380
Beckstead, H. D., 4887
Bedell, S. E., 5307
Belgrave, B. E., 5308, 5309
Bell, M., 3415
Belleau, R., 4026, 4028
Bellville, J. W., 3309, 3310, 3311, 4985, 4986, 5198
Bemporad, B., 5347
Ben-David, M., 4200
Ben-Zvi, Z., 3312, 3313, 4221, 4412, 4413, 5227
Bender, P. E., 5491
Benowitz, N., 4110, 4111, 4227
Benowitz, N. L., 3314, 3315, 3316, 3317, 3318, 3319, 3764, 5302, 5310
Bensemana, D., 3320, 3802
Berant, M., 4688
Bercht, C. A. L., 3053, 3054, 3321, 3322, 4209, 4210, 4297
Berg, J. R., 5273
Bergen, J. R., 3312
Berger, L. H., 3557
Bergquist, E., 4538
Berlo, J. M., 5068, 5070
Bernardi, R., 3261
Bernstein, J. G., 3323, 3868, 4429

Berthiaume, A., 3895, 4218
Bertuletti, G., 3820
Bertulli, G., 3324
Besch, N. F., 3325, 3326, 3327, 4897, 4898, 4899, 5581, 5582, 5583
Besch, P. K., 3325, 3326, 4897, 4898, 4899, 5581, 5583
Besserer, K., 4952
Beuthin, F., 3328
Beutler, J. A., 5311, 5312
Beyer, J. M., 5066
Bhakuni, D. S., 3329
Bhardwaj, S. L., 3092
Bhargava, H. N., 3330, 3331, 3332, 3333, 3334
Bhargava, K. P., 5020
Bhattacharya, P., 3463
Bhattacharya, S. K., 3810, 4872, 5398
Bhattacharyya, A. K., 5541
Bhattacharyya, P., 3462
Bhattacharyya, S. C., 5614
Bickel, P., 3618, 3619, 5239
Bieniek, D., 3335, 4480, 4481
Bier, M. M., 3336
Bigger, J. F., 3857, 3858
Biggs, D. A., 3055, 4575
Billets, S., 3337, 3727, 4720, 5083
Billings, A. A., 4835, 4836
Billings, D. K., 3084
Binder, M., 3207, 3208, 3338, 3339, 3340, 4375, 5313
Bindon, J., 3902, 3903
Bindra, Jasjit S., 5659
Binitie, A., 3341
Bino, T., 3813
Bird, K. D., 5308, 5309
Birmingham, M. K., 3300, 3342
Biswas, B., 3343, 3344, 4652
Bjorkroth, U., 5556
Blackly, P. H., 3345
Blaine, J. D., 3346, 4054, 4055
Blake, D. A., 5235
Blakey, D., 3347
Blamire, J., 4366, 5494, 5495
Blanchard, W. B., 3259
Blanchard, William B., 5660
Blevins, R. D., 3348, 3349
Blizard, J., 3350
Bloch, E., 3351, 4184, 5392
Bloom, A. S., 3352, 3353, 3354, 3355, 3356, 3357, 3358, 3359, 3360, 3609, 3890

Bloom, R., 3056
Bloomquist, E. R., 3057
Blum, K., 3361
Blumenthal, M., 4409, 5249
Boeren, E. G., 3362, 3363, 3671, 3681, 3682, 5314
Boger, E., 3899
Bogg, R. A., 3364, 3365
Bohlmann, F., 5315
Bohm, B. A., 5346
Bohm, L. R., 5542
Boisio, M. L., 3366
Bolger, James W., 5661, 5662
Bolton, J. R., 4154, 5461
Bond, C. R., 5566
Bond, W. H., 4521
Bondarenko, T. T., 3225
Bondy, G. P., 4567, 4568
Bonfiglio, J. F., 5318
Bonifazi, A., 3788
Bonuccelli, C. M., 5316
Boon, A., 3416
Bopp, B. A., 3640
Borg, J., 3367
Borgen, L. A., 3587
Borison, H. L., 3368, 4316, 5485
Borison, R., 5124
Borison, R. L., 4364
Borys, H., 4148
Borys, H. K., 4034, 4144, 5073, 5317, 5319, 5343, 5457, 5609
Borzelleca, J. F., 4320, 4321, 4322, 4323, 5171, 5172
Bos, R., 3960, 3961, 3962, 3963, 4345
Boucher, F., 3369, 3580, 3581, 4595, 4596
Bouhuys, A., 3370
Boulougouris, J., 4964, 4966
Boulougouris, J. C., 3371, 3372, 4275, 4967, 4968
Bourassa, M., 3068, 3069
Bourdon, R., 3373, 3374, 4792, 5238, 5421, 5572
Bourke, D. I., 4346
Bourn, W. M., 3815, 5318
Boutet, M., 3375, 4758
Bowd, A., 3376, 3377
Bowker, L. H., 3378
Bowman, F. J., 3357, 4914
Bowman, K., 3857, 3858, 3959, 3864

Bowman, K. A., 3866
Boyd, E. H., 3379, 3380, 3381
Boyd, E. S., 3379, 3380, 3381
Bozzetti, L. P., 3346, 4054, 4055
Brachet, P., 3385
Bracs, P., 3382
Bradley, S. G., 3383, 4511, 4668, 5543
Brady, K. T., 3384
Braenden, O. J., 4202
Braithwaite, R. A., 3797
Bram, S., 3385
Brand, S. N., 4613
Branda, L. A., 3386
Brannan, M. D., 3387, 3388
Braude, M., 3467, 3743
Braude, M. C., 3389, 3390, 3391, 3694, 3742, 4303, 4304, 4672, 4673, 4675, 4677, 4678, 4738, 4739, 4742, 4744, 5045, 5226
Braut-Boucher, F., 5320
Brecher, E. M., 3392
Brennan, J. S., 4910
Brenninkmeijer, C. A. M., 4313
Briant, R. H., 5201
Bridges, C. I., 4368
Briggs, A. H., 3361
Bright, T. P., 3393, 3394
Brightwell, D., 4453, 4454, 4460
Brightwell, D. R., 4459, 4461
Brill, H., 3081
Brill, N. G., 4584
Brin, S. C., 5196
Brine, D., 4617, 4618, 5562
Brine, D. R., 4619, 4746, 5146, 5147, 5148, 5149, 5150, 5621, 5622, 5623
Brine, G. A., 5622
Britton, E. L., 3505
Bro, P., 3395
Brody, A. R., 3585, 5363
Brombeer, J., 4955
Bromley, B., 3396
Bromley, B. L., 3397, 3834
Bron, B., 3398, 3399
Brook, J. S., 3400, 3401
Brosius, K., 3353
Brosius, K. K., 3354
Brown, A., 3402
Brown, B., 3194, 3195, 3196, 3403, 3404, 3747
Brown, D. J., 3393, 3394, 3698, 3700, 4325, 4326, 4392, 4393

Brown, J. D., 4661
Brown, J. E., 3405, 3406, 3407
Brown, J. K., 3408
Brown, L. E., 3379, 3380, 3381
Brown, R. D., 4356
Brown, Z. W., 3220
Brownell, B., 5281
Bruce, W. R., 5635
Brugaard, G., 4697
Bruneel, N., 5116
Brunk, S. F., 3409, 4560, 4561, 4562, 4563
Brunnemann, K. D., 3410, 3411, 3991
Brunner, T. F., 3412
Bryant, P. J., 5111, 5112, 5113, 5615
Bryson, J. B., 3109
Buchsbaum, H., 3519
Buckingham, G. A., 3413
Buckley, J. P., 4046, 4047, 4049, 4050, 3051,
    4052, 4289, 5267
Buelke, J., 5155
Bueno, O. F. A., 3414
Bullock, Francis J., 5663
Burch, L. S., 5156
Burdsal, C., 3415
Burgers, P. C., 3416
Burkett, S. R., 3417, 3418
Burns, M., 3419
Burrell, C. D., 3420
Bursey, J. T., 4746, 5149, 5150, 5623
Burstein, S., 3058, 3312, 3313, 3421, 3422,
    3423, 3424, 3425, 3426, 3427, 3428, 3568,
    3569, 4411, 5321, 5322, 5323
Bursuker, I., 3280
Burton, T. A., 5324
Bush, F. W., 5325
Butcher, R. W., 5462, 5463
Butler, J. L., 3429
Butler, J. R., 3430, 4712
Butler, M. C., 4869
Butler, R. C., 3431
Buyniski, J. P., 5415

Cabral, R. M., 5197
Cairns, E. R., 4310, 4311
Cais, M., 3432
Calanca, A., 3546
Calandra, J. C., 5226
Calihan, M., 4592
Calil, H. M., 3433, 4864
Calvarese, B., 5007, 5009

Cameron, I. L., 5243
Cami, J., 4223
Campbell, I., 3434
Campbell, R. L., 3876
Campo, R. A., 3059
Campos Rodriguez, R., 3435
Canale, M., 3436
Candela, R. G., 5326
Canter, A., 3409, 4560, 4561, 4562, 4563
Caolo, M. A., 5327
Capek, R., 3437, 3696
Capelle, N., 3438
Carasso, R. L., 3439
Carbol, L., 4010
Carchman, R., 5193
Carchman, R. A., 3440, 3441, 3442, 3690, 3920,
    3921, 3924, 4509, 4513, 5158, 5159, 5194,
    5250, 5254, 5328, 5329
Carder, B., 3443, 3444, 3597
Carlin, A. S., 3052, 3060, 3445
Carlini, E., 4409
Carlini, E. A., 3061, 3062, 3063, 3414, 3446,
    3447, 3448, 3449, 3450, 3451, 4408, 4489,
    4516, 4785, 5330, 5350
Carnevale, A., 3474, 3823, 3824, 5400
Carney, J. M., 3452, 4377, 4378, 5331
Caron, P., 4643
Carpenter, R. A., 4438
Carpi, A., 3051
Carr, J. D., 4673, 4677
Carr, R. R., 3453
Carranza, J., 3454
Carroll, R., 5283
Carter, W. E., 3455, 3745, 4138
Carvalho, F. V., 4588
Cassidy, J., 3263
Casswell, S., 3456
Castracane, V. D., 4113
Castro, M. E., 5332
Cates, W., 3457
Cates, W., Jr., 3458
Catz, C. S., 5399
Cavness, C., 3722, 3723
Cely, W., 3104, 3459
Chailakhyan, M. Kh., 5465, 5466
Chait, L. D., 3197
Chakravarty, I., 3460, 3461, 3462, 3463, 3464,
    4825, 5333, 5334
Chambers, J. W., 4321

Chan, A., 4887
Chan, M. L., 3064
Chan, M. Y., 3465
Chan, W. R., 3466
Chan, Y. M., 5375
Chance, M. R. A., 3559, 3560, 3561
Chandra, S., 3107
Chandrasekharan, V., 5614
Chang, A. E., 5335
Chao, F., 3853
Chao, F.-C., 3467, 4288, 5411
Chapman, L. F., 4782, 4783, 5336, 5571
Chapuis, L., 5481
Chari-Bitron, A., 3468, 5337
Charlebois, A. T., 5389, 5390
Charles, R., 5338
Chase, A. R., 3469
Chase, R., 3190
Chatterjee, D. K., 3808
Check, W. A., 5339
Cheema, A. M. 3470
Cheney, D. L., 4715, 4716, 5549
Cheng, F. P., 5081
Cheng, J. T., 3204
Cheng, P. C., 5080, 5610, 5612
Chesher, G. B., 3222, 3382, 3471, 3472, 3473,
    3784, 4039, 4347, 4348, 4349, 4350, 5184,
    5308, 5309, 5340, 5341, 5492, 5634
Chester, A. B., 5426
Chiang, C. Y., 4239
Chiarotti, M., 3474, 3825, 3826, 3827, 4604,
    5342, 5400
Chiavarelli, S., 3788, 5257
Chin, L., 3516
Chiu, P., 3475, 3476, 5073, 5074, 5343
Chiu, S. Y., 4989
Chmela, Z., 4878
Chmelikova, M., 4011, 4012
Choisy, G., 5344
Choisy, H., 5344
Chopa, G. S., 3477
Choulis, N. H., 3478, 5345
Christensen, D. H., 4619
Christensen, S. B., 3479
Christie, R. L., 4584
Christie, R. M., 3480
Chrusciel, T. L., 3481
Chung, J. P. C., 4274
Chusid, M. J., 3482

Cisin, I. H., 4452, 5503
Clark, C., 3535
Clark, J. H., 4116
Clark, M. N., 5346
Clark, R., 5353
Clark, S., 4332, 4469, 4470
Clark, S. C., 3483, 3484
Clark, W. C., 5347
Clarke, D. E., 3485
Clarke, E. G. C., 5251
Clarke, P. A., 5384
Clarke, R. C., 3486
Clayton, R. R., 5530
Clemens, J., 4247
Clerk, S. H., 4829
Clewe, G. L., 3119, 4360
Clopton, J. M., 5348
Clopton, P. L., 5348, 5444
Clough, J. M., 5026, 5027, 5028, 5598
Co, B. T., 3487
Cocchia, M. A., 4927, 4928, 4929
Cockerham, W., 3488
Cockerham, W. C., 3489
Coffman, C. B., 3490, 3491, 3492
Coggins, W. J., 3493, 3494, 3969, 4138
Cohen, D. R., 3495
Cohen, H. B., 3828
Cohen, M. I., 5424
Cohen, M. J., 3496, 4537, 4717
Cohen, S., 3497, 3498, 3499, 3500, 3501, 350
    3503, 3504, 4178, 4559
Cohn, R. A., 3065
Cole, J. O., 3066
Coleman, J. H., 3505
Collier, G., 5169
Collins, F., 3889
Collins, F. G., 3506, 5252, 5349
Collu, R., 3507, 3508
Comitas, L., 3509, 4762
Condes, M., 3730
Conley, J., 3224
Connell, P. H., 3510
Connor, T., 4242, 4984
Consroe, P., 3511, 3512, 3513, 3514, 35
    4386, 4387, 4388, 5350
Consroe, P. F., 3515, 3516, 3518, 3519, 40
    4095, 4220
Contreras, C. M., 3730
Cook, C. E., 3520, 5253, 5351

Cooler, P., 3521, 3522
Cooper, H., 3523
Cooper, J. T., 3524
Coper, H., 3067, 3950, 4335, 4336, 4337, 4338
Corcoran, M. E., 3525, 5140, 5141, 5142
Cordell, G. A., 3713
Cordova, T., 3269
Corin, E., 5127
Cormier, D., 3068, 3069
Cornett, T., 4453, 4454, 4455, 4456
Cornett, T. L., 4458, 4459, 4460, 4461, 5505
Corrigan, D., 3526
Cosson, L., 3369, 4595, 4596
Costa, E., 4715, 4716, 5549
Costa, G., 3527, 3528, 3592, 3593, 3594
Costa, L., 4640, 4644, 5538
Cote, G., 4027
Cote, M. G., 4365
Cottereau, M. J., 3529
Coulston, Frederick, 5678
Coutts, R. T., 4171, 5352
Cox, B., 3530
Coyle, I., 3531
Cozens, D. D., 5353
Crabtree, R., 4247
Crabtree, R. E., 4759
Craigmill, A., 4945
Craigmill, A. L., 4514, 4941, 4942, 4943, 4944, 5354
Cranston, J. W., 5025
Craven, C., 3476, 3532
Crawford, H., 3925
Crawford, H. J. W., 3070
Crawford, R. D., 4072
Crawford, W. J., 3213, 3533, 3534, 5355
Creagan, E. T., 5391
Crippa, O., 4484
Crocco, J., 5558
Crockett, D., 3535
Crombie, L., 3536, 3537, 3538, 3539, 3540, 3541, 5356, 5357
Crombie, W. M. L., 3536, 3537, 3538, 3539, 3540, 3541, 3542, 3543, 5356, 5357
Cronquist, A., 4888
Cross, C. E., 3544
Cross, H. J., 3071, 4163, 5472
Cross, J. K., 3406
Crow, F. W., 4021
Crowl, C. P., 4722, 4757

Cruickshank, E. K., 3545
Cuendet, J. F., 3546
Cunha, J., 4785
Curnow, D. H., 3586
Currie, R. F., 3547
Curry, C. L., 3213, 3534
Curtis, B., 3548, 4869
Cushman, P., 3549, 3551, 3552, 3553, 3554, 3555, 3556
Cushman, P., Jr., 3550
Cuskey, W. R., 3557
Cutler, M. G., 3558, 3559, 3560, 3561
Cutting, M., 4616
Cutting, M. B., 4018, 4315

Dadisch, G. L., 5358
Daenens, P., 5116
Dagirmanjian, R., 3653, 3830, 5372
Dahiya, M. S., 3562, 3563, 3564, 3565, 3566, 3567
Dahl, C. J., 3413
Dahlstrom, G., 4803
Dahmen, J., 5200, 5532
Daley, J. D., 3386
Dallmer, J., 5058
Dalterio, S., 3568, 3569
Dalterio, S. L., 5359
Dalterio, S. L. S., 3570
Dalton, B., 4248, 4630
Dalton, W. S., 3571, 3572, 3573, 3574, 3575, 3576, 5531
Dalzell, G. R. 5094
Dalzell, H. C., 3899, 4703, 4704, 4705, 4706, 4707, 4708, 4709, 5095, 5096, 5097, 5098, 5099, 5418
Dalzell, Haldean C., 5698, 5703
Dalzell, Haldean Cloyce, 5699, 5700, 5701, 5702, 5714
Dani, S., 3432
Daniel, S. A., 5360
Darley, C. F., 3161, 3577, 4637, 4751, 5050, 5051
Das, P. K., 4871, 4872, 4873, 4874, 4875, 4876
Daskalopoulos, N., 3578
Dassel, P. M., 5361
Datta, J., 4658
Datta, S. C., 4825
Daul, C. B., 3579
Davalos, S. G., 3580, 3581

Davidson, S. T., 4418
Davies, B. H., 3582, 3849
Davies, P., 5362
Davis, C. M., 3724
Davis, C. S., 3583
Davis, E. M., 3584
Davis, E. R., 4277
Davis, G. L., 3071
Davis, G. S., 3585, 5363
Davis, K. H., 4618, 4619, 4620, 5622
Davis, K. R., 4208
Davis, L. J., 4549
Davis, R. E., 3586
Davis, W. M., 3587
Dawley, H. H., 5364
Dawson, W. W., 3494, 3588, 3589
Day, N., 5276
Day, W. A., 3259
Day, William A., 5652, 5653, 5664, 5665
Dayanandan, P., 3590
De Carvalho, F. V., 3596
De Faubert Maunder, M. J., 3072, 3073, 3591
De Jong, Y., 5033, 5034, 5035
De Nie, L. C., 4860
De Pasquale, A., 3592, 3593, 3594, 5365
De Pasquale, R. C., 3527
De Souza, H., 3595, 3596
De Wied, D., 5119
Dean, J., 3968
Dean, J. C., 5426
Dean, L. M., 4535
Deb, G., 3343
Deboer, B., 5437
Debski, B. F., 3752
Decauchereux, J.-F., 3989
Deets, A. C., 4463
Deikel, S. M., 3597
Del Basso, P., 3051
Del Castillo, J., 3598
Delaney, G. V., 3108
Deliyannakis, E., 3074
Dell, D. D., 3599
Della Fera, M. A., 4154, 5461
Dellarco, A. J., 5440
Dembo, R., 3600, 3601
Denie, J. C., 4862
Der Marderosian, A. H., 5311
Derenzo, E. V., 4982
Dermarderosian, A., 5312

Desoize, B., 3132, 3602, 3603, 3604, 3605, 3606, 3607, 4523, 4524, 4525, 4533, 4534, 5304, 5366, 5367
Detels, R., 5037, 5038
Detrick, R., 3608
Dettbarn, W.-D., 3988
Dewey, W. L., 3121, 3198, 3199, 3352, 3353, 3354, 3357, 3358, 3383, 3609, 3610, 3611, 3690, 3752, 3755, 3922, 3923, 4074, 4075, 4076, 4077, 4078, 4079, 4080, 4081, 4082, 4140, 4141, 4263, 4322, 4323, 4378, 4379, 4380, 4381, 4382, 4385, 4509, 4510, 4653, 4654, 4708, 4939, 5212, 5250, 5254, 5262, 5328, 5368, 5630, 5631
Dey, S. K., 3344
Dezelsky, T. L., 5057
Dhingra, R. C., 4464
Di Ciommo, M., 3612
Di Cuneo, F., 4615
Di Napoli, T., 4292
Diamantis, W., 4920, 4921, 5369
Dibenedetto, M., 3613, 3614
Digregorio, J., 4520
Dijkstra, G., 3416
Dike, S. Y., 3615, 3616
Dikstein, S., 4409, 5249
Dimartino, R., 4928
Dimascio, A., 4544
Dimen, E., 5171
Dimen, E. M., 5172
Dingell, J. V., 4167
Dintcheff, B. A., 5276
Dionyssiou-Asteriou, A., 3617, 4193
Dipasqua, A. C., 3108
Dirdano, D. A., 3821
Dittrich, A., 3075, 3618, 3619, 5239
Dixit, B. N., 4922
Dixit, V. P., 3620, 3621, 3622, 3623, 3624
Dodder, R. A., 3972
Dodge, D. L., 3625, 3626
Dodge, P., 5218
Dodge, P. W., 4710
Doekel, R., 5245, 5246, 5247
Doggett, S., 4483
Dogra, R. K. S., 4829
Dolby, T. W., 3627, 3628
Dollery, C. T., 5201
Domey, R., 3361
Domino, E., 3629

Domino, E. F., 3630, 3631, 4228
Domino, R. J., 4227
Doms, D. J., 4293
Donelson, A. C., 3630
Doorenbos, N. J., 4680
Doran, K. M., 5415
Dorn, N., 3510
Dornbush, R., 4965, 5136
Dornbush, R. L., 3632, 3633, 3634, 3635, 3636, 4968
Dorr, M., 3637
Dorr, R., 3968
Dorus, W., 4843
Doughty, P. L., 3455
Doyle, O. L., 5575, 5576
Doyle, W. J., 4857
Drachler, D. H., 3638
Drath, D. B., 5370
Dren, A., 5218
Dren, A. T., 3639, 3640, 3665, 4236, 4710
Dren, Anthony Thomas, 5666
Drew, W., 4454
Drew, W. G., 3830, 4453, 4459
Drewnowski, A., 3641, 3642, 3643
Driessen, R. A., 5371
Driscoll, P., 5111
Drouga, M., 4123
Du Toit, B. M., 3076, 3644, 3645, 3646, 3647
Dua, R. D., 4540
Dube, K. C., 3648, 3649
Dubowski, K. M., 4787, 4788, 4789
Ducharme, J. R., 3508
Ducrey, N., 3546
Dudley, S., 4616
Duggan, J. F., 3650
Dukes, M. N. G., 3651
Dumetz, J., 4506, 5061
Duncan, D. F., 3652
Duncan, G. E., 3653, 5372
Dunnigan, D., 5218
Dunnigan, D. A., 5236
Dupont, R. L., 3654, 3655, 3656, 3657, 3658, 3659, 3875, 5373
Dusek, D., 3304
Dustman, R. E., 4270, 4626
Dvilanski, A., 4260, 4265
Dvorak, M., 3133
Dwivedi, C., 3660
Dwyer, W. O., 5555

Dykstra, L., 3077
Dykstra, L. A., 3661
Dyrenfurth, T., 3956

Earnhardt, J. T., 3197, 3198, 3199, 3662, 3663, 3664, 4378
Eastwood, M. E., 4312
Eaton, B. J., 4226
Ebert, D. M., 3640, 3665
Ebert, Donn Myron, 5666
Ebner, K. E., 4699
Edelson, J., 4920
Edelstein, E. L., 4817
Edery, H., 3209, 3666, 3836, 5313, 5532
Edson, P. H., 4389
Edward, C., 5277
Edwards, G., 3078, 3667
Egan, S. M., 3668
Eich, J. E., 4980
Eichel, G. R., 3669
Eimstad, W. M., 4722, 4757
Einhorn, L., 4960
Einhorn, L. H., 4521, 5426
Einstein, R., 3670, 3978
Eisenstein, D., 3513
Ejchental, B., 4175
Ekert, H., 5374
El-Bayoumi, A., 4120
El-Feraly, F., 3337
El-Feraly, F. S., 3426, 3671, 3672, 3673, 3674, 3683, 4580, 4582, 4583, 5375
El-Yousef, M. K., 3768
Elie, R., 3789
Ellingboe, J., 4430, 4431, 4432, 4433
Elliott, H. W., 3675, 3828
Elliott, R. A., 3876
Ellis, C. G., 3676, 3677
Ellis, G. J., 5376, 5590
Ellis, N. M., 5008
Ellner, M., 3678, 3679
Elsmore, T. F., 3680
Elsohly, M. A., 3362, 3671, 3672, 3681, 3682, 3683, 3684, 3685, 3686, 3687, 5080, 5081, 5314, 5375, 5611, 5612
Elsohly, Mahmoud A., 5667
Ely, D. L., 3688
Emanuelson, I., 5534
Emboden, W., 3079
Emboden, W. A., 3080, 3689

End, D., 5250, 5254
End, D. W., 3690, 5328, 5329
Endo, M., 3691
Engen, T., 3975
Ercan, Z. S., 4153, 5078
Erdmann, G., 3173, 3692, 4117, 4118, 4119
Erickson, P. G., 3693, 5377
Erikson, D., 3292
Erikson, D. J., 4924
Ernst, C. A. S., 5276
Esber, H. J., 3694, 3695, 4743
Eschenmoser, Albert, 5668
Esplin, B., 3437, 3696
Estevez, V. S., 4802
Etevenon, P., 5378, 5379
Evans, M., 3756
Evans, M. A., 3697, 3698, 3699, 3700, 3701
Evans, R. G., 3702
Evans, W. E., 3505
Eysenck, S., 5409

Fabre, L. F., 3703, 4960
Fager, Earl E., 5669
Fager, Earl Elmer, 5670
Faggioni, R., 3546
Fahndrich, C., 4338
Fahndrich, Ch., 4335, 4336, 4337
Fahrenholtz, Kenneth E., 5671
Fahrenholtz, Kenneth Earl, 5672
Fairbairn, J. W., 3704, 3705, 3706, 4755, 4756
    5380
Fairlie, K., 3707
Fairshter, R. D., 3708
Falek, A., 3709
Falk, L., 4551, 5527
Falvello, L., 4103
Fann, W. E., 4031
Farag, A., 4161
Farber, M. O., 3393, 3394
Farber, S. J., 3710
Farkas, J., 3711
Farnsworth, D. L., 3081, 3082, 3712
Farnsworth, N. R., 3083, 3713
Farrell, T. R., 4112
Fatray, Z., 3714
Fauci, A. S., 3482
Fauman, B., 3715
Fauman, M., 3715
Faust, R., 4131

Fazel, A., 5122
Fedora, D., 5170
Feeney, D. M., 3716, 3717, 3718, 3719, 5381
Fehr, K. A., 3720, 3721
Fehr, K. O., 5382
Fein, A., 3892
Feinberg, I., 3722, 3723
Feinglass, S. J., 3361
Fenimore, D. C., 3724
Fennessy, M. R., 3725, 3726, 5021, 5022, 5023,
    5024, 5596, 5597
Fenney, D. M., 5179
Fenselau, C., 3727, 4306, 4589
Fentiman, A. F., 5266
Fentiman, A. F., Jr., 4244
Fenz, W. D., 3728
Ferguson, Clyde Parker, Jr., 5638
Fernandes, M., 3067, 3950
Fernandez, E., 4896
Fernandez, E. O., 3265, 3729, 5295
Fernandez-Guardiola, A., 3730
Fernandez-Salas, A., 3494, 4138
Ferraro, D. P., 3084, 3090, 3731, 3732, 3733,
    3734, 3735, 3736, 3737, 4272
Ferry, D. G., 4311
Fetterman, P. S., 3337, 5082
Fetterold, D. J., 3737
Fidell, L. S., 4666
Field, B. I., 4974
Fink, M., 3634, 3738, 3739, 3740, 4965, 4966,
    5136
Finkelfarb, E., 3414
Fiori, A., 3474, 3827
First, M. W., 5432, 5433
Fisher, A., 3741
Fisher, H., 4401
Fisher, S., 4156
Fitzgerald, M., 5105
Fitzgerald, M. P., 5483, 5484
Fitzjarrell, A. T., 5423
Fitzsimmons, R. C., 4044
Fleischman, R. W., 3742, 3743, 4740, 4741,
    4744, 5045, 5383, 5560
Fletcher, J., 5000, 5593
Fletcher, J. M., 3744, 3745, 4784
Flom, M. C., 3194, 3195, 3196, 3403, 3404,
    3746, 3747
Florvaag, E., 3748, 3749
Floyd, T., 3722

Fogg, C. P., 4901, 4902
Foltz, R. L., 3608, 4244, 5266, 5384
Fonseka, K., 3207, 3750, 3751
Foote, R. S., 4102
Forbes, J. E., 3752
Forbes, Roger, 3541
Ford, R. D., 3085, 3289, 3753, 3754, 3755
Ford, T. M., 5043
Forman, E. J., 5029
Forney, R., 3574, 3756, 4248
Forney, R. B., 3393, 3394, 3572, 3573, 3575, 3576, 3700, 3701, 4325, 4326, 4392, 4393, 4987, 4988, 5531
Forrest, D. V., 3757
Forrest, I., 3853
Forrest, I. S., 3179, 3467, 4288
Forsyth, R., 4766, 4767
Fort, J., 3758
Fourniat, M. C., 3761
Fournier, A., 4234
Fournier, E., 3759, 3990, 4792, 5320, 5572
Fournier, G., 3580, 3581, 3760, 3761, 5255, 5385
Fowler, M. S., 4648
Fowler, R., 3288, 4543, 5386
Fox, B. L., 3707
Fox, F. J., 5387
Fox, J., 4175
Fox, S., 4981
Frank, I. M., 3762, 3966, 5011, 5271
Frank, M., 3763
Frankenheim, J. M., 3127
Franklin, R. M., 4957
Franks, H. M., 3471, 3472
Fredericks, A. B., 3764
Frederickson, R. C. A., 3765
Fredrickson, J. M., 4277
Freedman, A. M., 3633, 3634, 4966
Freedman, D. X., 3766, 5388
Freemon, F. R., 3767, 3768
Frei, E., 4772, 4773, 4774, 5567
Freidman, M. A., 5071
Fried, P. A., 3769, 3770, 3771, 5389, 5390
Friedlander, M., 4260
Friedman, E., 3772, 3773, 3979, 3980, 3981, 4504
Friedman, J. G., 3774
Friedman, M. A., 3441, 3775, 3776, 3777, 3778, 3779, 3780, 4509, 5222, 5223, 5224, 5225, 5256, 5272, 5604

Friedrich-Fiechtl, J., 3781
Frischknecht, H. R., 3782, 3783, 5161
Frizza, J., 3784
Frommer, R., 3439
Froscher, W., 3399
Fry, D., 4369, 5026
Frytak, S., 5391
Fu, T., 4400
Fu, T.-K., 3123, 4401
Fujimoto, G., 3351
Fujimoto, G. I., 4184, 5392
Fujiwara, M., 3785, 5091, 5092, 5234, 5393
Fukuda, D., 3786
Fukuda, D. S., 3178, 5292
Fukuda, David S., 5673
Fullerton, D. S., 4214
Funderburk, W., 5193
Furnas, B. E., 4521
Furr, M., 3787

Gado, W., 3487
Gaensler, E., 5105, 5106
Gaensler, E. A., 5107
Gagliardi, L., 3788, 5257
Gagne, D., 3286
Gagnon, M.-A., 3789
Gailis, L., 4027
Gaines, L. S., 3429
Galanter, M., 3790, 4981
Galbraith, G., 3791
Galbreath, C., 3291
Galchus, D. S., 3792
Galchus, K. E., 3792
Gallant, D., 3272
Galliher, J. F., 3793
Gallup, G. G., 4389
Gambaro, V., 5268
Gammon, C. B., 5025
Gan, O. H. M., 5111, 5112, 5113, 5615, 5616
Gangadhara, M., 3794
Gantt, C., 4958
Ganz, V. P., 3795
Garber, A. S., 3796
Garcia, J. F., 3110
Garcin, F., 4683
Gardner, E., 3351
Gardner, M., 4116
Gardner, M. J., 5452
Garey, R. E., 5423

Garrett, C. P. O., 3797
Garrett, E. R., 3798, 3799, 3800, 3801, 5394, 5395
Garriott, J. C., 4299
Gascon, A. L., 3320, 3802
Gash, A., 3803
Gasser, J. C., 3309, 3310
Gastaut, H., 5018
Gaul, C. C., 3804
Gawin, F. H., 3805
Gay, J. R., 5364
Gehlen, W., 3399
Gelbart, S. S., 3533
Gelfand, J. A., 3482
Geller, I., 3806
Genest, P., 3807
Gentile, V., 3825, 3827, 5400
Gentner, W. A., 3490. 3491, 3492
Georgotas, A., 5396
Gerber, M. L., 4001
Gergen, K. J., 3086
Gergen, M. K., 3086
Gerlach, D., 4056
Gerrein, J. R., 4731
Gershon, H., 3432
Gershon, S., 3367, 3772, 3773, 3979, 3980, 3981, 3982, 3983, 3984, 3985
Ghia, J., 3876, 4686
Ghoneim, M. T., 4339, 5397
Ghosh, A., 4719
Ghosh, J. J., 3290, 3294, 3343, 3343, 3460, 3461, 3462, 3463, 3464, 3808, 3809, 4475, 4476, 4477, 4478, 4479, 4652, 4655, 4656, 4657, 4658, 4659, 4779, 4780, 4825, 5333, 5334
Ghosh, P., 3140, 3810, 5398
Giacoia, G. P., 5399
Gianutsos, R., 3811
Gibbins, R. J., 3812
Gibbs, F. A., 3087
Gibermann, E., 3813
Gilbert, J. C., 3814
Gildea, M. L., 3815
Gilhooley, R. A., 5386
Gill, E. W., 3816, 3817, 4233
Gillespie, H., 3998
Gillespie, H. K., 3098, 3999, 4536
Giminez, Ma P., 5548
Ginsberg, I. J., 3818
Ginsburg, H. J., 3819

Giono-Barber, H., 3820
Giono-Barber, P., 3820
Girdano, D. D., 3821
Giusti, G. V., 3822, 3823, 3824, 3825, 3826, 3827, 4604, 5342, 5400
Glass, R. M., 5401
Glatt, H., 5402
Globus, G. G., 3828
Gobar, A. H., 3829
Godbold, J. C., 5403
Goel, S., 5019
Goett, J. M., 5404
Goetz, R. R., 5347
Golani, H. C., 4539, 4540
Goldbaum, D., 5123
Goldberg, I., 5405
Goldberg, N. H., 5335
Goldfrank, L., 5406
Goldman, H., 3830
Goldman, R., 3280, 3281, 3282, 3970, 4702
Goldstein, F. J., 3831
Goldstein, H., 3832
Goldstein, R., 5055
Goldstein, S., 3524
Golub, M. S., 5407
Gonzalez-Estrada, T., 3730
Goo, G. P., 5336, 5571
Goode, E., 3088, 3833
Goode, M., 5408
Goodstadt, M. S., 5377
Goodwin, D., 3973
Goodwin, D. W., 3487, 4622
Gordon, J., 3396
Gordon, J. H., 3397, 3834
Gordon, R., 3835
Gordon, R. J., 3835
Gori, G. B., 3991, 4605
Gorshkova, L., 4824
Gorski, R. A., 3834
Gossop, M., 5409
Gothilf, S., 3813
Gottesfeld, Z., 3666, 3836
Gottschalk, L. A., 3837, 4665
Gough, A. L., 3838, 3839, 3840, 3841
Gough, N. E., 3838
Gouvier, W. D., 5410
Gouyette, A. J., 3798, 5395
Graffeo, A. P., 5384
Graham, B. F., 5608

Graham, J., 4627, 4628
Graham, J. D. P., 3089, 3582, 3668, 3842, 3843, 3844, 3845, 3846, 3847, 3848, 3849, 3850, 3930, 3931, 5207
Graham, L., 4630
Granchelli, F. E., 4600
Granchelli, Felix E., 5686, 5688, 5689, 5690, 5691, 5704
Grant-Whyte, H., 3851
Gray, J. A., 3641
Gray, R., 4929
Green, D. E., 3467, 3852, 3853, 4288, 5411
Green, H. I., 3854
Green, K., 3855, 3856, 3857, 3858, 3859, 3860, 3861, 3862, 3863, 3864, 3865, 3866, 3867, 5412, 5413, 5414
Green, M. L., 4712
Greenberg, G., 3415
Greenberg, I., 3218, 3273, 3868, 3869, 3870, 4422, 4423, 4434, 4435
Greenberg, J. H., 3871, 3872, 3873, 3874, 4025
Greene, M. H., 3875
Greenfield, T. K., 4181
Greenley, J. R., 3818
Gregg, J., 3521, 4686
Gregg, J. M., 3522, 3876, 3877, 4679
Grenier, M. L., 4173
Grey, A. C., 3850
Grieco, M., 3551
Griffin, B. S., 3878
Griffin, C. T., 3878
Griffith, R., 5303
Grilly, D. M., 3879
Grinker, J. A., 3642, 3643
Grisham, M. G., 3090
Gross, S. J., 3880, 3881, 4916
Grote, H., 3882, 3883
Grove, R. N., 4683
Grupp, S. E., 3091, 4301
Gugelmann, A., 4313
Guinn, R., 3884
Guire, K., 4991
Guiusti, G. V., 3474
Gulas, I., 3885
Gulliani, G. L., 4030
Gunn, C. G., 4787, 4788, 4789
Gupta, B. N., 4829
Gupta, C. L., 3622
Gupta, L., 3092

Gupta, M. L., 4930
Gupta, M. N., 3279
Gupta, R. C., 3886, 5552
Gupta, S., 3551
Gupta, S. B., 3107
Gupta, S. P., 3648, 3649
Gupta, Y. K., 3279
Gustafsson, B., 3208
Gutierrez, R., 4223
Gutshall, P. L., 5111, 5112, 5113, 5615
Gylys, J. A., 5415

Haar, J., 3887
Haas, A. E., 5588
Haavik, C. O., 3355, 3356, 3359, 3506, 3888, 3889, 3890, 5252, 5258, 5349, 5416
Habib, A., 4120
Haddad, L. M., 3891
Hadley, K., 5154
Hadley, K. W., 3992, 5082, 5083
Haegerstrom-Portnoy, G., 3194, 3196, 3403, 3404
Haertzen, C. A., 5259
Hagaman, E. W., 3260
Hagel, D., 3892
Hahn, P., 3901
Hahn, P. M., 3503, 3762
Halikas, J. A., 3893
Halki, J. J., 3093
Hall, F. B., 3894
Hallas, R., 5218
Halldin, M., 5277, 5417, 5628
Halle, S., 3895, 4218
Halloin, T. J., 3360
Hamed, A., 3896
Hamed, A. T., 4048
Hammill, S., 5245, 5246, 5247
Hammond, C. T., 3897, 3898
Hanas, L., 5260
Handrick, G. R., 3899, 4706, 4707, 4708, 4709, 5094, 5095, 5096, 5097, 5098, 5099, 5418
Handrick, Richard, 5705
Haney, A., 3900
Haney, A. W., 3304
Hanin, I., 3773
Hanley, J., 3901
Hanna, J. M., 3902, 3903
Hansteen, R. W., 3142, 3904
Hanus, L., 3905, 3906, 3907, 3908, 3909, 3910, 3911, 3912, 4201, 4202, 5264

Harakal, J. J., 4924
Harbison, R., 4361
Harbison, R. D., 3119, 3660, 3699, 3700, 3913, 4360, 4362, 4363
Harclerode, J., 3832, 4281, 4282, 4543, 4811, 5419, 5440
Harclerode, J. E., 3431
Hardman, H. F., 3355, 3890, 3914, 4007, 5258, 5416
Hardy, N., 3759, 5353
Harmon, J. W., 3094, 3915, 4848
Harper, C. E., 5012, 5013, 5014
Harper, I., 3916
Harper, J. W., 3917
Harrell, A. V., 4452
Harris, L., 4686
Harris, L. S., 3127, 3198, 3199, 3353, 3354, 3383, 3384, 3440, 3442, 3610, 3611, 3661, 3778, 3918, 3919, 3920, 3921, 3922, 3923, 3924, 4078, 4082, 4140, 4141, 4263, 4323, 4377, 4379, 4380, 4381, 4382, 4385, 4509, 4510, 4511, 4512, 4513, 4653, 4654, 4913, 5158, 5159, 5171, 5172, 5225, 5250, 5254, 5262, 5331, 5420, 5510, 5543
Harris, Louis Selig, 5674, 5680
Harris, R. T., 4328
Harris, L. S., 3121
Harrison, J. E., 4921
Harshman, R. A., 3925
Hart, D. R., 4284
Hart, R. H., 3926, 3927
Hartel, F. W., 5401
Hartelius, J., 3928, 3929
Hartley, J. P. R., 3930, 3931, 5207
Hartmann, R. J., 3806
Harvey, D. J., 3932, 3933, 3934, 3935, 3936, 3937, 3938, 3939, 3940, 3941, 3942, 3943, 3944, 3945, 3946, 3947, 3948, 4383, 4384, 5353, 5421, 5422
Harvey, T. M., 4746, 5149, 5150
Harvey, W. M., 3149
Hashim, G., 3556
Hasleton, S., 3949
Hattendorf, C., 3950
Hattendorf, M., 3950
Hattori, T., 3951
Hauck, V. G., 3095
Hawes, M. L., 3520, 5253
Hawkins, B. J., 5403

Hawks, D., 3952, 4186, 4187
Hayden, D. W., 3742, 3743, 5561
Hayden, R., 4742
Hays, J. R., 3056
Hayward, A., 4491
Head, K., 4306
Heath, R. G., 3579, 3917, 3953, 3954, 5423, 5512
Hecht, E., 3925
Heer-Carcano, L., 5163
Heerma, W., 3322, 3363, 3416, 4209, 4210
Hein, K., 5424
Hembree, M. W., 3955
Hembree, W. C., 3956, 3957, 4016
Hembree, W. C., III, 5425, 5431
Hemphill, J. K., 3958, 3959, 5086, 5087, 5088
Henderson, A. H., 3850
Hendriks, H., 3960, 3961, 3962, 3963, 4345
Henke, G., 3964
Henri, E., 4598, 4599
Henrich, R., 4492, 4494
Henrich, R. T., 4493, 4495, 5511
Henriksson, B. G., 3965, 4059, 4060, 4061, 4062, 4070
Henry, J. P., 3688
Henry, J. T., 5084
Hensley, V. R., 3471
Hensley, W. J., 3471
Hepler, R. S., 3966, 3967, 5017
Heppner, G. H., 4262, 5482
Herd, R., 3118
Herlihy, P., 4704, 4705
Herlihy, Patricia, 5702
Herman, T. E., 3968
Herman, T. S., 5426
Hermans, A. J. M., 5438
Hernandez-Bolanos, J., 3494, 3969
Herning, R. I., 4112, 5302, 5427
Hershkowitz, M., 3970, 5428, 5429
Herweijer, J. J., 4698
Hewes, C. R., 3765
Heyman, I. A., 4304
Hickcox, P., 4640
Hidy, B. J., 5384
Hildebrand, D. C., 3971
Hill, R., 4338
Hill, R. D., 3972
Hill, S. Y., 3487, 3973, 4622
Hillestad, A., 3974, 3975, 3976, 5219

Hindmarch, I., 3670, 3977, 3978

Hinds, W. C., 5432, 5433

Hine, B., 3772, 3979, 3980, 3981, 3982, 3983, 3984, 3985

Hirano, H., 4849, 4850, 4851

Hirom, P. C., 5261

Hirsch, C. A., 5040

Hirschhorn, I. D., 3096

Ho, B. T., 3986, 4079, 4081, 4082, 4199, 4802, 4865

Hobbs, D. T., 4649

Hochhauser, M., 3987

Hoekman, T. B., 3988

Hoellinger, H., 3438, 3989, 3990, 4234, 4792, 5320, 5572

Hoffman, F. M., 4175

Hoffmann, D., 3410, 3411, 3991

Hoffmann, E., 5315

Hofmann, A. A., 5300

Hofmann, S., 5270

Holley, J. H., 3992, 5083

Hollister, L. E., 3097, 3098, 3993, 3994, 3995, 3996, 3997, 3998, 3999, 4000, 4001, 4133, 4134, 4135, 4136, 4137, 4290, 4536, 5273, 5430, 5455

Holmstedt, B., 4002

Holt, S., 5338

Hong, S. K., 3902

Hood, L. V. S., 4003

Hooks, N. T., 5259

Hooyman, J. T., 5134

Horn, A. H., 3724

Hornung, R., 4004

Horowitz, L. G., 4005

Horowitz, M., 4006

Horvath, S. M., 5298

Hosko, M. J., 3914, 4007, 4794, 4795, 4796, 4797, 4798, 4799

Hosokawa, M., 4818

Hosoya, E., 4032

Hoton-Dorge, M., 3099

Houser, V. P., 4008

Howes, J. F., 4009, 4576, 4577, 4578, 4601, 4603, 4705, 4707, 4708, 4709, 5094

Hoyer, G. A., 5129

Hrbek, J., 3128, 3133, 4010, 4011, 4012, 4013, 4014, 4015, 4414, 4415, 4542, 4878, 4879, 5498

Hruban, L., 3910

Hsu, J., 3602, 4524, 4533

Hsu, M. H., 5085

Hu, M. W., 4722

Hu, W. M., 4757

Huang, H. F. S., 4016, 5425, 5431

Huber, G., 4017, 4592

Huber, G. L., 4018, 4315, 5362, 5370, 5432, 5433

Hubert, G., 5128

Hudiburg, R. A., 4069

Hudson, G., 3819

Huertas, V. E., 3710

Huey, L., 5348

Huff, S. R., 4719

Huffman, S., 3302

Hughes, Gordon A., 5675

Hughes, I., 3978

Hughes, I. E., 3670

Hughes, P. H., 4843

Hughes, R. B., 4019, 5434

Hughes, W., 3958

Hulbert, S., 4501

Humphries, S. V., 5435, 5436

Hundleby, J. D., 4438

Hunt, C. A., 3799, 3800, 3801, 4020, 5395

Hunt, D. F., 4021

Hunter, S. A., 3422, 3423, 3424, 3425, 5322, 5323

Huot, J., 4022

Huott, A. D., 3074

Husain, S., 4023, 4024, 4673, 4674, 4675, 4676, 4678, 5437

Huszar, L. A., 4025

Huthsing, K. B., 3737

Huy, N. D., 3375, 3807, 4026, 4027, 4028, 4029, 4758

Hyun, B. H., 4030

Ibii, N., 5092

Ibrahim, M. F. K., 4713

Ibrahim, M. K. F., 3142

Ichael, E. D., 5298

Ilaria, R. L., 4031

Inamdar, J. A., 3794

Inayama, S., 4032

Inayat, Y., 3470

Inciardi, J. A., 5186

Ingall, G. B., 4033, 4034, 5319

Innemee, H. C. 5438

Irvin, J. E., 4035
Issidorides, M. R., 4036, 4970, 4971, 5439
Itagaki, B., 3902, 3903
Itokawa, H., 4037, 4038, 5004
Ivins, N. J., 3292
Izquierdo, I., 3100

Jackson, D. M., 3222, 3382, 3471, 3472, 3473, 3784, 4039, 4347, 4348, 4349, 4350, 5184, 5308, 5309, 5341, 5492, 5569, 5634
Jacobs, B. L., 4040
Jacobs, J. A., 5440
Jacobs, S., 5298
Jacobsen, L. B., 4545
Jaerbe, T. U. C., 5441
Jaffe, J., 5519
Jaffe, J. H., 4041
Jagoda, A., 4140, 4141
Jain, G. C., 3563, 3564, 3565, 3566
Jain, H. C., 3623
Jain, M. P., 4826
Jaiswal, V. S., 3130
Jakubovic, A., 4042, 4043, 4044, 5442, 5443, 5490
Jamieson, S. V., 5356
Jampolsky, A., 3195
Jandhyala, B., 3485
Jandhyala, B. S., 3896, 4045, 4046, 4047, 4048, 4049, 4050, 4051, 4052, 4053, 4289, 5267
Jandu, B. S., 3477
Janicki, B. W., 5196
Janowsky, D., 3803
Janowsky, D. S., 3346, 4054, 4055, 5348, 5444
Jansen Van Ryssen, F. W., 4974
Jansing, R. L., 4483, 5588
Janzen, H. 4056
Jarbe, T. U. C., 3965, 4057, 4058, 4059, 4060, 4061, 4062, 4063, 4070, 5445
Jardillier, J.-C., 3603, 5366, 5446
Jarosz, C. J., 3688
Jarvik, L., 4398
Jarvik, L. F., 3123, 4400, 4401
Jarvik, M. E., 4064, 5447
Jasso, N. K., 4065
Jay, W. M., 5521, 5522
Jayaraman, J., 5511
Jen, Timothy Y., 5675
Jering, H., 5448, 5449, 5602
Jessor, R., 4066, 5450

Jessor, R. L., 4067
Jessor, S. L., 4067
Jimenez-Antillon, C. F., 3589
Jimenez, Cardosa, E., 5125
Jiminez-Antillon, C. F., 3494
Jochimsen, P. R., 4068
Joe, G. W., 4069
Joffe, P., 4519
Johansson, J. O., 3965, 4060, 4061, 4062, 4070
Johnson, B. D., 3101
Johnson, C. K., 4071
Johnson, D. D., 4072
Johnson, D. N., 3752
Johnson, D. W., 3259, 3260
Johnson, J. E., 3126
Johnson, J. J., 5155
Johnson, K., 4141
Johnson, K. M., 3357, 3358, 3609, 3986, 4073, 4074, 4075, 4076, 4077, 4078, 4079, 4080, 4081, 4082, 4162, 5262, 5368
Johnson, M. Ross, 5676
Johnson, M. H., 4083
Johnson, M. R., 4084, 5507
Johnson, Michael R., 5677
Johnson, W. T., 4085
Johnston, L. D., 4086, 5451
Johnstone, R. E., 4087, 4346
Joneja, M. G., 4088, 4089, 4090, 4091
Jones, A. D., 4092
Jones, B., 3511, 3512, 3517, 3904
Jones, B. C., 3515, 3516, 4093, 4094, 4095, 4220
Jones, D. L., 4096
Jones, G. R., 5352
Jones, H., 4100
Jones, H. B., 4097, 4098, 4099, 4100
Jones, J. J., 5306
Jones, J. S., 4101
Jones, L. A., 3203, 4102
Jones, L. V., 4910
Jones, P. G., 4103, 4104, 4105
Jones, R., 3722, 3723, 4106
Jones, R. T., 3102, 3194, 3195, 3196, 3314, 3315, 3316, 3317, 3318, 3319, 3403, 3404, 3746, 3747, 4107, 4108, 4109, 4110, 4111, 4112, 4227, 4614, 5302, 5310, 5427
Jones, S. E., 3968, 5426
Jordan, V. C., 4113
Josephy, Y., 3432

Jou, S., 4492
Joyce, C. R. B., 4114
Judd, L. L., 5348, 5444
Jui, P. Y., 4889
Juneja, R. C., 4115
Jurk, I. H., 5374
Jusko, W. J., 4116, 5452
Just, W. W., 3692, 4117, 4118, 4119

Kabarity, A., 4120
Kaga, C. S., 4357
Kairys, D. J., 4543
Kaiserman, M. Z., 4091
Kaistha, K. K., 4121
Kajima, M., 4122
Kaklamani, E., 4123
Kalant, H., 3720, 3721, 4860, 4861, 4862, 5382
Kalofoutis, A., 4124, 4193, 5453
Kam, J. K., 4722, 4757
Kamali, K., 4125
Kamath, M., 3615
Kanakis, C., 4126, 4127, 4129, 4130, 4464,
    5454
Kanakis, C., Jr., 4128
Kandel, D., 4131, 4132
Kandel, D. B., 4606
Kanter, S., 5273
Kanter, S. L., 4133, 4134, 4135, 4136, 4137,
    4290, 5411, 5455
Kapil, R. S., 4342, 4343, 4344
Kaplan, J., 3103
Kaplan, J. N., 3467, 5456
Kapsabelis, G., 5293
Kapsambelis, V., 4497
Karacan, I., 4138
Karalis, D., 4123
Karasek, D. E., 4139
Karasek, F. W., 4139
Karbowski, M., 4140, 4141
Karler, R., 3104, 3459, 3476, 3532, 4034, 4142,
    4143, 4144, 4145, 4146, 4147, 4148, 4893,
    4894, 4895, 5073, 5074, 5075, 5076, 5077,
    5317, 5319, 5343, 5457, 5458, 5609
Karliner, J. S., 3803
Karniol, I. G., 4149, 4515, 5002, 5003
Karr, G., 4332, 4469, 4470
Kasprzak, A., 3120
Kass, M. A., 5405
Kassouny, M., 3406

Kassouny, M. E., 3407
Kau, D. L. K., 4994, 4995
Kaufman, P. B., 3590
Kaufman, R. H., 3326
Kaushal, R., 4205
Kay, E. J., 4150
Kaymakcalan, S., 3105, 4151, 4152, 4153, 5078,
    5299, 5459, 5460
Kazakoff, C. W., 4171
Keeler, M. H., 3106
Keim, D. A., 4154, 5117, 5461, 5618
Keim, K. L., 3147
Keller, J. K., 4600
Keller, W. J., 5318
Kelley, J. A., 4155
Kelley, P. R., 3469
Kelly, L. A., 5462, 5463
Kelly, R. J., 4156
Kelly, S., 3727
Kelly, S. F., 4156
Kemal, M., 5464
Kempfert, K. D., 4908
Kennard, O., 4103, 4104, 4105
Kennedy, J. S., 3127
Kephalas, T. A., 3214, 4157, 4785, 5279
Keplinger, M. L., 5226
Kessler, R. C., 4132
Kessler, R. R., 5434
Kettenes-Van Den Bosch, J., 4158, 4159, 4160
Khalaf, A. S., 4161
Khalil, S. K. W., 4690, 5464
Khan, I., 4160
Khan, M. A., 3116
Khanna, J. M., 4860, 4863
Khare, B. P., 3107
Khristolyubova, N. A., 3225
Khryanin, V. N., 5465, 5466
Khurana, R., 3552, 3553, 3554, 3555, 3556
Kiburis, J., 3214, 4157, 5279
Kielholz, P., 5467, 5468
Kiernan, C. J., 3359, 3360
Kieslich, K., 5129, 5130
Kilbee, G. W., 5357
Kilbey, M. M., 4162
Killam, E. E. K., 3853
Kim, K., 3857, 3858, 3860, 3861, 3862, 3863,
    3864, 3865
Kim, S. H., 4139
Kimlicka, T. M., 4163

Kimmel, G. L., 4618
King, F. W., 3885
King, L. J., 4164, 4370, 5027, 5028, 5029, 5206, 5598
King, M. R., 4165
King, T. M., 5235
Kinzer, G. W., 5068, 5070
Kirchegessner, W. G., 3108
Kirk, T., 4712
Kirkham, N., 5338
Kirtany, J. K., 4166
Kiuchi, M., 4682
Klager, K., 4240, 4241
Klausner, H. A., 3988, 4167
Klein, A. L., 3894
Klein, V., 4346
Kleinsmith, L. J., 3628
Klinge, V., 4168
Klipec, W. D., 5469
Klitzner, M. D., 4717
Klonoff, H., 3535, 4169
Kluin-Neleman, J. C., 5470
Klykken, P., 5263
Klykken, P. C., 4170, 5510
Knapp, J. E., 3687, 4294, 4880, 5085
Knaus, E. E., 4171
Knezek, L. D., 5578
Knight, F., 4172
Knight, R. C., 3109
Knights, R. M., 4173
Knobel, E., 4149, 4515
Knobloch, L. C., 4923, 4924, 4926
Knox, G. V., 3721, 5382
Kochansky, G. E., 4777
Koe, B. K., 5507
Koerner, A., 5469
Koh, S.-W., 4719
Kohn, P. M., 4174, 4175, 4439
Kokka, N., 3110
Kokkevi, A., 3635, 3636
Kolansky, H., 4176
Kolodny, R. C., 4177, 4178, 4179
Komenda, S., 3128, 3133, 4010, 4011, 4012, 4013, 4014, 4015, 4414, 4415, 4542, 5498
Kooshian, L. K., 3778
Kopell, B., 4752
Kopell, B. S., 3161, 3577, 4180, 4637, 4751, 4753, 4754, 5051, 5052, 5053
Kopplin, D. A., 4181

Korcok, M., 4182, 5471
Korte, F., 3298, 3335, 4195, 4196, 4197, 4198, 4211, 4212, 4295, 4296, 4480, 4481, 5486
Korte, Friedrich-Wilhelm, 5678
Kosersky, D. S., 4183
Kossoy, A. D., 5292
Kostellow, A. B., 4184, 5392
Kosviner, A., 4185, 4186, 4187
Kotb, N., 4161
Koukkou, M., 4188, 4189, 4190, 4191, 4192
Koup, J. R., 5452
Koutselinis, A., 4123, 4124, 4193, 5453
Kovacs, J. L., 3147
Koval, M., 3601
Kozhevnikova, S. K., 4194
Kraatz, A., 4198
Kraatz, U., 3298, 4195, 4196, 4197, 4198, 4211, 4212, 4295, 4296, 5486
Krakowiak, P. A., 5472
Krakowski, M. J., 3153
Kralik, P. M., 4199
Kramer, H. F., 3416
Kramer, J., 4200
Kramer, J. C., 3828
Krei, Joyce Ruth, 5714
Krejci, Z., 3128, 3133, 3910, 3911, 3912, 4201, 4202, 4414, 4415, 4542, 4878, 5264
Krell, M., 4991
Krieglstein, J., 4373
Krikorian, A. D., 4235
Krimmer, E. C., 3295, 3296, 3297, 4203, 4204, 4857
Krishnamurty, H. G., 4205, 4206
Kroll, P., 4207
Krup, M., 4808
Kuechenmeister, C. A., 4279, 4280
Kuehnle, J., 3274, 3275, 3276, 4208, 4432, 4433
Kuehnle, J. C., 3272, 3273, 3277, 3323, 3614, 3868, 3870, 4421, 4422, 4423, 4424, 4429, 4430, 4431, 4434, 4435, 4748, 4749
Kuhn, D., 3869
Kulp, R., 4915
Kulp, R. A., 4087, 4346
Kumar, A., 3648, 3649
Kumar, N., 3648, 3649
Kuo, E. H., 3694
Kuppers, F. J. E. M., 3322, 4209, 4210
Kuriyama, E., 4844

Kurth, H.-J., 4211, 4212
Kurzman, M. G., 4213, 4214
Kutsch, L. J. C., 4215
Kutscheid, B. B., 3900
Kvalseth, T. O., 4216, 4217
Kwon, W. J., 3903
Kyrkou, K. A., 4472

Labrecque, G., 3895, 4218
Lacerda, L. A., 5350
Lach, E., 5473
Ladewig, D., 5468
Ladriere, M. L., 4219
Laguarda, R., 4018, 4315
Laird, H., 3511, 3512, 3517
Laird, H. E., 4095
Laird, H. E., II, 4220
Lake, C. R., 3803
Lall, B., 5474
Lall, G., 5474
Lambert, J. 4550
Lame, M., 4023, 5437
Lander, N., 3451, 4221, 4409, 4410, 4412
Landreville, I., 3068
Lansky, D., 4222
Lapa, A. J., 4546, 5524, 5579
Lapointe, G., 4554
Laporte, J., 4223
Laporte, J.-R., 4223
Larsen, F., 4673
Larsen, F. F., 4224, 4677, 4678
Larson, J. W., 4441
Lash, S., 4973
Last, J. A., 3544
Laszlo, J., 5475
Latt, S. A., 4225
Latta, R. P., 4226
Lau, R. J., 4227, 4228
Lau-Cam, C. A., 4229, 4230, 5476
Laubie, M., 3578
Laurence, H. L., 5243
Laurent, B., 4028, 4231
Lavagnino, E., 3259
Lavagnino, Edward R., 5664, 5665
Laverty, V., 3892
Laverty, W., 4665
Law, B., 5477
Law, F. C. P., 4232, 5265
Lawrence, D. K., 3817, 4233

Lawton, R. L., 4068
Leander, J., 3207
Leander, K., 3208, 3209, 4375, 4564, 4565,
    4566, 5200, 5277, 5532, 5533, 5556
Leblanc, A. E., 3720, 3721
Leboeuf, G., 3508
Lecorsier, A., 4234
Ledbetter, M. C., 4235
Lee, C.-M., 4236
Lee, Cheuk M., 5715
Lee, Cheuk Man, 5679, 5680, 5681
Lee, G. M., 4237, 4571
Lee, J. H., 4471
Lee, M. L., 3299, 4238, 4555, 4556, 4557
Lee, Y. E., 5012, 5013, 5014
Lefkovitch, L. P., 4889
Lefkowitz, S. S., 4239, 4240, 4241, 4670
Legator, M. S., 4242, 4984
Leger, C., 3603, 3604, 3605, 5304, 5366, 5367
Legowska, Z., 4243
Legris, H., 5344
Lehmann, D., 4188, 4189, 4190, 4191, 4192
Lehrer, G. M., 3116
Leichner, P. P., 5444
Leigh, S., 3968
Leighty, E. G., 4244, 5266, 5478, 5479, 5480
Leiter, L., 3191
Lemberger, L., 3572, 3573, 3574, 3575, 3576,
    3701, 3756, 4245, 4246, 4247, 4248, 4249,
    4250, 4252, 4253, 4254, 4627, 4628, 4629,
    4630, 4981
Lemberger, Louis, 5654, 5655, 5656, 5657
Lemmi, H., 3505
Lenard, Katherine, 5710
Lenicque, P. M., 4597, 5255
Lenox, J. R., 3429
Lerer, B., 4817
Lerner, C. B., 3318, 4227
Lessin, P., 4682
Lessin, P. J., 3503, 3762, 4178, 4255, 4866
Letarte, J., 3508
Leuchtenberger, C., 3111, 4256, 4257, 4258, 5481
Leuchtenberger, R., 3111, 4256, 4257, 4258, 5481
Levander, S., 3208
Levett, A., 4259
Levi, R., 4260
Levin, A., 4812
Levin, K. J., 3876
Levin, S., 5044

Levine, M. M., 4538
Levisman, J. A., 5008
Levitan, D. E., 3220
Levy, J., 5263
Levy, J. A., 4170, 4261, 4262, 4263, 4510, 5482
Levy, M. H., 3854
Levy, R., 4264, 4265
Levy, S., 4266, 4267, 4314, 4410, 4412, 4413, 5227, 5277
Lewis, A., 4268
Lewis, C. R., 4269
Lewis, E. G., 4270, 4626
Lewis, G., 5612
Lewis, G. S., 4271, 5610
Lewis, M. F., 4272
Lewis, M. J., 3668, 3850, 4273
Lewis, M. L., 3089
Lewis, S. C., 3394
Lewis, S. J., 5024
Li, D. M. F., 4274
Li, H.-L., 3112, 3113
Liakopoulos, D., 4497, 5293
Liakos, A., 3371, 3372, 4275, 4964, 4966, 4967, 4968
Lichtenberg, D., 5006
Liddle, J., 5520
Lieber, M., 4276
Liebmann, J. A., 3705
Liedgren, S. R. C., 4277
Lief, P. L., 4087
Lima-De-Faria, A., 4278
Lin, D. C. K., 5384
Lin, K. N., 4554
Lin, W.-F., 5484
Lindgren, J.-E., 3207, 3209, 4374, 4375, 4551, 4552, 4553, 4564, 4565, 4566, 5230, 5232, 5277, 5533
Lindgren, J. E., 5228, 5231, 5278, 5528
Lindsey, C. J., 3063, 3448, 3449, 3450, 4516
Ling, G., 3159
Linton, P. H., 4279, 4280
List, A., 4281
List, A. F., 4282
Litt, I. F., 5424
Littleton, J. M., 4283, 4333
Litwack, A. R., 3811
Liu, J. H., 5483, 5484
Livne, A., 4260, 4264, 4265, 4806, 4807, 4808
Llamas, R., 4284
Llewellyn, G. C., 4285, 4286

Locke, D., 3915
Lockhart, A. B., 4287, 5188, 5189
Lodge, J., 5010
Lodge, J. W., 4572, 5009, 5015
Loeb, R. C., 4150
Loeffler, K. O., 3179, 3853, 4135, 4288, 5273, 5411
Loev, Bernard, 5682, 5683, 5684, 5685
Lohiya, N. K., 3620, 3621, 3624
Loizzo, A., 5208
Lokhandwala, M. F., 4053, 4289
Lomax, P., 3530, 5036
Lombrozo, L., 4136, 4290
London, S. W., 3368, 5485
Lonero, L., 3904
Longo, V. G., 5208
Loo, H., 3529
Lopata, A., 5291
Lopez-Artiguez, M., 4714
Loscalzo, B., 4291, 4292
Loskota, W. J., 3530, 5036
Lott, J. W., 4293
Lott, P. F., 4293
Lotter, H. L., 4294
Lotz, F., 4295, 4296, 5486
Loughnan, P., 5374
Louria, D. B., 3114
Lousberg, R. J. J. Ch., 3321, 3322, 4209, 4210, 4297, 4947
Lovegreen, P. D., 5112
Loveless, S. E., 4511, 4512
Low, C.-E., 4556, 4557
Lowe, D., 5419
Lowe, H. I. C., 4287
Lowry, W. T., 4298, 4299
Lubbe, K. E., 5308, 5309
Lubetkin, A. I., 5025
Lubin, D. J., 3913
Lubin, L., 3430
Lucas, W. L., 4300, 4301
Ludwig, B., 4056
Lukoff, I. F., 3400, 3401
Lundberg, G. D., 5552
Luteijn, J. M., 4948, 5487
Luteyn, J. M., 4302
Luthra, Y. K., 3695, 4303, 4304, 5488
Lutz, E. G., 5489
Lycko, E., 4056
Lyle, M. A., 4305, 4306, 4589, 4720
Lyle, Robert E., Jr., 5686

Lynch, J. J., 3526
Lynch, V. D., 4951
Lynn, Kathleen R., 5713
Lyons, A., 4150

McBay, A., 4307
McBay, A. J., 4308
McCabe, G. P., 4775
McCain, A. H., 3971
McCallum, N., 4410
McCallum, N. K., 4266, 4309, 4310, 4311, 4312, 4313, 4314, 4411, 4412
McCann, H. G., 4972
McCarthy, C., 4017
McCarthy, C. R., 4018, 4315
McCarthy, L. E., 3368, 4316, 5485
McCarthy, R. H., 5347
McCaughran, J. A., 3525
McChesney, J. D., 3064, 4317
McClean, D. K., 3125, 3177, 4318
McConnell, W. R., 4319, 4320, 4321, 4322, 4323
McCoy, D. J., 4324, 4325, 4326, 4988
McDonnell, J., 4230
McDougall, J., 3812
McFadden, M., 5168
McFarland, D., 4453, 4454, 4455, 4460
McFarland, D. J., 4459, 4461
McGeer, E. G., 5442, 5443
McGeer, P. L., 3951, 4042, 4043, 4044, 5442, 5443, 5490
McGlothlin, W., 4327
McGlothlin, W. H., 4501
McGowan, J. C., 3873
McGowan, W. T., 5280
McGuire, M. O., 4214
McIntyre, K. E., 4717
McKenna, G. J., 4473
McKenzie, C. E., 4673
McKillip, J., 3126
McLatchie, C., 5016
McLatchie, C. C., 4833
McLaughlin, C. L., 5282, 5491
McLaughlin, T., 4616
McLendon, D. M., 3703, 4162, 4328
McMahon, R., 4249
McMillan, D. E., 3077, 3127, 3661, 4329, 4330, 5441
McMillan, Moses W., 5658
McNamee, H. B., 3614
McNeil, J. R., 4072

Macakova, J., 4010, 4011, 4012, 4014, 4015, 4415
Macavoy, M. G. 4331
Maccannell, K., 4332, 4469, 4470
Macconaill, M., 3159
Machata, G., 5358
Machin, D., 4958
Macias, G.-S., 4917
Macindoe, J. H., 3915
Mackintosh, J. H., 3558, 3559, 3560, 3561
Maclean, B., 3484
Maclean, K. I., 4283, 4333
Madrid-Pedemonte, L., 3143
Maes, R. A. A., 5470
Magalhaes, C. C. P. B., 5330
Magence, D. N., 4334
Magnan, F., 4683, 4684
Magnan-Lapointe, F., 4758
Magnus, K. E., 3466
Magour, S., 4335, 4336, 4337, 4338
Mahajan, V., 4017
Mahfouz, M., 4339, 5397
Mahlberg, P. G., 3897, 3898, 3958, 3959, 5086, 5087, 5088
Maier, R., 4340
Maitre, L., 3115, 4340
Makar, A. B., 4339, 5397
Maker, H. S., 3116
Makino, H., 4849
Malhotra, R. K., 4719
Malik, O. P., 4341, 4342, 4343, 4344
Malingre, T. M., 3960, 3961, 3962, 3963
Malingre, Th., 4345
Malit, L. A., 4346
Malloy, K. P., 4049, 4050, 4051, 4052, 5267
Malone, M. H., 3408
Malor, R., 3222, 3784, 4039, 4347, 4348, 4349, 4350, 5340, 5341, 5492, 5634
Malor, R. M., 3473
Manaster, G. J., 4165
Manatt, M., 5493
Manfredi, R. A., 5440
Mangione, A., 5452
Manheimer, D. I., 4418
Mankin, D., 4150
Manning, F., 4352
Manning, F. J., 3117, 4351
Manno, B., 3118
Manno, B. R., 4353, 4354, 4355, 4356, 4357, 4358
Manno, J., 3118

Manno, B. R., 4353, 4354, 4355, 4356, 4357, 4358

Manno, J., 3118

Manno, J. E., 4353, 4354, 4355, 4356, 4357, 4358

Manocha, S. L., 5132

Mansur, E., 4765

Mantilla-Plata, B., 3119, 3913, 4359, 4360, 4361, 4362, 4363

Manys, S., 3120

Maple, P. J., 4364

March, J., 3723

Marcotte, J., 4365

Margolin, F., 4547

Margolis-Kazan, H., 4366, 5494, 5495

Mari, F., 3212

Marin, G., 4367

Marini, J. L., 4368

Marino, C., 5326

Markidou, S. G., 4472

Marks, D. F., 3307, 4331

Marks, V., 4164, 4369, 4370, 4998, 5026, 5027, 5028, 5029, 5030, 5496, 5598

Marozzi, E., 5268

Marshman, J. A., 3812, 4371

Martens, S., 4372

Martin, A., 5162, 5163

Martin, B., 3207, 3209, 4221, 4373, 4374, 4375, 4729, 5556, 5628

Martin, B. R., 3121, 3199, 3441, 3610, 3611, 3664, 3920, 3923, 3936, 3937, 3938, 3939, 3940, 3941, 3942, 4376, 4377, 4378, 4379, 4380, 4381, 4382, 4383, 4384, 4385, 5212, 5331, 5422, 5630

Martin, P., 3513, 4386, 4387, 4388

Martin, W. R., 4830

Martin, Yvonne C., 5713

Martinez, D., 4714, 5548

Martz, R., 3572, 3573, 3574, 3575, 3576, 3701, 3756, 4248

Marx, M. R., 3122

Maser, J. D., 4389

Maskarinec, M. P., 4390, 4391, 4392, 4393, 4556, 4558

Mason, D. L., 4545

Mason, J., 5170

Masoud, A. N., 4394, 4395, 5497

Masters, W. H., 4178, 4179

Masur, J., 5330

Mathe, A. A., 5104

Matkovics, B., 3714

Matsumoto, K., 4396, 4397

Matsumoto, Ken, 5687

Matsuyama, S., 3123, 4398

Matsuyama, S. S., 4399, 4400, 4401

Matte, A. C. 4402

Matthews, H. R., 4199

Mattox, K. L., 4403

Maugh, T. H., 3124, 4404

Maule, W. F., 4328

Maurin, J. F., 5128

May, E. L., 4381, 5210, 5211, 5212, 5631

May, J., 5124

Maybaum, J., 4405

Mazzi, G., 3212

Mazzone, G., 3264

Meacham, M. P., 3346, 4054, 4055

Mechoulam, B., 5227

Mechoulam, R., 3293, 3432, 3451, 4221, 4267, 4313, 4314, 4406, 4407, 4408, 4409, 4410, 4411, 4412, 4413, 5006

Medek, A., 3128, 3133, 4414, 4415, 4542, 5498

Meghal, S. K., 4610, 4611

Mehndiratta, S. S., 4416

Mehra, N., 3170

Mehrotra, N. K., 5499

Meisenberg, G., 3340

Meister, R. G., 4396, 4397

Melges, F. T., 4417

Melinek, M., 5406

Mellinger, G. D., 4418

Mello, N., 3870, 4431

Mello, N. K., 4419, 4420, 4421, 4422, 4423, 4424, 4429, 4434, 4435

Mellors, A., 3804, 3871, 3872, 3873, 3874, 4025, 4035, 4425, 5500

Melton, J., 4921, 5369

Mendelson, J. H., 3272, 3273, 3274, 3275, 3276, 3277, 3323, 3614, 3868, 3870, 4208, 4419, 4420, 4421, 4422, 4423, 4424, 4426, 4427, 4428, 4429, 4430, 4431, 4432, 4433, 4434, 4435, 4748, 4749

Mendhiratta, S. S., 4436

Mendleson, G., 4437

Mercer, G. W., 4438, 4439

Merchant, J. R., 3615, 3616

Merlini, L., 3261, 3262, 3612
Merriam, G., 4972
Merritt, J. C., 3213, 3534, 5355
Mertens, H. W., 4272
Messiha, F. S., 4440, 4441
Metzger, M. H., 4442
Meuwissen, O. J. A., 5470
Meyer, R. E., 4443, 4444
Michael, C. M., 3214, 4157, 5279
Michaels, R. J., 4236
Michaels, Raymond John, 5680
Michelson, A. E., 4507
Michihiro, F., 5093
Mickey, M. R., 4682
Miczek, K. A., 4445, 4446, 4447, 4448, 4449, 5501
Midalia, N. D., 3586
Middleton, B., 4592
Mihashi, S., 4038
Mikhael, M., 3487
Mikhail, M. M., 4339, 5397
Mikuriya, T. H., 4450, 4451
Mikus, P., 5105
Miles, C. G., 3812
Millart, H., 5344
Miller De Paiva, L., 5502
Miller, A. J., 4743
Miller, J. D., 4452, 5503
Miller, K. W., 4591
Miller, L., 4453, 4454, 4455, 4456
Miller, L. L., 4457, 4458, 4459, 4460, 4461, 5504, 5505
Miller, R. A., 4462
Miller, R. D., 3142, 3904
Miller, R. E., 4463
Miller, R. H., 4464
Milman, D. H., 4465, 5506
Milne, G. M., 5507, 5627
Milne, G. M., Jr., 4084
Milner, G., 4466, 4467, 4468
Milstein, M., 4494, 4495, 4496
Milstein, S. L., 3218, 4332, 4469, 4470
Mims, R. B., 4471
Mintz, J., 4957
Miran, M., 3600
Miranne, A. C., 5508, 5590
Miras, C., 4193
Miras, C. J., 3129, 3617, 4157, 4472
Mirin, S. M., 4473
Mishra, S. S., 4474

Mitoma, C., 4024, 4674, 4675
Mitra, G., 3808, 3809, 4475, 4476, 4477, 4478, 4659
Mitra, M. G., 4479
Miyake, T., 3309, 3310
Mobarak, Z., 4480, 4481
Mobilia, J., 5374
Modiano, A., 3432
Moertel, C. G., 5391
Moffat, A. C., 4482, 5027, 5089, 5206, 5477, 5598, 5629
Mohan Ram, H. Y., 3130, 4781, 5570
Mohan, D., 4700, 4701, 5547
Mole, M. L., 4880, 5083
Moll, H. R., 3095
Mon, M. J., 4483, 5509, 5588
Monroe, S., 3702
Montagna, M., 4484
Montana, E., 4485
Montero, J.-L., 4486
Montgomery, B. J., 4487
Montgomery, J., 4385
Monti, J. M., 3449, 4488, 4489, 5001
Moon, T. E., 3968
Moore, C. E., 4899
Moore, F., 4137
Moore, H. K., 4685
Moore, M., 3430
Moore, M. D., 4490
Moore, R., 3877
Moore, R. J., 4721
Moore, S. C., 3325
Moore, W. T., 4176
Moosmayer, A., 4952
Morahan, P. S., 5510
Moreno, L. N., 3260
Morgan, H. G., 4491
Mori, I., 4845, 4846, 4847
Morin, G., 3895, 4218
Morin, P. J., 3895, 4218
Morishima, A., 3602, 4492, 4493, 4494, 4495, 4496, 4523, 4524, 4525, 4533, 4534, 5511
Morishima, A., 3132
Moroni, F., 4715, 4716
Morrill, G. A., 3351, 4184, 5392
Morrissey, E. R., 4790
Morrissey, W., 5105
Mosca, L., 3324
Moschonas, D., 5365

Moschovakis, A., 4497, 5279, 5293
Mosher, R., 3159
Moskowitz, H., 4498, 4499, 4500, 4501, 4502, 5303
Mosnaim, A. D., 3143
Moss, D. E., 4503
Moss, I. R., 3772, 4504
Moss, S. W., 4030
Mott, J., 4505
Muchow, D. C., 3137
Mukerji, K. G., 4115
Mullane, J., 4017
Muller, P., 4506
Mullins, C. J., 4507
Munsen, A. E., 4508
Munson, A., 5263
Munson, A. E., 3383, 3440, 3921, 3924, 4170, 4263, 4382, 4509, 4510, 4511, 4512, 4513, 4913, 4914, 5194, 5510
Munson, J. A., 5194
Murison, G. L., 5593
Murphy, D. L., 4983
Murphy, P., 3160, 3161, 5053
Murphy, P. L., 3161
Murphy, S., 3830
Murray, T. F., 4514
Musty, R. E., 3449, 4149, 4515, 4516, 4517, 4590
Musumeci, M. R. 5455
Myers, W. A., 3917, 5423, 5512

Nadeau, A., 4028
Naditch, M. P., 3131, 4518, 4519
Nagle, B., 4520
Nagy, C., 5426
Nagy, C. M., 4521
Nahas, G., 3604, 3605, 3606, 3759, 3957, 4492, 4522, 4523, 4524, 4525, 5304, 5366, 5367, 5513, 5514
Nahas, G. G., 3132, 3602, 3603, 3607, 3955, 3956, 4016, 4493, 4494, 4495, 4496, 4526, 4527, 4528, 4529, 4530, 4531, 4532, 4533, 4534, 5238, 5353, 5425, 5431, 5511, 5515, 5516, 5517, 5518
Nail, R. L., 4535
Naimark, R. S., 4537
Naithani, S. C., 5586
Nakahara, H., 5574
Nakano, M., 4819

Nakano, S., 4536
Naliboff, B. D., 3496, 4537, 4717
Nalin, D. R., 4538
Nallan, G., 4456
Naor, Z., 3269
Narayanaswami, K., 4539, 4540
Natale, M., 5519
Nath, L. M., 4700, 4701, 5547
Nathan, I., 4265
Navaratnam, V., 4541
Navratil, J., 3128, 3133, 4013, 4015, 4414, 4415, 4542, 4878, 4879, 5498
Nayyar, V. L., 4115
Nazar, B., 4281, 4543, 5419
Nazar, B. L., 4282
Needham, L., 5520
Neidig, P. H., 4979
Neki, J. S., 4700, 4701, 5547
Neleman, F. A., 5470
Nemeth, D., 4241
Nersasian, R. R., 4005
Neu, C., 4544
New, P. F. J., 4208
Newell, F. W., 4960, 5521, 5522
Newman, W., 4150
Nguyen-Hoang-Nam, 3989, 3990, 4234, 4792, 5320, 5572
Nicar, M. J., 5523
Nichols, D. E., 4545
Nicolau, M., 4546, 5131, 5524
Nieburg, H. A., 4547
Niebyl, J. R., 5235
Nielson, P. J., 4979
Niemi, W. D., 5525
Nightingale, S. L., 3875, 5526
Nio, H. C., 5616
Nir, I., 3269
Nishimura, H., 4548
Nishioka, T., 4849, 4850, 4851, 4852, 4853
Nitake, M., 4549
Niu, H. C., 5113, 5615
Nogrady, S. G., 3930, 3931
Noirfalise, A., 4550
Nordqvist, M., 3209, 4221, 4374, 4375, 4551, 4552, 4553, 5201, 5269, 5527, 5528
Norris, S. A., 3819
Nosal, G., 4554
Novotny, M., 3299, 4238, 4391, 4392, 4393, 4555, 4556, 4557, 4558

Nowlan, R., 4559
Noyes, R., 3134, 3409, 4068, 4560, 4561
Noyes, R., Jr., 4562, 4563
Nugteren, D. H., 4948
Nunes, J. F., 4588
Nutter, C., 3482
Nyquist, S., 4281
Nyquist, S. E., 3832, 4811, 5419

O'Carroll, M., 4823
O'Connell, D., 4017, 4616
O'Connell, M. J., 5391
O'Donnell, J. A., 5529, 5530
O'Donnell, S., 4538
O'Fallon, J. R., 5391
O'Malley, P. M., 4086, 5451
O'Neil, J. D., 5531
O'Neill, C., 4485
O'Rear, C. E., 4285, 4286
Oakley, C., 3051
Oda, M., 4851
Odell, R. E., 4219
Odkvist, L. M., 4277
Oesch, F., 5402
Offermeier, J., 4974
Oguri, K., 5234, 5624, 5625
Ohlin, G. 4063
Ohlin, G. C., 4059, 5445
Ohlsson, A., 4564, 4565, 4566, 5278, 5402,
    5532, 5533, 5534, 5556
Okey, A. B., 4567, 4568, 4569
Olley, J. E., 3839, 3840, 3841
Olmsted, C. A., 4237, 4570, 4571
Olsen, D., M., 3476, 5343, 5609
Olsen, J., 5010
Olsen, J. L., 4572, 5009, 5015
Opelz, G., 4681, 4682
Orcutt, J. B., 3055
Orcutt, J. D., 3135, 4573, 4574, 4575
Orlina, A. R., 4835, 4836
Osawa, T., 5140
Osgood, P. F., 4009, 4576, 4577, 4578, 4579,
    4601
Oskoui, M., 5270
Ottersen, R., 4580
Ottersen, T., 3671, 4581, 4582, 4583, 4745
Overall, J. E., 4000, 4001

Pack, A. T., 4584

Padgett, D., 3867
Page, J. G., 4585, 4586, 5040
Pagel, M. L., 4587
Paknikar, S. K., 4166
Palermo Neto, J., 3595, 3596
Palermo, Neto, J. P., 4588
Pallante, S., 4306, 4589
Palmer, A. K., 5353
Panagopoulos, C., 3074
Panayiotopoulos, C., 5136
Panayiotopoulos, C. P., 3372, 3740
Pandina, R. J., 4590
Pang, K.-Y. Y., 4591
Panpanya, B., 4800
Papa, V. M., 5539
Papadakis, D., 4950
Papadakis, D. P., 3214, 4157
Papanikolaou, G., 4497, 5293
Paquin, D., 3069
Parad, R., 4592
Parekh, A. K., 4030
Parfrey, P. S., 4593, 4594
Pariani, H. K., 4053, 4289
Paris, M., 3369, 3580, 3760, 4595, 4596,
    4597, 4598, 4599, 5320
Paris, M. R., 3053, 3761, 5255, 5385
Paris, R. R., 4598, 4599
Parker, C. J., 5622
Parker, M. R., 5329
Parks, K. J., 4976
Pars, H. G., 4578, 4579, 4600, 4601, 4602,
    4603, 4709, 4710
Pars, Harry G., 5674, 5686, 5688, 5689,
    5690, 5691, 5692, 5698, 5703, 5704,
    5706, 5707
Paschal, D., 5520
Passatore, M., 3474, 3826, 3827, 4604
Pastier, D., 5065
Patel, A. H., 5135
Patel, A. R., 4605
Patel, D. D., 5135
Paton, S. M., 4606
Paton, W. D., 3136, 3936
Paton, W. D. M., 3937, 3938, 3939, 3940,
    3941, 3942, 3943, 3944, 3945, 3946,
    3947, 3948, 4383, 4384, 4607, 4608,
    4609, 4689, 5217, 5422, 5518, 5535,
    5632
Patwardan, G. M., 4610, 4611

Pauerstein, C. J., 3265, 3729, 5295, 5296, 5297
Paul, M. K., 4612
Paulsen, B. S., 3976
Payne, R. J., 4613
Pearl, J. M., 3631
Pechnick, R., 5444
Peck, P. L., 4503
Pedroni, G., 3324
Peek, L., 3430, 4712
Peeke, S. C., 4614
Peltzman, D. J., 5427
Peraita-Adrados, M. R., 5018
Perec, C. J., 4615
Pereira, W., 4017, 4018, 4315, 4616
Perez, J. M., 3589
Perez-Reyes, M., 4617, 4618, 4619, 4620, 5148
Perez-Vitoria, C., 4621
Perinetti Casoni, R., 4604
Perlman, D., 3547
Permutt, M. A., 4622
Perry, D. C., 4405
Perry, S., 5526
Persaud, T. V. N., 4623
Pertwee, R. G., 3814, 4624, 5536
Pesys, E., 4219
Pet, D., 4625
Peters, B. A., 4626
Petersen, B. A., 5384
Petersen, B. H., 4627, 4628, 4629, 4630
Petersen, R. C., 4631, 4632, 4633, 4634, 5537
Petersen, R. E., 4085
Petersson, K., 5200
Petit, L., 4635
Petroulakis, G., 4497, 5293
Petrus, R., 3966, 3967
Petrzilka, T., 4636
Petrzilka, Theodor, 5668, 5693, 5694, 5695, 5696, 5696
Petzel, T. P., 3126, 4334
Petzoldt, K., 5130
Pfefferbaum, A., 4637, 5051
Phoebe, C. H., 3687
Piall, E. M., 5028, 5029
Picchioni, A. L., 4220
Pichat, L., 3989
Pichon, J., 4635

Pickens, Joan T., 5380
Pickens, R., 3137
Piemme, T. E., 4638
Pieper, W. A., 4639
Pierozynski, G., 5157
Piga, A., 5115
Pihl, R. O., 3191, 3192, 4222, 4640, 4641, 4642, 4643, 4644, 4645, 4646, 4647, 5538
Pillard, R. C., 3138
Piraino, A., 4520
Piraux, M., 4122
Pirl, J. N., 5539
Pitt, C. G., 3520, 4648, 4649, 4650, 5253, 5540
Pizzitola, V., 5476
Plotnikoff, N. P., 4236, 4651, 4707, 4710
Pochay, V. E., 5432, 5433
Poddar, M. K., 3290, 3294, 3808, 3809, 4475, 4476, 4477, 4478, 4479, 4652, 4653, 4654, 4655, 4656, 4657, 4658, 4659, 5368
Pohl, K. D., 3139, 4660
Poklis, A., 4690
Polich, J. M., 4973
Pollack, C., 4592
Pomazol, R. J., 4661
Pomeranz, B., 3211
Pope, J. N., 3457
Popham, R. E., 4371
Porath, G., 5313, 5532
Porath, O., 4808
Post, R. D., 3060
Pouget, J. M., 4127, 4128, 5454
Pouget, M., 4129
Powell, K. E., 4662
Prabhu, G. G., 4700, 4701, 5547
Pradhan, S., 5541
Pradhan, S. N., 3140, 4663, 5541
Prakash, N., 5542
Prakash, R., 3837, 4664, 4665
Prasad, K. K., 4636
Prather, J. E., 4666
Prendergast, T. J., 3141
Preston, A., 5602
Preston, A. M., 5060
Preston, J., 4667
Price, L., 5370
Primavera, L. H., 4867

Pringle, H. L., 4668, 5543
Prioreschi, P., 4669
Prockop, L. D., 4803
Proctor, J. D., 3388
Profili, M., 5257
Pross, M., 5259
Pruess, M., 4241
Pruess, M. M., 4670
Pryor, G. T., 4024, 4224, 4671, 4672, 4673, 4674, 4675, 4676, 4677, 4678, 5576
Psaltis, P., 5617
Puder, M., 3269
Pundlik, M. D., 4610
Pundlik, M. G., 4611
Punjabi, E., 5361
Purnell, W. D., 4679
Purohit, V., 5544

Quero, A. M., 3761
Quimby, M. W., 4680

Rabii, J., 3397
Rachelefsky, G. S., 4681, 4682, 5017
Rackur, G., 5580
Radcliffe, S., 3582
Radouco-Thomas, C., 4683, 4684
Radouco-Thomas, S., 4683, 4684
Radstaak, D., 5170
Radwan, S. S., 4685
Raft, D., 3877, 4686
Ragonese, R. R., 4687
Ragusa, S., 5365
Raifman, M. A., 4688
Raine, J. M., 4689
Rainsbury, R., 3051
Raj, A. Y., 5636
Ram, H. Y. M., 5545
Ramanna, L., 5014
Randle, S., 3806
Rao, N. G. S., 4690, 5464
Rao, N. V. R., 4691
Rao, S. M., 4692
Rasmussen, K. E., 4693, 4694, 4695, 4696, 4697, 4698
Rauscher, F. P., 4983
Rawitch, A. B., 4699, 5025, 5122, 5546
Ray, R., 4700, 4701, 5547
Raymond, A., 4557
Raz, A., 3058, 3281, 3282, 3970, 4702

Razdan, R., 4170, 4602, 5263
Razdan, R. K., 3199, 3899, 3922, 4578, 4600, 4601, 4603, 4703, 4704, 4705, 4706, 4707, 4708, 4709, 4710, 5094, 5095, 5096, 5097, 5098, 5099, 5418
Razdan, Raj K., 5674, 5686, 5690, 5691, 5692, 5698, 5699, 5700, 5701, 5702, 5703, 5704, 5705, 5706, 5707, 5714
Reed, Jr., H. B. C., 4711
Regan, J. D., 3348, 3349
Regelson, W., 3430, 4712
Reid, L. D., 3142, 3308, 3904, 4713
Reinking, J., 3512
Reiss, S., 4831, 5009, 5010, 5015
Rennels, M., 4538
Rennick, P., 3631
Repetto, M., 4714, 5548
Revuelta, A. V., 4715, 4716, 5549
Reynolds, S., 3415
Rhead, J., 4538
Rhodes, M. L., 5237
Ricciardi, G., 5257
Rich, E., 3168
Rich, E. S., 4993
Richardson, A. H., 3557
Richter, J. A., 5550
Rickards, R. W., 3480
Rickles, W. H., 3496, 4537, 4717
Rieger, H., 4373
Rinder, I. D., 4718
Ritchie, J. M., 4989
Rittenhouse, J. D., 5551
Ritter, K. S., 4080
Ritzlin, R. S. 5552
Roberson, C., 3569
Robertson, J., 5117, 5618
Robertson, L. W., 4719, 4720
Robins, A., 5106
Robins, A. G., 5107
Robitscher, J., 3081
Rock, N. L., 4721
Rodda, B., 3756, 4248
Rodda, B. E., 3572, 3573, 3574, 3575, 3576, 3701
Rodgers, R., 4722
Rodriguez, M. B., 5059, 5060, 5602
Rodriquez, Ma. A., 5548
Roffman, R. A., 4723, 5553
Rogan, F., 3220

Rogers, C., 4724
Rogers, S., 3287
Rogers, W., 3319, 5310
Rohde, C., 4803
Rohrer, Roger 5546
Rollen, Z. J., 5520
Romanik, D. G., 5143
Romo-Quitanar, G., 5125
Ronald, R. C., 4722
Ronkainen, I., 5221
Rootman, I., 3484, 5554
Rose, R. M., 4725
Rose, S. E., 4726, 5555
Roseboom, H., 3798
Rosecrans, J. A., 3096
Rosell, S., 4727, 4728, 4729, 5556
Rosen, K., 4129
Rosen, K. M., 4127, 4128, 4130, 4464, 5454
Rosen, P., 3715
Rosenbaum, R., 5392
Rosenberg, C. M., 4730, 4731
Rosenberg, D., 5129
Rosenberg, E., 3759
Rosenberg, F. J., 4600
Rosenberg, J., 3319, 5310
Rosenblatt, J. E., 3768
Rosenbloom, M. J., 4751
Rosenblum, I., 4732
Rosenfeld, J., 4733, 4734, 5557, 5558
Rosenfeld, J. M., 3386, 4735
Rosenkrantz, H., 3694, 3695, 3742, 3743,
    4303, 4304, 4736, 4737, 4738, 4739,
    4740, 4741, 4742, 4743, 4744, 5045,
    5383, 5559, 5560, 5561
Rosenqvist, E., 4581, 4582, 4583, 4745
Rosenthal, D., 4746, 5016, 5149, 5150, 5562,
    5623
Rosenthal, D. L., 4833
Rosenthal, E., 3763
Rosenthal, F., 5563
Rosenthal, M. P., 4747
Rossi, A. M., 4429, 4748, 4749
Roth, S. H., 4750, 5564
Roth, W. T., 3161, 3577, 4180, 4637, 4751,
    4752, 4753, 4754, 5051, 5052, 5053
Rothschild, M., 4755
Rowan, M. G., 3705, 3706, 4755, 4756
Rowe, H., 4247, 4250, 4251, 4759
Rowley, G. L., 4757

Roy, A. N., 3279
Roy, P. E., 3375, 3807, 4026, 4027, 4028,
    4029, 4231, 4758
Rozhold, O., 3128
Rubenstein, K. E., 5565
Rubin, A., 4252, 4253, 4254, 4759
Rubin, J., 5391
Rubin, V., 4760, 4761, 4762
Rubottom, G. M., 3598
Rumbaugh, C. L., 3204
Russell, G. K., 4763
Russell, J. A., 5566
Russell, M. H., 5610
Russell, R. D., 4764
Ryan, C. W., 3259
Ryan, Charles W., 5660, 5708, 5709
Ryan, J. H., 3757
Rydberg, M., 5527
Ryman, T., 4551, 5527

Sa, L. M., 4765
Saayman, G. S., 4259
Sabelli, H. C., 3143, 4364, 5124
Sadava, S. W., 4766, 4767
Saha, S., 3290
Sahai, I., 4474
Salemink, C., 4768, 4769
Salemink, C. A., 3054, 3321, 3362, 4158,
    4159, 4160, 4209, 4210, 4302, 4770,
    4771, 4949, 4950
Salemink, C. A. L., 4948
Salgado, A., 3730
Sallan, S. E., 4772, 4773, 4774, 5567
Salmon, M., 3727
Salome, R., 4503
Salvendy, G., 4775
Salzman, C., 4776, 4777, 4778, 5568
Samba Murty, A. V. S. S., 4781
Samrah, H. M., 3321
San, R., 5240
Sanders, H. D., 3180
Sanders, J., 5569
Sanders, M. G., 4587
Sanders, V. M., 4511, 4512
Sands, R., 4517
Sangdee, P., 4144, 5457
Sangsingkeo, P., 4800
Santavy, F., 3144
Santo, J., 3892

Sanz, P., 5548
Sarath, G., 5570
Sarkar, C., 3809, 4779, 4780
Sarma, N. P., 4781
Sassenrath, E. N., 4782, 4783, 5336, 5571
Sathe, S., 4648
Sato, M., 5141
Satz, P., 3744, 3745, 4784
Saunders, M. E., 3874
Savaki, H. E., 4785
Savic, Y., 3303
Sawa, A., 4032
Saxena, A. K., 5499
Saxena, K. K., 4786
Saxena, S. C., 5484
Sayed, Y., 4650, 5540
Sazhko, M. M., 4824
Scarpignato, C., 3527, 3528, 3592
Schachter, E. N., 5473
Schaefer, C. F., 4787, 4788, 4789
Schaeffer, G. M., 4790
Schaller, J. L., 4357
Schanzlin, D. J., 5522
Scheelings, P., 5340
Schenk, J., 4791
Schentag, J. J., 4116, 5452
Scherer, S. E., 3145
Scherrmann, J., 3990
Scherrmann, J. M., 3438, 4792, 5572
Schiff, P. L., 3687, 4880, 5085
Schiff, P. L., Jr., 4294
Schill, T. R., 3702
Schlegel, R. P., 4793
Schleh, E., 4258
Schmeidler, J., 3601
Schmeling, W. T., 4794, 4795, 4796, 4797, 4798, 4799
Schmid, G., 4636
Schmitt, H., 3578
Schmitt, R. L., 4301
Schneider, A., 3111
Schneider, N. S., 4284
Schneider, R. J., 4800
Schnell, C., 4731
Schoenfeld, R. I., 4801
Schoolar, J. C., 4802
Schoor, M., 3346, 4054, 4055
Schopf, J., 3618
Schou, J., 3395, 4803, 5058

Schran, H., 4649
Schuckit, M. A., 4790
Schultes, R. E., 3146, 4804, 4805, 5573
Schultz, G. S., 4699
Schulz, J., 4712
Schurr, A., 4265, 4806, 4807, 4808
Schut, J., 4809
Schwam, J. S., 4810
Schwarz, S., 4811
Schweitzer, G., 4812
Schwin, R., 4622
Scoto, G. M., 3264
Seaton, A., 3582, 3849, 3930, 3931
Seehafer, R. W., 4813, 4814
Seffrin, J. R., 4813, 4814
Segal, B., 4815
Segal, M., 4816, 4817
Segal, Z., 4641
Segawa, M. 5574
Segawa, T., 4818, 4819
Segelman, A. B., 4820, 4821, 4822
Segelman, F. P., 4820, 4821, 4822
Sehgal, P. K., 3312
Seid, D. A., 5325
Seiden, R. H., 4823
Seigler, D. S., 3304
Seipp, C. A., 5335
Seligman, B. R., 4547
Seligmann, O., 4821, 4822
Sellers, M. L., 4424
Sells, S. B., 3148
Seltzman, H. H., 4650, 5540
Senchenko, G. I., 4824
Sengupta, D., 3462, 3463, 4825
Servi, S., 3261, 3262
Sethi, V. K., 4826
Sett, R., 5545
Seyfeddinipur, N., 4827
Shader, R. I., 4777, 4778
Shah, G., 5333
Shah, G. D., 5614
Shah, P. G., 5334
Shahar, A., 3813, 5337
Shalla, C. L., 5160
Shanahan, M. G., 4828
Shanker, R., 4829
Shannon, H. E., 4830
Shapiro, B., 5010

Shapiro, B. J., 4572, 4831, 4832, 4833, 4834, 5008, 5009, 5011, 5012, 5013, 5014, 5015, 5016, 5017, 5271
Shapiro, C. M., 4835, 4836
Shapiro, D., 3546
Shapiro, T. M., 3893
Sharma, A. N., 3623
Sharma, B. P., 4837
Sharma, G. K., 4838, 4839, 4840, 4841, 5610
Sharma, J. D., 5600, 5601
Sharma, S., 3419, 4502, 5303
Sharp, R., 3828
Shattuck, D., 4929
Shea, D., 4641, 4642, 4643, 4644, 4647, 5538
Shea, J. W., 5432, 5433
Sheard, M. H., 4368
Sheehan, John Clark, 5674
Shehorn, J., 3052
Sheldrick, G. M., 4103, 4105
Sheposh, J. P., 3109
Sheth, A. R., 3464, 5333, 5334
Shevin, R. L., 4842
Shick, J. F. E., 4843
Shieh, Y. N., 5484
Shiling, D. J., 5335
Shimomura, H., 4844
Shimp, R. G., 3865
Shinogi, M., 4845, 4846, 4847
Shiomi, H., 5574
Shipley, G., 4392, 4393
Shipp, D. A., 5235
Shirakawa, I., 4149, 4515
Shoemaker, R. H., 4848
Shorey, J. M., 5370
Shoupe, T. S., 3424, 3425, 5322, 5323
Shoyama, Y., 4849, 4850, 4851, 4852, 4853
Shrivastava, R. K., 3567
Shukla, S. R. P., 5039
Sidorenko, N. M., 4854
Sieber, M., 4855, 4856
Siegel, M. I., 4857
Siegel, P., 4857
Siemens, A. J., 3187, 4676, 4858, 4859, 4860, 4861, 4862, 4863, 5575, 5576
Sigal, H., 4645
Sigg, E. B., 3147
Sigg, T. D., 3147

Sihgh, H. H., 5544
Silcox, D., 4830
Siler-Kohdr, T. M., 5296, 5297
Silva, M. T. A., 4864
Silverman, P. B., 4865
Silverstein, M. J., 4682, 4866
Silvestro, J. R., 5577
Simmon, J., 4618
Simmonds, D., 3949
Simmons, G. A., 4018, 4315
Simmons, M., 5007
Simmons, M. S., 4831
Simon, G. S., 5172
Simon, L. M., 3714
Simon, W. E., 4867
Simpson, D. D., 3148, 3548, 4868, 4869
Singer, G., 3531, 5594
Singh, K., 5578
Singh, M., 4962
Singh, N., 4870
Singh, P., 4683, 4871
Singh, P. P., 4872, 4873, 4874, 4875, 4876
Singh, R., 5139
Singh, S., 5133
Single, E., 4132
Sinha, J. N., 5020
Sinnett, E. R., 3149
Siqueira, S. W., 5579
Siroka, A., 4010, 4011, 4012, 4013, 4014, 4015
Silva Prasad, J., 4206
Skelton, F. S., 4365
Skibba, J. L., 5252
Skinner, W. A., 5580
Sklenovsky, A., 4877, 4878, 4879
Skrabal, J., 4879
Slade, L. T., 3428
Slangen, J. L., 5119
Slatkin, D. J., 3687, 4294, 4880, 5085
Slavin, R. G., 4269
Small, E., 3150, 3151, 4881, 4882, 4883, 4884, 4885, 4886, 4887, 4888, 4889
Small, E. W., 3877
Smart, R. G., 3048, 3152, 3153, 4890, 4891
Smiley, K. A., 4892, 4893, 4894, 4895, 5609
Smith, C. B., 5296
Smith, C. G., 3265, 3325, 3326, 3729, 4896, 4897, 4898, 4899, 5295, 5297, 5581, 5582, 5583

Smith, C. M., 4900
Smith, D. E., 5187
Smith, G. M., 4901, 4902
Smith, G. V., 5483
Smith, H. W., 4903
Smith, Herchel, 5675
Smith, J. P., 4904
Smith, M. T., 3325, 5582
Smith, N., 4692
Smith, R. G., 3327, 4898, 5582, 5583
Smith, R. J., 4905, 4906, 4907
Smith, R. L., 5261
Smith, R. M., 4908
Smith, R. N., 4909, 4910, 4911, 4912, 5192
Smith, R. T., 4831
Smith, S. H., 4170, 4913, 4914, 5226, 5510, 5584
Smith, T. C., 4087, 4346, 4915
Smith, R. G., 5581
Snyder, J. A., 3599
Snyder, S. H., 3293
Soares, J. R., 3880, 3881, 4916, 5017
Sobrino Lazaro, G., 4917
Sofia, R. D., 3291, 3292, 3835, 4918, 4919, 4920, 4921, 4922, 4923, 4924, 4925, 4926, 5369, 5585
Solis, H., 3730
Solomon, J., 4927, 4928, 4929
Solomon, T. A., 4925
Somehara, T., 4851
Somers, R. H., 4418
Soni, C. M., 4930
Sorber, W. A., 3431
Sorfleet, P., 4931
Sornberger, C., 4592
Sornberger, G. C., 5362
Sorosiak, F. M., 4932
Soueif, M. I., 4933, 4934, 4935, 4936, 4937, 4938
Spadero, C., 3264
Sparkes, R. S., 4401
Spaulding, T. C., 4939
Spencer, C. P., 4541
Spiers, P., 4646, 4647
Spiker, M., 3719, 5179
Spikes, J. J., 5539
Spiteller, G., 3781, 3882, 3883
Sprague, G., 4945
Sprague, G. L., 4940, 4941, 4942, 4943, 4944

Sprague, R. A., 4744
Sprenge, L., 5169
Spronck, H. J. W., 4297, 4302, 4946, 4947, 4948, 4949, 4950, 5487
Srivastava, R. K., 4786, 5019, 5020
Srivastava, S. C., 4648
Srivastava, S. L., 5586
Srivastava, V. K., 4786, 5019, 5020
Staab, R. J., 4951
Staak, M., 4952
Staats, G. R., 4953, 4954, 5587
Stacey, B., 5185
Stahl, E., 4955
Stanley, J., 5235
Stanton, M. D., 3154, 4956, 4957
Stanyon, R., 3902, 3903
Staquet, M., 4958
Star, A. E., 4821
Stark, P., 3703, 4396, 4397, 4959, 4960, 5522
Starks, M., 4961
Starmer, G. A., 3471, 3472, 3784, 4039, 4350, 5184, 5308, 5309, 5569
Staub, J., 3779
Steadward, R. D., 4962
Steahly, L. P., 3336
Steen, J. A., 4272
Steer, R. A., 4125, 4809
Stefanis, C., 3371, 3372, 3740, 4275, 4963, 4964, 4965, 4966, 4967, 4968, 5136
Stefanis, C. N., 4969, 4970, 4971
Steffenhagen, R. A., 4972, 4973
Stein, G. S., 4483, 5588
Stein, J. I., 4810
Stein, J.L., 4483
Steinberg, H., 3637
Steinberg, S., 4974
Stenchever, M. A., 4975, 4976
Stenchever, M. R., 4976
Stepanov, G. S., 4977, 4978
Stermitz, F. R., 5327
Stern, W. C., 4040
Sternberg, P., 5521
Stewart, J., 4979
Stich, H., 5240
Stickgold, A., 3402
Stillman, R., 3504, 4980, 4981
Stillman, R. C., 4982, 4983, 5335
Stimmel, B., 5589
Stoeckel, M., 4242, 4984

Stoller, K., 4985
Stoller, K. P., 4986
Stone, C. J., 4987, 4988
Stone, G. C., 4614
Stone, L. H., 5376, 5590
Strahlendorf, H. K., 3831
Straight, R. C., 4626
Strasbaugh, J. E., 5585
Strauss, R. H., 3902, 3903
Strehlow, D., 3356
Strichartz, G. R., 4989
Stringaris, M. G., 3155
Stromberg, L., 4990
Stuart, R. B., 4991
Stueck, G. S., 5591
Suciu-Foca, N., 3132
Sugerman, A. A., 5592
Sulkowski, A., 3168, 4992, 4993, 5108, 5109
Sullivan, H., 4759
Sullivan, H. R., 4994, 4995
Sullivan, M. F., 4996, 4997
Sullivan, S. F., 4831
Sutker, L. S., 4784
Suzuki, J. S., 3414
Swann, D. A., 3376, 3377
Swanson, G. D., 3311, 4985, 4986, 5198
Swenson, E. W., 3494, 3969
Swonger, A. K., 4692
Symons, A. M., 4998
Szara, S., 3156, 3391, 3762, 4999
Szechtman, H., 5429
Szepsenwol, J., 5000, 5593
Szymkowska, K., 4243

Taboada, M. E., 5001
Tacker, H. L., 3505
Tadrus, R., 4121
Taguchi, V. Y., 4735
Takagi, H., 5574
Takahashi, R. N., 4149, 4515, 5002, 5003, 5594
Takeuchi, S., 4819
Takeya, K., 4037, 4038, 5004
Talbott, J. A., 5005
Tamir, I., 5006
Tanimura, T., 4548
Taplin, G. V., 5014

Tashkin, D. P., 4572, 4831, 4832, 4833, 4834, 5007, 5008, 5009, 5010, 5011, 5012, 5013, 5014, 5015, 5016, 5017, 5271, 5595
Tassinari, C. A., 5018
Taunton-Rigby, A., 3469
Tavendale, R., 4624, 5536
Tayal, G., 3092, 4786, 5019, 5020
Taylor, D. A., 3725, 3726, 5021, 5022, 5023, 5024, 5596, 5597
Taylor, Edward C., 5710
Taylor, P., 3425, 3426
Taylor, S. P., 5025
Teale, D., 5030
Teale, J. D., 3797, 4164, 4369, 4370, 4998, 5026, 5027, 5028, 5029, 5496, 5598
Tec, J., 3157
Tec, N., 3158
Teiger, D. G., 4600
Teitel, B., 5031
Telfer, M., 4835, 4836
Ten Ham, M., 3530, 5032, 5033, 5034, 5035, 5036, 5118
Tena, G., 5115
Tennant, F. S., 5037, 5599
Tennant, F. S., Jr., 5038
Teo, R. K. C., 3472
Terlouw, J. K., 3363, 3416, 4209, 4210
Terris, B. Z., 4709, 4710
Terris, Barbara Z., 5703
Testa, T., 5256
Tewari, S. N., 5600, 5601
Thacore, V. R., 5039
Thakkar, A. L., 5040
Thakur, R. S., 4826
Thel, E., 4118
Thel, S., 3692, 4117
Theuns, H., 3321
Thoden, J. S., 3159
Thomas, L. E., 4932
Thomas, R. J., 5041
Thomas, S. A., 4255
Thombs, M. J., 3534
Thompson, E. D., 5112, 5113, 5616
Thompson, G., 5042
Thompson, G. R., 5043, 5044, 5045
Thompson, T., 3137
Thorn, W. R., 4389, 5046

Thornby, J. I., 4138
Thoursen, K., 3690, 5250, 5254
Thysen, B., 3351
Tiess, D., 5047
Ting, T. L., 5558
Tinklenberg, J., 4752
Tinklenberg, J. R., 3160, 3161, 3162, 3577, 4180, 4637, 4751, 4753, 4754, 5048, 5049, 5050, 5051, 5052, 5053
Titus, H. W., 5054
Tocci, A. A., 4615
Todd, J., 5055
Tomassone, B. M., 4520
Tomer, K., 5622
Tomizawa, A., 4844
Tomlinson, K. R., 4823
Tonnesen, F., 4697
Toohey, J. V., 5056, 5057
Toomey, T. C., 3877
Topp, G., 5058
Toro, G., 4178, 4179
Toro-Goyco, E., 5000, 5059, 5060, 5448, 5449, 5593, 5602
Torrelio, M., 3772, 3979, 3980, 3981, 3982, 3983, 3984, 3985
Torres, L. M., 5080, 5081
Towell, B., 3376
Trajano, E., 3596
Tran Van Ky, P., 4506, 5061
Traub, S. H., 5062, 5063
Travis, R. P., 4280
Treffert, D. A., 5064
Treich, I., 5065
Tremblay, R., 4028
Trice, H. M., 5066
Trichopoulos, D., 4123
Triesman, D., 3163
Troiden, R. R., 3669
Trovato, A., 3593, 3594
Truant, G. S., 4569
True, J. H., 5067
True, W. R., 5067
Truitt, E. B., Jr., 5069, 5070
Truitt, E. B., 5068
Trulson, M. E., 4040
Trupin, E. W., 3445
Tubergen, D. G., 4227, 4228
Tuchinda, P., 5357
Tuchmann-Duplessis, H., 5603

Tucker, A. N., 5071, 5604
Tucker, L., 5605, 5606, 5607
Tucker, R. B., 5608
Tufik, S., 3448, 3450
Tulunay, F. C., 4152, 5299
Tumino, G., 5365
Tumrongrachaniti, S., 4800
Tunving, K., 5072
Turkanis, A., 4147
Turkanis, S., 3459, 4145
Turkanis, S. A., 3164, 3476, 4034, 4144, 4146, 4148, 4893, 4894, 4895, 5073, 5074, 5075, 5076, 5077, 5343, 5457, 5458, 5609
Turker, R. K., 4153, 5078
Turnbull, J. H., 3376, 3377
Turner, C., 3426
Turner, C. E., 3337, 3362, 3671, 3672, 3673, 3674, 3681, 3682, 3683, 3684, 3685, 3686, 3687, 3992, 4271, 4294, 4580, 4582, 4583, 4880, 5079, 5080, 5081, 5082, 5083, 5084, 5085, 5154, 5155, 5314, 5375, 5610, 5611, 5612
Turner, C. J., 5613
Turner, Carlton E., 5667
Turner, J. C., 3958, 3959, 5086, 5087, 5088
Tuttle, T., 3630
Twine, C. E., 4650, 5540
Twine, C. E., Jr., 4649
Twitchett, P. J., 5089
Twitchett, Peter J., 5711
Tylden, E., 3165, 3166
Tyrey, L., 5090
Tyrrell, E., 3901
Tyrrell, E. D., 3503, 3762

Uchtenhagen, A., 5468
Ueki, S., 3785, 5091, 5092, 5093, 5234, 5393
Uhlenhuth, E. H., 5401
Uhly, B., 3277
Uliss, D. B., 3899, 4708, 5094, 5096, 5097, 5098, 5099, 5418
Umekita, N., 4849
Unger, P. J., 4835, 4836
Ungerleider, J. T., 5283
Unnikrishnan, P., 5614
Urbanek, J. E., 5082
Uwaydah, E. M., 3452

Uwaydah, I. M., 4913
Uyeno, E., 5580
Uyeno, E. T., 3167, 5100, 5101, 5102

Vacc, N. A., 5577
Vachon, L., 3168, 4834, 4992, 4993, 5103, 5104, 5105, 5106, 5107, 5108, 5109
Vaille, C., 5110
Valencia, M., 5332
Valentine, J. L., 5111, 5112, 5113, 5615, 5616, 5617
Valio, I. F. M., 5114
Valle, J. R., 4546, 4765, 5114, 5131, 5524
Valle, J. R. D., 5579
Vallejo, E., 5115
Van Boven, M., 5116
van den Broek, G., 5117
van den Broek, G. W., 5618
Van Der Kolk, B. A., 4777, 4778
Van Dongen, J. P. C. M., 3322
van Klingeren, B., 5118
Van Noordwijk, J., 4160
Van Ooyen, R., 4297
Van Ree, J. M., 5119
Van Went, G. F., 5120
Van Zwieten, P. A., 5438
Vance, J. W., 5452
Vande Velde, V., 4122
Varanelli, C., 3312, 3427, 3428
Varano, A., 5312
Vardaris, R. M., 4699, 5025, 5121, 5122, 5183, 5546
Varma, D. R., 5123
Varma, S. D., 4822
Varma, V. K., 5202
Vassar, H. B., 4926
Vaughan, C. G., 4910, 4911, 4912
Vaziri, H., 4168
Vazquez, A. J., 3143, 5124
Vedlich, L., 4014
Vega-Franco, L., 5125
Velazquez y Cols, G. F., 5126
Verbeke, R., 5127
Vercruysse, A., 3223
Verin, Ph., 5128
Verma, O. P., 3623
Verma, S. K., 4436
Vernon, S., 3577
Vernot, E. T., 3831

Versteeg, K., 4068
Vidic, H. J., 5129, 5130
Vieira, J. E. V., 5114, 5131
Vijay, K. K., 5132
Vijayalakshmy, G., 5133
Vildy, A., 5128
Vinson, J. A., 5134, 5135, 5619
Virgo, B. B., 5620
Visser, J., 4345
Vitola, B. M., 4507
Volavka, J., 3740, 5136
Volkmar, F., 3795
Vossmer, A., 4929
Vree, T. B., 5137, 5138
Vyas, D. K., 5139

Wada, J. A., 3525, 5140, 5141, 5142
Wagner, D., 4619, 4620
Wagner, E. E., 5143
Wagner, H., 3169, 4821, 4822
Wake, A., 5141, 5142
Waldman, I., 4982
Waldmeier, P. C., 3115
Walker, A., 3793
Walker, J., 3722
Walker, J. M., 3723
Walker, L., 3547
Wall, M. E., 4617, 4618, 4619, 4620, 4746, 5144, 5145, 5146, 5147, 5148, 5149, 5150, 5621, 5622, 5623
Wallace, J. E., 3361
Wallace, L., 5151
Waller, C., 5154
Waller, C. W., 5152, 5153, 5155
Walsh, J. M., 5156
Walsworth, D., 3118
Wampler, K. S., 3149
Wangsness, P. J., 4154, 5461
Wardell, D., 3170
Warner, A. M., 5157
Warner, E. G., 3171
Warner, V. J., 4019
Warner, W., 3442, 5158, 5159, 5328
Warnock, G. R., 5160
Warren, J. W., 3458
Warren, M., 4665
Warrick, P., 4759
Waser, P. G., 3782, 3783, 5161, 5162, 5163, 5300

Wasserman, A. J., 3388
Watanabe, K., 5164, 5234, 5624, 5625
Waters, J. E., 3894
Waters, K. D., 5374
Watson, D., 3569
Watson, H. A., 3466
Watson, W. P., 3480
Watts, D. T., 5158
Watts, R. J., 5165
Way, E. L., 5166
Wayner, M. J., 3531
Weatherstone, R. M., 3849
Weber, E., 4242, 4984
Wechsler, H., 5167, 5168
Weckowicz, T. E., 5169, 5170
Wei, E. T., 5325
Weil, A. T., 5626
Weil, J., 5245
Weil, J. V., 5246, 5247
Weil, A., 3172
Weinberg, A. D., 5171, 5172
Weiner, B.-Z., 5173
Weingartner, H., 4980, 4981, 4982
Weinstein, M., 5174
Weinstein, R. M., 5175, 5176, 5177
Weisman, R., 5178
Weiss, G., 3719
Weiss, G. K., 5179
Weiss, S. T., 3082
Weissman, A., 5180, 5181, 5627
Weissman, B., 5104
Weisz, D. J., 5121, 5122, 5182, 5183
Weker, R. R., 5432
Weker, R. T., 5433
Welburn, P. J., 4039, 4350, 5184
Weller, R. A., 3893
Wells, B., 5185
Wells, L. E., 4085
Wenkert, E., 3260
Weppner, R. S., 5186
Werling, L. L., 5550
Werner, G., 3173, 3692, 4117, 4118, 4119
Wesson, D. R., 5187
West, L. E., 4585, 4586
West, M. E., 4287, 5188, 5189
Whalen, R. P., 5190
Wheals, B. B., 5191, 5192
Whetsell, C., 3064
Whitaker, Alison, 3541

White, A., 5193
White, A. C., 3442, 4513, 5194
White, E. R., 5195
White, H. B., 4279, 4280
White, S. C., 5196
Whitehead, P. C., 5197
Whitehouse, A., 5055
Whiteman, M., 3400, 3401
Wiberg, D. M., 5198
Wideburg, Norman E., 5669
Wideburg, Norman Earl, 5670
Widman, M., 3750, 3751, 5199, 5200, 5201,
    5228, 5229, 5230, 5231, 5232, 5417,
    5628
Wiechmann, M., 3692, 4117, 4118, 4119
Wieder, D. L., 5242
Wig, N. N., 4416, 4436, 5202
Wikler, A., 4453, 4454, 4459, 4461, 5203,
    5505
Wilcox, H. G., 4167
Wilcox, W. C., 4072
Willard, D. H., 4996, 4997
Willette, R. E., 5204, 5205
Willette, R. G., 5253
Williams, D., 3520
Williams, D. L., 4648, 4649, 4650, 5253,
    5540
Williams, J., 3089
Williams, P. J., 5564
Williams, P. L., 5027, 5089, 5206, 5477,
    5598, 5629
Williams, Peter L., 5711
Williams, R. L., 4138
Williams, S. J., 5207
Willinsky, M. D., 5208
Willis, R. J., 5613
Wilson, A. F., 3708
Wilson, C. W. M., 3174
Wilson, P. R., 5209
Wilson, R. S., 4381, 5210, 5211, 5212, 5630,
    5631
Win Pe, U., 5213, 5214, 5215
Winburn, G. M., 3056
Winek, C. L., 3175, 5216
Wing, D. R., 4689, 5217, 5632
Wingard, D. W., 5497
Winn, F. J., 4810
Winn, M., 4707, 5218
Winn, Martin, 5712, 5713, 5714

Winship-Ball, A., 3467
Winstead, D. K., 5364
Winternitz, F., 4486
Witayarut, C., 4800
Witschi, H., 4365
Woggon, B., 3075, 3176
Wojtulewicz, D., 4121
Wold, J. K., 3974, 3975, 3976, 5219
Wolfers, H., 4198
Wolkin, A., 3514
Wolkin, A. L., 3518
Wolkon, G. H., 4065
Wolkowitz, O., 4982
Wong, H. Z., 4181
Wong, R. J., 4311
Wood, C. D., 4356
Wood, G. C., 3519
Wood, P. G., 4994, 4995
Wood, P. L., 5549
Woodhouse, E. J., 5220
Woodrow, K. M., 3162
Woodside, A. G., 3305, 3306, 5221, 5306
Woodward, M. G., 5403
Woolsey, N. F., 5464
Wrenn, J. M., 3780, 5222, 5223, 5224, 5225, 5272
Wright, P. L., 5226
Wyatt, R. J., 4980, 4981, 4982, 4983
Wyllie, M. G., 3814
Wynder, E. L., 3991
Wynn, H., 3865, 3866, 3867
Wyss, U., 4192

Yagen, B., 4267, 4314, 4412, 4413, 5227
Yagi, M., 4853
Yamamoto, I., 5625
Yamamoto, T., 5092
Yamuchi, T., 4853
Yang, C., 5042
Yankelev, S., 5249
Yawney, C. D., 4371
Yehle, A. L., 5410, 5555
Yehuda, S., 3439
Yen, F.-S., 3123, 4400, 4401
Yisak, W., 5228, 5229, 5230

Yisak, W.-A., 5232
Yisak, W. A., 5231
Yonge, K. A., 5170
Yoshida, A., 5233
Yoshida, T., 3912, 4202
Yoshimura, H., 5234, 5624, 5625
Young, M. J., 3728
Young, P. R., 4236
Youngs, D. D., 5235
Yount, R., 5633
Yu, L., 3411
Yurchak, A. M., 4116

Zabrodin, G. D., 3225
Zaluzny, S. G., 5341, 5634
Zaugg, H. E., 4236, 5236
Zaugg, Harold E., 5715
Zaugg, Harold Elmer, 5681
Zavala, D. C. 5237
Zbinden, J., 4258
Zeidenberg, P., 3757, 3955, 3956, 3957, 5238, 5347, 5425, 5519
Zeindenberg, P., 5396
Zeskind, J. A., 3589
Ziedman, K., 4502
Zilkha, A., 5173
Zimmer, B. D., 5239
Zimmer, D., 3618, 3619, 4192
Zimmerman, A. M., 3177, 4318, 5240, 5241 5243, 5635, 5636
Zimmerman, D. H., 5242
Zimmerman, S., 5243, 5635, 5636
Zimmerman, S. B., 5241
Zimmermann, E., 3396, 3397, 3834
Zinberg, N., 4772
Zinberg, N. E., 4773, 4774, 5244, 5567 5637
Zolnierowicz, M., 4243
Zuardi, A. W., 5003
Zuskin, E., 3370
Zuurmond, T. J., 5281
Zwicker, A. P., 5350
Zwillich, C., 5245
Zwillich, C. W., 5246, 5247

SUBJECT INDEX

Referenced by annotation number.

ABBOTT-40656
  pharmacological aspects
    eyes, 3640
    intraocular pressure (IOP), 3640
ABBOTT-41988
  toxicology
    cardiovascular, 4773
    eyes, 5043
    subacute effects, 5044
ABBOTT-43981
  pharmacological aspects
    eyes, 3665
    intraocular pressure (IOP), 3665
ABSORPTION
  delta-9-THC, 4164
    dogs, 3611
    fasting, 4674
    feeding, 4674
    pharmacological aspects, 5261
    pigeon(s), 3611
    rats, 4674
    vehicle of administration, 4674
  marihuana
    review, 4663
  marihuana smoke
    humans, 4254
    lung(s), 4254
ABSTINENCE SYNDROME
  cannabidiol (CBD)
    mice, 3334
  cannabinol (CBN)
    mice, 3334
  delta-8-THC
    mice, 3334
  delta-9-THC
    mice, 3334
    rats, 3734, 4152
  11-hydroxy-delta-8-THC
    mice, 3334
ACCUMULATION
  delta-9-THC
    adipose, 5546
    mice, 5546
    sex accessory organs, 5546
  marihuana
    clinical aspects, 4531
    tissues, 3500, 4531
ACETYLCHOLINE (ACH)
  cannabidiol (CBD)
    brain, 3773, 4716
    hippocampus, 4715
    rats, 3773, 4715, 4716
    striatum, 4715
    synthesis, 3773
    turnover, 4715, 4716
  cannabinol (CBN)
    rats, 3629
  cannabis extract
    rats, 3264

ACETYLCHOLINE (continued)
  delta-8-THC
    brain, 3773
    metabolism, 3050
    rats, 3050, 3773
    synthesis, 3050, 3773
  delta-9-THC
    brain, 3773, 4140, 4141, 4716
    brain levels, 3630
    hippocampus, 4715
    in vitro, 4546, 4750
    metabolism, 3050
    mice, 4140, 4141
    neuromuscular transmission, 3988
    rats, 3050, 3629, 3630, 3773, 4715, 4716, 5372
    release, 4140
    stereospecificity, 4750
    striatum, 4715
    synaptic transmission, 4750
    synthesis, 3050, 3773, 4141
    turnover, 4715, 4716
    vas deferens, 4546
  11-hydroxy-delta-8-THC
    metabolism, 3050
    rats, 3050
    synthesis, 3050
  11-hydroxy-delta-9-THC
    brain, 5550
    rats, 5550
  SP-111
    in vitro, 4546
    vas deferens, 4546
ACETYLCHOLINESTERASE
  delta-9-THC
    adrenals, 3343
    in vitro, 4462
    membrane effects, 4231
    microsomal, 4657
    mitochondrial, 4657
    rats, 3343, 4503
    synaptosomal, 4657
    synaptosomes, 3809
  marihuana smoke
    cerebellum, 4303
    cerebrum, 4303
    chronic administration, 4303
    rats, 4303
ACHENE(S)
  cannabis
    domesticated plant, 4882
    wild plant, 4882
  Cannabis sativa
    development, 5542
    morphology, 5542
ACID(S)
  marihuana
    analysis, 4391
      GC/MS, 4391
    constituents of, 4391

ACTION POTENTIAL(S)
  delta-9-THC, 3190
  SP-111A, 3190
ACUTE EFFECT(S)
  marihuana
    review, 4527
ACUTE INTOXICATION
  hashish
    dogs, 4096
ACYLTRANSFERASE
  cannabigerol (CBG)
    in vitro, 3871
    lymphocytes, 3871
    mice, 3873
    synaptosomal, 3873
  cannabinol (CBN)
    in vitro, 3871
    lymphocytes, 3871
    mice, 3873
    synaptosomal, 3873
  delta-8-THC
    in vitro, 3871
    lymphocytes, 3871
    mice, 3873
    synaptosomal, 3873
  delta-9-THC
    in vitro, 3871
    lymphocytes, 3871
    mice, 3873
    synaptosomal, 3873
  ll-hydroxy-delta-9-THC
    mice, 3873
    synaptosomal, 3873
ACYLTRANSFERASE ACTIVITY
  cannabidiol (CBD)
    lymphocytes, 3872
  cannabigerol (CBG)
    lymphocytes, 3872
  cannabinoid(s)
    lymphocytes, 5500
    psychotomimetic activity, 5500
    synaptosomes, 5500
  cannabinol (CBN)
    lymphocytes, 3872
  delta-8-THC
    lymphocytes, 3872
  delta-9-THC
    lymphocytes, 3872
  ll-hydroxy-delta-9-THC
    lymphocytes, 3872
ADENYLATE CYCLASE
  cannabinol (CBN)
    brain, 3627
  delta-9-THC
    brain, 3627
    humans, 5333
    in vitro, 5333
    spermatozoa, 5333
  ll-hydroxy-delta-9-THC
    brain, 3627
ADIPOSE
  delta-9-THC
    accumulation, 5546
    mice, 5546
    sex accessory organs, 5546

ADMINISTRATION
  cannabinoid(s)
    research, 5340
ADOLESCENT(S)
  marihuana
    patterns of use, 5424
  marihuana smoke
    adverse effect(s), 5493
    detection, 5493
    review, 5493
  marihuana use
    attitude, 5451
    availability, 5451
    patterns of, 5451
    social interaction, 5451
ADRENAL FUNCTION
  delta-9-THC
    ascorbic acid, 3344
    rats, 3344
    steroids, 3344
  hashish
    ascorbic acid, 4292
    cholesterol, 4292
    corticosterones, 4292
    rats, 4291, 4292
    stress, 4291
ADRENALS
  delta-8-THC
    ascorbic acid, 4340
    cholesterol esterase, 4340
    rabbit(s), 4340
    rats, 4340
  delta-9-THC
    acetylcholinesterase, 3343
    ascorbic acid, 4340
    ATPase(s), 3343
    cholesterol esterase, 4340
    corticosterones, 3342
    histo chemistry, 3343
    organ weights, 5392
    pseudocholinesterase, 3343
    rabbit(s), 4340
    rats, 3342, 3343, 4340, 5392
    steroids
      synthesis, 5158
  dimethylheptylpyran (DMHP)
    ascorbic acid, 4340
    cholesterol esterase, 4340
    rabbit(s), 4340
    rats, 4340
  marihuana
    humans, 4617
  marihuana extract
    organ weights, 5392
    rats, 5392
ADRENERGIC NERVOUS SYSTEM
  cats
    cardiovascular effects, 5270
  delta-9-THC
    cardiovascular effects, 4128
    dogs, 4052
    heart rate, 4052
    humans, 4128
    intraocular pressure (IOP), 3860, 3864, 5413
    review, 5413

ADRENERGIC NERVOUS SYSTEM (continued)
  synthetic cannabinoids
    intraocular pressure (IOP), 5413
    review, 5413
ADRENOCORTICOTROPIC HORMONE (ACTH)
  cannabinol (CBN)
    release, 4080
  delta-8-THC
    rabbit(s), 4340
    rats, 4340
  delta-9-THC
    rabbit(s), 4340
    rats, 3110, 4340
    release, 4080
    secretion, 3110
  dimethylheptylpyran, (DMHP)
    rabbit(s), 4340
    rats, 4340
  ll-hydroxy-delta-9-THC
    release, 4080
ADULTERATION
  marihuana
    phencyclidine, 4688
ADVERSE EFFECT(S)
  cannabinoid(s)
    driving, 5496
  cannabis
    chronic use, 4934
    compared to:
        alcohol, 3243, 3854
    general information, 3854
    humans, 4471
    psychological aspects, 4934, 5072
    review, 3105, 5535
  delta-9-THC
    cancer, 4560, 4562, 4563
    humans, 3797
  hashish
    rats, 3438
    review, 3169, 4525
  immunosuppression, 4241
  marihuana, 3124, 3398, 3766, 4083, 4723
    acute effect(s), 3114
    amotivational syndrome, 3049
    anxiety, 3795
    brain, 3049, 3599
    Canada, 3048
    chromosomes, 3599
    chronic use, 3114, 3350, 4436, 4700
    cytotoxicity, 3049, 3916
    driving, 3599, 4498
    factors influencing use, 4519
    general information, 3138, 3657, 4097, 4530,
        5049
        physicians, 4099
    humans, 3049, 3231, 3350, 3651, 3655, 3848
        4030, 4098, 4151, 4518, 4519
    immune system, 3049, 3599, 4530
    intravenous administration, 3710, 4030
    lung(s), 3599, 3916
    macromolecular synthesis, 3049
    paraquat, 3544, 3708, 4549
    psychological aspects, 3131, 4041, 4518, 4519
    psychological effects, 5474
    psychological tests, 4436, 4700

marihuana (continued)
    review, 3231, 4151, 4466
    social interaction, 5474
    sociological aspects, 3231
    students, 3048
    testosterone, 3599
    therapy, 4030
  marihuana smoke
    psychological aspects, 5450
  marihuana use
    amotivational syndrome, 5506
    driving, 5503
    subjective effects, 5503
AGE
  cannabis
    cannabinoid content, 3591
    seeds, 5608
  cannabis plant
    cannabinoid content, 4698
  marihuana use, 5530
AGGRESSION
  delta-9-THC
    isolation, 5393
    rats, 5393, 5501
    route of administration, 5501
    strain difference, 5501
    vehicle of administration, 5501
  marihuana
    stress, 3241
AGGRESSIVE BEHAVIOR
  cannabidiol (CBD)
    mice, 5035
  cannabinoid(s)
    animals, 3732
  cannabis
    chronic use, 3186
    humans, 3078, 3186
    rats, 3182
    stress, 3062
  cannabis extract
    interaction with
        anticholinergic(s), 3595
    rats, 3446, 3595
    stress, 3446
  cannabis resin
    mice, 3560
  Cannabis sativa
    monkeys, 4407
    rats, 3061
    stress, 3061
  delta-8-THC
    animals, 3732
    rats, 3446
    stress, 3446
  delta-9-THC
    acute administration, 4446
    animals, 3732
    ant(s), 3783
    biogenic amine(s), 3450
    chronic administration, 4446
    compared to:
        alcohol, 5025
    gerbils, 3819
    humans, 5025
    mice, 4448, 5035

delta-9-THC (continued)
    monkeys, 3234, 4093, 4448
    rats, 3446, 3447, 3450, 3785, 4162, 4445, 4446,
        4448, 4449, 4588
    serotonin (5-hydroxytryptamine), 4588
    stress, 3446, 3785, 4588
  hashish
    mice, 4402
  marihuana
    animals, 3240, 4632
    biogenic amine(s), 3063
    crime, 3160
    delinquents, 5053
    humans, 3161, 3162, 4106, 4107, 4751, 4778
    monkeys, 3234
    rats, 3063, 4516
    stress, 3063
  marihuana extract
    biogenic amine(s), 3449, 3450
    rats, 3449, 3450, 4489
    REM sleep, 3449
    stress, 3449
  marihuana smoke
    chronic administration, 4303
    rats, 4303
AIRWAY CONDUCTANCE
  delta-9-THC
    aerosol, 4572
    humans, 4572, 5014
  marihuana smoke
    humans, 5014
ALCOHOL AND CANNABIS
  comparisons
    of use, 3233
ALCOHOL DEPENDENCE
  delta-9-THC, 4160
ALCOHOL WITHDRAWAL
  delta-9-THC
    convulsions, 4944
    mice, 4199, 4944
    nabilone (Lilly compound no. 109514), 4940
    therapy, 3498, 3734
  nabilone (Lilly compound no. 109514)
    convulsions, 4944
    mice, 4944
ALCOHOLISM
  cannabinoid(s)
    therapy, 3331
  cannabis
    therapy, 4731
  marihuana
    therapy, 4730
  synthetic cannabinoids
    therapy, 3331
ALKALINE PHOSPHATASE
  delta-9-THC
    rats, 4425
ALKALOID(S)
  cannabis
    anhydrocannabisativine, 3255
    cannabisativine, 3255
    constituents of, 3255, 3256, 3536, 4411, 5110,
        5154
    isolation, 3054
    seeds, 3054

ALKALOID(S) (continued)
  cannabis plant, 3685, 3787
  Cannabis sativa
    constituents of, 3673, 3674, 3684, 3686, 3906,
        4294, 4595, 4961, 5079, 5085
    pollen, 4595
    review, 3684
  hashish
    constituents of, 4770
  marihuana
    constituents of, 4770
ALKANE(S)
  cannabis
    analysis, 4695
  cannabis plant
    constituents of, 4698
ALLERGY
  cannabis
    humans, 3845
  delta-9-THC
    guinea pig(s), 4234, 5320
  hashish
    humans, 3748
  hemp
    lung(s), 4829
  marihuana extract
    humans, 4269
  marihuana smoke
    lung(s), 4284
  tetrahydrocannabivarolic acids
    guinea pig(s), 5320
ALVEOLAR MACROPHAGE(S)
  delta-9-THC
    cell membrane(s), 3468
    morphology, 3468
  marihuana smoke
    adverse effect(s), 4018
    anti-bacterial activity, 4315
    cell metabolism, 5370
    humans, 5363
    lung(s), 4018
    morphology, 3585, 5362, 5363
    protein levels, 5370
    rats, 4616, 5362, 5370
AMINES
  cannabis
    constituents of, 3536
AMINO ACID(S)
  cannabinol (CBN)
    in vitro, 5367
    uptake, 5367
  Cannabis sativa
    baboons, 5281
    constituents of, 5079
  delta-9-THC
    cellular effects, 5449
    in vitro, 5367, 5449
    uptake, 5367, 5449
AMINO SUGAR
  Cannabis sativa
    constituents of, 5219
    galactosamine, 5219
AMMONIA
  Cannabis sativa
    baboons, 5281

AMMONIA (continued)
  delta-9-THC
    dogs, 3594
AMOEBIC MENINGOENCEPHALITIS
  delta-9-THC
    in vitro, 5543
    inhibition, 5543
AMOTIVATIONAL SYNDROME
  cannabis
    chronic use, 3244
    humans, 3509, 3712, 4963
  marihuana, 3500, 5244
    chronic use, 3739
    humans, 3215, 3274, 3276, 3434, 3477, 3739,
      4107, 4420, 4444, 4529, 5291
    students, 4418
  marihuana smoke, 5450
AMPHETAMINE
  marihuana smoke
    gas chromatography, 4484
AMYGDALOID SEIZURE(S)
  delta-8-THC
    cats, 5141, 5142
  delta-9-THC
    cats, 5141, 5142
AMYLASE
  delta-9-THC
    rats, 4520
ANALGESIA
  benzopyranopyridine(s)
    cancer, 4068
    humans, 4068
  cannabidiol (CBD), 4918
    mice, 4926, 5184
    rats, 4926
  cannabinol (CBN), 4918
    humans, 4515
    mice, 4926, 5184
    rats, 4926
  cannabis
    humans, 3134
    mice, 4874
    rats, 4873, 4874
    tolerance, 4873
  delta-6a(10a)-THC
    carbocyclic analogs, 5218
    nitrogen analogs, 5218
    thio analogs, 5218
  delta-8-THC, 4918
    analog(s), 5210
    metabolites, 4084, 5210
    mice, 5210
    monkeys, 3077
    rats, 3983
    tolerance, 3983
  delta-9-THC, 3498, 4160, 4918
    analog(s), 4578, 4579, 5210
    biogenic amine(s), 3802
    cancer, 4561
    compared to:
      morphine, 3352
    dopamine (DA), 3320
    humans, 3409, 4515, 4561, 4562, 4563, 4686
    metabolites, 4084, 5210
    mice, 3352, 3918, 4578, 4926, 5184, 5210

delta-9-THC (continued)
    nitrogen analogs, 4958
    rats, 3320, 4786, 4926
    review, 3919, 5420
    serotonin (5-hydroxytryptamine), 3320
  dimethylheptylpyran (DMHP)
    mice, 4578
  9-hydroxy-9-*nor*-hexahydrocannabinol
    animals, 4408
    compared to:
      morphine, 3353, 3354
    interaction with
      naloxone, 3353
    mice, 3353, 3354, 3918, 4378, 5212
  marihuana, 3497
    humans, 3973
  marihuana extract
    mice, 4926
    rats, 4926
  SP-1
    mice, 4601
    rats, 4601
  SP-106
    mice, 4601
    rats, 4601
    review, 5420
  SP-111A
    mice, 4601
    rats, 4601
  SP-141
    mice, 4601
    rats, 4601
  SP-143
    mice, 4601
    rats, 4601
  SP-178
    mice, 4601
    rats, 4601
  SP-204
    mice, 4601
    rats, 4601
  tetrahydrocannabinol (THC)
    review, 5460
ANALGESIC
  cannabinoid(s), 3331
  delta-9-THC, 4708
    cancer, 3430, 4547, 4774
    humans, 3430, 4547, 4774
    set and setting, 4774
  marihuana
    cancer, 4547
    humans, 4182, 4547
  synthetic cannabinoids, 3331
ANALGESIC ACTIVITY
  cannabinoid(s)
    cannabidiol (CBD), 5569
    cannabinol (CBN), 5569
    delta-9-THC, 5569
    8 alpha, 11-dihydroxy-delta-9-THC, 5569
    11-hydroxy-delta-9-THC, 5569
    mice, 5569
  cannabis resin
    mechanism of action, 5398
    morphine, 5398
    rats, 5398

ANALGESIC ACTIVITY (continued)
  delta-9-THC
    constituents of, 4350
    mice, 3639, 5162
    nitrogen analogs, 4603
    review, 4603
    thio analogs, 4603
  hydroxylated cannabinoids
    mice, 5631
  marihuana smoke
    humans, 5347
  nantradol
    mice, 5507
    rats, 5507
    stereospecificity, 5507
  SP-1
    mice, 3639, 4602
  SP 80
    mice, 3639
  SP-106
    mice, 3639
  synthetic cannabinoids
    mice, 5162
ANALOG(S)
  cannabinoid(s)
    analgesic activity, 5630
    behavioral effect(s), 5630
    dogs, 5630
    mice, 5630
    structure-activity relationships, 5630
    synthesis, 5630
  delta-6a(10a)-THC
    structure-activity relationships, 4603
  delta-8-THC
    behavioral effect(s), 3121
    biological activity, 4705
    cardiovascular effects, 3121
    synthesis, 3298, 3616, 4196
  delta-9-THC
    analgesia, 4578
    biological activity, 4341
    CNS activity, 4708
    structure, 5094, 5327
    synthesis, 3616, 4341, 4411, 4486
  dimethylheptylpyran (DMHP)
    synthesis, 4703
  hexahydrocannabinol (HHC)
    synthesis, 3615
  tetrahydrocannabinol (THC)
    mice, 5614
    structure-activity relationships, 5614
    synthesis, 5614
ANALYSIS
  cannabichromene (CBC)
    high-pressure liquid chromatography (HPLC), 4911
    mass spectrometry, 5137
    quantitative, 4911
  cannabicyclol (CBL)
    mass spectrometry, 5137
  cannabidiol (CBD)
    abnormal isomer(s), 3261
    exhaled air, 3095
    gas liquid chromatography (GLC), 3095
    high-pressure liquid chromatography (HPLC), 4911
    mass spectrometry, 5137

cannabidiol (CBD) (continued)
    metabolites, 3207
    nuclear magnetic resonance (NMR), 3261
    quantitative, 4911
    thin layer chromatography (TLC), 3095
cannabidiolic acid
    gas liquid chromatography (GLC), 3413
    GC/MS, 3413
    high-pressure liquid chromatography (HPLC), 4911
    quantitative, 4911
    thin layer chromatography (TLC), 3413, 4201
cannabigerol (CBG)
    high-pressure liquid chromatography (HPLC), 4911
    quantitative, 4911
cannabigerolic acid
    gas liquid chromatography (GLC), 3413
    GC/MS, 3413
    high-pressure liquid chromatography (HPLC), 4911
    quantitative, 4911
    thin layer chromatography (TLC), 3413
cannabinoid acids
    thin layer chromatography (TLC), 4201
cannabinoids
    derivatives, 3932
      silyl, 3933
    gas chromatography, 4411, 4481
    gas liquid chromatography (GLC), 4310, 4410,
      5154
    GC/MS, 3108, 3933, 4411, 4481
    mass fragmentography, 4410, 5154
    mass spectrometry, 4410, 4566, 5371
    metabolites, 4290
    nuclear magnetic resonance (NMR), 4411, 5371
    plasma, 4566
    quantitative, 4310
    radiolabelled, 5371
    review, 5421
    thin layer chromatography (TLC), 4410, 4411,
      4481
    ultra violet (UV), 4411
cannabinol (CBN)
    abnormal isomer(s), 3261
    gas liquid chromatography (GLC)
      solid sample injection, 4694
    GC/MS, 5623
    mass spectrometry, 5137
    nuclear magnetic resonance (NMR), 3261
    silylation, 4694
cannabinol-7-oic acid
    high-pressure liquid chromatography (HPLC), 4911
    quantitative, 4911
    thin layer chromatography (TLC), 4201
cannabis
    cannabinoid content, 4226
    confiscated samples, 5080
    exhaled air, 3095
    forensic aspects, 5251
    gas chromatography, 5080
    gas liquid chromatography (GLC), 3095
    geographical origin, 3992
    high-pressure liquid chromatography (HPLC),
      5191, 5192
      compared to:
        gas liquid chromatography (GLC), 5192
        thin layer chromatography (TLC), 5192

cannabis (continued)
  thin layer chromatography (TLC), 3095, 5080
Cannabis sativa
  gas chromatography, 4610
  GC/MS, 3053
  smoke, 3565
  terpenes, 3053
  thin layer chromatography (TLC), 3565
delta-8-THC
  abnormal isomer(s), 3261
  mass spectrometry, 5137
  metabolites, 4244
  nuclear magnetic resonance (NMR), 3261
delta-9-THC
  abnormal isomer(s), 3261
  biological fluid(s), 4916, 5278, 5384
  exhaled air, 3095
  gas chromatography, 5278
  gas liquid chromatography (GLC), 3095, 4106
  GC/MS, 3363, 4106, 5278, 5623
  high-pressure liquid chromatography (HPLC), 4911
  humans, 5384
  mass fragmentography, 3363
  mass spectrometry, 4246, 5137
  metabolites, 3207, 3312, 4137, 4244, 4916
  nuclear magnetic resonance (NMR), 3261
  quantitative, 4911
  radioimmunoassay (RIA), 4106, 4246, 4916, 5278
  thin layer chromatography (TLC), 3095, 4137,
    5278
delta-9-THC oic acid A&B
  gas liquid chromatography (GLC), 3413
  GC/MS, 3413
  high-pressure liquid chromatography (HPLC), 4911
  quantitative, 4911
  thin layer chromatography (TLC), 3413, 4201
hashish
  gas chromatography, 4481
  GC/MS, 4481
  thin layer chromatography (TLC), 4481
hemp
  thin layer chromatography (TLC), 3270
ll-hydroxy-delta-9-THC
  biological fluid(s), 5384
  GC/MS, 5623
  humans, 5384
  mass fragmentography, 4735
  plasma, 4735
Lilly compound no. 109514
  mass spectrometry, 4994
  quantitative, 4994
marihuana, 5152
  confiscated samples, 5080
  gas chromatography, 5080
  gas liquid chromatography (GLC), 4557
  geographical origin, 4557
  high-pressure liquid chromatography (HPLC), 5027
  mass spectrometry, 4557
  metabolites, 4290
  radioimmunoassay (RIA), 5027
  review, 3239
  sterols, 4556
  thin layer chromatography (TLC), 5080
ll-*nor*-9-carboxy-delta-9-THC
  biological fluid(s), 4916, 5384

11-*nor*-9-carboxy-delta-9-THC (continued)
  GC/MS, 5623
  humans, 5384
  radioimmunoassay (RIA), 4916
street drugs
  GC/MS, 3108
ANATOMY
  hemp, 4854, 4977, 4978
ANDROGEN
  cannabis extract
    rats, 4393
  delta-9-THC
    rats, 4393
ANESTHESIA
  cannabidiol (CBD)
    in vitro tests, 4233
  cannabinol (CBN)
    in vitro tests, 4233
  delta-9-THC
    barbiturate(s), 5492
    humans, 4915
    in vitro tests, 4233
    mice, 5492
    tolerance, 5492
  7-hydroxy or ll-hydroxy-THC
    in vitro tests, 4233
ANESTHETIC(S)
  delta-9-THC
    review, 4603
ANGINA PECTORIS
  marihuana
    adverse effect(s), 3263
  marihuana smoke
    humans, 3837
ANHYDROCANNABISATIVINE
  Cannabis sativa
    constituents of, 3686, 3687,
  chemical aspects
    isolation, 3687
    structure, 3687
  hashish
    constituents of, 4770
  marihuana
    constituents of, 4770
ANOREXIA
  delta-9-THC
    rabbit(s), 3292, 5585
    rats, 3643
    review, 4603
  marihuana, 3497
ANTI-ANXIETY
  nabilone (Lilly compound no. 109514)
    clinical findings, 4960
    humans, 4960, 5178
ANTI-ANXIETY ACTIVITY
  Lilly compound no. 109514
    animals, 4959
  marihuana, 3497
  nabilone (Lilly compound no. 109514)
    humans, 3703, 3993, 4031, 4536
    stress, 4536
    therapy, 3703
ANTI-BACTERIAL ACTIVITY
  cannabidiol (CBD), 3498, 3564
    in vitro, 5118

ANTI-BACTERIAL ACTIVITY (continued)
Cannabis sativa
    essential oils, 3761
  delta-9-THC, 3498, 3564
    in vitro, 5118
  marihuana, 3497
    humans, 4182
  marihuana smoke
    alveolar macrophage(s), 4315
ANTIBIOTIC ACTIVITY
  cannabielsoic acid
    in vitro, 3711
ANTIBODIES
  cannabidiol (CBD)
    humans, 4835
  cannabinol (CBN)
    humans, 4835
  delta-8-THC
    humans, 4835
  delta-9-THC
    guinea pig(s), 4234
    humans, 4835
  marihuana
    humans, 4835
ANTIBODY RESPONSE
  delta-9-THC
    mice, 4629
  marihuana
    humans, 4836
ANTIBODY SYNTHESIS
  delta-9-THC
    mice, 4239
    spleen, 4239
ANTI-CONVULSANT ACTIVITY
  benzopyranopyridine(s)
    mice, 4651
  cannabidiol (CBD), 4918
    cortex, 5609
    cross tolerance
      diphenylhydantoin, 4146
      phenobarbital, 4146
    derivatives, 3451, 4409
    frog(s), 5076
    gerbils, 3530
    humans, 3498
    interaction with
      ethosuximide, 3518
    limbic, 5609
    mechanism of action, 5381, 5458
    mice, 3451, 3473, 4145, 4146
    posttetanic potentiation, 5076
    rats, 3475, 3514, 3518, 3814, 4146, 4409, 4892,
      5609
    review, 5381
    stereochemical features, 4104
    tolerance, 4146
  cannabinoid(s), 3331
    electrophysiology, 5458
    mechanism of action, 5458
    pharmacokinetics, 5458
    psychotomimetic activity, 5458
    review, 5381
  cannabinol (CBN), 4918
    frog(s), 5076
    gerbils, 3530

cannabinol (CBN) (continued)
  mice, 4145
  posttetanic potentiation, 5076
  rats, 3514
cannabis
  mice, 4874
  rats, 4873, 4874
  tolerance, 4873
cannabis resin
  catecholamines, 3810
  mechanism of action, 3810
  rats, 3810
  serotonin (5-hydroxytryptamine), 3810
delta-8-THC, 4918
  baboons, 5140
  cats, 5141, 5142
  humans, 3498
  mice, 3164, 3660, 4145
  rats, 3439, 3525
  tolerance, 3525
delta-8-THC-DMH
  rats, 3439
delta-9-THC, 4918
  baboons, 5140
  brain levels, 3104
  cats, 5141, 5142
  chickens, 4072
  cross tolerance
    diphenylhydantoin, 4146
    phenobarbital, 4146
  frog(s), 3459, 5075, 5076, 5077
  gerbils, 3530
  humans, 3498
  interaction with
    ethanol, 3696
  mechanism of action, 5381
  metabolites, 3459, 5077
  mice, 3104, 3164, 3459, 3473, 3660, 3696, 4145,
    4146, 4925
  nitrogen analogs, 4603
  posttetanic potentiation, 5075, 5076
  rabbit(s), 3512
  rats, 3104, 3459, 3475, 3514, 3525, 3814, 4146,
    4892
  review, 3919, 4603, 5381
  side effects, 3475
  thio analogs, 4603
  tolerance, 3525, 4146
dimethylheptylpyran (DMHP)
  mice, 3164, 4145
ll-hydroxy-delta-9-THC
  frog(s), 5075, 5076, 5077
  mice, 3164
  posttetanic potentiation, 5075, 5076
  rats, 3475
  side effects, 3475
marihuana
  agalactia, 3519
  humans, 3901, 4182
marihuana extract
  mice, 3660
SP-141
  mice, 4651
SP-143
  mice, 4651

ANTI-CONVULSANT ACTIVITY (continued)
SP-175
mice, 4651
rats, 3439
synthetic cannabinoids, 3331
ANTI-CONVULSANT EFFECT(S)
cannabidiol (CBD)
rats, 5073
delta-9-THC
compared to:
chlordiazepoxide, 4919
diphenylhydantoin, 4919
phenobarbital, 4919
gerbil, 5036
mice, 4919
rats, 3815, 5073
ANTI-CONVULSANT(S)
cannabis
therapeutic aspects, 4522
delta-8-THC, 4160
delta-9-THC, 4160
ANTI-ESTROGENIC
cannabis
rats, 3460
cannabis extract
rats, 3462
uterus, 3462
ANTI-FERTILITY
delta-9-THC, 4160
ANTI-FERTILITY ACTIVITY
delta-9-THC
review, 4603
ANTI-FUNGAL ACTIVITY
cannabidiol (CBD), 3563
delta-9-THC, 3563
ANTI-HISTAMINIC ACTIVITY
delta-8-THC, 4653
delta-9-THC
guinea pig(s), 3189
in vitro, 5078
ANTI-HYPERTENSIVE
cannabinoid(s), 3331
synthetic cannabinoids, 3331
ANTI-HYPERTENSIVE ACTIVITY
delta-6a(10a)-THC
carbocyclic analogs, 5218
nitrogen analogs, 5218
thio analogs, 5218
ANTI-INFLAMMATORY
delta-9-THC
animals, 4408
ANTI-INFLAMMATORY ACTIVITY
analysis
mice, 4874
rats, 4874
cannabidiol (CBD)
rats, 4009
cannabinoid(s), 3331
delta-8-THC, 4653
delta-9-THC, 4653
rats, 4009, 5019
review, 4603
olivetol
rats, 4009
synthetic cannabinoids, 3331

ANTI-NEOPLASTIC ACTIVITY
cannabichromene (CBC)
in vitro, 3442
cannabicyclol (CBL)
in vitro, 3442
cannabidiol (CBD)
in vitro, 3442, 3918
cannabinoid(s), 3921
structure-activity relationships, 3921
cannabinol (CBN)
in vitro, 3442
delta-8-THC
in vitro, 3442, 3918
delta-9-THC
analog(s), 3921
DNA synthesis, 5448
in vitro, 3442, 3918, 4513, 5194
in vivo, 5448
nucleotides, 5448
review, 4603
tissue culture, 3776
8 beta, ll-diOH-delta-9-THC
in vitro, 3442
marihuana, 3497, 3741
humans, 4182
ANTI-NEOPLASTIC TESTING
cannabidiol (CBD)
mice, 3775
delta-8-THC
mice, 3775
delta-9-THC
mice, 3775
ANTIASTHAMATIC
cannabinoid(s), 3331
synthetic cannabinoids, 3331
ANTIBODY FORMATION
cannabidiol (CBD)
humans, 4835
cannabinol (CBN)
humans, 4835
delta-8-THC
humans, 4835
delta-9-THC
humans, 4835
marihuana
humans, 4835
ANTICHOLINERGIC ACTIVITY
delta-8-THC, 4215
delta-9-THC, 4215
guinea pig(s), 3189
ANTICHOLINERGIC EFFECT
delta-9-THC
salivary glands, 4319
ANTIDEPRESSANT
cannabinoid(s), 3331
delta-9-THC, 3498, 4160, 4708
marihuana, 3497
synthetic cannabinoids, 3331
ANTIDIARRHEAL
cannabinoid(s), 3331
synthetic cannabinoids, 3331
ANTIDIARREAL ACTIVITY
delta-6a(10a)-THC
carbocyclic analogs, 5218
nitrogen analogs, 5218

delta-6a(10a)-THC (continued)
   thio analogs, 5218
ANTIEMETIC
  cannabinoid(s), 3331
  delta-9-THC, 4708
    cancer, 3239, 3430, 3498, 4408, 4772, 4773,
     5374, 5391
    chemotherapy, 5470, 5475, 5595
    humans, 3430, 3498, 4772, 4773, 5335, 5391,
     5470
    legal aspects, 5475
    pigeon(s), 5033
    plasma levels, 5335
    rats, 5033
    research, 5475
    review, 3919
    route of administration, 5335
    tolerance, 5335
  marihuana, 3497
    cancer, 3216, 3240, 5283
    chemotherapy, 5471, 5553
    humans, 3216, 3240, 5283, 5471
    route of administration, 5553
  nabilone (Lilly compound no. 109514)
    apomorphine, 5485
    cancer, 3968, 4960, 5178
    cancer therapy, 3253
    cats, 3368, 5485
    chemotherapy, 4521, 5485
    clinical findings, 4960
    digitalis, 5485
    dogs, 5415
    effectiveness, 5387
    humans, 3968, 4487, 4960, 5426, 5447
    mechanism of action, 5485
    nicotine, 5485
  synthetic cannabinoids, 3331
ANTI-EMETIC ACTIVITY
  nabilone (Lilly compound no. 109514)
    cats, 4316
ANTIMITOTIC
  cannabichromene (CBC)
    lymphocytes, 3602
  cannabicyclol (CBL)
    lymphocytes, 3602
  cannabinol (CBN)
    lymphocytes, 3602
  delta-8-THC
    lymphocytes, 3602
  delta-9-THC
    lymphocytes, 3602
  11-hydroxy-delta-8-THC
    lymphocytes, 3602
  11-hydroxy-delta-9-THC
    lymphocytes, 3602
  olivetol
    lymphocytes, 3602
ANTINEOPLASTIC
  cannabichromene (CBC)
    in vitro, 3440
  cannabicyclol (CBL)
    in vitro, 3440
  cannabidiol (CBD), 5071
    in vitro, 3440, 4509
    in vivo, 4509

ANTINEOPLASTIC (continued)
  cannabinol (CBN), 5071
    in vitro, 3440, 4509
    in vivo, 4509
  delta-8-THC, 4160, 5071
    in vitro, 3440, 4509
    in vivo, 4509
  delta-9-THC, 4160, 5071
    allylbenzene analog(s), 4545
    in vitro, 3440, 4509
    in vivo, 4509
  11-hydroxy-delta-9-THC, 5071
ANTINEOPLASTIC ACTIVITY
  cannabidiol (CBD)
    in vitro, 3924
    in vivo, 3924
  cannabinol (CBN)
    in vitro, 3924
    in vivo, 3924
  delta-8-THC
    in vitro, 3924
    in vivo, 3924
  delta-9-THC
    in vitro, 3924
    in vivo, 3924
ANTINEOPLASTIC TESTING
  delta-9-THC
    in vitro, 5193
ANTIPYRETIC
  cannabis
    mice, 4874
    rats, 4874
  delta-9-THC
    review, 4603
ANTITUSSIVE
  cannabidiol (CBD)
    cats, 3835
  cannabinoid(s), 3331
  cannabinol (CBN)
    cats, 3835
  delta-9-THC
    animals, 4408
    cats, 3835
  synthetic cannabinoids, 3331
ANTIULCER ACTIVITY
  delta-6a(10a)-THC
    carbocyclic analogs, 5218
    nitrogen analogs, 5218
    thio analogs, 5218
  delta-9-THC
    rats, 4921
ANXIETY
  delta-9-THC
    cardiovascular effects, 4328
    compared to:
      chlorpromazine, 4328
      diazepam, 4328
      morphine, 4328
    monkeys, 4328
  marihuana
    chronic use, 3795
    humans, 3893, 4106
    psychosis, 3172
    students, 3795

ANXIETY (continued)
  therapy
    diazepam, 3795
  nabilone (Lilly compound no. 109514)
    humans, 5401
APHRODISIAC(S)
  marihuana
    humans, 3805, 5364
APPETITE
  cannabinol (CBN)
    humans, 4870
  delta-9-THC, 4708
  marihuana
    humans, 3789
    interaction with
      amphetamine, 3789
APPETITE STIMULANT
  cannabinoid(s), 3331
  9-aza-cannabinol
    sheep, 5618
  synthetic cannabinoids, 3331
ARACHIDONIC ACID
  cannabichromene (CBC)
    HeLa cells, 3422, 3423
    in vitro, 3422
  cannabinol (CBN)
    HeLa cells, 3422, 3423
    in vitro, 3422
  delta-9-THC
    HeLa cells, 3422, 3423
    in vitro, 3422
ARYL HYDROCARBON HYDROXYLASE ACTIVITY
  delta-9-THC
    mice, 3777
ASCORBIC ACID
  delta-8-THC
    rabbit(s), 4340
    rats, 4340
  delta-9-THC
    rabbit(s), 4340
    rats, 4340
  dimethylheptylpyran, (DMHP)
    rabbit(s), 4340
    rats, 4340
  hashish
    adrenals, 4291
    stress, 4291
ASTHMA
  delta-9-THC, 4160, 4834
    aerosol, 5107
    bronchodilatation, 5015
    humans, 3180, 3931, 5009, 5207
    therapy, 3235, 3239, 3930, 4408, 4528
  marihuana
    bronchodilatation, 5012, 5105
    humans, 5011, 5012, 5473
    smoke, 5105
    tachycardia, 5105
    therapy, 3240, 3497, 4182, 5017, 5105
ATAXIA
  delta-8-THC
    analog(s)
      dogs, 4381
    gamma-amino-butyric acid (GABA), 3836
    rats, 3836

ATAXIA (continued)
  delta-9-THC
    analog(s)
      dogs, 4381
    dogs, 4379
    tolerance, 4379
  9-hydroxy-9-*nor*-hexahydrocannabinol
    dogs, 5212
  marihuana smoke
    chronic use, 4996
    dogs, 4996
    tolerance, 4996
ATPASE(S)
  cannabidiol (CBD)
    brain, 3970
    heart, 5349
    mice, 3970
    rats, 3814
    synaptosomal, 3814
  cannabinol (CBN)
    synaptic vesicles, 4570
  delta-9-THC, 4411, 4522
    adrenals, 3343
    brain, 3356, 3970
    gastrointestinal tract, 4825
    heart, 5349
    humans, 5333
    in vitro, 5333
    liver, 3808
    membrane effects, 4231
    membranes, 4022
    mice, 3356, 3970
    rats, 3343, 3808, 3814, 4825
    spermatozoa, 5333
    subcellular fractions, 3356
    synaptic vesicles, 4570, 4571
    synaptosomal, 3814
    tissue culture, 4022
  dimethylheptylpyran (DMHP)
    heart, 5349
  11-hydroxy-delta-9-THC
    synaptic vesicles, 4570
  olivetol
    synaptic vesicles, 4570
ATTENTION
  marihuana
    humans, 3168
ATTITUDE
  marihuana
    review, 3241
  marihuana use
    adolescent(s), 5451
    religious beliefs, 5613
ATTITUDES OF USERS
  ganja
    Jamaica, 4762
  hashish, 4004
  marihuana, 4793
    drug use, 3153
    psychological aspects, 4187
    students, 4187, 5577
    U.S.A., 5577
AUDITION
  delta-9-THC
    evoked potentials, 5427

delta-9-THC (continued)
  humans, 5427
AUTONOMIC NERVOUS SYSTEM EFFECT(S)
  delta-9-THC
    cardiovascular effects, 3764
    dogs, 4045, 4047
    humans, 3315, 5310
    marihuana, 5414
    monkeys, 3764
  marihuana
    adverse effect(s), 4992
    humans, 4992
AUTORADIOGRAPHY
  delta-8-THC, 3173
  delta-9-THC, 3173
AVOIDANCE BEHAVIOR
  cannabinoid(s)
    humans, 5477
  delta-9-THC
    rats, 4590

B

BARBITURATE WITHDRAWAL(S)
  delta-9-THC
    rats, 3815
BEAM TEST
  Cannabis sativa
    identification, 4230
BEHAVIOR
  delta-8-THC
    stress, 4333
  delta-9-THC
    adverse effect(s), 3258
  marihuana
    adverse effect(s), 4992
    humans, 4640
    intoxication, 4640
  marihuana smoke
    adverse effect(s), 4026
    chronic effects, 4026
    dogs, 4026
BEHAVIORAL EFFECT(S)
  cannabidiol (CBD)
    analog(s), 3199
    catecholamines, 3357
    mice, 3357
  cannabinol (CBN)
    catecholamines, 3357
    humans, 4870
    mice, 3357
  cannabis
    acute effect(s), 3062
    chronic effects, 3062
    humans, 3843
    mice, 5020
    rabbit(s), 5020
    rats, 5020
    review, 3062
    tolerance, 3062, 3769
  Cannabis sativa
    mice, 5559
    rats, 5559
  delta-8-THC
    analog(s), 3121, 3199

delta-8-THC (continued)
  dogs, 3121
  monkeys, 4732
  delta-9-THC, 3448, 4675
    adverse effect(s), 4744, 5156
    barometric pressure, 5156
    catecholamines, 3357
    cats, 3133, 4040
    duration, 3754
    electroencephalogram (EEG), 3516
    humans, 3697, 5207
    interaction with
      methamphetamine, 3515
      physostigmine, 4094
    mice, 3357, 4497
    monkeys, 4782
    nest building, 4497
    onset, 3754
    personality, 4782
    pigeon(s), 3435
    rabbit(s), 3515, 3516, 3517, 4094, 4386
    rats, 3754, 3755, 4744, 5021, 5156
    tolerance, 4386
  hexahydrocannabinol (HHC)
    catecholamines, 3357
    mice, 3357
  11-hydroxy-delta-9-THC
    duration, 3754
    onset, 3754
    rats, 3754, 3755
  Lilly compound no. 109514
    animals, 4959
  marihuana
    chronic use, 3454, 3894
    coordination, 3894
    humans, 3307, 3454, 3894, 4428
    memory, 3894
    mood, 4428
    motivation, 3894
    review, 3239
  marihuana extract
    pigeon(s), 3435
  marihuana smoke, 5070
    rats, 5068
    various fractions, 5068
  SP-1
    cats, 4602
    mice, 4602
    monkeys, 4602
    pigeon(s), 3435
  stress, 3448
  synthetic cannabinoids
    monkeys, 4732
BEHAVIORAL SCREEN
  marihuana smoke
    rats, 5068
    various fractions, 5068
BEHAVIORAL TERATOGENESIS
  delta-9-THC
    rats, 3531, 5122
  marihuana
    prenatal exposure, 5275
    rats, 5275
    sex differences, 5275

BENEFICIAL EFFECT(S)
  marihuana
    humans, 4752
BENEFIT(S)
  marihuana, 5244
BENZOPYRANOPYRIDINE(S)
  chemical aspects
    structure-activity relationships, 4601
  pharmacological aspects
    analgesia, 4601
    analgesic, 4068
    analgesic activity, 3639
    intraocular pressure (IOP), 3639
    sedative, 3639
    tranquilizing activity, 3639
  toxicology
    body weight, 5042
    food intake, 5042
    LD50, 5042
BENZOXOCINOL(S)
  chemical aspects
    structure, 3612
    synthesis, 3612
BIAS OF EXPERIMENTER
  marihuana, 3757
BINDING
  delta-8-THC
    phospholipids, 3438
  delta-9-THC
    microsomes, 5564
    rats, 5564
    salivary glands, 4320
    synaptosomes, 4411
BINDING SITES
  cannabinoid(s)
    lipids, 5340
    protein, 5340
BIOCHEMICAL EFFECT(S)
  delta-8-THC
    tissue culture, 4976
  delta-9-THC
    tissue culture, 4976
  marihuana extract
    tissue culture, 4976
BIOGENIC AMINE(S)
  aggressive behavior, 3448
  cannabidiol (CBD)
    brain, 4654
    dopamine (DA), 4654
    norepinephrine (NE), 4654
  cannabinol (CBN)
    brain, 4654
    dopamine (DA), 4654
    norepinephrine (NE), 4654
  cannabis
    humans, 4963
    hypothermia, 4875
    rats, 4875
  cannabis extract
    brain, 4656
    dopamine (DA), 4656
    guinea pig(s), 4161
    norepinephrine (NE), 4656
    rats, 3264, 3439
    serotonin (5-hydroxytryptamine), 4161

BIOGENIC AMINE(S) (continued)
  cannabis resin
    brain, 3592
    rats, 3592
  Cannabis sativa,
    aggressive behavior, 3061
    stress, 3061
  delta-8-THC
    brain, 3115, 4654
    dopamine (DA), 4654
    norepinephrine (NE), 4654
    rats, 3115
  delta-9-THC, 3448, 3609
    aggressive behavior, 3450
    analgesia, 3802
    behavioral effect(s), 3201
    brain, 3089, 3115, 3382, 3802, 4073, 4081, 4656,
      5023, 5574
    brain levels, 4652, 5021, 5597
    cats, 3201
    compared to:
      morphine, 3352
    dopamine (DA), 3352, 3382, 3726, 3831, 4215,
      4656, 5023
    heart, 3089
    5-hydroxyindoleacetic acid (5-HIAA), 3726
    hypothalamus, 3405
    in vitro, 5429
    mice, 3352
    muricide, 5574
    norepinephrine (NE), 3352, 3382, 3405, 3726,
      3802, 3831, 4081, 4215, 4656, 5023
    rats, 3089, 3115, 3382, 3405, 3407, 3450, 3507,
      3726, 4073, 4081, 4656, 5021, 5574, 5597
    serotonin (5-hydroxytryptamine), 3382, 3405,
      3726, 3802, 4076, 4078, 4081, 5023
    stereospecificity, 5429
    subcellular distribution, 5597
    synaptosomes, 5429
    tolerance, 5429
    uptake, 5429
  dimethylheptylpyran (DMHP)
    brain, 3115
    rats, 3115
  hashish
    brain, 3225
    rabbit(s), 3225
  9-hydroxy-9-nor-hexahydrocannabinol
    brain, 3353
    mice, 3353
  lung function
    aggressive behavior, 3449
    stress, 3449
  marihuana, 3448
    aggressive behavior, 3063
    rats, 3063
    stress, 3063
  marihuana extract
    aggressive behavior, 3450
    rats, 3450
BIOLOGICAL ACTIVITY
  Lilly compound no. 109514
    animals, 4959

BIOLOGICAL CONTROL
   Cannabis sativa
      fungus, 3971
      growth, 3971
BIOLOGICAL FLUID(S)
   cannabinoid(s)
      detection, 5623
      forensic aspects, 5340
      GC/MS, 5623
      humans, 5623
      separation, 5395
   cannabis
      analysis, 4522
BIOSYNTHESIS
   cannabinoid(s), 3536, 5340
      plant, 4122
   cannabinoid synthesis, 4853
   Cannabis sativa
      cannabichromene (CBC), 3329
      cannabidiol (CBD), 3329
      cannabinol (CBN), 3329
      delta-8-THC, 3329
      delta-9-THC, 3329
BIOTRANSFORMATION
   cannabidiol (CBD)
      metabolites, 4719
      microorganisms, 4305, 4719, 4720
   cannabinoid(s)
      in vitro, 4038
   cannabinol (CBN)
      metabolites, 4719
      microorganisms, 4305, 4719, 4720
   Cannabis sativa
      alcohol oxidase, 4038, 5004
   delta-6a(10a)-THC
      microorganisms, 3178, 3786
   delta-8-THC
      metabolites, 4719
      microorganisms, 4305, 4719, 4720
   delta-9-THC
      hydroxylation, 3480
      in vitro, 5269
      liver, 5269
      lung(s), 5269
      metabolites, 4719
      microorganisms, 3338, 3340, 3480, 4305, 4719, 4720
   marihuana
      metabolites, 5589
   nabilone (Lilly compound no. 109514)
      microorganisms, 3178
BLOOD
   cannabidiol (CBD)
      clotting factors, 4264, 4265
      humans, 4264, 4265
   delta-9-THC
      clotting factors, 4264, 4265
      detection, 5562
      humans, 4264, 4265
      methods, 5562
BLOOD-BRAIN BARRIER
   delta-8-THC
      lithium, 4817
      rats, 4817

BLOOD-BRAIN BARRIER (continued)
   delta-9-THC
      rats, 4803
      vehicle effect(s), 4803
   11-hydroxy-delta-9-THC
      rats, 4803
      vehicle effect(s), 4803
   marihuana
      chronic use, 3895
BLOOD CELLS
   cannabis
      adverse effect(s), 4969
      membrane effects, 4969
      morphology, 4963, 4969
   hashish
      chronic use, 4970
      histological changes, 4970
      humans, 4970
      lymphocytes, 4970
      morphology, 4970
      neutrophils, 4970
BLOOD CHEMISTRY
   delta-9-THC
      rabbit(s), 3292
   marihuana
      dogs, 4028
BLOOD CLEARANCE RATES
   cannabinol (CBN)
      tetrahydrocannabinol (THC), 4309
BLOOD FLOW
   delta-9-THC
      brain, 3830
      cerebellum, 3830
      hippocampus, 3830
      humans, 3319, 4275
      hypothalamus, 3830
   hashish
      humans, 4275
   marihuana
      humans, 4275
   marihuana smoke
      rats, 5383
BLOOD GASES
   biochemical effect(s)
      chromosome damage, 4534
      compared to:
         alcohol, 4534
         aspirin, 4534
         caffeine, 4534
      macromolecular synthesis, 4534
   cannabidiol (CBD)
      dogs, 3394
   Cannabis sativa
      biochemical effect(s), 5281
   delta-9-THC
      dogs, 3393
BLOOD GLUCOSE
   cannabis
      humans, 3097
   cannabis extract
      rabbit(s), 3470
      rats, 4930
   delta-9-THC
      Costa Rica, 3318
      growth hormone, 3318

BLOOD GLUCOSE (continued)
    humans, 3318
    insulin, 3318
  hashish
    rats, 4339
BLOOD PARAMETERS
  marihuana
    chronic effects, 3493
BLOOD LEVEL(S)
  delta-8-THC
    pharmacological aspects, 3208
    psychological aspects, 3208
  delta-9-THC
    animals, 5146
    humans, 4981
    metabolites, 5146
  nabilone (Lilly compound no. 109514)
    dogs, 4995
BLOOD PRESSURE
  cannabidiol (CBD)
    dogs, 3394
  Cannabis sativa
    dogs, 5188
  delta-8-THC
    dogs, 3387, 3388
    rats, 3198, 3342
  delta-9-THC
    adrenalectomy, 4274
    adrenergic nervous system, 4128
    cats, 3914, 4007, 4053, 4289
    central nervous system (CNS), 4053
    central nervous system mechanism, 3914, 4007
    humans, 3213, 3314, 3319, 3534, 3631, 3914, 4128, 5018, 5355
    intraocular pressure (IOP), 5355
    rats, 3198, 3342, 4183, 4274, 4520, 4576
    tolerance, 4183
  dimethylheptylpyran (DMHP)
    cats, 3914, 4007
    central nervous system mechanism, 3914, 4007
  hashish
    humans, 4827, 5018
  marihuana
    euphoria, 4643
    humans, 3533, 4643, 5298
  nabilone (Lilly compound no. 109514)
    humans, 4250
  SP-111A
    rats, 4576
BLOOD SUGAR
  delta-9-THC
    humans, 5239
BLOOD TEST(S)
  marihuana
    humans, 4428
BLOOD UREA NITROGEN
  delta-9-THC
    humans, 5239
BODY TEMPERATURE
  cannabidiol (CBD), 4918
    catecholamines, 3357
    mice, 3357, 3358, 5035
  cannabinoid(s)
    review, 5416

BODY TEMPERATURE (continued)
  cannabinol (CBN), 4918
    catecholamines, 3357
    humans, 4515
    mice, 3357, 3358
  cannabis
    mice, 4874
    rats, 4874
  delta-8-THC, 4918
    acute effect(s), 4070
    chronic effects, 4070
    rats, 3439, 4070
  delta-8-THC-DMH
    rats, 3439
  delta-9-THC, 4918
    acute effect(s), 4070
    animals, 3359
    biogenic amine(s), 5023
    catecholamines, 3357
    cats, 4795
    chronic effects, 4070
    humans, 4275, 4515
    interaction with
      depressant, 4671
      stimulants, 4671
    lactation, 3187
    mice, 3187, 3222, 3357, 3358, 4624, 5035, 5162, 5536
    rats, 3726, 4070, 4671, 4673, 4677, 4678, 4794, 4799, 5021, 5023, 5032, 5369, 5501
    review, 5416
    route of administration, 5501
    tolerance, 3222, 5023
    vehicle of administration, 5501
  dimethylheptylpyran (DMHP)
    cats, 4795
  hashish
    humans, 4275
  hexahydrocannabinol (HHC)
    catecholamines, 3357
    mice, 3357
  9-hydroxy-9-*nor*-hexahydrocannabinol
    mice, 3358
  11-hydroxy-delta-9-THC
    cats, 4795
    mice, 3358
  marihuana
    adverse effect(s), 4776
    clinical findings, 3323
    cold exposure, 3902, 3903
    environmental conditions, 3902, 3903
    humans, 3323, 3902, 3903, 4275, 4776
  SP-1
    rats, 5042
  SP 80
    rats, 5042
  SP-106
    rats, 5042
  SP-175
    rats, 3439
  synthetic cannabinoids
    mice, 5162
BODY WEIGHT
  cannabinoid(s)
    chronic effects, 3865

cannabinoid(s) (continued)
    rabbit(s), 3865
cannabinol (CBN)
    mice, 5359
Cannabis sativa
    baboons, 5281
delta-8-THC
    acute effect(s), 4070
    chronic effects, 4070
    rats, 3342, 4070
delta-9-THC
    acute effect(s), 4070
    chronic effects, 4027, 4070
    guinea pig(s), 4027
    mice, 4670, 5359
    rats, 3197, 3342, 4070, 5022, 5023
marihuana
    chronic administration, 4028
    dogs, 4028
marihuana extract
    adult, 5353
    fetus, 5353
    rabbit(s), 5353
marihuana smoke
    chronic effects, 4026, 4029
    dogs, 4026, 4029
    humans, 3868
    mice, 5171, 5172
    rats, 5370, 5431
SP-1
    chronic effects, 3865
    rabbit(s), 3865
SP-106
    chronic effects, 3865
    rabbit(s), 3865
SP-204
    chronic effects, 3865
    rabbit(s), 3865
BONE MARROW
    cannabidiol (CBD)
        mice, 3824
    cannabinol (CBN)
        mice, 3824
    delta-9-THC
        hyperplasia, 3823
        mice, 3824
BOTANICAL ASPECTS
    cannabis
        review, 3080, 4881
        wild plant, 4194
    Cannabis indica
        classification, 3083
    Cannabis sativa, 3900
        cannabinoid content, 3492, 3543, 4756
        classification, 3083
        growth, 3492
        herbicides, 3492
        photosynthesis, 3543
    marihuana, 4804
        sex differences, 3741
    paraquat
        gas chromatography, 5312
        identification, 5312
        temperature, 5312

BRAIN
    cannabidiol (CBD)
        acetylcholine (ACh), 4716
        mice, 3970
        monoamine oxidase (MAO), 4806, 4807
        neuronal activity, 4816
        rats, 3814, 4716
        synaptosomes, 3970
    cannabinoid(s)
        behavioral effect(s), 5504
        limbic, 5504
        neurotransmitters, 5368
        psychological aspects, 5504
        synaptosomes, 5368, 5428
    cannabinol (CBN)
        acetylcholine (ACh), 3629
        membrane-bound enzyme, 4570
        rats, 3629
    cannabis, 4522
        damage following cannabis use, 4763
        psychological aspects, 4763
        review, 5379
    cannabis extract
        damage, 4056
        dopamine (DA), 4656
        guinea pig(s), 4161
        norepinephrine (NE), 4656
        rabbit(s), 4056
        rats, 4056, 4656
        serotonin (5-hydroxytryptamine), 4161
        sodium-potassium adenosine triphosphatase (Na K
          ATPase), 4655
    cannabis resin
        catecholamines, 3810
        5-hydroxyindoleacetic acid (5-HIAA), 3592
        norepinephrine (NE), 3592
        rats, 3592, 3810
        serotonin (5-hydroxytryptamine), 3592, 3810
    Cannabis sativa
        adverse effect(s), 3562
        baboons, 5281
        pathology, 5281
    delta-8-THC
        concentration, 4118
        dopamine (DA), 3115
        norepinephrine (NE), 3115
        rats, 3920
        stereospecific binding, 3920
    delta-9-THC
        accumulation, 4618
        acetylcholine (ACh), 3629, 3630, 4140, 4716
        adverse effect(s), 3954, 4739
        amygdala, 4590
        ATPase(s), 3356
        biogenic amine(s), 3802
        blood flow, 3830
        catecholamines, 3360
        cats, 4796
        cellular respiration, 4282
        concentration, 4118
        cortex, 3204
        distribution, 3204, 3610, 3986, 4338
        dogs, 3610
        dopamine (DA), 3115, 3320, 3359, 4656
        fatty acids, 4878

delta-9-THC (continued)
  function, 3953
  functional changes, 3954
  humans, 4618
  5-hydroxyindoleacetic acid (5-HIAA), 4819
  hypothermia, 4796
  interaction with, 4282
    corticosterones, 4282
  intravenous administration, 3953
  lipid content, 4779, 4780
    subcellular distribution, 4779, 4780
  macromolecular synthesis, 5488
  membrane-bound ATPases, 3355
  membrane-bound enzyme, 4570, 4571
  metabolism, 4373
  metabolites, 4338
  mice, 3356, 3610, 3970, 4140, 4618, 5262
  monkeys, 3917, 3953, 3954
  monoamine oxidase (MAO), 4806, 4807
  neonates, 4554, 5488
  neuronal alterations, 4554
  neuronal activity, 4816
  norepinephrine (NE), 3115, 3320, 3359, 4656
  parasympathetic nervous system (PNS), 3653
  pathological study, 3954
  protein, 4304
  rabbit(s), 3204
  rats, 3320, 3610, 3629, 3630, 3653, 3986, 4237,
    4304, 4373, 4656, 4659, 4716, 4739, 4803,
    5059, 5488
  ribonucleic acid (RNA), 4304
  ribosomes, 4659
  route of administration, 4739
  septal region, 3917
  serotonin (5-hydroxytryptamine), 3320, 3986,
    4074, 5262
  serotonin levels, 4819
  sodium-potassium adenosine triphosphatase (Na K
    ATPase), 4655, 5059, 5492
  synaptosomes, 3970
    sodium-potassium adenosine triphosphatase (Na
      K ATPase), 4237
  trytophan, 5262
  ultrastructure, 3917
  uptake, 3204, 4803
  vehicle effect(s), 4803
dimethylheptylpyran (DMHP)
  dopamine (DA), 3115
  norepinephrine (NE), 3115
hashish
  biogenic amine(s), 3225
  electroencephalogram (EEG), 3225
  mechanism of action, 3225
hashish extract
  monoamine oxidase (MAO), 4806, 4807
11-hydroxy-delta-9-THC
  accumulation, 4618
  acetylcholine (ACh), 5550
  humans, 4618
  membrane-bound enzyme, 4570
  mice, 4618
  rats, 4803, 5550
  uptake, 4803
  vehicle effect(s), 4803

BRAIN (continued)
  LSD-25
    neonates, 4554
    neuronal alterations, 4554
  marihuana
    adverse effect(s), 4176, 4527
    function, 3953, 4711
    hemisphere, 3925
      differential effect, 4982
    humans, 3925, 4982
    inhalation, 3953
    monkeys, 3953
    retention, 4176
  marihuana smoke
    humans, 5136
  membrane permeability, 4571
  olivetol
    membrane-bound enzyme, 4570
  SP-111
    neuronal activity, 4816
  tetrahydrocannabinol (THC)
    distribution, 5490
    macromolecular synthesis, 5490
    metabolism, 5490
    morphological variations, 5490
    rats, 5490
    ribosomes, 5490
BRAIN DAMAGE
  cannabis
    humans, 3078
  delta-9-THC
    rats, 3258
BRAIN FUNCTION
  marihuana
    humans, 5291
BRAIN LEVELS
  cannabidiol (CBD)
    mice, 5319
  delta-9-THC
    animals, 5146
    anti-convulsant activity, 3104
    ant(s), 3782
    biogenic amine(s), 4652
    humans, 4619
    interaction with
      phencyclidine, 4514
    metabolites, 5146
    mice, 3104, 4514
    monkeys, 5331
    rats, 3104, 3755, 4514, 4652, 4673
  hashish
    gamma-amino-butyric acid (GABA), 4339
  11-hydroxy-delta-9-THC
    humans, 4619
    rats, 3755
BRAIN PATHOLOGY
  marihuana, 3240
    chronic use, 3739
    humans, 3347, 3392, 3487, 3739, 4208, 4632
BRONCHIAL TUBES
  cannabis smoke
    review, 3749
BRONCHODILATATION
  delta-9-THC, 4834
    aerosol, 5010, 5106, 5107

delta-9-THC (continued)
  airway conductance, 5106
  asthma, 3849
  compared to:
    isoproterenol, 5106
  guinea pig(s), 3189
  humans, 3498, 3501, 3582, 3849, 3930, 3931,
    4832, 5009, 5010, 5014, 5015, 5106, 5107,
    5207, 5271
  mechanism of action, 4832
  oral administration, 5010, 5271
  review, 3919
  route of administration, 5015
  smoking, 5010
marihuana
  chronic use, 3499
  compared to:
    isoproterenol, 5011
  humans, 3254, 3499, 5011, 5012, 5105
marihuana extract
  asthma, 3849
  humans, 3849
marihuana smoke
  humans, 4832, 5014, 5271
  mechanism of action, 4832
BUN (BLOOD UREA NITROGEN)
  delta-9-THC
    chronic effects, 5045
    rabbit(s), 5045
BUTYL HOMOLOG
  cannabidiol (CBD)
    cannabis
      constituents of, 3935
  cannabinol (CBN)
    cannabis
      constituents of, 3935
  delta-9-THC
    cannabis
      constituents of, 3935
  delta-9-THC oic acid A&B
    cannabis
      constituents of, 3935

C

CALCIUM LEVELS
  cannabidiol (CBD)
    heart, 5349
  delta-9-THC
    compared to:
      morphine, 5328
    heart, 5349
    hypothermia, 3889
    in vitro, 5328
    mice, 3889
  dimethylheptylpyran (DMHP)
    heart, 5349
CALLUS
  Cannabis sativa
    oxidation
      allylic alcohol(s), 4037
CANADA
  cannabinoid(s)
    detection, 5608
  cannabis
    patterns of use, 5554

CANADA (continued)
  marihuana use
    availability, 5332
    family relationships, 5332
    legal aspects, 5332
    students, 5332
CANCER
  cannabinoid(s)
    cellular respiration, 5604
    therapy, 3331
  cannabinol (CBN)
    therapy, 3498
  cannabis
    antiemetic, 5307
    humans, 5307
  delta-8-THC
    therapy, 3498
  delta-9-THC, 4708
    adverse effect(s), 4560, 4562, 4563
    analgesia, 4560, 4562, 4563
    analgesic, 4547
    antiemetic, 5374, 5391, 5470
    appetite, 4560
    children, 5374
    humans, 4547, 5335, 5391, 5470
    mood, 4560
    therapy, 3235, 3498
  marihuana
    analgesic, 4547
    antiemetic, 3216, 5283, 5471
    humans, 3254, 3741, 4547, 5283
    therapy, 3495, 3502
  nabilone (Lilly compound no. 109514)
    antiemetic, 4521, 5447
    humans, 5426, 5447
  synthetic cannabinoids
    therapy, 3331
  tetrahydrocannabinol (THC)
    therapeutic aspects, 4773
CANCER THERAPY
  nabilone (Lilly compound no. 109514)
    antiemetic, 3253
CANNABICHROMANON
  cannabis
    constituents of, 3781
  chemical aspects
    spectral data, 3781
C3-CANNABICHROMANONE
  analysis
    GC/MS, 3882
  Cannabis sativa
    constituents of, 3882
CANNABICHROMENE (CBC)
  adverse effect(s)
    cellular division, 3604
  analysis
    detection, 3374, 4911
    fluorometric, 3374
    gas liquid chromatography (GLC), 3286
    GC/MS, 3944
    high-pressure liquid chromatography (HPLC), 4911
    mass spectrometry, 3416, 5137
    separation, 3944
      cannabidiol (CBD), 3286
      cannabinol (CBN), 3286

analysis (continued)
  structure, 3416
  trimethylsilyl derivatives, 3944
biochemical effect(s)
  arachidonic acid, 3422, 3423
  cellular division, 3604
  chromosome damage, 4534
  compared to:
    alcohol, 4534
    aspirin, 4534
    caffeine, 4534
  macromolecular synthesis, 3440, 3442,
    4523, 4534
  prostaglandin synthesis, 3422
  thymidine uptake, 3604
Cannabis sativa
  constituents, 5082
  constituents of, 3562, 3691, 4480
chemical aspects
  gas liquid chromatography (GLC), 5083
  homologs, 3537
  propyl homologs, 4851
  separation
    cannabidiol (CBD), 5083
  synthesis, 3537, 3682
immunology
  antimitotic, 3602
  lymphocytes, 3602, 4523
marihuana
  constituents of, 3215, 3919, 4918, 5152
pharmacognosy
  biosynthesis, 3329
pharmacological aspects
  anti-neoplastic activity, 3442
  antineoplastic, 3440
  cardiovascular effects, 5531
  convulsions, 4387
  interaction with
    delta-9-THC, 5531
  motor activity, 5561
  prostaglandin synthesis, 3422
  respiration, 5531
  stimulant activity, 4387
  tolerance, 5561
toxicology
  growth profile, 5561
  inhalation toxicology, 4742, 5561
  lethality, 5561
  respiratory effects, 5561
  testicular effects, 5561
CANNABICHROMENIC ACID
  analysis
    gas liquid chromatography (GLC), 3539
    thin layer chromatography (TLC), 3539
  chemical aspects
    homologs
      synthesis, 3539
    synthesis, 3539
  marihuana
    constituents of 3919
CANNABICHROMEVARIN
  cannabis
    constituents of, 4851

CANNABICHROMEVARINIC ACID
  cannabis
    constituents of 4849
  chemical aspects
    synthesis, 4850
CANNABICITRAN
  chemical aspects
    homologs, 3537
    synthesis, 3537
CANNABICOUMARONON
  chemical aspects
    analog(s), 3883
    isolation, 3883
    structure, 3883
  hashish
    constituents of, 3883
CANNABICYCLOL (CBL)
  adverse effect(s)
    cellular division, 3604
  analysis
    detection, 3374
    fluorometric, 3374
    GC/MS, 3944
    mass spectrometry, 5137
    separation, 3944
    trimethylsilyl derivatives, 3944
  biochemical effect(s)
    cellular division, 3604
    chromosome damage, 4534
    compared to:
      alcohol, 4534
      aspirin, 4534
      caffeine, 4534
    macromolecular synthesis, 3440, 3442, 4523,
      4534
    thymidine uptake, 3604
  chemical aspects
    homologs, 3537
    synthesis, 3537
  immunology
    antimitotic, 3602
    lymphocytes, 3602, 4523
  marihuana
    constituents of, 3215, 3919, 4918
  pharmacological aspects
    anti-neoplastic activity, 3442
    antineoplastic, 3440
    convulsions, 4387
    stimulant activity, 4387
CANNABICYCLOLIC ACID
  analysis
    gas liquid chromatography (GLC), 3539
    thin layer chromatography (TLC), 3539
  chemical aspects
    homologs
      synthesis, 3539
    synthesis, 3539
CANNABIDIOL (CBD)
  adverse effect(s)
    cellular division, 3604
    muscular dystrophy, 3827
  analysis
    butyl homolog, 3935
    chemical tests, 3478

analysis (continued)
  colorametric method, 4658
  derivatives, 4171
  detection, 3212, 3374, 3376, 3478, 6164
      4395, 4484, 4565, 4658, 4911, 5028,
      5029, 5134, 5215
  exhaled air, 3095
  fluorometric, 3374, 3376
  gas chromatography, 4484, 4714
  gas liquid chromatography (GLC), 3095, 3286,
      3478, 3750, 4171
  GC/MS, 3935, 3944, 4565
  high-pressure liquid chromatography (HPLC),
      4171, 4911
  identification, 3179, 4171
      gas liquid chromatography (GLC), 3366
  liquid chromatography, 3750
  mass fragmentography, 4565
  mass spectrometry, 3339, 3416, 3478, 4171,
      5137
  metabolites, 3207, 3339, 3942, 4383
      GC/MS, 4305
  microscopic examination, 3478
  nuclear magnetic resonance (NMR),
      3261, 3339, 3478
  paper chromatography, 5215
  pyrolytic products, 4950
  radioimmunoassay (RIA), 5028, 5029
  review, 3478
  separation, 3179, 3750, 3944, 4171, 5134
      cannabichromene (CBC), 3286
      cannabinol (CBN), 3286
      phytosterols, 3366
  silyl derivatives, 3934
  structure, 3416
  thin layer chromatography (TLC), 3095, 3212,
      3478, 3750, 4395, 4484, 5134, 5257
      spray reagents, 3478
  trimethylsilyl derivatives, 3944
  ultra violet (UV), 3478
anti-neoplastic testing, 3775
behavioral effect(s)
  aggression, 5035
  analog(s), 3199
  catecholamines, 3357
  conditioned behavior, 3100, 3384, 4517, 5331
  consummatory behavior, 4923
  derivatives, 3664
  food deprivation, 4519
  gross behavior, 3664
  interaction with
      cannabinol (CBN), 5001
      delta-9-THC, 3384, 5001
      phencyclidine, 4987
  motor activity, 4987
  pseudoconditioning, 3100
  rats, 4816
  review, 4918
  sleep, 5001
biochemical aspects
  ATPase(s), 5349
  calcium levels, 5349
  microsomal metabolism, 5317
  microsomes, 5349

CANNABIDIOL (CBD) (continued)
  biochemical effect(s)
    brain levels, 5319
    cell membrane(s), 4702
    cellular division, 3604
    chromosome damage, 4534
    clotting factors, 4264, 4265
    compared to:
      alcohol, 4043, 4534
      aspirin, 4534
      caffeine, 4534
    hepatic metabolism, 5457
    interaction with
      follicle stimulating hormone (FSH), 5419
      luteinizing hormone (LH), 5419
      phospholipids, 3282
    macromolecular synthesis, 3440, 3442, 3775,
        4042, 4043, 4523, 4534, 5071
    membrane effects, 3282, 5006
    metabolism, 5269
    metabolites, 5457
    microsomal metabolism, 5319
    muscular dystrophy, 3474
    oxygen consumption, 3476
    platelets, 4264, 4265
    testicular effects, 5419
    thymidine uptake, 3604
  Cannabis sativa
    constituents, 5082
    constituents of, 3562, 3691, 3909, 5086
    content in plant, 5086
  chemical aspects
    analog(s), 3199
    biotransformation, 4305, 4719, 4720
    derivatives, 3144, 4650
    gas liquid chromatography (GLC), 5083
    glucuronides, 4306
    homologs, 3537
    metabolism, 3209
    metabolites, 3207, 3939, 4412, 4719, 4770,
        4918, 5147
      hydroxylated, 4221
      identification, 4375
    pyrolysis, 4302, 4949
    pyrolytic products, 4302, 4768, 4770, 4771,
        4946, 4947, 4948, 4949, 4950
      olivetol, 3285
    separation
      cannabichromene (CBD), 5083
    silyl derivatives, 3934
    smoke condensate analysis, 4950
    stereochemical features, 4104
    storage
      insects, 4755
    structure, 3144, 4103, 4583
    synthesis, 3261, 3537, 4221
      derivatives, 4650, 5173
      metabolites, 3207, 4221, 4412
  chemistry
    fluorescence, 3617
    pyrolytic products, 4209, 4210
  clinical findings, 3097
  endocrine effects
    compared to:
      delta-9-THC, 5440

endocrine effects (continued)
   corticosterone level, 5440
   steroids, 5159
   stress, 5440
hashish
   constituents of, 4770
immunology, 5243
   acyltransferase activity, 3872
   antibodies, 4835
   antibody formation, 4835
   cell-mediated immunity, 3550, 3554
   clinical findings, 4835
   lymphocytes, 3872, 4523
legal aspects, 3856
marihuana
   constituents of, 3215, 3919, 4770, 4918
neurochemical effects
   acetylcholine (ACh), 4715, 4716
   dopamine (DA), 4654
   gamma-amino-butyric acid (GABA), 4715
   glutamate, 4715
   monoamine oxidase (MAO), 4806, 4807, 4808
   norepinephrine (NE), 4654
neuropharmacological effects
   anti-convulsant activity, 5609
   brain, 4816
   catalepsy, 5380
   compared to:
      anti-convulsant(s), 5343, 5609
      chlorpromazine, 5380
      delta-9-THC, 5343
      11-hydroxy-delta-9-THC, 5343
   cortex, 5343
   epilepsy, 5343
   interaction with
      neurotransmitters, 4816
   nervous activity, 5609
   neuronal activity, 4816
neuropharmacology
   ganglionic transmission, 3752
neurophysiological effects
   posttetanic potentiation, 5076
neurophysiology
   evoked potentials, 5074
pathological study
   muscular dystrophy, 3822
pharmacognosy
   biosynthesis, 3329
pharmacokinetics
   disposition, 4253
   metabolism, 4253, 5317
   plasma levels, 4266
pharmacological aspects, 5034
   abstinence syndrome, 3334
   acetylcholine (ACh), 3773, 4715, 4716
   analgesia, 4918, 4926, 5184
   analog(s), 3199
   anesthesia, 4233
   anesthetic potentiation, 3784
   anti-bacterial activity, 3564, 5118
   anti-convulsant activity, 3451, 3473, 3475,
      3514, 3518, 3530, 3814, 4104, 4145, 4146,
      4409, 4892, 4918, 5076, 5381, 5458
   anti-convulsant effect(s), 5073
   anti-fungal activity, 3563

pharmacological aspects (continued)
   anti-inflammatory activity, 4009
   antineoplastic, 3440, 4509, 5071
   antineoplastic activity, 3442, 3918, 3924
   antitussive, 3835
   ATPase(s), 3814
   biogenic amine(s), 4654
   blood, 4264, 4265
   body temperature, 3357, 3358, 4918, 5035
   brain, 3814, 3970, 4654, 4716, 4806, 4807,
      4808
   cardiovascular effects, 3394, 3664, 4504
   catecholamines, 3357, 3358
   cell membrane(s), 3817
   clinical effects, 4248
   clotting factors, 4264, 4265
   compared to:
      alcohol, 5350
      delta-9-THC, 4892
      SKF-525a, 5319
   convulsions, 3513, 4387
   cross tolerance
      diphenylhydantoin, 4146
      phenobarbital, 4146
   derivatives, 3451, 3664, 4409
   disposition, 4253
   diuretic activity, 4924
   electroencephalogram (EEG), 3718, 4918
   epilepsy, 3718, 3719, 4388, 5179
   food intake, 4918, 4923
   guinea pig ileum, 4728
   heart, 4893, 4894
   hepatic enzymes, 4281
   hepatic metabolism, 3067, 3937, 4033, 4034,
      4144, 4148
   hypothermia, 3476
   interaction with
      alcohol, 5350
      aminopyrine, 3067
      amphetamine, 3067
      anesthetic(s), 3784
      anti-convulsant(s), 3514
      barbiturate(s), 4918
      cannabinol (CBN), 5184
      delta-9-THC, 3513, 3982, 3985, 4248, 4266
        4324, 4326, 5035, 5184
      ethanol, 3067, 4326, 4863
      ether, 4349
      ethosuximide, 3518
      hexabarbital, 3067, 4033, 4326
      insulin, 5034
      methamphetamine, 4325
      methaqualone, 4988
      morphine, 3067, 3980
      naloxone, 3333, 3980
      pentobarbital, 3067
      pentylenetetrazole, 4325,
      phenobarbital, 3473
      secobarbital, 3574, 3575, 4248
      strychnine, 4325,
   intraocular pressure (IOP), 3866, 4409
   liver, 4374, 4375, 4806, 4807
   membrane permeability, 3281, 3817
   membrane stability, 3281

pharmacological aspects (continued)
    metabolism, 3209, 3574, 3575, 3939, 3942
        4134, 4253, 4281, 4374, 4375, 4383, 4607,
        5148
    metabolites, 4144, 4148, 4374, 5457
    methadone withdrawal, 3984
    microsomal metabolism, 4326
    morphine withdrawal, 3333, 3334, 3980
    motor activity, 3451, 5561
    motor coordination, 5035
    motor performance, 5350
    muscular dystrophy, 3822, 3827, 4604
    neurochemical effects, 3970
    overview, 4412
    pharmacokinetics, 5457
    platelets, 4264, 4265
    prostaglandin synthesis, 4009, 4948
    pyrolytic products, 4948
    respiratory effects, 3394, 4504
    review, 3749, 4918
    seizures, 4892, 4895
    serotonin (5-hydroxytryptamine), 4597
    sleep, 4488
    sleep time, 3067, 3451, 4034, 4326, 4409,
        4988, 5319, 5457
    smooth muscle, 4729
    spontaneous activity, 4409
    stimulant activity, 4387
    testicular effects, 4281
    tolerance, 4033, 4145, 4146, 5561
    water intake, 4923
    withdrawal symptoms, 4147
    worms, 4597
physiological effects
    endocrine effects, 3327
psychological aspects
    cognitive function, 5309, 5350
    compared to:
        alcohol, 5350
    hypnotic, 5330
    interaction with
        alcohol, 5309, 5350
        delta-9-THC, 3573, 3576
    metabolism, 4164
    motor coordination, 5309
    perception, 5309, 5350
    performance, 3573, 5309
    subjective effects, 3573, 3576, 5350
review
    analysis, 3478
    disposition, 4253
    metabolism, 4253
therapeutic aspects
    anti-bacterial activity, 3498
    anti-convulsant activity, 3498
    epilepsy, 4408, 4528
    glaucoma, 3856
    intraocular pressure (IOP), 3498
toxicology
    bone marrow, 3824
    compared to:
        cannabinol (CBN), 5635
        delta-9-THC, 5635
    cytotoxicity, 4702
    growth profile, 5561

toxicology (continued)
    hyperplasia, 3825
    inhalation toxicology, 4742, 5561
    kidney, 3825
    LD50, 5380
    lethality, 5561
    macrophages, 4702
    mutagenesis, 3779
    neurotoxicity, 5609
    reproductive effects, 5635
    respiratory effects, 5561
    testicular effects, 3832, 5561
cis-CANNABIDIOL
    chemical aspects
        isomerization, 3899
        synthesis, 3899
CANNABIDIOLIC ACID
    analysis
        detection, 4911, 5215
        gas liquid chromatography (GLC), 3413
        GC/MS, 3413
        high-pressure liquid chromatography (HPLC),
            4911
        infrared (IR), 3910
        isolation, 3413
        mass spectrometry, 3910
        nuclear magnetic resonance (NMR), 3910
        paper chromatography, 5215
        separation, 3413
        spectral data, 3413
        thin layer chromatography (TLC), 3413, 4201
    cannabis
        constituents of, 3910
    Cannabis sativa
        constituents of, 3562, 3909
    chemical aspects
        ester, 3413
        photo-oxidation, 4166
        synthesis
            ester, 3413
    marihuana
        constituents of, 3919
CANNABIDIORCOL
    marihuana
        constituents of, 4918
CANNABIDIVARIN
    analysis
        detection, 3478
        gas liquid chromatography (GLC), 3478
CANNABIDIVARINIC ACID
    cannabis
        constituents of, 4849
    chemical aspects
        synthesis, 4850
CANNABIDIVAROL
    analysis
        detection, 3478
        gas liquid chromatography (GLC), 3478
    marihuana
        constituents of, 3919, 4918
CANNABIELSOIC ACID
    analysis
        GC/MS, 3882
    Cannabis sativa
        constituents of, 3882

CANNABIELSOIC ACID (continued)
  marihuana
    constituents of, 3919, 4918
  pharmacological aspects
    antibiotic activity, 3711
CANNABIELSOIN (CBE)
  chemical aspects
    isolation, 4946
    structure, 4946
    synthetic cannabinoids, 5095
C$_3$-CANNABIELSOIN
  analysis
    GC/MS, 3882
  Cannabis sativa
    constituents of, 3882
CANNABIFURAN
  cannabis
    constituents of, 3781
  chemical aspects
    spectral data, 3781
CANNABIGEROL (CBG)
  adverse effect(s)
    cellular division, 3604
  analysis
    detection, 3374, 3478, 4911
    fluorometric, 3374
    gas liquid chromatography (GLC), 3478
    GC/MS, 3944
    high-pressure liquid chromatography (HPLC), 4911
    separation, 3944, 4911
    trimethylsilyl derivatives, 3944
  biochemical effect(s)
    acyltransferase, 3871
    cellular division, 3604
    compared to:
      alcohol, 4043
    macromolecular synthesis, 4042, 4043, 4523
    phospholipids, 3871
    prostaglandin synthesis, 3428
    thymidine uptake, 3604
  Cannabis sativa
    constituents of, 3562, 3691
  chemical aspects
    compared to:
      resorcinol derivatives, 5315
    homologs, 3537
    propyl homologs, 4851
    pyrolytic products
      olivetol, 3285
    synthesis, 3537
  forensic aspects
    compared to:
      terpenoids, 5464
  immunology
    acyltransferase activity, 3872
    lymphocytes, 3872, 4523
  marihuana
    constituents of, 3919, 4918
  neurochemical effects
    acyltransferase, 3873
  pharmacological aspects
    anesthesia, 3873
CANNABIGEROLIC ACID
  analysis
    detection, 4911

analysis (continued)
    gas liquid chromatography (GLC), 3413, 3539
    GC/MS, 3413
    high-pressure liquid chromatography (HPLC), 4911
    isolation, 3413
    separation, 3413, 4911
    spectral data, 3413
    thin layer chromatography (TLC), 3413, 3539
  chemical aspects
    homologs
      synthesis, 3539
    synthesis, 3539
  homologs
    synthesis, 3539
  marihuana
    constituents of, 3919
CANNABIGERORCINIC ACID
  chemical aspects
    synthesis, 4850
CANNABIGEROVARIN
  cannabis
    constituents of, 4851
CANNABIGEROVARINIC ACID
  cannabis
    constituents of, 4849
  chemical aspects
    synthesis, 4850
CANNABINODIOL
  Cannabis sativa
    constituents of, 4297
CANNABINOID ACIDS
  analysis
    gas liquid chromatography (GLC), 3413
    GC/MS, 3413
    infrared (IR), 3911
    isolation, 3413
    mass spectrometry, 3911
    nuclear magnetic resonance (NMR), 3911
    review, 3413
    separation, 3413
    spectral data, 3413
    thin layer chromatography (TLC), 3413, 4201
    ultra violet (UV), 3911
  cannabis
    constituents of, 3255
  Cannabis sativa
    constituents of, 3337, 3911, 4853
  chemical aspects
    biosynthesis, 4853
    mass spectrometry, 3337
    synthesis, 4850
  review
    analysis, 3413
CANNABINOID CONTENT
  cannabis
    Belgium, 5116
    cannabidiol (CBD), 4371, 5115, 5116
    cannabinol (CBN), 4371, 5115
    characteristics, 4531
    classification, 5385
    Czechoslovakia, 4202, 5260
    delta-9-THC, 4371, 5115
    environmental conditions, 4202, 4531
    fertilizer, 4371
    flowers, 5260

cannabis (continued)
    France, 5385
    gas chromatography, 5260
    genetics, 4531
    geographical aspects, 5610
    geographical origin, 5115, 5116
    harvest, 4371
    India, 5610
    Jamaica, 4371
    light exposure, 3958
    nomenclature, 4531
    review, 4531
    seasonal variation, 4226
    South Africa, 4202
    Spain, 5115
    structure-activity relationships, 4531
    synthetic cannabinoids, 4531
    tetrahydrocannabinol acids, 5116
    Thailand, 4202
    Turkey, 4202
cannabis plant
    age, 4698
    gas liquid chromatography (GLC), 4698
    genetics, 5311
    Norway, 4697
    seeds
        variability, 4697
    taxonomy, 5311
Cannabis sativa
    age, 4961
    Canada, 3150
    cannabichromene (CBC), 5114
    cannabidiol (CBD), 3492
    cannabinol (CBN), 5114
    classification, 5612
    Czechoslovakia, 3909
    delta-9-THC, 3492, 5114
    environment, 4961
    France, 3580
    geographical origin, 3073, 3304, 3580, 3581,
        4887, 4974
    glands, 5087, 5088
    grafting, 3538
    inorganic elements, 3491
    Mexico, 3580, 3581, 3706
    phospholipids, 5114
    plant age, 5131
    seeds, 4610
    sex differences, 4961
    soil conditions, 3491
    strain difference, 3959
    tetrahydrocannabinol (THC), 4820
    Turkey, 3706
    variability, 5612
ganja
    cannabidiol (CBD), 4371
    cannabinol (CBN), 4371
    delta-9-THC, 4371
    fertilizer, 4371
    harvest, 4371
    Jamaica, 4371, 4762
hashish extract, 4961
hemp, 4824
    Burma, 3270
marihuana
    Brazil, 5003

marihuana (continued)
    confiscated samples, 4765
    geographical origin, 3215
CANNABINOID(S)
    adverse effect(s)
        cellular division, 3604
        driving, 5496
    analysis
        biological fluid(s), 4411, 4722, 5340, 5395, 5623
        Canada, 5608
        chromatography, 4961
        colorimetry, 4961
        compared to:
            gas liquid chromatography (GLC), 5621
            thin layer chromatography (TLC), 5621
        contact test, 5220
        dansyl derivatives, 5572
        derivatives, 5159
        detection, 3245, 3324, 3376, 3478, 3788, 3852,
            3932, 4142, 4229, 4288, 4369, 4370, 4565,
            4566, 4607, 4696, 4722, 4911, 5026, 5089,
            5220, 5326, 5665, 5600
        drug availability, 5496
        drugs of abuse, 4229
        EMIT (homogenous enzyme immunoassay), 5565
        fluorometric, 3376
        fluorometry, 4961
        forensic aspects, 5352, 5483, 5496
        fragmentation, 3933
        gas chromatography, 4411, 4481, 4696, 4950
        gas liquid chromatography (GLC), 3724, 4310,
            4410, 4694, 5154, 5268, 5395
        GC/MS, 3852, 3933, 3944, 4411, 4481, 4565,
            5150, 5384, 5422, 5621, 5623
        hashish, 5268
        high-pressure liquid chromatography (HPLC),
            3799, 4288, 4911, 5089, 5384, 5395, 5497,
            5598, 5629
        identification, 3108, 3324, 4394, 5497
        immunoassay, 4722
        interference with
            coffee, 4229
        lipids, 5557
        mass fragmentography, 4288, 4410, 4565, 4802,
            5154
        mass spectrometry, 4410, 5483
        metabolites, 4288, 5422, 5557, 5598
            thin layer chromatography (TLC), 4290
        methods, 5340, 5352
        nuclear magnetic resonance (NMR), 3261, 4411
        paper chromatography, 5215
        paraquat, 5621
        pyrolytic products, 4950
        quantitative, 4310
        radioimmunoassay (RIA), 3245, 4369, 4370,
            4441, 5026, 5351, 5496, 5598, 5629
        separation, 3944, 4714, 5352, 5386
        silyl derivatives, 3934
        silylation, 4694
        solid sample injection, 4694
        stability, 4142, 5084
        thin layer chromatography (TLC), 3324, 3478,
            4410, 4411, 4481, 4696, 4950, 5220, 5268,
            5572
            spray reagents, 3478

analysis (continued)
  trimethylsilyl derivatives, 3944
  ultra violet (UV), 4411
  urine, 5629
behavioral effect(s)
  aggressive behavior, 3732
  avoidance behavior, 5477
  conditioned behavior, 5331
  definition, 5627
  drug interactions, 3732
  food intake, 3732
  motor activity, 3732
  review, 3732, 4329
  tolerance, 3923
  unlearned behavior, 3732
  water intake, 3732
biochemical aspects
  binding sites, 5340
  membrane effects, 5340
  metabolites, 5340
biochemical effect(s)
  acyltransferase activity, 5500
  cell growth, 5588
  cellular division, 3604
  cellular effects, 5340, 5413, 5509, 5604
  chromosomes, 5588
  cyclic AMP, 5443
  deoxyribonucleic acid (DNA), 5366
  DNA synthesis, 5604
  gonadotropins, 5443
  lipid synthesis, 5500
  macromolecular synthesis, 4523, 5509, 5588
  membrane effects, 5366, 5500
  metabolism, 5413, 5422
  metabolites, 5478
  muscular dystrophy, 3474
  nucleic acids, 5588
  prostaglandin synthesis, 3421, 5413
  protein synthesis, 5442, 5443
  sodium-potassium adenosine triphosphatase (Na K ATPase), 5602
  testis(es), 5442
  testosterone synthesis, 5442, 5443
  thymidine uptake, 3604
botanical aspects
  age, 5608
  biosynthesis, 4122
  definition, 5627
cannabis
  constituents of, 3255, 3256, 3536, 4411
  high-pressure liquid chromatography (HPLC), 4909
  seeds
    detection, 4611
  separation, 4909
cannabis plant, 3787
Cannabis sativa
  constituents, 5082
  constituents of, 4595, 4961, 4079
  pollen, 4595
chemical aspects
  analog(s), 5630
  analysis, 5371, 5384, 5623
  benzoxocinol(s), 3612
  biosynthesis, 4122, 5340
  biotransformation, 3786, 4038

chemical aspects (continued)
  carbocyclic analogs, 4707
  characteristics, 5395
  definition, 5627
  degradation, 5316
  derivatives, 3541, 4650, 5540
    silyl, 3933
    synthesis, 4342, 4343, 4396, 4397, 4710
  detection, 4317, 5340, 5477
  epimerization, 5097
  extractions, 4912
  forensic aspects, 5477
  fragmentation, 5371
  HPLC/MS, 5477
  homologs
    pentyl, 4481
  C_3-homologs, 3882
  mass spectrometry, 5371
  metabolism, 4142, 4410
  metabolites, 4410, 5144
  nitrogen analogs, 4236, 5486
    synthesis, 4600
  nomenclature, 5144
  propyl homologs, 4481
  pyrolytic products, 4950
  radiolabelled, 5371
  review, 3479, 4411, 5144
  silyl derivatives, 3934
  smoke condensate analysis, 4950
  solvents
    ethanol, 4912
    methanol, 4912
  stability, 4142, 5316
  storage, 4912
  structure, 4410, 5413
    thio derivatives, 4212
  structure-activity relationships, 3335, 3442, 3479, 3866, 3921, 4396, 4411, 4607, 4653, 4668, 4707, 4913, 4918, 4961, 5340
  synthesis, 3241, 3261, 3541, 3682, 4142, 4410, 4411, 4961, 5144, 5357, 5371, 5486, 5487
    acids, 3541
    derivatives, 4342, 4343, 4344, 4396, 4397, 4650
    ester, 3541
    metabolites, 4411, 5096, 5144
    thio derivatives, 4212
  thio analogs, 4707, 4709
compared to:
  steroids, 3816
convulsions
  rabbit(s), 3511
cytogenic effects
  chromosome damage, 5636
  review, 5446
  spermatozoa, 5636
derivatives
  detection, 3672
detection
  derivatives, 3672
  spray reagents, 3672
  thin layer chromatography (TLC), 3672
electrophysiology
  anti-convulsant activity, 5458

CANNABINOID(S) (continued)
  endocrine effects
    hypothalamic pituary function, 5340
    review, 5340
  forensic aspects
    contact test, 5220
    detection, 4607, 5061, 5220
    geographical origin, 5061
  immunology
    cell-mediated immunity, 4653, 4913
    delayed hypersensitivity reaction, 5510
    host resistance, 5510
    humoral immunity, 4653, 4913
    immunosuppression, 5510, 5584
    lymphocytes, 4523
    structure-activity relationships, 4668
  marihuana smoke
    catatonia, 5279
    corneal reflex, 5279
    motor activity, 5279
    sleep time, 5279
    water pipes, 5279
  neurochemical effects
    acyltransferase, 3873
    analog(s), 3293
    brain, 5428
    dopamine (DA), 3293
    gamma-amino-butyric acid (GABA), 3293
    neurotransmitters, 5428
    norepinephrine (NE), 3293
    receptors, 5428
    serotonin (5-hydroxytryptamine), 3293
  neuropharmacological effects
    brain, 5368, 5504
    EEG changes, 5504
    limbic, 5504
    neurotransmitters, 5368
    synaptosomes, 5368
  9-nor-9-beta-hydroxy-hexahydrocannabinol, 4378
  pharmacognosy
    biosynthesis, 3329
    review, 3329
  pharmacokinetics
    compared to:
      diphenylhydantoin, 5458
    disposition, 4142
    excretion, 5621
  pharmacological aspects
    administration, 5340
    analgesic activity, 5569
    analog(s), 5630
    anesthesia, 3873
    anti-convulsant activity, 5458
    anti-neoplastic activity, 3442, 3921
    body temperature, 3358, 5416
    body weight, 3865
    brain, 3920
    cardiovascular effects, 5340
    catecholamines, 3358
    CNS activity, 4396
    compared to:
      dimethylheptylpyran (DMHP), 4600
      diphenylhydantoin, 5458
      ethosuximide, 5458
      phenobarbital, 5458

  pharmacological aspects (continued)
    convulsions, 4387
    definition, 5627
    derivatives, 4710
      CNS activity, 4397
    eyes, 3859, 3865
    gastrointestinal effects, 5340
    hypothermia, 5416
    intraocular pressure (IOP), 3859, 3866, 5413,
      5414
    liver weight, 3865
    microsomal metabolism, 3219
    muscular dystrophy, 4604
    nitrogen analogs, 4236, 4600
    ocular effects, 5340
    pharmacokinetics, 5395, 5623
    plasma levels, 5421
    prostaglandin synthesis, 3421
    respiratory effects, 5340
    review, 4329, 5340
    stereospecific binding, 3920
    stimulant activity, 4387
    tolerance, 3923
    vehicle effect(s), 5414
  physiological effects
    endocrine effects, 3351
    reproductive effects, 3351
    review, 3351
    sexual behavior, 3351
  psychological aspects
    cognitive processes, 5504
    subjective effects, 5504
    time perception, 5504
  review
    analysis, 4607, 5421
    behavioral effect(s), 3732, 4329
    biosynthesis, 3329
    chemical aspects, 4142, 5144
    endocrine effects, 3351
    metabolism, 5421
    pharmacognosy, 3329
    pharmacokinetics, 5421
    pharmacology, 4329
    reproductive effects, 3351
    sexual behavior, 3351
    structure-activity relationships, 3479
    teratogenic effects, 3351
    therapeutic aspects, 3237, 3498
  site of action, 3816
  therapeutic aspects
    alcoholism, 3331
    analgesic, 3331
    anti-convulsant activity, 3331, 5381
    anti-hypertensive, 3331
    anti-inflammatory activity, 3331
    antiasthmatic, 3331
    antidepressant, 3331
    antidiarrheal, 3331
    antiemetic, 3331
    antipyretic, 3331
    antitussive, 3331
    appetite stimulant, 3331
    cancer, 3331, 5604
    glaucoma, 3331
    history, 3498

therapeutic aspects (continued)
  morphine withdrawal, 3331
  review, 3237, 3331, 3498, 4408
therapeutic effects
  glaucoma, 5405, 5413
  intraocular pressure (IOP), 5405
  ocular effects, 5412
toxicology
  placental transfer, 3351
  teratogenic effects, 3351
  testis(es), 5442
9-AZA-CANNABINOL
  behavioral effect(s)
    compared to:
      delta-9-THC, 5491
    feeding, 5491
  pharmacological aspects
    appetite stimulant, 5618
    food intake, 5117, 5618
    gastric secretion, 5117
    gastrointestinal tract, 4154
    muscle, 4154
    stomach acids, 5618
  physiological effects
    compared to:
      benzodiazepine(s), 5461
    gastrointestinal effects, 5461
CANNABINOL (CBN)
  adverse effect(s)
    cellular division, 3604
    muscular dystrophy, 3827
  analysis, 4565
    butyl homolog, 3935
    chemical tests, 3478
    colorametric method, 4658
    derivatives, 4171
    detection, 3212, 3376, 3478, 4164, 4395, 4484,
      4565, 4658, 5028, 5029, 5089, 5134, 5149,
      5150, 5206, 5215, 5617
    exhaled air, 3095
    fluorometric, 3376
    gas chromatography, 4484, 4714
    gas liquid chromatography (GLC), 3095, 3286,
      3478, 3750, 4171
    GC/MS, 3935, 3944, 4155, 4565, 5149, 5150
    high-pressure liquid chromatography (HPLC),
      4171, 5089, 5206
    identification, 4171
      gas liquid chromatography (GLC), 3366
    liquid chromatography, 3750
    mass spectrometry, 3339, 3478, 4171, 5137
    metabolites, 3339, 3938, 3942, 5228, 5229,
      5230, 5232
      GC/MS, 4305
    microscopic examination, 3478
    nuclear magnetic resonance (NMR), 3261, 3339,
      3478
    paper chromatography, 5215
    plasma, 5149
    quantitative, 5149
    radioimmunoassay (RIA), 5028, 5029, 5206
    review, 3478
    saliva, 5617
    separation, 3750, 3944, 4171, 5134
      cannabichromene (CBC), 3286

separation (continued)
    cannabidiol (CBD), 3286
    phytosterols, 3366
    silyl derivatives, 3934
    thin layer chromatography (TLC), 3095, 3212,
      3478, 3750, 4395, 4484, 5134, 5257
      spray reagents, 3478
    trimethylsilyl derivatives, 3944
    ultra violet (UV), 3478
    urine, 4155
  behavioral effect(s)
    appetite, 4870
    catecholamines, 3357
    cognitive function, 4515
    consummatory behavior, 4923
    copulation, 5359
    interaction with
      cannabidiol (CBD), 5001
      delta-9-THC, 4515, 5001
    memory, 4870
    perception, 4515
    review, 4918
    sexual behavior, 3569, 3570, 4870
    sleep, 5001
    social behaivor, 4515
    time estimation, 4515
    vision, 4870
  biochemical effect(s)
    acyltransferase, 3871
    adenylate cyclase, 3627
    amino acid(s), 5367
    arachidonic acid, 3422, 3423
    ATPase(s), 4570
    brain, 3627
    cell growth, 3385
    cellular division, 3604
    cholesterol esterase, 5323
    compared to:
      alcohol, 4043
    cyclic AMP, 3627
    macromolecular synthesis, 3440, 3442, 4042,
      4043, 4523, 5071, 5367
    membrane-bound enzyme, 4570
    membrane effects, 4591, 5367
    muscular dystrophy, 3474
    oxygen consumption, 3476
    phosphodiesterase, 3627
    phospholipids, 3871, 4591
    progesterone, 5323
    prostaglandin synthesis, 3422
    synaptic vesicles, 4570
    thymidine uptake, 3604, 5367
  cannabis
    seeds
      detection, 4611
  Cannabis sativa
    constituents, 5082
    constituents of, 3562, 3691
  chemical aspects
    biotransformation, 4305, 4719, 4720
    derivatives, 4650
    glucuronides, 4306
    homologs, 3537
    identification
      metabolites, 3751

chemical aspects (continued)
  metabolism, 3209
  metabolites, 3207, 3427, 3939, 4719, 4770, 4918,
    5147, 5228, 5229
  pyrolytic products, 4770, 5487
  silyl derivatives, 3934
  structure, 4582
  synthesis, 3261, 3537, 4649
    derivatives, 4650
    metabolites, 3207, 5200
  ultra violet radiation, 3377
chemistry
  fluoresence, 3617
clinical findings, 3097
endocrine effects
  steroids, 5159
hashish
  constituents of 4770
immunology, 5243
  acyltransferase activity, 3872
  antibodies, 4835
  antibody formation, 4835
  antimitotic, 3602
  cell-mediated immunity, 3550, 3554, 4262, 5482
  clinical findings, 4835
  immunosuppression, 5482
  lymphocytes, 3602, 3872, 4523
marihuana
  constituents of, 3215, 3919, 4770, 4918
neurochemical effects
  acetylcholine (ACh), 3629
  acyltransferase, 3873
  adenylate cyclase, 3627
  cyclic AMP, 3627
  dopamine (DA), 4654
  norepinephrine (NE), 4654
  phosphodiesterase, 3627
neuropharmacology
  ganglionic transmission, 3752
neurophysiological effects
  posttetanic potentiation, 5076
pathological study
  muscular dystrophy, 3822
pharmacognosy
  biosynthesis, 3329
pharmacokinetics
  disposition, 4253, 4918
  excretion, 4918
  metabolism, 4253
pharmacological aspects
  abstinence syndrome, 3334
  acetylcholine (ACh), 3629
  analgesia, 4515, 4918, 4926, 5184
  anesthesia, 3873, 4233
  anti-convulsant activity, 3514, 3530, 4145, 4918,
    5076
  anti-neoplastic activity, 3442
  antineoplastic, 3440, 4509, 5071
  antineoplastic activity, 3924
  antitussive, 3835
  biogenic amine(s), 4654
  body temperature, 3357, 3358, 4515, 4918
  body weight, 5359
  brain, 3629, 4570, 4654
  brain levels
    cyclic AMP, 3628

pharmacological aspects (continued)
  cardiovascular effects, 4149, 4515
  catecholamines, 3357, 3358
  cell membrane(s), 3817
  compared to:
    delta-9-THC, 5544
    methadone, 5544
  convulsions, 3513, 4387
  disposition, 4253
  diuretic activity, 4924
  electroencephalogram (EEG), 4918
  eyes, 5042
  food intake, 4918, 4923
  guinea pig ileum, 4728
  heart, 4893, 4894
  hepatic metabolism, 3067, 5200
  hypothalamic pituary function, 5544
  hypothermia, 3476
  interaction with
    aminopyrine, 3067
    amphetamine, 3067
    anesthetic(s), 3784
    anti-convulsant(s), 3514
    bacterial lipopolysaccharide, 4511
    barbiturate(s), 4918
    cannabidiol (CBD), 5184
    delta-9-THC, 3985, 4149, 4412, 5184
    ethanol, 3067
    ether, 4349
    gonadotropins, 5544
    hexabarbital, 3067
    lipopolysaccharides, 4512
    morphine, 3067
    naloxone, 3333
    pentobarbital, 3067
  intraocular pressure (IOP), 3866, 5042
  membrane permeability, 3817
  metabolism, 3209, 3427, 3751, 3938, 3939, 3942,
    4134, 4253, 5148, 5228, 5229, 5230, 5231,
    5232
  morphine withdrawal, 3333, 3334
  muscular dystrophy, 3822, 3827, 4604
  overview, 4412
  plasma protein binding, 4312
  prostaglandin synthesis, 3422
  reproductive system, 5544
  review, 4918
  sleep time, 3067
  smooth muscle, 4729
  stimulant activity, 4387
  testicular effects, 5359
  testosterone synthesis, 3425
  tolerance, 4145
  water intake, 4923
pharmacology
  blood clearance rates, 4309
physiological effects
  adrenocorticotropic hormone (ACTH), 4080
  corticosterones, 4077, 4080
  endocrine effects, 3568, 5359
  follicle stimulating hormone (FSH), 3569, 3570
  luteinizing hormone (LH), 3569, 3570
  reproductive effects, 5359
  reproductive system, 3569, 3570
  testis(es), 3568

physiological effects (continued)
    testosterone levels, 3569, 3570, 5359
psychological aspects, 4149
    metabolism, 4164
review
    analysis, 3478
    disposition, 4253
    metabolism, 4253
therapeutic aspects
    cancer, 3498
    intraocular pressure (IOP), 3498
toxicology
    bone marrow, 3824
    compared to:
        cannabidiol (CBD), 5635
        cannabinol (CBN), 5635
    hyperplasia, 3825
    kidney, 3825
    occular toxicity, 5042
    reproductive effects, 5635
CANNABINOL-7-OIC ACID
analysis
    detection, 4911
    high-pressure liquid chromatography (HPLC), 4911
    thin layer chromatography (TLC), 4201
marihuana
    constituents of, 3919
CANNABIORCOL
marihuana
    constituents of, 4918
CANNABIRIPSOL
analysis
    identification, 5314
chemical aspects
    structure, 5314
    synthesis, 5314
CANNABIS
abuse of
    South Africa, 3851
adverse effect(s), 3243, 4465
    aggressive behavior, 3078
    blood cells, 4969
    brain, 4763
    brain damage, 3078
    carcinogenicity, 3078, 3230
    chronic effects, 4965
    chronic use, 3633
    compared to:
        hallucinogens, 5128
    diarrhea, 4538
    driving, 3078, 4437, 5030
    eyes, 5128
    feces, 5324
    general information, 3926
    hepatitis, 3458
    humans, 4763
    immunology, 4763
    intravenous administration, 4471
    liver, 4965
    lung(s), 4763
    mutagenicity, 3078
    personality, 3078
    poisoning, 3395
    progression to other drugs, 3078
    psychiatric aspects, 4763

adverse effects (continued)
    psychological aspects, 4763
    psychosis, 3078, 3228, 3529, 3633
    review, 3078, 3105
    spermatozoa, 4763
    spermatogenesis, 3955
    stomach acids, 4538
    teratogenic effects, 3078
    urine, 5324
analysis
    alkane(s), 4695
    biological fluid(s), 4522
    cannabinoid content, 4202, 5260, 5610
    cannabinoid(s), 3324, 4909, 5215
    color tests, 3542, 4243
    confiscated samples, 5080
    constituents of, 4411
    detection, 3212, 3288, 3542, 4243, 4369, 4952,
        4955
        cannabinoid(s), 4611
        thin layer chromatography (TLC), 4611
    exhaled air, 3095
    gas chromatography, 3288, 4952, 5047, 5080
    gas liquid chromatography (GLC), 3095, 3542,
        4202
    GC/MS, 4522
    geographical origin, 5047
    high-pressure liquid chromatography (HPLC),
        3288, 4909, 5191, 5192
        compared to:
            gas liquid chromatography (GLC), 5192
            thin layer chromatography (TLC), 5192
    identification, 3072, 3591
    infrared (IR), 3542
    mass spectrometry, 3542
    methods, 4531
    microscopic examination, 4952
    nuclear magnetic resonance (NMR), 3542
    paraquat, 5080
    radioimmunoassay (RIA), 3542, 4369, 4522
    smoke, 4157
    stability, 4539
    street samples, 4285
    thin layer chromatography (TLC), 3095, 3212,
        3288, 3324, 3542, 3591, 4202, 4243, 4952,
        4955, 5047, 5080
    ultra violet (UV), 3542
behavioral effect(s), 5020

    aggression, 3182, 3186
    aggressive behavior, 3062
    CNS depression, 3843
    conditioned behavior, 5498
    depressive effects, 4874
    EEG changes, 3769
    interaction with
        amphetamine, 3839
        syntostigmine, 4542
    locomotor activity, 4259, 4873
    motor reflex, 4542
    research efforts, 3735
    review, 3062
    sexual behavior, 3995
    social behavior, 4259
    stereotypy, 3839
    stimulant effects, 4874

behavioral effect(s) (continued)
    tolerance, 3062, 3456, 3769, 4108, 4522
biochemical effect(s)
    blood glucose, 3097
    cyclic AMP, 4963
    dopa beta-hydroxylase, 4949
    drug abuse, 5514
    nucleotides, 4969
    prostaglandin synthesis
        constituents of, 3426
    protein, 4036
    spermatozoa, 4036
books on:
    A Comprehensive Guide to the Cannabis Literature, 5274
    Cannabinoid Analysis in Physiological Fluids, 5619
    Cannabinoid Assays in Humans, 5204
    Cannabis and Culture, 4761
    Cannabis and Health, 3842
    Cannabis and Man, 3510
    Cannabis Now, 3848
    Chronic Cannabis Use, 3634
    Consequences of Alcohol and Marijuana Use, 5551
    Hashish: Studies of Long-Term Use, 4965
    Highlights from Drug Use Among American H.S. Students 1975-1977, 4086
    Highlights from the National Survey on Drug Abuse: 1977, 4452
    Highlights from the National Survey on Drug Abuse: 1979, 5503
    Keep off the Grass: a Sci. Enquiry into Biol. Effects of Marihuana, 5517
    Marihuana: An Annotated Bibliography, 5155
    Marihuana: Biological Effects, 5518
    Marihuana: Chemistry, Biochemistry and Cellular Effects, 4526
    Marihuana: Deceptive Weed, 4531
    Marihuana Research Findings: 1976, 4631
    Marihuana Today, 4763
    Marihuana Users and Drug Subculture, 3101
    Marijuana and Health Hazards: Methodological Issues in Current Research, 5048
    Marijuana Grower's Guide, 3763
    Marijuana Potency, 4961
    Parents, Peers and Pot, 5493
    Pharmacology of Marihuana, Vols 1 & 2, 3391
    Sensual Drugs: Deprivation and Rehabilitation of the Mind, 4100
    Some Recent Advances in the Study of Cannabis, 5340
    The Marihuana Muddle, 3091
    The Scientific Study of Marihuana, 3183
    The Therapeutic Potential of Marihuana, 3504
botanical aspects
    achene(s), 4882
    analysis, 4226
    anatomy, 4854, 4977, 4978
    cannabinoid content, 4202, 4226, 4371, 4531, 4824
    classification, 3146, 4885, 4886, 4889, 5340, 5573, 5610
    cultivation, 3763
    cytology, 4854, 4977, 4978
    development, 5466

botanical aspects (continued)
    ecological factors, 3486
    environment, 3192
    eradication, 3270
    fertilizer, 4371
    flowering, 3486
    gamma irradiation, 4844
    geographical origin, 3255, 4202
    harvest, 3763, 4371
    history, 3763
    life cycle, 3486
    morphological variations, 4844, 4882
    morphology, 3486, 5610
    nitrogen compounds, 3713
    phytosterols, 5570
    review, 3079, 3486, 3763, 4531, 4881
    seeds, 4844
    sex differences, 3486, 3763
    sexual function, 5466, 5570
    silver nitrate, 5570
    soil, 3763
    species, 3151, 4411, 4881, 4883, 4885, 4886, 4889
    stomato, 3794
    taxonomy, 3255, 3486, 3689, 3763, 3794, 4885, 4886, 4889
    trichomes, 3794
    wild plant, 4194
chemical aspects
    alkaloid(s), 3054
    biosynthesis, 3536
    butyl homolog
        cannabidiol (CBD), 3935
        cannabinol (CBN), 3935
        delta-9-THC, 3935
        delta-9-THC oic acid A & B, 3935
    cannabinoid content, 3958, 4371, 4531, 4824, 5115, 5116
    classification, 5340, 5484
    colorametic method, 5601
    constituents of, 3704, 4410, 4522
        alkaloid(s), 3255, 3256, 3536, 4411, 5110, 5154
        alkane(s), 4695
        amines, 3536
        cannabichromanon, 3781
        cannabichromene (CBC), 3536
        cannabichromevarin, 4851
        cannabichroevarinic acid, 4849
        cannabicitran, 3536
        cannabicyclol (CBL), 3536
        cannabidiol (CBD), 3536
        cannabidiolic acid, 3910
        cannabidivarinic acid, 4849
        cannabifuran, 3781
        cannabigerol (CBG), 3536
        cannabigerovarin, 4851
        cannabigerovarinic acid, 4849
        cannabinoid acids, 3255
        cannabinoid(s) 3255, 3256, 3536, 4411
        cannabinol (CBN), 3536
        cannabispiran (see also cannabispirone), 4580
        carbohydrates, 4411
        carboxylic acid, 3256, 4411
        carotenoid, 3120

constituents of (continued)
    cathine, 5110
    cathinone, 5110
    dehydrocannabifuran, 3781
    delta-8-THC, 3536
    delta-9-THC, 3536
    essential oils, 4411
    flavonoids, 3255, 3536
    glycoprotein, 3255
    heptacosane, 4695
    hydrocarbon, 3255, 3256, 3536
    minerals, 3120
    nonacosane, 4695
    novel cannabinoids, 3781
    phenols, 3255, 3256, 4411
    phosphorus, 4845
    polycyclic aromatic hydrocarbons, 3230
    propyl cannabinoid acids, 4849
    review, 3256, 4411
    steroids, 3255
    sugars, 3255, 3536
    terpenes, 3255, 3536
    tetrahydrocannabinol acids, 4596
    tetrahydrocannabivarinic acid, 4849
    tetrahydrocannabivarolic acids, 4596
    p-vinylphenol, 3426
  detection, 4691
  geographical aspects, 5115
  geographical origin, 4596, 5116
  identification, 5601
  nitrogen compounds, 3054
  nomenclature, 4411
  pyrolytic products, 3214, 3230, 3256, 3411, 4157,
    5340
  research, 5260, 5264
  review, 4411, 4531
  smoke condensate analysis, 3214, 3411
  structure-activity relationships, 3536
  synthesis, 3536
chemistry
  analysis, 3992
  constituents of, 3992, 4880
  geographical origin, 3992
classification, 4372
delta-9-THC
  cerebral cortex, 4095
  hippocampus, 4095
drug interactions
  alcohol, 4900
epidemiological study
  Canada, 5554
  characteristics of users, 3509, 4416
  drug use, 4531
  factors influencing use, 4936
  multiple drug use, 4541, 4936
  neurological effects, 3372
  patterns of use, 3205, 4541, 4936, 5127, 5554
  pharmacological aspects, 3372, 3545
  physiological effects, 3372, 3545
  problems, 4185
  progression to other drugs, 3205
  psychological aspects, 3545, 4172, 4416, 4936
  sociological aspects, 4416
  teratogenic effects, 4623
forensic aspects
  age, 3591

forensic aspects (continued)
  analysis, 5080, 5251
  classification, 4885, 4886, 4889
  color tests, 4411
  confiscated samples, 5080
  detection, 3288, 4411, 4550, 4660, 4952, 5191
  geographical origin, 3288, 3591, 5047, 5191
  identification, 3436, 4660
    species, 4442
  review, 4660
  species, 4298, 4299, 4885, 4886, 4889
  stability, 4539
  storage, 3591
general information, 4805
  adverse effect(s), 3854
  distribution, 3854
  legal aspects, 3854
  preparation, 3854
history
  Africa, 3076, 3644
  classification, 5573
  distribution, 3076
  drug use, 4531
  Jamaica, 3267
  legalization issue, 4531
  medicine, 4451
  review, 3113, 3704, 4531
humans
  chronic use, 3589
legal aspects, 3078, 3243, 3646, 3677, 3952, 4298
  decriminalization, 3928
    England, 5288
  definition, 5408
  England, 3238, 5287
  history, 3229
  possession, 5408
  regulation, 3229
  species, 4299
  trafficking, 3257, 5408
  use, 5408
neurochemistry
  review, 3844
neurochemical effects
  biogenic amine(s), 4963
  dopamine beta-hydroxylase, 4963
neuropharmacological effects
  neurotransmitters, 5340
neurophysiology
  electroencephalogram (EEG), 3087, 3097, 3738,
    3845, 4172, 4963
  REM sleep, 3097
neuropsychology
  Halstead tests, 3445
patterns of use, 4724
pharmacognosy
  aflatoxin, 4286
  classification, 3704
  fungal growth, 4286
  identification, 3704
  review, 3079
  species, 3079
pharmacological aspects
  analgesia, 3134, 4873, 4874
  anti-convulsant activity, 4873, 4874
  anti-inflammatory activity, 4874

pharmacological aspects (continued)
  antipyretic, 4874
  biogenic amine(s), 4875
  blood cells, 4963
  body temperature, 4874
  brain, 4522
  cardiovascular effects, 3097, 3227, 4280
  clinical findings, 3097
  compared to:
    alcohol, 3523
    reserpine, 4875
  dependence, 3854, 5340
  dependence liability, 3136
  drug dependence, 3136
  drug interactions, 5340
  electroencephalogram (EEG), 4280
  eyes, 3588
  heart rate, 4963
  hepatic enzymes, 4479
  hepatic metabolism, 3067
  hypothermia, 4873, 4875, 4876
  interaction with
    alcohol, 4331
    aminopyrine, 3067
    amphetamine, 3067, 4479
    atropine, 5498
    copper, 4876
    estradiol, 3460
    ethanol, 3067
    hexabarbital, 3067
    LSD-25, 4479
    morphine, 3067
    pentobarbital, 3067, 4479
    physostigmine, 5498
    reserpine, 4479
  intraocular pressure (IOP), 3588, 5568
  lung(s), 4522
  motor performance, 5568
  motor reflex, 5498
  performance, 4331
  physical dependence, 4812, 4968, 5203
  research, 5260, 5264
  review, 3436, 4727, 5233
  sleep time, 3067, 4873, 4876
  spermatozoa, 4963
  tolerance, 4812, 4873, 4876, 4963, 4968, 5203,
    5340
  tranquilizing activity, 5020
  uterine effects
    glycogen, 3460
  withdrawal symptoms, 4968
  withdrawal syndrome, 3523, 4812, 4963
physiological effects
  endocrine effects, 4522, 4727
  reproductive effects, 4522, 5139
  spermatozoa, 4036
  spermatogenesis, 3955, 4522
  testicular effects, 5139
psychiatric aspects
  intoxication, 3927
  psychosis, 3929
psychological aspects, 4100, 5110
  adverse effect(s), 4934, 5072
  amotivational syndrome, 3244, 3712, 4963
  analgesia, 3844

psychological aspects (continued)
  anti-convulsant activity, 3844
  body temperature, 3844
  brain, 3844
  cardiovascular effects, 3844
  cognitive function, 4701, 4934
  compared to:
    amphetamine, 3715
    hallucinogens, 5128
    LSD, 3715
    other drugs, 5626
    phencyclidine, 3715
  dependence, 5301
  drug abuse, 5514
  environmental conditions, 3667, 3929
  euphoria, 3529
  eyes, 3844
  flashbacks, 3667
  hallucinogenic effects, 3165
  intelligence tests, 4963
  interaction with
    alcohol, 3844
    amphetamine, 3844
    morphine, 3844
  memory, 3097
  mental illness, 4531
  motor activity, 3097
  neurosis, 4963
  perception, 3097, 5128
  performance, 3097, 3456, 4934
  personality, 3667, 4963, 5301
  psychosis, 3165, 3228, 3529, 3667, 3715, 4172,
    4531, 5568
  respiratory effects, 3844
  review, 3529, 3667, 3844, 4531
  schizophrenia, 3102
  subjective effects, 3738, 3843, 3845, 3854, 5128,
    5626
  tolerance, 3738, 3845, 5301
  withdrawal symptoms, 5301
psychopharmacological aspects
  compared to:
    tobacco, 4112
  methods, 4114
  self administration, 4112
  tolerance, 4112
registry, 4465
religious beliefs
  India, 3210
research, 3078
review
  adverse effect(s), 3078, 3105, 5535
  behavioral effect(s), 3062, 3769
  botanical aspects, 3486, 3763, 4881
  brain, 5379
  central nervous system (CNS), 5379
  CNS activity, 5535
  constituents of, 3256
  EEG changes, 3769
  forensic aspects, 4660
  history, 3113
  neurochemistry, 3844
  pharmacokinetics, 5535
  pharmacological aspects, 3436, 4727, 5233
  pharmacology, 3844

review (continued)
    psychological aspects, 3529, 3667
    reproductive effects, 5535
    respiratory effects, 5535
    sociological aspects, 3929
    teratogenic effects, 4623
    therapeutic aspects, 4451
seeds
    cannabinoid(s), 4611
sociological aspects, 3633
    amotivational syndrome, 3509
    chronic use, 5067
    compared to:
        alcohol, 4531
    education, 4531
    epidemiological study, 4185
    legalization issue, 4531
    motivation of use, 4531
    multiple drug use, 4531
    productivity, 4531
    progression to other drugs, 3854
    review, 3929, 4531
    social behavior, 3509
therapeutic aspects, 3846, 4727
    alcoholism, 4731
    anti-convulsant(s), 4522
    cancer, 5307
    gastric ulcers, 4101
    history, 4451, 4760
    review, 4451
therapeutic effects
    review, 4531
toxicology
    acute effect(s), 3845
    allergy, 3845
    chromosomes, 3845
    chronic effects, 4531
    immune response, 3845
    LD_{50}, 3845
    liver, 3845
    mutagenic effects, 4531
    review, 4531
    subacute effects, 4531
    teratogenic effects, 4531, 4623
trafficking, 4372
United Nations Narcotics Commission
    recommendations, 3256
vision
    intraocular pressure (IOP), 3589
    visual acuity, 3589
CANNABIS EXTRACT
analysis
    detection
        olivetol, 3285
    gas liquid chromatography (GLC), 4540
    stability, 4540
behavioral effect(s)
    acetylcholine (ACh), 3264
    aggressive behavior, 3446, 3595
    biogenic amine(s), 3264
    catalepsy, 3264
    compared to:
        alcohol, 3721
        ethanol, 3720
    discriminative stimulus, 4204

behavioral effects (continued)
    interaction with
        anticholinergic(s), 3595
    learning, 3720, 3721
    locomotor activity, 3264
    performance, 3720, 3721
    review, 3446
    stereotypy, 3264
biochemical effect(s)
    brain, 4655
    macromolecular synthesis, 3621
    sodium-potassium adenosine triphosphatase (Na K
        ATPase), 4655
neurochemical effects
    acetylcholine (ACh), 3264
    biogenic amine(s), 3264, 4656
    5-hydroxyindoleacetic acid (5-HIAA), 4161
    serotonin (5-hydroxytryptamine), 4161
pharmacological aspects
    biogenic amine(s), 4161, 4656
    blood glucose, 3470, 4930
    brain, 4161, 4655, 4656
    dopamine (DA), 3528
    food intake, 3181
    glucose tolerance, 3470
    glycogen, 4930
    interaction with
        estradiol, 3463
        insulin, 3470
    monoamine oxidase (MAO), 3463
    review, 3181
    serotonin (5-hydroxytryptamine), 4161
    stress, 3528
    water intake, 3181
physiological effects
    anti-estrogenic, 3462
    endocrine effects, 3462, 3621, 3624, 4393
    interaction with
        estradiol, 3462
    ovaries, 3620, 3621
    reproductive effects, 3620, 3621, 3623, 3624
    steroids, 4390, 4392, 4393
    testis(es), 3623
    testosterone, 4392
    uterus, 3462
review
    aggressive behavior, 3446
    food intake, 3181
    water intake, 3181
therapeutic aspects
    gastric ulcers, 3596
toxicology
    brain, 4056
    interaction with
        serotonin (5-hydroxytryptamine), 5255
    kidney, 4056
    reproductive system, 3622
    teratogenic effects, 3759
    worms, 5255
CANNABIS INDICA
analysis
    cannabinoid(s), 3223
    detection, 3223
    fast blue B salt, 3223

CANNABIS INDICA (continued)
  behavioral effect(s)
    interaction with
      amphetamine, 4871
    motor activity, 4871
    stereotypy, 4871
  botanical aspects
    classification, 3083
  chemical aspects
    cannabinoid(s), 3223
  pharmacological aspects
    interaction with
      aspirin, 4474
      diphenylhydantoin, 4474
      pentazocine, 4474
      pethidine, 4474
CANNABIS PLANT
  alkaloid(s)
    anhydrocannabisativine, 3685
    cannabisativine, 3685
    hordenine, 3685
  analysis
    detection, 4693
    gas chromatography, 4693
    inorganic elements, 4847
    neutron activation, 4847
    solid sample injection, 4693
    stability, 3705
  biochemical effect(s)
    phytosterols, 5465
  botanical aspects
    age, 4698
    cannabinoid content, 4697, 4698, 5385
    classification, 5385
    cultivation, 5311
    diseases, 4115
    sex differences, 4781
  chemical aspects
    cannabinoid content, 5311
    constituents of
      alkane(s), 4698
      inorganic elements, 4847
      South Africa, 5314
    stability, 3705
  chemistry
    alkaloid(s), 3787
    cannabinoids, 3787
  geographical origin, 3685
  phytochemistry
    structure, 3787
CANNABIS RESIN
  analysis
    GC/MS, 4990
    stability, 3705
    trace elements, 3964
  behavioral effect(s)
    aggressive behavior, 3560
    conditioned behavior, 3593
    feeding, 3560
    learned behavior, 3820
    sexual behavior, 3561
    social behavior, 3559, 3560
  biochemical effect(s)
    chromosomes, 5133
    mitosis, 5133

CANNABIS RESIN (continued)
  chemical aspects
    constituents of
      hexadecamide, 4910
      hydroxylated cannabinoids, 4990
      trace elements, 3964
    extractions, 4912
    geographical origin, 3964
    stability, 3705
  neuropharmacological effects
    catecholamines, 5398
    serotonin (5-hydroxytryptamine), 5398
  pathological study
    muscular dystrophy, 3822
  pharmacological aspects
    anti-convulsant activity, 3810
    biogenic amine(s), 3592, 3810
    brain, 3592, 3810
    hypothermia, 4872
    interaction with
      chlorpromazine, 4872
      reserpine, 4872
    muscular dystrophy, 3822
    stress, 3592
    tolerance, 4872
  physiological effects
    reproductive system, 4569
  psychological aspects
    analgesic activity, 5398
    interaction with
      morphine, 5398
    learning, 3820
  toxicology
    reproductive system, 4569
CANNABIS SATIVA
  analysis
    Beam test, 4230
    cannabinoid(s), 4610
    chemical tests, 3478
    detection, 3099, 3478, 3526, 4690
    Duquenois test, 4230
    essential oils, 3960
    flavonoids, 5346
    Furfural test, 4230
    gas chromatography, 4610
    gas liquid chromatography (GLC), 3478, 3909,
      4540
    geographical origin, 4846
    histochemical test, 3526
    hydrocarbon content, 4480
    identification, 3073, 3691, 4230, 4820
    mass spectrometry, 3478
    microscopic examination, 3478, 4690
    neutron activation, 4846
    nuclear magnetic resonance (NMR), 3478
    review, 3478, 3691
    separation
      phenols, 3099
    smoke, 3565
    stability, 4540
    storage, 4540
    taxonomy, 5346
    tetrahydrocannabinol (THC), 3303
      fast blue B salt, 4820

analysis (continued)
    thin layer chromatography (TLC), 3073, 3478,
        3565, 3909, 4690
        spray reagents, 3478
    ultra violet (UV), 3478
    x-ray, 3590
behavioral effect(s)
    aggressive behavior, 3061, 4407
    biogenic amine(s), 3061
    conditioned behavior, 3137
    interaction with
        apomorphine, 3061
        haloperidol, 3061
    psychosis, 4440, 4441
    review, 4407
    self administration, 3137
    stress, 3061
biochemical change(s)
    dopamine (DA), 4441
biochemical effect(s)
    amino acid(s), 5281
    ammonia, 5281
    cholesterol, 5281
    colchicine, 5365
    cyclic AMP, 5281
    essential oils
        prostaglandin synthesis, 3428
    glucose, 5281
botanical aspects, 3900
    achene(s), 5542
    biological control, 3971
    cannabinoid content, 3073, 3150, 3304, 3369,
        3491, 3492, 3538, 3543, 3580, 3581, 3959,
        4756, 5086, 5087, 5088, 5114, 5131
    chemotype, 3369
    chromosomes, 4278
    classification, 3083, 4680
    clones, 5088
    colchicine, 5365
    cultivation, 3150
    development, 5542
    diseases, 5586
    environment, 3369, 4961
    environmental conditions, 4840, 4887
    eradication, 3150
    essential oils, 3581
    flowers, 3073
    fungus, 3279, 3480
    geographical origin, 3073, 3304, 3369, 3491,
        3580, 3581, 4961
    glands, 3897
    grafting, 3538
    growth, 3490, 3492, 3959, 4006, 4840, 4961
    harvest, 4961
    herbicides, 3492, 4006
    hormonal effects, 3130
    insects, 3301
    leaves, 3073, 3840
    morphology, 3150, 3491, 3590, 3898, 4235, 4838,
        5542
    patterns of growth, 4680
    phospholipids, 5114
    phosphorus, 3304
    photosynthesis, 3543
    potency, 4961

botanical aspects (continued)
    pyridine hydroxylation, 3714
    review, 3080, 3691
    seeds, 3073, 3279, 3580, 4887, 4961
    sex differences, 3130, 4887
    species, 4961
    taxonomy, 4887, 4888
    trichomes, 3590, 4235
chemical aspects
    analysis
        GC/MS, 3053
    biotransformation, 4038, 5004
    callus, 4037
    cannabinoid acids, 3911
    cannabinoid content, 3491, 3580, 3581, 3909,
        4610, 4820, 4887, 4974, 5088, 5612
    cannabinoid(s), 5320
    classification, 5612
    constituents
        cannabichromene (CBC), 5082
        cannabidiol (CBD), 5082
        cannabinoid(s), 5082
        cannabinol (CBN), 5082
        delta-9-THC, 5082
    constituents of, 3974, 3975, 3976, 4974, 5083,
        5356
        alkaloids, 3673, 3674, 3684, 3686, 3687, 3906,
        3908, 4294, 4595, 4961, 5079, 5085
    amino acid(s), 5079
    amino sugar, 5219
    anhydrocannabisativine, 3686, 3687
    C_3-cannabichromanone, 3882
    cannabichromene (CBC), 3562, 3691, 4480
    cannabidiol (CBD), 3562, 3565, 3691, 3706, 3909
    cannabidiolic acid, 3562, 3909
    cannabielsoic acid, 3882
    C_3-cannabielsoin, 3882
    cannabigerol (CBG), 3562, 3691
    cannabinodiol, 4297
    cannabinoid acids, 3337
    cannabinoid(s), 3565, 3907, 3908, 4595, 4853,
        4961, 5079
    cannabinol (CBN), 3562, 3565, 3691
    cannabisativine, 3674, 4294, 5085
    cannabispiran (see also cannabispirone), 3540,
        3671, 4852
    beta-cannabispiranol (see also cannabispirol), 3362,
        3540, 4852
    cannabispirenone (see also dehydrocannabispiran),
        3322
    cannabispirone (see also cannabispiran), 3322
    cannabitriol, 3466, 3683
    canniprene, 3540
    cyclitols, 3907, 4205
    dehydrocannabispiran (see also cannabispirenone),
        3540, 3671, 4852
    delta-8-THC, 3691
    delta-9-THC, 3562, 3565, 3691, 3909, 4908
    delta-9-THC oic acid A & B, 3562, 3909
    dihydrostilbenes, 3540, 4159
    dihydrovomifoliol, 3321
    8,9-dihydroxy-delta-6a(10a)-THC, 3681
    9,10-dihydroxy-delta-6a(10a)-THC, 3681
    enzymes, 5079

constituents of (continued)
    essential oils, 3053, 3960, 3961, 3962, 3963, 4345, 4961
    fatty acids, 3907, 5079
    flavondiglycosides, 4595, 4598, 5079
    flavonoids, 3907, 4599
    galactosamine, 5219
    glycolipids, 4685
    glycoprotein, 5079, 5219
    glycosides, 4821, 4822
    hordenine, 3673
    hydrocarbon, 3907, 5079
    leaves, 4598
    lipids, 4685
    nitrogen compounds, 3684, 3906
    organic acids, 5079
    phenols, 3099, 3362, 3907, 4595
    phospholipids, 4685
    phytosterols, 3203, 3907
    pigments, 5079
    pollen, 4595
    protein, 5079
    review, 3335, 3684, 3760, 3907, 3908, 4607, 5079
    roots, 4826
    spiro-compounds, 4852, 5079
    steroids, 5079
    sterols, 4685
    steryl esters, 4685
    sugars, 3907, 4205, 5079
    terpenes, 3053, 3905, 3961, 5079
    terpenoids, 3908
    tetrahydrocannabinol (THC), 3706, 4480
    tetrahydrocannabinol acids, 3369
    tetrahydrocannabivarolic acids, 3369
    trace elements, 4846
    triglycerides, 4685
    vitamins, 5079
    vomifoliol, 3321
dihydrostilbenes, 5356
essential oils, 3581
euphoria, 3683
geographical origin, 3491, 3565, 3580, 3581, 3706, 4205, 4974
metabolites, 3907, 3908
pyrolytic products, 3203
review, 3691, 4407
spiro-compounds, 5356
storage
    insects, 4755
structure, 3466
structure-activity relationships
    cannabinoid(s), 3479
ecology, 3900
essential oils, 3962
forensic aspects
    color tests, 5164
    detection, 4690, 5061, 5164
    geographical origin, 3073, 3580, 3581, 5061
history
    review, 3691
legal aspects, 4961
    review, 3691
pharmacognosy
    chromosomes, 4278

CANNABIS SATIVA (continued)
    pharmacological aspects
        anti-bacterial activity, 3761
        blood gases, 5281
        cardiovascular effects, 5188
        compared to:
            pilocarpine, 5189
        dopamine (DA), 4440, 4441
        essential oils, 3761
        extrapyramidal system, 4440
        intraocular pressure (IOP), 5189
        motor activity, 4441
        review, 3691, 4407
        tranquilizing activity, 4407
    physiological effects
        cobalt, 5545
        sexual function, 5545
    reproductive effects
        ovaries, 5603
        prenatal development, 5603
        testis(es), 5603
    review
        analysis, 3478, 3691
        behavioral effect(s), 4407
        botanical aspects, 3691
        chemical aspects, 3335, 3691, 4407
            alkaloid(s), 3684
            constituents of, 3760
        constituents of, 3907, 3908, 4607
        history, 3691
        legal aspects, 3691
        metabolites, 3907, 3908
        pharmacological aspects, 3691, 4407
        therapeutic aspects, 4407
    therapeutic aspects
        glaucoma, 5189
        review, 4407
    therapeutic use
        insect repellent, 3107
    toxicology
        behavioral effect(s), 5559
        body weight, 5281
        brain, 3562, 5281
        chronic effects, 5281
        lung(s), 3562
        pathological study, 3092
        reproductive effects, 5559
        teratogenesis, 5559
CANNABIS SMOKE
    chemical aspects
        constituents of, 4771
        smoke condensate analysis, 4785
    pharmacological aspects
        catatonia, 4785
        corneal reflex, 4785
        lung(s), 3749
        motor activity, 4785
        respiratory effects, 3749
        review, 3749
        sleep time, 4785
    review
        respiratory effects, 3749
CANNABIS USE
    economic aspects
        cultivation, 4276

economic aspects (continued)
　distribution, 4276
　market structure, 4276
　Trinidad, 4276
history
　China, 3112
　review, 4002
increase in use, 3233
legal aspects, 3242
review
　history, 4002
sociological aspects
　distribution, 4276
　Trinidad, 4276
studies of groups, 4473
CANNABISATIVINE
Cannabis sativa
　constituents, 4294
　constituents of, 3674, 5085
　isolation, 5085
　roots, 5085
chemical aspects
　x-ray crystallography, 4294
hashish
　constituents of, 4770
marihuana
　constituents of, 4770
CANNABISPIRAN (see also cannabispirone)
cannabis
　constituents of, 4580
Cannabis sativa
　constituents of, 3540, 3671, 4852
chemical aspects
　isolation, 4852
　structure, 4852
　　x-ray crystallography, 3671
　synthesis, 5375
BETA-CANNABISPIRANOL (see also cannabispirol)
Cannabis sativa
　constituents of, 3362, 3540, 4852
chemical aspects
　isolation, 4852
　structure, 3362, 4852
CANNABISPIRENONE (see also dehydrocannabispiran)
Cannabis sativa
　constituents of, 3322
CANNABISPIRONE (see also cannabispiran)
Cannabis sativa
　constituents of, 3322
CANNABITRIOL
Cannabis sativa
　constituents of, 3466, 3683
　isolation, 3683
chemical aspects
　isolation, 3466
　structure, 3466
CANNABIVARICHROMENE
marihuana
　constituents of, 4918
CANNABIVAROL
marihuana
　constituents of, 3919, 4918
CANNIBALISM
delta-9-THC
　isolation, 5393
　rats, 5393

CANNIPRENE
Cannabis sativa
　constituents of, 3540
Chemical aspects
　isolation, 3540
　structure, 3540
CARBOCYCLIC ANALOGS
cannabinoid(s)
　biological activity, 4707
　synthesis, 4707
delta-9-THC
　pharmacological aspects, 4603
　structure-activity relationships, 4603
　therapeutic aspects, 4603
CARBOHYDRATES
cannabis
　constituents of, 4411
Cannabis sativa
　constituents of, 3974, 3975, 3976
CARBON MONOXIDE
marihuana smoke
　lung(s), 5432
　rats, 5432
CARBOXYLATED DERIVATIVES
cannabinoid(s)
　synthesis
　　cannabidiol (CBD), 5357
　　cannabinol (CBN), 5357
　　delta-8-THC, 5357
　　delta-9-THC, 5357
CARBOXYLIC ACID
cannabis
　constituents of, 3256, 4411
CARCINOGENICITY
Cannabis
　polycyclic aromatic hydrocarbons, 3230
marihuana, 4143
　identification, 5434
marihuana smoke, 3078
mice, 3991
　polycyclic aromatic hydrocarbons, 3991
CARCINOGENICITY OF
delta-9-THC
　review, 3733
CARCINOGENESIS
delta-9-THC
　mice, 5000, 5593
marihuana
　lung(s), 4256
　tissue cultures, 4256
marihuana smoke
　in vivo, 5481
　interaction with
　　L-cysteine, 4257
　　vitamin C, 4257
　mitosis, 5481
　rats, 5548
　tissue culture, 4257
CARDIAC OUTPUT
cannabidiol (CBD)
　dogs, 3394
delta-9-THC
　dogs, 3393, 4048

CARDIOVASCULAR
  toxicology
    subacute effects, 5044
  delta-9-THC
    blood pressure, 4245
    heart rate, 4245
    humans, 4245
  dimethylheptylpyran (DMHP)
    blood pressure, 4245
    heart rate, 4245
    humans, 4245
  11-hydroxy-delta-9-THC
    blood pressure, 4245
    heart rate, 4245
    humans, 4245
  nabilone (Lilly compound no. 109514)
    blood pressure, 4245
    heart rate, 4245
    humans, 4245
CARDIOVASCULAR EFFECTS
  cannabichromene (CBC)
    blood pressure, 5531
    heart rate, 5531
    rats, 5531
  cannabidiol (CBD)
    analog(s), 3199
    blood gases, 3394
    blood pressure, 3394
    cardiac output, 3394
    derivatives, 3664
    dogs, 3394, 3664, 4504
    heart rats, 3394
  cannabinoid(s)
    humans, 5340
  cannabinol (CBN)
    heart rate, 4515
    humans, 4149, 4515
  cannabis
    heart rate, 4280
    humans, 3227, 4280
  Cannabis sativa
    blood pressure, 5188
    contractile force, 5188
    dogs, 5188
    electrocardiogram (EKG), 5188
    heart rate, 5188
  delta-8-THC
    analog(s), 3121, 3199
      dogs, 4381
    blood pressure, 3198, 3387, 3388, 3662
    contractile force, 3387, 3388
    derivatives, 3387, 3388, 3664
    dogs, 3121, 3387, 3388, 3664
    heart rate, 3387, 3388, 3662
    monkeys, 4732
    rats, 3198, 3662
  delta-9-THC, 5310
    adrenalectomy, 4274
    adrenergic nervous system, 4128, 4273
    aerosol, 4572
    analog(s), 4579
      dogs, 4381
    anesthesia, 4046
    antiarrhythmic activity, 3876
    anxiety, 4328

delta-9-THC (continued)
  autonomic nervous system effect(s), 3764, 5454
  blood flow, 3319
  blood gases, 3393
  blood level(s), 4981
  blood pressure, 3197, 3198, 3213, 3314, 3319,
    3521, 3534, 3631, 3662, 3663, 3772, 3914,
    4007, 4053, 4127, 4128, 4183, 4274, 4289,
    4520, 4576, 5018, 5239, 5270, 5302, 5438,
    5454, 5531, 5579
  cardiac output, 3393, 4048
  cats, 3578, 3914, 4007, 4289, 4797, 5270, 5438
  central control, 4797
  central nervous system (CNS), 4053
  central nervous system mechanism, 3578, 3914,
    4007
  chronic effects, 4051
  consciousness, 4046
  contractile force, 3850, 4045
  dogs, 3393, 3578, 3664, 3772, 3896, 4045, 4046,
    4047, 4048, 4051, 4052, 4504
  echocardiogram, 4129
  electrocardiogram (EKG), 4129, 4464
  glaucoma, 3213
  guinea pig(s), 3051
  heart rate, 3197, 3213, 3250, 3314, 3319, 3393,
    3521, 3534, 3631, 3662, 3663, 3740, 3914,
    4007, 4048, 4049, 4050, 4052, 4053, 4127,
    4128, 4247, 4274, 4275, 4289, 4515, 4520,
    4572, 4576, 4579, 4671, 4678, 4915, 5018,
    5123, 5270, 5302, 5454, 5531, 5579
  humans, 3213, 3227, 3250, 3314, 3315, 3317,
    3483, 3521, 3534, 3631, 3697, 3740, 3914,
    4106, 4107, 4126, 4127, 4128, 4129, 4149,
    4247, 4275, 4346, 4464, 4515, 4572, 4603,
    4915, 4981, 5018, 5207, 5302, 5454
  hypertension, 5123
  hypotension, 3876
  in vitro, 3850, 4273, 4353
  interaction with
    anesthetic(s), 3896
    depressant, 4671
    oxymorphone, 4087
    pentobarbital, 4087
    stimulants, 4671
  mechanism of action, 3319, 4797, 5270
  monkeys, 3764, 4328
  nitrogen analogs, 4603
  perfused heart, 4353
  pulse rate, 5239
  rats, 3197, 3198, 3662, 3663, 4183, 4274, 4520,
    4576, 4577, 4578, 4671, 4678, 5123, 5531,
    5579
  reflexes, 4797
  regional blood flow, 4045, 4048
  review, 3483, 4603
  stress, 4981
  subjective effects, 4981
  tachycardia, 4577, 4578
  theory of mechanism of effect, 4289
  thio analogs, 4603
  tolerance, 3197, 3317, 3764, 4183
  total peripheral resistance, 4049
  ventricles, 4048, 4050

CARDIOVASCULAR EFFECTS (Continued)
  dimethylheptylpyran (DMHP)
    blood pressure, 3914, 4007
    cats, 3914, 4007
    central nervous system mechanism, 3914, 4007
    heart rate, 3914, 4007
    rats, 4577, 4578
    tachycardia, 4577, 4578
  hashish
    blood pressure, 4827, 5018
    heart rate, 4275, 4827, 5018
    humans, 4275, 4827, 5018
  hexahydrocannabinol (HHC)
    dogs, 3664
  11-hydroxy-delta-9-THC
    blood pressure 4358
    heart rate, 4247, 4358
    humans, 4247
    in vitro, 4353, 4354
    perfused heart, 4353, 4354
    rats, 4358
  marihuana, 3215, 3499
    acute effect(s), 3762, 5589
    adverse effect(s), 4664
    angina pectoris, 3241
    blood pressure, 3533, 3762, 4643, 4665, 4993,
      5108
    chronic effects, 3503, 3762, 5589
    clinical findings, 3323
    contractile force, 4665
    contractility, 4664
    dogs, 3375
    exercise, 3159, 4831
    forearm blood flow, 4537
    heart rate, 3159, 3240, 3273, 3533, 3762, 3812,
      3902, 3903, 4275, 4279, 4537, 4559, 4642,
      4643, 4644, 4665, 4717, 4788, 4789, 4964,
      4993, 5052, 5108
    humans, 3159, 3241, 3273, 3323, 3483, 3503,
      3533, 3762, 3812, 3902, 3903, 4106, 4107,
      4130, 4275, 4279, 4428, 4429, 4537, 4559,
      4632, 4664, 4665, 4717, 4788, 4789, 4831,
      4964, 4993, 5052, 5108
    interaction with
      propranolol, 4993
      stress, 4537
    mechanism of action, 5589
    oral surgery, 4005
    review, 3483, 5589
    stress, 4005
    tolerance, 3273, 3812
  marihuana smoke
    angina pectoris, 3837
    blood pressure, 3701, 5338
    chronic use, 4996
    dogs, 4996, 4997
    electrocardiogram (EKG), 5338
    heart rate, 3701, 3803, 4996, 4997, 5247, 5338,
    humans, 3701, 3803, 3847, 5008, 5247, 5338
    tolerance, 4996, 4997
    ventricular function, 3803
  nabilone (Lilly compound no. 109514)
    blood pressure, 4250
    heart rate, 4250, 5401
    humans, 4250, 5401

  nabilone (continued)
    hypotension, 5401
  SP-1
    mice, 4602
  SP-111A
    blood pressure, 4576
    heart rate, 4576
    rats, 4576
  synthetic cannabinoids
    monkeys, 4732
CAROTENOID
  cannabis
    constituents of, 3120
  hemp
    constituents of, 3120
CATALEPSY
  cannabidiol (CBD)
    mice, 5380
    route of administration, 5380
  cannabis extract
    acetylcholine (ACh), 3264
    rats, 3264
  delta-6a(10a)-THC
    chickens, 4389
  delta-8-THC
    chickens, 4389
    phospholipids, 5234
  delta-9-THC
    chickens, 4389
    dopamine (DA), 3841
    extrapyramidal system, 3840
    gamma-amino-butyric acid (GABA), 3666
    mice, 5380
    rats, 3666, 3840, 3841, 5091
    route of administration, 5380
  11-hydroxy-delta-9-THC
    extrapyramidal system, 3840
    rats, 3840
CATATONIA
  cannabis smoke
    mice, 4785
CATECHOLAMINES
  cannabidiol (CBD)
    dopamine (DA), 3357
    mice, 3357, 3358
    norepinephrine (NE), 3357
    synthesis, 3358
  cannabinol (CBN)
    dopamine (DA), 3357
    mice, 3357, 3358
    norepinephrine (NE), 3357
    synthesis, 3358
  cannabis resin
    analgesic activity, 5398
    anti-convulsant activity, 3810
    rats, 3810, 5398
  delta-9-THC
    adrenal levels, 4477
    aggressive behavior, 3450
    dogs, 4047
    dopamine (DA), 3357, 3360
    mice, 3357, 3358, 3360
    norepinephrine (NE), 3357, 3360
    rats, 4477
    synthesis, 3358, 3360

CATECHOLAMINES (continued)
  hexahydrocannabinol (HHC)
    dopamine (DA), 3357
    mice, 3357
    norepinephrine (NE), 3357
  9-hydroxy-9-*nor*-hexahydrocannabinol
    mice, 3358
    synthesis, 3358
  11-hydroxy-delta-9-THC
    mice, 3358
    synthesis, 3358
  marihuana extract
    aggressive behavior, 3450
CATHINE
  cannabis
    constituents of, 5110
CATHINONE
  cannabis
    constituents of, 5110
CELL DIVISION
  delta-9-THC
    bone marrow, 4091
    in vitro, 3125, 4091, 4318
    tissue culture, 4022
CELL GROWTH
  cannabinoid(s)
    inhibition, 5588
  cannabinol (CBN)
    mold(s), 3385
  chromosomes
    HeLa cells, 5588
  delta-9-THC
    in vitro, 4318, 5241
    mold(s), 3385
  marihuana smoke
    tissue culture, 4258
CELL MEMBRANE(S)
  cannabidiol (CBD)
    adverse effect(s), 4702
    in vitro, 3817
    macrophages, 4702
  cannabinol (CBN)
    in vitro, 3817
  delta-9-THC
    adverse effect(s), 4702
    in vitro, 3817
    macrophages, 4702
    morphology, 3468
    red blood cells, 3468
  marihuana
    review, 5513
CELL METABOLISM
  marihuana
    adverse effect(s), 3240, 3347, 4632
CELL-MEDIATED IMMUNITY
  cannabidiol (CBD)
    in vitro, 3550, 3554
  cannabinol (CBN)
    in vitro, 3550, 3554
    inhibition, 5482
    mice, 4262, 5482
  delta-8-THC, 4914
    anti-histaminic activity, 4653, 4913
    derivatives, 4914
    inhibition, 5482

delta-8-THC (continued)
    lymphocytes, 4653, 4913
    mice, 5482
  delta-9-THC, 4914
    chronic use, 4627
    humans, 3553, 3555, 4106, 4107, 4627
    in vitro, 3550, 3554
    lymphocytes, 4653, 4913
    mechanism of action, 4510
    mice, 4241, 4262, 4629
    review, 4737
    rosette formation, 3556
    tolerance, 4510
  8,9-epoxyhexahydrocannabinol
    mice, 4170
  marihuana
    assays, 4508
    chronic use, 4627, 4682, 4866
    humans, 3132, 3551, 3554, 4106, 4107, 4532,
      4627, 4682, 4866
    in vitro, 3552
    review, 4398, 4737
  olivetol
    in vitro, 3550
CELLULAR DIVISION
  cannabichromene (CBC)
    adverse effect(s), 3604
  cannabicyclol (CBL)
    adverse effect(s), 3604
  cannabidiol (CBD)
    adverse effect(s), 3604
  cannabigerol (CBG)
    adverse effect(s), 3604
  cannabinol (CBN)
    adverse effect(s), 3604
  delta-8-THC
    mitotic index, 3177
  delta-9-THC
    adverse effect(s), 3604
    in vitro, 3524
    mitotic index, 3177
    tissue culture, 3524
    volvox, 5494, 5495
  marihuana
    mitotic index, 4028
CELLULAR EFFECTS
  cannabinoid(s)
    cancer, 5604
    cellular respiration, 5340, 5604
    DNA synthesis, 5604
    distribution, 5509
    enzyme activity, 5340
    HeLa cells, 5509
    lipids, 5340
    macromolecular synthesis, 5509
    mice, 5604
    nucleic acids, 5340
    prostaglandins, 5340
    review, 5340
  delta-8-THC
    macromolecular synthesis, 5329
    membrane effects, 5329
  delta-9-THC
    cyclic AMP, 5462
    fibroblasts, 5463

delta-9-THC (continued)
  heart, 5344
  macromolecular synthesis, 5329
  membrane effects, 5329
  morphology, 5463
  protein kinase, 5463
  review, 5413
marihuana smoke
  cell growth, 5481
  in vivo, 5481
  mitosis, 5481

CELLULAR IMMUNITY
delta-9-THC, 4261
  age, 4670
  mice, 4263, 4670
marihuana
  chronic use, 4630
  humans, 4630

CELLULAR RESPIRATION
delta-9-THC
  brain, 4282
  interaction with
    corticosterones, 4282
    ethanol, 4282

CENTRAL NERVOUS SYSTEM (CNS)
cannabinoid(s)
  cognitive function, 5340
  electroencephalogram (EEG), 5340
  memory, 5340
  perception, 5340
cannabis
  behavioral effect(s), 5379
  electroencephalogram (EEG), 5379
  electrophysiology, 5379
  epilepsy, 5379
  memory, 5379
  neurotransmitters, 5379
  tolerance, 5379
  ultrastructural changes, 5379
  withdrawal symptoms, 5379
delta-9-THC
  adverse effect(s), 4528
  hypothermia, 5258
  mice, 5258
  review, 5413
hydroxylated cannabinoids
  dogs, 5631
marihuana, 3632
  atrophic change(s)
    humans, 3241
marihuana smoke
  inhibition, 4740
  rats, 4740
  stimulation, 4740

CNS ACTIVITY
cannabinoid(s)
  derivatives, 4397
  rats, 4186, 4396
cannabis
  review, 5535
delta-9-THC
  analog(s), 4708
  dogs, 4708
marihuana smoke
  chronic administration, 4303

CNS ACTIVITY (continued)
nabilone (Lilly compound no. 109514)
  humans, 4250
  sedative effect, 4250

CNS DEPRESSION
delta-9-THC
  cats, 3730
  humans, 3730
  interaction with
    datura, 3566
  rats, 3566, 4058
  tolerance, 4058

CENTRAL NERVOUS SYSTEM MECHANISM
delta-9-THC
  anticholinergic effect, 3768
  cardiovascular effects, 3578
  cats, 3578
  dogs, 3578
  humans, 3768
  taste, 3220

CEREBRAL CORTEX
delta-9-THC
  compared to:
    pentobarbital, 3379, 3380
  differential effect, 3379
  evoked potentials, 3380
  monkeys, 3379, 3380
marihuana
  atrophic change(s), 3487, 4208
  humans, 3487, 4208

CEREBRAL DOMINANCE
marihuana
  humans, 4982

CHARACTERISTICS
cannabinoid(s)
  binding, 5395
  degradation, 5395
  solubility, 5395

CHARACTERISTICS OF USERS
cannabis
  chronic use, 4416
  India, 4416
  Jamaica, 3509
chemistry
  education, 4507
ganja
  Jamaica, 4762
hashish, 3176
  chronic use, 3129
  Greece, 3371, 4967
marihuana, 4165, 4169, 4584, 4867, 5175
  adolescent(s), 4067, 4843
  age, 4069, 4507,
  Canada, 3069, 4612
  chronic use, 3454
  compared to:
    alcohol, 3365, 3978
    tobacco, 3978
  Costa Rica, 3455
  cross cultural research, 3069
  Egypt, 4933, 4938
  England, 3166, 4505
  Ireland, 4593
  multiple drug use
    heroin, 4809

516

marihuana (continued)
  Nepal, 4837
  nutrition, 3586
  personality, 4150, 4163, 4174, 4646
  psychological aspects, 3583
  races, 4507
  religion, 4507
  sex differences, 4666
  social behavior, 3068, 3071
  sociological aspects, 3057, 4174
  students, 3364, 3365, 3601, 3626, 3670, 3818,
    3978, 4066, 4125, 4150, 4174, 4300, 4439,
    4612, 4667, 4764, 5143
  teachers, 4612
  U.S.A., 3069, 3236, 3419
  youths, 4065
marihuana smoke
  psychological aspects, 4367
  sociological aspects, 4367
  students, 4367
CHEMICAL ASPECTS
  marihuana, 4804
  review, 3922
CHEMOTHERAPY
  delta-9-THC
    humans, 4547
  marihuana
    antiemetic, 5553
    humans, 4547
    route of administration, 5553
  nabilone (Lilly compound no. 109514)
    antiemetic, 5485
    cats, 5485
CHEMOTYPE
  Cannabis sativa
    geographical origin, 3369
    South Africa, 3369
CHOLESTEROL
  Cannabis sativa
    baboons, 5281
  hashish
    adrenals, 4291
    stress, 4291
CHOLESTEROL ESTERASE
  cannabinol (CBN)
    ovaries, 5323
  delta-8-THC
    rabbit(s), 4340
    rats, 4340
  delta-9-THC
    adrenals, 3424
    in vitro, 5322
    mice, 5322
    ovaries, 3424, 5323
    rabbit(s), 4340
    rats, 3424, 4340
  dimethylheptylpyran (DMHP)
    rabbit(s), 4340
    rats, 4340
  11-hydroxy-delta-9-THC
    ovaries, 5323
  hydroxylated cannabinoids
    ovaries, 5323

CHOLINE
  delta-9-THC
    brain, 4141
    brain levels, 5632
    environmental conditions, 5632
    mice, 4075, 4141, 5632
    synaptosomal, 4075
    uptake, 4075, 4141
CHROMATOGRAPHY
  cannabinoid(s), 4961
  marihuana
    forensic aspects, 5476
CHROMOSOME DAMAGE
  blood gases
    lymphocytes, 4534
  cannabichromene (CBC)
    lymphocytes, 4534
  cannabicyclol (CBL)
    lymphocytes, 4534
  cannabidiol (CBD)
    lymphocytes, 4534
  cannabinoid(s)
    mice, 5636
    spermatozoa, 5636
  delta-9-THC
    bone marrow, 4091
    in vitro, 4091
    lymphocytes, 4534
  hashish, 4525
    in vitro, 4472
    plant material, 4120
  marihuana, 3240, 4975
    humans, 3123, 3347, 4529
    lymphocytes, 4401
  olivetol
    lymphocytes, 4534
CHROMOSOMES
  cannabinoid(s)
    HeLa cells, 5588
    protein, 5588
  cannabis
    adverse effect(s), 3845
  cannabis resin
    mitosis, 5133
  Cannabis sativa
    characteristics, 4278
  delta-9-THC
    adverse effect(s), 5240
    lymphocytes, 4494, 4496
  ganja
    humans, 4762
  11-hydroxy-delta-9-THC
    adverse effect(s), 5240
  marihuana
    adverse effect(s), 3215, 4632
    chronic use, 3807
    dogs, 3807
    humans, 4400
    lymphocytes, 3807
    review, 4398
    tissue culture, 3807
  olivetol, 4493
    in vitro, 4492
    lymphocytes, 4494, 4496

CHRONIC ADMINISTRATION
  delta-9-THC
    behavioral effect(s), 3241
    body weight, 5571
    monkeys, 5571
    rats, 4304
    reproductive effects, 5571
  marihuana
    humans, 3241
    learning, 3241
CHRONIC EFFECTS
  cannabis
    humans, 4965
    review, 4531
  Cannabis sativa
    baboons, 5281
  delta-9-THC
    guinea pig(s), 4027
    humans, 4106
    rats, 3823
  hashish
    adverse effect(s), 3744, 4935
    Egypt, 3744, 4935
  marihuana, 4143
    clinical findings, 3493
    Costa Rica, 3493
    humans, 3239, 4106, 4964
    neurosis, 4964
    psychosis, 4964
    review, 4527
  marihuana smoke
    dogs, 4029
    toxicology, 4029
CHRONIC USE
  cannabis
    Costa Rica, 3633
    Greece, 3633
    India, 3633
    Jamaica, 3633
  marihuana
    adverse effect(s), 3481, 3893, 5373
ALPHA-CHYMOTRYPSIN
  delta-9-THC
    in vitro, 4462
CIGARETTE PREPARATION
  marihuana
    smoke condensate analysis, 4605
CLASSIFICATION
  cannabis
    botanical aspects, 3146
    cannabinoid content, 3704
    chemical aspects, 5340
    hallucinations, 5573
    hallucinogens, 3146
    history, 5573
    India, 5610
    narcotic, 4372
    plant, 4886, 4889, 5340
    radiolabelled, 5484
    United Nations Narcotics Commission, 4372
  cannabis plant
    cannabinoid content, 5385
    France, 5385
  Cannabis sativa, 4680
    cannabinoid content, 5612

CLASSIFICATION (continued)
  marihuana
    hypnotic, 3149
    sedative, 3149
CLEARANCE RATES
  marihuana
    humans, 5452
    theophylline, 5452
CLINICAL ASPECTS
  asthma, 5105
  marihuana
    poisoning, 5406
CLINICAL EFFECTS
  cannabidiol (CBD)
    humans, 4248
    interaction with
      delta-9-THC, 4248
      secobarbital, 4248
  delta-9-THC
    humans, 4248
    interaction with
      cannabidiol (CBD), 4248
      secobarbital, 4248
  marihuana
    humans, 4248
    interaction with
      secobarbital, 4248
CLINICAL FINDINGS
  cannabidiol (CBD)
    humans, 3097
    immunology, 4835
  cannabinol (CBN)
    humans, 3097
    immunology, 4835
  cannabis
    humans, 3097
  chemistry
    immunology, 4835
  delta-6a(10a)-THC
    humans, 3097
  delta-8-THC
    humans, 3097
    immunology, 4835
  delta-9-THC
    humans, 3097, 4110
    immunology, 4835
  ganja
    humans, 4762
  marihuana
    acute effect(s), 3762
    chronic effects, 3503, 3762
    humans, 3250, 3503, 3762, 4030, 4110
  synhexyl
    humans, 3097
CLONES
  Cannabis sativa
    cannabinoid content, 5088
CLOTTING FACTORS
  cannabidiol (CBD)
    humans, 4264, 4265
  delta-9-THC
    humans, 4264, 4265
COBALT
  Cannabis sativa
    flowers, 5545
    sexual function, 5545

COGNITIVE FUNCTION
   cannabidiol (CBD)
      humans, 5309, 5350
   cannabinol (CBN)
      humans, 4515
   cannabis
      chronic use, 4701, 4934
      humans, 4701, 4934
   delta-9-THC
      humans, 3631, 3636, 4110, 4515, 4626, 5308
   hashish
      humans, 3636
   marihuana
      chronic use, 4173
      clinical aspects, 5489
      humans, 3636, 3925, 4107, 4110, 4173, 4426
         4457
      review, 4173, 5489
COGNITIVE PROCESSES
   cannabinoid(s)
      limbic, 5504
   delta-9-THC
      humans, 3471
   marihuana
      humans, 3367, 3429, 3535, 4279
   marihuana smoke
      humans, 5170
   marihuana use
      chronic use, 5547
      humans, 5547
      India, 5547
COLCHICINE
   Cannabis sativa
      cannabinoid content, 5365
      morphological variations, 5365
COLOR TESTS
   Cannabis sativa
      detection, 5164
COLORAMETRIC METHOD
   cannabis extract
      identification, 5601
COLORIMETRY
   cannabinoid(s), 4961
COMPARISONS
   cannabidiol (CBD)
      rats, 4374
CONDITIONED BEHAVIOR
   cannabidiol (CBD)
      food intake, 5331
      interaction with
         delta-9-THC, 3384
      monkeys, 3384, 5331
      rats, 3100, 4517
      route of administration, 5331
   cannabinoid(s)
      food intake, 5331
      monkeys, 5331
      route of administration, 5331
   cannabis
      cats, 5498
   Cannabis sativa
      monkeys, 3137
      response rates, 3137
   delta-8-THC
      animals, 3289

delta-8-THC (continued)
   monkeys, 3085
   pigeon(s), 3085
   rats, 3085, 4062, 4692
   spiders, 3085
   tolerance, 3289
delta-9-THC
   animals, 3289, 4352
   aversive stimulus, 5404
   cats, 3128, 4415
   chronic effects, 4684
   compared to:
      anti-anxiety drug(s), 3806
   fasting, 4674
   feeding, 4674
   food intake, 5331
   interaction with
      cannabidiol (CBD), 3384
      depressant, 4671
      pentobarbital, 4330
      stimulants, 4671
   metabolism, 3587
   metabolites, 3753
   mice, 4684, 5162
   monkeys, 3085, 3137, 3384, 4377, 5331
   non-human primates, 4639
   pigeon(s), 3085, 3127, 3661, 4330, 5404, 5410
   rabbit(s), 5555
   rats, 3085, 3090, 3096, 3117, 3140, 3593, 3753,
      3806, 4062, 4224, 4351, 4671, 4673, 4674,
      4677, 4678, 4692, 4864, 5032, 5163, 5183,
      5318
   response rates, 3137, 5410
   review, 3733, 3919
   route of administration, 5331
   spiders, 3085
   taste, 3220
   tolerance, 3096, 3127, 3289, 3587, 3919, 4330,
      4351, 5032
   vehicle of administration, 4674
hexahydrocannabinol (HHC)
   rats, 3753
9-hydroxy-9-*nor*-hexahydrocannabinol
   food intake, 5331
   monkeys, 5331
   route of administration, 5331
11-hydroxy-delta-9-THC
   food intake, 5331
   monkeys, 4377, 5331
   rats, 3753
   route of administration, 5331
marihuana
   cats, 4414
   interaction with
      nicotine, 4414
marihuana extract
   rats, 4517
nabilone (Lilly compound no. 109514)
   monkeys, 3381
SP-1
   pigeon(s), 3059
SP-111
   pigeon(s), 3661
synthetic cannabinoids
   mice, 5162

CONDITIONED SPEECH CONNECTIONS
  delta-9-THC
    humans, 4010, 4012, 4015
CONFISCATED SAMPLES
  cannabis
    analysis, 5080
    cannabinoid(s), 5080
  marihuana
    analysis, 3118, 5080
    cannabinoid content, 4765
    cannabinoid(s), 3118, 5080
CONSCIOUSNESS
  delta-9-THC
    humans, 3618
CONSTITUENTS OF
  cannabis, 3704
    cannabichromene (CBC), 3992
    cannabidiol (CBD), 3992
    steroids, 4880
  cannabis resin
    hexadecamide, 4910
  Cannabis sativa
    cannabichromene (CBC), 5083
    cannabidiol (CBD), 5083
    carbohydrates, 3974, 3975, 3976
    delta-9-THC, 4908
    essential oils, 3962
    flavonoids, 4599
    glycoprotein, 3974, 3975, 3976
    glycosides, 4822
    phenols, 3099
    protein, 3974, 3975, 3976
    review, 3907, 3908
    roots, 4826
    Thailand, 5356
  cannabis smoke, 4771
  hashish, 5138
  marihuana smoke
    acidic fraction, 4158
    basic fraction, 4158
    neutral fraction, 4158
CONSUMMATORY BEHAVIOR
  cannabidiol (CBD)
    rats, 4923
  cannabinol (CBN)
    rats, 4923
  delta-9-THC
    rats, 3407, 4923
CONTACT TEST
  cannabinoid(s)
    humans, 5220
    thin layer chromatography (TLC), 5220
  marihuana
    humans, 5220
    thin layer chromatography (TLC), 5220
CONTAMINANT
  marihuana
    paraquat, 5622
CONTRACTILE FORCE
  Cannabis sativa
    dogs, 5188
  delta-8-THC
    dogs, 3387, 3388
  delta-9-THC
    in vitro, 3850

CONVULSIONS
  cannabichromene (CBC)
    rabbit(s), 4387
  cannabicyclol (CBL)
    rabbit(s), 4387
  cannabidiol (CBD)
    cats, 3718
    dogs, 3718
    humans, 3718
    rabbit(s), 3513, 3718, 4387
  cannabinol (CBN)
    rabbit(s), 3513, 4387
  delta-8-THC
    rabbit(s), 4387
  delta-9-THC
    cats, 3718
    dogs, 3718, 4218
    humans, 3718
    interaction with
      ethanol, 4941
    mice, 4941, 5354
    rabbit(s), 3512, 3513, 3718, 4387
    tolerance, 5354
  11-hydroxy-delta-9-THC
    rabbit(s), 4387
  nabilone (Lilly compound no. 109514)
    mice, 5354
  SP-111A
    rabbit(s), 4387
COORDINATION
  delta-9-THC
    chronic use, 3635
    humans, 3635
  hashish
    chronic use, 3635
    humans, 3635
  marihuana
    chronic use, 3635, 4937
    humans, 3635, 4937
COPULATION
  cannabinol (CBN)
    mice, 5359
  delta-9-THC
    mice, 5359
  marihuana smoke
    pregnancy, 5389
    rats, 5389
CORNEAL REFLEX
  cannabis smoke
    rabbit(s), 4785
CORPUS LUTEUM
  delta-9-THC
    monkeys, 3729
    rabbit(s), 5296
CORRELATES OF USE
  marihuana
    age, 3833
    personality, 3833
    political ideology, 3833
    religion, 3833
    sexual attitudes, 3833
    students, 3821
CORTEX
  cannabidiol (CBD)
    rats, 5343

CORTEX (continued)
    delta-9-THC
        rats, 5343
    11-hydroxy-delta-9-THC
        rats, 5343
CORTICOSTERONE LEVEL
    cannabidiol (CBD)
        electrical stimulation, 5440
        plasma levels, 5440
        rats, 5440
    delta-9-THC
        electrical stimulation, 5440
        plasma levels, 5440
        rats, 5440
CORTICOSTERONES
    cannabinol (CBN)
        brain, 4080
        brain levels, 4077
        mice, 4077, 4080
        plasma levels, 4077, 4080
        uptake, 4080
    cannabis extract
        plasma levels, 4390, 4393
    delta-8-THC
        rabbit(s), 4340
        rats, 4340
    delta-9-THC
        aggressive behavior, 4588
        blood levels, 3359
        brain, 4080
        brain levels, 4077
        mice, 4077, 4080
        plasma levels, 3342, 3507, 4077, 4080, 4390,
            4393, 4478
        rabbit(s), 4340
        rats, 3342, 3507, 4340, 4478, 4558, 4588
        uptake, 4080
    dimethylheptylpyran (DMHP)
        rabbit(s), 4340
        rats, 4340
    hashish
        blood level(s), 4291
        stress, 4291
    11-hydroxy-delta-9-THC
        brain, 4080
        brain levels, 4077
        mice, 4077, 4080
        plasma levels, 4077, 4080
        uptake, 4080
CORTISOL
    marihuana smoke
        humans, 4178
        plasma levels, 4178
COSTA RICA
    delta-9-THC
        humans, 3318
        interaction with
            insulin, 3318
CREATININE PHOSPHOKINASE (CPK)
    delta-9-THC
        rats, 4356
CREATIVITY
    marihuana
        humans, 5051
CRIME
    marihuana, 5291
        aggressive behavior, 3160

CRIME (continued)
    marihuana smoke, 5450
CROSS CULTURAL RESEARCH
    marihuana
        characteristics of users, 3069
        Costa Rica, 3745
        Egypt, 3745
        Greece, 3745
        Jamaica, 3745
CROSS-REACTIVITY
    delta-9-THC
        cannabichromene (CBC), 3469
        cannabicyclol (CBL), 3469
        cannabidiol (CBD), 3469
        cannabidiolic acid, 3469
        cannabinol (CBN), 3469
        delta-8-THC, 3469, 3520
        metabolites, 3469
CROSS TOLERANCE
    delta-9-THC
        alcohol, 5575
        ethanol, 4858, 4942, 4943
        11-hydroxy-delta-9-THC, 3754
        morphine, 5634
        pentobarbital, 4330
        rats, 5575, 5634
    marihuana smoke
        delta-9-THC, 3770
        rats, 3770
CULTIVATION
    cannabis
        environment, 3763
        Trinidad, 4276
    cannabis plant
        cannabinoid content, 5311
        morphological variations, 5311
    Cannabis sativa
        Canada, 3150
    marihuana
        legal aspects, 5373
CULTURAL USE
    marihuana
        history, 3893
CURRENT USE
    marihuana
        U.S.A., 3893
CYCLIC AMP
    cannabicyclol (CBL)
        fibroblasts, 5462, 5463
    cannabidiol (CBD)
        fibroblasts, 5462, 5463
    cannabinoid(s)
        in vitro, 5443
        protein synthesis, 5443
        testosterone synthesis, 5443
    cannabinol (CBN)
        brain, 3627, 3628
        fibroblasts, 5462, 5463
        mice, 3628
    cannabis
        humans, 4963
    Cannabis sativa
        biochemical effect(s), 5281
    delta-8-THC
        metabolism, 3050

delta-8-THC (continued)
  rats, 3050
  synthesis, 3050
delta-9-THC
  brain, 3627, 3628
  fibroblasts, 5462, 5463
  metabolism 3050
  mice, 3628
  protein kinase, 5462, 5463
  rats, 3050
  synthesis, 3050
11-hydroxy-delta-8-THC
  metabolism, 3050
  rats, 3050
  synthesis, 3050
11-hydroxy-delta-9-THC
  brain, 3627, 3628
  mice, 3628
tetrahydrocannabinol (THC), 3627
CYCLITOLS
  Cannabis sativa
    constituents of, 4205
CYTOCHROME P450
  delta-9-THC
    rats, 4811
    testis(es), 4811
  11-hydroxy-delta-8-THC
    liver, 5625
    microsomal metabolism, 5625
CYTOGENIC EFFECTS
  marihuana
    adverse effect(s), 4776
    humans, 4776
CYTOLOGICAL CHANGES, 4399
  delta-8-THC
    in vitro, 4399
    in vivo, 4399
    tissue culture, 4976
  delta-9-THC
    in vitro, 4399
    in vivo, 4399
    tissue culture, 4976
  marihuana
    humans, 4399
  marihuana extract
    tissue culture, 4976
  marihuana smoke
    tissue culture, 4258
CYTOLOGY
  hemp, 4854, 4977, 4978
CYTOTOXICITY
  cannabidiol (CBD)
    macrophages, 4702
  delta-9-THC
    macrophages, 4702

D

DANSYL DERIVATIVES
  cannabinoid(s)
    biological fluid(s), 5572
    detection, 5572
DECISION-MAKING
  marihuana, 4355
    humans, 4789
    students, 4766

DECOMPOSITION
  delta-9-THC
    synthetic, 4271
DECRIMINALIZATION
  cannabis, 3928
  marihuana, 3232, 3249, 4490, 4828
    attitude, 3241, 5285, 5578
    Australia, 5209
    economic aspects, 5373
    medical aspects, 5373
    morals and ethics, 4633
    patterns of use, 3557
    review, 5285
    sociological aspects, 5373
    U.S.A., 3345, 3453, 3584, 3887
DEFECATION
  delta-9-THC
    rats, 4864
DEFINITION
  cannabinoid(s)
    behavioral effect(s), 5627
    botanical aspects, 5627
    pharmacological aspects, 5627
    structure, 5627
  cannabis
    Australia, 5408
  hashish
    Australia, 5408
DEGRADATION
  cannabinoid(s)
    light exposure, 5316
    mechanism of action, 5316
    solvents, 5316
    temperature, 5316
  delta-8-THC
    acid(s), 3798
    cannabis, 5611
    epoxy metabolites, 5611
    hydroxylated metabolites, 5611
  delta-9-THC
    acid(s), 3798
    cannabis, 5611
    epoxy metabolites, 5611
    hydroxylated metabolites, 5611
DEHYDROCANNABIFURAN
  cannabis
    constituents of, 3781
  chemical aspects
    spectral data, 3781
DEHYDROCANNABISPIRAN (*see also* CANNABISPI-
RENONE)
  Cannabis sativa
    constituents of, 3540, 3671, 4852
  chemical aspects
    isolation, 4852
    structure, 4852
      x-ray crystallography, 3671
DELAYED HYPERSENSITIVITY REACTION
  cannabinoid(s)
    mice, 5510
  marihuana extract
    mice, 5510
DELTA-6A(7)-THC
  chemical aspects
    synthesis, 3262

DELTA-6A(10A)-THC
  behavioral effect(s)
    catalepsy, 4389
    tonic immobility, 4389
  chemical aspects
    analog(s), 4603
    biotransformation, 3178, 3786
    nitrogen analogs
      synthesis, 4600
    oxidation products, 4704
    structure-activity relationships, 4603
  clinical findings, 3097
  pharmacological aspects
    analgesia, 5218
    anti-hypertensive activity, 5218
    antidiarreal activity, 5218
    antiulcer activity, 5218
    hypnotic, 5218
    tranquilizing activity, 5218
DELTA-7-THC
  behavioral effect(s)
    interaction with
      delta-9-THC, 5313
    monkeys, 5313
  chemical aspects
    stereochemical features, 5313
    synthesis, 5313
DELTA-8-THC
  adverse effect(s)
    review, 3246
  analysis
    attitudes of users, 4119
    autoradiography, 3173, 4117
    blood, 3208
    chemical tests, 3478
    derivatives, 4171
    detection, 3208, 3376, 3478, 4118, 4119, 4564,
      4565, 5029, 5215
      free radical immunoassay, 3432
    fluorometric, 3376, 4118, 4119
    gas liquid chromatography (GLC), 3478, 3750,
      4171
    GC/MS, 3208, 3944, 4565
    high-pressure liquid chromatography (HPLC), 4171
    identification, 3179, 4171
    liquid chromatography, 3750
    mass fragmentography, 3208, 4565, 5533
    mass spectrometry, 3416, 3478, 4119, 4171, 5137
    metabolites, 3941, 3942, 3945, 4244, 5417
      GC/MS, 4305
    microscopic examination, 3478
    nuclear magnetic resonance (NMR), 3260, 3261,
      3478
    paper chromatography, 5215
    radioimmunoassay (RIA), 5029
    review, 3478
    separation, 3179, 3750, 3944, 4171
    structure, 3416
    thin layer chromatography (TLC), 3478, 3750
      spray reagents, 3478
    trimethylsilyl derivatives, 3944
    ultra violet (UV), 3478
  anti-neoplastic testing, 3775
  behavioral effect(s), 4732
    aggressive behavior, 3446, 3732

behavioral effect(s) (Continued)
  analog(s), 3121, 3199
    ataxia, 4381
    tolerance, 4381
  catalepsy, 4389
  conditioned behavior, 3085, 3289, 4062, 4692
  derivatives, 3664
  discriminative properties, 3289, 4203
  discriminative stimulus, 4204
  drug discrimination, 4061
  food intake, 3732
  gross behavior, 3664
  monkeys, 5532
  motor activity, 3732
  review, 3446, 3732, 4160, 4918
  stress, 4333
  tolerance, 3289
  tonic immobility, 4389
  unlearned behavior, 3732
  water intake, 3732
biochemical effect(s)
  acyltransferase, 3871
  ascorbic acid, 4340
  cellular division, 3177
  cellular effects, 5329
  cholesterol esterase, 4340
  chromosomes, 4976
  compared to:
    alcohol, 4043
  cytological changes, 4399, 4976
  distribution, 5277
  drug metabolism, 3177
  enzyme induction, 5225
  interaction with
    steroids, 5329
  macromolecular synthesis, 3440, 3441, 3442,
    3775, 4042, 4043, 4523, 5071
  metabolism, 5417
  metabolites, 5266, 5277
  microbiological transformation, 5130
  mitotic index, 3177
  phospholipids, 3871
  RNA polymerase, 5225
  tyrosine aminotransferase, 5222, 5225
Cannabis sativa
  constituents of, 3691
chemical aspects
  analog(s), 3199, 4196, 4705
  biotransformation, 4305, 4719, 4720, 5129
  degradation, 3798, 5611
  derivatives, 4195
  glucuronides, 4306, 5624
    synthesis, 5227
  homologs, 3537, 4195
  hydrolysis
    phospholipids, 5234
  7-hydroxy, 5129
  hydroxylated metabolites, 5532
  isomers, 4160, 5098
  keto analogs, 3260
  mass spectrometry, 4032
  metabolism, 4267
  metabolites, 4267, 4296, 4314, 4719, 4770, 4918
  nitrogen analogs, 4295

chemical aspects (continued)
   NMR spectra, 3260
   oxidation products, 4032
   oxygen analog(s), 4197
   pyrolytic products, 4770
   receptors, 3598
   stability, 3798
   structure, 3260
     thio derivatives, 4212
   structure-activity relationships, 3598, 4084, 4195,
     4196, 4653, 4913
   sulfate, 5624
   synthesis, 3208, 3261, 3335, 3537, 4160, 4635,
     4649, 5046, 5099
     analog(s), 3298, 3616, 4196
     derivatives, 4195, 5173
     glucuronides, 5227
     homologs, 4195
     metabolites, 4296
     oxygen analog(s), 4197
     phospholipids, 5234
     radiolabelled, 3989
     thio analogs, 3616
     thio derivatives, 4212
   transformation
     9-hydroxy-9-*nor*-hexahydrocannabinol, 4636
clinical findings, 3097
forensic aspects
   detection, 4118
hashish
   constituents of, 4770
immunology
   acyltransferase activity, 3872
   antibodies, 4835
   anti-histaminic activity, 4653, 4913
   antibody formation, 4835
   antimitotic, 3602
   cell-mediated immunity, 4653, 4913, 4914, 5482
   clinical findings, 4835
   derivatives, 4914
   humoral immunity, 4653, 4913, 4914
   immunosuppression, 5482
   lymphocytes, 3602, 3872, 4523
interaction with
   bacterial lipopolysaccharide, 4512
marihuana
   constituents of, 3215, 3919, 4770, 4918
neurochemical effects
   acyltransferase, 3873
   dopamine (DA), 4283, 4654
   norepinephrine (NE), 4654
neuropharmacology
   gamma-amino-butyric acid (GABA), 3836
   ganglionic transmission, 3752
neurophysiological effects
   electroencephalogram (EEG), 5208
pharmacognosy
   biosynthesis, 3329
pharmacokinetics
   binding, 3438
   disposition, 4253
   distribution, 3173, 3438, 3951, 4118, 4119
   metabolism, 4253
pharmacological aspects
   abstinence syndrome, 3334

pharmacological aspects (continued)
   acetylcholine (ACh), 3050, 3773
   amygdaloid seizure(s), 5141, 5142
   analgesia, 3077, 3983, 4084, 4918, 5210
   analog(s), 3121, 3199
     cardiovascular effects, 4381
   anesthesia, 3873
   anti-convulsant activity, 3164, 3439, 3525, 3660,
     4145, 4918, 5140, 5141, 5142
   anti-inflammatory activity, 4653, 4913
   anti-neoplastic activity, 3442, 3918
   anticholinergic activity, 4215
   antineoplastic, 3440, 4509, 5071
   antineoplastic activity, 3924
   ataxia, 3836
   biogenic amine(s), 3115, 4654
   blood-brain barrier, 4817
   blood level(s), 3208
   blood pressure, 3342
   body temperature, 3439, 4070, 4918
   body weight, 3342, 4070
   brain, 3115, 3920, 4118, 4654
   cardiovascular effects, 3121, 3198, 3387, 3388,
     3662, 3664, 4732
   compared to:
     chlorpromazine, 3077
     delta-9-THC, 3465
     epinephrine, 5249
     morphine, 3077
     nalorphine, 3077
     pentazocine, 3077
     pilocarpine, 5249
   convulsions, 4387
   cross tolerance
     delta-9-THC, 3085
   cyclic AMP, 3050
   dependence liability, 4160
   derivatives, 3387, 3388, 3664
   disposition, 4253
   distribution, 4117
   dopamine (DA), 4283, 4333
   electroencephalogram (EEG), 4918
   enzyme induction, 5223, 5224, 5225
   eyes, 4620
   food intake, 3181, 4070, 4918
   gamma-amino-butyric acid (GABA), 3836
   glaucoma, 5249
   guinea pig ileum, 4728
   heart, 4893, 4894
   heart rate, 3983
   hepatic enzymes, 5223
   hepatic metabolism, 3465, 3937, 4267, 5222
   hypothermia, 3983
   interaction with
     amphetamine, 4160
     atropine, 4160
     bacterial lipopolysaccharide, 4511
     barbiturate(s), 4918
     glaucagon, 5224
     hydrocortisone, 5223, 5224
     lithium, 4817
     naloxone, 3333
     norepinephrine (NE), 4160
     pentobarbital, 4160
     trytophan, 5224
     Tween 80, 3485

pharmacological aspects (continued)
  intraocular pressure (IOP), 3866, 4620, 5249
  lethal synergism, 4511
  metabolism, 3941, 3942, 4117, 4244, 4253, 4412, 4413, 5211
  metabolites, 3945, 4084, 4620, 4729, 5556
  monoamine oxidase (MAO), 3485
  morphine withdrawal, 3332, 3333, 3334, 3979
  norepinephrine (NE), 4333
  organ weights, 3342
  phospholipids, 5234
  protein binding, 3438
  psychotomimetic activity
    derivatives, 5173
  psychotropic drugs, 5556
  review, 3181, 3329, 4160, 4918
  salivary glands, 4118
  serotonin (5-hydroxytryptamine), 4597
  smooth muscle, 4729, 5556
  stereospecific binding, 3920
  stimulant activity, 4387
  stress, 4283
  testosterone, 3465
  tolerance, 3085, 3525, 3983, 4145, 4160
  water intake, 3181, 4070
  worms, 4597
physiological effects
  adrenals, 4340
  endocrine effects, 4340
psychological aspects
  blood level(s), 3208
rats
  analysis, 3478
review
  aggressive behavior, 3446
  behavioral effect(s), 3732
  discriminative properties, 3289, 4203
  disposition, 4253
  food intake, 3181
  metabolism, 4253
  water intake, 3181
therapeutic aspects
  anti-convulsant activity, 3498
  anti-convulsant(s), 4160
  antineoplastic, 4160
  cancer, 3498
  intraocular pressure (IOP), 3498, 4160
  morphine withdrawal, 4160
toxicology
  LD$_{50}$, 3919
  motor activity, 3164
  mutagenesis, 3779, 4399
  reproduction, 3919
  review, 4160
DELTA-8-THC-DMH
  pharmacological aspects
    anti-convulsant activity, 3439
    body temperature, 3439
DELTA-8-THC-OIC ACID
  analysis
    gas liquid chromatography (GLC), 3472, 3539
    thin layer chromatography (TLC), 3539
  chemical aspects
    homologs
      synthesis, 3539
    synthesis, 3539

DELTA-8-THC-OIC ACID (continued)
  marihuana
    constituents of, 3919
DELTA-9-THC
  adverse effect(s), 3797
    cell division, 4091
    cellular division, 3604
    chromosome damage, 4091
    chromosomes, 5240
    compared to:
      alcohol, 3404, 3904
    driving, 3904
    gynecomastia, 3094
    interaction with
      diethylstilbesterol, 3094
    motor coordination, 5391
    muscular dystrophy, 3826, 3827
    nuclear changes, 5328
    premedication, 3876
    red blood cells, 5337
    review, 3246
    sedation, 5335
    sedative, 5391
    subjective effects, 5391, 5470
    testis(es), 3915
    vision, 3404
    visual acuity, 3404
  aflatoxin
    muscular dystrophy, 5400
  amphetamine
    clinical aspects, 3756
  analysis, 3520
    attitudes of users, 4119
    autoradiography, 3173, 4117
    biological fluid(s), 3800, 4722, 5111
    blood, 5562
    butyl homolog, 3935
    chemical tests, 3478
    colorametric method, 4658
    decomposition, 4271
    derivatives, 4021, 4171, 5558
    detection, 3064, 3139, 3206, 3212, 3373, 3374, 3376, 3469, 3478, 3608, 3707, 3724, 3800, 3880, 3881, 3946, 3990, 4021, 4118, 4119, 4135, 4139, 4164, 4288, 4311, 4395, 4484, 4564, 4565, 4658, 4722, 4733, 4734, 4746, 4757, 4792, 4911, 5026, 5028, 5029, 5111, 5112, 5113, 5134, 5135, 5149, 5150, 5206, 5215, 5300,
    exhaled air, 3095
    fluorometric, 3373, 3374, 3376, 4118, 4119
    forensic aspects, 5539, 5562, 5615
    gas chromatography, 3139, 4311, 4484, 4714, 5300
    gas liquid chromatography (GLC), 3095, 3478, 3707, 3724, 3750, 3800, 4106, 4171
    GC/MS, 3363, 3608, 3935, 3944, 3946, 4021, 4106, 4565, 4746, 5149, 5150, 5411
    high-pressure liquid chromatography (HPLC), 3799, 3800, 4171, 4288, 4911, 5111, 5113, 5206, 5273, 5616
    HPLC/MS, 4135
    identification, 3064, 3179, 3206, 4171, 4394
      gas liquid chromatography (GLC), 3366
      metabolites, 3943

analysis (continued)
  immunoassay, 4722, 4757
  liquid chromatography, 3750
  mass fragmentography, 3206, 3363, 4288, 4565, 4734, 4802, 5533
  mass spectrometry, 3339, 3416, 3478, 4119, 4171, 4246, 5137
  metabolites, 3207, 3338, 3339, 3936, 3940, 3941, 3942, 3943, 3946, 4020, 4133, 4135, 4137, 4244, 4288, 4482, 4551, 4553, 4722, 4734, 4802, 4916, 5145, 5273, 5527, 5528
    GC/MS, 3312, 4305, 4384
    radioimmunoassay (RIA), 3880
    thin layer chromatography (TLC), 3312
  methods, 5539
  microscopic examination, 3478
  nuclear magnetic resonance (NMR), 3260, 3261, 3338, 3339, 3478
  paper chromatography, 5215
  plasma, 4746, 5149
  plasma chromatography, 4139
  probability based matching (PBM), 5411
  quantitative, 5149
  radioimmunoassay (RIA), 3206, 3469, 3880, 3881, 4106, 4246, 4916, 5026, 5028, 5029, 5206
    cross-reactivity, 3469, 3520
  review, 3478
  separation, 3179, 3750, 3944, 4171, 5134
    cannabinoid(s), 3799
    metabolites, 3799
    phytosterols, 3366
  silyl derivatives, 3934
  stability, 4271
  structure, 3416
  thin layer chromatography (TLC), 3095, 3139, 3212, 3478, 3750, 4135, 4395, 4484, 5134, 5257
    spray reagents, 3478
  trimethylsilyl derivatives, 3944
  ultra violet (UV), 3478
anti-neoplastic activity, 3690
anti-neoplastic testing, 3775
behavioral effect(s), 3732, 3755, 4040, 4094, 4675, 5021, 5207
  adverse effect(s), 3258, 5156
  aggression, 3447, 3450, 3819, 4445, 5035, 5501
  aggressive behavior, 3234, 3446, 3448, 3732, 3783, 3785, 4093, 4162, 4443, 4446, 4448, 4449, 4588
  analog(s)
    ataxia, 4381
    tolerance, 4381
  ataxia, 4379
  avoidance behavior, 4590
  barometric pressure, 5156
  behavioral teratogenesis, 3531
  biogenic amine(s), 3201, 3448
  cannabis, 4095
  carcinogenicity of, 3733
  catalepsy, 3841, 4389, 5091
  catecholamines, 3357
  chronic administration, 3241
  cognitive function, 4515

behavioral effect(s) (continued)
  compared to:
    alcohol, 4449
    amphetamine, 3783, 5102, 5119, 5318
    anti-anxiety drug(s), 3806
    9-Aza-cannabinol, 5491
    chlordiazepoxide, 4449
    chlorpromazine, 5119
    cocaine, 3137
    ethanol, 5382
    11-hydroxy-delta-9-THC, 3754
    lithium, 5404
    LSD, 3783, 4801, 5163
    mescaline, 4801, 5318
    metabolites, 5441
    morphine, 3096, 4684, 5119
    nalorphine, 5119
    pentobarbital, 5318, 5445
    phencyclidine, 3137
    psilocybin, 5318
  conditioned behavior, 3085, 3090, 3096, 3117, 3127, 3128, 3137, 3140, 3289, 3384, 3435, 3587, 3661, 3733, 3753, 3806, 3919, 4062, 4224, 4330, 4351, 4352, 4377, 4415, 4443, 4639, 4671, 4673, 4674, 4677, 4678, 4684, 4692, 4864, 5032, 5162, 5163, 5183, 5318, 5331, 5404, 5410, 5555
  consummatory behavior, 3407, 4923
  copulation, 5359
  cross tolerance, 3770
  defecation, 4864
  discrimination, 5441, 5445, 5469
  discriminative properties, 3289, 4203
  discriminative stimulus, 3733, 4204, 5180, 5280
  dominance, 3167
  drug discrimination, 3096, 3295, 3414, 3433, 3753, 3869, 3965, 4059, 4060, 4061, 4062, 4063, 4865, 5180, 5181
  drug vehicle, 4945
  electrical stimulation, 5541
  electroencephalogram (EEG), 3201, 3516, 4095, 4189, 4386
  emotional aspects, 4454
  environmental conditions, 5536
  feeding, 5491
  food intake, 3642, 3643, 3732
  gross behavior, 3664, 3953, 4684
  gross behavioral change(s), 3954
  hallucinations, 4189
  head-twitching, 4864
  hypothalamus, 3308
  interaction with
    alcohol, 4677, 4943
    American Indian(s), 5092
    amphetamine, 5429
    anti-histaminic, 5091
    anti-Parkinsonian drug(s), 5091
    antidepressant, 5091, 5092
    antihistamine(s), 5092
    apomorphine, 4220, 5092, 5429
    arecoline, 4095
    atrophine, 5092
    atropinemethylbromide, 4415
    caffeine, 3517, 4220
    cannabidiol (CBD), 3384, 3732, 4059, 5001

interaction with (continued)
    cannabinol (CBN), 3732, 4059, 4515, 5001
    carbachol, 5372
    chlordiazepoxide, 4677
    cocaine, 3517, 4220
    delta-8-THC, 4059
    L-dopa, 5092
    estrogen, 3834, 4588
    methamphetamine, 3515, 3517, 3698, 3700, 4220
    naltrexone, 4063
    neuroleptic drugs, 5092
    nicotine, 3128, 3133, 4095
    pentobarbital, 4330, 5445
    phencyclidine, 4672, 4673, 4987
    phenobarbital, 3587, 4677
    phenoxybenzamine, 4063
    physostigmine, 4095
    progesterone, 4588
    propranolol, 4063
    serotonin (5-hydroxytryptamine), 5092
    SKF-525A, 3587
  learned behavior, 4683
  learning, 5100, 5101, 5382
  locomotor activity, 3643, 3698, 3700, 4335, 4684 5100, 5101, 5318, 5372
  maternal behavior, 3184, 5407, 5456
  memory, 4454, 4460
  motility, 5091
  motivation, 5183
  motor activity, 3187, 3202, 3222, 3688, 3732 3783, 4220, 4336, 4338, 4447, 4671, 4678 4683, 4987, 5501, 5541
  muricide, 3785, 4446, 4447, 4818, 5091, 5092 5382, 5501, 5574
  neo-natal development, 5571
  nest building, 4497
  non-human primates, 4639
  operant behavior, 3296, 3680, 4865
  partial reinforcement, 3641
  perception, 4515
  performance, 4272, 4463, 4678, 4683, 4943, 4945
  personality, 4782
  prenatal exposure, 5382
  punishment, 4801
  rabbit(s), 3511
  rats, 4816
  REM sleep, 3447, 3448, 3450
  review, 3289, 3446, 3732, 3733, 4443, 4446 4531, 4918, 5093, 5336
  self administration, 3137, 5119, 5594
  serotonin (5-hydroxytryptamine), 4588
  sexual behavior, 3569, 3570, 4739, 5102, 5295
  shock avoidance, 4008
  sleep, 3046, 5001
  social behavior, 3234, 3558, 3637, 3688, 3834, 4071, 4093, 4515, 4684, 5161, 5336
  social interaction, 5501
  state-dependent learning, 3869, 5163
  stereotypy, 3841, 5429
  stimulant effects, 3143
  stress, 3448, 4588
  time estimation, 4515

behavioral effect(s) (continued)
  tolerance, 3096, 3127, 3222, 3289, 3435, 3680, 3734, 3754, 3919, 3923, 4058, 4108, 4224, 4330, 4335, 4351, 4352, 4379, 4386, 5163, 5336
  tonic immobility, 4389
  unlearned behavior, 3732, 4443
  water intake, 3642, 3732, 3737, 5372
  withdrawal symptoms, 5022
behavioral model(s)
  social behavior, 4783
biochemical aspects
  accumulation, 5546
  adipose, 5546
  ATPase(s), 5349
  calcium levels, 5349
  choline, 5632
  compared to:
    phenobarbital, 5632
  disposition, 5576
  distribution, 5546
  metabolism, 5546
  microsomal metabolism, 5317
  microsomes, 5349
  radiolabelled, 5576
biochemical effect(s)
  acetylcholinesterase, 3343, 4231, 4462, 4657
  acyltransferase, 3871
  adenylate cyclase, 3627, 5333
  alkaline phosphatase, 4425
  alveolar macrophage(s), 3468
  amino acid(s), 5367, 5449
  ammonia, 3594
  amylase, 4520
  anti-neoplastic activity, 5448
  arachidonic acid, 3422, 3423
  ascorbic acid, 4340
  ATPase(s), 3343, 3356, 4022, 4231, 4411, 4522, 4570, 4571, 4825, 5333
  binding, 4411, 5564
  biogenic amine(s), 5429, 5597
  biotransformation, 5269
  blood glucose, 3318
  brain, 3355, 3356, 3627, 4304, 4655, 4779, 4780, 4878, 5059, 5262, 5488, 5492
  brain levels, 5331
  calcium levels, 5328
  cell division, 3125, 4022, 4318
  cell growth, 3385, 4318, 5241
  cell membrane(s), 3468, 4425, 4702
  cellular division, 3177, 3524, 3604, 4483, 4528, 5495
  cellular effects, 5329, 5344, 5462, 5463
  cholesterol esterase, 3424, 4340, 5322, 5323
  chromosome damage, 4534
  chromosomes, 4494, 4496, 4976
  alpha-chymotrypsin, 4462
  clotting factors, 4264, 4265
  compared to:
    alcohol, 4043, 4534
    aspirin, 4534
    caffeine, 4534
    cannabicyclol (CBL), 5462, 5463
    cannabidiol (CBD), 5429, 5462, 5463
    cannabinol (CBN), 5462, 5463

biochemical effect(s) (continued)
    ethanol, 5463
    glycosides, 5602
    11-hydroxy-delta-9-THC, 5479,
    11-palmitoyloxy-delta-9-THC, 5479
    psychotropic drugs, 5304
    SP-111, 5429
  corticosterones, 3342
  cyclic AMP, 3627, 4603, 5462, 5463
  cytological changes, 4399, 4976
  deoxyribonucleic acid (DNA), 5328
  DNA levels, 3287
  DNA synthesis, 3348, 3605, 4366, 4494, 4496, 4681, 5495
  drug metabolism, 3177
  enzyme induction, 3780, 5225, 5272
  fatty acids, 4878
  glucose, 3594
  glucose metabolism, 4023, 5437
  glutamate synthetase, 4657
  glycogen levels, 3287
  heart, 5344
  hepatic enzymes, 3780
  hydroxylated metabolites, 5527
  insulin, 3594
  interaction with
    anti-inflammatory activity, 5380
    cannabidiol (CBD), 5429
    follicle stimulating hormone (FSH), 5419
    hydrocortisone, 5272
    luteinizing hormone (LH), 5419
    phospholipids, 3282
    solvents, 5564
    steroids, 3780, 5329
  lactic dehydrogenase (LDH), 4425
  lactic dehydrogenase isozymes (LDH), 4357
  lipase, 4462
  lipid content, 4479, 4780
  lipid synthesis, 3177
  lipoprotein(s), 4167, 4357, 5065
  lymphocytes, 4425, 5304
  lysosomes, 4425
  macromolecular synthesis, 3125, 3177, 3348, 3349, 3440, 3442, 3603, 3606, 3607, 3690, 3775, 3776, 4022, 4042, 4043, 4318, 4411, 4483, 4513, 4522, 4523, 4524, 4528, 4533, 4534, 5071, 5193, 5194, 5241, 5367
  mechanism of action, 4877
  membrane-bound ATPases, 3355, 3506, 3888, 4657
  membrane-bound enzyme, 4231, 4570, 4571
  membrane effects, 3282, 4877, 5006, 5304, 5367, 5448
  membrane stability, 4231
  membranes, 4022, 4879
  metabolism, 5278, 5331, 5378
  metabolites, 5266, 5269, 5321
  microsomal metabolism, 5265, 5479
  mitochondria
    electron transport system, 3300
  mitochondrial respiration, 3300, 3342
  monoamine oxidase (MAO), 3290
  muscular dystrophy, 3474
  neuronal membrane(s), 4657
  nucleotides, 5448, 5449, 5602

biochemical effect(s) (continued)
  oxygen consumption, 3476
  phosphodiesterase, 3627, 5333
  phospholipase, 4877
  phospholipids, 3871, 4411, 4879, 5492
  platelets, 4264, 4265
  progesterone, 5323
  prostaglandin synthesis, 3422, 3428
  prostaglandins, 4603, 5380
  protein levels, 3287
  protein synthesis, 3348, 5328
  pseudocholinesterase, 3343, 4462
  radioimmunoassay (RIA), 5564
  review, 4411
  RNA levels, 3287
  RNA polymerase, 5225
  RNA synthesis, 3348, 5328
  ribosomes, 4659
  SGOT (serum glutamic oxaloacetic transaminase), 4425
  SGPT (serum glutamic pyruvic transaminase), 4425
  sodium-potassium adenosine triphosphatase (Na K ATPase), 4237, 4655, 5059, 5060, 5492, 5602
  steroids, 4558
  subcellular distribution, 3690
  synaptic vesicles, 4570, 4571
  testicular effects, 5419, 5437
  testosterone synthesis, 5322
  thymidine uptake, 3604, 3605, 5367, 5449
  tissue culture, 3690
  tissue respiration, 3532
  tyrosine aminotransferase, 5222, 5225
  vitamins, 5342
cannabis
  seeds
    detection, 4611
Cannabis sativa
  constituents, 5082
  constituents of, 3562, 3691, 3909
cardiovascular effects
  heart rate, 5267
  interaction with
    anesthetic(s), 5267
chemical aspects
  analog(s), 4341, 4411, 4578, 4579, 4708, 5094, 5327
    synthesis, 4486
  analysis, 5278
  biotransformation, 3338, 3340, 3480, 4305, 4719, 4720
  carbocyclic analogs, 4603, 4918
  decomposition, 4271
  degradation, 3798, 5611
  derivatives, 4650
  extractions, 4802, 5320
  glucuronides, 4306
  homologs, 3537
  hydroxylated metabolites, 5418
  isomers, 4160, 5098
  keto analogs, 3260
  mass fragmentography, 3363
  mass spectrometry, 4032
  metabolism, 3209, 3340, 4411
  metabolites, 3207, 3939, 3947, 3948, 4314, 4384, 4482, 4589, 4607, 4719, 4770, 4918, 5147

528

chemical aspects (continued)
  nitrogen analogs, 4603
  NMR spectra, 3260
  oxidation products, 4032
  oxygen analog(s), 4197
  pyrolytic products, 4770
  receptors, 3598
  review
    structure-activity relationships, 4603
  silyl derivatives, 3934
  stability, 3798, 4271
  storage
    insects, 4755
  structure, 3260, 5340
  structure-activity relationships, 3598, 4076, 4078,
    4084, 4411, 4578, 4579, 4653, 4913, 5094,
    5146
    analog(s), 4603
    carbocyclic analogs, 4603
    nitrogen analogs, 4603
    review, 4603
    thio analogs, 4603
  synthesis, 3139, 3261, 3335, 3537, 4160, 4635,
    4649, 4706, 5418, 5487
    analog(s), 3616, 4411
    derivatives, 4650
    metabolites, 3207, 4589, 4648, 5096
    oxygen analog(s), 4197
    radiolabelled, 3989
    thio analogs, 3616
  thio analogs, 4198, 4603, 4918
chemistry
  fluorescense, 3617
clinical findings, 3097
compared to:
  steroids, 3816
constituents of
  Cannabis sativa, 4908
detection
  GC/MS, 3727
  hops plant, 3727
drug discrimination
  gerbils, 4057
drug interactions, 4675
electroencephalogram (EEG), 3511, 4094, 4188
endocrine effects, 4782
  compared to:
    cannabidiol (CBD), 5440
  corticosterone level, 5440
  dihydrotestosterone, 5296
  estrogen, 3461
  estrogen-receptor binding, 4848
  estrogenic activity, 5620
  gonadotropic effects, 5296
  interaction with
    gonadotropins, 5297
  luteinizing hormone (LH), 5297
  ovum, 5620
  progesterone, 5297
  progesterone levels, 5296
  steroids, 5159
  stress, 5440
  testosterone, 5296, 5297
  uterus, 5620

DELTA-9-THC (continued)
  epidemiological study
    psychological aspects, 3075
  forensic aspects
    detection, 4118, 4311
  general information
    contaminated
      phencyclidine, 5187
  hashish
    Austria, 5358
    constituents of, 4770
  hemp
    constituents of, 3912
  history
    review, 5093
  immune system
    lymphocytes, 3874, 4025
  immunology, 4743, 5243
    acyltransferase activity, 3872
    allergy, 4234
    antibodies, 4234, 4835
    antibody response, 4629
    antibody formation, 4835
    antimitotic, 3602
    cell-mediated immunity, 3550, 3553, 3554, 3555,
      3556, 4106, 4107, 4241, 4262, 4510, 4627,
      4629, 4653, 4737, 4913, 4914
    cellular immunity, 4261, 4263, 4670
    clinical findings, 4835
    derivatives, 4914
    hematology, 3553
    humoral immunity, 3431, 3553, 3555, 4240,
      4241, 4261, 4263, 4510, 4629, 4653, 4670,
      4736, 4737, 4913, 4914
    immunosuppression, 3695, 4017, 4603, 4668
    lymphocyte function, 4628, 4681
    lymphocytes, 3602, 3606, 3872, 4227, 4228,
      4240, 4523, 4533, 4670, 5304
    macromolecular synthesis, 4533
    macrophages, 3804
    reticuloendothelial system (RES), 4261
    spleen, 4239
    tolerance, 3695
  interaction with
    alcohol, 3994
    amphetamine, 3756
    cannabinoid(s), 3994
    methamphetamine, 3756
    muscular coordination, 4671
    naloxone, 3609
    other drugs, 3994
    reserpine, 3609
    stimulants, 3511
  legal aspects, 3856
    medical use, 5567
    research, 5567
  locomotor activity
    mice, 3756
  marihuana
    constituents of, 3215, 3919, 4770, 4918
    high-pressure liquid chromatography (HPLC), 5455
  memory, 4753
  metabolites
    distribution, 3609

DELTA-9-THC (Continued)
  neurochemistry
    choline, 4075
    serotonin (5-hydroxytryptamine), 4074
    trytophan, 4075
  neurochemical effects
    acetylcholine (ACH), 3629, 3630, 4140, 4141,
      4715, 4716
    acetylcholinesterase, 3809
    acyltransferase, 3873
    adenylate cyclase, 3627
    analog(s), 3293
    biogenic amine(s), 3382, 3507, 4656, 5023, 5574
    catecholamines, 3360
    choline, 4141
    cyclic AMP, 3627
    dopamine (DA), 3293, 3320, 3359, 3382, 3508
    gamma-amino-butyric acid (GABA), 3293, 4715
    ganglioside, 3809
    glutamate, 4715
    5-hydroxyindoleacetic acid (5-HIAA), 3508
    membrane-bound ATPases, 3355
    mitochondria, 3809
    monoamine oxidase (MAO), 3290, 3809, 4806,
      4807, 4808
    neurotransmitters, 4603
    norepinephrine (NE), 3293, 3320, 3359, 3382,
      3508, 5104
    phosphodiesterase, 3627
    phospholipids, 3809
    serotonin (5-hydroxytryptamine), 3293, 3320,
      3382, 3508, 3986
    sodium-potassium adenosive triphosphatase (Na
      K ATPase), 3809, 5059
    synaptosomes, 3809
  neuropharmacological effects
    acetylcholine (ACH), 5372
    adrenergic nervous system, 5413
    audition, 5427
    brain, 3917, 4590, 4816
    cardiovascular effects, 5454
    catalepsy, 5380
    central nervous system (CNS), 5413
    compared to:
      anti-convulsant(s), 5343
      cannabidiol (CBD), 5343, 5549
      chlorpromazine, 5380
      ethanol, 5382
      11-hydroxy-delta-9-THC, 5343
    convulsions, 5354
    cortex, 5343
    electroencephalogram (EEG), 3917, 5378, 5382,
      5427
    epilepsy, 5343
    evoked potentials, 5427
    extrapyramidal system, 3838
    hippocampus, 5549
    5-hydroxyindoleacetic acid (5-HIAA), 5596
    interaction with
      alcohol, 5354
      cannabidiol (CBD), 5354
      cannabinol (CBN), 5354
      carbachol, 5372
      diazepam, 5354
      neurotransmitters, 4816

DELTA-9-THC (Continued)
    membrane effects, 5525
    neuronal alterations, 5250
    neurotoxicity, 5254
    neurotransmitters, 5541
    neuronal activity, 4816
    seizures, 5372
    septal region, 5549
    serotonin (5-hydroxytryptamine), 5596
    sodium conductance, 4989
    synapse, 3917
    synaptic transmission, 5525
    tolerance, 5354
  neuropharmacology
    action potential(s), 3190
    analog(s), 4076, 4078
    catalepsy, 3840
    central nervous system mechanism, 3220
    cerebral cortex, 3379, 3380
    conditioned behavior, 3220
    electrophysiology, 4270
    evoked potentials, 3380
    extrapyramidal system, 3840
    gamma-amino-butyric acid (GABA), 3666
    hypothermia, 4796
    metabolites, 4076, 4078
    neuronal activity, 3190, 5182
    serotonin (5-hydroxytryptamine), 4076, 4078
    synaptic transmission, 3190, 3211
    synaptosomes, 4076, 4078
  neurophysiological effects
    posttetanic potentiation, 5075, 5076
    septal region, 5512
    ultrastructural changes, 5512
  neurophysiology, 3631
    electroencephalogram (EEG), 3250, 3722, 3730,
      3740, 3953, 3954, 4106, 4192, 4220, 4754
    evoked potentials, 3147, 5074
    ganglionic transmission, 3147
    sleep, 4106
    synaptic transmission, 3437
  pathological study
    muscular dystrophy, 3822
  pharmacognosy
    biosynthesis, 3329
  pharmacokinetics
    absorption, 3611, 4164
    blood level(s), 4981, 5146
    brain, 3204, 4618
    brain levels, 3104, 3782, 4514, 4619, 4673
    compared to:
      LSD, 3782
    disposition, 3312, 3467, 3801, 3853, 4232, 4253,
      4379, 4382, 4522, 4619, 4676, 4862, 4918
    distribution, 3173, 3250, 3611, 3692, 3986, 4118,
      4119, 4164, 4246, 4336, 4337, 4338, 4363,
      4376, 4377, 4380, 4385, 4607, 4608, 4618,
      5394
    dogs, 3801
    excretion, 3312, 3467, 3801, 3853, 4020, 4164,
      4246, 4522, 4676, 4862, 4918, 5394
    flash analysis, 4676
    half-life, 3782, 4020
    interaction with
      cannabidiol (CBD), 4862

interaction with (continued)
    cannabigerol (CBG), 4862
    cannabinol (CBN), 4412, 4862
    endotoxin, 4382, 4385
    SKF-525A, 4862
  liver, 4035
  metabolism, 3312, 3801, 4020, 4164, 4253, 4313, 4377, 4522, 4862, 5317, 5394
  metabolites, 3467, 3853, 4246, 4338, 4861, 5146
  plasma levels, 3611, 4246, 4266, 4361, 4385, 4619, 4673, 5146, 5278
  protein binding, 4020, 4313
  review, 3250, 5278, 5394
pharmacological aspects, 4675
  absorption, 4674, 5261
  abstinence syndrome, 3334, 3734, 4152
  acetylcholine (ACh), 3050, 3629, 3630, 3773, 4140, 4141, 4546, 4715, 4716, 4750
  acetylcholinesterase, 3343, 4503
  adrenals, 3343
  adrenergic nervous system, 3860, 3864, 4052, 4128, 5270
  alcohol withdrawal, 3734, 4199, 4940, 4944
  amygdaloid seizure(s), 5141, 5142
  analgesia, 3320, 3352, 3409, 3802, 3918, 3919, 4084, 4515, 4561, 4578, 4579, 4686, 4786, 4918, 4926, 5184, 5210
    nitrogen analogs, 4958
  analgesic 3430, 4547, 4712, 4774
  analgesic activity, 4350, 4603, 5162
  analog(s), 4341, 4578, 4579, 4708, 5094
    cardiovascular effects, 4381
  anesthesia, 3873, 4233, 4915, 5492
  anesthetic potentiation, 3784
  anesthetic(s), 4603
  anorexia, 3643, 4603
  anti-bacterial activity, 3564, 5118
  anti-convulsant activity, 3104, 3164, 3459, 3473, 3475, 3512, 3514, 3525, 3530, 3660, 3696, 3814, 3919, 4072, 4145, 4146, 4603, 4892, 4918, 4925, 5075, 5076, 5077, 5140, 5141, 5142, 5381
  anti-convulsant effect(s), 3815, 4919, 5036, 5073
  anti-fertility activity, 4603
  anti-fungal activity, 3563
  anti-histaminic activity, 3189, 5078
  anti-inflammatory activity, 4009, 4603, 4653, 4913, 5019
  anti-neoplastic activity, 3442, 3776, 4513, 4603, 4651, 5194
  anticholinergic activity, 3189, 4215
  anticholinergic effect, 4319
  antidepressant, 4712,
  antiemetic, 3430, 3919, 4712, 4772, 5033
  antineoplastic, 3440, 4509, 4545, 5071
  antineoplastic activity, 3924
  antineoplastic testing, 5193
  antipyretic, 4603
  antitussive, 3835
  antiulcer activity, 4921
  anxiety, 4328
  appetite, 4712
  asthma, 3930, 3931, 5015
  ATPase(s), 3343, 3808, 3814, 4825
  autonomic nervous system effect(s), 3315, 3764, 4045, 5414

pharmacological aspects (continued)
  barbiturate withdrawal(s), 3815
  biogenic amine(s), 3089, 3115, 3352, 3405, 3407, 3450, 3609, 3726, 3802, 3831, 4073, 4076, 4078, 4081, 4215, 4364, 4652, 4656, 5021, 5023
  blood, 4264, 4265
  blood-brain barrier, 4803
  blood flow, 3830, 4275
  blood pressure, 3342, 5355
  blood sugar, 5239
  blood urea nitrogen, 5239
  body temperature, 3187, 3222, 3357, 3358, 3359, 3726, 4070, 4275, 4515, 4624, 4671, 4673, 4677, 4678, 4794, 4795, 4799, 4918, 5021, 5023, 5032, 5035, 5162, 5369, 5416, 5501, 5536
  body weight, 3197, 3342, 4070, 5022, 5023, 5359
  brain, 3115, 3204, 3320, 3359, 3360, 3610, 3629, 3630, 3653, 3802, 3814, 3830, 3954, 3970, 3986, 4081, 4118, 4140, 4141, 4237, 4282, 4373, 4570, 4571, 4655, 4656, 4659, 4716, 4796, 4803, 4806, 4807, 4808, 4819
  brain levels, 3104, 3755
    cyclic AMP, 3628
  bronchodilatation, 3189, 3919, 3930, 3931, 5009, 5010, 5015, 5106, 5271
  calcium levels, 3889
  cancer, 4547, 4712
  carbocyclic analogs, 4603
  cardiovascular effects, 3051, 3197, 3198, 3250, 3314, 3317, 3393, 3483, 3521, 3578, 3631, 3663, 3664, 3740, 3876, 3914, 4007, 4049, 4050, 4051, 4052, 4126, 4127, 4128, 4129, 4149, 4245, 4247, 4273, 4275, 4289, 4328, 4346, 4353, 4504, 4515, 4520, 4572, 4576, 4579, 4671, 4915, 4981, 5018, 5123, 5207, 5239, 5270
  catalepsy, 3666, 3840
  catecholamines, 3357, 3358, 3360, 4047, 4477
  cell division, 4091
  cell membrane(s), 3817
  cellular respiration, 4282
  central nervous system (CNS), 5258
  CNS activity, 4708
  CNS depression, 3566, 3730, 4058
  central nervous system mechanism, 3768
  cerebral cortex, 3379, 3380
  chemotherapy, 4547
  choline, 4075, 4141
  chromosome damage, 4091
  chronic effects, 4106
  clinical effects, 4248
  clinical findings, 4110
  clotting factors, 4264, 4265
  cognitive function, 4626
  compared to:
    alcohol, 3403, 4546, 5575
    aspirin, 3802, 4113, 4920
    barbiturate(s), 5282
    benzodiazepine(s), 5282
    cannabidiol (CBD), 4892
    cannabinol (CBN), 5544
    chloral hydrate, 4544
    chlordiazepoxide, 4925, 5341

pharmacological aspects
  compared to (continued)
    chlorpromazine, 3888, 4328
    delta-8-THC, 3465
    diazepam, 3522, 4328
    diphenylhydantoin, 4925
    epinephrine, 4347
    ethanol, 5524
    haloperidol, 5341
    indomethacin, 3058
    isoproterenol, 5015, 5106, 5271
    LSD, 3098
    marihuana smoke, 5271
    methadone, 5544
    morphine, 3352, 3802, 4328, 5341, 5459
    morphine withdrawal, 3888
    pentobarbital, 4986
    reserpine, 4073
  convulsions, 3512, 3513, 3718, 4218, 4387, 4941
  corticosterones, 3359
  cross tolerance, 4943, 5575, 5634
    delta-8-THC, 3085
    diphenylhydantoin, 4146
    ethanol, 4858, 4942
    phenobarbital, 4146
  cyclic AMP, 3050
  cytochrome P450, 4811
  dependence liability, 4152
  derivatives
    analgesic, 4068
  dietary effects, 4608
  disposition, 3853, 4253
  distribution, 3610, 3611, 3692, 4117, 4215, 4531,
    4608, 4674, 4860, 5058
  diuretic activity, 4924
  dopamine (DA), 4200, 4348
  dosage, 3296
  drug interactions, 4531, 5575
  electroencephalogram (EEG), 3046, 3718, 4188,
    4373, 4918
  emesis, 4830
  endocrine effects, 4699, 5581
    corticosterones, 4478
  enzyme induction, 5223, 5224, 5225
  epilepsy, 3718, 3719, 4072, 4388, 5179
  euphoria, 3430
  excretion, 3853, 4860, 5269
  eyes, 3250, 3522, 3546, 3588, 3855, 3857, 3858,
    3859, 3860, 3862, 3867, 4110, 4620
  extrapyramidal system, 3841
  false hormone, 3156
  fatty acids, 4347
  food intake, 3181, 3405, 3406, 3642, 3643, 4070,
    4918, 4923, 5022, 5282, 5501
  free fatty acids, 4348
  gamma-amino-butyric acid (GABA), 3666
  ganglionic transmission, 3147, 3831
  gastrointestinal effects, 4039
  gastrointestinal tract, 4603, 4920
  glaucoma, 3213, 3251, 4603, 5355
  glucose, 5034
  beta-glucuronidase, 4811
  gamma-glutamyl transpeptidase, 4811
  growth, 5501
  hallucinations, 4188

pharmacological aspects (continued)
  heart, 3850, 4893, 4894
  heart rate, 4673, 4677, 5355
  hepatic enzymes, 4281, 5223
  hepatic function, 3808
  hepatic metabolism, 3067, 3313, 3465, 3777,
    3778, 3937, 3947, 4148, 5145, 5222
  higher brain function, 4014
  histamine, 5024
  history, 3390
  hormonal effects, 3269
  5-hydroxyindoleacetic acid (5-HIAA), 4819
  hyperthermia, 3888
  hypnotic, 4544
  hypothalamic pituary function, 5544, 5581
  hypothalamus, 4795
  hypothermia, 3197, 3352, 3476, 3532, 3609,
    3725, 3889, 3890, 4058, 4503, 4796, 4798,
    4872, 5252, 5258
  interaction with
    acetylcholine (ACh), 3765
    alcohol, 4107, 4199, 4677
    aminopyrine, 3067
    amphetamine, 3067, 3361, 3840, 3950, 4106,
      4107, 4336, 4859, 4860, 4918
    anesthetic(s), 3784, 3896, 4048, 4918
    anti-convulsant(s), 3513, 3514
    antipyrene, 3316
    apomorphine, 4830
    aspirin, 4671
    atropine, 3227, 3317, 3319, 3653, 3876, 5302,
      5310
    bacterial lipopolysaccharide, 4511, 4512
    barbiturate(s), 4860, 4918
    caffeine, 4671
    calcium chloride, 3890
    cannabichromene (CBC), 5531
    cannabidiol (CBD), 3513, 3571, 3982, 3985,
      3998, 4106, 4107, 4248, 4324, 4326, 4443,
      4607, 5035, 5058, 5184
    cannabinol (CBN), 3985, 3998, 4106, 4107,
      4149, 4412, 4443, 5002, 5058, 5184
    carbachol, 3653
    carbon tetrachloride, 4475
    chlordiazepoxide, 4671, 4677, 5634
    chlorpromazine, 4872
    clomipramine, 3726, 5022
    cocaine, 4024, 4671, 4678
    corticosterones, 4282
    d-amphetamines, 4678
    Datura, 3566
    delta-9-THC, 4266
    desmethylimipramine, 3668, 4671
    diazepam, 4915
    diphenylhydantoin, 4671
    estradiol, 4567
    estrogen, 5593
    ethanol, 3067, 3316, 3696, 4282, 4326, 4858,
      4863, 4940, 4941, 4942
    ether, 4349
    fungal infection, 4347
    glucagon, 5224
    gondotropins, 5544
    haloperidol, 5634

532

pharmacological aspects
  interaction with (continued)
    hexabarbital, 3067, 4326
    hydrocortisone, 4274, 5223, 5224
    6-hydroxy-dopamine, 3668
    insulin, 5034
    isoprenaline, 3227
    isoproterenol, 5270
    local anesthetics, 3876
    LSD, 4478, 4671
    mescaline, 4860
    methamphetamine, 3700, 4325, 4671
    methaqualone, 4671, 4988
    3-methylcolanthrene, 3777
    morphine, 3067, 3765, 3980, 4860, 5299
    naloxone, 3333, 3352, 3765, 3980, 5634
    nicotine, 3133, 4414, 4671, 4678
    oral administration, 3777
    oxymorphone, 4087, 4915
    papaverine, 3861
    penicillin G, 4218
    pentobarbital, 3067, 3316, 4045, 4051, 4087, 4915
    pentylenetetrazole, 4325
    phencyclidine, 4024, 4514, 4671, 4672, 4673
    phenobarbital, 3473, 4024, 4361, 4478, 4671, 4677
    phenoxybenzamine, 3862
    phentolamine, 3862, 4053, 4289
    phenylephrine, 3227
    2-phenylethylamine, 5124
    physostigmine, 3768, 4094, 4106, 4107, 4503
    pilocarpine, 4520
    probenecid, 4819
    propranolol, 3317, 3319, 3862, 3930, 5270, 5302, 5310
    prostaglandins, 3862, 4039
    reserpine, 3986, 4079, 4082, 4478, 4872
    secobarbital, 4106, 4248
    SKF-525A, 4361, 4860
    sodium chloride, 3890
    sotalol, 3862
    strychnine, 4325
    tolbutamide, 4671
    trytophan, 5224
    Tween 80, 3485
    verapamil, 3861
    vitamins, 5400
  interactions
    hexamethonium, 4794
    6-hydroxy-dopamine, 4794
  intestinal motility, 3222
  intoxication, 3999
  intraocular pressure (IOP), 3251, 3521, 3522, 3534, 3546, 3588, 3855, 3857, 3858, 3859, 3860, 3861, 3862, 3864, 3866, 3867, 3919, 4620, 4679, 5355, 5414
  kidney, 4153
  lactation, 3467
  lethal synergism, 4511
  lipid peroxidation, 4475
  lipids, 3280
  lipoprotein(s), 4167
  liver, 3280, 4035, 4475, 4476, 4806, 4807
  liver function tests, 5239

pharmacological aspects (continued)
  locomotor activity, 5299
  lung(s), 3180, 3849, 4048, 4050, 4153, 4832, 5010, 5014, 5104, 5106
  lung function, 3931
  lymphocytes, 4025
  mechanism of action, 4082, 4603, 4657
  membrane-bound enzyme, 3294
  membrane permeability, 3281, 3813, 3817
  membrane stability, 3281
  membranes, 4879
  metabolism, 3209, 3250, 3312, 3692, 3919, 3936, 3939, 3940, 3941, 3942, 3943, 3948, 3999, 4106, 4107, 4117, 4134, 4232, 4244, 4249, 4252, 4253, 4281, 4373, 4412, 4443, 4531, 4589, 4607, 4860, 4861, 5058, 5148, 5195, 5199, 5201, 5211, 5261
  metabolites, 3459, 3853, 3859, 4084, 4148, 4337, 4412, 4620, 4729, 5077
  methadone withdrawal, 3984
  microsomal metabolism, 3219, 3316, 4326, 4476
  microsomal protein, 3777
  microsomes, 3280
  mitotic index, 4091
  monoamine oxidase (MAO), 3294, 3485, 4983
  morphine withdrawal, 3330, 3332, 3333, 3334, 3444, 3734, 3765, 3979, 3980, 3982, 3985
  motor activity, 3197
  motor coordination, 5035
  motor performance, 5575
  muscular dystrophy, 3822, 3826, 3827, 4604
  narcotic withdrawal, 3597
  neurochemical effects, 3970, 4304
  neurologic function, 5018
  neuromuscular transmission, 3988
  nitrogen analogs, 4603, 4958
  norepinephrine (NE), 4546, 5104
  ocular effects, 5413
  organ weights, 3342
  ovaries, 3269
  ovulation, 3269
  oxygen consumption, 4624, 5252
  pain, 3730, 3877
  parasympathetic nervous system (PNS), 3653, 4321, 4322
  pharmacokinetics, 5413, 5575
  physical dependence, 3734, 4106, 4110, 4111, 4160
  placental transfer, 3386
  plasma levels, 3755, 3993
  plasma protein binding, 4312
  platelets, 4260, 4264, 4265, 4983
  premedication, 4346
  prostaglandin synthesis, 3058, 3422, 4009, 4113
  prostaglandins, 4153
  pseudocholinesterase, 3343, 4462
  psychological dependence, 4160
  pulse rate, 4454
  pupil size, 3403, 4275
  receptor binding, 5583
  red blood cells, 5239
  regional blood flow, 4045, 4049
  reproductive system, 5544
  respiration, 4346, 5531

pharmacological aspects (continued)
respiratory effects, 3393, 3521, 3849, 3896, 4050, 4106, 4107, 4275, 4504, 4572, 4832, 4915, 5009, 5014, 5207
review, 3181, 3250, 3329, 3483, 3749, 3919, 4106, 4107, 4443, 4531, 4603, 4918, 5093, 5199, 5233
ribosomes, 4659
route of administration, 3296, 5414
saliva, 4321, 4322, 4520
salivary glands, 4118, 4319, 4320
salivation, 4323
sedative, 4364, 4603
seizures, 4892, 4895
serotonin (5-hydroxytryptamine), 3986, 4074, 4200, 4597, 4818, 4922
serotonin levels, 3725, 4081, 4162, 4819
side effects, 5405
skin conductance, 4275
sleep, 3046, 3722, 4544, 5018
sleep time, 3067, 4326, 4988, 5162, 5541
smooth muscle, 4051, 4729, 5524
sodium, 4919
sorbitol dehydrogenase, 4811
speech, 4014
spermatozoa, 3813
spinal cord, 4795
spleen, 4239
stimulant activity, 4364, 4387
stimulant effects, 5124
stress, 3527, 3877, 4282, 4981
subjective effects, 4626
synaptic transmission, 3211, 4750
synaptosomes, 4025
testicular effects, 4281, 5359
testis(es), 4023, 4811
testosterone, 3465
testosterone synthesis, 3425
thio analogs, 4603
tolerance, 3085, 3197, 3222, 3250, 3317, 3525, 3530, 3610, 3611, 3740, 3771, 3923, 4045, 4058, 4106, 4110, 4111, 4145, 4146, 4152, 4160, 4183, 4252, 4304, 4336, 4337, 4376, 4531, 4678, 4858, 4872, 5018, 5023, 5036, 5414, 5541, 5575
tranquilizing activity, 3430, 4603
trytophan, 4075
tumor growth, 4545
uptake, 3668
uterus, 4113, 5583
vas deferens, 3668, 4546, 5524
vasoconstriction, 3663
vehicle effect(s), 5414
visual acuity, 5555
visual tracking, 4986
water intake, 3181, 3642, 3737, 4070, 4923, 5501
white blood cells, 5239
withdrawal symptoms, 4111, 4147, 5022, 5341
worms, 4597
physiological effects
adrenal function, 3344
adrenals, 3342, 4340, 5158
adrenocorticotropic hormone (ACTH), 4080
autonomic nervous system effect(s), 5310

physiological aspects (continued)
cardiovascular effects, 5302, 5310
cellular division, 5494
corpus luteum, 5296
corticosterones, 4077, 4080
deoxyribonucleic acid (DNA), 5494
discrimination, 5360
electroencephalogram (EEG), 5302
endocrine effects, 3110, 3234, 3318, 3325, 3326, 3327, 3342, 3351, 3396, 3397, 3461, 3464, 3507, 3508, 3568, 3694, 3915, 4106, 4107, 4247, 4340, 4393, 4411, 4558, 4689, 4737, 4896, 4898, 4899, 4998, 5294, 5334, 5359
estradiol, 4567
estrogenic activity, 4568, 4927, 4928, 4929
follicle stimulating hormone (FSH), 3569, 3570, 4898
gonadotropic effects, 4898
growth, 5494
hippocampus, 5121
hypothalamic pituitary function, 3110, 4348, 4899, 4998, 5294, 5334
hypothermia, 5310
interaction with
methadone, 5360
thyroid release hormone, 5294
17-ketosteroids, 3567
luteinizing hormone (LH), 3569, 3570, 4898, 5090, 5295
morphology, 5494
ovulation, 5296
pituitary function, 3396, 4898
prolactin, 4200
prolactin levels, 4689
reproductive effects, 3351, 3461, 4896, 5295, 5359
reproductive system, 3569, 3570, 4689
review, 3351
serum prolactin, 5294
sexual behavior, 3351, 4106
steroids, 4390, 4392, 4393, 5158
testis(es), 3568, 3915
testosterone, 4392
testosterone levels, 3569, 3570, 4998, 5359
thyroxine, 4543
vision, 4726
volvox, 5494
physiology
endocrine effects, 4848
psychological aspects, 3768, 4149, 4712
aggression, 5393
aggressive behavior, 5025
cannabalism, 5393
cognitive function, 3631, 3636, 4110, 5308
cognitive processes, 3471
compared to:
alcohol, 4753, 5025
hallucinogens, 3618
pentobarbital, 4985
conditioned speech connections, 4010, 4012, 4015
consciousness, 3618
coordination, 3635
electroencephalogram (EEG), 3723
euphoria, 3075, 4679
hallucinations, 3075, 3618, 4192

psychological aspects (continued)
    interaction with
        alcohol, 3472, 5308
        cannabidiol (CBD), 3573, 3576
        ethanol, 3471
        tobacco, 4011
    learning, 5109
    memory, 3202, 3631, 3635, 4753, 4754, 4980, 5109
    metabolism, 4164
    mood, 3740, 5018
    motor coordination, 4217
    motor performance, 3471, 3636, 5308
    nervous activity, 4012
    perception, 3471, 3636, 5308
    performance, 3250, 3573, 3631, 3635, 3904, 4011, 4110, 4272, 4754, 5109
    psychosis, 3619, 4915
    psychoticism, 3619
    reaction time, 3730, 5308
    reflexes, 3730
    review, 5336
    sleep, 3723, 4544, 4603
    speech, 5519
    state-dependent learning, 4980
    stress, 3877, 4981
    subjective effects, 3250, 3573, 3576, 3631, 4110, 4247, 4981, 5239, 5302
    time estimation, 3635, 3730, 5302
    visual tracking, 4985
psychological effects
    analgesia, 4686
    electroencephalogram (EEG), 3517
    subjective effects, 4245, 5335
psychopharmacological aspects
    discriminative stimulus, 3297, 5180, 5181
    drug discrimination, 5180, 5181
    euphoria, 3098
psychosis
    memory, 3577
reproductive effects, 5390
    adrenals, 5392
    chronic administration, 5571
    estrogenic activity, 5582
    estrus cycle, 5392
    gonadotropins, 5582
    histological changes, 5582
    interaction with
        estrogen, 5582
    lactation, 5593
    mortality, 5593
    neo-natal development, 5488, 5571
    ovaries, 5392
    ovulation, 5582
    prenatal development, 5571
    uterus, 5392
review, 3435, 3732
    aggressive behavior, 3446, 4446
    analysis, 3478
    behavioral effect(s), 3733, 4443, 5093
        tolerance, 3734
    biochemical effect(s), 3177
    cardiovascular effects, 3483
    discriminative properties, 3289, 4203
    disposition, 4253

review (continued)
    distribution, 4607
    endocrine effects, 3351
    fetal development, 3699
    food intake, 3181
    history, 5093
    metabolism, 3936, 4253, 5199
    mutagenesis, 4225
    pharmacokinetics, 3250
    pharmacological aspects, 3250, 3919, 4107, 4443, 5093, 5233
    radioimmunoassay (RIA), 3520
    reproductive effects, 3351
    sexual behavior, 3351
    teratogenic effects, 3351, 3699, 3743
    therapeutic aspects, 3498, 4408
    water intake, 3181
site of action, 3816
sleep, 3767
sociological aspects
    medical use, 5567
street samples, 3408
therapeutic aspects, 4009
    adverse effect(s), 4560, 4562, 4563
    alcohol dependence, 4160
    alcohol withdrawal, 3498
    amoebic meningoencephalitis, 5543
    analgesia, 3498, 4160
    anti-bacterial activity, 3498
    anti-convulsant activity, 3498
    anti-convulsant(s), 4160
    anti-fertility, 4160
    anti-inflammatory, 4408
    antidepressant, 3498, 4160
    antiemetic, 3239, 3498, 4408, 5335, 5374, 5391, 5475, 5595
    antineoplastic, 4160
    antitussive, 4408
    asthma, 3180, 3235, 3239, 3930, 4160, 4408, 4528, 4834, 5009, 5107
    bronchodilatation, 3498, 3501, 3582, 4834, 5009, 5010, 5106, 5107
    cancer, 3235, 3498, 4560, 4562, 4563, 5335, 5374, 5391
    cardiovascular effects, 5438
    compared to:
        cannabinoid(s), 5543
        clotting factors, 5438
    glaucoma, 3235, 3521, 3534, 3856, 3864, 4408, 4528
    homologs, 3993
    hypertension, 4408
    intraocular pressure (IOP), 3239, 3498, 3501, 4160, 5438
    morphine withdrawal, 3498
    neurological effects, 5339
    plasma levels, 5391
    preanesthetic medication, 3498, 4408
    review, 3498, 4408, 5405
    sedative, 3498, 3501
therapeutic effects
    analgesia, 5420
    antiemetic, 5470
    cancer, 5470

therapeutic effects (continued)
  compared to:
    diazepam, 5420
    SP-106, 5420
  glaucoma, 5414
  review, 5420
therapy
  review, 4603
toxicology, 3797
  allergy, 5320
  anorexia, 3292, 5585
  behavioral effect(s), 4744, 5156
  behavioral teratogenesis, 3531, 5122
  blood chemistry, 3292
  body weight, 4027, 4670
  bone marrow, 3823, 3824
  brain, 3953, 4554, 4739
  brain damage, 3258
  BUN (blood urea nitrogen), 5045
  carcinogenesis, 5000, 5593
  cardiovascular effects, 3051, 3393
  cellular division, 3524
  central nervous system (CNS), 4528
  chromosomes, 4493
  chronic effects, 3823, 4027, 4744
  compared to:
    cannabidiol (CBD), 5635
    cannabinol (CBN), 5635
    LSD, 4225
    tobacco, 4225
  cytotoxicity, 4702
  dermal effects, 3292, 5045
  electrolytes, 4027
  endocrine effects, 4143
  estrus cycle, 4184
  false hormone, 3156
  fetal development, 3699, 4184
  fetus, 5585
  glycerol, 4356
  growth, 4744
  hematology, 4744, 5045
  hyperglycemia, 4744
  hyperplasia, 3825
  inhalation, 4739
  interaction with
    bacterial endotoxin(s), 3383
    phenobarbital, 3913, 4359, 4362
    SKF-525A, 3913, 4359, 4362
  kidney, 3825
  LD_{50}, 3919, 5380
  lung(s), 4739
  macrophages, 4702
  mitochondria, 4607
  motor activity, 3164
  mutagenesis, 3779, 4225, 4399, 5120, 5240, 5402
  mutagenic effects, 3119, 4493, 4984, 5325
  mutagenic tests, 4242
  neo-natal development, 5407
  neonates, 4554, 5000
  organ weights, 4027, 4356, 4744
  pathological study, 4027
  placental transfer, 3351, 4361, 4362, 5122
  prenatal development, 4361
  prenatal exposure, 5407

toxicology (continued)
  reproductive effects, 3093, 3116, 3389, 4359, 4360, 4362, 5100, 5585, 5635
  reproductive system, 3265, 3729, 4184, 4528, 4687, 4689, 5000, 5226
  reproduction, 3919
  respiratory effects, 3393
  review, 3699, 4225
  self administration, 3116
  serum enzymes, 4356, 5045
  SGOT (serum glutamic oxaloacetic transaminase), 4744
  SGPT (serum glutamic pyruvic transaminase), 4744
  spermatogenesis, 4528
  spleen, 4670
  stress, 4857
  subacute study, 3292
  teratogenesis, 5585
  teratogenic effects, 3116, 3119, 3291, 3351, 3699, 3743, 3913, 4044, 4088, 4089, 4090, 4143, 4184, 4359, 4360, 4361, 4362, 4857, 5041, 5100, 5101, 5122, 5226
  testicular effects, 3832
  urinalysis, 4744
  vehicle of administration, 5413
DELTA-9-THC OIC ACID A & B
  analysis
    butyl homolog, 3935
    detection, 4552, 4911
    gas liquid chromatography (GLC), 3413, 3539
    GC/MS, 3413, 3935
    high-pressure liquid chromatography (HPLC), 4911
    isolation, 3413
    mass fragmentography, 4552
    separation, 3413
    spectral data, 3413
    thin layer chromatography (TLC), 3413, 3539, 4201
  Cannabis sativa
    constituents of, 3562, 3909
  chemical aspects
    ester, 3413
    homologs, 3539
      synthesis, 3539
    structure, 4745
    synthesis, 3539
      ester, 3413
  hemp
    constituents of, 3912
  marihuana
    constituents of, 3919, 4918
    high-pressure liquid chromatography (HPLC), 5455
DELTA-9-TETRAHYDROCANNABIORCOL
  marihuana
    constituents of, 4918
DELTA-9-TETRAHYDROCANNABIVARIN
  analysis
    detection, 3478
    gas liquid chromatography (GLC), 3478
DELTA-9-TETRAHYDROCANNABIVAROL
  analysis
    detection, 3478
    gas liquid chromatography (GLC), 3478
  marihuana
    constituents of, 3919, 4918

DEOXYRIBONUCLEIC ACID (DNA)
cannabinoid(s)
  lymphocytes, 5366
delta-9-THC
  in vitro, 5328
  volvox, 5494
hashish
  humans, 5439
  spermatozoa, 5439
  white blood cells, 5439
marihuana
  adverse effect(s), 3709
marihuana smoke
  metabolism, 4258
  tissue culture, 4258
DNA BREAKS
cannabidiol (CBD)
  tissue cultures, 3779
delta-8-THC
  tissue cultures, 3779
delta-9-THC
  tissue cultures, 3779
DNA LEVELS
delta-9-THC
  in vitro, 3287
  liver, 3287
DNA SYNTHESIS
blood gases
  in vitro, 4534
  lymphocytes, 4534
cannabichromene (CBC)
  in vitro, 3440, 4534
  lymphocytes, 4534
cannabicyclol (CBL)
  in vitro, 3440, 4534
  lymphocytes, 4534
cannabidiol (CBD), 5071
  in vitro, 3440, 4534
  lymphocytes, 4534
cannabinoid(s)
  cellular respiration, 5604
cannabinol (CBN), 5071
  in vitro, 3440
delta-8-THC, 5071
  in vitro, 3440
  tissue culture, 3441
delta-9-THC, 4366, 5071
  adverse effect(s), 4528
  bacteria, 3177
  HeLa cells, 4483
  humans, 4681
  in vitro, 3440, 3603, 3605, 3607, 4318, 4513,
    4534, 4758
  lymphocytes, 3603, 3606, 3607, 4494, 4496,
    4524, 4533, 4534
  tissue culture, 3348, 3776
  tissue cultures, 3349
  volvox, 5495
11-hydroxy-delta-9-THC, 5071
marihuana
  humans, 3111
  in vitro, 3111
  lung(s), 3111
olivetol
  in vitro, 4534
  lymphocytes, 4494, 4496, 4534

DEPENDENCE
cannabis
  humans, 3854, 5301, 5340
  subjective effects, 5301
marihuana
  adolescent(s), 5493
  humans, 3174, 3241
  interaction with
    heroin, 3174
tetrahydrocannabinol (THC)
  review, 5460
  withdrawal symptoms, 5460
DEPENDENCE LIABILITY
cannabis, 3136
delta-8-THC, 4160
delta-9-THC, 4160
  rats, 4152
DEPRESSIVE EFFECTS
cannabis
  mice, 4874
  rats, 4874
DERIVATIVES
cannabidiol (CBD)
  identification, 4171
  optical derivation, 3144
  pharmacological aspects, 4409
  side chain, 4650
  stability, 4171
  synthesis, 4650
cannabinoid(s)
  CNS activity, 4397
  detection, 3932
  GC/MS, 3933
  side chain, 5540
  silyl, 3933
  synthesis, 3541, 4342, 4343, 4396, 4397, 5540
cannabinol (CBN)
  identification, 4171
  side chain, 4650
  stability, 4171
  synthesis, 4650
delta-8-THC
  identification, 4171
  NMR spectra, 4195
  stability, 4171
  synthesis, 4195
delta-9-THC
  alkylation, 5558
  detection, 5558
  identification, 4171
  side chain, 4650
  stability, 4171
  synthesis, 4650
hexahydrocannabinol (HHC)
  pharmacological aspects, 5580
  synthesis, 5580
11-hydroxy-delta-9-THC
  alkylation, 5558
  detection, 5558
tetrahydrocannabinol (THC)
  pharmacological aspects, 5580
  synthesis, 5580
DERMAL EFFECTS
delta-9-THC
  chronic effects, 5045
  rabbit(s), 3292, 5045

DETECTION
cannabichromene (CBC)
fluorometric, 3374
urine, 3374
cannabicyclol (CBL)
fluorometric, 3374
urine, 3374
cannabidiol (CBD), 4164
biological fluid(s), 3376, 4484
chemical tests, 3478
colorametric method, 4658
colorimetry, 3788
fluorometric, 3374, 3376
gas chromatography, 4484
gas liquid chromatography (GLC), 3478
GC/MS, 4565
mass spectrometry, 3478
metabolites
GC/MS, 4383
microscopic examination, 3478
nuclear magnetic resonance (NMR), 3478
paper chromatography, 5215
plasma, 4565, 5029
plasma levels, 5028
radioimmunoassay (RIA), 5028, 5029
thin layer chromatography (TLC), 3212, 3478,
4395, 4484
ultra violet (UV), 3478
urine, 3374
cannabidiolic acid
colorimetry, 3788
paper chromatography, 5215
cannabidivarin
gas liquid chromatography (GLC), 3478
cannabidivarol
gas liquid chromatography (GLC), 3478
cannabigerol (CBG)
fluorometric, 3374
gas liquid chromatography (GLC), 3478
urine, 3374
cannabinoid(s)
biological fluid(s), 3245, 3852, 5061, 5326, 5340
blood, 4370, 5477
cannabis
seeds, 4611
contact test, 5220
derivatives, 3932
drugs of abuse, 4229
EMIT (homogenous enzyme immunoassay), 5565
fast blue B salt, 3223
fingernails, 5061
gas chromatography, 4317
GC/MS, 3852, 3932
hand test, 5326
high-pressure liquid chromatography (HPLC), 4317
histochemical method, 3223
humans, 5220, 5477
immunoassay, 4722
interference with
coffee, 4229
metabolites, 3852, 5026, 5565
methods, 5326, 5600
overview, 4142
plasma, 4566
radioimmunoassay (RIA), 3245, 4369, 4370, 5026

cannabinoid(s) (continued)
thin layer chromatography (TLC), 3324, 3672,
5134, 5220, 5600
urine, 4370, 4722, 5026, 5477
cannabinol (CBN), 4164
biological fluid(s), 3376, 4484, 5150
chemical tests, 3478
colorametric method, 4658
colorimetry, 3788
fluorescence, 5089
fluorometric, 3376
fluorometry, 5617
gas chromatography, 4484
gas liquid chromatography, (GLC), 3478
GC/MS, 4155, 4565, 5149, 5150
high-pressure liquid chromatography (HPLC),
5089, 5206, 5617
humans, 5150
mass spectrometry, 3478
metabolites, 5206
microscopic examination, 3478
nuclear magnetic resonance (NMR), 3478
paper chromatography, 5215
plasma, 4565, 5029, 5149, 5206
plasma levels, 5028
quantitative, 5150, 5206
radioimmunoassay (RIA), 5028, 5029, 5206
saliva, 5617
thin layer chromatography (TLC), 3212, 3478,
4395, 4484
ultra violet (UV), 3478
urine, 4155
cannabis
color tests, 3542, 4243
consumption, 4550
forensic aspects, 4660
gas chromatography, 3288, 4952
gas liquid chromatography (GLC), 3542
geographical origin, 3288
high-pressure liquid chromatography (HPLC),
3288, 5191
infrared (IR), 3542
mass spectrometry, 3542
microscopic examination, 4952
nuclear magnetic resonance (NMR), 3542
radioimmunoassay (RIA), 3542, 4369
spray reagents, 4691
teeth, 4550
thin layer chromatography (TLC), 3212, 3288,
3542, 4243, 4952
ultra violet (UV), 3542
Cannabis indica
cannabinoid(s), 3223
fast blue B salt, 3223
histochemical method, 3223
cannabis plant
gas chromatography
solid sample injection, 4693
qualitative, 4693
quantitative, 4693
Cannabis sativa
biological fluid(s), 5061
chemical tests, 3478
color tests, 5164
false positives, 4690

538

Cannabis sativa (continued)
    fast blue B salt, 4690
    fingernails, 5061
    gas liquid chromatography (GLC), 3478
    histochemical test, 3526
    mass spectrometry, 3478
    microscopic examination, 3478, 4690
    nuclear magnetic resonance (NMR), 3478
    phenols, 3099
    thin layer chromatography, 3478, 4690
    ultra violet (UV), 3478
chemistry
    street samples, 4506
delta-8-THC
    autoradiographic, 4119
    biological fluid(s), 3376
    blood, 3208
    blood level(s), 4564
    chemical tests, 3478
    fluorometric, 3376, 4118
    free radical immunoassay, 3432
    gas liquid chromatography (GLC), 3478
    GC/MS, 3208, 4565
    mass fragmentography, 3208, 4564
    mass spectrometry, 3478, 4119
    microscopic examination, 3478
    nuclear magnetic resonance (NMR), 3478
    paper chromatography, 5215
    plasma, 4565, 5029
    radioimmunoassay (RIA), 5029
    saliva, 4119
    salivary glands, 4118
    thin layer chromatography (TLC), 3478
    ultra violet (UV), 3478
    urine, 3432
delta-9-THC, 4164
    autoradiographic, 4119
    bile, 5113
    biological fluid(s), 3376, 3469, 3520, 3799, 3800,
       3880, 3881, 3990, 4484, 4792, 5111, 5135,
       5150
    blood, 3206, 4311, 4734
    blood level(s), 4564
    brain, 4311, 5113
    chemical tests, 3478
    colorametric method, 4658
    colorimetry, 3788
    dansyl derivatives, 4792
    derivatives, 4021, 5558
        fluorescent, 5135
    EMIT (homogenous enzyme immunoassay), 4757
    exercise, 5615
    feces, 4288
    fluorometric, 3373, 3374, 3376, 4118
    gas chromatography, 3139, 4484
    gas liquid chromatography (GLC), 3478, 3800,
       5558
        solid sample injection, 3707
    GC/MS, 3608, 3946, 4021, 4565, 4733, 4746,
       5149, 5150
    heart, 3946
    high-pressure liquid chromatography (HPLC),
       3064, 3799, 3800, 4288, 5111, 5112, 5113,
       5206
    HPLC/MS, 4135, 5111, 5615

delta-9-THC (continued)
    humans, 3724, 5150, 5300
    immunoassay, 4722, 4757
    liver, 3946
    lung(s), 3946
    marihuana smoke, 5112
    mass fragmentography, 3206, 4288, 4564, 4734
    mass spectrometry, 3478, 4119, 5111, 5558
    metabolism, 3374
    metabolites, 3800, 3881, 3946, 4133, 4135, 4288,
       4722, 4734, 5026, 5206
        radioimmunoassay (RIA), 3880
    microscopic examination, 3478
    nuclear magnetic resonance (NMR), 3478
    paper chromatography, 5215
    plasma, 3608, 4565, 4733, 4746, 5029, 5113,
       5149, 5206
    plasma chromatography, 4139
    plasma levels, 5028, 5300
    quantitative, 3469, 3520, 3707, 3880, 4792, 5111,
       5150, 5206
    radioimmunoassay (RIA), 3206, 3469, 3520,
       3880, 3881, 5026, 5028, 5029, 5206
    radiolabelled, 4792
    saliva, 4119
    salivary glands, 4118
    serum, 3724
    thin layer chromatography (TLC), 3139, 3212,
       3478, 4135, 4395, 4484, 4792, 5135
    ultra violet (UV), 3478
    urine, 3373, 3374, 4135, 4722, 4734, 4757, 5026
delta-9-THC oic acid A & B
    mass fragmentography, 4552
delta-9-tetrahydrocannabivarin
    gas liquid chromatography (GLC), 3478
delta-9-tetrahydrocannabivarol
    gas liquid chromatography (GLC), 3478
drugs of abuse
    high-pressure liquid chromatography (HPLC), 3064
hashish
    biological fluid(s), 5061
    fingernails, 5061
    headspace volatiles, 4003
    street samples, 4506
    terpenes, 3892
    thin layer chromatography (TLC), 4955
hemp
    street samples, 4506
hops plant
    delta-9-THC, 3727
    GC/MS, 3727
11-hydroxy-delta-9-THC
    blood, 4734
    derivatives, 5558
    gas liquid chromatography (GLC), 5558
    GC/MS, 4155, 4733, 5149, 5150
    humans, 5150
    immunoassay, 4722
    mass fragmentography, 4734
    mass spectrometry, 5558
    plasma, 4733, 5149
    plasma levels, 5028
    quantitative, 5150
    radioimmunoassay (RIA), 5028
    urine, 4133, 4155, 4722

DETECTION (continued)
  hydroxylated cannabinoids
    high-pressure liquid chromatography (HPLC), 5206
    plasma, 5206
    radioimmunoassay (RIA), 5206
  marihuana
    biological fluid(s), 5061
    cannabinoid content, 4765
    color tests, 4019
    contact test, 5220
    fingernails, 5061
    gas liquid chromatography (GLC), 4765, 5144
      solid sample injection, 3707
    GC/MS, 4155
    headspace volatiles, 4003
    high-pressure liquid chromatography (HPLC), 5027
    humans, 5220
    metabolites, 4136, 4155
    quantitative, 3707
    radioimmunoassay (RIA), 5027
    terpenes, 3892
    thin layer chromatography (TLC), 4019, 4136, 4765, 5144, 5214, 5220
    urine, 4136
  marihuana smoke
    biological fluid(s), 4484
    thin layer chromatography (TLC), 4484
  nabilone (Lilly compound no. 109514)
    blood, 4995
    dogs, 4995
  11-nor-9-carboxy-delta-9-THC
    biological fluid(s), 3880
    quantitative, 3880
    radioimmunoassay (RIA), 3880
  olivetol
    GC/MS, 4565
    plasma, 4565
  synthetic cannabinoids
    biological fluid(s), 3241, 3800
    gas liquid chromatography (GLC), 3800
    high-pressure liquid chromatography (HPLC), 3800
    metabolites, 3800
  tetrahydrocannabinol (THC)
    densitometry, 3303
    gas chromatography
      solid sample injection, 4696
    quantitative, 3303
    thin layer chromatography (TLC), 4696
  tetrahydrocannabinol acids
    colorimetry, 3788
    mass fragmentography, 4552
DEVELOPMENT
  cannabis
    phytosterols, 5466
    sexual function, 5466
  Cannabis sativa
    achene(s), 5542
    morphology, 5542
DIABETES MELLITUS
  marihuana
    humans, 3336
    therapy, 3336
DIARRHEA
  cannabis
    humans, 4538

DIETARY EFFECTS
  delta-9-THC
    toxicity, 4608
DIHYDROSTILBENES
  Cannabis sativa
    cannabidihydrophenanthrene, 5356
    constituents of, 3540, 4159
    Thailand, 5356
  chemical aspects
    isolation, 3540, 4159
    structure, 3540, 4159
DIHYDROTESTOSTERONE
  delta-9-THC
    blood level(s), 5296
    rabbit(s), 5296
DIHYDROVOMIFOLIOL
  Cannabis sativa
    constituents of, 3321
8 BETA, 11-DIHYDROXY-DELTA-9-THC
  biochemical effect(s)
    macromolecular synthesis, 3442
  pharmacological aspects
    anti-neoplastic activity, 3442
8,9-DIHYDROXY-DELTA-6A(10A)-THC
  Cannabis sativa
    constituents of, 3681
  chemical aspects
    isolation, 3681
    structure, 3681
9,10-DIHYDROXY-DELTA-6A(10A)-THC
  Cannabis sativa
    constituents of, 3681
  chemical aspects
    isolation, 3681
    structure, 3681
DIMETHYLHEPTYLPYRAN (DMHP)
  biochemical aspects
    ATPase(s), 5349
    calcium levels, 5349
    microsomes, 5349
  biochemical effect(s)
    ascorbic acid, 4340
    cholesterol esterase, 4340
  chemical aspects
    ester, 4603
    synthesis
      analog(s), 4703
  pharmacological aspects
    analgesia, 4578
    analog(s), 4703
    anti-convulsant activity, 3164, 4145
    biogenic amine(s), 3115
    body temperature, 4795
    brain, 3115
    cardiovascular effects, 3914, 4007, 4245, 4577, 4578
    hypothalamus, 4795
    metabolism, 4249
    review, 4603
    spinal cord, 4795
    tolerance, 4145
  physiological effects
    adrenals, 4340
    endocrine effects, 4340

DIMETHYLHEPTYLPYRAN (DMHP) (continued)
  psychological effects
    subjective effects, 4245
  toxicology
    motor activity, 3164
DISCRIMINATION
  delta-9-THC
    pigeon(s), 5360, 5441, 5445, 5469
    rats, 5441
  marihuana
    humans, 3218
DISCRIMINATIVE PROPERTIES
  delta-8-THC
    animals, 3289, 4203
    metabolites, 3289
    review, 3289
  delta-9-THC
    animals, 3289, 4203
    metabolites, 3289
    review, 3289
  hashish
    animals, 4203
  11-hydroxy-delta-9-THC
    animals, 4203
  marihuana
    animals, 4203
    constituents of, 4203
  marihuana extract
    animals, 4203
DISCRIMINATIVE STIMULUS
  cannabis extract
    animals, 4204
  delta-8-THC
    animals, 4204
  delta-9-THC, 3297
    animals, 4204
    pigeon(s), 5280
    rats, 5180, 5181
    review, 3733
  hashish
    animals, 4204
  11-hydroxy-delta-9-THC
    animals, 4204
DISEASES
  cannabis plant
    India, 4115
  Cannabis sativa
    leaves, 5586
DISPOSITION
  cannabidiol (CBD)
    animals, 4253
    humans, 4253
    metabolites, 4253
    review, 4253
  cannabinoid(s)
    overview, 4142
  cannabinol (CBN), 4918
    animals, 4253
    humans, 4253
    metabolites, 4253
    review, 4253
  delta-8-THC
    animals, 4253
    humans, 4253
    metabolites, 4253

delta-8-THC (continued)
  review, 4253
delta-9-THC, 4522, 4918
  animals, 4253
  bile, 5576
  blood, 5576
  brain, 4619
  dogs, 3801, 4379
  humans, 4253
  in vitro, 4232
  interaction with
    cannabidiol (CBD), 4862
    cannabigerol (CBG), 4862
    cannabinol (CBN), 4862
    endotoxin, 4382
    SKF-525A, 4862
  international control, 3801
  label from, 4676
  lung(s), 4232
  metabolites, 4253
  mice, 4382
  monkeys, 3312, 3467, 3853
  rats, 4676, 4862, 5576
  review, 4253
  synaptic vesicles, 4379
  tissues, 5576
  tolerance, 4379
  urine, 5576
11-hydroxy-delta-9-THC
  brain, 4619
marihuana
  humans, 5017
marihuana smoke
  humans, 4254
nabilone (Lilly compound no. 109514)
  humans, 4759
DISTRIBUTION
  cannabis
    Africa, 3076
    history, 3076
  cannabis use
    economic aspects, 4276
    Trinidad, 4276
  delta-8-THC
    autoradiography, 4117
    brain, 3951
    humans, 3438
    metabolites, 5277
    monkeys, 3173, 4117, 4118, 4119
    rats, 3951
    salivary glands, 4118
    synapse, 3951
  delta-9-THC, 4164
    acute administration, 4363
    adipose, 4215
    animals, 4246
    autoradiography, 4117
    brain, 3692, 3986, 4337, 4338, 4376, 4377, 4380
    chronic administration, 4363
    dogs, 3610, 3611, 4376, 4380
    fasting, 4674
    fat, 4608
    feeding, 4674
    fetus, 4380
    heart, 4608

delta-9-THC (continued)
humans, 4246, 5058
interaction with
amphetamine, 4336
cannabidiol (CBD), 5058
cannabinol (CBN), 5058
endotoxin, 4385
kidney, 4215
liver, 4215, 4608
lung(s), 4215
metabolites, 4246, 4338
mice, 3610, 4385, 4608, 5546
monkeys, 3173, 3692, 4117, 4118, 4119, 4377
pancreas, 4215
pharmacokinetics, 5394
pigeon(s), 3611
plasma levels, 4674
radiolabelled, 4860
rats, 3610, 3986, 4337, 4674, 4860
review, 3250, 4531, 4607
route of administration, 4363
salivary glands, 4118
serotonin (5-hydroxytryptamine), 3986
skin, 4608
spleen, 4608
subcellular, 3610, 3986, 4336, 4338, 4607
subcellular fractions, 4376
tissues, 5546
vehicle effect(s), 4363
vehicle of administraton, 4674
9-alpha, 10-alpha-epoxyhexahydro-cannabinol
rats, 5534
11-hydroxy-delta-9-THC
brain, 4377
monkeys, 4377
marihuana
review, 4663
tetrahydrocannabinol (THC)
cells, 5490
lactation, 5490
neonates, 5490
rats, 5490
tissues, 5490
DISTRIBUTION OF LABEL FROM THC, 3609
DIURETIC ACTIVITY
cannabidiol (CBD)
hypothalamic pituitary function, 4924
rats, 4924
tolerance, 4924
cannabinol (CBN)
hypothalamic pituitary function, 4924
rats, 4924
tolerance, 4924
delta-9-THC
hypothalamic pituitary function, 4924
rats, 4924
tolerance, 4924
DOMINANCE
delta-9-THC
rats, 3167
marihuana
cerebral, 3499
DOPA BETA-HYDROXYLASE
cannabis
plasma levels, 4969

DOPAMINE (DA)
cannabidiol (CBD)
mice, 3357, 3970
uptake, 3970
cannabinol (CBN)
mice, 3357
cannabis extract
brain, 4656
rats, 4656
receptor interaction, 3528
Cannabis sativa
humans, 4440, 4441
metabolism, 4441
delta-8-THC
central nervous system (CNS), 4333
rats, 3115, 4283, 4333
stress, 4283
striatum, 4283
uptake, 4283
delta-9-THC
analgesia, 3320
analog(s)
brain, 3293
synaptosomes, 3293
uptake, 3293
brain, 3089, 3293, 3320, 3359, 3382, 3508, 4073, 4656
brain levels, 5023
central nervous system mechanism, 4348
compared to:
morphine, 3352
heart, 3089
mice, 3352, 3357, 3970
rabbit(s), 3831
rats, 3089, 3115, 3320, 3382, 3508, 4073, 4656, 5023
synaptosomal, 3360
synaptosomes, 3293
synthesis, 3359
uptake, 3293, 3970
dimethylheptylpyran (DMHP)
rats, 3115
hexahydrocannabinol (HHC)
mice, 3357
9-hydroxy-9-nor-hexahydrocannabinol
brain, 3353
mice, 3353
marihuana
aggressive behavior, 3063
DOPAMINE BETA-HYDROXYLASE
cannabis
humans, 4963
DOSAGE
delta-9-THC
operant behavior, 3296
rats, 3296
route of administration, 3296
DRIVING
cannabis
accidents, 5030
adverse effect(s), 3078, 4437
delta-9-THC
adverse effect(s), 3904
compared to:
alcohol, 3904

delta-9-THC (continued)
  humans, 3904
  hashish
    adverse effect(s), 4827
  marihuana, 4106, 4500
    adverse effect(s), 3152, 3240, 3247, 3741, 4107,
      4307, 4466, 4467, 4498, 4499, 4501, 4632,
      4776, 5027
    beneficial effect(s), 4307
    blood level(s), 4307
    compared to:
      alcohol, 3879, 4502
      barbiturate(s), 3879
      LSD, 3879
    humans, 4107, 4776, 5291
    students, 3152, 3879
  review
    adverse effect(s), 4499
DRUG ABUSE
  cannabis
    adverse effect(s), 4100
    biochemical effect(s), 5514
    psychological aspects, 5514
  drug interactions
    alcohol, 4900
  hashish, 3175
  marihuana, 3148, 3175, 3875
    adolescent(s), 5493
    alcohol, 5493
    children, 5493
    education, 4491
    legal aspects, 3081, 3101
    medical aspects, 3081
    prisoners, 4368
    problems, 4810
    sociological aspects, 3081
    South Africa, 3851
    tolerance, 5493
DRUG ABUSE PREVENTION
  marihuana
    effectiveness, 3600
    high school, 3600
    humans, 3278
DRUG ABUSE RESEARCH
  marihuana
    government programs and funding, 3656
DRUG AVAILABILITY
  cannabinoid(s)
    urine, 5496
  marihuana use, 5530
DRUG DEPENDENCE
  cannabis, 3136
  marihuana
    Mexico, 4917
DRUG DISCRIMINATION
  delta-8-THC
    ditran, 4061
    phencyclidine, 4061
  delta-9-THC
    alcohol, 3295, 4057
    amphetamine, 3414, 3433, 3965, 4057
    apomorphine, 3414, 3433
    bemegride, 4057
    cannabidiol (CBD), 3414, 3965, 4059, 5180, 5181
    cannabinol (CBN), 3414, 3965, 4059, 5180, 5181

delta-9-THC (continued)
    chlordiazepoxide, 3295
    chlorpromazine, 3414, 3433
    delta-8-THC, 3295, 4059
    derivatives, 3753
    DH-524, 4057
    diazepam, 3433
    ditran, 3965, 4061
    ethanol, 3414
    gerbils, 4060
    harmaline, 3433
    harmine, 3433
    hexahydrocannabinol (HHC), 5180, 5181
    11-hydroxy-delta-8-THC, 3295
    11-hydroxy-delta-9-THC, 5180, 5181
    LSD-25, 3433, 3965
    mescaline, 3433
    metabolites, 3753
    morphine, 3096, 3433
    nabilone (Lilly compound no. 109514), 5180,
      5181
    pentobarbital, 3295, 3414, 3433, 3965, 4060
    phencyclidine, 4061
    pigeon(s), 3965, 4059
    psilocin, 3433
    psilocybin, 3433, 3869
    psychotropic drugs, 3965
    rats, 3295, 3869, 4062, 4063
DRUG EFFECTS
  marihuana
    culture, 3669
    Jamaica, 3669
    U.S.A., 3669
DRUG INFORMATION CENTER
  marihuana
    Canada, 3484
DRUG INTERACTIONS
  cannabichromene (CBC)
    delta-9-THC, 5531
  cannabidiol (CBD)
    alcohol, 5309, 5350
    aminopyrine, 3067
    amphetamine, 3067
    anesthetic(s), 3784
    anti-convulsant(s), 3514
    barbiturate(s), 4918
    cannabinol (CBN), 5001, 5569
    delta-9-THC, 3384, 3473, 3573, 3576, 3982, 3985,
      4248, 4326, 5001
    ethanol, 3067, 4326, 4863
    ether, 4349
    ethosuximide, 3518
    follicle stimulating hormone (FSH), 5419
    hexabarbital, 3067, 4033, 4326
    luteinizing hormone (LH), 5419
    methaqualone, 4988
    morphine, 3067, 3980
    naloxone, 3980
    neurotransmitters, 4816
    pentobarbital, 3067
    phencyclidine, 4987
    phenobarbital, 3473
    secobarbital, 3574, 3575, 4248
  cannabinoid(s), 3732

DRUG INTERACTIONS (continued)

cannabinol (CBN)
  aminopyrine, 3067
  amphetamine, 3067
  anesthetic(s), 3784
  anti-convulsant(s), 3514
  bacterial lipopolysaccharide, 4511
  barbiturate(s), 4918
  cannabidiol (CBD), 5001
  delta-9-THC, 3985, 4412, 4515, 5001
  ethanol, 3067
  ether, 4349
  gonadotropins, 5544
  hexabarbital, 3067
  lipopolysaccharides, 4512
  morphine, 3067
  pentobarbital, 3067

cannabis
  alcohol, 4331
  aminopyrine, 3067
  amphetamine, 3067, 3839, 4479
  atropine, 5498
  copper, 4876
  estradiol, 3460, 3462
  ethanol, 3067
  hexabarbital, 3067
  LSD-25, 4479
  morphine, 3067
  pentobarbital, 3067, 4479
  physostigmine, 5498
  reserpine, 4479
  review, 5340
  syntostigmine, 4542

cannabis extract
  estradiol, 3463
  serotonin (5-hydroxytryptamine), 5255

Cannabis indica
  aspirin, 4474
  diphenylhydantoin, 4474
  pentazocine, 4474
  pethidine, 4474

cannabis resin
  chlorpromazine, 4872
  morphine, 5398
  reserpine, 4872

delta-7-THC
  delta-9-THC, 5313

delta-8-THC
  amphetamine, 4160
  atropine, 4160
  bacterial lipopolysaccharide, 4511
  barbiturate(s), 4918
  hydrocortisone, 5223
  lipopolysaccharides, 4512
  lithium, 4817
  pentobarbital, 4160
  steroids, 5329

delta-9-THC
  acetylcholine (ACh), 3765
  alcohol, 3472, 3994, 4107, 4199, 4677, 5308, 5354, 5575
  American Indian(s), 5092
  aminopyrine, 3067
  amphetamine, 3067, 3361, 3756, 3950, 4106, 4107, 4336, 4859, 4860, 4918, 5429

delta-9-THC (continued)
  anesthetic(s), 3784, 3896, 4048, 4918, 5267
  anti-convulsant(s), 3513, 3514
  anti-histaminic, 5091
  anti-inflammatory activity, 5380
  anti-Parkinsonian drug(s), 5091
  antidepressant, 5091, 5092
  antihistamine(s), 5092
  antipyrene, 3316
  apomorphine, 4220, 4830, 5092, 5429
  arecoline, 4095
  aspirin, 4671
  atropine, 3227, 3317, 3319, 3653, 3876, 5092, 5302, 5310
  atropinemethylbromide, 4415
  bacterial lipopolysaccharide, 4511
  barbiturate(s), 4860, 4918
  binding, 5564
  caffeine, 3517, 4220, 4671
  calcium chloride, 3890
  cannabidiol (CBD), 3384, 3473, 3513, 3571, 3573, 3576, 3732, 3982, 3985, 3998, 4059, 4106, 4107, 4248, 4266, 4324, 4326, 4607, 4862, 5001, 5035, 5058, 5354, 5429, 5569
  cannabigerol (CBG), 4862
  cannabinoid(s), 3994
  cannabinol (CBN), 3732, 3985, 3998, 4059, 4106, 4107, 4149, 4412, 4515, 4862, 5001, 5002, 5058, 5354, 5569
  carbachol, 3653, 5372
  chlordiazepoxide, 4671, 4677, 5634
  chlorpromazine, 4872
  clomipramine, 3726, 5022
  cocaine, 3517, 4024, 4220, 4671, 4678
  corticosterones, 4282
  d-amphetamines, 3697, 4678
  delta-8-THC, 4059
  depressant, 5541
  desmethylimipramine, 3668, 4671
  diazepam, 4915, 5354
  diphenylhydantoin, 4671
  L-dopa, 5092
  endotoxin, 4385
  estradiol, 4567
  estrogen, 4588, 5582, 5593
  ethanol, 3067, 3316, 3471, 3696, 4282, 4326, 4858, 4863, 4940, 4941, 4942
  ether, 4349
  follicle stimulating hormone (FSH), 5419
  gonadotropins, 5297, 5544
  haloperidol, 5634
  hexabarbital, 3067, 4326
  humans, 3571, 5310
  hydrocortisone, 4274, 5223, 5272
  6-hydroxy-dopamine, 3668
  isoprenaline, 3227
  isoproterenol, 5270
  lipopolysaccharides, 4512
  local anesthetics, 3876
  LSD, 4478, 4671
  luteinizing hormone (LH), 5419
  mescaline, 4860
  methadone, 5360
  methamphetamine, 3515, 3517, 3698, 3700, 3756, 4220, 4671

delta-9-THC (continued)
  methaqualone, 4671, 4988
  3-methylcolanthrene, 3777
  mice, 5299
  monkeys, 5294, 5297
  morphine, 3067, 3352, 3765, 3980, 4860, 5299
  naloxone, 3609, 3765, 3980, 5569, 5634
  neuroleptic drugs, 5092
  neurotransmitters, 4816
  nicotine, 3128, 3133, 4095, 4414, 4671, 4678
  oral administration, 3777
  other drugs, 3994
  oxymorphone, 4915
  papaverine, 3861
  penicillin G, 4218
  pentobarbital, 3067, 3316, 4045, 4051, 4330, 4915, 5445
  phencyclidine, 4024, 4514, 4671, 4672, 4673, 4987
  phenobarbital, 3473, 3913, 4024, 4359, 4361, 4362, 4478, 4671, 4677
  phenoxybenzamine, 3862
  phentolamine, 3862, 4053, 4289
  phenylephrine, 3227
  2-phenylethylamine, 5124
  physostigmine, 4095, 4106, 4107, 4503
  pilocarpine, 4520
  probenecid, 4819
  progesterone, 4588
  propranolol, 3317, 3319, 3862, 3930, 5270, 5302, 5310
  prostaglandins, 3862, 4039
  rats, 5575
  reserpine, 3609, 3986, 4079, 4082, 4478, 4872
  review, 4531
  secobarbital, 4106, 4248
  serotonin (5-hydroxytryptamine), 5092
  SKF-525A, 3913, 4359, 4361, 4362, 4860, 4862
  sodium chloride, 3890
  solvents, 5564
  sotalol, 3862
  steroids, 3780, 5329
  stimulants, 3511, 5541
  thyroid release hormone, 5294
  tolbutamide, 4671
  verapamil, 3861
  vitamins, 5400
hashish
  phenitrone, 4939
  sociological interaction, 5435
  tobacco, 5599
marihuana
  alcohol, 3241, 4992, 5493, 5529
  amphetamine, 3789, 5157
  anesthetic(s), 3675
  atropine, 4005
  disulfiram, 4730
  dopamine (DA), 4516
  epinephrine, 4005
  haloperidol, 3052
  nicotine, 4414
  norepinephrine (NE), 4516
  norethynodiel, 4617
  paraquat, 5284
  penicillin, 3895

marihuana (continued)
  propranolol, 5108
  review, 4663, 5589
  secobarbital, 3572, 4248
  serotonin (5-hydroxytryptamine), 4516
  sociological interaction, 5435
  theophylline, 4116
  tobacco, 5493, 5529
marihuana extract
  cannabidiol (CBD), 4517
marihuana smoke
  alcohol, 5303
  delta-9-THC, 5390
  methaqualone, 5633
  vitamins, 5431
nabilone (Lilly compound no. 109514)
  ethanol, 4940
neurophysiology
  naloxone, 4316
SP-111
  neurotransmitters, 4816
tetrahydrocannabinol (THC)
  morphine, 5460
  naloxone, 5460
DRUG METABOLISM
  delta-8-THC, 3177
  delta-9-THC, 3177
DRUG USE
  cannabis
    history, 4531
    Indian Hemp Commission Report, 4531
    La Guardia Report, 4531
    National Commission on Marihuana, 4531
    United Nations Narcotics Commisssion, 4531
  Costa Rica, 3494
  marihuana
    adolescent(s), 5493
    behavior, 5493
    detection, 5493
    environmental conditions, 4001
    habituation, 3716
    psychosis, 3188
    punishment, 5493
    related to
      alcohol, 5037, 5038
      coffee, 5037, 5038
      smoking, 5037, 5038
    research, 3655
    students, 4766, 4891, 5056
    Switzerland, 4855, 4856
DRUG VEHICLE
  delta-9-THC
    behavioral effect(s), 4945
DRUGS OF ABUSE
  analysis
    detection, 3064
    identification, 3064
DUQUENOIS TEST
  Cannabis sativa
    identification, 4230

E

ECHOCARDIOGRAM
  delta-9-THC
    humans, 4129
ECOLOGICAL FACTORS
  cannabis
    review, 3486
ECOLOGY
  Cannabis sativa, 3900
ECONOMIC BENEFITS
  marihuana, 3791
EDUCATION
  cannabis
    public health, 4531
  marihuana
    drug abuse, 4491
    drug use, 4764
    students, 4764
EFFLUX
  delta-9-THC
    salivary glands, 4320
ELECTRICAL STIMULATION
  delta-9-THC
    rats, 5541
ELECTROCARDIOGRAM (EKG)
  Cannabis sativa
    dogs, 5188
  delta-9-THC
    humans, 4129
ELECTROENCEPHALOGRAM (EEG)
  cannabidiol, (CBD), 3718, 4918
  cannabinol (CBN), 4918
  cannabis, 3087
    chronic use, 3738, 4172
    humans, 3097, 3845, 4172, 4280, 4963
  delta-8-THC, 4918
    cortex, 5208
    hippocampus, 5208
    rabbit(s), 5208
  delta-9-THC, 3718, 4918
    amygdala, 3954
    audition, 5427
    behavioral effect(s), 3201, 3516
    cats, 3201, 3730
    compared to:
      alcohol, 4754
    evoked potentials, 5427
    hallucinations, 4188, 4189, 4192
    hippocampus, 3954
    humans, 3250, 3722, 3730, 3740, 4106, 4188,
      4189, 4192, 4754, 5302, 5378, 5427
    interaction with
      arecoline, 4095
      caffeine, 4220
      cocaine, 4220
      methamphetamine, 4220
      nicotine, 4095
      physostigmine, 4095
    intravenous administration, 3953
    monkeys, 3046, 3917, 3953, 3954
    rabbit(s), 3516, 3517, 4094, 4095, 4220, 4386
    rats, 4373, 5382
    REM sleep, 3723
    review, 5378

delta-9-THC (continued)
    septal region, 3954
    sleep, 3046
    tolerance, 4386
  delta-9-tetrahydrocannabivarol
    interaction with
      apomorphine, 4220
  electroencephalogram (EEG)
    marihuana extract
      humans, 3722
  ganja
    humans, 4762
  hashish
    chronic use, 4966
    hallucinations, 3086
    humans, 3086, 3129, 4827, 4966
  marihuana, 4109
    hallucinations, 4191
    humans, 3239, 3901, 4106, 4107, 4191, 4279
    inhalation, 3953
    monkeys, 3953
    review, 5489
  marihuana extract
    humans, 3722
  marihuana smoke
    humans, 5136
  tetrahydrocannabinol (THC)
    hallucinations, 4190
    humans, 4190
EEG CHANGES
  cannabinoid(s)
    limbic, 5504
  cannabis
    behavioral effect(s), 3769
ELECTROLYTES
  delta-9-THC
    blood level(s), 4027
ELECTRON TRANSPORT SYSTEM
  delta-9-THC
    brain, 3300
    in vitro, 3300
    mitochondria, 3300
ELECTROPHYSIOLOGY
  cannabinoid(s)
    anti-convulsant activity, 5458
  delta-9-THC
    animals, 4270
    brain, 4270
    hippocampus, 5121
    humans, 4270
EMESIS
  delta-9-THC
    dogs, 4830
EMIT (HOMOGENOUS ENZYME IMMUNOASSAY)
  cannabinoid(s)
    detection, 5565
    metabolites, 5565
EMOTIONAL ASPECTS
  delta-9-THC
    humans, 4454
  marihuana
    motivation of use, 5566
    students, 5566
  marihuana smoke
    humans, 5348

EMPLOYMENT
  marihuana
    use, 5377
ENDOCRINE EFFECTS
  cannabidiol (CBD)
    follicle stimulating hormone (FSH), 3327
    luteinizing hormone (LH), 3327
    monkeys, 3327
  cannabinol (CBN)
    follicle stimulating hormone (FSH), 5359
    luteinizing hormone (LH), 5359
    mice, 3568, 5359
    testosterone, 3568, 5359
  cannabis
    follicle stimulating hormone (FSH), 4522
    luteinizing hormone (LH), 4522
    testosterone, 4727
  cannabis extract
    chronic administration, 3621
    estradiol, 3462
    estrogen, 3621
    gerbils, 3621
    mice, 3624
    testosterone, 3624
  delta-8-THC
    adrenocorticotropic hormone (ACTH), 4340
    corticosterones, 4340
    rabbit(s), 4340
    rats, 4340
  delta-9-THC
    adrenocorticotropic hormone (ACTH), 3110, 4340
    chronic administration, 3318
    corticosterones, 3342, 3507, 4340, 4558
    Costa Rica, 3318
    estradiol
      receptor binding, 4699
    estrogen, 4558, 4896
    follicle stimulating hormone (FSH), 3327, 3508, 3694, 3915, 4898, 5334, 5359, 5581
    growth hormone, 3110, 3318, 3507, 3508, 3694
    humans, 3318, 4106, 4107, 4247
    hypothalamic pituitary function, 4998
    interaction with
      insulin, 3318
    luteinizing hormone (LH), 3325, 3326, 3327, 3464, 3508, 3694, 4898, 4899, 5334, 5359, 5581
    mice, 3568, 4689, 5359
    monkeys, 3234, 3325, 3326, 3327, 4782, 4896, 4898, 4899, 5581
    ovariectomy, 4898
    prolactin, 3396, 3397, 3464, 3507, 4247, 5294, 5334
    prolactin levels, 4689
    rabbit(s), 4340
    rats, 3110, 3342, 3396, 3387, 3508, 3694, 4340, 4998, 5334
    review, 4737, 5294
    testosterone, 3568, 3915, 4558, 4782, 4899, 5359
    testosterone levels, 4998
  dimethylheptylpyran (DMHP)
    adrenocorticotropic hormone (ACTH), 4340
    corticosterones, 4340
    rabbit(s), 4340
    rats, 4340

ENDOCRINE EFFECTS (continued)
  ganja
    humans, 4762
    steroids, 4762
    thyroid, 4762
  hashish
    adrenal function, 4292
    corticosterones, 4291
    pituitary function, 4292
    rats, 4291
  11-hydroxy-delta-9-THC
    humans, 4247
    prolactin, 4247
  marihuana, 3215
    adverse effect(s), 4776
    chronic use, 3499
    estrogen, 4621
    follicle stimulating hormone (FSH), 3549, 3956, 3957
    gynecomastia, 3241
    humans, 3239, 3499, 3956, 3957, 4106, 4107, 4177, 4429, 4430, 4432, 4433, 4725, 4776, 4787
    luteinizing hormone (LH), 3499, 3549, 3956, 3957, 4107, 4430
    monkeys, 3234
    review, 4737, 5551
    testosterone, 3239, 3549, 3774, 3957, 4107, 4177, 4179, 4429, 4430, 4432, 4433, 4725, 4787
    testosterone levels, 3241, 3499
  marihuana extract
    adrenal cortex, 3351
    corticosterones, 3351
    estrogen, 3351
    hypothalamic pituitary function, 3351
    luteinizing hormone (LH), 3351
    prolactin, 3351
    review, 3351
    testosterone, 3351
  marihuana smoke
    cortisol, 4178
    follicle stimulating hormone (FSH), 4178
    humans, 4178
    luteinizing hormone (LH), 4178
    testosterone, 4178
  tetrahydrocannabinol (THC)
    follicle stimulating hormone (FSH), 4897
    luteinizing hormone (LH), 4897
    monkeys, 4897
ENDOCRINE SYSTEM
  marihuana
    adverse effect(s), 3240, 3347, 4632
    gynecomastia, 3347
ENVIRONMENT
  cannabis
    cultivation, 3763
  Cannabis sativa
    chemotype, 3369
  marihuana
    motivation of use, 5566
    students, 5566
ENVIRONMENTAL CONDITONS
  cannabis
    subjective effects, 3929

ENVIRONMENTAL CONDITIONS (continued)
Cannabis sativa
growth, 4840, 4887
leaves, 4840
delta-9-THC
body temperature, 5536
mice, 5536
marihuana
euphoria, 4641, 4718
subjective effects, 4092
ENZYME ACTIVITY
hashish
brain, 5397
liver, 5397
rabbit(s), 5397
serum, 5397
ENZYME INDUCTION
delta-8-THC
glucagon, 5224
hydrocortisone, 5224
mice, 5223, 5224, 5225
rats, 5224
RNA polymerase, 5225
trytophan, 5224
tyrosine aminotransferase, 5225
delta-9-THC
glucagon, 5224
hydrocortisone, 5224
liver, 3780, 5272
mechanism of action, 5272
mice, 5223, 5224, 5225, 5272
rats, 3780, 5224
RNA polymerase, 5225
trytophan, 5224
tyrosine aminotransferase, 5225, 5272
ENZYMES
Cannabis sativa
constituents of, 5079
EPIDEMIOLOGICAL STUDY
marihuana
adverse effect(s), 5551
amotivational syndrome, 5551
driving, 5551
family relationships, 5551
sexual attitudes, 5551
EPILEPSY
cannabidiol (CBD), 3718
animals, 4388
cats, 3719
dogs, 3719, 5179
rats, 5343
therapy, 4408, 4528
delta-9-THC, 3718
animals, 4388
cats, 3719
chickens, 4072
dogs, 3719, 5179
rats, 5343
11-hydroxy-delta-9-THC
rats, 5343
marihuana
animals, 4388
therapy, 3497

EPIMERIZATION
cannabinoid(s)
mechanism, 5097
8,9-EPOXYHEXAHYDROCANNABINOL
immunology
cell-mediated immunity, 4170
humoral immunity, 4170
immunoglobulins, 5263
9-ALPHA, 10-ALPHA-EPOXYHEXAHYDRO-CANNABI-NOL
biochemical effect(s)
metabolites, 5534
chemical aspects
transformation, 4636
pharmacological aspects
distribution, 5534
excretion, 5534
toxicology
mutagenesis, 5402
ERADICATION
Cannabis sativa
Canada, 3150
2,4-dichlorophenoxyacetic acid (2,4-D), 3150
hemp
Burma, 3270
ESSENTIAL OILS
cannabis
constituents of, 4411
Cannabis sativa
alkane(s), 3962
analysis, 3960
anti-bacterial activity, 3761
constituents of, 3960, 3963, 4345, 4961
geographical origin, 3581
Mexico, 3581
terpenes, 3053, 3961
pharmacological aspects
prostaglandin synthesis, 3421
ESTER
cannabidiolic acid
analysis, 3413
decarboxylation, 3413
synthesis, 3413
delta-9-THC oic acid A & B
analysis, 3413
decarboxylation, 3413
synthesis, 3413
dimethylheptylpyran (DMHP)
structure-activity relationships, 4603
ESTRADIOL
delta-9-THC
binding, 4567
mice, 4567
receptor binding, 4699
ESTROGEN
cannabis extract
rats, 4390, 4393
delta-9-THC
monkeys, 4896
rats, 3461, 4390, 4393, 4558
uterus, 3461
ESTROGEN-RECEPTOR BINDING
delta-9-THC
in vitro, 4848

548

ESTROGEN-RECEPTOR BINDING (continued)
  11-hydroxy-delta-9-THC
    in vitro, 4848
ESTROGENIC ACTIVITY
  delta-9-THC, 4568, 4927
    mice, 5620
    monkeys, 5582
    rats, 4928, 4929
    receptor binding, 5582
    uterus, 4929
ESTRUS CYCLE
  delta-9-THC
    mice, 4184
    rats, 5392
  marihuana extract
    mice, 4184
    rats, 5392
EUPHORIA
  cannabis
    humans, 3529
  Cannabis sativa
    constituents of 3683
    isolation, 3683
  delta-9-THC
    cancer, 3430
    compared to:
      LSD, 3098
    humans, 3075, 3098, 3430, 4679
  marihuana
    aversive stimulus, 4644
    blood pressure, 4643
    environmental conditions, 4641
    heart rate, 4642, 4643, 4644
    humans, 4641, 4642, 4643, 4644, 4749, 4993
    mood, 4749
    stress, 4641
  marihuana smoke
    inhalation, 5238
EVOKED POTENTIALS
  cannabidiol (CBD)
    rats, 5074
  delta-9-THC
    audition, 5427
    cats, 3147
    cerebral cortex, 3380
    compared to:
      pentobarbital, 3380
    conditioned behavior, 3380
    dose dependent, 5427
    humans, 5427
    monkeys, 3380
    rats, 5074
    reaction time, 5427
  marihuana
    humans, 4180
EXCRETION
  cannabinoid(s)
    half-life, 5621
    humans, 5621
    intravenous administration, 5621
  cannabinol (CBN), 4918
  delta-9-THC, 4164, 4522, 4918
    animals, 4246
    biliary, 4860
    bile, 4020, 4861

delta-9-THC (continued)
    dogs, 3801, 4020
    feces, 3312, 3467, 4020
    humans, 4246
    interaction with
      cannabidiol (CBD), 4862
      cannabigerol (CBG), 4862
      cannabinol (CBN), 4862
      SKF-525A, 4862
    metabolites, 3312, 3467, 4246, 4861
    milk, 3467
    monkeys, 3312, 3467, 3853
    pharmacokinetics, 5394
    rats, 4676, 4860, 4862
    review, 5269
    urine, 3312, 3467, 3853
  9-alpha, 10-alpha-epoxyhexahydrocannabinol
    rats, 5534
  marihuana smoke
    feces, 4254
    humans, 4254
    urine, 4254
  nabilone (Lilly compound no. 109514)
    humans, 4759
    lung(s), 4759
    morphine withdrawal, 4759
    urine, 4759
EXERCISE
  marihuana
    cardiovascular effects, 4831
    heart rate, 5017
    humans, 4831, 5298
    performance, 5017
    respiratory effects, 4831
EXTRACTIONS
  cannabis resin
    cannabinoid(s), 4912
  delta-9-THC
    biological fluid(s), 4802
    cannabis plant, 5320
    solvent systems, 4802
  tetrahydrocannabivarolic acids
    cannabis plant, 5320
EYES
  ABBOTT-40656
    rabbit(s), 3640
  ABBOTT-41988
    toxicity, 5043
  ABBOTT-43981
    rabbit(s), 3665
  cannabinoid(s)
    chronic effects, 3865
    rabbit(s), 3865
  cannabis, 3588
    adverse effect(s), 5128
    humans, 5128
  delta-9-THC, 3588
    blood flow, 3867
    humans, 3250, 3522, 3546, 3855, 4110
    intraocular pressure (IOP), 3859
    rabbit(s), 3857, 3858, 3859, 3860, 3867
  hashish
    adverse effect(s), 5467
  marihuana
    adverse effect(s), 4776

marihuana (continued)
    humans, 3493, 3503, 3747, 4110, 4776
    intraocular pressure (IOP), 3503
    rabbit(s), 3966
    visual tracking, 3747
marihuana smoke
    humans, 3746
SP-1
    chronic effects, 3865
    monkeys, 3863
    rabbit(s), 3857, 3858, 3863, 3865
SP-106
    chronic effects, 3865
    monkeys, 3863
    rabbit(s), 3857, 3858, 3863, 3865
SP-111A
    intraocular pressure (IOP), 3859
    rabbit(s), 3859
SP-204
    chronic effects, 3865
    monkeys, 3863
    rabbit(s), 3863, 3865
synthetic cannabinoids
    rabbit(s), 3640
EXTRAPYRAMIDAL SYSTEM
    Cannabis sativa
        humans, 4440
    delta-9-THC
        acetylcholine (ACh), 3838
        catalepsy, 3840
        dopamine (DA), 3838, 3841
        rats, 3840, 3841
    11-hydroxy-delta-9-THC
        catalepsy, 3840
        rats, 3840

F

F$_2$ GENERATION
    marihuana smoke
        body weight, 5390
        neo-natal development, 5390
FACTORS INFLUENCING USE
    cannabis
        Egypt, 4936
    marihuana, 3106, 3138, 4165, 4954, 5177
        adolescent(s), 3400
        Costa Rica, 3455
        Egypt, 4938
        family relationships, 3157
        humans, 3275, 4953
        mood, 3275
        sex differences, 4666
        sociological aspects, 3057
        students, 3060, 3278, 3418, 3601, 3649, 3972, 4175, 4901
        tolerance, 3275
        youths, 3082, 3157, 4065, 4606
FALSE HORMONE
    delta-9-THC, 3156
FAMILY RELATIONSHIPS
    marihuana
        adolescent(s), 5493
        drug abuse, 5493
    marihuana use, 5530

FAST BLUE B SALT
    marihuana
        detection, 5476
FATTY ACIDS
    Cannabis sativa
        constituents of, 5079
    delta-9-THC
        brain stem, 4878
        cortex, 4878
        hypothalamus, 4878
        mice, 4347
FECES
    cannabis
        humans, 5324
FEEDING
    9-Aza-cannabinol
        sheep, 5491
    cannabis resin
        mice, 3560
    delta-9-THC
        sheep, 5491
        stereospecificity, 5491
FERTILITY
    delta-9-THC
        rats, 5390
    marihuana smoke
        rats, 5390
FETAL DEVELOPMENT
    delta-9-THC
        animals, 3699
        mice, 4184
        rats, 4687
        review, 3699
    marihuana
        animals, 3699
        review, 3699
    marihuana extract
        mice, 4184
FETUS
    delta-9-THC
        body weight, 5585
        lethality, 5585
        rabbit(s), 5585
    marihuana smoke
        rats, 5389
FLASH ANALYSIS
    delta-9-THC
        rats, 4676
FLASHBACKS
    cannabis
        dosage, 3667
        environmental conditions, 3667
        personality, 3667
    marihuana
        humans, 3402, 4444, 4957
FLAVONDIGLYCOSIDES
    Cannabis sativa
        constituents of, 4595, 4598, 5079
        leaves, 4598
        pollen, 4595
FLAVONOIDS
    cannabis
        constituents of, 3255, 3536
    Cannabis sativa
        constituents of, 4599
        variability, 5346

FLOWERS
   Cannabis sativa
      cannabinoid content, 3073
      geographical origin, 3073
FLOWERING
   cannabis, 3486
FLUORESCENCE
   cannabidiol (CBD), 3617
   cannabinol (CBN), 3617
   delta-9-THC, 3617
FLUOROMETRY
   cannabinoid(s), 4961
FLYING PERFORMANCE
   marihuana
      adverse effect(s), 3240, 4632
      humans, 3346
   marihuana smoke
      performance, 4054, 4055
FOLKLORE
   marihuana
      India, 4839, 4841
FOLLICLE STIMULATING HORMONE (FSH)
   cannabidiol (CBD)
      monkeys, 3327
   cannabinol (CBN)
      mice, 3569, 3570
   delta-9-THC
      blood level(s), 4898
      mice, 3569, 3570
      monkeys, 3327, 4898
      ovariectomy, 4898
      plasma levels, 3694
      rats, 3508, 3694, 3915
   marihuana
      blood level(s), 4016
      humans, 3549, 3956, 3957, 4016
      plasma levels, 3549, 3957
   marihuana smoke
      humans, 4178
      plasma levels, 4178
   tetrahydrocannabinol (THC)
      monkeys, 4897
FOOD DEPRIVATION
   cannabidiol (CBD)
      rats, 4517
   marihuana extract
      rats, 4517
FOOD INTAKE
   cannabidiol (CBD), 4918
      rats, 4923
   cannabinoid(s)
      animals, 3732
   9-Aza-cannabinol
      sheep, 5117, 5618
   cannabinol (CBN), 4918
      rats, 4923
   delta-8-THC, 4918
      acute effect(s), 4070
      animals, 3732
      chronic effects, 4070
      rats, 4070
   delta-9-THC
      acute administration, 3642
      acute effect(s), 4070
      animals, 3732

delta-9-THC (continued)
      biogenic amine(s), 3405
      chronic administration, 3642
      chronic effects, 4070
      rats, 3405, 3406, 3642, 3643, 4070, 4923, 5022, 5282, 5501
      route of administration, 5282, 5501
      tolerance, 5501
      vehicle of administration, 5501
   marihuana
      humans, 3789
      interaction with
         amphetamine, 3789
      rats, 4738
   marihuana smoke
      chronic effects, 4026, 4029
      dogs, 4026, 4029
      humans, 3868
   SP-1
      rats, 5042
   SP-80
      rats, 5042
   SP-106
      rats, 5042
FOREARM BLOOD FLOW
   marihuana
      humans, 4537
      interaction with
         stress, 4537
FORENSIC ASPECTS
   cannabinoid(s)
      biological fluid(s), 5496
      cannabis plant, 5483
      detection, 5477
      HPLC/MS, 5477
      nabilone (Lilly compound no. 109514), 5352
   cannabis
      color tests, 4411
      detection, 4411
      species
         classification, 4298, 4299
   delta-9-THC
      analysis, 5539
      blood, 5539
      detection, 5562
      exercise, 5615
      HPLC/MS, 5615
      humans, 5615
      methods, 5562
   marihuana
      chemical tests, 5523
      detection, 3241, 4308
FRAGMENTATION
   cannabinoid(s)
      mechanism, 5371
FREE FATTY ACIDS
   delta-9-THC
      central nervous system mechanism, 4348
      mice, 4348
      plasma levels, 4348
FREE RADICAL IMMUNOASSAY
   delta-8-THC
      urine, 3432
FUNGAL GROWTH
   cannabis
      aflatoxin, 4286

FUNGAL INFECTION
marihuana
humans, 3482
FUNGUS
Cannabis sativa
seeds, 3279
FURFURAL TEST
Cannabis sativa
identification, 4230

G

GALACTOSAMINE
Cannabis sativa
constituents of, 5219
GAMMA-AMINO-BUTYRIC ACID (GABA)
cannabidiol (CBD)
brain levels, 4715
mice, 3970
rats, 4715
uptake, 3970
delta-8-THC
ataxia, 3836
cerebellum, 3836
rats, 3836
delta-9-THC
analog(s)
brain, 3293
synaptosomes, 3293
uptake, 3293
brain, 3293
brain levels, 4715
catalepsy, 3666
cerebellum, 3666
mice, 3970
rats, 3666, 4715
synaptosomes, 3293
uptake, 3293, 3970
hashish
rats, 4339
GAMMA IRRADIATION
cannabis
morphological variations, 4844
seeds, 4844
GANGLIONIC TRANSMISSION
cannabidiol (CBD)
rats, 3752
tolerance, 3752
cannabinol (CBN)
rats, 3752
delta-8-THC
rats, 3752
delta-9-THC
cats, 3147
11-hydroxy-delta-9-THC
rats, 3752
GANGLIOSIDE
delta-9-THC
mitochondria, 3809
synaptosomes, 3809
GANJA
analysis
cannabinoid content, 4762
botanical aspects
cannabinoid content, 4371

botanical aspects (continued)
fertilizer, 4371
harvest, 4371
chemical aspects
cannabinoid content, 4371
epidemiological study
attitudes of users, 4762
characteristics of users, 4762
patterns of use, 4762
history
rats, 4762
legal aspects
review, 4762
neurophysiology
electroencephalogram (EEG), 4762
patterns of use, 4724
pharmacological aspects
acute effect(s), 4762
clinical findings, 4762
hematology, 4762
respiratory effects, 4762
physiological effects
endocrine effects, 4762
psychological aspects
memory, 4762
motor coordination, 4762
perception, 4762
performance, 4762
personality, 4762
review
history, 4762
legal aspects, 4762
toxicology
chromosomes, 4762
GAS CHROMATOGRAPHY
delta-9-THC
humans, 5300
plasma levels, 5300
GAS LIQUID CHROMATOGRAPHY (GLC)
cannabinoid(s)
analysis, 5268, 5395
homologs, 3537
GASTRIC SECRETION
9-Aza-cannabinol
sheep, 5117
GASTRIC ULCERS
cancer
therapy, 4101
cannabis extract
rats, 3596
GASTROINTESTINAL EFFECTS
cannabinoid(s)
humans, 5340
9-Aza-cannabinol
action potential(s), 5461
contraction, 5461
sheep, 5461
stomach acids, 5461
delta-9-THC
mice, 4039
motility, 4039
prostaglandins, 4039
GASTROINTESTINAL TRACT
9-Aza-cannabinol
contractile force, 4154

9-Aza-cannabinol (continued)
   muscle, 4154
   sheep, 4154
  delta-9-THC
   nitrogen analogs, 4603
   rats, 4920
   review, 4603
   thio analogs, 4603
  marihuana
   adverse effect(s), 3494, 4527
   cats, 4414
   chronic use, 3494
   interaction with
   nicotine, 4414
GC/MS
  cannabinoid(s)
   analysis, 5384
   biological fluid(s), 5384, 5621, 5623
   biotransformation, 5422
   detection, 5623
   humans, 5623
   identification, 5422
   liver, 5422
   quantitative, 5422
  delta-9-THC
   analysis, 5411
   humans, 5411
   metabolites, 5411
   urine, 5411
  paraquat
   marihuana smoke, 5621
GENERAL INFORMATION
  cannabis
   adverse effect(s), 3926
   pharmacological aspects, 4805
  marihuana, 3659
   adverse effect(s), 3082, 4097, 4468
   humans, 3217
   physicians, 3657, 4097
GEOGRAPHICAL ORIGIN
  cannabis
   age, 3591
   analysis, 3992
   cannabinoid content, 3591, 4202, 5115, 5116
   cannabinoid(s), 5047
   constituents of, 4596
   Czechoslovakia, 4202
   detection, 3288
   high-pressure liquid chromatography (HPLC), 5191
   South Africa, 4202, 4596
   Spain, 5115
   storage, 3591
   Thailand, 4202
   Turkey, 4202
  cannabis plant
   alkaloid(s), 3685
  cannabis resin
   trace elements, 3964
  Cannabis sativa
   analysis, 3565
   Canada, 4974
   cannabinoid content, 3073, 3304, 3580, 3581, 3706, 4974
   constituents of, 4205
   England, 4974

Cannabis sativa (continued)
   essential oils, 3581
   France, 3580
   India, 3565
   inorganic elements, 3491
   Japan, 4846
   Mexico, 3580, 3581, 3706
   potency, 4961
   soil conditions, 3491
   South Africa, 4974
   Sweden, 4974
   trace elements, 4846
   Turkey, 3706
   U.S.A., 4974
  hashish
   potency, 4961
GESTATION, EFFECTS ON
  delta-9-THC
   rats, 3093
GLANDS
  Cannabis sativa
   ultrastructure, 3897
GLAUCOMA
  cannabidiol (CBD)
   therapy, 3856
  cannabinoid(s)
   potency, 5405
   review, 5413
   therapy, 3331
  Cannabis sativa
   humans, 5189
  delta-8-THC
   rabbit(s), 5249
  delta-9-THC
   blood pressure, 5355
   cardiovascular effects, 3213
   humans, 3213, 3251, 3534, 5355, 5414
   monkeys, 5414
   rabbit(s), 5414
   review, 4603, 5405, 5413
   therapy, 3235, 3521, 3534, 3856, 3864, 4408, 4528
  marihuana
   government programs and funding, 5286
   humans, 3251, 3533, 3967, 5289
   rabbit(s), 3966
   research, 5286
   review, 5405
   therapy, 3254, 3495, 3497, 3502, 3533, 3741, 3856, 3919, 4182, 5017
  marihuana smoke
   humans, 4287, 5414
  nabilone (Lilly compound no. 109514)
   humans, 5521, 5522
   rabbit(s), 5521, 5522
  synthetic cannabinoids
   therapy, 3331
GLUCOSE
  cannabidiol (CBD)
   blood, 5034
   rabbit(s), 5034
   rats, 5034
  Cannabis sativa
   baboons, 5281

GLUCOSE (continued)
  delta-9-THC
    blood, 5034
    dogs, 3594
    rabbit(s), 5034
    rats, 5034
GLUCOSE METABOLISM
  delta-9-THC
    in vitro, 5437
    rats, 4023
    testis(es), 4023, 5437
  marihuana
    humans, 4622
GLUCOSE TOLERANCE
  cannabis extract
    rabbit(s), 3470
BETA-GLUCURONIDASE
  delta-9-THC
    rats, 4811
    testis(es), 4811
GLUCURONIDES
  cannabidiol (CBD)
    characteristics, 4306
    mice, 3937, 3942
    synthesis, 4306
  cannabinol (CBN)
    characteristics, 4306
    mice, 3938, 3942
    rats, 3938
    synthesis, 4306
  delta-8-THC
    characteristics, 4306
    excretion, 5624
    hydrolysis, 5624
    mice, 3937, 3942
    rats, 5624
    synthesis, 4306, 5227, 5624
    toxicity, 5624
  delta-9-THC
    characteristics, 4306
    mice, 3937, 3942
    synthesis, 4306
  5-hydroxy-delta-9-THC
    synthesis, 4589
  11-hydroxy-delta-9-THC
    synthesis, 4589
GLUTAMATE
  cannabidiol (CBD)
    brain levels, 4715
    rats, 4715
  delta-9-THC
    brain levels, 4715
    rats, 4715
GLUTAMATE SYNTHETASE
  delta-9-THC
    microsomal, 4657
    mitochondrial, 4657
    synaptosomal, 4657
GAMMA-GLUTAMYL TRANSPEPTIDASE
  delta-9-THC
    rats, 4811
    testis(es), 4811
GLYCEROL
  delta-9-THC
    blood level(s), 4356

GLYCOGEN
  cannabis extract
    liver, 4930
    rats, 4930
GLYCOGEN LEVELS
  delta-9-THC
    in vitro, 3287
    liver, 3287
GLYCOPROTEIN
  cannabis
    constituents of, 3255
  Cannabis sativa
    constituents of, 3974, 3975, 3976, 5079, 5219
GLYCOSIDES
  Cannabis sativa
    constituents of, 4821
  chemical aspects
    isolation, 4821
    structure, 4821
  constituents of
    Cannabis sativa, 4822
GONADAL FUNCTION
  marihuana
    humans, 3957
GONADOTROPIC EFFECTS
  delta-9-THC
    mechanism of action, 4898
    monkeys, 4898, 5296
    rabbit(s), 5296
GONADOTROPINS
  cannabinoid(s)
    in vitro, 5443
    protein synthesis, 5443
    testosterone synthesis, 5443
  delta-9-THC
    follicle stimulating hormone (FSH), 5582
    hypothalamus, 5582
    luteinizing hormone (LH), 5582
    monkeys, 5582
    progesterone, 5582
GOVERNMENT PROGRAMS AND FUNDING
  marihuana, 3654
    National Institute on Drug Abuse (NIDA), 3656
    U.S.A., 5607
GRAFTING
  Cannabis sativa
    cannabinoid content, 3538
GROSS BEHAVIOR
  cannabidiol (CBD)
    derivatives, 3664
    dogs, 3664
  delta-8-THC
    derivatives, 3664
    dogs, 3664
  delta-9-THC
    chronic effects, 4684
    dogs, 3664
    intravenous administration, 3953
    mice, 4684
    monkeys, 3953
  hexahydrocannabinol (HHC)
    dogs, 3664
  marihuana
    inhalation, 3953
    monkeys, 3953

GROSS BEHAVIORAL CHANGE(S)
  delta-9-THC
    monkeys, 3954
  synthetic cannabinoids
    mice, 5162
GROUP INTERACTION
  marihuana
    humans, 4429
GROWTH
  Cannabis sativa
    environment, 4961
    environmental conditions, 4840
    herbicides, 4006
    nitrogen, 3490
    paraquat, 3492
    phosphorus, 3490
    potassium, 3490
    seeds, 4961
    species, 4961
    strain difference, 3959
  delta-9-THC
    chronic administration, 4744
    rats, 4744, 5501
    route of administration, 5501
    strain difference, 5501
    volvox, 5494
  marihuana
    rats, 4738
GROWTH HORMONE
  delta-9-THC
    humans, 3318
    interaction with
      insulin, 3318
    plasma levels, 3507, 3694
    rats, 3110, 3507, 3508, 3694
    secretion, 3110
GROWTH PROFILE
  cannabichromene (CBC)
    rats, 5561
  cannabidiol (CBD)
    rats, 5561
  marihuana
    rats, 5561
    Turkey, 5561
GUINEA PIG ILEUM
  cannabidiol (CBD)
    acetylcholine (ACh), 4728
  cannabinol (CBN)
    acetylcholine (ACh), 4728
  delta-8-THC
    acetylcholine (ACh), 4728
  11-hydroxy-delta-8-THC
    acetylcholine (ACh), 4728
GYNECOMASTIA
  delta-9-THC
    rats, 3094
  marihuana
    estrogen, 4621
    humans, 3248, 4621
  marihuana smoke
    humans, 3457

H

HABITUATION
  marihuana
    humans, 3716
  marihuana use
    humans, 5259
HALF-LIFE
  delta-9-THC
    ant(s), 3782
    dogs, 4020
  nabilone (Lilly compound no. 109514)
    humans, 4759
HALLUCINATIONS
  delta-9-THC
    electroencephalogram (EEG), 4188, 4189, 4192
    humans, 3075, 3618, 4188, 4189, 4192
  hashish
    electroencephalogram (EEG), 3086
    humans, 3086
  marihuana
    electroencephalogram (EEG), 4191
    humans, 4191
    monkeys, 4064
  tetrahydrocannabinol (THC)
    electroencephalogram (EEG), 4190
    humans, 4190
HALLUCINOGENIC EFFECTS
  cannabis
    chronic effects, 3165
HALLUCINOGENS
  delta-9-THC, 4804
  marihuana
    monkeys, 4064
HALSTEAD TESTS
  cannabis
    humans, 3445
HARVEST
  cannabis, 3763
  Cannabis sativa, 4961
  hashish, 4961
HASHISH
  adverse effect(s)
    acute intoxication, 4096
    allergy, 3748
    chromosome damage, 4525
    chronic use, 3744, 4935
    eyes, 5467
    hepatitis, 3638
    rats, 3438
    review, 3169, 3176, 4525
  analysis, 3565
    cannabinoid(s), 4481, 5215
    delta-9-THC, 5358, 5552
    detection, 3892, 4506, 4955
    gas chromatography, 4003, 4481, 4506
    GC/MS, 4481
    geographical origin, 4003
    headspace volatiles, 4003
    microscopic examination, 4506
    street samples, 5552
    thin layer chromatography (TLC), 4481, 4506, 4955
    vapor phase, 3892

HASHISH (continued)
  antagonism
    phenitrone, 4939
  behavioral effect(s)
    aggressive behavior, 4402
    discriminative properties, 4203
    discriminative stimulus, 4204
    motor activity, 4402
  biochemical effect(s)
    ascorbic acid, 4291
    cells, 4970
    cholesterol, 4291
    chromosome damage, 4472
    enzyme activity, 5397
    monoamine oxidase (MAO), 5397
    phospholipids, 5453
  botanical aspects
    chromosome damage, 4120
    geographical origin, 4961
    harvest 4961
    mitosis, 4120
    potency, 4961
  cannabinoid(s)
    analysis, 5268
  chemical aspects
    constituents of, 3565, 5138
      alkaloid(s), 4770
      anhydrocannabisativine, 4770
      cannabicoumaronon, 3883
      cannabidiol (CBD), 4770
      cannabinol (CBN), 4770
      cannabisativine, 4770
      delta-8-THC, 4770
      delta-9-THC, 4770
      indoles, 4770
      review, 4770
      terpenes, 3892
    geographical origin, 3565
    sample variation, 5138
  cytogenic effects
    deoxyribonucleic acid (DNA), 5439
    macromolecular synthesis, 5439
    mitosis, 5439
    morphology, 5439
  epidemiological study
    characteristics of users, 3129, 3176, 3371, 4967
    compared to:
      methaqualone, 4721
    drug abuse, 3175
    market structure, 4931
    multiple drug use, 4721
    patterns of use, 3176, 3829, 4181, 4223, 4931
    progression to other drugs, 4721
    sociological aspects, 3371, 3829, 4931
  forensic aspects
    analysis
      headspace volatiles, 4003
    detection, 4506, 5061
    geographical origin, 5061
  general information
    driving, 4827
  history, 3169
    review, 3155, 3169, 3176
    use, 5563
  immunology
    lymphocytes, 4123, 4124

HASHISH (continued)
  legal aspects
    definition, 5408
  neuropharmacology
    electroencephalogram (EEG), 3129
  neurophysiology
    electroencephalogram (EEG), 3086, 3225, 4827
  pharmacological aspects
    adrenal function, 4292
    antagonism, 4939
    biogenic amine(s), 3225
    blood flow, 4275
    blood glucose, 4339
    body temperature, 4275
    brain, 3225
    brain levels, 4339
    cardiovascular effects, 4275, 4827, 5018
    clinical findings, 3155
    interaction with
      phenitrone, 4939
    leukocytes, 4193
    lipids, 4193
    neurologic function, 5018
    neurotransmitters
      gamma-amino-butyric acid (GABA), 4339
    phospholipids, 4193
    pituitary function, 4292
    pupil size, 4275
    respiratory effects, 4275
    review, 3155, 3176
    skin conductance, 4275
    sleep, 5018
    stress, 4292
  physiological effects
    adrenal function, 4291
    corticosterones, 4291
    endocrine effects, 4291, 4292
    hypothalamic pituitary function, 4291
    stress, 4291
  psychiatric aspects
    subjective effects, 5435
  psychological aspects
    attitudes of users, 4004
    chronic effects, 3744, 4935
    cognitive function, 3636
    compared to:
      alcohol, 4417
    coordination, 3635
    electroencephalogram(EEG), 4966
    hallucinations, 3086
    memory, 3635, 4417
    mood, 5018
    motor performance, 3636
    paranoia, 4417
    perception, 3636
    performance, 3635, 4967
    personality, 4966, 4967
    psychosis, 4966
    review, 3155
    social behavior, 4966
    subjective effects, 3169
    time estimation, 3635
    tracking, 4417
  review, 4525
    adverse effect(s), 3169, 3176
    chemical aspects, 4770

review (continued)
    clinical findings, 3155
    discriminative properties, 4203
    history, 3155, 3169, 3176
    pharmacological aspects, 3155, 3176
    psychological aspects, 3155
    sociological aspects, 3155
    therapeutic aspects, 4770
  sociological aspects
    compared to:
      ethanol, 5563
    drug interactions, 5435
    review, 3155
    social behavior, 3371, 4967
    use, 5563
  street samples, 3408
  therapeutic aspects, 4406
  toxicology
    blood cells, 4970
    chromosome damage, 4472
    chronic effects, 4935
    interaction with
      tobacco, 5599
    lactic dehydrogenase (LDH), 4339
    overdose, 3829
    respiratory effects, 5599
    SGOT (serum glutamic oxaloacetic transaminase), 4339
    sperms, 4970
HASHISH EXTRACT
  chemical aspects
    cannabinoid content, 4961
  neurochemical effects
    monoamine oxidase (MAO), 4806, 4807
  pharmacological aspects
    brain, 4806, 4807
    liver, 4806, 4807
HASHISH, RESIN, AND OILS
  street samples, 3408
HASHISH SMOKE
  chemical aspects
    compared to:
      tobacco, 5293
    pyrolytic products, 5293
  psychopharmacological aspects
    reaction time, 5293
HEAD-TWITCHING
  delta-9-THC
    mice, 4864
HEADACHE
  marihuana, 3505
HEADSPACE VOLATILES
  hashish
    analysis, 4003
    gas chromatography, 4003
  marihuana
    analysis, 4003
    gas chromatography, 4003
HEALTH HAZARDS
  marihuana
    humans, 5523
  marihuana use
    humans, 5468
HEARING
  marihuana
    humans, 4277

HEART
  cannabidiol(CBD)
    contractility, 4893, 4894
    heart rate, 4893, 4894
    in vitro, 4893, 4894
    rats, 4893, 4894
  cannabinol (CBN)
    contractility, 4893, 4894
    heart rate, 4894
    in vitro, 4893, 4894
    rats, 4893, 4894
  delta-8-THC
    contractility, 4893, 4894
    heart rate, 4893, 4894
    in vitro, 4893, 4894
    rats, 4893, 4894
  delta-9-THC
    adrenergic nervous system, 4273
    contractile force, 3850
    contractility, 4893, 4894
    enzyme activity, 5344
    glucose metabolism, 5344
    heart rate, 4893, 4894, 5344
    in vitro, 3850, 4273, 4893, 4894
    rats, 4893, 4894
  marihuana
    adverse effect(s), 5589
    chronic use, 3375
    dogs, 3375
    histological changes, 3375
HEART RATE
  cannabidiol (CBD)
    dogs, 3394
  cannabis
    humans, 4963
  Cannabis sativa
    dogs, 5188
  delta-8-THC
    dogs, 3387, 3388
    rats, 3983
    tolerance, 3983
  delta-9-THC
    adrenalectomy, 4274
    adrenergic nervous system, 4128
    aerosol, 4572
    analog(s), 4579
    cats, 3914, 4007, 4053, 4289
    central nervous system (CNS), 4053
    central nervous system mechanism, 3914, 4007
    chronic effects, 4052
    dogs, 3393, 4048, 4050, 4052, 5267
    humans, 3213, 3314, 3319, 3534, 3631, 3740, 3803, 3914, 4128, 4572, 5018, 5302, 5355
    mechanism of action, 5267
    rats, 4274, 4520, 4576, 4673, 4677, 4678, 5123
    subjective effects, 5302
  dimethylheptylpyram (DMHP)
    cats, 3914, 4007
    central nervous system mechanism, 3914, 4007
    humans, 3914
  hashish
    humans, 4827, 5018
  marihuana
    acute effect(s), 3762

marihuana (continued)
   chronic effects, 3762
   euphoria, 4643, 4644
   humans, 3273, 3533, 3762, 3812, 3902, 3903,
      4643, 4644, 4717, 4788, 5052, 5105, 5298,
      5505
   plasma levels
      tetrahydrocannabinol (THC), 4788
   subjective effects, 3762
   tolerance, 3273, 3812
marihuana smoke
   chronic effects, 4026
   dogs, 4026, 4997
   humans, 5247
   tolerance, 4997
nabilone (Lilly compound no. 109514)
   humans, 4250
SP-111A
   rats, 4576
HEMATOLOGY
   delta-9-THC
      chronic effects, 5045
      humans, 3553
      rabbit(s), 5045
      rats, 4744
   ganja
      humans, 4762
   marihuana
      adverse effect(s), 4776
      humans, 4030, 4776
   marihuana smoke
      chronic effects, 4026
      dogs, 4026
HEMOLYSIS
   hemp
      humans, 5499
      sheep, 5499
HEMP
   adverse effect(s)
      psychosis, 3341
      respiratory system, 3370
   analysis
      detection, 4506
      gas chromatography, 4506
      microscopic examination, 4506
      thin layer chromatography (TLC), 3270, 4506
   botanical aspects
      anatomy, 4287, 4854, 4977, 4978
      cannabinoid content, 4824
      cytology, 4854, 4977, 4978
      eradication, 3270
   chemical aspects
      cannabinoid content, 3270, 4824
      constituents of
         carotenoid, 3120
         delta-9-THC, 3912
         delta-9-THC oid acid A & B, 3912
         minerals, 3120
   forensic aspects
      detection, 4506
   immunology
      allergy, 4829
   psychological aspects
      psychosis, 3341

HEMP (continued)
   toxicology
      hemolysis, 5499
      immunological effects, 5499
      lung(s), 4829
      lymph nodes, 4829
HEPATIC ENZYMES
   cannabidiol (CBD)
      rats, 4281
   cannabis
      rats, 4479
   delta-8-THC
      mice, 5223
   delta-9-THC
      acute administration 3808
      chronic administration, 3808
      induction, 3780
      mice, 5223
      rats, 3780, 4281
HEPATIC FUNCTION
   delta-9-THC
      acute administration, 3808
      chronic administration, 3808
      rats, 3808
HEPATIC METABOLISM
   cannabidiol (CBD), 5457
      cytochrome P450, 4033
      glucuronides, 3937, 3942
      humans, 4148
      inhibition, 4144
      mice, 3937, 3942, 4033, 4034, 4144, 4148
      microsomal, 4148
      microsomal induction, 4034
      rats, 3067, 4148
      subchronic administration, 4034
   cannabinol (CBN)
      glucuronides, 3938, 3942
      mice, 3938, 3942
      rabbit(s), 5200
      rats, 3067, 3938
   cannabis
      rats, 3067
   delta-8-THC
      glucuronides, 3937, 3942
      hexahydrocannabinol (HHC), 3941
      mice, 3937, 3941, 3942, 3945, 5222
      testosterone, 3465
      tyrosine aminotransferase, 5222
   delta-9-THC
      aryl hydrocarbon hydroxylase activity, 3777
      glucuronides, 3937, 3942
      guinea pig(s), 3936
      hexahydrocannabinol (HHC), 3941
      humans, 4148, 5145
      hydroxylation, 3947
      mice, 3777, 3778, 3936, 3937, 3940, 3941, 3942,
         3947, 4148, 5222
      microsomal, 3778, 4148
      rats, 3067, 3936, 4148
      review, 3936
      testosterone, 3465
      tyrosine aminotransferase, 5222
HEPATITIS
   cannabis
      humans, 3458

HEPATITIS (continued)
  hashish
    humans, 3638
HEPTACOSANE
  analysis
    quantitative, 4695
  cannabis
    constituents of, 4695
HERBICIDES
  Cannabis sativa
    paraquat, 3492
HETEROCYCLIC DERIVATIVES OF CANNABINOIDS
  cannabinoid(s)
    synthesis, 4344
HEXADECAMIDE
  constituents of
    cannabis resin, 4910
  identification
    GC/MS, 4910
HEXAHYDROCANNABINOL (HHC)
  behavioral effect(s)
    catecholamines, 3357
    conditioned behavior, 3753
    gross behavior, 3664
    self administration, 3452
  chemical aspects
    analog(s)
      synthesis, 3615
    derivatives, 5580
    homologs
      structure, 4105
    synthesis
      analog(s), 3615
  pharmacological aspects
    body temperature, 3357
    cardiovascular effects, 3664
    catecholamines, 3357
    derivatives, 5580
    structure-activity relationships, 5580
HIGH-PRESSURE LIQUID CHROMATOGRAPHY (HPLC)
  cannabinoid(s)
    biological fluid(s), 5384, 5598
    cannabis plant, 5497
    detection, 5497
    hashish, 5497
    separation, 5384, 5395, 5598
    urine, 5629
  delta-9-THC, 3064
    humans, 5616
    milk, 5273
    plasma, 5616
    urine, 5273
  drugs of abuse, 3064
  marihuana
    decarboxylation, 5455
    delta-9-THC, 5455
    delta-9-THC oic acid A & B, 5455
  11-*nor*-9-carboxy-delta-9-THC
    humans, 5616
    plasma, 5616
HPLC/MS
  cannabinoid(s)
    blood, 5477
    detection, 5477
    urine, 5477

HIGHER BRAIN FUNCTION
  delta-9-THC
    humans, 4014
HIPPOCAMPUS
  delta-9-THC
    acetylcholine (ACh), 5549
    anesthesia, 5121
    electrophysiology, 5121
    interaction with
      dopamine (DA), 5549
      endorphine, 5549
    rats, 5549
HISTAMINE
  delta-9-THC
    brain, 5024
    gastrointestinal tract, 5024
    heart, 5024
    liver, 5024
    lung(s), 5024
    rats, 5024
HISTOCHEMICAL TEST
  Cannabis sativa
    detection, 3526
HISTOLOGICAL CHANGES
  delta-9-THC
    monkeys, 5582
    reproductive system, 5582
HISTORY
  cannabinoid(s)
    therapeutic aspects, 3498
  cannabis
    Africa, 3644
    Asia, 3113
    distribution, 3076
    Jamaica, 3267
    legal aspects, 3229
    medicine, 4451
    pharmacological aspects, 4805
    plant, 3763
    review, 3113
    therapeutic aspects, 4760
  cannabis use
    China, 3112
    review, 4002
  delta-9-THC
    pharmacological aspects, 3390
  ganja
    Jamaica, 4762
    review, 4762
  hashish
    review, 3169
  marihuana, 3215
    chemical aspects, 3390
    cultural use, 3080
    general information, 4530
    Greece, 3412
    Italy, 3412
    legal aspects, 3268
    medicine, 3412
    pharmacological aspects, 3390
    research, 3390
    review, 3080
    therapeutic aspects, 5216
    U.S.A., 3268, 3658

HOMOLOGS
  cannabichromene (CBC), 3537
  cannabicitran, 3537
  cannabicyclol (CBL), 3537
  cannabidiol (CBD), 3537
  cannabigerol (CBG), 3537
  cannabinoid(s)
    pentyl, 4481
  cannabinol (CBN), 3537
  delta-8-THC, 3537
    NMR spectra, 4195
    synthesis, 4195
  delta-9-THC, 3537
    therapeutic aspects, 3993
  tetrahydrocannabinol (THC)
    mice, 5614
    structure-activity relationships, 5614
    synthesis, 5614
HOPS PLANT
  analysis
    delta-9-THC, 3727
    GC/MS, 3727
HORDENINE
  Cannabis sativa
    constituents of, 3673
HORMONAL EFFECTS
  Cannabis sativa
    sex differences, 3130
  delta-9-THC
    hypothalamic pituitary function, 3267
    ovaries, 3269
    rats, 3269
HOST RESISTANCE
  cannabinoid(s)
    mice, 5510
  marihuana extract
    mice, 5510
HUMANS
  cannabis
    genetics, 5048
    review, 4763, 5048
    testosterone levels, 5048
  chronic use
    pharmacology, 3494
  electroencephalogram (EEG)
    correlated with task, 4754
  immunology, 4404
  reproduction, 4404
HUMORAL IMMUNITY
  delta-8-THC, 4914
    anti-histaminic activity, 4653, 4913
    derivatives, 4914
    spleen, 4653, 4913
  delta-9-THC, 4261, 4914
    age, 4670
    humans, 3553, 3555
    mechanism of action, 4510
    mice, 3431, 4240, 4241, 4263, 4629, 4670
    rats, 4736
    review, 4737
    spleen, 4653, 4913
    tolerance, 4510
  8,9-epoxyhexahydrocannabinol
    mice, 4170

HUMORAL IMMUNITY
  marihuana
    assays, 4508
    chronic use, 4630, 4682
    humans, 3551, 4630, 4682
    inhalation, 4736
    rats, 4736
    review, 4398, 4737
HYDROCARBON
  cannabis
    constituents of, 3255, 3256
  Cannabis sativa
    constituents of, 5079
HYDROCARBON CONTENT
  cannabis, 3536
  Cannabis sativa
    analysis, 4480
HYDROLYSIS
  delta-8-THC
    phospholipids, 5234
7-HYDROXY OR 11-HYDROXY-THC
  pharmacological aspects
    anesthesia, 4233
8-BETA-HYDROXY-DELTA-9-THC
  biochemical effect(s)
    compared to:
      alcohol, 4043
    macromolecular synthesis, 4042, 4043
  chemical aspects
    structure, 4581
9-HYDROXY-9-*NOR*-HEXAHYDROCANNABINOL
  analgesia, 3609
  behavioral effect(s)
    ataxia, 5212
    conditioned behavior, 5331
    locomotor activity, 5212
  interaction with
    naloxone, 3609
  pharmacological aspects
    analgesia, 3353, 3354, 3918, 4378, 5212
    biogenic amine(s), 3353
    body temperature, 3358
    brain, 3353
    catecholamines, 3358
    compared to:
      delta-8-THC, 5212
      delta-9-THC, 5212
      morphine, 3353, 3354, 5212
    morphine withdrawal, 4378
  therapeutic aspects
    analgesia, 4408
11-HYDROXY-DELTA-8-THC
  analysis
    GC/MS, 3944
    identification, 3179
    separation, 3179, 3944
    trimethylsilyl derivatives, 3944
  biochemical effect(s)
    cytochrome P450, 5625
    macromolecular synthesis, 4523
    microsomal metabolism, 5480, 5625
    oxidation, 5625
  immunology
    antimitotic, 3602
    lymphocytes, 3602, 4523

11-HYDROXY-DELTA-8-THC (continued)
  pharmacological aspects
    abstinence syndrome, 3334
    acetylcholine (ACh), 3050
    cyclic AMP, 3050
    guinea pig ileum, 4728
    interaction with
      naloxone, 3333
    intraocular pressure (IOP), 3866
    morphine withdrawal, 3333, 3334
11-HYDROXY-DELTA-9-THC
  adverse effect(s)
    chromosomes, 5240
  analysis
    biological fluid(s), 4722
    derivatives, 5558
    detection, 4133, 4722, 4733, 4734, 5028, 5149,
      5150, 5558
    GC/MS, 4155, 5149, 5150
    immunoassay, 4722
    mass fragmentography, 4734, 4735
    plasma, 5149
    quantitative, 5149
    radioimmunoassay (RIA), 5028
    silyl derivatives, 3934
    thin layer chromatography (TLC), 4133
    urine, 4155
  behavioral effect(s), 3755
    compared to:
      delta-9-THC, 3754
    conditioned behavior, 3753, 4377, 5331
    discriminative properties, 4203
    discriminative stimulus, 4204
    tolerance, 3754
  biochemical effect(s)
    adenylate cyclase, 3627
    ATPase(s), 4570
    brain, 3627
    cholesterol esterase, 5323
    compared to:
      alcohol, 4043
      delta-9-THC, 5479
      11-palmitoyloxy-delta-9-THC, 5479
    cyclic AMP, 3627
    macromolecular synthesis, 4042, 4043, 4523, 5071
    membrane-bound enzyme, 4570
    microsomal metabolism, 5479, 5480
    phosphodiesterase, 3627
    progesterone, 5323
    synaptic vesicles, 4570
  chemical aspects
    silyl derivatives, 3934
  endocrine effects
    estrogen-receptor binding, 4848
  immunology
    acyltransferase activity, 3872
    antimitotic, 3602
    lymphocytes, 3602, 3872, 4523
  neurochemical effects
    acyltransferase, 3873
    adenylate cyclase, 3627
    cyclic AMP, 3627
    phosphodiesterase, 3627
  neuropharmacological effects
    acetylcholine (ACh), 5550

neuropharmacological effects (continued)
    brain, 5550
    compared to:
      alcohol, 5550
      anti-convulsant(s), 5343
      barbiturate(s), 5550
      cannabidiol (CBD), 5343
      chlordiazepoxide, 5550
      delta-9-THC, 5343
    cortex, 5343
    epilepsy, 5343
  neuropharmacology
    catalepsy, 3840
    extrapyramidal system, 3840
    ganglionic transmission, 3752
  neurophysiological effects
    posttetanic potentiation, 5075, 5076
  pharmacokinetics
    brain, 4618
    brain levels, 4619
    disposition, 4619
    distribution, 4377, 4618
    metabolism, 4377
    plasma levels, 4619
  pharmacological aspects
    anesthesia, 3873
    anti-convulsant activity, 3164, 3475, 4145, 5075,
      5076, 5077
    antineoplastic, 5071
    blood-brain barrier, 4803
    body temperature, 3358, 4795
    brain, 4570, 4803
    brain levels, 3755
      cyclic AMP, 3628
    cardiovascular effects, 4245, 4247, 4353, 4354,
      4358
    catalepsy, 3840
    catecholamines, 3358
    convulsions, 4387
    hypothalamus, 4795
    interaction with
      amphetamine, 3840
    intraocular pressure (IOP), 3866
    metabolism, 5148
    morphine withdrawal, 3332
    plasma levels, 3755
    spinal cord, 4795
    stimulant activity, 4387
    tolerance, 4145
  physiological effects
    adrenocorticotropic hormone (ACTH), 4080
    corticosterones, 4077, 4080
    endocrine effects, 4247
  physiology
    endocrine effects, 4848
  psychological aspects
    subjective effects, 4247
  psychological effects
    subjective effects, 4245
  review
    discriminative properties, 4203
  toxicology
    motor activity, 3164
    mutagenesis, 5240

5-HYDROXYINDOLEACETIC ACID (5-HIAA)
cannabis extract
excretion, 4161
guinea pig(s), 4161
delta-9-THC
brain, 3508, 4819, 5596
brain levels, 5023
hypothermia, 5023
rats, 3508, 3726, 4819, 5023, 5596
HYDROXYLATED CANNABINOIDS
analysis
detection, 5206
GC/MS, 4990
high-pressure liquid chromatography (HPLC), 5206
radioimmunoassay (RIA), 5206
behavioral effect(s)
central nervous system (CNS), 5631
biochemical effect(s)
cholesterol esterase, 5323
progesterone, 5323
cannabis resin
constituents of, 4990
chemical aspects
structural identification, 5129
synthesis, 5631
pharmacological aspects
analgesic activity, 5631
HYDROXYLATED METABOLITES
delta-8-THC
behavioral effect(s), 5532
monkeys, 5532
synthesis, 5532
delta-9-THC
GC/MS, 5527
nuclear magnetic resonance (NMR), 5527
rabbit(s), 5527
synthesis, 5418
urine, 5527
HYPERGLYCEMIA
delta-9-THC
rats, 4744
HYPERPLASIA
cannabidiol (CBD)
kidney, 3825
cannabinol (CBN)
kidney, 3825
delta-9-THC
kidney, 3825
HYPERTENSION
delta-9-THC
rats, 5123
therapy, 4408
HYPERTHERMIA
delta-9-THC
mice, 3888
HYPNOTIC
cannabidiol (CBD)
humans, 5330
delta-6a(10a)-THC
carbocyclic analogs, 5218
nitrogen analogs, 5218
thio analogs, 5218
delta-9-THC
humans, 4544

HYPNOTIC SUSCEPTIBILITY
marihuana
humans, 3052
interaction with
haloperidol, 3052
HYPOTHALAMIC PITUITARY FUNCTION
cannabinoid(s)
review, 5340
cannabinol (CBN)
rats, 5544
delta-9-THC
dopamine (DA), 4348
follicle stimulating hormone (FSH), 5581
luteinizing hormone (LH), 5581
mice, 4348
monkeys, 4899, 5581
rats, 3110, 4998, 5294, 5334, 5544
hashish
rats, 4291
stress, 4291
HYPOTHALAMUS
delta-9-THC
body temperature, 4795
cats, 4795
rats, 3308
stimulation, 3308
dimethylheptylpyran (DMHP)
body temperature, 4795
cats, 4795
11-hydroxy-delta-9-THC
body temperature, 4795
cats, 4795
HYPOTHERMIA
cannabidiol (CBD)
mechanism of action, 3476
cannabinoid(s)
mechanism of action, 5416
tolerance, 5416
cannabinol (CBN)
mechanism of action, 3476
cannabis
biogenic amine(s), 4875
interaction with
copper, 4876
rats, 4873, 4875, 4876
tolerance, 4873, 4876
cannabis resin
mechanism of action, 4872
rats, 4872
tolerance, 4872
delta-8-THC
phospholipids, 5234
rats, 3983
tolerance, 3983
delta-9-THC
calcium levels, 3889
cats, 4796
central nervous system mechanism, 4798
compared to:
morphine, 3352
humans, 5310
mechanism of action, 3476, 4796, 4872, 5252, 5258
mice, 3352, 3889, 3890, 5252, 5258
rats, 3197, 3725, 4058, 4503, 4798, 4872, 5032

delta-9-THC (continued)
   tissue respiration, 3532
   tolerance, 3197, 4058, 4872, 5032
  Lilly compound 109514
   rats, 4586
   tolerance, 4586
  nabilone (Lilly compound 109514)
   rats, 4585
   tolerance, 4585

I

IDENTIFICATION
  cannabidiol (CBD)
   derivatives, 4171
   gas liquid chromatography (GLC), 4171
   high-pressure liquid chromatography (HPLC),
     4171, 5497
   mass spectrometry, 4171
  cannabinoid(s)
   color tests, 4394
   fluorometric, 3179
   GC/MS, 3108
   thin layer chromatography (TLC), 3324
  cannabinol (CBN)
   derivatives, 4171
   gas liquid chromatography (GLC), 4171
   high-pressure liquid chromatography (HPLC), 4171
   mass spectrometry, 4171
  cannabiripsol
   GC/MS, 5314
  cannabis, 3704
   fast blue B salt, 3072
   forensic aspects, 3436, 4660
   geographical origin, 3591
   species, 4442
   thin layer chromatography (TLC), 3591
  cannabis extract
   colorametric method, 5601
   flowers, 5601
   leaves, 5601
  Cannabis sativa
   Beam test, 4230
   Duquenois test, 4230
   Furfural test, 4230
   geographical origin, 3073
   tetrahydrocannabinol (THC)
     fast blue B salt, 4820
   thin layer chromatography (TLC), 3073
  delta-8-THC
   blood level(s), 4564
   derivatives, 4171
   gas liquid chromatography (GLC), 4171
   high pressure liquid chromatography (HPLC),
     4171, 5497
   mass fragmentography, 4564
   mass spectrometry, 4171
  delta-9-THC
   blood, 3206
   blood level(s), 4564
   color tests, 4394
   derivatives, 4171
   gas liquid chromatography (GLC), 4171
   high-pressure liquid chromatography (HPLC),
     3064, 4171, 5497

delta-9-THC (continued)
   mass fragmentography, 4564
   mass spectrometry, 4171
   metabolites, 3943, 4551, 4553
  drugs of abuse
   high-pressure liquid chromatography (HPLC), 3064
  marihuana
   carcinogenesis, 5434
   legal aspects, 4442
   microscopic examination, 5213
   species, 4442
   street drugs, 5213
   thin layer chromatography (TLC), 5213, 5434
  marihuana smoke
   polycyclic aromatic hydrocarbons, 3299
  street drugs
   GC/MS, 3108
  terpenoids
   forensic aspects, 5464
IMMUNE RESPONSE
  cannabis
   humans, 3845
IMMUNE SYSTEM
  marihuana
   adverse effect(s), 3240, 3741, 4527, 4530, 4632,
     4776, 5017
   humans, 3241, 4776
   lymphocytes, 3241
   review, 4404
IMMUNOGLOBULINS
  8,9-epoxyhexahydrocannabinol
   immunosuppression, 5263
   lymphocytes, 5263
   mice, 5263
  marihuana
   chronic use, 3579
   monkeys, 3579
IMMUNOLOGICAL EFFECTS
  hemp
   hemolysis, 5499
   humans, 5499
   sheep, 5499
IMMUNOLOGY
  antibody formation, 4404
  cannabidiol (CBD)
   acyltransferase activity, 3872
   lymphocytes, 3872
   mice, 5243
  cannabigerol (CBG)
   acyltransferase activity, 3872
   lymphocytes, 3872
  cannabinol (CNB)
   acyltransferase activity, 3872
   lymphocytes, 3872
   mice, 5243
  cannabis
   immunosuppression, 4763
   review, 5048
  delta-8-THC
   acyltransferase activity, 3872
   lymphocytes, 3872
  delta-9-THC
   acyltransferase activity, 3872
   lymphocytes, 3872
   macrophages, 3804

delta-9-THC (continued)
   mice, 5243
   rats, 4743
11-hydroxy-delta-9-THC
   acyltransferase activity, 3872
   lymphocytes, 3872
marihuana
   humans, 3893
review, 4404
IMMUNOSUPPRESSION
  cannabinoid(s)
   mice, 5510, 5584
  cannabinol (CBN)
   mice, 5482
  delta-8-THC
   mice, 5482
  delta-9-THC
   in vitro, 4668
   lung(s), 4017
   mechanism of action, 4668
   mice, 4241
   structure-activity relationships, 4668
   tolerance, 3695
  marihuana
   humans, 3392, 4529
  marihuana extract
   mice, 5510
  marihuana smoke
   lung(s), 4017
  synthetic cannabinoids
   mice, 5584
IMPOTENCE
  marihuana
   humans, 3392, 4529
INCREASE IN USE
  marihuana, 3659
   adolescent(s), 3217
INDOLES
  hashish
   constituents of, 4770
  marihuana
   constituents of, 4770
INFLAMMATION
  marihuana smoke
   rats, 5383
INFRARED (IR)
  paraquat
   analysis, 5312
INHALATION
  marihuana
   humans, 5537
   lung damage, 5537
   rats, 4738
   toxicity, 4738
INHALATION TOXICOLOGY
  cannabichromene (CBC)
   organ weights, 4742
   rats, 4742, 5561
  cannabidiol (CBD)
   organ weights, 4742
   rats, 4742, 5561
  marihuana
   organ weights, 4742
   rats, 4742, 5561
   Turkey, 5561

INHALATION TOXICOLOGY (continued)
  marihuana smoke
   chronic effects, 5383
   rats, 5383
INORGANIC ELEMENTS
  cannabis plant
   constituents of, 4847
   neutron activation, 4847
INSECT REPELLENT
  Cannabis sativa, 3107
INSECTS
  cannabidiol (CBD)
   storage, 4755
  Cannabis sativa
   India, 3301
  delta-9-THC
   storage, 4755
INSULIN
  cannabis extract
   rabbit(s), 3470
   release, 3470
  delta-9-THC
   dogs, 3594
INTELLIGENCE
  marihuana
   chronic use, 4784
   humans, 4784
INTELLIGENCE TESTS
  cannabis
   humans, 4963
INTERACTION WITH THC
  other drugs, 4675
INTERNATIONAL CONTROL
  marihuana
   history, 5517
INTESTINAL MOTILITY
  delta-9-THC
   mice, 3222
   tolerance, 3222
INTOXICATION
  cannabis
   psychiatric aspects, 3927
   psychosis, 3927
  delta-9-THC
   correlated with
    metabolism, 3999
  marihuana
   behavior, 4640
   humans, 4640, 4647
   meditation, 3790
   psychological aspects, 3790
   stress, 4647
INTRAOCULAR PRESSURE (IOP)
  ABBOTT-40656
   rabbit(s), 3640
  ABBOTT-43981
   rabbit(s), 3665
  cannabidiol (CBD)
   derivatives, 4409
   humans, 3498
   rabbit(s), 4409
  cannabinoid(s)
   chronic effects, 3865
   potency, 5405
   rabbit(s), 3865

cannabinoid(s) (continued)
review, 5412, 5413, 5414
route of administration, 5413
cannabinol (CBN)
dogs, 5042
humans, 3498
cannabis, 3588, 3589
chronic use, 3589
humans, 3589
Cannabis sativa
dogs, 5189
humans, 5189
delta-8-THC, 4160
glaucoma, 5249
humans, 3498, 4620
metabolites, 4620
rabbit(s), 5249
delta-9-THC, 3588, 4160
adrenergic nervous system, 3860, 3864
blood pressure, 5355
cats, 5438
central nervous system, 3857
glaucoma, 3534
humans, 3251, 3498, 3501, 3521, 3522, 3534,
3546, 3855, 4620, 4679, 5355
in vitro, 3859
mechanism of action, 3861, 5438
metabolites, 3859, 4620
prostaglandin synthesis, 5413
rabbit(s), 3251, 3639, 3857, 3858, 3859, 3860,
3861, 3862, 3864, 3867
review, 3919, 5405, 5413, 5414
route of administration, 5405, 5413
therapy, 3239
marihuana
chronic use, 3499
glaucoma, 3533
humans, 3240, 3251, 3499, 3533, 3967
rabbit(s), 3966
review, 5405
route of administration, 5405
tolerance, 5405
marihuana smoke
humans, 3746, 4287, 5103
review, 5414
nabilone (Lilly compound 109514)
clinical findings, 4960
humans, 4960, 5178, 5521, 5522
rabbit(s), 5521, 5522
SP-1
central nervous system mechanism, 3857
chronic effects, 3865
dogs, 5042
monkeys, 3863
rabbit(s), 3639, 3857, 3858, 3863, 3865
SP-80
dogs, 5042
rabbit(s), 3639
SP-106
central nervous system mechanism, 3857
chronic effects, 3865
dogs, 5042
monkeys, 3863
rabbit(s), 3639, 3857, 3858, 3863, 3865

INTRAOCULAR PRESSURE (IOP) (continued)
SP-111A
in vitro, 3859
metabolites, 3859
rabbit(s), 3859
SP-204
chronic effects, 3865
monkeys, 3863
rabbit(s), 3863, 3865
synthetic cannabinoids
rabbit(s), 3640
review, 5413
route of administration, 5413
tolerance, 5413
ISOLATION
cannabidiolic acid, 3413
cannabielsoin (CBE)
hashish, 4946
cannabigerolic acid, 3413
Cannabis sativa
glycosides, 4821
delta-9-THC oic acid A & B, 3413
ISOMERIZATION
cis-cannabidiol, 3899
ISOMERS
delta-8-THC
synthesis, 5098
delta-9-THC
synthesis, 5098

K

KETO ANALOGS
delta-8-THC
NMR spectra, 3260
structure, 3260
delta-9-THC
NMR spectra, 3260
structure, 3260
KETOACIDOSIS
marihuana
humans, 3336
therapy, 3336
17-KETOSTEROIDS
delta-9-THC
adrenals, 3567
excretion, 3567
liver, 3567
metabolism, 3567
rats, 3567
spleen, 3567
testis(es), 3567
KIDNEY
cannabidiol (CBD)
hyperplasia, 3825
cannabinol (CBN)
hyperplasia, 3825
cannabis extract
damage, 4056
rabbit(s), 4056
rats, 4056
delta-9-THC
hyperplasia, 3825
in vitro, 4153
prostaglandins, 4153
rabbit(s), 4153

L

LACTATION
delta-9-THC
excretion, 3467
metabolites, 3467
mice, 5593
monkeys, 3467
marihuana
adverse effect(s), 5515
marihuana smoke
neonates, 5399
LACTIC DEHYDROGENASE (LDH)
delta-9-THC
rats, 4425
hashish
rats, 4339
LACTIC DEHYDROGENASE ISOZYMES (LDH)
delta-9-THC
rats, 4357
LEARNED BEHAVIOR
cannabis resin
monkeys, 3820
delta-9-THC
chronic administration, 4683
mice, 4683
marihuana
animals, 3240
humans, 3218
LEARNING
cannabis extract
acute effect(s), 3721
chronic effects, 3721
chronic use, 3720
maze, 3721
rats, 3720, 3721
cannabis resin
monkeys, 3820
delta-9-THC
humans, 5109
delta-9-THC
humans, 5109
neonates, 5100, 5101
rats, 5100, 5382
marihuana
animals, 3185
anticholinergic effect, 3496
humans, 3168, 3185, 3496, 4255, 4645, 5109
review, 3185
LEAVES
Cannabis sativa
cannabinoid content, 3073
environmental conditions, 4840
geographical origin, 3073
LEGAL ASPECTS
cannabis
Australia, 3229
compared to:
alcohol, 3243
decriminalization, 3928
England, 3078, 3238, 5287, 5288
general information, 3854
history, 3229
legalization issue, 3078
prohibition, 3078

cannabis (continued)
regulation, 3229
South Africa, 3646, 3677
species, 4298, 4299
United Kingdom, 3952
U.S.A., 3243
Cannabis sativa, 4961
cannabis use, 3242
ganja
Jamaica, 4762
marihuana, 3091, 3217, 3231, 3758, 3791, 3793,
3856, 4308, 4450, 4669, 4723, 4804, 4991
arrests, 4085
Australia, 3949, 5209
availability, 3284
Canada, 3693, 4182
decriminalization, 3232, 3249, 3392, 3453, 3557,
3584, 3887, 4213, 4490, 4633, 4747, 4828,
4972, 5054, 5186
drug abuse, 3101
drug use, 4890
England, 3848, 3977, 4268
epidemiological study, 4085
general information, 4999
history, 3268, 3658
identification, 4214
species, 4442
legalization issue, 3124, 3916, 4083, 4151, 4268
patterns of use, 3557
penalties, 4842
possession, 4214
recommendations, 4625
review, 3268, 4890
sociological aspects, 3103
U.S.A., 3103, 3114, 3268, 3345, 3453, 3693,
3893, 4842
marihuana use
history, 5517
LEGALIZATION ISSUE
cannabis
review, 4531
marihuana
attitude, 5578
demographic aspects, 5578
England, 5409
history, 4531
review, 4531
U.S.A., 3106, 3833
LD$_{50}$
cannabidiol (CBD)
mice, 5380
cannabis
animals, 3844
delta-8-THC
review, 3919
delta-9-THC
mice, 5380
review, 3919
SP-1
mice, 4602
rats, 5042
SP-80
rats, 5042
SP-106
rats, 5042

LETHAL SYNERGISM
  cannabinol (CBN)
    bacterial lipopolysaccharide, 4511
  delta-8-THC
    bacterial lipopolysaccharide, 4511
  delta-9-THC
    bacterial lipopolysaccharide, 4511
LETHALITY
  cannabichromene (CBC)
    rats, 5561
  cannabidiol (CBD)
    rats, 5561
  marihuana
    rats, 5561
    Turkey, 5561
  marihuana smoke
    chronic effects, 5383
    rats, 5383
LEUKOCYTES
  hashish
    humans, 4193
LIFE CYCLE
  cannabis, 3486
LIGHT ADAPTATION
  marihuana
    humans, 3194
LILLY COMPOUND NO. 109514
  analysis
    quantitative, 4994
  behavioral effect(s), 4959
  pharmacokinetics
    half-life, 4994
    metabolites, 4994
  pharmacological aspects
    anti-anxiety activity, 4959
    biological activity, 4959
    compared to:
      dimethylheptylpyran (DMHP), 4586
    cross tolerance
      dimethylheptylpyran (DMHP), 4586
    hypothermia, 4586
    tolerance, 4251, 4586
    tranquilizing activity, 4251
LIMBIC
  cannabinoid(s)
    review, 5504
LIPASE
  delta-9-THC
    in vitro, 4462
LIPID CONTENT
  delta-9-THC
    brain, 4779, 4780
      subcellular distribution, 4779, 4780
    rats, 4779, 4780
LIPID PEROXIDATION
  delta-9-THC
    liver, 4475
    rats, 4475
LIPID SYNTHESIS
  cannabinoid(s)
    lymphocytes, 5500
    synaptosomes, 5500
  delta-9-THC
    bacteria, 3177

LIPIDS
  cannabinoid content
    analysis, 5557
    GC/MS, 5557
    plasma, 5557
  Cannabis sativa
    constituents of, 4685
  delta-9-THC
    in vitro, 3280
  hashish
    humans, 4193
    plasma levels, 4193
  marihuana smoke
    chronic effects, 4026
    dogs, 4026
LIPOLYSIS
  marihuana extract
    adipocyte(s), 5217
    albumin, 5217
    norepinephrine (NE), 5217
    rats, 5217
LIPOPROTEIN(S)
  delta-9-THC
    binding, 4167
    humans, 4167, 5065
    plasma, 4167
  rats, 4167, 4357
LITHIUM
  delta-8-THC
    blood-brain barrier, 4817
    rats, 4817
LIVER
  cannabidiol (CBD)
    metabolism, 4374, 4375
    metabolites
      dioxygenated, 4374
      hydroxylated, 4375
    monoamine oxidase (MAO), 4806, 4807
    rats, 4375
  cannabis
    adverse effect(s), 3845, 4965
  cannabis extract
    damage, 4056
    rabbit(s), 4056
    rats, 4056
  delta-9-THC
    chronic administration, 4476
    enzyme activity, 4475
    lipid peroxidation, 4475
    lipids, 3280
    microsomal metabolism, 4476
    microsomes, 3280
    monoamine oxidase (MAO), 4806, 4807
    rats, 3280, 4475
    uptake, 4035
  hashish extract
    monoamine oxidase (MAO), 4806, 4807
  marihuana
    adverse effect(s), 4527
LIVER FUNCTION TESTS
  delta-9-THC
    humans, 5239
LIVER WEIGHT
  cannabinoid(s)
    chronic effects, 3865
    rabbit(s), 3865

LIVER WEIGHT (continued)
  SP-1
    chronic effects, 3865
    rabbit(s), 3865
  SP-106
    chronic effects, 3865
    rabbit(s), 3865
  SP-204
    chronic effects, 3865
    rabbit(s), 3865
LOCOMOTOR ACTIVITY
  cannabis
    baboons, 4259
    rats, 4873
  cannabis extract
    catecholamines, 3264
    rats, 3264
  delta-9-THC, 3756
    chronic effects, 4684
    interaction with
      methamphetamine, 3698, 3700
    mice, 3698, 4684, 5299
    neonates, 5100, 5101
    rats, 3643, 4335, 5100, 5318, 5372
    tolerance, 4335
  9-hydroxy-9-*nor*-hexahydrocannabinol
    mice, 5212
  LSD-25
    toxicology
      brain, 4554
      neonates, 4554
LUNG(S)
  cannabis, 4522
    general, 4763
  Cannabis sativa
    adverse effect(s), 3562
  delta-9-THC
    adverse effect(s), 4739
    airway conductance, 5106
    blood flow, 4048, 4050
    bronchodilatation, 3849, 4832, 5106
    dogs, 4048, 4050
    guinea pig(s), 4153, 5104
    humans, 3180, 3582, 3849, 4832, 5014
    in vitro, 4153
    norepinephrine (NE), 5104
    prostaglandins, 4153
    rats, 4739
    route of administration, 4739
    vital capacity, 3582
  hemp
    allergy, 4829
    damage, 4829
    guinea pig(s), 4829
    pathological study, 4829
  marihuana
    adverse effect(s), 3392, 3482, 3741, 4527, 4592
    alveolar macrophage(s), 4592
    anti-bacterial activity, 4592
    bronchodilatation, 5012
    cytotoxicity, 3111
    emphysema, 4403
    humans, 3111, 3392, 3482, 4529, 5012
  marihuana extract
    bronchodilatation, 3849
    humans, 3849

LUNG(S) (continued)
  marihuana smoke
    adverse effect(s), 3585, 4616, 4758, 5103
    airway conductance, 5016
    alveolar macrophage(s), 3585, 4018, 4315, 4616, 5383
    anti-bacterial activity, 4315
    aryl hydrocarbon hydroxylase activity, 4365
    bacteria, 5433
    bronchodilatation, 4832
    cholesterol, 5383
    chronic administration, 5560
    chronic effects, 5383
    chronic use, 3969, 5016
    clearance rates, 5432
    dogs, 4758
    humans, 3969, 4832, 5014, 5016
    immune system, 5432
    immunology, 5423
    immunosuppression, 5433
    microsomal metabolism, 4365
    pathology, 5560
    rats, 4365, 4616, 5383, 5432, 5433, 5560
    sex differences, 5560
LUNG FUNCTION
  delta-9-THC
    humans, 3931
LUTEINIZING HORMONE (LH)
  cannabidiol (CBD)
    monkeys, 3327
  cannabinol (CBN)
    mice, 3569, 3570
  delta-9-THC
    blood level(s), 3464, 4898, 5090, 5295
    mice, 3569, 3570
    monkeys, 3325, 3326, 3327, 4898, 4899, 5297
    ovariectomy, 4898, 5090
    plasma levels, 3694
    rabbit(s), 5295
    rats, 3464, 3508, 3694, 5090
  marihuana
    blood level(s), 4016
    chronic use, 3499
    humans, 3499, 3549, 3956, 3957, 4016, 4107, 4430, 4431
    plasma levels, 3549, 3957, 4430, 4431
  marihuana smoke
    humans, 4178
    plasma levels, 4178
  tetrahydrocannabinol (THC)
    monkeys, 4897
LYMPH NODES
  hemp
    damage, 4829
    guinea pig(s), 4829
LYMPHOCYTE FUNCTION
  delta-9-THC
    humans, 4628, 4681
  marihuana
    humans, 4628
LYMPHOCYTES
  cannabichromene (CBC)
    antimitotic, 3602
    macromolecular synthesis, 4523
  cannabicyclol (CBL)
    antimitotic, 3602

cannabicyclol (CBL) (continued)
    macromolecular synthesis, 4523
cannabidiol (CBD)
    acyltransferase activity, 3872
    macromolecular synthesis, 4523
    mice, 3872
cannabigerol (CBG)
    acyltransferase activity, 3872
    macromolecular synthesis, 4523
    mice, 3872
cannabinol (CBN)
    acyltransferase activity, 3872
    antimitotic, 3602
    macromolecular synthesis, 4523
    mice, 3872
delta-8-THC
    acyltransferase activity, 3872
    antimitotic, 3602
    macromolecular synthesis, 4523
    mice, 3872
delta-9-THC
    acyltransferase activity, 3872, 3874, 4025
    age, 4670
    antimitotic, 3602
    chromosomes, 4494, 4496
    DNA synthesis, 4494, 4496
    growth, 5304
    humans, 4227, 4228
    in vitro, 4240
    in vivo, 4240
    macromolecular synthesis, 3606, 4523
    membrane effects, 5304
    membranes, 4425
    mice, 3872, 4240, 4670
    rats, 4425
hashish
    chronic use, 4123
    humans, 4123, 4970
    lipids, 4124
    phospholipids, 4124
    thymidine uptake, 4124
11-hydroxy-delta-8-THC
    antimitotic, 3602
    macromolecular synthesis, 4523
11-hydroxy-delta-9-THC
    acyltransferase activity, 3872
    antimitotic, 3602
    macromolecular synthesis, 4523
    mice, 3872
marihuana
    chromosome damage, 4401
    chronic use, 3579
    humans, 4227, 4228, 5196
    monkeys, 3579
marihuana smoke
    mitosis, 5511
olivetol
    antimitotic, 3602
    chromosomes, 4494, 4496
    DNA synthesis, 4494, 4496
LYSOSOMES
delta-9-THC
    enzymes, 4425
    membranes, 4425
    rats, 4425

M

M-WAVE BEHAVIOR
    nabilone (Lilly compound no. 109514)
        monkeys, 3381
MACROMOLECULAR SYNTHESIS
    cannabichromene (CBC)
        lymphocytes, 4523
        tissue cultures, 3442
    cannabicyclol (CBL)
        lymphocytes, 4523
        tissue cultures, 3442
    cannabidiol (CBD), 5071
        lymphocytes, 4523
        rats, 4042, 4043
        testis(es), 4042, 4043
        tissue cultures, 3442
    cannabigerol (CBG)
        lymphocytes, 4523
        rats, 4042, 4043
        testis(es), 4042, 4043
    cannabinoid(s)
        deoxyribonucleic acid (DNA), 5588
        HeLa cells, 5509, 5588
        nucleic acids, 5509
        protein synthesis, 5509
        radioimmunoassay (RIA), 5588
        ribonucleic acid (RNA), 5588
    cannabinol (CBN)
        in vitro, 5367
        lymphocytes, 4523
        rats, 4042, 4043
        testis(es), 4042, 4043
        tissue cultures, 3442
    cannabis extract
        ovaries, 3621
    delta-8-THC, 5071
        lymphocytes, 4523
        rats, 4042, 4043
        testis(es), 4042, 4043
        tissue cultures, 3442
    delta-9-THC, 4411, 5071
        bacteria, 3177
        deoxyribonucleic acid (DNA), 4522, 5193, 5194
        DNA synthesis, 3349, 3606, 3776, 4022, 4318,
            4513, 4524, 4533, 5241
        HeLa cells, 4483
        in vitro, 3125, 4318, 4513, 5194, 5241, 5367
        lymphocytes, 3606, 4523, 4524, 4533
        protein, 3349, 4522, 5193
        protein synthesis, 3606, 4318, 4533, 5241
        rats, 4042, 4043
        ribonucleic acid (RNA), 4522
        RNA synthesis, 3349, 3606, 3776, 4022, 4318,
            4524, 4533, 5241
        testis(es), 4042, 4043
        tissue culture, 3348, 3690, 4022
        tissue cultures, 3349, 3442
        tolerance, 5193
    8 beta, 11-dihydroxy-delta-9-THC
        tissue cultures, 3442
    hashish
        humans, 5439
        spermatozoa, 5439
        white blood cells, 5439

MACROMOLECULAR SYNTHESIS (continued)
  8-beta-hydroxy-delta-9-THC
    rats, 4042, 4043
    testis(es), 4042, 4043
  11-hydroxy-delta-8-THC
    lymphocytes, 4523
  11-hydroxy-delta-9-THC, 5071
    lymphocytes, 4523
    rats, 4042, 4043
    testis(es), 4042, 4043
  marihuana, 3239
    adverse effect(s), 3500
    lymphocytes, 4532
MACROPHAGES
  cannabidiol (CBD)
    pathology, 4702
  delta-9-THC, 3804
    pathology, 4702
MAMMARY GLANDS
  delta-9-THC
    growth, 4689
    mice, 4689
MARIHUANA
  abuse of, 3420
  adverse effect(s), 3049, 3124, 3398, 3599, 3655,
    3766, 3848, 4083, 4098, 4723
    accumulation, 3500
    acute effect(s), 3114
    adolescent(s), 5493
    aggressive behavior, 4107
    amotivational syndrome, 3274, 3276, 3477, 3500,
      3739, 4107, 4529, 5244, 5291, 5506
    angina pectoris, 3263
    anxiety, 3795
    autonomic nervous system effect(s), 4992
    behavior, 4992
    body temperature, 4776
    brain, 4176
    brain function(s), 5291
    brain pathology, 3240, 3347, 3392, 3487, 3739,
      4208, 4632
    cancer, 3741
    carcinogenesis, 5548
    cell metabolism, 3240, 3347, 4632
    cerebral cortex, 3487, 4208
    chromosome, damage, 3240, 3347, 4401, 4529
    chromosomes, 3215, 4632
    chronic use, 3114, 3477, 3481, 3494, 3893
    cognitive function, 5489
    compared to:
      alcohol, 3266, 4592, 5551
      heroin, 5468
      tobacco, 3263, 4592, 5537
    contaminant, 5622
    cytogenic effects, 4776
    cytotoxicity, 3916
    diabetes mellitus, 3336
    driving, 3239, 3240, 3247, 3741, 4107, 4307,
      4466, 4467, 4498, 4499, 4632, 4776, 5027,
      5291
    endocrine effects, 4776, 5551
    endocrine system, 3240, 3347, 4632
    epidemiological study, 5551
    exercise, 5017
    eyes, 4776

adverse effect(s) (continued)
  flying performance, 3240, 4632
  fungal infection, 3482
  gastrointestinal tract, 3494
  general information, 3082, 3138, 3657, 4097,
    4468, 5049
    physicians, 4099
  government programs and funding, 5607
  gynecomastia, 3248, 4621
  headache, 3505
  health hazards, 5468, 5523
  heart rate, 5017
  hematology, 4776
  immune system, 3240, 3741, 4632, 4776, 5017
  immunosuppression, 3392, 4529
  impotence, 3392, 4529
  inhalation, 5537
  interaction with
    alcohol, 4992
    amphetamine, 5157
  intravenous administration, 3710, 4030
  ketoacidosis, 3336
  lactation, 5515
  lung(s), 3392, 3482, 3741, 3916, 4529, 4592
  macromolecular synthesis, 3500
  memory, 5291
  motor activity, 3142, 3741, 4776
  neurological effects, 3477, 4776
  neuropharmacological effects, 5551
  oral epithelium, 4615, 5160
  oral surgery, 4005
  overdose, 3266
  overview, 4999
  paranoia, 5187, 5489
  paraquat, 3544, 3708, 4549, 4662, 4906, 5190
  paraquat contamination, 5237
  perception, 4776
  performance, 3500, 3893, 4107, 4176, 4776
  personality, 3347, 5126, 5291
  pharmacological aspects, 5551
  physical activity, 3274, 3276
  poisoning, 5361, 5403
  pregnancy, 3247, 5515
  progression to other drugs, 4466
  psychological aspects, 5005
  psychological effects, 4776, 5551
  psychosis, 3106, 3172, 3247, 3250, 3481, 3739,
    4107, 5291, 5489
  psychosocial aspects, 5126
  pulmonary effects, 5284
  pyrolytic products, 5548
  reproductive system, 3248
  research, 3328, 5607
  respiratory effects, 3347, 4776
  respiratory system, 3500
  review, 3231, 3240, 3246, 3250, 3392, 3481,
    3500, 3651, 3741, 4107, 4151, 5285, 5517,
    5592, 5637
  sexual behavior, 3477, 3494
  side effects, 5436
  sleep, 3274, 3276
  teratogenesis, 5551
  testis(es), 4176
  testosterone, 3494
  therapy, 3082, 5187

adverse effect(s) (continued)
    time estimation, 4176
    toxic delirium, 4107
    visual tracking, 3142
analysis, 5152
    biological fluid(s), 5144
    carcinogenicity, 5434
    chromatography, 5476
    color tests, 4019, 5214
    comparisons
        thin layer chromatography (TLC), 4290
    confiscated samples, 3118, 5080
    contact test, 5220
    cyanide, 3411
    delta-9-THC, 5455, 5552
    delta-9-THC oic acid A & B, 5455
    detection, 3707, 3892, 4019, 4136, 4155, 4506,
        5027, 5144, 5214, 5220
    EMIT (homogenous enzyme immunoassay), 3239
    forensic aspects, 3241
    gas chromatography, 4003, 4506, 5003, 5080
    gas liquid chromatography (GLC), 3707, 4557,
        5144
    GC/MS, 4155, 4556
    geographical origin, 4003
    headspace volatiles, 4003
    high-pressure liquid chromatography (HPLC), 5455
    identification, 5213, 5434
    mass spectrometry, 4557
    metabolites, 4136, 4155
    microscopic examination, 4506
    paraquat, 4121, 4293, 5080, 5081, 5345, 5501,
        5520, 5622
    pyrolytic products, 3410, 4391
        GC/MS, 4391
    quantitative, 3707
    radioimmunoassay (RIA), 3239
    review, 3239
    separation
        cannabidiol (CBD), 3366
        cannabinol (CBN), 3366
        delta-9-THC, 3366
        phytosterols, 3366
    spectrophotometry, 5476
    sterols, 4556
    street drugs, 5213
    street samples, 3493, 4285, 5552
    thin layer chromatography (TLC), 3239, 4019,
        4136, 4506, 5080, 5144, 5214, 5220, 5434
    vapor phase, 3892
behavioral effect(s), 3307, 3454
    aggression, 3241
    aggressive behavior, 3063, 3161, 3162, 3234,
        3240, 4516, 4632, 4778
    compared to:
        alcohol, 4419, 5069
        heroin, 4419
    conditioned behavior, 4414
    constituents of
        discriminative properties, 4203
    coordination, 3894
    decision-making, 4789
    discrimination, 3218
    drug use, 5493
    gross behavior, 3953

behavioral effect(s) (continued)
    hallucinations, 4064
    interaction with
        d-amphetamines, 3697
        dopamine (DA), 4516
        norepinephrine (NE), 4516
        serotonin (5-hydroxytryptamine), 4516
    intoxication, 4640, 4647, 4777
    learned behavior, 3218, 3240
    memory, 3218, 3894
    mood, 4428
    motivation, 3894, 4419
    neo-natal exposure, 3241
    operant behavior, 3870, 4435
    operant work, 4422, 4423
    perception, 4789
    review, 3239, 4778, 5069, 5093
    self administration, 3870
    sexual behavior, 3997, 4638, 5165
    social behavior, 3234, 3240, 3252, 4419, 4632,
        4777, 5176
    stress, 3063, 4632
    suggestibility, 3070
    tolerance, 3443, 3731, 3736
beneficial effect(s)
    driving, 4307
benefit(s), 5244
bibliography, 4587
biochemical aspects
    biotransformation, 5589
    metabolites, 3241
biochemical effect(s)
chromosome damage, 4975
    chromosomes, 4400
    compared to:
        tobacco, 3111
    cytological changes, 4399
    deoxyribonucleic acid (DNA), 3709
    DNA synthesis, 3111
    macromolecular synthesis, 3239, 4256, 4532
    metabolism, 5523
botanical aspects, 4804
    cannabinoid content, 3215
    National Institute on Drug Abuse (NIDA), 5606
    sex differences, 3741
    species, 4884
    standardized samples, 5606
cannabinoid(s)
    benzopyranopyridine(s), 5486
chemical aspects
    cannabinoid content, 5003
    cigarette preparation
    constituents of, 4158
        acid(s), 4391
        alkaloid(s), 4770
        anhydrocannabisativine, 4770
        cannabichromene (CBC), 3215, 3919, 4918,
            5144, 5152
        cannabichromenic acid, 3919
        cannabicyclol (CBL), 3215, 3919, 4918, 5144
        cannabidiol (CBD), 3215, 3919, 4770, 4918,
            5144
        cannabidiolic acid, 3919
        cannabidiorcol, 4918
        cannabidivarol, 3919, 4918

constituents of (continued)
    cannabielsoic acid, 3919, 4918
    cannabigerol (CBG), 3919, 4918, 5144
    cannabigerolic acid, 3919
    cannabinoid(s), 4391
    cannabinol (CBN), 3215, 3919, 4770, 4918,
      5144
    cannabinol-7-oic acid, 3919
    cannabiorcol, 4918
    cannabisativine, 4770
    cannabivarichromene, 4918
    cannabivarol, 3919, 4918
    delta-8-THC, 3215, 3919, 4770, 4918, 5144
    delta-8-THC-oic acid, 3919
    delta-9-THC, 3215, 3919, 4770, 4918, 5144
    delta-9-THC-oic acid A & B, 3919, 4918
    delta-9-tetrahydrocannabiorcol, 4918
    delta-9-tetrahydrocannabivarol, 3919, 4918
    indoles, 4770
    phenols, 4391
    polycyclic aromatic hydrocarbons, 4555
    review, 4770
    beta-sitosterol, 3215
    sterols, 4556
    terpenes, 3892
  forensic aspects, 5523
  geographical origin, 4557
  history, 3390
  metabolism, 3240, 4632
  pyrolytic products, 4158, 4555
  review, 3239, 3922, 4918
  smoke condensate analysis, 3991, 4017, 4102,
    4158, 4238, 4391, 4555, 4605
  structure-activity relationships, 4663, 4918
clinical aspects
  accumulation, 4531
  flashbacks, 3402
  metabolism, 4531
  performance, 4531
  potency, 4531
  review, 4531
  subjective effects, 4531
  tolerance, 4531
  users vs nonusers, 4531
clinical findings, 3250
cytogenic effects
  cell membrane(s), 5513
  compared to:
    neuroleptic drugs, 5513
driving, 4106, 4500, 4502
  adverse effect(s), 4498
drug abuse, 3101
  education, 4491
  legal aspects, 3081
  medical aspects, 3081
  problems, 4810
  sociological aspects, 3081
drug dependence, 4917
drug use, 3655, 4902
  theory of mechanism of effect, 3716
economic benefits, 3791
epidemiological study, 5169
  adolescent(s), 5424
  adverse effect(s), 3048, 3131, 3350, 3599, 3795,
    4176, 5503
  attitude, 3241

epidemiological study (continued)
  attitudes of users, 3153, 4187, 4793, 5577
  beneficial effect(s), 3599, 4752
  characteristics of users, 3057, 3069, 3071, 3166,
    3236, 3364, 3365, 3419, 3454, 3455, 3583,
    3586, 3601, 3626, 3670, 3818, 3977, 3978,
    4065, 4066, 4067, 4069, 4125, 4150, 4163,
    4165, 4169, 4174, 4300, 4367, 4416, 4439,
    4505, 4507, 4584, 4593, 4612, 4646, 4666,
    4667, 4764, 4809, 4837, 4843, 4867, 4933,
    4938, 5143, 5175
  cognitive function, 4426
  compared to: 4932
    alcohol, 3055, 3152, 3302, 3365, 3417, 3488,
      3670, 3792, 3821, 3879, 4132, 4424, 4438,
      4485, 4573, 4575, 4752, 4764, 4790, 4813,
      4856, 4973, 5167, 5291, 5529, 5566
    amphetamine, 3875, 4814
    barbiturate(s), 3879, 4814
    cigarette smoking, 4856
    cocaine, 3875
    drugs, 4856
    heroin, 3091, 3174, 3875, 4956
    LSD, 3131, 3879, 4957
    mescaline, 3131
    other drugs, 5248
    tobacco, 3302, 3670, 3792, 3821, 4438, 4932,
      4973, 5291, 5529
  correlates of use, 3821
  cross cultural research, 3069, 3745
  driving, 3152, 3879, 4501
  drug abuse, 3148, 3175, 3875, 4368
  drug abuse prevention, 3278, 3600
  drug effects, 3669
  drug information center, 3484
  drug use, 4855, 4856, 5037, 5038
  education, 4764
  emotional aspects, 5566
  environment, 5566
  factors influencing use, 3057, 3060, 3082, 3106,
    3138, 3157, 3278, 3400, 3418, 3455, 3601,
    3649, 3972, 4065, 4165, 4175, 4606, 4666,
    4901, 4938, 4953, 4954, 5177
  increase in use, 3217, 3659
  interaction with
    tobacco, 5529
  legal aspects, 3345, 3949, 4085, 4890, 4972
  motivation, 4426, 5508
  motivation of use, 3091, 3398, 3419, 4186, 4219,
    4301, 4573, 4661, 4752, 4813, 5126, 5143,
    5175, 5177, 5306
  multiple drug use, 3091, 3145, 3148, 3174, 3302,
    3378, 3488, 3489, 3548, 3586, 3626, 3649,
    3792, 3875, 3885, 3987, 4065, 4125, 4132,
    4168, 4169, 4368, 4421, 4424, 4535, 4666,
    4791, 4800, 4809, 4814, 4856, 4868, 5143,
    5174, 5538
  patterns of use, 3048, 3055, 3056, 3084, 3088,
    3091, 3106, 3126, 3145, 3148, 3154, 3166,
    3174, 3191, 3233, 3236, 3239, 3240, 3278,
    3477, 3488, 3494, 3548, 3626, 3658, 3659,
    3670, 3717, 3741, 3875, 3978, 4066, 4131,
    4132, 4169, 4473, 4505, 4535, 4573, 4800,
    4813, 4814, 4823, 4856, 4869, 4956, 5126,
    5167, 5248

epidemiological study (continued)
performance, 4426
personality, 3885, 4222, 4867
physiological changes, 4426
predicting drug use, 3047, 3141, 3170, 3240, 3305, 3306, 3878, 3885, 3972, 4067, 4125, 4175, 4300, 4301, 4606, 4632, 4646, 4767, 4793, 5285
progression to other drugs, 3166, 3174, 3652, 4131, 4507, 4535, 4809, 4868, 4869, 4956, 5197
psychological aspects, 3131, 3583, 4175, 4187, 4367, 4416, 4606, 4790, 4901, 4933, 4957, 5185, 5221
psychosis, 3166, 4207
racial differences, 3792
related to
alcohol, 5037, 5038
coffee, 5037, 5038
smoking, 5037, 5038
relaxation, 4575
religious beliefs, 4222, 4594
review, 3239, 3919
sex differences, 4606, 4666, 5168
sexual behavior, 3088, 3415, 5364
social behavior, 4575
social problems, 3224
sociological aspects, 3056, 3057, 3109, 3126, 3141, 3157, 3415, 3417, 3418, 4168, 4219, 4367, 4416, 4438, 4573, 4574, 4584, 4723, 4767, 5066, 5185
subjective effects, 4000, 5538
teratogenic effects, 4548
tobacco, 4132
folklore
India, 4839, 4841
forensic aspects
analysis, 3118, 4557, 5080
headspace volatiles, 4003
cannabinoid content, 4765
color tests, 4019
confiscated samples, 3118, 4765, 5080
contact test, 5220
detection, 3881, 4019, 4308, 4506, 4765, 5061, 5220
fast blue B salt, 5476
geographical origin, 4557, 5061
species, 4884
taxonomy, 4884
general information
adulteration, 4688
adverse effect(s), 4530
availability, 3284
government programs and funding, 3654
history, 4530
multiple drug use, 3654
overdose
therapy, 3891
paraquat, 4405, 4662, 4907
paraquat contamination, 4549, 5081, 5237
paraquat spraying, 4905
physicians, 3217, 3657, 4097
potency, 4979
regulated marketing, 3796
street samples, 4688

MARIHUANA (continued)
history, 3215, 3658, 5216
international control, 5517
legal aspects, 3268, 5517
medicine, 3412
research, 5517
review, 3080, 5093
use, 5517
immunology
adverse effect(s), 4530
antibodies, 4835
antibody response, 4836
antibody formation, 4835
cell-mediated immunity, 3132, 3551, 3552, 3554, 4106, 4107, 4398, 4508, 4532, 4627, 4682, 4737, 4866
cellular immunity, 4630
clinical findings, 4835
humoral immunity, 3551, 4398, 4508, 4630, 4682, 4736, 4737
immune system, 4404
immunoglobulins, 3579
lymphocyte function, 4628
lymphocytes, 3579, 4227, 4228, 5196
red blood cells, 4836
reticulocytosis, 4836
review, 3893, 4398, 4404
legal aspects, 3091, 3101, 3103, 3114, 3124, 3217, 3231, 3658, 3758, 3791, 3793, 3848, 3856, 3949, 3977, 4083, 4151, 4182, 4213, 4268, 4308, 4450, 4625, 4669, 4723, 4747, 4804, 4842, 4972, 4991, 5408
arrests, 4085
availability, 3284
Canada, 3693
compared to:
alcohol, 3758
other drugs, 3420
tobacco, 3758
decriminalization, 3232, 3241, 3249, 3345, 3453, 3557, 3584, 3887, 4490, 4828, 5054, 5186, 5209, 5285, 5578
general information, 4999
history, 3268
identification, 4214
species, 4442
legalization issue, 3106, 3833, 3916
medical use, 5553, 5605
Mexico, 4917
paraquat, 4906
patterns of use, 3557
political ideology, 5637
possession, 4214
regulation, 5526
review, 3268, 5285
trafficking, 5285
U.S.A., 3693
memory, 4456, 4748
morals and ethics
compared to:
other drugs, 3420
neuropharmacological effects
electroencephalogram (EEG), 5489
neurophysiology, 4784
electroencephalogram (EEG), 3239, 3901, 3953, 4106, 4107, 4109, 4138

neurophysiology (continued)
    neural transmission, 3613
    REM sleep, 4107, 4138
    sleep, 4106
pharmacokinetics
    absorption, 4663
    disposition, 5017
    distribution, 4663
    metabolism, 4663
    review, 3922
pharmacological aspects
    acute effect(s), 3762, 5291
    adrenals, 4617
    aggressive behavior, 4751
    analgesia, 3973
    analgesic, 4547
    anti-convulsant activity, 3519, 3901
    antiemetic, 3216, 5283
    appetite, 3789
    asthma, 5012
    biogenic amine(s), 3063
    blood-brain barrier, 3895
    blood chemistry, 4028
    blood flow, 4275
    blood parameters, 3493
    blood test(s), 4428
    body temperature, 3323, 3902, 3903, 4275
    body weight, 4028
    brain, 4711, 4982
    cancer, 4547
    cardiovascular effects, 3159, 3215, 3240, 3273,
        3323, 3375, 3483, 3499, 3503, 3533, 3697,
        3762, 3812, 3902, 3903, 4005, 4106, 4107,
        4130, 4275, 4428, 4429, 4537, 4559, 4632,
        4642, 4643, 4644, 4664, 4665, 4717, 4788,
        4789, 4831, 4964, 4993, 5052, 5108, 5589
    cellular division, 4028
    central nervous system (CNS), 3632
    cerebral dominance, 4982
    chemotherapy, 4547
    chronic effects, 3239, 3493, 3762, 4106
    clearance rates, 5452
    clinical findings, 3503, 3762, 4110
    compared to:
        alcohol, 3193, 3311, 3747, 5069
        barbiturate(s), 3747
        chlorpromazine, 5283
        ethanol, 4663
        isoproterenol, 5012
        LSD, 4663
        pentobarbital, 3311
        tobacco, 4028, 4116
    dependence, 3174, 3241, 5493
    drug interactions, 4663, 5589
    epilepsy, 4388
    exercise, 4831
    eyes, 3215, 3493, 3503, 3747, 3966, 4110
    food intake, 3789
    gastrointestinal tract, 4414
    glaucoma, 3251
    glucose metabolism, 4622
    hearing, 4277
    heart, 3375
    heart rate, 5105, 5505
    history, 3390

pharmacological aspects (continued)
    interaction with
        amphetamine, 3789
        anesthetic(s), 3675
        atropine, 4005
        chlorpromazine, 3063
        d-amphetamines, 3697
        disulfiram, 4730
        epinephrine, 4005
        haloperidol, 3063
        nicotine, 4414
        norethynodiel, 4617
        penicillin, 3895
        propranolol, 4993, 5108
        secobarbital, 4248
        stress, 4537
        theophylline, 4116
    intraocular pressure (IOP), 3251, 3499, 3533,
        3966, 3967
    light adaptation, 3194
    lung(s), 5012
    medical use, 5523
    memory, 3811, 4459, 4751
    metabolism, 4106
    monoamine oxidase (MAO), 4983
    motor activity, 5561
    ocular effects, 5405
    overview, 4999
    pain, 4469
    perception, 4751
    physical dependence, 3239, 3240, 3247, 3739,
        4106, 4107, 4110, 4632
    platelets, 4983
    psychosis, 3399
    pupil size, 4275
    respiratory effects, 3159, 3215, 3283, 3309, 3310,
        3311, 3323, 3499, 3503, 4106, 4107, 4275,
        4428, 4429, 4632, 4831, 5013, 5198, 5245,
    review, 3250, 3481, 3483, 3893, 3922, 4106,
        4107, 4918, 5069, 5093, 5132, 5406, 5591
    seizures, 3717
    sexual behavior, 4751
    skin conductance, 4275, 4537, 4717
    sputum analysis, 4833
    stress, 4005
    testosterone levels, 4028
    tolerance, 3239, 3240, 3241, 3273, 3309, 3310,
        3739, 3893, 3922, 4106, 4107, 4110, 4527,
        4559, 4617, 4632, 4663, 5291, 5493, 5561
    vision, 3193, 3194, 3195, 3973
    visual acuity, 3195
    visual tracking, 3747
    withdrawal syndrome, 5031
physiological effects, 3728
    aphrodisiac(s), 5364
    blood pressure, 5298
    cardiovascular effects, 4279
    electroencephalogram (EEG), 4279
    endocrine effects, 3215, 3234, 3239, 3499, 3549,
        3774, 3956, 3957, 4106, 4107, 4177, 4179,
        4429, 4430, 4432, 4433, 4621, 4725, 4737,
        4787
    exercise, 5298
    follicle stimulating hormone (FSH), 4016
    gonadal function, 3957

574

physiological effects (continued)
  heart rate, 4642, 5298
  luteinizing hormone (LH), 4016, 4431
  pulmonary effects, 5298
  reproductive effects, 4177, 4404
  reproductive system, 3248, 4016
  respiratory effects, 3283
  review, 4404, 5591
  sexual behavior, 4106, 5364
  sexual function, 4107
  spermatozoa, 4016
  spermatogenesis, 3956, 4016
  sperms, 3957, 4971
  steroids, 4005
  testosterone, 4016, 4431
psychological aspects
  adverse effect(s), 4041, 4436, 4518, 4519, 4700, 5474
  aggressive behavior, 3161, 3162, 4106, 4778, 5053
  amotivational syndrome, 3215, 3434, 4418, 4444
  anxiety, 3172, 3893, 4106
  attention, 3168
  bias of experimenter, 3757
  brain, 3925
  brain function(s), 3745
  characteristics of users, 3068, 3071
  chronic effects, 4964
  chronic use, 3870
  classification
    hypnotic, 3149
    sedative, 3149
  cognitive function, 3636, 3925, 4107, 4110, 4173, 4457
  cognitive processes, 3367, 3429, 3535, 4279, 5547
  compared to:
    alcohol, 4180, 4279, 4355, 4502, 4713, 5053
    psychotropic drugs, 5388
  coordination, 3635, 4937
  creativity, 5051
  decision-making, 4355, 4766
  dominance, 3499
  drug abuse, 5493
  drug use, 3716, 4001, 4766
  electroencephalogram (EEG), 4191
  environmental conditions, 4001, 4092, 4641, 4718
  euphoria, 4559, 4641, 4642, 4643, 4644, 4749, 4993
  evoked potentials, 4180
  factors influencing use, 3275
  family relationships, 5493
  flashbacks, 3402, 4444, 4957
  flying performance, 3346
  group interaction, 4429
  habituation, 3716, 5259
  hallucinations, 4191
  hypnotic susceptibility, 3052
  intelligence, 3745, 4784
  interaction with
    haloperidol, 3052
    secobarbital, 3572
  intoxication, 3790
  learning, 3168, 3185, 3496, 4255, 4645, 5109
  memory, 3122, 3185, 3577, 3635, 3973, 4429, 4453, 4455, 4456, 4458, 4459, 4461, 4937, 4980, 5050, 5109

psychological aspects (continued)
  memory impairment, 5505
  mood, 4107, 4429, 4443, 4749
  motivation, 3434, 4255, 4645
  motivation of use, 3398, 5151, 5306, 5388, 5472, 5502
  motor coordination, 4217, 4470
  motor performance, 3367, 3636, 4713
  operant behavior, 4429
  operant work, 4434
  perception, 3196, 3636, 3828, 4107, 4332, 4457, 4470, 4500, 4501, 4645, 4713, 4903
  performance, 3215, 3239, 3240, 3307, 3346, 3434, 3499, 3503, 3572, 3635, 3893, 4013, 4106, 4110, 4216, 4255, 4434, 4443, 4540, 4614, 4645, 4713, 4775, 4937, 4962, 5109
  personality, 3745, 4646, 4784, 4815, 4901, 5174, 5291
  predicting drug use, 5259
  productivity, 3434
  psychosis, 3172, 3188, 3239, 3650, 3893, 4106, 4207, 4444, 5005, 5039, 5064, 5506
  reaction time, 4614, 4645
  related to
    heroin abusers, 5530
  review, 3185, 3239, 3250, 4443
  schizophrenia, 3650, 5039
  self administration, 3275
  set and setting, 4903
  sex differences, 4013
  sexual behavior, 4427, 5291
  sleep, 3200, 4138
  social behavior, 3068, 3071, 4429, 4901
  state-dependent learning, 3973, 4457, 4980
  stress, 3364, 4641
  subjective effects, 3250, 3273, 3503, 3572, 3702, 3728, 3762, 3848, 4106, 4107, 4109, 4110, 4537, 4903, 5052, 5108, 5435, 5505
  suggestibility, 4156
  time estimation, 3168, 3635, 4937
  time perception, 5052
  tolerance, 3273
  toxic delirium, 3893, 4106
  use, 5530
  vision, 3196
  visual acuity, 4502
  visual tracking, 4500
psychological effects
  review, 5591
psychopharmacological aspects
  amotivational syndrome, 4420
  multiple drug use, 4420
  self administration, 4420
psychosocial aspects, 5169, 5202
  memory, 4637
  review, 4634
reaction time, 4748
research, 3328, 4632, 4634, 5152
  bias of experimenter, 3163
  government programs and funding, 3656
  history, 3390
  National Institute on Drug Abuse (NIDA), 3996, 4904
  problems, 3066
  recommendations, 3241
  review, 5516

research (continued)
    standardized samples, 5153
    United Nations Narcotics Commission, 4904
    World Health Organization (WHO), 4904
review
    adverse effect(s), 3240, 3250, 3392, 3481, 3500,
        3741, 3893, 4107, 4151, 4466, 4467
        driving, 4499
    aggressive behavior, 4778
    behavioral effect(s), 5069, 5093
    cardiovascular effects, 3483
    chemical aspects, 3922, 4663, 4770
    chromosomes, 4398
    cognitive function, 4173
    constituents of
        discriminative properties, 4203
    fetal development, 3699
    general information, 3215
    history, 3080, 4663, 5093
    immune system, 4404
    immunology, 4398
    learning, 3185
    legal aspects, 3268, 3392, 5285
    memory, 3185
    patterns of use, 3919, 4663
    pharmacokinetics, 3922, 4663
    pharmacological aspects, 3250, 3481, 3893, 3922,
        4107, 4663, 5069, 5093
    pharmacology, 5132
    psychological aspects, 3250, 3893, 4443
    psychosocial aspects, 4634
    reproductive effects, 4404
    sociological aspects, 3833, 3893
    teratogenic effects, 3699
    therapeutic aspects, 3215, 3893, 3922, 4770, 5017
    toxicology, 3922, 4527, 4663, 5132
sociological aspects, 3103, 3109, 3659, 3758, 4450,
    4574, 5169, 5242
    adverse effect(s), 3231, 5474
    aggressive behavior, 3160
    aphrodisiac(s), 3805
    attitude, 3241
    characteristics of users, 3455
    compared to:
        alcohol, 3135
        other drugs, 3420
    correlates of use, 3833
    crime, 3160, 5291
    cultural use, 3893
    current use, 3893
    decriminalization, 4633
    drug interactions, 5435
    factors influencing use, 3275, 3400, 3455
    legal aspects, 3241, 3893, 4633
    legalization issue, 5578
    medical use, 3893
    morals and ethics, 4633
    motivation of use, 3833, 5472, 5590
    multiple drug use, 3833
    parental influence, 5590
    patterns of use, 3884, 5376, 5587
    peer influence, 5590
    progression to other drugs, 3158
    recreational use, 3893
    review, 3833, 3893, 5637

sociological aspects (continued)
    sex differences, 3192, 5587
    sexual activity, 3805
    sexual behavior, 3378
    social interaction, 3192, 3272, 3277
    socioeconomic activity, 3884
street samples, 3408
therapeutic aspects, 3420, 3599, 5216
    alcoholism, 4730, 4731
    analgesia, 3497, 3893
    analgesic, 4182
    anorexia, 3497
    anti-anxiety activity, 3497
    anti-bacterial activity, 3497, 4182
    antibiotic activity, 3893
    anti-convulsant activity, 3893, 4182
    anti-neoplastic activity, 3497, 3741, 3893, 4182
    antidepressant, 3497, 3893
    antiemetic, 3240, 3497, 3893, 5553
    aphrodisiac(s), 3893
    asthma, 3240, 3497, 4182, 5011, 5017, 5105
    bronchodilatation, 3254, 3893, 5011, 5105
    cancer, 3254, 3495, 3502, 5283, 5553
    epilepsy, 3497
    glaucoma, 3254, 3495, 3497, 3502, 3533, 3741,
        3856, 3919, 3966, 3967, 4182, 5017, 5286
    intraocular pressure (IOP), 3240, 3893
    medical use, 5605
    overview, 3996
    preanesthetic medication, 3497, 4182
    review, 3215, 3241, 3893, 3922, 5017, 5637
    sedative, 3893
    substitute for
        heroin, 3679
    therapy, 5436
therapeutic effects
    antiemetic, 5471
    asthma, 5473
    cancer, 5471
    glaucoma, 5289
    pulmonary effects, 5473
toxicology, 4613, 4663
    acute effect(s), 4527
    behavioral effect(s), 3241
    brain, 3953, 4527
    carcinogenicity, 4143
    carcinogenesis, 4256
    cardiovascular effects, 3241
    chromosome damage, 3123
    chromosomes, 3807, 4398
    chronic effects, 4143, 4527
    chronic use, 3241
    clinical aspects, 5406
    clinical findings, 4030
    endocrine effects, 3241
    fetal development, 3699
    food intake, 4738
    gastrointestinal tract, 4527
    growth, 4738
    growth profile, 5561
    heart, 5589
    hematology, 4030
    immune system, 3241, 4527
    inhalation, 4738
    inhalation toxicology, 4742, 5561

toxicology (continued)
  interaction with
    alcohol, 3241
    paraquat, 5284
  intravenous administration, 3241
  lethality, 5561
  liver, 4527
  lung(s), 3111, 4403, 4527
  mutagenesis, 3250, 3709, 4256, 4398, 4399
  mutagenic effects, 3123, 4400, 4527, 4975
  mutagenic tests, 4495
  nervous system, 3241
  organ weights, 4738
  overdose, 5589
  paraquat, 5305
  peripheral nervous system, 3614
  poisoning, 5406
  psychological aspects, 3241
  pulmonary effects, 3241
  respiratory effects, 5561
  respiratory system, 4403, 5007
  review, 3699, 3922, 4527, 5132
  sex differences, 4738
  teratogenesis, 3250, 4398
  teratogenic effects, 3699, 3893, 4143, 4527, 4548, 4975
  testicular effects, 5561
  water intake, 4738
trafficking, 3171
trauma, 3676
MARIHUANA EXTRACT
  adverse effect(s)
    maternal behavior, 5276
    prenatal exposure, 5276
  behavioral effect(s)
    aggression, 3450
    aggressive behavior, 3449, 4489
    biogenic amine(s), 3449
    conditioned behavior, 3435, 4517
    discriminative properties, 4203
    food deprivation, 4517
    interaction with
      cannabidiol, (CBD), 4517
    REM sleep, 3450, 4489
    sex differences, 3065
    sleep, 4489
    tolerance, 3435
  biochemical effect(s)
    chromosomes, 4976
    cytological changes, 4976
    lipolysis, 5217
  immunology
    allergy, 4269
    delayed hypersensitivity reaction, 5510
    host resistance, 5510
    immunosuppression, 5510
  neurophysiology
    electroencephalogram (EEG), 3722
  pharmacological aspects
    analgesia, 4926
    anti-convulsant activity, 3660
    biogenic amine(s), 3450
    lipolysis, 5217
    lung(s), 3849
    respiratory effects, 3849
    sleep, 3722

MARIHUANA EXTRACT (continued)
  physiological effects
    endocrine effects, 3351
    reproductive effects, 3351
    review, 3351
    sexual behavior, 3351
  reproductive effects
    adrenals, 5392
    estrus cycle, 5392
    maternal behavior, 5276
    ovaries, 5392
    uterus, 5392
  review, 3435
    discriminative properties, 4203
    endocrine effects, 3351
    reproductive effects, 3351
    sexual behavior, 3351
    teratogenic effects, 4326
  toxicology
    behavioral teratogenesis, 5275
    body weight, 5353
    estrus cycle, 4184
    fetal development, 4184
    placental transfer, 3351
    prenatal exposure, 5275
    reproductive effects, 3389
    reproductive system, 4184, 5226
    skeleton, 5353
    teratogenic effects, 3351, 4184, 5226
MARIHUANA SMOKE
  adverse effect(s)
    allergy, 4284
    alveolar macrophage(s), 4018, 5362, 5363
    body weight, 5431
    compared to:
      tobacco, 5362, 5363
    gynecomastia, 3457
    lactation, 5399
    lung(s), 4018, 4284, 5016, 5103
    seminal vesicle, 5431
    spermatozoa, 5431
    testis(es), 5431
  analgesic activity, 5347
  analysis
    delta-8-THC, 4564
    delta-9-THC, 4564
    detection, 4484
    gas chromatography, 4484
    GC/MS, 4238
    identification
      GC/MS, 3299
      nuclear magnetic resonance (NMR), 3299
      polycyclic aromatic hydrocarbons, 3299
    nuclear magnetic resonance (NMR), 4238
    polycyclic aromatic hydrocarbons, 4238
    review, 4531
    thin layer chromatography (TLC), 4484
  behavioral effect(s), 5070
    aggressive behavior, 4303
    amotivational syndrome, 5450
    ataxia, 4996
    behavioral screen, 5068
    CNS activity, 4303
    compared to:
      heroin, 3271

behavioral effect(s) (continued)
   crime, 5450
   cross tolerance, 3770
   motor activity, 3770, 4303, 5172
   personality, 5450
   self administration, 3271
   social behavior, 3271
   stimulant activity, 4303
   tolerance, 3770, 4303, 5560
   various fractions, 5068
biochemical effect(s)
   cell growth, 4258
   cytological changes, 4258
   deoxyribonucleic acid (DNA), 4258
   nucleic acids, 5125
brain, 5136
chemical aspects
   cannabinoid(s), 5279
   carbon monoxide, 5432
   constituents of
      polycyclic aromatic hydrocarbons, 4238
   particulate matter, 5432
   pyrolytic products, 5432
   water pipes, 5279
clinical aspects
   interaction with
      methaqualone, 5633
compared to:
   tobacco, 5103
delta-8-THC
   mitosis, 5511
electroencephalogram (EEG), 5136
epidemiological study
   compared to:
      other drugs, 5450
   patterns of use, 5450
immunology
   immunosuppression, 4017
   lung(s), 5423, 5433
inhalation
   metabolites, 5238
neurochemical effects
   acetylcholinesterase, 4303
   ribonucleic acid (RNA), 4303
neurophysiological effects
   septal region, 5512
   ultrastructural changes, 5512
pharmacokinetics
   absorption, 4254
   disposition, 4254
   excretion, 4254
   metabolism, 4254
pharmacological aspects
   anti-bacterial activity, 4315
   body weight, 3868, 5171, 5172, 5370
   bronchodilatation, 5271
   cardiovascular effects, 3701, 3803, 3837, 3847,
      4996, 4997, 5008, 5247
   central nervous system (CNS), 4740
   compared to:
      delta-9-THC, 5271
      isoproterenol, 5271
      tobacco, 5370
   euphoria, 5238
   eyes, 3746

pharmacological aspects (continued)
   food intake, 3868
   intraocular pressure (IOP), 3746, 4287, 5414
   lung(s), 3969, 4315, 4365, 4832, 5014, 5016
   metabolic rate, 5247
   microsomal metabolism, 4365
   motor activity, 5171
   norepinephrine (NE), 3803
   respiratory effects, 3969, 4832, 4996, 4997, 5014,
      5246, 5247
   tolerance, 4997
physiological effects
   copulation, 5389
   endocrine effects, 4178
   F_2 generation, 5390
   fetus, 5389
   interaction with
      alcohol, 5303
      delta-9-THC, 5390
   neo-natal development, 5389, 5390
   reproductive effects, 5389, 5390
   testis(es), 4178
   visual tracking, 5303
psychological aspects, 3837
   cognitive processes, 5170
   emotional aspects, 5348
   humans, 3837
   memory, 4054, 5347
   motor activity, 3701
   perception, 5348
   performance, 4054, 4055
   psychotomimetic activity, 5279
   social interaction, 5396
   subjective effects, 5348, 5396, 5444
   time estimation, 4054
   withdrawal symptoms, 5396
reproductive effects
   interaction with
      vitamins, 5431
   spermatozoa, 5425
   testis(es), 5431
research
   patterns of use, 5450
sociological aspects
   adverse effect(s), 5450
   emotional aspects, 5348
   perception, 5348
   social interaction, 5396
   sociological interaction, 5444
therapeutic aspects
   angina pectoris, 3837
   glaucoma, 4287
therapeutic effects
   glaucoma, 5414
   intraocular pressure (IOP), 5103
toxicology
   alveolar macrophage(s), 3585, 4616, 5370
   behavior, 4026
   blood flow, 5383
   body weight, 4026, 4029
   brain, 5125
   carcinogenicity, 3991, 4257
   cardiovascular effects, 5338
   carcinogenesis, 5481
   cellular effects, 5481

578

toxicology (continued)
  chronic effects, 4029
  compared to:
    tobacco, 3585, 3991, 5370, 5432, 5481, 5560
  food intake, 4026, 4029
  heart rate, 4026
  hematology, 4026
  inflammation, 5383
  inhalation toxicology, 5383
  lethality, 5383
  lipids, 4026
  lung(s), 3585, 4616, 4758, 5383, 5432, 5560
  lymphocytes, 5511
  neo-natal development, 3771
  neurotoxicity, 4303
  organ weights, 4029
  pathology, 5560
  placental transfer, 3771
  pulmonary effects, 5338, 5383
  reproductive effects, 5125
  respiratory effects, 4758
  respiratory system, 4740
  serum enzymes, 5338
  sex differences, 3742
  spermatozoa, 5425
  spermatogenesis, 5425
  teratogenic effects, 3771, 4741, 4951
  testicular effects, 5383
  tolerance, 3742
  vitamin C, 5481
MARIHUANA USE
  adverse effect(s)
    chronic use, 5373
  England, 3226
  epidemiological study
    adolescent(s), 5451
    Canada, 5332
    compared to:
      other drugs, 5332
    Mexico, 5332
  general information, 3226
  legal aspects
    cultivation, 5373
    decriminalization, 5373
    employment, 5377
    legalization issue, 5409
    medical use, 5373
  psychological aspects
    attitude, 5451
  sociological aspects
    attitude, 5613
    parental influence, 5451
    patterns of use, 5613
    peer influence, 5451
MARKET STRUCTURE
  cannabis
    Trinidad, 4276
  hashish
    Canada, 4931
MASS FRAGMENTOGRAPHY
  delta-8-THC
    humans, 5533
    plasma, 5533
    silylation, 5533

MASS FRAGMENTOGRAPHY (continued)
  delta-9-THC
    humans, 5533
    plasma, 5533
    silylation, 5533
MASS SPECTROMETRY
  cannabinoid(s)
    cannabis plant, 5483
    forensic aspects, 5483
    fragmentation, 5371
    radiolabelled, 5371
MATERNAL BEHAVIOR
  delta-9-THC
    chronic administration, 5407, 5456
    mice, 3184
    monkeys, 5407, 5456
    neo-natal development, 5407
  marihuana extract
    neo-natal development, 5276
    rats, 5276
MECHANISM OF ACTION
  delta-8-THC
    analgesia, 5211
    metabolism, 5211
  delta-9-THC
    analgesia, 5211
    brain, 4082, 4877
    membranes, 4877
    metabolism, 4249, 5211
    neuronal membrane(s), 4657
    psychological aspects, 4249
    rats, 4082
MEDICAL USE
  delta-9-THC
    antiemetic, 5567
    legal aspects, 5567
  marihuana
    antiemetic, 5553, 5605
    chemotherapy, 5553
    humans, 5523
    intraocular pressure (IOP), 5605
    legal aspects, 5373, 5553, 5605
    review, 5605
  tetrahydrocannabinol (THC)
    therapeutic aspects, 4773
MEMBRANE-BOUND ATPASES
  delta-9-THC
    brain, 3355
    heart, 3506
    mice, 3506, 3888
    microsomal, 4657
    mitochondrial, 4657
    subcellular fractions, 3355
    synaptosomal, 4657
MEMBRANE-BOUND ENZYME
  cannabinol (CBN)
    ATPase(s), 4570
    synaptic vesicles, 4570
  delta-9-THC
    acetylcholinesterase, 4231
    ATPase(s), 4231, 4570, 4571
    mitochondria, 3294
    platelets, 3294
    rats, 3294
    synaptic vesicles, 4570, 4571

MEMBRANE-BOUND ENZYME (continued)
  11-hydroxy-delta-9-THC
    ATPase(s), 4570
      synaptic vesicles, 4570
  olivetol
    ATPase(s), 4570
      synaptic vesicles, 4570
MEMBRANE EFFECTS
  cannabidiol (CBD)
    nuclear magnetic resonance (NMR), 5006
    phospholipids, 3282
    physical work capacity, 5006
  cannabinoid(s)
    acyltransferase activity, 5500
    anesthetic potentiation, 5340
    calcium levels, 5500
    lipid solubility, 5366
    lymphocytes, 5366, 5500
    membrane permeability, 5340
    membrane stability, 5340
    nucleoside uptake, 5366, 5500
    synaptosomes, 5500
  cannabinol (CBN)
    in vitro, 4591, 5367
    mitochondria, 4591
    red blood cells, 4591
  delta-9-THC
    eel, 5525
    excitability, 5525
    in vitro, 5367
    lymphocytes, 5304
    membrane-bound enzyme, 5448
    neurotransmitters, 4877
    nuclear magnetic resonance (NMR), 5006
    nucleoside uptake, 5304
    phospholipids, 3282
    physical work capacity, 5006
MEMBRANE PERMEABILITY
  cannabidiol (CBD)
    in vitro, 3281, 3817
  cannabinol (CBN)
    in vitro, 3817
  delta-9-THC
    in vitro, 3281, 3813, 3817
    potassium, 3813
    spermatozoa, 3813
MEMBRANE STABILITY
  cannabidiol (CBD)
    in vitro, 3281
  delta-9-THC
    enzymes, 4231
    in vitro, 3281
MEMBRANES
  delta-9-THC
    ATPase(s), 4022
    brain, 4879
MEMORY
  cannabinol (CBN)
    humans, 4870
  cannabis
    humans, 3097
  delta-9-THC
    chronic use, 3635
    compared to:
      alcohol, 4754

delta-9-THC (continued)
    humans, 3631, 3635, 4454, 4460, 4753, 4754,
      4980, 5109
    mice, 3202
    recall, 3577, 4460
    recognition, 3577
    retention, 3577, 4460
  ganja
    humans, 4762
  hashish
    chronic use, 3635
    compared to:
      alcohol, 4417
    humans, 3635, 4417
  marihuana
    acquisition, 3185
    animals, 3185
    chronic use, 3635, 3811, 4937
    humans, 3122, 3185, 3218, 3635, 3811, 3973,
      4429, 4453, 4455, 4456, 4458, 4459, 4461,
      4637, 4748, 4751, 4933, 4937, 4980, 5050,
      5109, 5291
    recall, 3185, 3577, 4453, 4455, 4456, 4458, 4459,
      4637
    recognition, 3577
    retention, 3577
    review, 3185
    storage, 4455, 4459
    visual, 4461
  marihuana smoke
    adverse effect(s), 5347
    humans, 4054, 5347
    mechanism of action, 5347
    pain, 5347
MEMORY IMPAIRMENT
  marihuana
    humans, 5505
MENTAL ILLNESS
  cannabis
    review, 4531
METABOLIC RATE
  marihuana smoke
    humans, 5247
METABOLISM
  cannabidiol (CBD), 4164
    animals, 4253
    guinea pig(s), 3939
    humans, 4253, 5148
    7-hydroxy, 4253
    hydroxylation, 5148
    in vitro, 5269
    inhibition, 4144
    interaction with
      secobarbital, 3574, 3575
    liver, 4034, 4144, 4374, 4375
    mice, 3939, 4034, 4144, 4383
    microsomal, 4281, 4607
    monkeys, 3209
    rats, 3939, 4281, 4374, 4375
    review, 4253, 5269
    steroids, 4281
    subchronic administration, 4034
  cannabinoid(s), 4410, 5144
    in vivo, 5422
    overview, 4142

cannabinoid(s) (continued)
  patterns of, 5422
  review, 5421
cannabinol (CBN), 4164
  animals, 4253
  feces, 5231
  guinea pig(s), 3939
  humans, 4253, 5148
  7-hydroxy, 4253
  hydroxylation, 5148
  in vitro, 3751
  mice, 3427, 3939
  monkeys, 3209
  rabbit(s), 5200
  rats, 3751, 3939, 5230, 5231, 5232
  review, 4253
cannabis
  review, 5413
delta-8-THC
  analgesia, 5211
  animals, 4253
  cannabinol (CBN), 4412
  glucuronides, 4413
  humans, 4253
  7-hydroxy, 4253
  hydroxylation, 5211, 5417
  in vitro, 5417
  liver, 5417
  mechanism of action, 5211
  mice, 4267
  monkeys, 4117, 5417
  rats, 4244
  review, 4253
delta-9-THC, 4164, 4522
  analgesia, 5211
  animals, 4253
  biochemical effect(s), 5278
  brain, 3312, 3692, 4373
  cannabinol (CBN), 4313, 4412
  cannabinol-7-oic acid, 3312
  correlated with
    intoxication, 3999
  dogs, 3801, 4020, 5201
  guinea pig(s), 3939
  humans, 3250, 4106, 4107, 4253, 4411, 5058,
    5148
  7-hydroxy, 4253
  hydroxylation, 4249, 5148, 5195, 5211
  in vitro, 3943, 4232, 4861, 5201
  in vivo, 4861
  interaction with
    cannabidiol (CBD), 4411, 4862, 5058
    cannabigerol (CBG), 4862
    cannabinol (CBN), 4411, 4862, 5058
    SKF-525A, 4411, 4862
  liver, 3313, 3943, 3948
  lung(s), 4232, 5201
  mechanism of action, 4249, 5211
  metabolites, 5199
  mice, 3939, 3948, 4411, 5317, 5546
  microorganisms, 3340
  microsomal, 3313, 4281, 4411, 4607, 4860
  monkeys, 3209, 3312, 3692, 4117, 4377, 4411,
    5378
  pharmacokinetics, 5394

delta-9-THC (continued)
  pharmacological aspects, 4249, 5261
  psychological aspects, 4249
  rabbit(s), 3313, 4411
  rats, 3939, 4244, 4281, 4313, 4373, 4411, 4860,
    4861, 4862, 5317
  review, 3250, 3919, 4253, 4531, 4607
  steroids, 4281
  tissues, 5546
  tolerance, 4252
dimethylheptylpyran (DMHP)
  mechanism of action, 4249
  pharmacological aspects, 4249
  psychological aspects, 4249
11-hydroxy-delta-9-THC
  humans, 5148
  monkeys, 4377
marihuana, 3240, 4632
  clinical aspects, 4531
  humans, 4106
  hydroxylation, 5523
  review, 4663
marihuana smoke
  humans, 4254
  liver, 4254
nabilone (Lilly compound no. 109514)
  dogs, 4759
  humans, 4759
11-palmitoyloxy-delta-9-THC
  cholesterol, 5478
  hydrolysis, 5478
  lipase, 5478
tetrahydrocannabinol (THC)
  age, 5490
  brain, 5490
  humans, 5628
  in vivo, 5628
  liver, 5628
  monkeys, 5628
  rats, 5490
METABOLITES
cannabidiol (CBD), 4770, 5457
  analysis, 3207, 3939
  biotransformation, 4305, 4719
  detection, 4383
    GC/MS, 3942
  dioxygenated, 4374
  GC/MS, 4383, 5147
  humans, 4134
  hydroxylated, 3207, 3209, 3339, 4148
  hydroxylation, 5147
  identification, 3339, 4375
  liver, 4375
  mass spectrometry, 3339
  mice, 4144, 4383
  monkeys, 3209
  nuclear magnetic resonance (NMR), 3339
  rats, 4375
  structure, 4918
  synthesis, 3207, 4221, 4412
  thin layer chromatography (TLC), 4134
  urine, 4134
cannabinoid(s)
  analysis
    thin layer chromatography (TLC), 4290

cannabinoid(s) (continued)
  biological activity, 5478
  biological fluid(s), 3852, 4410
  detection, 3852
  GC/MS, 3852, 5422
  identification, 5422
  in vivo, 5422
  plasma, 5144
  quantitative, 5422
  retention, 5478
  structure, 4410, 5340
  synthesis, 4410, 5144
  urine, 4290, 5144
cannabinol (CBN), 4770
  analysis, 3207, 3939
    GC/MS, 5228, 5229
  biotransformation, 4305, 4719
  cannabinol-7-oic acid, 5229
  detection
    GC/MS, 3938, 3942
  fatty acid conjugates, 5228
  feces, 5229, 5230, 5232
  GC/MS, 5147
  humans, 4134
  hydroxylated, 3207, 3209, 3339
  hydroxylation, 5147
  identification, 3339, 3751, 5230, 5232
  isolation, 5232
  mass spectrometry, 3339
  mice, 3427
  monkeys, 3209
  nuclear magnetic resonance (NMR), 3339
  rats, 5229
  structure, 4918
  synthesis, 3207, 5200
  thin layer chromatography (TLC), 4134
  urine, 4134, 5230
Cannabis sativa
  review, 3907, 3908
delta-8-THC, 4770
  biotransformation, 4305, 4719
  cannabinol (CBN), 4314
  conjugation, 4244
  detection
    GC/MS, 3941, 3942, 3945
  distribution, 5277
  fatty acid conjugates, 5266
  glucuronides, 4267, 4413
  guinea pig(s), 5277
  hexahydrocannabinol (HHC), 3941
  11-hydroxy-delta-8-THC, 4244
  hydroxylated, 4296
  identification, 5277, 5417
  mice, 4267, 5277
  psychotropic drugs, 5556
  rabbit(s), 5277
  rats, 4314, 5266
  side chain, 4296
  smooth muscle, 5556
  structure, 4267, 4918
  synthesis, 4296, 5277
delta-9-THC, 4770
  acidic cannabinoid(s), 5145
  analysis, 3207, 3939, 3948, 4020, 4133, 4137,
    4482, 4802, 4916, 5557

delta-9-THC (continued)
  animals, 4384
  bile, 4861, 5269
  biological fluid(s), 5273
  biotransformation, 4305, 4719
  blood level(s), 5146
  brain, 4337
  brain levels, 5146
  cannabinol (CBN), 4314, 5321
  carboxylic acid, 5269
  conjugation, 4244
  detection, 3946, 4135
    EMIT (homogenous enzyme immunoassay),
      4757
    GC/MS, 3940, 3941, 3942
    immunoassay, 4757
    mass spectrometry, 3936
    radioimmunoassay (RIA), 5026
  excretion, 3467, 4246, 4861, 5269
  extractions, 4802
  fatty acid conjugates, 5266
  feces, 3853, 5145
  gas chromatography, 4482
  GC/MS, 3946, 3947, 3948, 4482, 5147, 5528,
    5557
  glucuronides, 4589
  hexahydrocannabinol (HHC), 3941
  high-pressure liquid chromatography (HPLC),
    4020, 4482, 5273
  humans, 4134, 4137, 4553
  hydroxy, 3948
  11-hydroxy-delta-9-THC, 3853, 4244, 5145
  hydroxylated, 3207, 3209, 3338, 3339, 4148
  hydroxylation, 5147
  identification, 3339, 4551, 4553, 4607, 5528
    GC/MS, 4384
  in vitro, 5269
  lipids, 5557
  liver, 3313, 3948, 4589
  lung(s), 5201
  mass spectrometry, 3339
  mice, 3948
  microorganisms, 3338
  monkeys, 3209, 3853
  nuclear magnetic resonance (NMR), 3339, 5528
  pharmacological aspects, 4412
  pharmacology, 4164
  plasma, 4553
  rabbit(s), 3313, 4551, 5528
  radioimmunoassay (RIA), 4482
  radiolabelled, 3943
  rats, 4314, 4337, 4861, 5266
  review, 5269, 5321
  route of administration, 5321
  separation, 4133
  structure, 3943, 4918
  synthesis, 3207, 4589, 4648, 5096
  thin layer chromatography (TLC), 4020, 4134,
    4482
  urine, 4133, 4134, 4135, 4551, 4553, 4757,
    5026, 5145, 5269, 5528
9-alpha, 10-alpha-epoxyhexahydrocannabinol
  GC/MS, 5534
  hydroxylated, 5534
  in vitro, 5534

METABOLITES (continued)
Lilly compound no. 109514
half-life, 4994
marihuana
analysis
thin layer chromatography (TLC), 4290
cannabinol (CBN), 4155
detection, 4155
11-hydroxy-delta-9-THC, 4155
route of administration, 3241
thin layer chromatography (TLC), 4136
toxicology, 3241
urine, 4136, 4155, 4290
marihuana smoke
inhalation, 5238
urine, 5238
nabilone (Lilly compound no. 109514)
dogs, 4759
humans, 4759
tetrahydrocannabinol (THC)
biological fluid(s), 5598
radioimmunoassay (RIA), 5598
METHADONE WITHDRAWAL
cannabidiol (CBD)
rats, 3984
delta-9-THC
rats, 3984
METHODS
cannabinoid(s)
analysis, 5340
detection, 4531, 5352
cannabis
psychopharmacological aspects, 4114
delta-9-THC
detection, 5539
MEXICO
marihuana use
availability, 5332
family relationships, 5332
legal aspects, 5332
students, 5332
MICROBIOLOGICAL TRANSFORMATION
delta-8-THC
hydroxylated cannabinoids, 5130
nabilone (Lilly compound no. 109514)
hydroxylation, 5292
in vitro, 5292
stereospecificity, 5292
MICROSCOPIC EXAMINATION
hashish
street samples, 4506
hemp
street samples, 4506
marihuana
street samples, 4506
MICROSOMAL INDUCTION
cannabidiol (CBD)
liver, 4034
mice, 4034
subchronic administration, 4034
MICROSOMAL METABOLISM
cannabidiol (CBD)
mice, 4326, 5317, 5319
rats, 5317

MICROSOMAL METABOLISM (continued)
delta-9-THC
chronic administration, 4476
humans, 3219, 3316
liver, 4476, 5265
lung(s), 5265
mice, 4326, 5317
rabbit(s), 5265
rats, 4476, 5317, 5479
11-hydroxy-delta-8-THC
fatty acid conjugates, 5480
in vitro, 5480
inhibition, 5625
liver, 5625
11-hydroxy-delta-9-THC
fatty acid conjugates, 5480
in vitro, 5480
rats, 5479
marihuana smoke
aryl hydrocarbon hydroxylase activity, 4365
lung(s), 4365
rats, 4365
11-palmitoyloxy-delta-9-THC
rats, 5479
MICROSOMAL PROTEIN
delta-9-THC
mice, 3777
MICROSOMES
cannabidiol (CBD)
heart, 5349
delta-9-THC
enzyme activity, 3280
heart, 5349
liver, 3280
rats, 3280
dimethylheptylpyran (DMHP)
heart, 5349
MILITARY
a coping device, 4473
cannabis, 4473
MINERALS
cannabis
constituents of, 3120
hemp
constituents of, 3120
MITOCHONDRIA
delta-9-THC
adverse effect(s), 4607
electron transport system, 3300
liver, 4607
monoamine oxidase (MAO), 3809
MITOCHONDRIAL RESPIRATION
delta-9-THC
brain, 3300
in vitro, 3300, 3342
MITOSIS
cannabis resin
chromosomes, 5133
hashish
arrests, 5439
plant material, 4120
white blood cells, 5439
marihuana smoke
humans, 5511
lymphocytes, 5511

MITOTIC INDEX
  delta-9-THC
    bone marrow, 4091
    mice, 4091
  marihuana
    dogs, 4028
MONKEYS
  delta-8-THC
    behavioral effect(s), 5313
  9-*nor*-9-beta-hydroxy-hexahydrocannabinol
    analgesia, 4378
    morphine withdrawal, 4378
MONOAMINE OXIDASE (MAO)
  cannabidiol (CBD)
    brain, 4806, 4807, 4808
    liver, 4806, 4807
    motochondria, 4806, 4807, 4808
    phospholipids, 4808
  cannabis extract
    rats, 3463
    uterus, 3463
  delta-8-THC
    rats, 3485
  delta-9-THC
    brain, 3290, 4806, 4807, 4808
    heart, 3290
    humans, 4983
    kidney, 3290
    liver, 3290, 4806, 4807
    mitochondria, 3294, 3809, 4806, 4807, 4808
    phospholipids, 4808
    platelets, 3294, 4983
    rats, 3290, 3294, 3485
  hashish
    brain, 5397
    liver, 5397
    rabbit(s), 5397
  hashish extract
    brain, 4806, 4807
    liver, 4806, 4807
    mitochondria, 4806, 4807
  marihuana
    humans, 4983
    platelets, 4983
MOOD
  delta-9-THC
    humans, 3740, 5018
  hashish
    humans, 5018
  marihuana
    euphoria, 4749
    humans, 4107, 4429, 4443, 4749
MORALS AND ETHICS
  marihuana
    decriminalization, 4633
MORPHINE WITHDRAWAL
  cannabidiol (CBD)
    mice, 3333, 3334
    naloxone, 3333
    rats, 3980
  cannabinoid(s)
    therapy, 3331
  cannabinol (CBN)
    mice, 3333, 3334
    naloxone, 3333

MORPHINE WITHDRAWAL (continued)
  delta-8-THC
    dopamine (DA), 3979
    interaction with
      haloperidol, 3979
    mice, 3332, 3333, 3334
    naloxone, 3333
    rats, 3979
  delta-9-THC
    dopamine (DA), 3979
    guinea pig(s), 3765
    interaction with
      cannabidiol (CBD), 3982, 3985
      cannabinol (CBN), 3985
      haloperidol, 3979
    mice, 3330, 3332, 3333, 3334
    naloxone, 3333
    nitrogen analogs, 4603
    rats, 3444, 3979, 3980, 3982, 3985
    therapy, 3498, 3734
    thio analogs, 4603
  9-hydroxy-9-*nor*-hexahydrocannabinol
    monkeys, 4378
  11-hydroxy-delta-8-THC
    mice, 3333, 3334
    naloxone, 3333
  11-hydroxy-delta-9-THC
    mice, 3332
  synthetic cannabinoids
    therapy, 3331
MORPHOLOGICAL VARIATIONS
  cannabis
    domesticated plant, 4882
    gamma irradiation, 4844
    wild plant, 4882
MORPHOLOGY
  cannabis
    environmental conditions, 5610
    India, 5610
    review, 3486
  Cannabis sativa, 3898, 4838
    achene(s), 5542
    Canada, 3150
    development, 5542
    inorganic elements, 3491
    soil conditions, 3491
    trichomes, 3590, 4235
  delta-9-THC
    Volvox, 5494
  hashish
    spermatozoa, 5439
    white blood cells, 5439
MORTALITY
  delta-9-THC
    mice, 5593
    neonates, 5593
MOTILITY
  delta-9-THC
    rats, 5091
MOTIVATION
  delta-9-THC
    rats, 5183
  marihuana
    euphoria, 4645
    humans, 3434, 4255, 4419, 4426, 4645
    students, 5508

MOTIVATION OF USE
  cannabis
    review, 4531
  marihuana, 3091, 3398, 3833, 4301, 5126, 5175,
    5177
    adolescent(s), 5472, 5590
    availability, 5472
    compared to:
      alcohol, 4573
    environment, 5566
    factors influencing use, 5450
    family relationships, 5472
    humans, 4752, 5388
    parental influence, 5502
    psychological aspects, 5151
    social interaction, 5472
    students, 4186, 4219, 4661, 4813, 5143, 5306,
      5566
    subjective effects, 3419, 5472
MOTOR ACTIVITY
  cannabichromene (CBC)
    rats, 5561
  cannabidiol (CBD)
    derivatives, 3451
    mice, 3451, 4987
    rats, 5561
  cannabinoid(s)
    animals, 3732
  cannabis
    humans, 3097
  Cannabis indica
    mice, 4871
  Cannabis sativa
    humans, 4441
  cannabis smoke
    mice, 4785
  delta-8-THC
    adverse effect(s), 3164
    animals, 3732
  delta-9-THC
    adverse effect(s), 3164
    animals, 3732
    ant(s), 3783
    brain, 4338
    chronic administration, 4683
    chronic effects, 4447
    distribution, 4338
    interaction with
      amphetamine, 4336
      apomorphine, 4220
      caffeine, 4220
      cocaine, 4220
      depressant, 4671
      methamphetamine, 4220
      rats, 4336
      stimulants, 4671
    mice, 3187, 3202, 3222, 3688, 4683, 4987
    muricide, 4447
    rabbit(s), 4220
    rats, 3197, 4338, 4447, 4671, 4678, 5501, 5541
    route of administration, 5501
    strain difference, 5501
    tolerance, 3197, 3222, 5501
    vehicle of administration, 5501

MOTOR ACTIVITY (continued)
  dimethylheptylpyran (DMHP)
    adverse effect(s), 3164
  hashish
    mice, 4402
  11-hydroxy-delta-9-THC
    adverse effect(s), 3164
  marihuana
    adverse effect(s), 3741, 4776
    humans, 3142, 4776
    rats, 5561
    Turkey, 5561
  marihuana smoke
    chronic administration, 4303
    humans, 3701
    mice, 5171, 5172
    rats, 3770, 4303
    tolerance, 3770
MOTOR COORDINATION
  cannabidiol (CBD)
    humans, 5309
    mice, 5035
  delta-9-THC
    humans, 4217, 5391
    mice, 5035
    reaction time, 4217
  ganja
    humans, 4762
  marihuana
    humans, 4217, 4470
    reaction time, 4217
MOTOR PERFORMANCE
  cannabidiol (CBD)
    humans, 5350
  cannabis
    humans, 5568
  delta-9-THC
    humans, 3471, 3636, 5308
    rats, 5575
  hashish
    humans, 3636
  marihuana
    driving, 3241
    flying, 3241
    humans, 3367, 3636, 4713
MOTOR REFLEX
  cannabis
    cats, 5498
    interaction with
      syntostigmine, 4542
MOUTH
  cannabis manifestations, 5160
MULTIPLE
  marihuana
    students, 4132
MULTIPLE DRUG USE
  cannabis
    Egypt, 4936
    Malaysia, 4541
    review, 4531
  hashish
    methaqualone, 4721
  marihuana, 3091, 3148, 3833, 4169, 4535, 4868
    adolescent(s), 3488, 3489, 4168
    Australia, 3586

marihuana (continued)
    compared to:
        alcohol, 3488, 3489, 3987, 4420, 4421, 4424,
            4856
        amphetamine, 3145, 3875
        barbiturate(s), 3548
        cigarette smoking, 4791, 4856
        cocaine, 3548, 3875
        drugs, 4856
        hallucinogens, 3145
        heroin, 3548, 3875
        LSD, 3145
        opiates, 4791
        tobacco, 4421
    correlates of use, 5538
    heroin, 3174, 4809
    humans, 4420, 4421
    patterns of use, 3378
    prisoners, 4368
    progression to other drugs, 3654
    self administration, 4620
    sex differences, 4666
    students, 3302, 3378, 3586, 3626, 3649, 3792,
        3885, 3987, 4125, 4814, 5143, 5174
    Thailand, 4800
    U.S. army, 4800
    youths, 4065
MURICIDE
    delta-9-THC, 5092
        acute administration, 4446
        biogenic amine(s), 5574
        chronic administration, 4446
        chronic effects, 4447
        food intake, 5501
        motor activity, 4447
        rats, 3785, 4818, 5091, 5382, 5501, 5574
        route of administration, 5501
        serotonin (5-hydroxytryptamine), 4818
        strain difference, 5501
        vehicle of administration, 5501
MUSCLE
    cannabidiol (CBD)
        biochemical change(s), 3827
        histological changes, 3827
    9-Aza-cannabinol
        contractile force, 4154
        gastrointestinal tract, 4154
        sheep, 4154
    cannabinol (CBN)
        biochemical change(s), 3827
        histological changes, 3827
    delta-9-THC
        biochemical change(s), 3827
        histological changes, 3827
        mice, 3826
MUSCULAR COORDINATION
    delta-9-THC
        interaction with
            depressant, 4671
            stimulants, 4671
        rats, 4671
    marihuana
        humans, 4933

MUSCULAR DYSTROPHY
    cannabidiol (CBD)
        biochemical effect(s), 3474
        mice, 3474, 3822, 3827, 4604
        pathological study, 3822
    cannabinol (CBN)
        biochemical effect(s), 3474
        mice, 3474, 3822, 3827, 4604
        pathological study, 3822
    cannabis resin
        mice, 3822
        pathological study, 3822
    delta-9-THC
        biochemical effect(s), 3474
        mice, 3474, 3822, 3826, 3827, 4604, 5400
        pathological study, 3822
MUTAGENSIS
    cannabidiol (CBD)
        DNA breaks, 3779
        tissue cultures, 3779
    delta-8-THC
        DNA breaks, 3779
        in vitro, 4399
        in vivo, 4399
        tissue cultures, 3779
    delta-9-THC
        compared to
            LSD, 4225
            tobacco, 4225
        DNA breaks, 3779
        in vitro, 4399, 5120, 5240, 5402
        in vivo, 4399
        saliva, 4225
        tissue cultures, 3779
    9-alpha, 10-alpha-epoxyhexahydrocannabinol
        in vitro, 5402
    11-hydroxy-delta-9-THC
        in vitro, 5240
    marihuana
        chromosome damage, 3709
        humans, 3250, 4399
        lung(s), 4256
        methodology, 3709
        review, 4398
        tissue cultures, 4256
    olivetol
        chromosomes, 4492
        in vitro, 4492
MUTAGENICITY
    cannabis
        animals, 3078
MUTAGENIC EFFECTS
    cannabis
        review, 4531
    delta-9-THC
        compared to:
            tobacco smoke, 5325
        lymphocytes, 4493
        mice, 3119, 4984
        pyrolytic products, 5325
    marihuana, 4975
        humans, 3123, 4400
        review, 4527

MUTAGENIC EFFECTS (continued)
olivetol
lymphocytes, 4493
MUTAGENIC TESTS
delta-9-THC
in vitro, 4242
in vivo, 4242
marihuana
lymphocytes, 4495
mitotic index, 4495

N

NABILONE (LILLY COMPOUND NO. 109514)
adverse effect(s)
compared to:
prochlorperazine, 5426
orthostatic hypotension, 4031
side effects, 5426
analysis
detection, 4995
behavioral effect(s)
compared to:
amphetamine, 3381
chlordiazepoxide, 3381
chlorpromazine, 3381
diazepam, 3381
meprobamate, 3381
pentobarbital, 3381
conditioned behavior, 3381
M-wave behavior, 3381
biochemical effect(s)
microbiological transformation, 5292
chemical aspects
biotransformation, 3178
polymorphism, 5040
solubility
vehicle of administration, 5048
synthesis, 3259
neuropharmacological effects
convulsions, 5354
pharmacokinetics
blood level(s), 4995
disposition, 4759
excretion, 4759
half-life, 4759
metabolism, 4759
pharmacological aspects
alcohol withdrawal, 4940, 4944
anti-anxiety, 4960
anti-anxiety activity, 3703, 3993, 4031, 4536
antiemetic, 3253, 3368, 3968, 4960
antiemetic activity, 4316
cancer therapy, 3253
cardiovascular effects, 4245, 4250, 5401
CNS activity, 4250
clinical findings, 4960
compared to:
diazepam, 3993, 4536
hypothermia, 4585
interaction with
ethanol, 4940
naloxone, 4316
intraocular pressure (IOP), 4960
tolerance, 5522

NABILONE (continued)
psychological aspects
anxiety, 5401
subjective effects, 5401
psychological effects
subjective effects, 4245
therapeutic aspects
anti-anxiety, 5178
anti-anxiety activity, 3703, 4031
antiemetic, 3368, 4487, 5387, 5415, 5426
cancer, 5426
compared to:
prochlorperazine, 5387, 5426
glaucoma, 5522
intraocular pressure (IOP), 5178, 5522
therapeutic effects
antiemetic, 4521, 5447, 5485
cancer, 4521, 5447, 5485
compared to:
prochlorperazine, 4521, 5485
glaucoma, 5521
intraocular pressure (IOP), 5521
side effects, 5485
tolerance, 5521
NANTRADOL
pharmacological aspects
analgesic activity, 5507
compared to:
delta-9-THC, 5507
opiates, 5507
NARCOTIC WITHDRAWAL
delta-9-THC, 3597
NARCOTICS AND CANNABIS
morphine
withdrawal, 3981
NATIONAL INSTITUTE ON DRUG ABUSE (NIDA)
marihuana
standardized material, 5606
NEO-NATAL DEVELOPMENT
delta-9-THC
adverse effect(s), 5571
behavioral effect(s), 5407, 5571
biochemical effect(s), 5488
lactation, 5488
macromolecular synthesis, 5488
monkeys, 5407, 5571
prenatal exposure, 5407
marihuana smoke
fertility, 5390
organ weights, 5390
rats, 3771, 5389, 5390
NEO-NATAL EXPOSURE
marihuana
learning, 3241
NEONATES
delta-9-THC
adverse effect(s), 5000
mice, 5000
NERVOUS ACTIVITY
cannabidiol (CBD)
action potential(s), 5609
duration, 5609
rats, 5609
delta-9-THC
humans, 4012

NEURAL TRANSMISSION
   marihuana
      chronic use, 3613
      humans, 3613
NEUROCHEMICAL EFFECTS
   cannabidiol (CBD)
      ATPase(s), 3970
      dopamine (DA), 3970
      gamma-amino-butyric acid (GABA), 3970
      mice, 3970
      norepinephrine (NE), 3970
      serotonin (5-hydroxytryptamine), 3970
   delta-9-THC
      acetylcholinesterase activity, 4304
      ATPase(s), 3970
      dopamine (DA), 3970
      gamma-amino-butyric acid (GABA), 3970
      mice, 3970
      norepinephrine (NE), 3970
      rats, 4304
      serotonin (5-hydroxytryptamine), 3970
NEUROLOGIC FUNCTION
   delta-9-THC
      humans, 5018
   hashish
      humans, 5018
NEUROLOGICAL EFFECTS
   cannabis
      chronic use, 3372
      humans, 3372
   delta-9-THC
      humans, 5339
   marihuana
      adverse effect(s), 4776
      chronic use, 3477
      humans, 3477, 4776
NEUROMUSCULAR TRANSMISSION
   delta-9-THC
      acetylcholine (ACH), 3988
      rats, 3988
NEURONAL ACTIVITY
   delta-9-THC
      in vitro, 3190
   SP-111A
      in vitro, 3190
NEURONAL ALTERATIONS
   delta-9-THC
      cell growth, 5250
      macromolecular synthesis, 5250
   marihuana
      humans, 3614
      peripheral nervous system, 3614
NEURONAL MEMBRANE(S)
   delta-9-THC
      acetylcholinesterase, 4657
      glutamate synthetase, 4657
      membrane-bound ATPases, 4657
NEUROPHARMACOLOGICAL EFFECTS
   marihuana
      review, 5551
NEUROPHYSIOLOGY
   marihuana
      chronic use, 4784
      humans, 4784

NEUROPSYCHOLOGY
   cannabis
      humans, 3445
NEUROSIS
   cannabis
      humans, 4963
NEUROTOXICITY
   cannabidiol (CBD)
      rats, 5609
   delta-9-THC
      distribution, 5254
      mechanism of action, 5254
      uptake, 5254
   marihuana smoke
      rats, 4303
NEUROTRANSMITTERS
   cannabinoid(s)
      brain, 5368, 5428
      in vitro, 5428
      in vivo, 5428
      rats, 5368
      release, 5368
      synaptosomes, 5368, 5428
      uptake, 5368, 5428
   cannabis
      review, 5340
   delta-9-THC
      behavioral effect(s), 5541
      brain, 5541
      rats, 5541
NEUTROPHILS
   hashish
      humans, 4970
NEURONAL ACTIVITY
   cannabidiol (CBD)
      cerebellum, 4816
      hippocampus, 4816
      rats, 4816
   delta-9-THC
      cerebellum 4816
      hippocampus, 4816, 5182
      rats, 4816
   SP-111
      cerebellum, 4816
      hippocampus, 4816
      rats, 4816
NITROGEN ANALOGS
   cannabinoid(s)
      benzopyranopyridine(s), 5486
      pharmacological aspects, 4236
      structure-activity relationships, 4602
      synthesis, 4236, 5486
   delta-6a(10a)-THC
      pharmacology, 4600
      synthesis, 4600
   delta-8-THC
      synthesis, 4295
   delta-9-THC
      analgesic, 4958
      humans, 4958
      pharmacological aspects, 4603
      structure-activity relationships, 4603
      therapeutic aspects, 4603

NITROGEN COMPOUNDS
  cannabis, 3713
    isolation, 3054
    seeds, 3054
  Cannabis sativa
    constituents of, 3684, 3906
    review, 3684
NOMENCLATURE
  cannabinoid(s), 5144
NONACOSANE
  analysis
    quantitative, 4695
  cannabis
    constituents of, 4695
11-*NOR*-9-CARBOXY-DELTA-9-THC
  analysis
    detection, 3880
    high-pressure liquid chromatography (HPLC), 5616
    radioimmunoassay (RIA), 3880, 4916
NOREPINEPHRINE (NE)
  cannabidiol (CBD)
    mice, 3357, 3970
    uptake, 3970
  cannabinol (CBN)
    mice, 3357
  cannabis extract
    brain, 4656
    rats, 4656
  cannabis resin
    brain, 3592
    rats, 3592
  delta-8-THC
    central nervous system (CNS), 4333
    rats, 3115, 4333
  delta-9-THC
    analog(s)
      brain, 3293
      synaptosomes, 3293
      uptake, 3293
    brain, 3089, 3293, 3320, 3359, 3382, 3508, 3802, 4073, 4656
    brain levels, 5023
    compared to:
      morphine, 3352
    consummatory behavior, 3407
    guinea pig(s), 5104
    heart, 3089
    humans, 3803
    hypothalamus, 3405, 3407
    in vitro, 4546
    lung(s), 5104
    mice, 3352, 3357, 3970
    plasma levels, 3803
    rabbit(s), 3831
    rats, 3089, 3115, 3320, 3382, 3405, 3407, 3508, 4073, 4656, 5023
    synaptosomal, 3360, 4081
    synaptosomes, 3293
    synthesis, 3359
    uptake, 3293, 3970
    vas deferens, 4546
  dimethylheptylpyran (DMHP)
    rats, 3115
  hexahydrocannabinol (HHC)
    mice, 3357

NOREPINEPHRINE (continued)
  9-hydroxy-9-*nor*-hexahydrocannabinol
    brain, 3353
    mice, 3353
  SP-111
    in vitro, 4546
    vas deferens, 4546
NOVEL CANNABINOIDS
  cannabis
    constituents of, 3781
  chemical aspects
    spectral data, 3781
NUCLEIC ACIDS
  cannabinoid(s)
    HeLa cells, 5588
    synthesis, 5588
    turnover, 5588
  marihuana smoke
    brain, 5125
    fetus, 5125
    pregnancy, 5125
NUCLEOTIDES
  cannabis
    plasma levels, 4969
  delta-9-THC
    anti-neoplastic activity, 5448
    cellular effects, 5449
    in vitro, 5449
    inhibition, 5602
    sodium-potassium adenosine triphosphatase (Na K ATPase), 5602
    uptake, 5449

O

OCULAR EFFECTS
  cannabinoid(s)
    glaucoma, 5412
    humans, 5340
    intraocular pressure (IOP), 5412
    review, 5412
  delta-9-THC
    review, 5413
  marihuana
    review, 5405
  synthetic cannabinoids
    adverse effect(s), 5413
OCULAR TOXICITY
  SP-1
    dogs, 5042
  SP 80
    dogs, 5042
  SP-106
    dogs, 5042
OLIVETOL
  analysis
    detection, 4565
    GC/MS, 4565
    mass fragmentography, 4565
  biochemical effect(s)
    ATPase(s), 4570
    chromosome damage, 4534
    chromosomes, 4492, 4494, 4496
    compared to:
      alcohol, 4534

compared to (continued)
    aspirin, 4534
    caffeine, 4534
  DNA synthesis, 4494, 4496
  macromolecular synthesis, 4534
  membrane-bound enzyme, 4570
  synaptic vesicles, 4570
cannabidiol (CBD)
  pyrolytic products, 3285
cannabigerol (CBG)
  pyrolytic products, 3285
chemical aspects
  synthesis, 4206
    derivatives, 4302
immunology
  antimitotic, 3602
  cell-mediated immunity, 3550
  lymphocytes, 3602
pharmacological aspects
  anti-inflammatory activity, 4009
  brain, 4570
  prostaglandin synthesis, 4009
toxicology
  chromosomes, 4493
  mutagenesis, 4492
  mutagenic effects, 4493

OPERANT BEHAVIOR
delta-9-THC
  chronic administration, 3680
  dosage, 3296
  monkeys, 3680
  rats, 3296, 4865
  route of administration, 3296
  tolerance, 3680
marihuana
  chronic use, 3870
  humans, 3870, 4429, 4435

OPERANT WORK
marihuana
  humans, 4422, 4423, 4434

ORAL EPITHELIUM
marihuana
  adverse effect(s), 4615
  humans, 5160

ORAL SURGERY
marihuana
  adverse effect(s), 4005

ORGAN WEIGHTS
delta-8-THC
  rats, 3342
delta-9-THC
  chronic administration, 4744
  chronic effects, 4027
  guinea pig(s), 4027
  rats, 3342, 4356, 4744
marihuana
  rats, 4738
marihuana smoke
  chronic effects, 4029
  dogs, 4029

ORGANIC ACIDS
Cannabis sativa
  constituents of, 5079

ORTHOSTATIC HYPOTENSION
nabilone (Lilly compound no. 109514)
  humans, 4031

OVARIES
cannabis extract
  chronic administration, 3620, 3621
  gerbils, 3621
  histological changes, 3620
Cannabis sativa
  adverse effect(s), 5603
delta-9-THC
  organ weights, 5392
  rats, 5392
marihuana extract
  organ weights, 5392
  rats, 5392

OVERDOSE
hashish
  therapy, 3829
marihuana
  adverse effect(s), 5589
  compared to:
    alcohol, 3266
    therapy, 3266
    diazepam, 3891

OVERVIEW
cannabidiol (CBD)
  pharmacological aspects, 4412
cannabinol (CBN)
  pharmacological aspects, 4412
marihuana
  adverse effect(s), 4999
  pharmacological aspects, 4999
  therapeutic aspects, 3996

OVULATION
delta-9-THC
  monkeys, 3729, 5582
  rabbit(s), 3265, 5296
  rats, 3269

OVUM
delta-9-THC
  mice, 5620

OXIDATION
11-hydroxy-delta-8-THC
  inhibition, 5625
  liver, 5625
  microsomes, 5625

OXIDATION PRODUCTS
delta-6a(10a)-THC
  biological activity, 4704
delta-8-THC
  mass spectrometry, 4032
delta-9-THC
  mass spectrometry, 4032

OXYGEN ANALOG(S)
delta-8-THC
  synthesis, 4197
delta-9-THC
  synthesis, 4197

OXYGEN CONSUMPTION
cannabidiol (CBD)
  brain, 3476
  heart, 3476
  liver, 3476
  skeletal muscle, 3476
cannabinol (CBN)
  brain, 3476
  heart, 3476

cannabinol (CBN) (continued)
  liver, 3476
  skeletal muscle, 3476
delta-9-THC
  brain, 3476
  heart, 3476
  in vitro, 5252
  liver, 3476, 5252
  mice, 4624, 5252
  skeletal muscle, 3476

P

PAIN
  delta-9-THC
    humans, 3730, 3877
  marihuana
    humans, 4469
11-PALMITOYLOXY-DELTA-9-THC
  biochemical effect(s)
    compared to:
      delta-9-THC, 5479
      11-hydroxy-delta-9-THC, 5479
    metabolism, 5478
    microsomal metabolism, 5479
PARANOIA
  hashish
    compared to:
      alcohol, 4417
      humans, 4417
  marihuana
    chronic use, 5489
    clinical aspects, 5489
    humans, 5187
    review, 5489
PARAQUAT
  analysis
    anti-neoplastic testing, 4293
    colorametric method, 4293
    gas chromatography, 4293
    GC/MS, 5621
    infrared (IR), 5312
    marihuana, 4293
    spectrophotometry, 4293
  clinical aspects
    botanical aspects, 5312
  marihuana
    adverse effect(s), 3544, 3708, 4662, 4906, 5190
    analysis, 4121, 5080, 5081, 5622
    contaminated, 4121, 4907
    detection, 5345, 5622
    general information, 4662, 4906
    high-pressure liquid chromatography (HPLC), 5520
    humans, 5305
    identification, 5501, 5520
    legal aspects, 4906
    Mexico, 4405
    pulmonary effects, 4662
    pyrolytic products, 5622
    thin layer chromatography (TLC), 5345
  toxicology, 4405
PARAQUAT CONTAMINATION
  marihuana, 5081
    general information, 4549
    lung damage, 5237
    rabbit(s), 5237

PARAQUAT SPRAYING
  marihuana
    Mexico, 4905
PARASYMPATHETIC NERVOUS SYSTEM (PNS)
  delta-9-THC
    brain, 3653
    cats, 4321, 4322
    discrimination, 4322
    rats, 3653
    saliva, 4321, 4322
PARENTAL INFLUENCE
  marihuana
    predicting drug use, 5590
  marihuana use
    adolescent(s), 5451
PARTIAL REINFORCEMENT
  delta-9-THC
    rats, 3641
PARTICULATE MATTER
  marihuana smoke
    lung(s), 5432
    rats, 5432
PATENTS (see U.S. Patents)
PATHOLOGICAL STUDY
  Cannabis sativa
    brain, 3092
    heart, 3092
    kidney, 3092
    liver, 3092
    rats, 3092
    spleen, 3092
  delta-9-THC
    adrenals, 4027
    kidney, 4027
    liver, 4027
    spleen, 4027
PATHOLOGY
  marihuana smoke
    lung(s), 5560
    rats, 5560
PATTERNS OF GROWTH
  Cannabis sativa
    soil conditions, 4680
PATTERNS OF USE
  Cannabis
    Canada, 5554
    Egypt, 4936
    Jamaica, 4724
    Malaysia, 4541
    students, 5127
    Sweden, 3205
    Zaire, 5127
  ganja
    Jamaica, 4724, 4762
  hashish, 3176
    Afghanistan, 3829
    Canada, 4931
    increase in use, 4181
    Spain, 4223
    students, 4181, 4223
  marihuana, 3091, 3233, 3875, 4169, 4327, 4535, 4573, 4723, 5285
    adolescent(s), 3217, 3221, 3400, 3401, 3488, 3489, 4131, 4168, 4843, 4932, 5063, 5235, 5424

marihuana (continued)

age, 3241, 5538

attitude, 5450

Canada, 3048, 3191, 3547, 4612, 4767

characteristics of users, 4066

chemistry, 4932

chronic use, 3977

Colombia, 5248

compared to:

    alcohol, 3055, 3417, 3670, 4424, 4855, 4856, 4973, 5167, 5235

    cigarette smoking, 4855, 4856

    drugs, 4856

    heroin, 4956

    tobacco, 3670, 4932, 4973, 5235

Costa Rica, 3494

decriminalization, 3557

demographic aspects, 5503

drug abuse, 3148

drug availability, 4891

education, 3241

England, 3166, 3174, 3977, 4186, 4505, 5044

epidemiological study, 5057

epileptics, 3717

family relationships, 5503

frequency, 5538

general information, 3658

geographical aspects, 3241

Germany, 4791

heavy users, 5202

heroin abusers, 3678

humans, 4767

increase in use, 4181

India, 3477, 3648, 5202

Ireland, 4593, 4594

Jamaica, 3669

legal aspects, 3305

military, 4473, 4956

motivation, 5376

onset, 5450

performance and behavior, 4902

personality, 5174

predicting drug use, 3305, 5450, 5529

prisoners, 4368

races, 3241

racial differences, 3792

religion, 5613

review, 3239, 3919, 4663

Scotland, 5185

sex differences, 3221, 3241, 3378, 3548, 4632, 4666, 4932, 5168, 5376, 5587

sexual behavior, 3088

South Africa, 3645, 3647

Spain, 4223

students, 3055, 3056, 3084, 3088, 3126, 3145, 3191, 3240, 3278, 3418, 3547, 3625, 3626, 3648, 3659, 3670, 3818, 3821, 3878, 3884, 3978, 4066, 4132, 4150, 4181, 4186, 4223, 4334, 4439, 4485, 4593, 4612, 4661, 4667, 4813, 4814, 4823, 4891, 4902, 4972, 4973, 4991, 5055, 5062, 5167, 5168, 5248,

Switzerland, 4855, 4856

teachers, 4612

Thailand, 4800

marihuana (continued)

U.S.A., 3106, 3236, 3239, 3241, 3669, 3741, 4132, 4632, 4663, 4868, 4869, 4890, 5126, 5291, 5450, 5503, 5577

U.S. Army, 4800

Vietnam, 3154, 4956

PEER INFLUENCE

marihuana

    predicting drug use, 5590

marihuana use, 5530

    adolescent(s), 5451

PERCEPTION

cannabidiol (CBD)

    humans, 5309, 5350

cannabinol (CBN)

    humans, 4515

cannabis

    humans, 3097, 5128

delta-9-THC

    humans, 3471, 3636, 4515, 5308

ganja

    humans, 4762

hashish

    humans, 3636

marihuana

    adverse effect(s), 4776

    auditory, 3828

    color tests, 3196

    humans, 3196, 3636, 3828, 4107, 4332, 4457, 4470, 4500, 4501, 4645, 4713, 4751, 4776, 4789, 4903

    visual, 4470

marihuana smoke

    humans, 5348

PERFORMANCE

cannabidiol (CBD)

    humans, 5309

    interaction with

        delta-9-THC, 3573

cannabis

    adverse effect(s), 4934

    chronic use, 4934

    humans, 3097, 3456, 4331, 4934

    motivation, 3456

cannabis extract

    acute effect(s), 3721

    chronic effects, 3721

    chronic use, 3720

    maze, 3721

    rats, 3720, 3721

delta-9-THC

    attitude, 4272

    baboons, 4272

    chronic administration, 4683

    chronic use, 3635, 3904

    compared to:

        alcohol, 4754

    drug vehicle, 4945

    humans, 3250, 3631, 3635, 3904, 4011, 4110, 4754, 5109

    hypoxia, 4272

    interaction with

        alcohol, 4943

        cannabidiol (CBD), 3573

        tobacco, 4011

delta-9-THC (continued)
  mice, 4683, 4943, 4945
  monkeys, 4463
  rats, 4678
ganja
  humans, 4762
hashish
  chronic use, 3635, 4967
  humans, 3635
marihuana
  adverse effect(s), 3500, 4176, 4776
  chronic effects, 3503
  chronic use, 3499, 3635, 4937
  clinical aspects, 4531
  driving, 3239
  flying, 3346
  humans, 3215, 3239, 3307, 3346, 3434, 3499,
    3503, 3635, 3893, 4106, 4107, 4110, 4216,
    4255, 4426, 4434, 4443, 4540, 4614, 4645,
    4713, 4775, 4776, 4933, 4937, 4962, 5109
  interaction with
    secobarbital, 3572
  motivation, 4645
  physical activity, 4962
  sex differences, 4013
  training, 3307
marihuana smoke
  flying performance, 4054, 4055
  humans, 4054, 4055
PERFORMANCE IN OFFSPRING
delta-9-THC
  rats, 3093
PERIPHERAL NERVOUS SYSTEM
mariuana
  humans, 3614
  neuronal alterations, 3614
PERSONALITY
cannabis
  adverse effect(s), 3078
  humans, 3078, 4963
  use, 5301
delta-9-THC
  monkeys, 4782
ganja
  humans, 4762
hashish
  chronic use, 4966, 4967
  humans, 4966
marihuana
  adverse effect(s), 5126
  chronic use, 4784, 5126
  drug use, 4222, 4646, 4867
  humans, 3347, 4784, 4815, 5291
  predicting drug use, 3885
  psychological aspects, 5174
  students, 3885, 4901
  users vs nonusers, 5450
PHARMACOKINETICS
cannabidiol (CBD), 5457
cannabinoid(s)
  dogs, 5395
  humans, 5632
  review, 5421
cannabis
  review, 5535

PHARMACOKINETICS (continued)
delta-9-THC
  blood clearance rates, 5575
  review, 5413
  vehicle of administration, 5413
marihuana
  absorption, 3922
  distribution, 3922
  review, 3922, 4663
PHARMACOLOGICAL ASPECTS
cannabis
  chronic use, 3372, 3545
  humans, 3372, 3545
delta-9-THC, 4675
marihuana
  review, 3922, 4663, 5406, 5551
PHARMACOLOGY
chronic use, 3494
PHENOLS
cannabis
  cannabispiran (see also cannabispirone), 3255
  constituents of, 3255, 3256, 4411
Cannabis sativa
  constituents of, 4595
  pollen, 4595
marihuana
  analysis, 4391
  GC/MS, 4391
  constituents of, 4391
PHOSPHODIESTERASE
cannabinol (CBN)
  brain, 3627
delta-9-THC
  brain, 3627
  humans, 5333
  in vitro, 5333
  spermatozoa, 5333
11-hydroxy-delta-9-THC
  brain, 3627
PHOSPHOLIPASE
delta-9-THC
  brain, 4877
PHOSPHOLIPIDS
cannabigerol (CBG)
  turnover, 3871
cannabinol (CBN)
  membrane effects, 4591
  turnover, 3871
Cannabis sativa
  cannabinoid content, 5114
delta-8-THC
  turnover, 3871
delta-9-THC, 4411
  brain, 4879
  distribution, 5492
  membranes, 4879
  mice, 5492
  mitochondria, 3809
  synaptosomes, 3809
  turnover, 3871
hashish
  humans, 4193
  plasma levels, 4193
  red blood cells, 5453

PHOSPHORUS
cannabis
neutron activation analysis, 4845
Cannabis sativa, 3304
PHOTO-OXIDATION
cannabidiolic acid
product(s), 4166
PHYSICAL ACTIVITY
marihuana
humans, 3274, 3276
PHYSICAL DEPENDENCE
cannabis
humans, 4812, 4968, 5203
delta-9-THC
humans, 4106, 4110, 4111
rats, 3734
marihuana, 3239, 4632
chronic use, 3240, 3739
humans, 3247, 3739, 4106, 4107, 4110
tetrahydrocannabinol (THC)
humans, 5430
monkeys, 5430
PHYSIOLOGICAL CHANGES
marihuana
humans, 4426
PHYSIOLOGICAL EFFECTS
cannabis
chronic use, 3372, 3545
humans, 3372, 3545
delta-9-THC
blood pressure, 5310
forearm blood flow, 5310
heart rate, 5310
humans, 5310
marihuana
chronic use, 3728
humans, 3728
PHYTOSTEROLS
cannabis
sexual function, 5570
cannabis plant
sex differences, 5465
Cannabis sativa
constituents of, 3203
PIGMENTS
Cannabis sativa
constituents of, 5079
PITUITARY FUNCTION
delta-9-THC
monkeys, 4898
rats, 3396
hashish
rats, 4292
PLACENTAL TRANSFERS
delta-9-THC, 3351
humans, 3386
interaction with
phenobarbital, 4361, 4362
SKF-525A, 4361, 4362
mice, 4361, 4362
rats, 5122
marihuana, 3351
marihuana smoke
rats, 3771

PLASMA CHROMATOGRAPHY
delta-9-THC, 4139
PLASMA LEVELS
cannabidiol (CBD)
interaction with
delta-9-THC, 4266
rats, 4266
cannabinoid(s)
route of administration, 5421
delta-9-THC
animals, 4246
antiemetic, 5391
biological activity, 3993
dogs, 3611
humans, 4246, 4619, 5391
interaction with
cannabidiol (CBD), 4266
endotoxin, 4385
phenobarbital, 4361
SKF-525A, 4361
metabolites, 4246
mice, 4361, 4385
pigeon(s), 3611
psychological aspects, 4619
rats, 3755, 4266, 4673
route of administration, 5278
11-hydroxy-delta-9-THC
humans, 4619
psychological aspects, 4619
rats, 3755
PLASMA PROTEIN BINDING
cannabinol (CBN)
interaction with
delta-9-THC, 4312
rats, 4312
delta-9-THC
interaction with
cannabinol (CBN), 4312
rats, 4312
PLATELETS
cannabidiol (CBD)
humans, 4264, 4265
delta-9-THC
humans, 4260, 4264, 4265, 4983
monoamine oxidase (MAO), 4983
ultrastructural changes, 4260
marihuana
humans, 4983
monoamine oxidase (MAO), 4983
POISONING
cannabis
humans, 3395
marihuana
dogs, 5403
gastrointestinal effects, 5361
humans, 5361, 5406
oral administration, 5403
POLYCYCLIC AROMATIC HYDROCARBONS
cannabis
carcinogenicity, 3230
constituents of, 3230
chemical aspects
structure, 3299
marihuana, 4555

POLYCYCLIC AROMATIC HYDROCARBONS (cont.)
  marihuana smoke
    analysis, 4238
    GC/MS, 3299
    identification, 3299
    nuclear magnetic resonance (NMR), 3299
POLYMORPHISM
  nabilone (Lilly compound no. 109514)
    solubility, 5040
POSSESSION
  cannabis
    attitude, 5408
    Australia, 5408
    legal aspects, 5408
POSTTETANIC POTENTIATION
  cannabidiol (CBD)
    frog(s), 5076
  cannabinol (CBN)
    frog(s), 5076
  delta-9-THC
    frog(s), 5075, 5076
  11-hydroxy-delta-9-THC
    frog(s), 5075, 5076
POTENCY
  Cannabis sativa
    geographical origin, 4961
  hashish
    geographical origin, 4961
  marihuana, 4979
    analysis, 4531
    clinical aspects, 4531
PREANESTHETIC MEDICATION
  delta-9-THC, 4408
    humans, 3498
  marihuana, 3497, 4182
PREDICTING DRUG USE
  marihuana, 3047, 4301, 4632, 4767, 4793, 5285
    adolescent(s), 3141
    behavioral model(s), 3305, 3306, 4067
    humans, 5259
    personality, 3885, 4646
    students, 3170, 3240, 3306, 3878, 3885, 3972,
      4125, 4175, 4300
    youths, 4606
PREGNANCY
  marihuana
    adverse effect(s), 3247, 5515
PREMEDICATION
  delta-9-THC
    adverse effect(s), 3876
    humans, 4346
PRENATAL DEVELOPMENT
  Cannabis sativa
    adverse effect(s), 5603
  delta-9-THC
    adverse effect(s), 5571
    interaction with
      phenobarbital, 4361
      SKF-525A, 4361
    mice, 4361
    monkeys, 5571
    pathology, 5571
PRENATAL EXPOSURE
  delta-9-THC
    behavioral effect(s), 5382

delta-9-THC (continued)
    chronic administration, 5407
    maternal behavior, 5407
    monkeys, 5407
    rats, 5382
  marihuana extract
    behavioral teratogenesis, 5275
    neo-natal development, 5276
    rats, 5275, 5276
    sex differences, 5275
PREPARATION
  cannabis, 3854
PROBABILITY BASED MATCHING (PBM)
  delta-9-THC
    analysis, 5411
    biological fluid(s), 5411
    GC/MS, 5411
PRODUCTIVITY
  cannabis
    review, 4531
  marihuana
    humans, 3434
PROGESTERONE
  cannabinol (CBN)
    ovaries, 5323
    synthesis, 5323
  delta-9-THC
    monkeys, 5297
    ovaries, 5323
    synthesis, 5323
  11-hydroxy-delta-9-THC
    ovaries, 5323
    synthesis, 5323
  hydroxylated cannabinoids
    ovaries, 5323
    synthesis, 5323
PROGESTERONE LEVELS
  delta-9-THC
    blood level(s), 5296
    monkeys, 5296
    rabbit(s), 5296
PROGRESSION TO OTHER DRUGS
  cannabis, 3078, 3205
  heroin, 3854
  hashish
    methaqualone, 4721
  marihuana, 3158, 4507, 4535, 4868
    drug use, 4131
    England, 3166
    heroin, 3166, 3174, 3652, 4809, 4956
    LSD, 5197
    opiates, 5197
PROLACTIN
  delta-9-THC
    blood level(s), 3464, 4247, 5294
    central nervous system mechanism, 4200
    dopamine (DA), 4200
    humans, 4247
    monkeys, 5294
    plasma levels, 3507, 4200
    rats, 3396, 3397, 3464, 3507
    release, 3396, 3397, 4200
    serotonin (5-hydroxytryptamine), 4200
  11-hydroxy-delta-9-THC
    blood level(s), 4247

11-hydroxy-delta-9-THC (continued)
   humans, 4247
PROLACTIN LEVELS
  delta-9-THC
   mice, 4689
PROPYL CANNABINOID ACIDS
  cannabis
   constituents of, 4849
PROPYL HOMOLOGS
  cannabichromene (CBC), 4851
  cannabigerol (CBG), 4851
  cannabinoid(s), 4481
PROSTAGLANDIN SYNTHESIS
  cannabichromene (CBC)
   HeLa cells, 3422
   in vitro, 3422
  cannabidiol (CBD)
   in vitro, 4009
   pyrolytic products, 4948
  cannabigerol (CBG)
   seminal vesicle, 3428
  cannabinoid(s)
   tissue cultures, 3421
  cannabinol (CBN)
   HeLa cells, 3422
   in vitro, 3422
  cannabis
   constituents of
    p-vinylphenol, 3426
   seminal vesicle, 3426
  Cannabis sativa
   essential oils, 3428
  delta-9-THC
   HeLa cells, 3422
   in vitro, 3058, 3422, 4009
   rats, 4113
   review, 5413
   seminal vesicle, 3428
   uterus, 4113
  essential oils
   Cannabis sativa, 3421
  olivetol
   in vitro, 4009
PROSTAGLANDINS
  delta-9-THC
   kidney, 4153
   lung(s), 4153
   mice, 5380
   release, 4153
PROSTATE
  cannabis resin
   rats, 4569
PROTEIN
  cannabis
   humans, 4036
   spermatozoa, 4036
  Cannabis sativa
   constituents of, 3974, 3975, 3976, 5079
  delta-9-THC
   tissue cultures, 3349
PROTEIN BINDING
  delta-8-THC
   humans, 3438
  delta-9-THC
   dogs, 4020

delta-9-THC (continued)
   plasma, 4020
   rats, 4313
PROTEIN LEVELS
  delta-9-THC
   in vitro, 3287
   liver, 3287
PROTEIN SYNTHESIS
  blood gases
   in vitro, 4534
   lymphocytes, 4534
  cannabichromene (CBC)
   in vitro, 4534
   lymphocytes, 4534
  cannabicyclol (CBL)
   in vitro, 4534
   lymphocytes, 4534
  cannabidiol (CBD)
   in vitro, 4534
   lymphocytes, 4534
  cannabinoid(s)
   cannabidiol (CBD), 5443
   cannabigerol (CBG), 5443
   cannabinol (CBN), 5443
   delta-9-THC, 5443
   8-beta-hydroxy-delta-9-THC, 5443
   11-hydroxy-delta-9-THC, 5443
   in vitro, 5443
   rats, 5442
   SP-111A, 5443
   testis(es), 5442
  delta-8-THC
   tissue culture, 3441
  delta-9-THC
   adverse effect(s), 4528
   bacteria, 3177
   HeLa cells, 4483
   in vitro, 3603, 3607, 4318, 4534, 5241, 5328
   lymphocytes, 3603, 3606, 3607, 4533, 4534
   tissue culture, 3348
  olivetol
   in vitro, 4534
   lymphocytes, 4534
PSEUDOCHOLINESTERASE
  delta-9-THC
   adrenals, 3343
   in vitro, 4462
   rats, 3343
PSEUDOCONDITIONING
  cannabidiol (CBD)
   rats, 3100
PSYCHIATRIC ASPECTS
  cannabis
   use, 4763
  marihuana
   opinions, 5048
PSYCHOLOGICAL ASPECTS
  cannabinol (CBN)
   humans, 4149
  cannabis
   chronic use, 3545, 4172, 4416, 4936
   drug abuse, 4100
   humans, 3545, 4172
   psychosis, 4416
   reviewed, 4763

PSYCHOLOGICAL ASPECTS
  delta-9-THC, 3768, 4708
    epidemiological study, 3075
    euphoria, 3075
    hallucinations, 3075
    humans, 4149
    interaction with
        alcohol, 3472
  humans, 3768
  marihuana
    characteristics of users, 3583
    chronic use, 3870
    drug use, 4175, 4606, 5185
    humans, 5221
    memory, 4933
    muscular coordination, 4933
    performance, 4933
    review, 3241
    students, 4790
    suggestibility, 4156
    vision, 4933
  marihuana smoke
    characteristics of users, 4367
    humans, 3837
  motivation
    cannabis use, 4837
PSYCHOLOGICAL EFFECTS
  marihuana
    adverse effect(s), 4776
    humans, 4776
    review, 5551
PSYCHOSIS
  cannabis, 3165
    chronic use, 3633, 4172
    compared to:
      amphetamine, 3715
      LSD, 3715
      phencyclidine, 3715
    dosage, 3667
    environmental conditions, 3667
    humans, 3078, 3228, 3529, 4172
    intoxication, 3927
    military, 5568
    personality, 3667
    review, 4531
  Cannabis sativa
    humans, 4440, 4441
  delta-9-THC, 3619
    humans, 4915
    therapy, 4915
  hashish
    chronic use, 4966
    diagnosis, 3399
    humans, 3399, 4966
  hemp
    children, 3341
  marihuana, 3106
    adolescent(s), 5506
    anxiety, 3172
    chronic use, 3650, 3739, 5489
    clinical aspects, 5489
    drug use, 3166, 4207
    flashbacks, 3188
    humans, 3239, 3247, 3481, 3650, 3739, 3893,
      4106, 4107, 4444, 5039, 5291

marihuana (continued)
    paranoia, 5039
    schizophrenics, 5064
    therapy, 5005
PSYCHOSOCIAL ASPECTS
  cannabis use, 4837
  marihuana
    adverse effect(s), 5126
    cognitive processes, 5169, 5202
    heavy users, 5169
    humans, 5202
    personality, 5196
    review, 4634
PSYCHOTICISM
  delta-9-THC, 3619
PSYCHOTOMIMETIC ACTIVITY
  delta-8-THC
    derivatives, 5173
  marihuana smoke
    humans, 5279
PSYCHOTROPIC DRUGS
  delta-8-THC, 5556
  synthetic cannabinoids, 5556
PULMONARY EFFECTS
  marihuana
    fibrosis, 5284
    humans, 3241, 5284, 5298, 5473
    interaction with
      paraquat, 5284
    oxygen consumption, 5298
    ventilation, 5298
  marihuana smoke
    chronic effects, 5383
    humans, 5338
    rats, 5383
PULSE RATE
  delta-9-THC
    humans, 4454
PUNISHMENT
  delta-9-THC
    rats, 4801
PUPIL SIZE
  delta-9-THC
    humans, 3403, 4275
  hashish
    humans, 4275
  marihuana
    humans, 4275
PYRIDINE HYDROXYLATION
  Cannabis sativa
    in vitro, 3714
PYROLYSIS
  cannabidiol (CBD), 4302
  nitrogen, 4949
PYROLYTIC PRODUCTS
  cannabidiol (CBD), 4770, 4771, 4948
    analysis, 4209, 4950
    cannabielsoin (CBE), 4946
    isolation, 4949
    olivetol, 3285
      derivatives, 4302
    pharmacology, 4768
    prostaglandin synthesis, 4948
    structure, 4210, 4947, 4949
    synthesis, 4302

cannabidiol (CBD) (continued)
  water pipes, 4950
cannabigerol (CBG)
  olivetol, 3285
cannabinoid(s)
  analysis, 4950
  water pipes, 4950
cannabinol (CBN)
  synthesis, 5487
cannabis
  analysis, 4157
  cannabicitran, 3214
  cannabicyclol (CBL), 3214
  cannabidiol (CBD), 3214
  cannabifuran, 3214
  cannabinol (CBN), 3214
  cannabinol methyl ether, 3214
  constituents, 5340
  cyanide, 3411
  dehydrocannabifuran, 3214
  delta-8-THC, 3214
  delta-9-THC, 3214
  gas liquid chromatography (GLC), 4157
  mass spectrometry, 4157
  polycyclic aromatic hydrocarbons, 3230
Cannabis sativa
  sterols, 3203
delta-8-THC, 4770
delta-9-THC, 4770
hashish smoke
  mice, 5293
marihuana, 4158, 5432
  acid(s), 4391
  ammonia, 3410
  analysis, 4391
  compared to:
    tobacco, 4555
  phenols, 4391
  polycyclic aromatic hydrocarbons, 4555
marihuana smoke
  carcinogenesis, 5548
  rats, 5548

R

RACIAL DIFFERENCES
  marihuana
    students, 3792
  marihuana use
    U.S.A., 5530
RADIOIMMUNOASSAY (RIA)
  cannabinoid(s)
    biological fluid(s), 5598
    blood, 5496
    review, 5351
    urine, 5496, 5629
  delta-9-THC
    binding, 5564
    rats, 5564
    synaptosomes, 5564
  tetrahydrocannabinol (THC)
    rabbit(s), 5253
RADIOLABELLED
  cannabinoid(s)
    fragmentation, 5371

cannabinoid(s) (continued)
  metabolism, 5371
  review, 5371
  synthesis, 5371
delta-8-THC
  synthesis, 3989
delta-9-THC
  rats, 5576
  route of administration, 5576
  synthesis, 3989
RATS
  behavior
    abstinence attenuating effect(s), 3981
  cannabidiol (CBD)
    behavioral effect(s), 4816
  Cannabis sativa
    behavioral effect(s), 4407
  cardiovascular effects
    growth
      hypothermia, 3197
      motor activity, 3197
  delta-9-THC
    behavioral effect(s), 4816
  SP-111
    behavioral effect(s), 4816
REACTION TIME
  delta-9-THC
    humans, 3730, 5308
  hashish smoke
    mice, 5293
  marihuana
    humans, 4614, 4645, 4748
RECEPTOR BINDING
  delta-9-THC
    estradiol, 5583
    in vitro, 5583
    uterus, 5583
  tetrahydrocannabinol (THC)
    structure-activity relationships, 5313
RECEPTORS
  cannabinoid(s)
    dopamine (DA), 5428
    mechanism of action, 5428
  delta-8-THC
    central nervous system (CNS), 3598
    compared to:
      thujone, 3598
    psychotomimetic activity, 3598
  delta-9-THC
    central nervous system (CNS), 3598
    compared to:
      thujone, 3598
    psychotomimetic activity, 3598
RECOMMENDATIONS
  marihuana
    research, 3241
RECREATIONAL USE
  marihuana
    U.S.A., 3893
RED BLOOD CELLS
  delta-9-THC
    humans, 5239
    in vitro, 5337
    membrane effects, 5337
    rats, 3823

RED BLOOD CELLS (continued)
  marihuana
    humans, 4836
REFLEXES
  delta-9-THC
    humans, 3730
REGIONAL BLOOD FLOW
  delta-9-THC
    dogs, 4045, 4049
REGISTRY
  cannabis
    adverse effect(s), 4465
REGULATED MARKETING
  marihuana
    tax revenue, 3796
REGULATION
  cannabis
    South Africa, 3229
  marihuana
    medical use, 5526
    research, 5526
RELAXATION
  marihuana
    compared to:
      alcohol, 4575
RELIGIOUS BELIEFS
  cannabis
    India, 3210
  marihuana
    drug use, 4222
    patterns of use, 4594
REM SLEEP
  cannabidiol (CBD)
    rats, 4488, 5001
  cannabinol (CBN)
    rats, 5001
  cannabis
    humans, 3097
  delta-9-THC
    rats, 3447, 3450, 5001
  marihuana
    chronic use, 4138
    humans, 4107
    sleep, 4138
  marihuana extract
    rats, 3450, 4489
REPRODUCTIVE EFFECTS
  cannabidiol (CBD)
    mice, 5635
    spermatozoa, 5635
    spermatogenesis, 3351
  cannabinol (CBN)
    copulation, 5359
    mice, 5359, 5635
    spermatozoa, 5635
  cannabis, 4522
    pigeon(s), 5139
    review, 5535
    testicular effects, 5139
  cannabis extract
    chronic administration, 3620, 3621
    estrus cycle, 3620
    gerbils, 3621
    mice, 3620, 3624
    ovaries, 3620, 3621

cannabis extract (continued)
    protein synthesis, 3621
    rats, 3620
    RNA synthesis, 3621
    sex accessory organs, 3624
    testicular function, 3623
    testosterone, 3624
  Cannabis sativa
    adult, 5559
    fetus, 5559
    mechanism of action, 5559
    mice, 5559
    rats, 5559
  delta-9-THC
    agalactia, 3389
    animals, 3389
    copulation, 5359
    estrogen, 3461
    fertility, 5390
    gestation, effects on, 3093
    lactation, 3351
    mice, 3116, 4359, 4360, 4362, 5359, 5635
    monkeys, 4896
    neo-natal development, 5390
    ovulation, 5295
    performance in offspring, 3093
    pregnancy, 3351
    prenatal growth, 4360
    rabbit(s), 5295, 5585
    rats, 3093, 3461, 5100, 5390
    review, 3351
    route of administration, 3389
    spermatozoa, 5635
    spermatogenesis, 3351
    testicular function, 3351
    uterus, 3461
  marihuana
    agalactia, 3389
    animals, 3389
    humans, 4177
    review, 4404
    route of administration, 3389
    sperms, 4177
  marihuana extract
    lactation, 3351
    pregnancy, 3351
    review, 3351
    spermatogenesis, 3351
    testicular function, 3351
  marihuana smoke
    brain, 5125
    fertility, 5390
    fetus, 5389
    neo-natal development, 5390
    nucleic acids, 5125
    rats, 5125, 5389, 5390
REPRODUCTIVE SYSTEM
  cannabinol (CBN)
    mechanism of action, 5544
    mice, 3569, 3570
    prostate, 5544
    seminal vesicle, 5544
    testosterone, 5544
  cannabis extract
    spermatogenesis, 3622

cannabis extract (continued)
  testicular effects, 3622
cannabis resin
  prostate, 4569
  seminal vesicle, 4569
  testis(es), 4569
  uterus, 4569
delta-9-THC
  adverse effect(s), 4528
  corpus luteum, 3729
  fetal development, 4687
  mammary glands, 4689
  mechanism of action, 5544
  mice, 3569, 3570, 4184, 4689, 5000
  monkeys, 3729
  ovulation, 3265, 3729
  prostate, 5544
  rabbit(s), 3265, 5226
  rats, 4687, 5226
  seminal vesicle, 5544
  testosterone, 5544
marihuana
  gynecomastia, 3248
  humans, 4016
  spermatozoa, 4016
  spermatogenesis, 4016
marihuana extract
  mice, 4184
  rabbit(s), 5226
  rats, 5226
REPRODUCTION
delta-8-THC
  review, 3919
delta-9-THC
  review, 3919
RESEARCH
cannabis, 3078
  chemical aspects, 5260, 5264
  Czechoslovakia, 5260, 5264
  pharmacological aspects, 5260, 5264
delta-9-THC
  antiemetic, 5567
  legal aspects, 5567
marihuana, 4632, 5152
  adverse effect(s), 3328
  bias of experimenter, 3163
  government programs and funding, 5607
  history, 5517
  National Institute on Drug Abuse (NIDA), 3996,
    4904
  problems, 3066, 3163, 4634
  United Nations Narcotics Commission, 4904
  U.S.A., 4634, 5607
  World Health Organization (WHO), 4904
RESEARCH EFFORTS
cannabis
  behavioral effect(s), 3735
RESPIRATION
cannabichromene (CBC)
  rats, 5531
delta-9-THC
  humans, 4346
  rats, 5531

RESPIRATORY EFFECTS
cannabichromene (CBC)
  rats, 5561
cannabidiol (CBD)
  dogs, 3394, 4504
  rats, 5561
cannabinoid(s)
  humans, 5340
cannabis
  review, 5535
cannabis smoke
  bronchial tubes, 3749
  review, 3749
delta-9-THC
  acute effect(s), 5014
  aerosol, 4572
  airway conductance, 4572, 5014
  asthma, 5207
  bronchodilatation, 3849, 4106, 4832, 5009, 5014,
    5207
  chronic effects, 5014
  dogs, 3393, 3896, 4050, 4504
  humans, 3521, 3849, 4106, 4107, 4275, 4572,
    4832, 4915, 5014, 5207
  interaction with
    anesthetic(s), 3896
    oxymorphone, 4087
    pentobarbital, 4087
ganja
  humans, 4762
hashish
  humans, 4275, 5599
  pathology, 5599
marihuana, 3215
  acute effect(s), 5013
  adverse effect(s), 3347, 4776
  bronchodilatation, 3499, 4106
  chronic effects, 3503
  chronic use, 3309, 3499
  clinical findings, 3323
  exercise, 3159, 4831
  humans, 3159, 3283, 3309, 3310, 3311, 3323,
    3347, 3499, 3503, 4106, 4107, 4275, 4428,
    4429, 4632, 4776, 4831, 5013, 5198
  rats, 5561
  tolerance, 3309, 3310
  Turkey, 5561
  ventilation, 3159
marihuana extract
  bronchodilatation, 3849
  humans, 3849
marihuana smoke
  acute effect(s), 5014
  adverse effect(s), 4758
  airway conductance, 5014
  bronchodilatation, 4832, 5014
  chronic effects, 5014
  chronic use, 3969, 4996
  dogs, 4758, 4996, 4997
  humans, 3969, 4832, 5014, 5245, 5246, 5247
  tolerance, 4996
SP-1
  rats, 5042

RESPIRATORY EFFECTS (continued)
SP 80
rats, 5042
SP-106
rats, 5042
RESPIRATORY SYSTEM
hemp workers
adverse effect(s), 3370
marihuana
adverse effect(s), 3500, 5007
compared to:
tobacco, 5007
emphysema, 4403
humans, 4403, 5007
marihuana smoke
adverse effect(s), 4740
chronic effects, 4740
rats, 4740
RETICULOENDOTHELIAL SYSTEM (RES)
delta-9-THC, 4261
RETICULOCYTOSIS
marihuana
humans, 4836
REVIEW
cannabichromene (CBC)
mass spectrometry, 5137
cannabicyclol (CBL)
mass spectrometry, 5137
cannabidiol (CBD)
analysis, 3478
behavioral effect(s), 4918
disposition, 4253
mass spectrometry, 5137
metabolism, 4253
pharmacological aspects, 3749, 4918
cannabinoid acids
analysis, 3413
cannabinoid(s)
analysis, 3478, 4411
behavioral effect(s), 3732, 4329
biosynthesis, 3329
chemical aspects, 5144
cytogenic effects, 5446
endocrine effects, 5340
intraocular pressure (IOP), 5414
pharmacognosy, 3329
pharmacological aspects, 5340
pharmacology, 4329
structure-activity relationships, 3479, 4411
therapeutic aspects, 3237, 3331, 4408
cannabinol (CBN)
analysis, 3478
behavioral effect(s), 4918
disposition, 4253
mass spectrometry, 5137
metabolism, 4253
pharmacokinetics, 4918
pharmacological aspects, 4918
cannabis
adverse effect(s), 3078, 4100
analysis, 4411
behavioral effect(s), 3062, 3769
biotransformation, 4531
botanical aspects, 3079, 3486, 3763, 4531, 4881

cannabis (continued)
chemical aspects, 4411, 4531
constituents of, 3256
constituents of, 4411
drug use, 4531
EEG changes, 3769
forensic aspects, 4660
history, 4531
neurochemistry, 3844
pharmacognosy, 3079
pharmacological aspects, 3436, 4727, 5233
pharmacology, 3844
psychological aspects, 3529, 3667, 4531
sociological aspects, 3929, 4531
taxonomy, 3255
teratogenic effects, 4623
therapeutic aspects, 4451
therapeutic effects, 4531
toxicology, 4531
cannabis extract
food intake, 3181
water intake, 3181
Cannabis sativa
analysis, 3478
chemical aspects, 3335, 4407
alkaloid(s), 3684
constituents of, 3760, 3905, 3907, 3908
metabolites, 3907, 3908
constituents of, 5079
pharmacological aspects, 4407
therapeutic aspects, 4407
cannabis smoke
respiratory effects, 3749
delta-8-THC
adverse effect(s), 3246
analysis, 3478
behavioral effect(s), 3732, 4160, 4918
discriminative properties, 3289, 4203
disposition, 4253
food intake, 3181
mass spectrometry, 5137
metabolism, 4253
pharmacological aspects, 3329, 4160, 4918
therapeutic aspects, 4160
toxicology, 4160
water intake, 3181
delta-9-THC
adverse effect(s), 3246
aggressive behavior, 4446
analgesia, 5420
analysis, 3478, 5278
behavioral effect(s), 3435, 3732, 3733, 4443, 4531, 4918, 5093
biochemical effect(s), 3177, 4411
cardiovascular effects, 3483
chemical aspects
structure-activity relationships, 4603
discriminative properties, 3289, 4203
disposition, 4253
endocrine effects, 3351, 4411
fetal development, 3699
food intake, 3181
hepatic metabolism, 3936
history, 5093
intraocular pressure (IOP), 5414

delta-9-THC (continued)
    mass spectrometry, 5137
    metabolism, 4253, 5199, 5278
    pharmacokinetics, 3250, 4918, 5278, 5394
    pharmacological aspects, 3250, 3329, 3749, 3919,
        4107, 4443, 4531, 4603, 4918, 5093, 5233,
        5459
    radioimmunoassay (RIA), 3520
    reproductive effects, 3351
    sexual behavior, 3351
    teratogenic effects, 3351, 3699, 3743
    therapeutic aspects, 3498, 4160, 4603
    therapeutic effects, 5405
    water intake, 3181
dimethylheptylpyran (DMHP)
    pharmacological aspects, 4603
ganja
    history, 4762
    legal aspects, 4762
hashish
    adverse effect(s), 3169, 3176
    chemical aspects, 4770
    clinical findings, 3155
    discriminative properties, 4203
    history, 3155, 3169, 3176
    pharmacological aspects, 3155, 3176
    psychological aspects, 3155
    sociological aspects, 3155
    therapeutic aspects, 4770
11-hydroxy-delta-9-THC
    discriminative properties, 4203
marihuana
    adverse effect(s), 3231, 3240, 3246, 3250, 3392,
        3481, 3500, 3651, 3741, 3893, 4107, 4151,
        5517, 5592, 5637
    driving, 4499
    aggressive behavior, 4778
    analysis, 3239
    behavioral effect(s), 3239, 5069, 5093, 5336
    botanical aspects, 3215
    cardiovascular effects, 3483
    chemical aspects, 3239, 3922, 4663, 4770, 4918
    chromosomes, 4398
    clinical aspects, 4531
    cognitive function, 4173
    constituents of, 3215
        discriminative properties, 4203
    endocrine effects, 3351
    epidemiological study, 3239
    fetal development, 3699
    history, 4663, 5093
    humans, 5336
    immune system, 4404
    immunology, 4398
    patterns of use, 3919, 4663
    pharmacokinetics, 3922, 4663
    pharmacological aspects, 3215, 3250, 3481, 3893,
        3922, 4107, 4663, 4918, 5069, 5093, 5591
    pharmacology, 5132
    physiological effects, 5591
    political ideology, 5637
    psychological aspects, 3185, 3239, 3250, 3893,
        4443, 5336
    psychological effects, 5591
    psychosocial aspects, 4634

marihuana (continued)
    reproductive effects, 3351, 4404
    research, 5516, 5517
    sexual behavior, 3351
    sociological aspects, 3833, 3893, 5637
    structure-activity relationships, 4918
    teratogenic effects, 3351, 3699
    therapeutic aspects, 3215, 3241, 3893, 3922,
        4770, 5017, 5637
    toxicology, 3922, 4527, 4663, 5132
marihuana extract
    behavioral effect(s), 3435
    discriminative properties, 4203
marihuana smoke
    analysis, 4531
    intraocular pressure (IOP), 5414
marihuana use
    adverse effect(s), 5285
    legal aspects, 5285
SP-1
    behavioral effect(s), 3435
SP-106
    analgesia, 5420
synthetic cannabinoids
    chemical aspects, 4918
        structure-activity relationships, 4603
    pharmacological aspects, 4603
    structure-activity relationships, 4918
    therapeutic aspects, 3331, 4603
tetrahydrocannabinol (THC)
    behavioral effect(s), 4329
    pharmacology, 4329
RIBONUCLEIC ACID (RNA)
delta-9-THC
    bacteria, 3177
marihuana smoke
    brain, 4303
    rats, 4303
RNA LEVELS
delta-9-THC
    in vitro, 3287
    liver, 3287
RNA POLYMERASE
delta-8-THC
    mice, 5225
delta-9-THC
    mice, 5225
RNA SYNTHESIS
blood gases
    in vitro, 4534
    lymphocytes, 4534
cannabichromene (CBC)
    in vitro, 4534
    lymphocytes, 4534
cannabicyclol (CBL)
    in vitro, 4534
    lymphocytes, 4534
cannabidiol (CBD)
    in vitro, 4534
    lymphocytes, 4534
delta-8-THC
    tissue culture, 3441
delta-9-THC
    adverse effect(s), 4528
    HeLa cells, 4483

delta-9-THC (continued)
  in vitro, 3603, 3607, 4318, 4534, 5241, 5328
  lymphocytes, 3603, 3606, 3607, 4524, 4533, 4534
  tissue culture(s), 3348, 3349, 3776
  olivetol
    in vitro, 4534
    lymphocytes, 4534
RIBOSOMES
  delta-9-THC
    brain, 4659
    cortex, 4659
    hypothalamus, 4659
    rats, 4659
    ribonucleic acid (RNA), 4659
ROUTE OF ADMINISTRATION
  delta-9-THC
    dosage, 3296
    monkeys, 5414
    operant behavior, 3296
    rabbit(s), 5414
    rats, 3296

S

SALIVA
  cannabinol (CBN)
    detection, 5617
  delta-9-THC
    cats, 4321, 4322
    discrimination, 4322
    parasympathetic nervous system (PNS), 4321, 4322
    rats, 4520
SALIVARY GLANDS
  delta-8-THC
    monkeys, 4118
  delta-9-THC
    accumulation, 4118
    animals, 4319
    anticholinergic effect, 4319
    binding, 4320
    blood flow, 4319
    efflux, 4320
    in vitro, 4320
    monkeys, 4118
    uptake, 4320
SALIVATION
  delta-9-THC
    cats, 4323
    dogs, 4323
    electrical stimulation, 4323
SAMPLE VARIATION
  hashish, 5138
SCHIZOPHRENIA
  cannabis, 3102
  marihuana
    chronic use, 3650
    humans, 3650, 5039
    paranoia, 5039
SCHIZOPHRENICS
  marihuana
    adverse effect(s), 5064

SEDATION
  delta-9-THC
    humans, 5335
SEDATIVE
  delta-9-THC, 3498
    biogenic amine(s), 4364
    humans, 3501, 5391
    nitrogen analogs, 4603
    rabbit(s), 4364
    review, 4603
    thio analogs, 4603
  SP-1
    cats, 3639
  SP 80
    cats, 3639
  SP-106
    cats, 3639
SEDATIVE EFFECT
  nabilone (Lilly compound no. 109514)
    humans, 4250
SEEDS
  cannabis
    gamma irradiation, 4844
    morphological variations, 4844
  Cannabis sativa, 4887
    cannabinoid content, 3073, 3580
    fungus, 3279
    geographical origin, 3073, 3580
SEIZURES
  cannabidiol (CBD)
    hippocampus, 4895
    limbic, 4892
    rats, 4892, 4895
    thujone, 4895
  delta-9-THC
    hippocampus, 4895
    limbic, 4892
    rats, 4892, 4895, 5372
    thujone, 4895
  marihuana
    epileptics, 3717
SELF ADMINISTRATION
  cannabis
    humans, 4112
    tolerance, 4112
  Cannabis sativa
    monkeys, 3137
  delta-9-THC
    body weight, 5594
    compared to:
      amphetamine, 5119
      chlorpromazine, 5119
      morphine, 5119
      nalorphine, 5119
    food deprivation, 5594
    mice, 3116
    monkeys, 3137
    rats, 5119, 5594
  hexahydrocannabinol (HHC)
    monkeys, 3452
  marihuana
    compared to:
      alcohol, 4420
    humans, 3275, 3870, 4420
    mood, 3275

marihuana (continued)
  multiple drug use, 4420
marihuana smoke
  humans, 3271
  social behavior, 3271
SEMINAL VESICLE
  cannabis resin
    rats, 4569
  marihuana smoke
    rats, 5431
SEPARATION
  cannabichromene (CBC)
    cannabidiol (CBD), 3286
    cannabinol (CBN), 3286
  cannabidiol (CBD)
    cannabichromene, (CBC), 3286
    cannabinol (CBN), 3286
    gas liquid chromatography (GLC), 4171
    high-pressure liquid chromatography (HPLC), 4171
    hydroxylated metabolites, 3750
    mass spectrometry, 4171
    phytosterols, 3366
  cannabidiolic acid, 3413
  cannabigerol (CBG)
    cannabigerolic acid, 4911
  cannabigerolic acid, 3413
  cannabinoid(s)
    gas chromatography, 4714
    GC/MS, 3944
    high-pressure liquid chromatography (HPLC), 3179
    methods, 5352
    phytosterols, 3366
    thin layer chromatography (TLC), 5134, 5386
    trimethylsilyl derivatives, 3944
  cannabinol (CBN)
    cannabichromene (CBC), 3286
    cannabidiol (CBD), 3286
    gas liquid chromatography (GLC), 4171
    high-pressure liquid chromatography (HPLC), 4171
    hydroxylated metabolites, 3750
    mass spectrometry, 4171
    phytosterols, 3366
  Cannabis sativa
    phenols, 3099
  delta-8-THC
    gas liquid chromatography (GLC), 4171
    high-pressure liquid chromatography (HPLC), 4171
    hydroxylated metabolites, 3750
    mass spectrometry, 4171
  delta-9-THC
    gas liquid chromatography (GLC), 4171
    high-pressure liquid chromatography (HPLC), 4171
    hydroxylated metabolites, 3750
    mass spectrometry, 4171
    phytosterols, 3366
  delta-9-THC oic acid A & B, 3413
SEPTAL REGION
  delta-9-THC
    gamma-amino-butyric acid (GABA), 5549
    rats, 5549
    ultrastructural changes, 5512
  marihuana smoke
    monkeys, 5512
    ultrastructural changes, 5512

SEROTONIN (5-HYDROXYTRYPTAMINE)
  cannabidiol (CBD)
    mice, 3970
    uptake, 3970
    worms, 4597
  cannabis extract
    brain levels, 4161
    guinea pig(s), 4161
    metabolism, 4161
    plasma levels, 4161
  cannabis resin
    analgesic activity, 5398
    anti-convulsant activity, 3810
    brain, 3592
    brain levels, 5398
    rats, 3592, 3810
  delta-8-THC
    worms, 4597
  delta-9-THC
    aggressive behavior, 4588
    analgesia, 3320
    analog(s), 4076, 4078
      brain, 3293
      synaptosomes, 3293
      uptake, 3293
    behavioral effect(s), 3201
    brain, 3293, 3320, 3382, 3802, 3986, 4073, 4074, 5596
    brain levels, 4922, 5023
    cats, 3201
    consummatory behavior, 3407
    distribution, 3986
    hypothalamus, 3405, 3407
    in vitro, 4076, 4078
    metabolites, 4076, 4078
    mice, 3970, 4074
    muricide, 4818
    rats, 3320, 3382, 3405, 3407, 3725, 3986, 4073, 4588, 4818, 4922, 5023, 5596
    synaptosomal, 4081
    synaptosomes, 3293, 4076, 4078
    synthesis, 4074
    turnover, 5596
    uptake, 3293, 3970, 4076, 4078
    worms, 4597
SEROTONIN LEVELS
  delta-9-THC
    brain, 4162, 4819
    rats, 3527, 4162, 4819
    stress, 3527
SERUM ENZYMES
  delta-9-THC
    creatinine phosphokinase (CPK), 4356
    rats, 4356
    SGOT (serum glutamic oxaloacetic transaminase), 4356
    SGPT (serum glutamic pyruvic transaminase), 4356
  marihuana smoke
    humans, 5338
SET AND SETTING
  marihuana
    humans, 4903
    subjective effects, 4903

SEX ACCESSORY ORGANS
  cannabis extract
    mice, 3624
    testosterone, 3624
SEX DIFFERENCES
  cannabis
    plant, 3763
    review, 3486
  cannabis plant, 4781
  Cannabis sativa
    hormonal effects, 3130
    plant, 4887
    potency, 4887
  marihuana
    adolescent(s), 3221
    botanical aspects, 3741
    characteristics of users, 4666
    drug use, 4606
    humans, 3192
    patterns of use, 4666, 5168
    performance, 4013
    rats, 4738
    social interaction, 3192
    toxicity, 4738
    use, 5587
  marihuana extract
    distribution, 3065
    endocrine effects, 3065
    metabolism, 3065
  marihuana smoke
    toxicology, 3742
SEXUAL ACTIVITY
  marihuana
    humans, 3805
SEXUAL BEHAVIOR
  cannabinol (CBN)
    humans, 4870
    mice, 3569, 3570
  cannabis
    humans, 3995
  cannabis resin
    mice, 3561
  delta-9-THC
    animals, 3351
    dominance, 5102
    humans, 3351, 4106
    mice, 3569, 3570
    rabbit(s), 5295
    rats, 4739, 5102
    review, 3351
  marihuana
    adverse effect(s), 3477
    attitude, 5364
    characteristics of users, 3415
    chronic use, 3494
    humans, 3477, 3494, 3997, 4106, 4427, 4638,
      4751, 5165, 5291, 5364
    patterns of use, 3088
    students, 3088, 3378
  marihuana extract
    animals, 3351
    humans, 3351
    review, 3351
SEXUAL FUNCTION
  cannabis
    phytosterols, 5466

cannabis (continued)
    plant, 5570
  Cannabis sativa
    cobalt, 5545
    flowers, 5545
SGOT (SERUM GLUTAMIC OXALOACETIC TRANS-
AMINASE)
  delta-9-THC
    chronic administration, 4744
    chronic effects, 5045
    rabbit(s), 5045
    rats, 4356, 4425, 4744
  hashish
    rats, 4339
SGPT (SERUM GLUTAMIC PYRUVIC TRANSAMIN-
ASE)
  delta-9-THC
    chronic administration, 4744
    chronic effects, 5045
    rabbit(s), 5045
    rats, 4356, 4425, 4744
SHOCK AVOIDANCE
  delta-9-THC
    monkeys, 4008
SIDE EFFECTS
  delta-9-THC
    review, 5405
  marihuana
    review, 5436
  nabilone (Lilly compound no. 109514)
    behavioral effect(s), 5485
    cats, 5485
    humans, 5426
  SP-106
    humans, 5420
SILVER NITRATE
  cannabis
    sexual function, 5570
SILYL DERIVATIVES
  cannabidiol (CBD)
    characteristics, 3934
    GC/MS, 3934
  cannabinol (CBN)
    characteristics, 3934
    GC/MS, 3934
  delta-9-THC
    characteristics, 3934
    GC/MS, 3934
  11-hydroxy-delta-9-THC
    characteristics, 3934
    GC/MS, 3934
BETA-SITOSTEROL
  marihuana
    constituents of, 3215
SKELETON
  marihuana extract
    fetus, 5353
    rabbit(s), 5353
SKIN CONDUCTANCE
  delta-9-THC
    humans, 4275
  hashish
    humans, 4275
  marihuana
    humans, 4275, 4537, 4717
    interaction with
      stress, 4537

SLEEP
  cannabidiol (CBD)
    rats, 4488, 5001
  cannabinol (CBN)
    rats, 5001
  delta-9-THC
    electroencephalogram (EEG), 3046
    humans, 3722, 3767, 4106, 4544, 4603, 5018
    monkeys, 3046
    rats, 5001
    REM sleep, 3723
  hashish
    humans, 5018
  marihuana
    chronic administration, 3200
    chronic use, 4138
    humans, 3274, 3276, 4106, 4138
    monkeys, 3200
  marihuana extract
    humans, 3722
    rats, 4489
SLEEP TIME
  cannabidiol(CBD), 5457
    derivatives, 3451, 4409
    hexabarbital, 4034
    interaction with
      methaqualone, 4988
    mice, 3451, 4034, 4409, 4988, 5319
    pentobarbital, 4409
    rats, 3067
    tolerance, 5319
  cannabinol (CBN)
    rats, 3067
  cannabis
    interaction with
      copper, 4876
    mice, 4876
    rats, 3067, 4873, 4876
    tolerance, 4873, 4876
  cannabis smoke
    barbiturate(s), 4785
    mice, 4785
  delta-8-THC
    phospholipids, 5234
  delta-9-THC
    interaction with
      methaqualone, 4988
    mice, 4988, 5162
    rats, 3067, 5541
  SP-1
    mice, 4602
  synthetic cannabinoids
    mice, 5162
SMOKE CONDENSATE ANALYSIS
  cannabidiol (CBD)
    gas chromatography, 4950
    thin layer chromatography (TLC), 4950
  cannabinoid(s)
    gas chromatography, 4950
    thin layer chromatography (TLC), 4950
  cannabis, 3214
    cyanide, 3411
  marihuana, 4017, 4158, 4605
    acid(s), 4102, 4391
    base(s), 4102

marihuana (continued)
  compared to:
    tobacco, 4555
  gas chromatography, 4102
  GC/MS, 4102, 4238
  nuclear magnetic resonance (NMR), 4238
  phenols, 4102, 4391
  polycyclic aromatic hydrocarbons, 3991, 4238, 4555
SMOOTH MUSCLE
  cannabidiol (CBD)
    in vitro, 4729
  cannabinol (CBN)
    in vitro, 4729
  delta-8-THC
    contraction, 5556
    in vitro, 4729
    metabolites, 4729
  delta-9-THC
    blood vessels, 4051
    contraction, 5524
    dogs, 4051
    in vitro, 4729
    metabolites, 4729
  SP-111
    contraction, 5524
  synthetic cannabinoids
    contraction, 5556
SOCIAL BEHAVIOR
  cannabinol (CBN)
    humans, 4515
  cannabis
    baboons, 4259
    humans, 3509
  cannabis resin
    mice, 3559, 3560
  delta-9-THC
    acute administration, 5336
    aggression, 5336
    animals, 3351
    ant(s), 5161
    biogenic amine(s), 3834
    chronic administration, 5336
    chronic effects, 4684
    estrogen, 3834
    humans, 3351, 4515
    mice, 3558, 3637, 3688, 4684
    monkeys, 3234, 4071, 4093, 4783, 5336
    rats, 3834
    review, 3351
    sex differences, 3234
  hashish
    chronic use, 4966, 4967
    Greece, 4967
    humans, 3371, 4966
  marihuana, 3252
    animals, 3240, 4632
    characteristics of users, 3068, 3071
    compared to:
      alcohol, 4575
    humans, 4419, 4429, 4575, 4777, 5176
    monkeys, 3234
    sex differences, 3234
    students, 4901

SOCIAL BEHAVIOR (continued)
 marihuana smoke
  humans, 3271
  self administration, 3271
SOCIAL INTERACTION
 delta-9-THC
  rats, 5501
   route of administration, 5501
   strain difference, 5501
   vehicle of administration, 5501
 marihuana
  humans, 3192, 3272, 3277
  sex differences, 3192
 marihuana smoke
  humans, 5396
SOCIAL PROBLEMS
 marihuana
  deafness, 3224
SOCIOECONOMIC ACTIVITY
 marihuana
  students, 3884
SOCIOLOGICAL ASPECTS
 cannabis
  characteristics of users, 4416
  chronic use, 3633, 4416, 5067
  Costa Rica, 5067
  epidemiological study, 4185
  problems, 4185
  review, 3929
  social behavior, 4416
 compared to:
  alcohol, 3758
  tobacco, 3758
 hashish
  Afghanistan, 3829
  Canada, 4931
 marihuana, 3135, 3659, 4450, 4574, 4723, 5242
  adolescent(s), 4168
  age, 4219
  attitudes of users, 3415
  characteristics of users, 3057, 4584
  compared to:
   alcohol, 4573, 5066
   tobacco, 5066
  Costa Rica, 3455
  drug use, 4438, 5185
  epidemiological study, 3109
  factors influencing use, 3057, 3157, 3418
  family relationships, 3141, 4438
  humans, 4767, 5169
  legal aspects, 3103
  motivation of use, 4573
  parental influence, 3417
  religious beliefs, 3417
  sex differences, 4219
  sexual behavior, 3415
  students, 3056, 3109, 3126, 4219, 5066
  youths, 3157
 marihuana smoke
  characteristics of users, 4367
SOCIOLOGICAL INTERACTION
 marihuana smoke
  humans, 5444

SODIUM
 delta-9-THC
  plasma levels, 4919
SODIUM CONDUCTANCE
 delta-9-THC
  frog(s), 4989
  nerve fibers, 4989
SODIUM-POTASSIUM ADENOSINE TRIPHOSPHA-
TASE (Na K ATPASE)
 cannabinoid(s)
  enzyme activity, 5602
 cannabis extract
  microsomes, 4655
  rats, 4655
  synaptosomes, 4655
 delta-9-THC
  binding, 5602
  brain, 5059
  in vitro, 5060
  inhibition, 5602
  mice, 5492
  microsomes, 4655
  nucleotides, 5602
  pharmacokinetics, 5492, 5602
  rats, 4237, 4655, 5059
  synaptosomes, 3809, 4237, 4655, 5492
SOIL
 cannabis
  plant, 3763
SOLID SAMPLE INJECTION
 cannabinol (CBN)
  gas liquid chromatography (GLC), 4694
SORBITOL DEHYDROGENASE
 delta-9-THC
  rats, 4811
  testis(es), 4811
SOUTH AFRICA
 cannabis plant
  hydroxylated cannabinoids, 5314
SP-1
 behavioral effect(s), 4602
  conditioned behavior, 3059, 3435
  self administration, 3639
  tolerance, 3435
 pharmacological aspects
  analgesia, 4601
  analgesic activity, 3639, 4602
  body temperature, 5042
  body weight, 3865
  cardiovascular effects, 4602
  compared to:
   dimethylheptylpyran (DMHP), 4602
   morphine, 4602
  eyes, 3857, 3858, 3863, 3865, 5042
  intraocular pressure (IOP), 3639, 3857, 3858,
   3863, 5042
  liver weight, 3865
  respiratory effects, 5042
  sedative, 3639
  sleep time, 4602
  tranquilizing activity, 3639
 review, 3435
 toxicology
  body weight, 5042
  food intake, 5042

toxicology (continued)
    LD50, 3639, 4602, 5042
    occular toxicity, 5042
SP 80
  behavioral effect(s)
    self administration, 3639
  pharmacological aspects
    analgesic activity, 3639
    body temperature, 5042
    eyes, 5042
    intraocular pressure (IOP), 3639, 5042
    respiratory effects, 5042
    sedative, 3639
    tranquilizing activity, 3639
  toxicology
    body weight, 5042
    food intake, 5042
    LD50, 3639, 5042
    occular toxicity, 5042
SP-106
  behavioral effect(s)
    self administration, 3639
  pharmacological aspects
    analgesia, 4601
    analgesic activity, 3639
    body temperature, 5042
    body weight, 3865
    eyes, 3857, 3858, 3863, 3865, 5042
    intraocular pressure (IOP), 3639, 3857, 3858, 3863, 5042
    liver weight, 3865
    respiratory effects, 5042
    sedative, 3639
    tranquilizing activity, 3639
  therapeutic effects
    analgesia, 5420
    compared to:
      delta-9-THC, 5420
      secobarbital, 5420
    review, 5420
    side effects, 5420
  toxicology
    body weight, 5042
    food intake, 5042
    LD50, 3639, 5042
    occular toxicity, 5042
SP-111
  behavioral effect(s)
    conditioned behavior, 3661
    rats, 4816
  neuropharmacological effects
    brain, 4816
    interaction with
      neurotransmitters, 4816
    neuronal activity, 4816
  pharmacological aspects
    acetylcholine (ACh), 4546
    compared to:
      alcohol, 4546
      ethanol, 5524
    norepinephrine (NE), 4546
    smooth muscle, 5524
    vas deferens, 4546, 5524

SP-111A
  neuropharmacology
    action potential(s), 3190
    neuronal activity, 3190
    synaptic transmission, 3190
  pharmacological aspects
    analgesia, 4601
    cardiovascular effects, 4576
    convulsions, 4387
    eyes, 3859
    intraocular pressure (IOP), 3859
    stimulant activity, 4387
SP-141
  pharmacological aspects
    analgesia, 4601
    anti-convulsant activity, 4651
SP-143
  pharmacological aspects
    analgesia, 4601
    anti-convulsant activity, 4651
SP-175
  pharmacological aspects
    anti-convulsant activity, 3439, 4651
    body temperature, 3439
SP-178
  pharmacological aspects
    analgesia, 4601
SP-204
  pharmacological aspects
    analgesia, 4601
    body weight, 3865
    eyes, 3863, 3865
    intraocular pressure (IOP), 3863
    liver weight, 3865
SPECIES
  cannabis
    classification, 3151
    legal aspects, 4298, 4299
    plant, 4411, 4881, 4883, 4884, 4885, 4886, 4889
    review, 3079
SPECTRAL DATA
  cannabidiolic acid, 3413
  cannabigerolic acid, 3413
  delta-9-THC oic acid A & B, 3413
SPECTROPHOTOMETRY
  marihuana
    forensic aspects, 5476
SPEECH
  delta-9-THC
    humans, 4014, 5519
SPERMATOZOA
  cannabinoid(s)
    mice, 5636
    morphology, 5636
  cannabis
    humans, 4036
    morphology, 4963
    production, 4763
    protein, 4036
    testosterone, 4963
  delta-9-THC
    humans, 5333
    in vitro, 3813
    membrane permeability, 3813

SPERMATOZOA (continued)
  marihuana
    humans, 4016
    morphology, 4016
  marihuana smoke
    concentration, 5425
    humans, 5425
    morphology, 5425, 5431
    mortality, 5425
    rats, 5431
SPERMATOGENESIS
  cannabis, 4522
    chronic use, 3955
    humans, 3955
  cannabis extract
    dogs, 3622
  delta-9-THC
    adverse effect(s), 4528
  marihuana
    humans, 3956, 4016
  marihuana smoke
    humans, 5425
SPERMS
  hashish
    chronic use, 4970
    histological changes, 4970
    humans, 4970
    morphology, 4970
  marihuana
    humans, 3957, 4177, 4971
    semen, 3957
SPINAL CORD
  delta-9-THC
    body temperature, 4795
    cats, 4795
  dimethylheptylpyran (DMHP)
    body temperature, 4795
    cats, 4795
  11-hydroxy-delta-9-THC
    body temperature, 4795
    cats, 4795
SPIRO-COMPOUNDS
  Cannabis sativa
    cannabispiradienone, 5356
    cannabispirenone (see also dehydrocannabispiran),
      5356
    constituents of, 4852, 5079
    Thailand, 5356
  chemical aspects
    isolation, 4852
    structure, 4852
SPLEEN
  delta-9-THC
    adverse effect(s), 4670
    antibody synthesis, 4239
    mice, 4239
SPONTANEOUS ACTIVITY
  cannabidiol (CBD)
    derivatives, 4409
    mice, 4409
SPRAY REAGENTS
  cannabinoid(s), 3672
  cannabis
    phenols, 4691

SPUTUM ANALYSIS
  marihuana
    humans, 4833
STABILITY
  cannabinoid(s)
    chloroform, 5084, 5316
    ethanol, 5316
    overview, 4142
  cannabis
    storage, 4539
  cannabis plant
    light, 3705
    temperature, 3705
  cannabis resin
    light, 3705
    temperature, 3705
  delta-8-THC
    acid(s), 3798
  delta-9-THC
    acid(s), 3798
    synthetic, 4271
STANDARDIZED MATERIAL
  marihuana
    research, 5606
STANDARDIZED SAMPLES
  marihuana
    availability, 5153
STATE-DEPENDENT LEARNING
  delta-9-THC
    humans, 4980
    rats, 3869, 5163
  marihuana
    humans, 3973, 4457, 4980
STEREOCHEMICAL FEATURES
  cannabidiol (CBD)
    anti-convulsant activity, 4104
  delta-7-THC, 5313
STEREOSPECIFIC BINDING
  delta-8-THC
    brain, 3920
    rats, 3920
STEREOTYPY
  cannabis
    interaction with
      amphetamine, 3839
  cannabis extract
    dopamine (DA), 3264
    rats, 3264
  Cannabis indica
    mice, 4871
  delta-9-THC
    dopamine (DA), 3841
    mice, 5429
    rats, 3841
STEROIDS
  cannabidiol (CBD)
    mice, 5159
    synthesis, 5159
  cannabinol (CBN)
    mice, 5159
    synthesis, 5159
  cannabis
    constituents of, 3255
  cannabis extract
    androgen, 4392, 4393

cannabis extract (continued)
  conjugated, 4390
  corticosterones, 4390, 4393
  estrogen, 4390, 4393
  rats, 4390, 4392, 4393
  testosterone, 4390, 4393
Cannabis sativa
  constituents of, 5079
delta-9-THC
  androgen, 4392, 4393
  conjugated, 4390
  corticosterones, 4390, 4393
  estrogen, 4390, 4393
  metabolism, 4558
  mice, 5159
  rats, 4390, 4392, 4393, 4558
  synthesis, 5158, 5159
  testosterone, 4390, 4393
ganja
  humans, 4762
STEROLS
  marihuana
    analysis
      GC/MS, 4556
    constituents of, 4556
STIMULANT ACTIVITY
  cannabichromene (CBC)
    rabbit(s), 4387
  cannabicyclol (CBL)
    rabbit(s), 4387
  cannabidiol (CBD)
    rabbit(s), 4387
  cannabinol (CBN)
    rabbit(s), 4387
  delta-8-THC
    rabbit(s), 4387
  delta-9-THC
    biogenic amine(s), 4364
    2-phenylethylamine, 4364
    rabbit(s), 4364, 4387
  11-hydroxy-delta-9-THC
    rabbit(s), 4387
  marihuana smoke
    rats, 4303
    tolerance, 4303
  SP-111A
    rabbit(s), 4387
STIMULANT EFFECTS
  cannabis
    mice, 4874
    rats, 4874
  delta-9-THC
    2-phenylethylamine, 3143, 5124
    rabbit(s), 3143
STOMACH ACIDS
  9-Aza-cannabinol
    sheep, 5618
  cannabis
    compared to:
      alcohol, 4538
    humans, 4538
STOMATO
  cannabis
    taxonomy, 3794

STORAGE
  cannabidiol (CBD)
    insects, 4755
  cannabis
    cannabinoid content, 3591
    geographical origin, 3591
  delta-9-THC
    insects, 4755
STREET SAMPLES
  delta-9-THC
    hashish extract, 3408
    hashish, resin, and oils, 3408
    marihuana, 3408
    phencyclidine, 3408
  hashish
    subjective effects, 5552
    U.S.A., 5552
  marihuana
    cannabinoid content, 5552
    contaminated, 4285
    Costa Rica, 3493
    phencyclidine, 4688
    subjective effects, 5552
    U.S.A., 5552
  tetrahydrocannabinol (THC)
    contaminated, 3886
STRESS
  cannabidiol (CBD)
    corticosterone level, 5440
    rats, 5440
  cannabis extract
    dopamine (DA), 3528
    homovanillic acid (HVA), 3528
  cannabis resin
    biogenic amine(s), 3592
    rats, 3592
Cannabis sativa
    aggressive behavior, 3061
    rats, 3061
  delta-9-THC
    cellular respiration, 4282
    corticosterone level, 4588, 5440
    dopamine (DA), 4283
    humans, 3877, 4981
    rats, 3527, 4283, 4588, 4857, 5440
    serotonin levels, 3527
    subjective effects, 4981
    teratogenic effects, 4857
  hashish
    adrenal function, 4291
    ascorbic acid, 4291, 4292
    cholesterol, 4291, 4292
    hypothalamic pituitary function, 4291
    rats, 4291, 4292
  marihuana
    animals, 4632
    euphoria, 4641
    humans, 3364, 4005, 4641
    oral surgery, 4005
  nabilone (Lilly compound no. 109514)
    humans, 4536
STRUCTURE
  cannabichromene (CBC)
    mass spectrometry, 3416

STRUCTURE (continued)
cannabidiol (CBD), 3144
derivatives, 3144
mass spectrometry, 3416
pyrolytic products, 4947
x-ray crystallography, 4583
x-ray diffraction, 4103
cannabielsoin (CBE)
infrared (IR), 4946
mass spectrometry, 4946
nuclear magnetic resonance (NMR), 4946
cannabinoid(s), 4410
review, 5413
thio derivatives, 4212
cannabinol (CBN)
x-ray crystallography, 4582
cannabiripsol, 5314
Cannabis sativa
glycosides, 4821
cannabispiran (see also cannabispirone)
x-ray, 4580
delta-8-THC, 3260
keto analogs, 3260
mass spectrometry, 3416
nuclear magnetic resonance (NMR), 4212
thio derivatives, 4212
delta-9-THC, 3260, 5340
keto analogs, 3260
mass spectrometry, 3416
delta-9-THC oic acid A & B, 4745
hexahydrocannabinol (HHC)
homologs, 4105
8-beta-hydroxy-delta-9-THC
x-ray crystallography, 4581
nuclear magnetic resonance (NMR), 4212
synthetic cannabinoids
camphane moiety, 4166
review, 5413
THC-iso
mass spectrometry, 3416
STRUCTURE-ACTIVITY RELATIONSHIPS
benzopyranopyridine(s)
analgesia, 4601
cannabinoid(s), 3335, 3536, 4411, 4918, 4961, 5340
anti-neoplastic activity, 3921
carbocyclic analogs, 4707
derivatives, 4396
immunology, 4668
nitrogen analogs, 4602
thio analogs, 4602, 4707
delta-6a(10a)-THC, 4603
delta-8-THC, 4195, 4196, 4653
analgesic activity, 4084
compared to:
thujone, 3598
delta-9-THC, 4653
analgesic activity, 4084
analog(s), 4076, 4078, 4411, 4578, 4579, 5094
carbocyclic analogs, 4603
chemical aspects, 5146
compared to:
thujone, 3598
metabolites, 4076, 4078
nitrogen analogs, 4603
thio analogs, 4603

STRUCTURE-ACTIVITY RELATIONSHIPS (cont.)
hexahydrocannabinol (HHC)
analgesia, 5580
body temperature, 5580
derivatives, 5580
locomotor activity, 5580
mice, 5580
marihuana
review, 4663
synthetic cannabinoids, 4918
tetrahydrocannabinol (THC)
analgesia, 5580
body temperature, 5580
derivatives, 5580
locomotor activity, 5580
mice, 5580
SUBACUTE EFFECTS
ABBOTT-41988
rats, 5044
cannabis
review, 4531
SUBACUTE STUDY
delta-9-THC
rabbit(s), 3292
SUBCELLULAR DISTRIBUTION
delta-9-THC, 3690
SUBJECTIVE EFFECTS
cannabidiol (CBD)
humans, 5350
interaction with
delta-9-THC, 3573, 3576
cannabinoid(s)
limbic, 5504
mechanism of action, 5504
cannabis, 3843
consciousness, 5128
environmental conditions, 3854
humans, 3738, 3854, 5626
mood, 5128
sensory associations, 5128
tolerance, 3845
delta-9-THC
blood level(s), 4981
cardiovascular effects, 4981
humans, 3250, 3631, 4110, 4245, 4247, 4626, 4981, 5239, 5302, 5335, 5391, 5470
interaction with
cannabidiol (CBD), 3573, 3576
stress, 4981
dimethylheptylpyran (DMHP)
humans, 4245
hashish, 3169
sociological interaction, 5435
11-hydroxy-delta-9-THC
humans, 4245, 4247
marihuana, 4109
acute effect(s), 3762
chronic effects, 3503, 3762
chronic use, 3728
clinical aspects, 4531
environment, 3848
guilt, 3702
heart rate, 3762

marihuana (continued)
    humans, 3250, 3273, 3503, 3728, 3762, 4000,
        4106, 4107, 4110, 4537, 4903, 5052, 5108,
        5505, 5538
    interaction with
        secobarbital, 3572
        stress, 4537
    sociological interaction, 5435
    tolerance, 3273
  marihuana smoke, 5348
    humans, 5396, 5444
  nabilone (Lilly compound no. 109514)
    humans, 4245, 5401
SUGARS
  cannabis
    constituents of, 3255, 3536
  Cannabis sativa
    constituents of, 4205, 5079
SUGGESTIBILITY
  marihuana
    humans, 3070, 4156
SULFATE
  delta-8-THC
    excretion, 5624
    hydrolysis, 5624
    rats, 5624
    synthesis, 5624
    toxicity, 5624
SYNAPSE
  delta-9-THC
    monkeys, 3917
    ultrastructure, 3917
SYNAPTIC TRANSMISSION
  delta-9-THC
    acetylcholine (ACh), 4750
    action potential(s), 5525
    cats, 3437
    crayfish, 3211
    eel, 5525
    endplate potential, 5525
    in vitro, 3190, 4750
    isomers, 4750
    spinal cord, 3437
    stereospecificity, 4750
  SP-111A
    in vitro, 3190
SYNAPTIC VESICLES
  cannabinol (CBN)
    ATPase(s), 4570
  delta-9-THC
    ATPase(s), 4570
  11-hydroxy-delta-9-THC
    ATPase(s), 4570
  olivetol
    ATPase(s), 4570
SYNAPTOSOMES
  cannabinoid(s)
    brain, 5368
    neurotransmitters, 5368
  delta-9-THC
    acetylcholinesterase, 3809
    acyltransferase activity, 4025
    analog(s), 4076, 4078
    in vitro, 4076, 4078
    metabolites, 4076, 4078

delta-9-THC (continued)
    serotonin (5-hydroxytryptamine), 4076, 4078
    sodium-potassium adenosine triphosphatase (Na K
      ATPase), 3809
SYNHEXYL
  clinical findings, 3097
SYNTHESIS
  cannabichromene (CBC), 3537, 3682
  cannabichromevarinic acid
    radiolabelled, 4850
  cannabicitran, 3537
  cannabicyclol (CBL), 3537
  cannabidiol (CBD), 3537
    derivatives, 5173
    glucuronides, 4306
    hydroxylated, 4221
    metabolites, 4221
  cis-cannabidiol, 3899
  cannabidivarinic acid
    radiolabelled, 4850
  cannabigerol (CBG), 3537
  cannabigerorcinic acid
    radiolabelled, 4850
  cannabigerovarinic acid
    radiolabelled, 4850
  cannabinoid(s), 3536, 4411, 4961
    acid(s), 3541
    analog(s), 3241, 5236
    cannabidiol (CBD)
      abnormal isomer(s), 3261
    cannabinol (CBN)
      abnormal isomer(s), 3261
    carboxylated derivatives, 5357
    constituents, 3241
    delta-8-THC
      abnormal isomer(s), 3261
    delta-9-THC
      abnormal isomer(s), 3261
    derivatives, 3541, 4342, 4343, 4396, 4397, 4710
    ester, 3541
    metabolites, 4410, 4411, 5144
    nitrogen analogs, 4602, 5486
    overview, 4142
    radiolabelled, 5371
    thio analogs, 4602
    thio derivatives, 4212
  cannabinol (CBN), 3537
    deuterium labelled, 4649
    glucuronides, 4306
    isomers, 5487
    metabolites, 5200
    pyrolytic products, 5487
    radiolabelled, 4649
  cannabiripsol, 5314
  cannabispiran (see also cannabispirone)
    chemical aspects, 5375
  chemical aspects
    heterocyclic derivatives of cannabinoids, 4344
  delta-6a(7)-THC, 3262
  delta-8-THC, 3537, 4160, 4635, 5046, 5099
    analog(s), 3298, 3616, 4196
    chemical aspects, 3208
    derivatives, 4195, 5173
    dioxygenated, 4649
    glucuronides, 4306, 5227

delta-8-THC (continued)
  homologs, 4195
  metabolites, 4296
  nitrogen analogs, 4295
  oxygen analog(s), 4197
  phospholipids, 5234
  radiolabelled, 3989, 4649
  stereospecific, 3335
  thio analogs, 3616
  thio derivatives, 4212
delta-7-THC, 5313
delta-9-THC, 3139, 3537, 4160, 4635, 4706
  analog(s), 3616, 4411, 4486
  chemical aspects, 5418
  deuterium labelled, 4649
  glucuronides, 4306
  in vitro, 5333
  isomers, 5487
  metabolites, 4648
  oxygen analog(s), 4197
  radiolabelled, 3989, 4649
  stereospecific, 3335
  thio analogs, 3616
dimethylheptylpyran (DMHP)
  analog(s), 4703
hexahydrocannabinol (HHC)
  analog(s), 3615
5-hydroxy-delta-9-THC
  glucuronides, 4589
11-hydroxy-delta-9-THC, 4589
  glucuronides, 4589
nabilone (Lilly compound no. 109514), 3259
olivetol, 4206
synthetic cannabinoids, 5095
tetrahydrocannabinol (THC)
  derivatives, 4710
  thio derivatives, 4211
SYNTHETIC
  cannabinoid(s)
    chemical aspects
      nitrogen analogs, 4602
    structure-activity relationships, 4602
    synthesis, 4602
    thio analogs, 4602
SYNTHETIC CANNABINOIDS
  analysis
    biological fluid(s), 3800
    detection, 3800, 4995
    fragmentation, 3933
    gas liquid chromatography (GLC), 3800
    GC/MS, 3933
    high-pressure liquid chromatography (HPLC), 3800
    mass fragmentography, 5154
  behavioral effect(s), 3199, 4732, 4959
    ataxia, 4381
    conditioned behavior, 3381, 5162
    gross behavior, 3664
    gross behavioral change(s), 5162
    M-wave behavior, 3381
  benzopyran derivative(s)
    conditioned behavior, 3059
  biochemical aspects
    detection, 3241

SYNTHETIC CANNABINOIDS (continued)
  chemical aspects, 3199
    biotransformation, 3178
    delta-6a(10a)-THC, 4918
    derivatives
      silyl, 3933
    dimethylheptylpyran (DMHP), 4918
    nabilone (Lilly compound no. 109514), 4918
    review
      structure-activity relationships, 4603
    structure, 4166, 5413
    structure-activity relationships, 4653, 4913, 4918
      review, 4603
    synthesis, 3259, 3298, 3615, 3899, 4195, 5095, 5236
  clinical findings, 3097
  immunology, 4914
    cell-mediated immunity, 4653, 4913
    humoral immunity, 4653, 4913
    immunosuppression, 5584
  pharmacokinetics
    blood level(s), 4995
  pharmacological aspects, 3199
    adrenergic nervous system, 5413
    alcohol withdrawal, 4944
    analgesia, 3354, 4378, 4958
    analgesic, 4068
    analgesic activity, 5162
    anti-anxiety, 4960
    anti-anxiety activity, 3993, 4031, 4536, 4959
    anti-convulsant activity, 4651
    antiemetic, 4960
    biological activity, 4959
    body temperature, 5162
    cardiovascular effects, 3664, 4250, 4381, 4732
    CNS activity, 4250
    delta-6a(10a)-THC, 4918
    dimethylheptylpyran (DMHP), 4918
    eyes, 3640
    intraocular pressure (IOP), 3640, 3866, 4960, 5413
    morphine withdrawal, 4378
    nabilone (Lilly compound no. 109514), 4918
    review, 4603
    route of administration, 5413
    sleep time, 5162
    smooth muscle, 5556
  review
    pharmacological aspects, 4603
    therapeutic aspects, 4603
  therapeutic aspects, 3498, 4487
    alcoholism, 3331
    analgesic, 3331
    anti-anxiety, 5178
    anti-convulsant activity, 3331
    anti-hypertensive, 3331
    anti-inflammatory activity, 3331
    antiasthmatic, 3331
    antidepressant, 3331
    antidiarrheal, 3331
    antiemetic, 3331, 5178
    antipyretic, 3331
    antitussive, 3331

therapeutic aspects (continued)
  appetite stimulant, 3331
  cancer, 3331
  glaucoma, 3331
  intraocular pressure (IOP), 5178
  morphine withdrawal, 3331
  review, 3331, 4603
toxicology
  eyes, 5043
  ocular effects, 5413
  subacute effects, 5044

T

TACHYCARDIA
delta-9-THC
  animal model, 4577
  rats, 4578
dimethylheptylpyran (DMHP)
  rats, 4578
TAXONOMY
cannabis, 3689
  plant, 3763, 4884, 4885, 4886, 4889
  review, 3255, 3486
  stomato, 3794
  trichomes, 3794
  Cannabis sativa, 4887, 4888
  flavonoids, 5346
TERATOGENESIS
Cannabis sativa
  review, 5559
delta-9-THC
  rabbit(s), 5585
marihuana
  humans, 3250
  review, 4398, 5551
TERATOGENIC EFFECTS
cannabis
  animals, 3078
  humans, 4623
  review, 4531, 4623
cannabis extract
  rabbit(s), 3759
delta-9-THC
  animals, 3351
  chickens, 4044
  constituents of, 4359
  fetal development, 3351
  hamsters, 3699, 4089
  interaction with
    phenobarbital, 4361
    SKF-525A, 4361
  metabolites, 3913
  mice, 3116, 3119, 3743, 3913, 4088, 4090, 4184,
    4360, 4361, 4362
  rabbit(s), 3699, 5226
  rats, 3291, 3699, 4857, 5100, 5101, 5122, 5226
  review, 3351, 3699
  route of administration, 4090
  stress, 4857
  zebrafish embryo, 5041
marihuana, 4143, 4975
  animals, 3893

marihuana (continued)
  epidemiological study, 4548
  hamsters, 3699
  humans, 4548
  rabbit(s), 3699
  rats, 3699
  review, 3699, 4527
marihuana extract
  animals, 3351
  fetal development, 3351
  mice, 4184
  rabbit(s), 5226
  rats, 5226
  review, 3351
marihuana smoke
  mice, 4741, 4951
  rats, 3771, 4741
TERPENES
cannabis
  constituents of, 3255, 3536
Cannabis sativa
  constituents of, 3905, 3961, 5079
  review, 3905
constituents of,
  Cannabis sativa, 3053
hashish
  constituents of, 3892
marihuana
  constituents of, 3892
TERPENOIDS
chemical aspects
  identification, 5464
TESTICULAR EFFECTS
cannabichromene (CBC)
  rats, 5561
cannabidiol (CBD)
  enzyme changes, 3832, 4281
  rats, 3832, 4281, 5419, 5561
  testosterone, 4281
  testosterone synthesis, 5419
cannabinol (CBN)
  mice, 5359
cannabis
  pigeon(s), 5139
cannabis extract
  dogs, 3622
delta-9-THC
  enzyme changes, 3832, 4281, 5419
  glucose metabolism, 5437
  in vitro, 5437
  mice, 5359
  microsomes, 5419
  rats, 3832, 4281, 5419
  review, 5419
  testosterone, 4281
  testosterone synthesis, 5419
marihuana
  rats, 5561
  Turkey, 5561
marihuana smoke
  rats, 5383
TESTICULAR FUNCTION
cannabis extract
  toads, 3623

TESTIS(ES)
  cannabinoid(s)
    nucleotides, 5442
    protein synthesis, 5442
    rats, 5442
    testosterone levels, 5442
  cannabinol (CBN)
    mice, 3568
  cannabis resin
    rats, 4569
  Cannabis sativa
    adverse effect(s), 5603
  delta-9-THC
    cytochrome P450, 4811
    glucose metabolism, 4023
    beta-glucuronidase, 4811
    gamma-glutamyl transpeptidase, 4811
    histological changes, 3915
    mice, 3568
    rats, 3915, 4811
    sorbitol dehydrogenase, 4811
    spermatogenesis, 3915
  marihuana
    retention, 4176
  marihuana smoke
    adverse effect(s), 5431
    humans, 4178
    rats, 5431
    spermatogenesis, 4178
TESTOSTERONE
  cannbinol (CBN)
    mice, 3568
    secretion, 3568
  cannabis, 4727
  cannabis extract
    plasma levels, 4390, 4392, 4393
    rats, 4392
    urine, 4392
  delta-8-THC
    in vitro, 3465
    metabolism, 3465
  delta-9-THC
    blood level(s), 5296
    in vitro, 3465
    metabolism, 3465
    mice, 3568
    monkeys, 3899, 5297
    plasma levels, 4390, 4392, 4393
    rabbit(s), 5296
    rats, 3915, 4392, 4558
    secretion, 3568
    urine, 4392
  marihuana
    blood level(s), 4016
    chronic use, 3494
    humans, 3494, 3549, 3774, 3957, 4016, 4107, 4177, 4179, 4429, 4430, 4431, 4432, 4433, 4725, 4787
    plasma levels, 3494, 3549, 3774, 3957, 4179, 4430, 4431, 4433, 4787
  marihuana smoke
    humans, 4178
    plasma levels, 4178

TESTOSTERONE LEVELS
  cannabinol (CBN)
    mice, 3569, 3570, 5359
    plasma, 3569, 3570
  delta-9-THC
    mice, 3569, 3570, 5359
    plasma, 3569, 3570
    rats, 4998
  marihuana
    chronic administration, 4028
    chronic use, 3499
    dogs, 4028
    humans, 3499
TESTOSTERONE SYNTHESIS
  cannabinoid(s)
    cannabidiol (CBD), 5443
    cannabigerol (CBG), 5443
    cannabinol (CBN), 5443
    delta-9-THC, 5443
    8-beta-hydroxy-delta-9-THC, 5443
    11-hydroxy-delta-9-THC, 5443
    in vitro, 5443
    inhibition, 5442
    rats, 5442
    SP-111A, 5443
  cannabinol (CBN)
    mice, 3425
  delta-9-THC
    in vitro, 5322
    metabolism, 5322
    mice, 3425, 5322
TETRAHYDROCANNABINOL (THC)
  analysis
    densitometry, 3303
    detection, 3303, 4696
    gas chromatography, 4696
    thin layer chromatography (TLC), 4696
  biochemical aspects
    brain, 5490
    metabolism, 5490
  biochemical effect(s)
    metabolism, 5628
    radioimmunoassay (RIA), 5253
  Cannabis sativa
    constituents of, 4480
  chemical aspects
    analog(s), 5614
      carbocyclic, 4710
      nitrogen, 4710
    derivatives, 5580
      ester, 4710
    homologs, 5614
    synthesis
      thio derivatives, 4211
  epidemiological study
    street samples, 3886
  neurophysiology
    electroencephalogram (EEG), 4190
  pharmacokinetics
    distribution, 5490
  pharmacological aspects
    analgesia, 5460
    antiemetic, 4773

pharmacological aspects (continued)
  behavior
    abstinence attenuating, 3981
    blood clearance rates, 4309
    compared to:
      morphine, 5460
    dependence, 5460
    derivatives, 5580
    interaction with
      morphine, 5460
      naloxone, 5460
    memory, 4754
    physical dependence, 5430
    receptor binding, 5313
    structure-activity relationships, 5580
    tolerance, 5430, 5460
  physiological effects
    endocrine effects, 4897
  psychological aspects
    hallucinations, 4190
  therapeutic aspects
    antiemetic, 4773
    asthma, 5105
    cancer, 4773
    humans, 5105
    medical use, 4773
TETRAHYDROCANNABINOL ACIDS
  analysis
    detection, 4552
    mass fragmentography, 4552
  cannabis
    constituents of, 4596
  Cannabis sativa
    constituents of, 3369
TETRAHYDROCANNABIVARINIC ACID
  cannabis
    constituents of, 4849
TETRAHYDROCANNABIVAROLIC ACIDS
  cannabis
    constituents of, 4596
  Cannabis sativa
    constituents of, 3369
  chemical aspects
    extractions, 5320
  toxicology
    allergy, 5320
THC-ISO
  analysis
    mass spectrometry, 3416
    structure, 3416
THERAPEUTIC ASPECTS
  cannabinoid(s)
    review, 4770
  cannabis, 3846
    history, 4451
    review, 4451
  hashish, 4406
  marihuana
    analgesia, 3599
    anesthesia, 3599
    antibiotic activity, 3599
    anti-convulsant activity, 3599
    antiemetic, 3599
    appetite stimulant, 3599
    bronchodilatation, 3599

  history, 5216
    intraocular pressure (IOP), 3599
    psychotherapy, 3599
  substitute for
    heroin, 3679
THERAPEUTIC EFFECTS
  cannabis
    review, 4531
THERAPY
  marihuana
    adverse effect(s), 3082, 5187
    review, 5436
THIN LAYER CHROMATOGRAPHY (TLC)
  cannabidiol (CBD), 5134
    analysis, 5257
  cannabinoid(s)
    analysis, 5268
    biological fluid(s), 5572
    dansyl derivatives, 5572
    homologs, 3537
  cannabinol (CBN), 5134
    analysis, 5257
  delta-9-THC, 5134
    analysis, 5257
  marihuana
    carcinogenesis, 5434
THIO ANALOGS
  cannabinoid(s)
    biological activity, 4707, 4709
    structure-activity relationships, 4602
    synthesis, 4707
  delta-8-THC
    synthesis, 3616
  delta-9-THC
    pharmacological aspects, 4603
    structure, 4198
    structure-activity relationships, 4603
    synthesis, 3616, 4198
    therapeutic aspects, 4603
THIO DERIVATIVES
  cannabinoid(s)
    synthesis, 4212
  delta-8-THC
    synthesis, 4212
  tetrahydrocannabinol (THC)
    synthesis, 4211
THYMIDINE UPTAKE
  cannabichromene (CBC), 3604
  cannabicyclol (CBL), 3604
  cannabidiol (CBD), 3604
  cannabigerol (CBG), 3604
  cannabinol (CBN), 3604
    in vitro, 5367
  delta-9-THC, 3604
    cellular effects, 5449
    in vitro, 3605, 5367, 5449
    inhibition, 5449
    membrane effects, 3605
THYROID
  ganja
    humans, 4762
THYROXINE
  delta-9-THC
    acute effect(s), 4543

delta-9-THC (continued)
    blood level(s), 4543
    chronic effects, 4543
    rats, 4543
TIME ESTIMATION
  cannabinol (CBN)
    humans, 4515
  delta-9-THC
    chronic use, 3635
    humans, 3635, 3730, 4515, 5302
  hashish
    chronic use, 3635
    humans, 3635
  marihuana
    adverse effect(s), 4176
    chronic use, 3635, 4937
    humans, 3168, 3635, 4937
  marihuana smoke
    humans, 4054
TIME PERCEPTION
  cannabinoid(s)
    limbic, 5504
  marihuana
    humans, 5052
TISSUE CULTURE
  delta-9-THC
    disposition, 3690
TISSUE RESPIRATION
  delta-9-THC
    brain, 3532
    heart, 3532
    hypothermia, 3532
    liver, 3532
    skeletal muscle, 3532
TOLERANCE
  cannabichromene (CBC)
    rats, 5561
  cannabidiol (CBD)
    anti-convulsant activity, 4145, 4146
    diuretic activity, 4924
    ganglionic transmission, 3752
    hepatic metabolism, 4033
    rats, 5561
  cannabinol (CBN)
    anti-convulsant activity, 4145
    diuretic activity, 4924
  cannabis, 4522
    adverse effect(s), 4963
    behavioral effect(s), 3062, 3456, 4108
    chronic use, 3769
    dispositional, 5203
    humans, 3456, 3738, 4108, 4112, 4812, 4963,
      4968, 5203, 5301, 5340
    rats, 4873
    self administration, 4112
    subjective effects, 3845
  cannabis resin
    hypothermia, 4872
    rats, 4872
  delta-8-THC
    analgesia, 3984
    analog(s)
      behavioral effect(s), 4381
    animals, 4160
    anti-convulsant activity, 3525, 4145

delta-8-THC (continued)
    behavioral effect(s), 3085, 3289
   heart rate, 3983
   humans, 4160
   hypothermia, 3983
   monkeys, 3085
   pigeon(s), 3085
   rats, 3085, 3983
   spiders, 3085
delta-9-THC
  analog(s)
    behavioral effect(s), 4381
  animals, 4160, 4252, 4352
  anti-convulsant activity, 3525, 3530, 4145, 4146
  ataxia, 4996
  behavioral effect(s), 3085, 3096, 3289, 3435,
    3611, 3734, 3754, 4058, 4108, 4224, 4379,
    4386, 4678, 5032, 5163, 5336, 5541
  blood pressure, 3197
  body temperature, 3222, 4678
  brain, 4376
  cardiovascular effects, 3317, 3764, 4183, 4996,
    5018
  CNS depression, 4058
  chronic administration, 3680
  conditioned behavior, 3127, 4330, 4351, 4352
  convulsions, 5354
  dispositional, 4252
  distribution, 3610, 3923
  diuretic activity, 4924
  dogs, 3610, 3611, 4376, 4379, 4996
  electroencephalogram (EEG), 3771, 4386
  gerbil, 5036
  heart rate, 4678
  humans, 3250, 3317, 3740, 4106, 4108, 4110,
    4111, 4160
  hypothermia, 3197, 4058, 4872, 5032
  immunosuppression, 3695
  intestinal motility, 3222
  intraocular pressure (IOP), 5414
  locomotor activity, 4335
  mechanism of effects, 3610
  metabolic, 3923, 4335, 4336, 4376
  monkeys, 3085, 3680, 3764, 5336
  motor activity, 3222
  operant behavior, 3680
  pigeon(s), 3085, 3611
  pregnancy, 4376
  psychological aspects, 3740
  rats, 3085, 3197, 3771, 4058, 4152, 4304, 4335,
    4337, 4351, 4858, 4872, 5163, 5541, 5575
  respiratory effects, 4996
  review, 3734, 4531
  spiders, 3085
  vagal effects, 4045
dimethylheptylpyran (DMHP)
  anti-convulsant activity, 4145
11-hydroxy-delta-9-THC
  behavioral effect(s), 3754
Lilly compound no. 109514
  hypothermia, 4586
  rats, 4586
marihuana, 3239, 3240
  adolescent(s), 5493
  behavioral effect(s), 3443, 3731, 3736, 5560

marihuana (continued)
  cardiovascular effects, 4559
  chronic use, 3739, 4632
  clinical aspects, 4531
  environmental conditions, 3443
  euphoria, 4559
  heart rate, 3812
  humans, 3241, 3309, 3739, 3812, 3893, 4106,
    4107, 4110, 4617, 5291
  physical dependence, 3893
  physiological effects, 4527
  psychological aspects, 4527
  rats, 5561
  respiratory effects, 3309
  review, 3922, 4663
  Turkey, 5561
marihuana extract
  behavioral effect(s), 3435
marihuana smoke
  behavioral effect(s), 4303
  heart rate, 4997
  motor activity, 3770
  rats, 3770, 4303
  toxicology, 3742
nabilone (Lilly compound no. 109514)
  hypothermia, 4585
  intraocular pressure (IOP), 5521, 5522
  rabbit(s), 5521
SP-1
  behavioral effect(s), 3435
tetrahydrocannabinol (THC)
  review, 5430, 5460
TONIC IMMOBILITY
  delta-6a(10a)-THC
    chickens, 4389
  delta-8-THC
    chickens, 4389
  delta-9-THC
    chickens, 4389
TOXIC DELIRIUM
  marihuana
    humans, 3893, 4106, 4107
TOXICOLOGY
  delta-9-THC
    humans, 3797
  marihuana
    humans, 4613
    review, 3241, 3922, 4663
  marihuana smoke
    chronic administration, 3742
    rats, 3742
TRACE ELEMENTS
  Cannabis sativa
    constituents of, 4846
    geographical origin, 4846
  constituents of
    cannabis resin, 3964
TRACKING
  hashish
    compared to:
      alcohol, 4417
    humans, 4417
TRAFFICKING
  cannabis, 4372
    attitude, 5408

cannabis (continued)
  Australia, 5408
  legal aspects, 5408
  Pakistan, 3257
marihuana
  legal aspects, 5285
  Mexico, 3171
  Middle East, 3171
TRANQUILIZING ACTIVITY
  cannabis
    mice, 5020
    rabbit(s), 5020
    rats, 5020
  Cannabis sativa
    monkeys, 4407
  delta-6a(10a)-THC
    carbocyclic analogs, 5218
    nitrogen analogs, 5218
    thio analogs, 5218
  delta-9-THC
    cancer, 3430
    humans, 3430
    mice, 3639
    nitrogen analogs, 4603
    review, 4603
    thio analogs, 4603
  Lilly compound no. 109514
    humans, 4251
  SP-1
    mice, 3639
  SP 80
    mice, 3639
  SP-106
    mice, 3639
TRANSFORMATION
  delta-8-THC
    9-hydroxy-9-*nor*-hexahydrocannabinol, 4636
    9-alpha, 10-alpha-epoxyhexahydrocannabinol
    chemical aspects, 4636
TRICHOMES
  cannabis
    taxonomy, 3794
  Cannabis sativa
    calcification, 3590
    morphology, 3590
    silification, 3590
    ultrastructure, 4235
TRINIDAD
  cannabis use
    distribution, 4276
    economic aspects, 4276
TRYTOPHAN
  delta-9-THC
    mice, 4075
    synaptosomal, 4075
    uptake, 4075
TUMOR GROWTH
  delta-9-THC
    allylbenzene analog(s), 4545
TYROSINE AMINOTRANSFERASE
  delta-8-THC
    liver, 5222
    mice, 5222, 5225
  delta-9-THC
    liver, 5222,

delta-9-THC (continued)
  mice, 5222, 5225

U

ULTRA VIOLET RADIATION
  cannabinol (CBN)
    fluorescence, 3377
    product(s), 3377
ULTRASTRUCTURAL CHANGES
  delta-9-THC
    monkeys, 5512
    septal region, 5512
  marihuana smoke
    monkeys, 5512
    septal region, 5512
UPTAKE
  delta-9-THC
    liver, 4035
    salivary glands, 4320
UNITED NATIONS NARCOTICS COMMISSION
  cannabis
    recommendations, 3256
UNLEARNED BEHAVIOR
  cannabinoid(s)
    animals, 3732
  delta-8-THC
    animals, 3732
  delta-9-THC
    animals, 3732
URINALYSIS
  delta-9-THC
    rats, 4744
U.S. PATENTS
  2,419,934, 5639
  2,419,935, 5640
  2,419,936, 5641
  2,419,937, 5642
  2,509,386, 5643
  2,509,387, 5644
  3,325,489, 5661
  3,325,490, 5662
  3,388,136, 5710
  3,493,579, 5686
  3,507,885, 5672
  3,514,464, 5690
  3,535,327, 5645
  3,560,528, 5693
  3,562,312, 5668
  3,576,798, 5645
  3,576,887, 5675
  3,632,595, 5645
  3,635,993, 5691
  3,636,058, 5671
  3,639,427, 5704
  3,649,650, 5706
  3,654,312, 5688
  3,656,906, 5663
  3,668,224, 5694
  3,676,462, 5689
  3,694,464, 5638
  3,734,930, 5705
  3,799,946, 5682
  3,808,234, 5669
  3,822,188, 5670

U.S. PATENTS (continued)
  3,833,616, 5695
  3,856,820, 5683
  3,856,821, 5684
  3,856,823, 5685
  3,873,576, 5696
  3,878,219, 5679
  3,883,551, 5707
  3,886,184, 5687
  3,888,946, 5692
  3,901,926, 5713
  3,920,705, 5697
  3,928,598, 5647
  3,929,835, 5714
  3,941,782, 5674
  3,944,673, 5648
  3,953,603, 5646
  3,968,125, 5649
  3,987,188, 5650
  4,024,275, 5651
  4,025,516, 5699
  4,025,536, 5678
  4,025,630, 5666
  4,036,857, 5700
  4,049,653, 5712
  4,051,152, 5702
  4,054,582, 5660
  4,064,009, 5673
  4,066,667, 5680
  4,075,230, 5652
  4,087,545, 5654
  4,087,546, 5655
  4,087,547, 5656
  4,088,777, 5657
  4,102,902, 5653
  4,111,942, 5681
  4,116,979, 5701
  4,126,694, 5698
  4,126,695, 5703
  4,131,614, 5708
  4,133,819, 5677
  4,137,232, 5715
  4,140,701, 5709
  4,143,139, 5659
  4,148,809, 5664
  4,152,450, 5665
  4,152,451, 5658
  4,187,076, 5667
  4,209,520, 5676
  4,233,030, 5711
URINE
  cannabinoid(s)
    detection, 5629
  cannabis
    humans, 5324
USE
  cannabis
    Australia, 5408
    crime, 5408
  hashish
    history, 5563
    sociological aspects, 5563
  marihuana
    age, 5530

marihuana (continued)
   behavioral effect(s), 5530
   drug abuse, 5517
   drug availability, 5530
   epidemiological study, 5530
   family relationships, 5530
   history, 5517
   motivation, 5517, 5530
   peer influence, 5530
   racial differences, 5530
USERS VS NONUSERS
  marihuana
   clinical aspects, 4531
UTERINE EFFECTS
  cannabis
   glycogen, 3460
   rats, 3460
UTERUS
  cannabis extract
   glycogen, 3462
   water uptake, 3462
  cannabis resin
   rats, 4569
  delta-9-THC
   estradiol, 5583
   mice, 5620
   organ weights, 5392
   prostaglandin synthesis, 4113
   rats, 4113, 4929, 5392
   receptor binding, 5583
  marihuana extract
   organ weights, 5392
   rats, 5392

V

VAPOR PHASE
  hashish
   terpenes, 3892
  marihuana
   terpenes, 3892
VAS DEFERENS
  delta-9-THC
   acetylcholine (ACh), 4546
   contraction, 4546, 5524
   in vitro, 4546
   interaction with
    desmethylimipramine, 3668
    6-hydroxy-dopamine, 3668
   norepinephrine (NE), 4546
   uptake, 3668
  SP-111
   acetylcholine (ACh), 4546
   contraction, 4546, 5524
   in vitro, 4546
   norepinephrine (NE), 4546
VASOCONSTRICTION
  delta-9-THC
   rats, 3663
VEHICLE EFFECT(S)
  cannabinoid(s)
   intraocular pressure (IOP), 5414
   monkeys, 5414
   rabbit(s), 5414

VEHICLE EFFECT(S) (continued)
  delta-9-THC
   intraocular pressure (IOP), 5414
   monkeys, 5414
   rabbit(s), 5414
VEHICLE OF ADMINISTRATION
  delta-9-THC
   adverse effect(s), 5413
VENTRICLES
  delta-9-THC
   contractile force, 4048
   dogs, 4050
VENTRICULAR FUNCTION
  delta-9-THC
   humans, 3803
P-VINYLPHENOL
  cannabis
   constituents of, 3426
   prostaglandin synthesis, 3426
VITAMINS
  Cannabis sativa
   constituents of, 5079
  delta-9-THC
   rabbit(s), 5342
VITAMIN C
  marihuana smoke
   carcinogenesis, 5481
   in vitro, 5481
VISION
  cannabinol (CBN)
   humans, 4870
  cannabis, 3589
   chronic use, 3589
   humans, 3589
  delta-9-THC
   humans, 3404, 4985
   rats, 4726
  marihuana
   color tests, 3196
   compared to:
    alcohol, 3193
   humans, 3193, 3194, 3195, 3196, 3973, 4933
   light adaptation, 3194
VISUAL ACUITY
  delta-9-THC
   humans, 3404
   mechanism of action, 5555
   rabbit(s), 5555
  marihuana
   compared to:
    alcohol, 4502
   humans, 3195, 4502
VISUAL TRACKING
  delta-9-THC
   compared to:
    pentobarbital, 4986
   humans, 4985, 4986
   performance, 4986
  marihuana
   humans, 3142, 3747, 4500
  marihuana smoke
   compared to:
    alcohol, 5303
   humans, 5303

VOLVOX
  delta-9-THC
    growth, 5494
    morphology, 5494
    reproduction, 5494
VOMIFOLIOL
  Cannabis sativa
    constituents of, 3321

W

WATER INTAKE
  cannabidiol (CBD)
    rats, 4923
  cannabinoid(s)
    animals, 3732
  cannabinol (CBN)
    rats, 4923
  delta-8-THC
    acute effect(s), 4070
    animals, 3732
    chronic effects, 4070
    rats, 4070
  delta-9-THC
    acute administration, 3642
    acute effect(s), 4070
    animals, 3732
    chronic administration, 3642
    chronic effects, 4070
    rats, 3642, 3737, 4070, 4923, 5372, 5501
    route of administration, 5501
    tolerance, 5501
    vehicle of administration, 5501
  marihuana
    rats, 4738
WATER PIPES
  marihuana smoke
    cannabinoid content, 5279

WHITE BLOOD CELLS
  delta-9-THC
    humans, 5239
    rats, 3823
WITHDRAWAL SYMPTOMS
  cannabidiol (CBD)
    convulsions, 4147
    mice, 4147
  cannabis
    anxiety, 5301
    compared to:
      alcohol, 3523
    humans, 3523, 5301
    sleep, 5301
  delta-9-THC
    convulsions, 4147
    humans, 4111
    mice, 4147
    morphine, 5341
    rats, 5022, 5341
  marihuana smoke
    humans, 5396
WITHDRAWAL SYNDROME
  cannabis
    humans, 4812, 4963, 4968
  marihuana
    humans, 5031
WORMS
  cannabis extract
    LD50, 5255

X

X-RAY
  cannabispiran (see also cannabispirone)
    structure, 4580